THE OFFICIAL RFU CLUB DIRECTORY 2002-2003

THE OFFICIAL RFU CLUB DIRECTORY 2002-2003

ALL RFU AFFILIATED CLUBS INCLUDED

EDITOR & STATISTICIAN
STEPHEN MCCORMACK

Queen Anne Press

First published in Great Britain in 2002 by
Queen Anne Press
a division of Lennard Associates Limited
Mackerye End, Harpenden
Hertfordshire AL5 5DR

A CIP catalogue record for this book
is available from the British Library

ISBN 1 85291 645 1

The publishers wish to confirm that the views expressed in articles and reviews in this publication are not necessarily those of the Rugby Football Union, any sponsor or indeed agencies employed by the RFU or sponsors.

Compiled, typeset and designed by
Tony Williams Publishing
Helland, North Curry, Taunton TA3 6DU

Printed and bound in Great Britain by
Butler & Tanner, Frome & London

INDEX

SIX NATIONS CHAMPIONSHIP

(Sponsored by Lloyds TSB) 2001-02

ROUND ONE
Saturday, 2nd February 2002

SCOTLAND 3-29 ENGLAND

At Murrayfield.
Attendance: 67,500 Half-time: 3-12

SCOTLAND: G Metcalfe (Glasgow); B Laney (Edinburgh), J McLaren (Glasgow), G Townsend (Castres), J Paterson (Edinburgh); D Hodge (Edinburgh), B Redpath (Sale); T Smith (Northampton), G Bulloch (Glasgow), M Stewart (Northampton), J White (Glasgow), S Murray (Saracens), S Grimes (Newcastle), B Pountney (Northampton)(captain), S Taylor (Edinburgh). Replacement: G Graham (Newcastle) for Smith 62 mins..

Scorer: Pen: Hodge.

ENGLAND: J Robinson (Sale); A Healey (Leicester), W Greenwood (Harlequins), M Tindall (Bath), B Cohen (Northampton); J Wilkinson (Newcastle), K Bracken (Saracens); G Rowntree (Leicester), S Thompson (Northampton), J White (Bristol), R Hill (Saracens), M Johnson (Leicester)(captain), B Kay (Leicester), N Back (Leicester), J Worsley (Wasps). Replacementts: N Duncombe (Harlequins) for Bracken 41 mins., D Grewcock (Bath) for Kay 67 mins., I Balshaw (Bath) for Tindall 72 mins., J Leonard (Harlequins) for White 73 mins., C Hodgson (Sale) for Wilkinson 80 mins..New caps: Thompson, Duncombe.

Scorers: Tries: Robinson (2), Tindall, Cohen. Pen: Wilkinson. Cons: Wilkinson (2), Hodgson.

Man of the Match: W Greewnood (England).
Referee: S Walsh, New Zealand.

FRANCE 33-12 ITALY

At Stade de France, Paris
Half-time: 19-12

FRANCE: N Jeanjean (Toulouse); A Rougerie (Montferrand), D Traille (Pau), T Marsh (Montferrand), D Bory (Montferrand); G Merceron (Montferrand), P Michalek (Toulouse); J-J Crenca (Agen), Y Bru (Toulouse), P de Villiers (Stade Francais), S Betsen (Biarritz), D Auradou (Stade Francais), T Privat (Beziers), S Hall (Beziers), O Magne (Montferrand)(captain). Replacements: X Garbajosa (Toulouse) for Jenajean 53 mins., R Ibanez (Castres) for Bru 59 mins., F Pelous (Toulouse) for Auradou 59 mins., A Albouy (Castres) for Michalek 80 mins.. Yellow card: Auradou 23-33 mins..

Scorers : Tries: Traille, Betsen. Pens: Merceropn (7). Con: Merceron.

ITALY: P Vaccari (Calvisano); R Pedrazzi (Viadana), C Stoica (Castres), L Martin (Northampton), D Dallan (Treviso); D Dominguez (Stade Francais), A Troncon (Montferrand); A Lo Cicero (Toulouse), A Moscardi (Treviso)(captain), A Muraro (Padova), Mauro Bergamasco (Treviso), C Checchinato (Treviso), S Dellape (Viadana), M Botolami (Padova), M Phillips (Viadana). Replacements: G De Carli (Calvisano) for Lo Cicero 28-31 mins. (temp.) and 57 mins., A Moreno (Agen) for Muraro 57 mins., M Giacheri (Sale) for Dellape 72 mins., MIrco Bergamsaco (Padova) for Vaccari 72 mins., A Persico (Viadana) for Mauro Bergamasco 80+ mins.. Temp. replacement: Mirco Bergamasco for Pedrazzi 47-50 mins.. Yellow cards: Checchinato 35-45 mins., Botolami 44-54 mins., Phillips 55-65 mins., Dominguez 62-72 mins..

Scorer: Pens: Dominguez (4). .

Man of the Match: D Traille (France).
Referee: A Lewis, Ireland.

Sunday, 3rd February 2002.

IRELAND 54-10 WALES

at Lansdowne Road, Dublin
Attendance: 48,898 Half-time: 24-3

IRELAND: G Dempsey (Terenure College); G Murphy (Leicester), B O'Driscoll (Blackrock College), K Maggs (Bath), D Hickie (St Mary's College); D Humphreys (Dungannon), P Stringer (Shannon); P Clohessy (Young Munster), F Sheahan (Cork Constitution)), J Hayes (Shannon), S Easterby (Llanelli), M Galwey (Shannon)(captain), P O'Connell (Young Munster), D Wallace (Garryowen), A Foley (Shannon). Replacements: G Longwell (Ballymena) for O'Connell 32 mins., P Wallace (Blackrock College) for Clohessy 70 mins., S Byrne (Blackrock College) for Sheahan 70 mins., K Gleason (St Mary's College) for Galwey 70 mins., R O'Gara (Cork Constitution) for Humphreys 75 minuters, R Henderson (Young Munster) for Hickie 75 mins., G Easterby (Llanelli) for Stringer 77 mins.. New caps: O'Connell, Gleason.
Scorers : Tries: Murphy (2), O'Connell (10, Hickie, Gleason, O'Gara. Pens: Humphreys (6). Cons: Humphreys 2), O'Gara.
WALES; K Morgan (Swansea); D James (Bridgend), J Robinson (Cardiff), I Harris (Cardiff), C Morgan (Cardiff); S Jones (Llanelli), R Howley (Cardiff); S John (Cardiff), R McBryde (Llanelli), C Anthony (Newport), N Budgett (Ebbw Vale), C Quinnell (Cardiff), C Wyatt (Llanelli), S Quinnell (Llanelli)(captain), M Williams (Cardiff). Replacements: I Gough (Newport) for Wyatt 4 mins., A Marinos (Newport) for Robinson 10 mins., D Peel (Llanelli) for Howley 55 mins., D Jones (Neath) for John 55 mins., Williams for McBryde 70 mins.. New caps: C Morgan, Marinos.
Scorer: Try: S Jones. Pen: S Jones. Con: S Jones.
Man of the Match: D Humphreys (Ireland).
Referee: P Deluca, Argentina.

ROUND TWO
Saturday, 16th February 2002.

ENGLAND 45-11 IRELAND

At Twickenham
Attendance: 75,000 Half-time: 31-6

ENGLAND: J Robinson (Sale); A Healey (Leicester), W Greenwood (Harlequins), M Tindall (Bath), B Cohen (Northampton); J Wilkinson (Newcastle), K Bracken (Saracens); G Rowntree (Leicester), S Thompson (Northampton), P Vickery (Gloucester), R Hill (Saracens), M Johnson (Leicester)(captain), B Kay (Leicester), N Back (Leicester), J Worsley (Wasps). Replacements: J Leonard (Harlequins) for Rowntree 16 mins., I Balshaw (Bath) for Healey 60 mins., L Moody (Leicester) for Hill 60 mins., D Grewcock for Johnson 60 mins., C Hodgson (Sale) for Wilkinson 77 mins., N Duncombe (Harlequins) for Bracken 77 mins..
Scorers : Tries: Greenwood (2), Wilkinson, Cohen, Worsley, Kay. Pen: Wilkinson. Cons: Wilkinson (6).
IRELAND; G Dempsey (Terenure College); G Murphy (Leicester), B O'Driscoll (Blackrock College), K Maggs (Bath), D Hickie (St Mary's College); D Humphreys (Dungannon), P Stringer (Shannon); P Clohessy (Young Munster), F Sheahan (Cork Constitution), J Hayes (Shannon), E Miller (Terenure College), M Galwey (Shannon)(captain), M O'Kelly (St Mary's College), D Wallace (Garryowen), A Foley (Shannon). Replacements: R Henderson (Young Munster) for Murphy 8 mins., R O'Gara (Cork Constitution) for Henderson 41 mins., S Byrne (Blackrock College) for Sheahan 52 mins., G Longwell (Ballymena) for Galwey 56 mins., S Easterby (Llanelli) for Miller 56 mins., P Wallace (Blackrock College) for Clohessy 78 mins..
Scorers : Try: O'Gara, Pens: Humphreys (2)
Referee: P Marshall, Australia.

ITALY 12-29 SCOTLAND

At Flaminio Stadium, Rome.
Attendance: 34,000 Half-time: 9-9

ITALY: P Vaccari (Calvisano); R Pedrazzi (Viadana), Mirko Bergamasco (Padova), C Stoica (Castres), D Dallan (Treviso); D Dominguez (Stade Francais), A Troncon (Montferrand); F Pucciariello (Gloucester), A Moscardi (Treviso)(captain), G De Carli (Calvisano), Mauro Bergamasco (Treviso), M Bertolami (Padova), S Dellape (Viadana), C Checchinato (Treviso), M Phillips (Viadana). Replacements: A Moreno (Worcester) for Pucciariello 52 mins., A Lo Cicero (Toulouse) for De Carli 60 mins., M Giacheri (Sale) for Dellape, L Martin (Bedford) for Vaccari 69 mins., R Pez (Rotherham) for Dominguez 80 mins., A Persico (Treviso) for Phillips 80 mins.. Yellow cards: Mauro Bergamasco 15-25 mins., Dallaep 50-60 mins..
Scorer: Pens: Dominguez (4).

SCOTLAND: B Laney (Edinburgh); G Metcalfe (Glasgow), J McLaren (Glasgow), A Henderson (Glasgow), J Paterson (Edinburgh); G Townsend (Castres), B Redpath (Sale)(captain); T Smith (Northampton), G Bulloch (Glasgow), M Stewart (Northampton), J White (Glasgow), S Murray (Saracens), S Grimes (Newcastle), A Mower (Newcastle), S Taylor (Edinburgh). Replacements: G Graham (Newcastle) for Stewart 59 mins., M Leslie (Edinburgh) for Mower 69 mins. Yellow card: Mower 15-25 mins.
Scorers : Tries: Townsend, Laney. Pens: Laney (5). Cons: Laney (2).
Man of the Match: S Taylor (Scotland).
Referee: K Deaker, New Zealand.
NB: B Laney's 24 points were a Six Nations record for Scotland.

WALES 33-37 FRANCE

At Millennium Stadium, Cardiff
Attendance: 72,500 Half-time: 19-24

WALES: K Morgan (Swansea); D James (Bridgend), T Shanklin (Saracens), A Marinos (Newport), C Morgan (Cardiff); S Jones (Llanelli), R Howley (Cardiff); S John (Cardiff), R McBryde (Llanelli), C Anthony (Newport), N Budgett (Bridgend), C Quinnell (Cardiff), A Moore (Swansea), M Williams (Cardiff), S Quinnell (Llanelli)(captain). Replacements: B Williams (Neath) for McBryde 62 mins., I Gough (Newport) for C Quinnell 67 mins., Jones for John 67 mins., R Williams (Cardiff) for Marinos 70 mins.. Yellow card: S Quinnell 40+1-47 mins..
Scorers : Tries: C Quinnell, Budgett, K Morgan. Pens: Jones (4). Cons: Jones (3).
FRANCE: N Brusque (Biarritz); A Rougerie (Montferrand), D Traille (Pau), A Marsh (Montferrand), X Garbajosa (Touolouse); G Merceron (Montferrand), P Mignoni (Beziers); J-J Crenca (Agen), R Ibanez (Castres)(captain), P de Villiers (Stade Francais), S Betsen (Biarritz), T Privat (Beziers), O Brouzet (Northampton), I Harinordoquy (Pau), S Hall (Beziers). Replacements: F Pelous (Toulouse) for Privat 60 mins., S Bruno (Beziers) for Ibanez 65 mins., A Audebert (Montferrand) for Hall 68 mins., Milloud for Crenca 80 mins.. New caps: Brusque, Harinordoquy, Bruno.
Scorers : Tries: Marsh (2), Rougerie. DG: Merceron. Pens: Merceron (4), Traille. Cons: Merceron (2).
Man of the Match: S Betsen (France).
Referee: D McHugh, Ireland. .

ROUND THREE
Saturday, 2nd March 2002.

FRANCE 20-15 ENGLAND

At Stade de France, Paris
Attendance: 80,000 Half-time: 17-7

FRANCE: N Brusque (Biarritz); A Rougerie (Montferrand), A Marsh (Montferrand), D Traille (Pau), D Bory (Montferrand); G Merceron (Montferrand), F Galthie (Stade Francais)(captain); J-J Crenca (Agen), R Ibanez (Castres), P de Villiers (Stade Francais), O Magne (Montferrand), D Auradou (Stade Francais), O Brouzet (Northampton), S Betsen (Biarritz), I Harinordoquy (Pau). Replacements: F Pelous (Toulouse) for Auradout 60 mins., O Milloud (Bourgoin) for Crenca 60 mins., P Mignoni (Beziers) for Galthie 66 mins., O Azam (Gloucester) for Ibanez 74 mins., R Martin (Stade Francais) for Harinordoquy 78 mins.. Temp. replacement: Martin for Betsen 57-63 mins.. No new caps.
Scorers : Tries: Merceron, Harinordoquy. Pens: Merceron (2). Cons: Merceron (2).

ENGLAND: J Robinson (Sale); A Healey (Leicester), W Greenwood (Harlequins), M Tindall (Bath), B Cohen (Northampton); J Wilkinson (Newcastle), K Bracken (Saracens); G Rowntree (Leicester), S Thompson (Northampton), P Vickery (Gloucester), R Hill (Saracens), M Johnson (Leicester)(captain), B Kay (Leicester), N Back (Leicester), J Worsley (Wasps). Replacements: H Paul (Gloucester) for Tindall 39 mins., J Leonard (Harlequins) for Rowntree 74 mins., D Luger (Harlequins) for Wilkinson 74 mins., D West (Leicester) for Thompson 74 mins., D Grewcock (Bath) for Kay 74 mins.. Temp. replacement: M Corry (Leicester) for Back 47-54 mins..
Scorers : Tries: Robinson, Cohen. Pen: Wilkinson. Con: Wilkinson.
Man of the Match: P de Villiers (France).
Referee: A Watson, South Africa.

IRELAND 43-22 SCOTLAND

At Lansdowne Road, Dublin
Attendance: 48,898 Half-time: 22-12

IRELAND: G Dempsey (Terenure College); S Horgan (Lansdowne), B O'Driscoll (Blackrock College), K Maggs (Bath), D Hickie (St Mary's College); D Humphreys (Dungannon), P Stringer (Shannon); P Clohessy (Young Munster), F Sheahan (Cork Constitution), J Hayes (Shannon), E Miller (Terenure College), M Galwey (Shannon)(captain), M O'Kelly (St Mary's College), D Wallace (Garryowen), A Foley (Shannon). Replacements: S Byrne (Blackrock College) for Sheahan 36 mins., S Easterby (Llanelli) for Miller 48 mins., G Longwell (Ballymena) for Galwey 72 mins., R O'Gara (Cork Constitution) for Humphreys 75 mins., P Wallace (Blackrock Coll.) for Clohessy 75 mins., Easterby for Stringer 80mins..
Scorers : Tries: O'Driscoll (3), Horgan, G Easterby. Pens: Humphreys (4). Cons: Humphreys (2), O'Gara.
SCOTLAND: B Laney (Edinburgh); G Metcalfe (Glasgow), J McLaren (Glasgow), A Henderson (Glasgow), J Paterson (Edinburgh); G Townsend (Castres), B Redpath (Sale)(captain); T Smith (Northampton), G Bulloch (Glasgow), M Stewart (Northampton), J White (Glasgow), S Murray (Saracens), A Grimes (Newcastle), B Pountney (Northampton), S Taylor (Edinburgh). Replacements: M Leslie (Edinburgh) for White 58 mins., G Graham (Newcastle) for Stewart 63 mins., K Logan (Wasps) for Metcalfe 72. Yellow card: Pountney 59 mins..
Scorers : Try: Leslie. Pens: Laney (4). Con: Laney.
Man of the Match: B O'Driscoll (Ireland).
Referee: N Whitehouse, Wales.

WALES 44-20 ITALY

At Millennium Stadium, Cardiff.
Attendance: 58,900

WALES: K Morgan (Swansea); D James (Bridgend), T Shanklin (Saracens), A Marinos (Newport), C Morgan (Cardiff); S Jones (Llanelli), R Howley (Cardiff); I Thomas (Ebbw Vale), R McBryde (Llanelli), C Anthony (Newport), N Budgett (Bridgend), I Gough (Newport), A Moore (Swansea), M Williams (Cardiff), S Quinnell (Llanelli)(captain). Replacements: R Williams (Cardiff) for Shanklin 23 mins., C Wyatt (Llanelli) for Moore 51 mins., D Peel (Llanelli) for Howley 51 mins., I Harris (Cardiff) for K Morgan 58 mins., B Williams (Neath) for McBryde 59 mins., B Sinkinson (Neath) for Quinnell 63 mins., S John (Cardiff) for Anthony 75 mins..
Scorers : Tries: K Morgan, James, R Williams, Quinnell, Marinos. Pens: S Jones (3). Cons: S Jones (5).
ITALY: G Peens (Piacenza); R Pedrazzi (Viadana), Mirco Bergamasco (Padova), C Stoica (Castres), N Mazzucato (Treviso); R Pez (Rotherham), A Troncon (Montferrand); G de Carli (Calvisano), A Moscardi (Treviso)(captain), S Perugini (L'Aquila), A Persico (Viadana), M Giacheri (Sale), M Bertolami (Padova), Mauro Bergamasco (Treviso), C Checchinato (Treviso). Replacements: A Lo Cicero (Toulouse) for de Carli 47 mins., M Phillips (Viadana) for Giacheri 59 mins., F Mazzariol (Treviso) for Pez 64 mins., G Raineri (Roma) for Mirco Bergamasco 66 mins., A Benatti (Viadana) for Pedrazzi 66 mins., F Pucciariello (Gloucester) for Perugini 66 mins.. Yellow card: Persico 49-59 mins..
Scorers: Tries: Cnecchinato, Raineri. Pens: Pez, Peens. Cons: Pez, Peens.
Man of the Match: C Morgan (Wales).
Referee: C White, England.

ROUND FOUR
Saturday, 23rd March 2002.

ENGLAND 50-10 WALES

At Twickenham.
Attendance: 75,000 Half-time: 19-3

ENGLAND: A Healey (Leicester); D Luger (Harlequins), W Greenwood (Harlequins), M Tindall (Bath), B Cohen (Northampton); J Wilkinson (Newcastle), K Bracken (Saracens); G Rowntree (Leicester), S Thompson (Northampton), J White (Bristol), L Moody (Leicester), D Grewcock (Bath), B Kay (Leicester), N Back (Leicester)(captain), R Hill (Saracens). Replacements: M Dawson (Northampton) for Bracken 60 mins., T Stimpson (Leicester) for Tindall 64 mins., D West (Leicster) for Thompson 67 mins., J Worsley (Wasps) for Hill 82 mins.. Temp. replacements: M Corry (Leicester) for Kay 20-27 mins., Worsley for Moody 43-52 mins..
Scorers : Tries: Luger (2), Greenwood, Wilkinson, Stimpson.
WALES: K Morgan (Swansea); D James (Bridgend), G Thomas (Bridgend), A Marinos (Newport), C Morgan (Cardiff); I Harris (Cardiff), R Howley (Cardiff); I Thomas (Ebbw Vale), R
McBryde (Llanelli), C Anthony (Newport), N Budgett (Ebbw Vale), A Moore (Swansea), C Wyatt (Llanelli), M Williams (Cardiff), S Quinnell (Llanelli)(captain). Replacements: R Williams (Cardiff) for G Thomas 49 mins., C Charvis (Swansea) for M Williams 51 mins., G Llewellyn (Neath) for Wyatt 54 mins., D Peel (Llanelli) for Howley 60 mins., B Williams (Neath) for McBryde 67 mins..
Scorer: Try: Harris. Pen: Harris. Con: Harris.
Man of the Match: W Greenwood (England).
Referee: A Cole, Australia.

IRELAND 32-17 ITALY

At Lansdowne Road, Dublin.
Attendance: 48,898 Half-time: 19-0

IRELAND: G Dempsey (Terenure College); J Kelly (Cork Constitution), B O'Driscoll (Blackrock College), S Horgan (Lansdowne), D Hickie (St Mary's College); D Humphreys (Dungannon)(captain), P Stringer (Shannon); P Clohessy (Young Munster), S Byrne (Blackrock College), J Hayes (Shannon), E Miller (Terenure College), G Longwell (Ballymena), M O'Kelly (St Mary's College), D Wallace (Garryowen), A Foley (Shannon). Replacements: P O'Connell (Young Munster) for o'Kelly 71 mins., P Wallace (Blackrock College) for Clohessy 75 mins., E Miller (Terenure College) for D Wallace 78 mins., T Howe (Ballymena) for Hickie 79 mins.. Temp. replacement: R O'Gara (Cork Constitution) for Humphreys 32-40 mins.. New cap: Kelly.

Scorers : Tries: Kelly (2), Hickie. Pens: Humphreys (4), O'Gara. Con: O'Gara.

ITALY: G Peens (Piacenza); N Mazzucato (Treviso), C Stoica (Castres), G Raineri (Roma), D Dallan (Treviso); D Dominguez (Stade Francais), A Troncon (Montferrand); G de Carli (Calvisano), A Moscardi (Treviso)(captain), S Perugini (L'Aquila), A Persico (Viadana), M Bortolami (Padova), M Giacheri (Sale), Mauro Bergamasco (Treviso), M Phillips (Viadana). Replacements: F Pucciariello (Gloucester) for Persico 26 mins., Pucciariello for Perugini 37 mins., S Dallape (Viadana) for Bortolami 61 mins., A de Rossi (Calvisano) for Phillips 67 mins.. Yellow cards: Perugini 27-37 mins., de Carli 34 mins..

Scorers : Tries: Bergamasco, di Carli. DG: Preens. Cons: Dominguez (2).
Man of the Match: J Kelly (Ireland).
Referee: R Dickson, Scotland.

SCOTLAND 10-22 FRANCE

At Murrayfield.
Attendance: 65,562 Half-time: 3-10

SCOTLAND: B Laney (Edinburgh); G Metcalfe (Glasgow), J McLaren (Glasgow), J Leslie (Northampton), J Paterson (Edinburgh); G Townsend (Castres), B Redpath (Sale)(captain); T Smith (Northampton), G Bulloch (Glasgow), M Stewart (Northampton), M Leslie (Edinburgh), S Murray (Saracens), J White (Glasgow), B Pountney (Northampton), S Taylor (Edinburgh). Replacements: G Graham (Newcastle) for Stewart 60 mins., S Grimes (Newcastle) for Murray 63 mins., R Russell (Saracens) for Bulloch 75 mins., K Logan (Wasps) for McLaren 78 mins.. Temp. replacement: J Petrie (Glasgow) for M Leslie 29-34 mins..

Scorers : Try: Redpath. Pen: Laney. Con: Laney.

FRANCE: N Brusque (Biarritz); A Rougerie (Montferrand), A Marsh (Montferrand), D Traille (Pau), D Bory (Montferrand); G Merceron (Montferrand), F Galthie (Stade Francais)(captain); J-J Crenca (Agen), R Ibanez (Biarritz), J-B Poux (Narbonne), S Betsen (Biarritz), F Pelous (Toulouse), O Brouzet (Northampton), O Magne (Montferrand), I Harinordoquy (Pau).
Replacements: J Marlu (Montferrand) for Brusque 48 mins., S Marconnet (Stade Francais) for Poux 53 mins., T Privat (Beziers) for Pelous 65 mins., R Martin (Stade Francais) for Betsen 77 mins..

Scorers : Tries: Marsh (2), Galthie. Pen: Merceron. Cons: Merceron (2).
Man of the Match: F Galthie (France).
Referee: A Rolland, Ireland. .

ROUND FIVE

Saturday, 6th April 2002

FRANCE 44-5 IRELAND

At Stade de France, Paris.
Attendance: 79,978 Half-time: 28-5

FRANCE: N Brusque (Biarritz); A Rougerie (Montferrand), T Marsh (Montferrand), D Traille (Pau), D Bory (Montferrand); G Merceron (Montferrand), F Galthie (Stade Francais)(captain); J-J Crenca Agen), R Ibanez (Castres), P de Villiers (Stade Francais), S Betsen (Biarritz), F Pelous (Toulouse), O Brouzet (Northampton), O Magne (Montferrand), I Harinordoquy (Pau).
Replacements: J-P PPoux (Narbonne) for de Villiers 663 mins., F Gelez ((Agen) for

Merceron 64 mins., D Auradou (Stade Francais) for Brouzet 73 mins., J Marlu (Montferrand) for Bory 75 mins., P Mignoni (Beziers) for Galthie 75 mins., O Azam (Gloucester) for Ibanez 75 mins., R Martin (Stade Francais) for Magne 75 mins..
Scorers : Tries: Betsen (2), Brusque (2), Rougerie. Pens: Merceron (4), Gelez. Cons: Merceron (2).
IRELAND: G Dempsey (Terenure College); S Horgan (Lansdowne), B O'Driscoll (Blackrock College), R Henderson (Young Munster), D Hickie (St Mary's College); D Humphreys (Dungannon), P Stringer (Shannon); P Clohessy (Young Munster), K Wood (Harlequins (captain), J Hayes (Shannon), S Easterby (Llanelli), G Longwell (Ballymena), M O'Kelly (St Mary's College), D Wallace (Garryowen), A Foley (Shannon). Replacements: R O'Gara (Cork Constitution) for Humphries 45 mins., K Gleeson (Young Munster) for D Wallace 49 mins., O Wallace (Blackrock College) for Clohessy 52 mins., P O'Connell (Young Munster) for Longwell 64 mins..
Scorer: Try: Wood.
Man of the Match: G Merceron (France).
Referee: P O'Brien, New Zealand.

NB: P Clohessy (Ireland) retired from international rugby after this match.

WALES 22-27 SCOTLAND

At The Millennium Stadium, Cardiff.
Attendance: 74,000 Half-time: 9-15

WALES: K Morgan (Swansea); R Williams (Cardiff), M Taylor (Swansea), A Marinos (Newport), C Morgan (Cardiff); S Jones (Llanelli), R Howley (Cardiff); I Thomas (Ebbw Vale), B Williams (Neath), C Anthony (Newport), N Budgett (Bridgend), I Gough (Newport), A Moore (Swansea), M Williams (Cardiff), C Charvis (Swansea)(captain). Replacements: C Wyatt (Llanelli) for Moore 14 mins., G Thomas (Bath) for Budgett 41 mins., I Harris (Cardiff) for Marinos 44 mins., R McBryde (Llanelli) for B Williams 44 mins., S John (Cardiff) for I Thomas 57 mins., D Peel (Llanelli) for Howley 54 mins., D James (Bridgend) for C Morgan 70 mins..
Scorers : Try: R Williams. Pens: S Jones (5). Con: S Jones.
SCOTLAND: B Laney (Edinburgh); K Logan (Wasps), J McLaren (Glasgow), J Leslie (Northampton), C Paterson (Edinburgh); G Townsend (Castres), B Redpath (Sale)(captain); T Smith (Northampton), G Bulloch (Glasgow), M Stewart (Northampton), M Leslie (Edinburgh), S Murray (Saracens), J White (Glasgow), B Pountney (Northampton), S Taylor (Edinburgh). Replacements: G Graham (Newcastle) for Stewart 41 mins., S Grimes (Newcastle) for White 57 mins., G Metcalfe (Glasgow) for Logan 60 mins., J Petrie (Glasgow) for M Leslie 70 mins., D Hodge (Edinburgh) for Laney 80 mins..
Scorers : Tries: Bulloch (2). Pens: Laney (4), Hodge.Con: Laney. .
Man of the Match: S Murray (Scotland).
Referee: J Jutge, France. .
NB: Robert Howley (Wales) retired from international rugby after this match.

Sunday, 7th April 2002.

ITALY 9-45 ENGLAND

At Flamino Stadium, Rome.
Attendance: 26,000 Half-time: 3-24
ITALY: G Peens (Piacenza); N Mazzucato (Treviso), C Stoica (Castres), G Raineri (Roma), D Dallan (Treviso); D Dominguez (Stade Francais), A Troncon (Montferrand); G De Carli (Calvisano), A Moscardi (Treviso)(captain), F Pucciariello (Gloucester), A Persico (Viadana), M Bortolami (Viadana), M Giacheri (Sale), Mauro Bergamasco (Treviso), M Phillips (Viadana). Replacements: C Zanoletti (Calvisano) for Raineri 49 mins., A de Rossi (Calvisano) for Phillips 49 mins., C Nieto (GRAN Parma) for Pucciariello 58 mins., S Dallape (Viadana) for Giacheri 58 mins., R Pez (Rotherham) for Peens 74 mins., Puccariello for de Carli 80 mins., M Mazzantini (Treviso) for Stoica 83 mins..
Scorer: Pens: Dominguez (3).
ENGLAND: J Robinson (Sale); D Luger (Harlequins), W Greenwood (Harlequins), M Tindall (Bath), B Cohen (Northampton); J Wilkinson (Newcastle), K Bracken (Saracens); G Rowntree (Leicester), S Thompson (Northampton), J White (Bristol), L Moody (Leicester), D Grewcock (Bath), B Kay (Leicester), N Back (Leicester)(captain), R Hill (Saracens). Replacements: J Leonard (Saracens) for Rowntree 56 mins., M Johnson (Leicester) for Grewcock 19-23 mins. (temp.) and 56 mins., L Dallaglio (Wasps) for Back 56 mins., M Dawson (Northampton) for Bracken 56 mins., A Healey (Leicester) for Cohen 70 mins., D West (Leicester) for Thompson 72 mins., C Hodgson (Sale) for Tindall 77 mins..
Scorers : Tries: Greenwood (2), Cohen, Robinson, Dallaglio, Healey. Pen: Wilkinson. Cons: Wilkinson (5), Dawson.
Man of the Match: W Greenwood (England).
Referee: M Lawrence, Souh Africa.

NB: For the first time during the season's Six Nations matches Italy incurred no yellow cards.

FINAL TABLE & STATISTICS

Final Table	P	W	L	F	A	Pts
France	5	5	0	156	75	10
England	5	4	1	184	53	8
Ireland	5	3	2	145	138	6
Scotland	5	2	3	91	128	4
Wales	5	1	4	199	188	2
Italy	5	0	5	70	183	0

Leading Points Scorers

Pts	Name	Tries	Conv	Pens	DG's
80	Gerald Merceron (France)	1	9	18	1
75	Jonny Wilkinson (England)	2	19	8	1
64	Stephen Jones (Wales)	1	10	13	-
60	B.J Laney (Scotland)	1	5	15	-
56	David Humphreys (Ireland)	-	4	16	-
37	Diego Dominguez (Italy)	-	2	11	-
25	Will Greenwood (England)	5	-	-	-
20	Jason Robinson (England)	4	-	-	-
20	Tony Marsh (France)	4	-	-	-
19	Ronan O'Gara (Ireland)	2	3	1	-
456	**Total**	**20**	**52**	**82**	**2**

Leading Try Scorers

Tries	Name	1st Half	2nd Half	Home	Away
5	Will Greenwood (England)	3	2	3	2
4	Jason Robinson (England)	3	1	0	4
4	Tony Marsh (France)	3	1	0	4
3	Ben Cohen (England)	2	1	1	2
3	Dan Luger (England)	0	3	2	1
3	Brian O'Driscoll (Ireland)	1	2	3	0
3	Serge Betsen (France)	1	2	3	0
2	Geordan Murphy (Ireland)	1	1	2	0
2	Jonny Wilkinson (England)	1	1	2	0
2	Rhys Wiliams (Wales)	0	2	2	0
2	Gordon Bulloch (Scotland)	2	0	0	2
2	Dennis Hickie (Ireland)	0	2	2	0
2	John Kelly (Ireland)	1	1	2	0
2	Ronan O'Gara (Ireland)	0	2	1	1
2	Nicolas Brusque (France)	1	1	2	0
2	Aurelien Rougerie (France)	1	1	1	1

Kicking Strike Rate

		Conversions		Penalties		TOTAL	
S/R%	Player	Att	Suc	Att	Suc	Att	Suc
100	Hodgson, Charles (England)	1	1	-	-	1	1
100	Peens, Gert (Italy)	1	1	-	-	1	1
100	Dawson, Matt (England)	1	1	-	-	1	1
100	Pez, Ramiro (Italy)	1	1	2	2	3	3
93.1	Wilkinson, Jonny (England)	20	19	9	8	29	27
92	Jones, Stephen (Wales)	10	10	15	13	25	23
81.25	Dominguez, Diego (Italy)	2	2	14	11	16	13
80	O'Gara, Ronan (Ireland)	4	3	1	1	5	4
76.92	Laney, B.J (Scotland)	6	5	20	15	26	20
71.05	Merceron, Gerald (France)	14	9	24	18	38	27
68.97	Humphreys, David (Ireland)	12	4	17	16	29	20
66.67	Harris, Iestyn (Wales)	1	1	2	1	3	2
50	Gelez, Francois (France)	1	-	1	1	2	1
33.33	Traille, Damien (France)	-	-	3	1	3	1
33.33	Hodge, Duncan (Scotland)	-	-	6	2	6	2
0	Paterson, Chris (Scotland)	-	-	1	-	1	0
0	Paul, Henry (England)	1	-	-	-	1	0
76.84(Ave.)	TOTAL	75	57	115	89	190	146

ZURICH

PREMIERSHIP

CLUBS

LEAGUE TABLE

									HOME									AWAY								
														For		Against							For		Against	
	P	W	D	L	F	A	PD	Pts	W	D	L	F	A	Tries	Pens	Tries	Pens	W	D	L	F	A	Tries	Pens	Tries	Pens
Leicester Tigers	22	18	0	4	658	349	309	83	11	0	0	340	135	37	32	6	29	7	0	4	318	214	35	27	13	40
Sale Sharks	22	14	1	7	589	517	72	69	8	1	2	312	242	36	26	21	31	6	0	5	277	275	31	26	26	33
Gloucester	22	14	0	8	692	485	207	68	10	0	1	429	189	44	41	19	17	4	0	7	263	296	24	29	26	38
London Irish	22	11	3	8	574	465	109	57	8	1	2	308	215	26	44	17	29	3	2	6	266	250	20	42	20	40
Northampton Saints	22	12	1	9	506	426	80	56	7	1	3	295	190	29	34	16	23	5	0	6	211	236	19	29	20	34
Newcastle Falcons	22	12	1	9	490	458	32	56	8	1	2	280	182	27	32	18	23	4	0	7	210	276	16	29	22	46
London Wasps	22	12	0	10	519	507	12	54	8	0	3	312	186	23	45	14	30	4	0	7	207	321	19	25	27	44
Bristol Shoguns	22	9	1	12	591	632	-41	50	6	1	4	355	290	34	43	32	27	3	0	8	236	342	21	29	34	39
Harlequins	22	5	3	14	434	507	-73	35	5	0	6	276	235	23	42	21	27	0	3	8	158	272	10	25	31	19
Saracens	22	7	0	15	425	671	-246	34	5	0	6	251	323	19	39	35	32	2	0	9	174	348	14	28	33	39
Bath	22	7	0	15	311	524	-213	33	7	0	6	193	183	12	38	13	30	0	0	11	118	341	9	19	34	36
Leeds Tykes	22	6	0	16	406	654	-248	28	5	0	6	340	259	18	28	26	28	1	0	10	318	395	20	18	42	36

REVIEW

Leicester Tigers took the Premiership title for a fourth successive season to equal the record of Bath. It was done with ease and they ended the season 14 points clear of second placed Sale Sharks. The Tigers maintained their superb home form and went through another league campaign with a 100% record at Welford Road as they finished the season with 83 points, one more than they achieved last season. Tim Stimpson again topped the points scorers for a third consecutive season whilst wingers Geordan Murphy and Steve Booth shared the try scorers title.

Sale had their best ever season in league rugby with an excellent second place in the Premiership – previous best was fourth place back in 1994-95 and their first top ten finish since 1997-98. Sale lost four of their first eight games of the season before turning it round. After that they lost just three of their remaining 14 league matches and climbed up the table to second place and with it Qualification for the Heineken Cup for the first time. Right winger, Mark Cueto topped the try scorers in the Zurich Premiership in his first season of senior rugby with 13 whilst Charlie Hodgson topped the points scorers with a new club record of 273 point, 27 more than Shane Howarth scored in 1997-98. In the process Hodgson set new records for conversions and penalties in a season with 44 and 48 respectively and equalled the record for points in a match with 27 against Leeds Tykes last November.

Gloucester finished third, for the second time in three seasons, just one behind second placed Sale Sharks. The Cherry & Whites had an impressive record with just one home defeat, against Leicester Tigers, and 10 victories at Kingsholm. Nearly half the Gloucester points came from new boy Ludovic Mercier who scored 334 points out of the 692 they scored. Mercier set a new Gloucester record for a season, 52 more than the previous record set by Simon Mannix in 1999-00. It is also the second highest total in a Premiership season after Barry Everitt's 343 points also set this season. New England Sevens star James Simpson-Daniel topped the try scorers list along with Junior Paramore with nine, which equals the Gloucester record for a league campaign.

London Irish achieved their best ever finish in the top division with fourth place, three better than their previous best reached back in 1998-99. Barry Everitt made a huge contribution to their success with 343 points out of the 579 that they scored in the Premiership. In that 343 points Everitt set new club records for penalties and drop goals with 83 and eight respectively. The Irish finished the season with a run of bad form with three defeats and a draw from their last four Premiership matches.

Northampton Saints recovered after a terrible start to finish the season a creditable fifth. They managed just two wins in their opening nine matches before finding some form. After the defeat at home to Bristol in late November the Saints won ten of their remaining 13 Premiership matches to climb up the table. Paul Grayson had his best ever season for Northampton and set a new record for points in a season with 238, 19 more than his previous record. England winger Ben Cohen topped the try scorers for the third consecutive season with eight tries, one short of his best haul from the previous season.

Newcastle Falcons finished six but failed to qualify for the Heineken Cup for the coming season with Bristol getting to the play off finals at Twickenham. The Falcons got off to an excellent start to the season and lost just one of their opening eight matches. After that they had a mid season slump with six defeats in eight matches before finding their early season form again. England international Jonny Wilkinson again topped the points scorers for the fourth season running and scored over 200 for the second season to equal Rob Andrews record. In the try-scoring department Michael Stephenson top the list for a second successive season and he will hope to build on his England caps.

London Wasps recovered from a dreadful start to the season suffering a run of six successive defeats, their worst ever run in league rugby. At the turn of the year their fortunes changed and they went on to win nine of their remaining 11 Premiership matches, under two coaches, and ended the season with a run of six consecutive victories. Alex King topped the points scorers list for the first time and ended Kenny Logan's run of three years as leading scorer for the club. King set a new record for drop goals in a season with nine as well as setting a new record for drop goals in a match with two against Leicester King also set a new record of nine penalties in a match during the home defeat to Newcastle in November.

Bristol managed a top eight finish against most peoples expectations and them went on to reach the Zurich Play off final and in the process qualify for the Heineken Cup for the coming season at the expense of Newcastle Falcons. Argentinean international Felipe Contepomi topped the points scorers for a second successive season and in the process broke Mark Taunton's record of 221 points in a season. Not content with that he also topped the try scorers list with nine. Bristol did well early on in the season with six wins and a draw in their opening ten Premiership matches. After that they struggled with just two wins from 10 matches and dropped down the table before getting two wins from their final three matches.

Harlequins found themselves in trouble after a mid season slump which saw them lose eight consecutive matches and slip to the bottom of the Premiership. They then managed two wins and a draw from their final six Premiership matches, which included an emphatic win over Leeds Tykes, which proved vital to pull them clear. They managed just five wins all season but did pick up three draws in their 22 matches. Paul Burke topped the points scorers for the second season running with 258 points, the second highest total by a Quins player in league rugby. Burke also equalled the Quins record of seven penalties in a match twice in home matches during September.

Saracens finished 10th in the Premiership which was their worst placing since retuning to the top flight back in 1995-96. They got off to a good start to the season with three wins in four matches but after that they managed just four more in 18 league matches and ended the season with six straight defeats. Like Bath they struggled to score tries and managed just 33 all season with Tim Horan topping the try scoring list with just four. Outside half Luke Smith topped the points scoring with 194 and equalled the club and league record of nine penalties in a match in the home win against Gloucester last September.

Bath had their worst ever season in league rugby finishing second bottom (11th) having never previously finished worse than sixth. They were the lowest points scorers in the division with just 311, 95 fewer than Leeds Tykes. They were also the lowest try scorers with just 21 scored in 22 Premiership matches and just five of those coming from the forwards. They suffered their worst ever defeat in league rugby when their West Country rivals Gloucester 68-12 at Kingsholm thrashed them as they also conceded a record nine tries. Iain Balshaw did set a new record with three dropped goals in a league campaign, including a new record of two in a match.

Leeds Tykes finished bottom after putting up a brave display but with the Rotherham "affair" it did not matter and Leeds survive to fight another season. The Tykes finished bottom five points adrift of the rest. They managed just one away win all season at Saracens whom they did the double over. At the end of the season they lost eight consecutive Premiership matches despite having the South African internationals Braam van Straatan and Japie Mulder on board. One bright spot was the form of Danny Scarborough who finished second in the try scores list with 12.

2001-02 RECORD REVIEW
Individual Records

The ALL-TIME RECORDS for MOST POINTS IN A MATCH, MOST POINTS IN A SEASON & MOST TRIES IN A MATCH can be found in the Records Section for this division.

MOST POINTS - IN A MATCH

David Walder's record from last season remained intact but three men did get within three points of the record. Alex King three times scored 27 points or morebeat Saracens in November. Two other players came close to the record with both Tim Stimpson and Felipe Contepomi scoring 31 points in a match to move to joint third on the all time list.
The London Wasps left wing Kenny Logan had two big points returns during the season - he scored 29 points against Sale late in the season and 28 points two weeks previously against Rotherham.

Most Points in a Match 2001-02

29 Luke Smith	Saracens v Gloucester	08.09.01
29 Felipe Contepomi	Bristol v Leeds	23.09.01
29 Alex King	Wasps v Leeds	18.11.01
28 Paul Burke	Harlequins v Saracens	16.11.01
28 Tim Stimpson	Leicester v Bath	22.09.01

EVOLUTION OF RECORD - Points in a match

21 Ian Aitchison	Waterloo v Sale	02.01.88
23 Jamie Salmon	Quins v Waterloo	27.02.88
24 Dusty Hare	Leicester v Rosslyn P.	19.11.88
26 John Liley	Leicester v Bedford	23.09.89
27 David Pears	Quins v Bedford	14.10.89
28 Martin Strett	Orrell v Rosslyn P.	21.03.92
31 John Liley	Leicester v Rosslyn P.	21.03.92
32 Niall Woods	Lon. Irish v Harlequins	25.04.98
32 David Walder	Newcastle v Saracens	26.11.00

MOST POINTS - IN A SEASON

Two players broke the record for most points in a season set by John Schuster back in 1998-99. Barry Everitt was the first to break the record and ended the season on 343, 12 points better than the previous record. The on the final day of the season Gloucester's Ludovic Mercieralso passed the old record by three points to finish on 334.
In third place was Sale's Charlie Hodgson with 273 which broke the Sale record for a season held by Shane Howarth. Other players setting club records were Northampton's Paul Grayson who improved his old club record of 219 to 238 and Felipe Contepomi who beat Mark Tainton's record for points in a season for Brsitol with 221 points.

EVOLUTION OF RECORD - Points in a season

126	Dusty Hare	Leicester	1987-88
126	*John Liley*	*Leicester*	*1989-90*
126	*Rob Andrew*	*Wasps*	*1990-91*
202	Jez Harris	Leicester	1993-94
272	John Liley	Leicester	1996-97
291	Gareth Rees	Wasps	1996-97
331	John Schuster	Harlequins	1998-99
343	Barry Everitt	London Irish	2001-02

MOST TRIES - IN A MATCH

The record set by Ryan Constable was safe and never really challenged last season. We saw just three hat tricks all season. They all came late in the season with Sale'sMartin Shaw leading the way with three tries against Bristol on the 13th April.
Next to achieve the feat was Leicester openside flanker Neil Back at home to Leeds Tykes. The final hatt rick of the season came from James Simpson-Daniel as GLoucester thrashed Bath during May.

EVOLUTION OF RECORD - Tries in a match
(Only the first to reach the figure is shown)

3	Peter Shillingford	Moseley v Wasps	05.02.88
4	Gary Hartley	Nottingham v Bedford	18.11.89
5	Kenny Logan	Wasps v Orrell	22.03.97
6	Ryan Constable	Saracens v Bedford	16.04.00

MOST TRIES - IN A SEASON

Nobody came near to breaking the record of 17 tries in a season. Sale right winger Mark Cueto finished as leading try scorer in his first seaosn of senior rugby. He finished one clear of the Leeds Tykes full back Danny Scarborough who was playing in the Premiership for the first time.

EVOLUTION OF RECORD - Tries in a season

11	Andrew Harriman	Harlequins	1987-88
11	*Daren O'Leary*	*Harlequins*	*1993-94*
14	Daren O'Leary	Harlequins	1995-96
16	Adedayo Adebayo	Bath	1996-97
17	Domonic Chapman	Richmond	1997-98

ALL-TIME RECORDS - Tries in a season

17	Domonic Chapman	Richmond	1997-98
16	Adedayo Adebayo	Bath	1996-97
16	Neil Back	Leicester	1998-99
15	Daren O'Leary	Harlequins	1996-97
15	Iain Balshaw	Bath	1999-00
14	Daren O'Leary	Harlequins	1995-96
14	Tom Beim	Sale	1997-98
13	Steven John	West Hartlepool	1996-97
13	Tom Beim	Sale	1996-97
13	Gary Armstrong	Newcastle	1997-98
13	Mark Cueto	Sale Sharks	2001-02

MOST CONVERSIONS - IN A MATCH

This record was never seriously challenged. The best return during the season was six conversions in a match by five different players.

EVOLUTION OF RECORD - Conversions in a match

10	Stuart Barnes	Bath v Bedford	13.01.90
13	Rich Butland	Richmond v Bedford	17.05.99

ALL-TIME RECORDS - Conversions in a match

13	Rich Butland	Richmond v Bedford	17.05.99
10	Stuart Barnes	Bath v Bedford	13.01.90
9	Paul Challinor	Quins v W. Hartlepool	23.03.96
8	Martin Strett	Orrell v Rosslyn P.	28.04.90
8	Will Carling	Quins v Orrell	05.10.96
8	Mike Catt	Bath v Sale	26.04.97
8	Niall Woods	Lon. Irish v Harlequins	25.04.98
8	Mike Catt	Bath v London Scottish	16.05.99
8	Alex King	Wasps v Bedford	26.03.00

MOST CONVERSIONS - IN A SEASON

Gloucester's new signing had an excellent first season and came within four of the record of 52 conversions in a season with his 48 as he smashed the club record for points in a season. His 48 conversions put him sixth on the all time list and beat the previous best for Gloucester by 12. Also getting into the top ten was Charlie Hodgson,England and Sale fly half, who moved into joint 11th on the list.

EVOLUTION OF RECORD - Conversions in a season

15	Dusty Hare	Leicester	1987-88
29	Stuart Barnes	Bath	1989-90
43	Jonathon Callard	Bath	1995-96
51	Jonathon Callard	Bath	1996-97
52	Gavin Johnson	Saracens	1998-99

ALL-TIME RECORDS - Conversions in a season

52	Gavin Johnson	Saracens	1998-99
52	Tim Stimpson	Leicester	1999-00
51	Jonathon Callard	Bath	1996-97
51	Jonny Wilkinson	Newcastle	1998-99
50	Mike Catt	Bath	1998-99
48	Ludovic Mercier	Gloucester	2001-02
47	Thierry Lacroix	Saracens	1999-00
47	Kenny Logan	London Wasps	2000-01
46	Jarod Cunningham	London Irish	1999-00
45	Gareth Rees	Wasps	1996-97
44	Rob Andrew	Newcastle	1997-98
44	Charlie Hodgson	Sale	2001-02
43	Jonathon Callard	Bath	1995-96
42	Shane Howarth	Sale	1998-99
39	Shane Howarth	Sale	1997-98
39	Joel Stransky	Leicester	1997-98

2001-02 RECORD REVIEW continued

MOST PENALTIES - IN A MATCH

This was where all the activity was last season. Gloucesters Simon Mannix equaled the record of nine penalties in a match. He did so against Harlequins to equal the record Thierry Lacroix set the previous season. Two other player moved into joint third on the all time list after kicking eight penalties in a match. They were Tim Stimpson in Leicesters home win against Gloucester and Jarrod Cunningham for London Irish against Bristol.
Five other players kicked seven penalties in a match and moved into joint sixth on the all time list. London Irishs new kicking star Barry Everitt achieved this feat twice.

EVOLUTION OF RECORD

6	Dusty Hare	Leicester v Rosslyn P.	19.11.88
7	David Pears	Quins v Rosslyn P.	07.12.91
8	John Liley	Leicester v Bristol	28.10.95
9	Thierry Lacroix	Saracens v Wasps	07.11.99
9	Simon Mannix	Gloucester v Harlequins	23.09.00

ALL-TIME RECORDS

9	Thierry Lacroix	Saracens v Wasps	07.11.99
9	Simon Mannix	Gloucester v Harlequins	23.09.00
9	Luke Smith	Saracens v Gloucester	08.09.01
9	Alex King	Wasps v Newcastle	11.11.01
8	John Liley	Leicester v Bristol	28.10.95
8	Jarrod Cunningham	London Irish v Bristol	10.09.00
8	Tim Stimpson	Leicester v Gloucester	02.12.00
8	Barry Everitt	London Irish v Bath	10.04.02
7	David Pears	Quins v Rosslyn P.	07.12.91
7	Jez Harris	Leicester v Bristol	11.12.93
7	Rob Andrew	Wasps v Orrell	11.12.93
7	Jez Harris	Leicester v Gloucester	29.01.94
7	Mark Tainton	Bristol v Leicester	05.1194
7	John Liley	Leicester v Bath	07.09.96
7	Simon Mannix	Sale v Northampton	08.03.97
7	Paul Grayson	N'hampton v Richmond	08.03.97
7	Shane Howarth	Sale v Wasps	18.04.98
7	Joel Stransky	Leicester v London Irish	
7	Steven Vile	W Hartlepool v Richmond	
7	Tim Stimpson	Leicester v Newcastle	
7	Tim Stimpson	Leicester v Gloucester	08.04.00
7	Paul Grayson	Northampton v Leicester	29.04.00
7	Nicky Little	Sale v Bath	19.08.00
7	Tim Stimpson	Leicester v Lon. Wasps	18.11.00
7	Barry Everitt	Lon. Irish v Harlequins	19.11.00
7	Kevin Sorrell	Saracens v Harlequins	17.12.00
7	Barry Everitt	London Irish v Bristol	24.02.01
7	Paul Burke	Harlequins v Lon Irish	01.09.01
7	Barry Everitt	Lon Irish v Leeds	09.09.01
7	Paul Burke	Harlequins v Wasps	22.09.01
7	Alex King	Wasps v Leicester	31.03.02
7	Barry Everitt	Lon Irish v Newcastle	08.05.02

MOST PENALTIES - IN A SEASON

Barry Everitt in his record breaking season broke this record as well adding six penalties to the previous total of 77 which has not been challenged since in was set by John Schuster back in 1998-99. Also getting into the all time top ten was Gloucester's Ludovic Mercier who kicked 64 penalties to move into joint fourth on the list. Finally we had Quins' Paul Burke make it into seevnth on the all time list.

EVOLUTION OF RECORD - Penalties in a season

31	Dusty Hare	Leicester	1987-88
31	Michael Corcoran	London Irish	1992-93
41	Jez Harris	Leicester	1993-94
56	Mark Tainton	Bristol	1994-95
64	John Liley	Leicester	1995-96
77	John Schuster	Harlequins	1998-99

ALL-TIME RECORDS - Penalties in a season

83	Barry Everitt	London Irish	2001-02
77	John Schuster	Harlequins	1998-99
66	Jarod Cunningham	Lon Irish	1999-00
64	John Liley	Leicester	1995-96
64	Ludovic Mercier	Gloucester	2001-02
63	T Stimpson	Leicester	1999-00
62	Gareth Rees	Wasps	1996-97
62	Simon Mannix	Gloucester	1999-00
62	Paul Burke	Harlequins	2001-02
58	Mark Mapletoft	Gloucester	1996-97
58	Michael Lynagh	Saracens	1997-98
58	Mark Mapletoft	Gloucester	1997-98
58	Gavin Johnson	Saracens	1998-99
58	Paul Grayson	Northampton	2000-01
57	Gareth Rees	Wasps	1997-98
57	Tim Stimpson	Leicester	2000-01
56	Mark Tainton	Bristol	1994-95

MOST DROP GOALS - IN A MATCH

This record was not challenged with nobody managing more than one drop goal in a match.

ALL-TIME RECORDS - Drop Goals in a match

3	John Steele	Northampton v Wasps	23.09.91
3	Jez Harris	Leicester v Wasps	23.11.91
3	Jez Harris	Leicester v Bath	15.04.95
3	Matthew McCarthy	Orrell v W. Hartlepool	07.12.96

2001-02

ZURICH PREMIERSHIP

MOST POINTS

POINTS			T	C	P	DG
343	Barry Everitt	London Irish	2	30	83	8
334	Ludovic Mercier	Gloucester	2	48	64	12
273	Charlie Hodgson	Sale	7	44	48	2
258	Paul Burke	Harlequins	3	21	62	5
238	Paul Grayson	Northampton	1	31	55	2
221	Felipe Contepomi	Bristol	9	25	40	2
215	Jonny Wilkinson	Newcastle	5	29	43	-
212	Tim Stimpson	Leicester	5	29	43	-
194	Luke Smith	Saracens	1	12	53	2
183	Alex King	Wasps	-	24	36	9
132	Braam van Straaten	Leeds Tykes	-	15	33	1
130	Shane Drahm	Brsitol	1	16	30	1
129	Olly Barkley	Bath	2	7	35	-
121	Kenny Logan	Wasps	3	5	32	-
112	Andy Goode	Leicester	4	16	15	5
75	David Walder	Newcastle	2	4	16	3
73	Matt Perry	Bath	2	3	17	2
65	Mark Cueto	Sale	13	-	-	-

MOST PENALTIES

83	Barry Everitt	London Irish
64	Ludovic Mercier	Gloucester
62	Paul Burke	Harlequins
55	Paul Grayson	Northampton
53	Luke Smith	Saracens
48	Charlie Hodgson	Sale
43	Jonny Wilkinson	Newcastle
43	Tim Stimpson	Leicester
40	Felipe Contepomi	Bristol
36	Alex King	Wasps
35	Olly Barkley	Bath
33	Braam van Straatan	Leeds Tykes
32	Kenny Logan	Wasps
30	Shane Drahm	Bristol
17	Matt Perry	Bath
16	David Walder	Newcastle

MOST TRIES

13	Mark Cueto	Sale
12	Danny Scarborough	Leeds Tykes
9	Junior Paramore	Gloucester
9	Geordan Murphy	Leicester
9	Jason Robinson	Sale
9	Steve Booth	Leicester
9	Felipe Contepomi	Bristol
9	James Simpson-Daniel	Gloucester
8	Ben Cohen	Northampton
8	Michael Stephenson	Newcastle
7	Steven Hanley	Sale
7	Charlie Hodgson	Sale
7	Tom May	Newcastle
7	Philip Christophers	Bristol

MOST CONVERSIONS

48	Ludovic Mercier	Gloucester
44	Charlie Hodgson	Sale
32	Jonny Wilkinson	Newcastle
31	Paul Grayson	Northampton
30	Barry Everitt	London Irish
29	Tim Stimpson	Leicester
25	Felipe Contepomi	Bristol
24	Alex King	Wasps
21	Paul Burke	Harlequins
16	Shane Drahm	Bristol
16	Andy Goode	Leicester
15	Braam van Straatan	Leeds Tykes
12	Luke Smith	Saracens
10	Jon Benson	Leeds Tykes

MOST DROP GOALS

12	Ludovic Mercier	Gloucester
9	Alex King	Wasps
8	Barry Everitt	London Irish
5	Andy Goode	Leicester
5	Paul Burke	Harlequins
3	Jonny Wilkinson	Newcastle
3	David Walder	Newcastle
3	Dan Parks	Leeds Tykes
2	Steve Booth	Leicester
2	Matt Perry	Bath
2	Luke Smith	Saracens

ZURICH PREMIERSHIP

FIXTURES 2002-03

Away Teams

	HOME TEAMS	Bath	Bristol	Gloucester	Leeds Tykes	Leicester Tigers	London Irish	London Wasps	NEC Harlequins	Newcastle Falcons	Northampton	Sale Sharks	Saracens	
1	Bath	XXX	23-11	28-09	26-10	26-04	14-09	10-05	28-12	10-05	15-03	09-11	19-04	1
2	Bristol	03-05	XXX	15-03	01-02	28-09	16-11	19-04	26-10	09-11	14-09	28-12	31-08	2
3	Gloucester	08-02	21-09	XXX	23-11	10-05	30-11	04-01	26-04	06-03	02-11	07-09	05-10	3
4	Leeds Tykes	04-01	05-10	03-05	XXX	31-08	07-09	30-11	06-03	08-02	16-11	21-09	02-11	4
5	Leicester Tigers	05-10	08-02	16-11	26-04	XXX	03-05	02-11	07-09	21-09	30-11	06-03	04-01	5
6	London Irish	31-08	10-05	09-11	19-04	23-11	XXX	28-09	15-03	28-12	26-10	01-02	14-09	6
7	London Wasps	06-03	07-09	26-10	09-11	28-12	08-02	XXX	10-05	26-04	01-02	23-11	21-09	7
8	NEC Harlequins	02-11	04-01	31-08	14-09	19-04	21-09	16-11	XXX	05-10	03-05	08-02	30-11	8
9	Newcastle Falcons	16-11	30-11	14-09	28-09	15-03	02-11	31-08	01-02	XXX	19-04	26-10	03-05	9
10	Northampton	21-09	06-03	28-12	10-05	09-11	04-01	05-10	23-11	07-09	XXX	26-04	08-02	10
11	Sale Sharks	30-11	02-11	19-04	15-03	14-09	05-10	03-05	28-09	04-01	31-08	XXX	16-11	11
12	Saracens	07-09	26-04	01-02	28-12	26-10	06-03	15-03	09-11	23-11	28-09	10-05	XXX	12
		1	2	3	4	5	6	7	8	9	10	11	12	

BATH RUGBY

Director of Rugby	Jack Rowell
Team Director	Michael Foley
Co-Coaches	Brian Smith
	Richard Graham
Chief Executive	Andrew Brownsword
General Manager	Bob Calleja
Commercial Manager	Tim Davies
Ticket Office Manager	Sarah Dade
Press Officer	Dom Rumbles

Bath Rugby,
11 Argyle Street,
Bath BA2 4BQ
01225 325200 (Office)
01225 325201 (Fax)

email: dom.rumbles@bathrugby.com

Whilst the 2001-02 season was undoubtedly one of great disappointment, Bath Rugby's Team Director Mike Foley can look forward to the new campaign of Zurich Premiership and Parker Pen Challenge Cup fixtures confident that the foundations have been laid for his side to challenge for honours.

Jack Rowell has returned as Director of Rugby to the club he left eight years ago after winning five league and eight cup titles, and the club has also been active on the player recruitment front. In come French International prop Alessio Galasso, Australian International second/back row Mark Connors, former Wales captain Jonathan Humphreys, England A flanker Adam Vander, Chris Malone and Ross Blake to bolster a squad that already boasts a number of World Class players.

It promises to be a far cry from a season which witnessed a horrendous injury list, a change in coaching staff at the top and a string of frustrating results that left the club fighting for its very Premiership status during the final months of a tense and highly competitive Zurich Premiership campaign.

Despite pundits having Jon Callard's side enlisted as second favourites to lift the Zurich Premiership title, things could not have started worse for Bath Rugby as the club had a lengthy injury list before the season even kicked off. That list included England trio Mike Catt, Mike Tindall and Iain Balshaw and was soon to have the names of Matt Perry, Dan Lyle and Gareth Cooper added to it. Four straight defeats in the Zurich Premiership left the club in the unaccustomed position at the foot of the table as Europe approached.

The Heineken Cup though, was to prove a timely boost to a side that had just recorded its worst-ever start to a Premiership campaign. Nobody gave Jon Callard's side a hope in what was aptly titled 'the pool of death'-that is everyone except for Callard and his team of young charges. With Mike Catt back fit pulling the shots at fly half, the side regained direction allowing the likes of Kevin Maggs and Mike Tindall to return to International class form.

Interestingly, Europe was also to signal the end of Bath Rugby's try-scoring drought in dramatic fashion. Tom Voyce scored a hat-trick against a much-fancied Swansea side and went on to score six tries in the Pool stages (a record by a Bath Rugby player) as the club sailed through Pool three without dropping a point. High optimism was soon to be scotched though as Bath Rugby lost a tough Heineken Cup quarter-final against Llanelli at the Rec.

Jon Callard's departure in March left Mike Foley at the helm of a club struggling with a massive injury list. Matt Perry, Mike Catt, Andy Williams, Gareth Cooper, Iain Balshaw and Mike Tindall all ended the season injured and it was down to the club's depth of talented youngsters to steer Bath Rugby away from the threat of relegation. In the event, relegation was abolished, but a young side had done enough to finish above Leeds in the Premiership.

Bath Rugby once again provided players for the Lloyds TSB Six Nations Championship and Investec Internationals with Mike Tindall, Mike Catt, Kevin Maggs, Danny Grewcock, Steve Borthwick, Gareth Cooper and Gavin Thomas all adding to their caps.

BATH

Comp	Date	H/A	Opponents	Result & Score	Att	15	14	13	12	11
ZP	02-09	A	Leeds Tykes	L 6-10	5181	Thirlby/2p	Voyce	Maggs	Cox	Danielle
ZP	08-09	A	Northampton Saints	L 7-26	10241	Thirlby	Voyce	Maggs	Cox	Danielle
ZP	15-09	H	Saracens	L 20-27	7968	Balshaw	Thirlby	Maggs	Cox	Danielle/t
ZP	22-09	A	Leicester Tigers	L 9-48	15145	Perry	Balshaw	Tindall	Cox	Danielle
ZP	13-10	H	Sale	W 20-17	7875	Perry/t4pdg	Balshaw	Tindall	Barklay	Voyce
ZP	20-10	A	Harlequins	L 8-15	5328	Bellinger	Thirlby	Crockett	Cox	Voyce
ZP	11-11	H	London Irish	W 19-11	7656	Perry/c4p	Voyce	Balshaw	Tindall/t	Danielle
ZP	18-11	A	Bristol	L 17-31	10021	Perry/p	Voyce	Crockett	Balshaw	Danielle
ZP	25-11	H	Newcastle Falcons	W 24-9	7903	Perry/tc4p	Danielle	Maggs/t	Balshaw	Voyce
ZP	02-12	A	London Wasps	L 10-23	6240	Perry/cp	Balshaw	Maggs	Tindall	Voyce
ZP	08-12	H	Gloucester	W 12-9	8200	Perry/3p	Balshaw/dg	Maggs	Tindall	Voyce
ZP	29-12	H	Bristol	W 15-9	8200	Balshaw	Thirlby	Barklay/5p	Tindall	Voyce
ZP	09-02	H	Harlequins	W 18-9	8200	Perry/dg	Balshaw	Maggs	Barklay/cp	Voyce
ZP	23-02	A	Sale	L 14-20		Perry	Balshaw	Maggs	Tindall	Voyce
ZP	09-03	H	Leicester Tigers	L 9-27	8200	Balshaw	Danielle	Maggs	Tindall	Voyce
ZP	17-03	A	Saracens	L 11-33	10828	Balshaw	Voyce	Crockett	Tindall/t	Danielle
ZP	30-03	H	Northampton Saints	L 11-29	8200	Balshaw	Danielle	Crockett	Tindall/p	Thirlby
ZP	10-04	A	London Irish	L 15-31	6055	Thirlby	Voyce	Tindall	Barklay/3p	Danielle
ZP	13-04	H	Leeds Tykes	W 23-12	8129	Thirlby	Danielle/t	Tindall	Barklay/t2c3p	Voyce
ZP	28-04	A	Newcastle Falcons	L 9-36	5430	Thirlby	Voyce	Tindall	Barklay/3p	Danielle
ZP	04-05	A	Gloucester	L 12-68	11000	Thirlby	Voyce	Cox/t	Davy	Danielle
ZP	12-05	H	London Wasps	L 22-24	8200	Thirlby/2p	Danielle	Cox	Davy	Voyce
HC	29-09	A	Biarritz	W 14-6	6500	Perry/3p	Balshaw	Maggs	Tindall	Voyce/t
HC	06-10	H	Swansea	W 38-9	7727	Perry/3c4p	Balshaw	Maggs/t	Tindall	Voyce/3t
HC	27-10	A	Edinburgh Reivers	W 37-6		Perry/t4c3p	Balshaw	Barklay	Maggs	Voyce/t
HC	03-11	H	Edinburgh Reivers	W 17-10	7811	Perry/4p	Balshaw	Maggs	Barklay	Voyce/t
HC	05-01	A	Swansea	W 24-12		Balshaw	Thirlby	Barklay/c4p	Tindall	Maggs/t
HC	12-01	H	Biarritz	W 31-13		Perry/t	Thirlby	Barklay/c3p	Tindall/2t	Maggs/t
HC	26-01	H	Llanelli	L 10-27	8200	Perry	Balshaw	Barklay/cp	Tindall	Maggs
PGC	15-12	H	London Irish	L 12-20	5332	Perry/3p	Balshaw	Maggs	Tindall	Danielle

** after opponents name indicates a penalty try. Brackets after a player's name indicates he was replaced. eg (a) means he was replaced by replacement code "a" and so on. / after a player or replacement name is followed by any scores he made - eg /t, /c, /p, /dg or any combination of these*

EVER PRESENT None

Most Appearances:
19: Oliver Barkley (1), David Barnes (4), Steve Borthwick (1), Tom Voyce (2).

PLAYERS USED

31 plus one as a replacement only

MOST POINTS

Pts	Player	T	C	P	DG
129	O Barkley	2	7	35	-
73	M Perry	2	3	17	2
13	M TIndall	2	-	1	-
12	R Thirlby	-	-	4	-

MATCH FACTS

10	9	1	2	3	4	5	6	7	8
Perry	Cooper	Barnes	Long	Mallett	Gabey	Borthwick	El Abd	Beattie	Lyle
Barklay/c	Cooper/t	Emms	Regan	Mallett	Borthwick	Grewcock	El Abd	Beattie	Thomas
Barklay/5p	Cooper	Barnes	Regan	Mallett	Borthwick	Grewcock	Thomas	Thomas	Lyle
Barklay/3p	Williams	Barnes	Regan	Mallett	Borthwick	Grewcock	Thomas	Thomas	Lyle
Catt	Williams	Barnes	Long	Mallett	Borthwick	Grewcock	Gabey	Thomas	Lyle
Barklay/p	Williams/t	Barnes	Regan	Mallett	Gabey	Beattie	Thomas	Thomas	Lyle
Barklay	Cooper	Barnes	Long	Emms	Borthwick	Gabey	Scayesbrook	Beattie	Lyle
Barklay/t2c	Cooper/t	Emms	Long	Mallett	Gabey	Beattie	El Abd	Scayesbrook	Lyle
Barklay	Cooper	Barnes	Long	Mallett	Borthwick	Gabey	Scayesbrook	Beattie	Lyle
Catt	Cooper	Barnes	Regan	Mallett	Borthwick	Grewcock	Thomas	Scayesbrook	Gabey/t
Catt	Cooper	Barnes	Regan	Mallett	Borthwick	Grewcock	Thomas	Scayesbrook	Gabey
Catt	Williams	Barnes	Long	Mallett	Borthwick	Grewcock	Thomas	Gabey	Thomas
Catt/t	Cooper	Barnes	Regan	Emms	Borthwick	Grewcock	Thomas	Thomas	Lyle/t
Barklay/3p	Chrystie(a/t)	Barnes	Regan	Emms	Borthwick	Grewcock	Thomas	Thomas	Gabey
Barklay/3p	Dalzell	Barnes	Regan	Mallett	Borthwick	Grewcock	Thomas	Thomas	Lyle
Barklay/2p	Dalzell	Barnes	Regan	Mallett	Borthwick	Grewcock	Thomas	Thomas	Lyle
Barklay/p(b/t)	Dalzell	Barnes	Long	Mallett	Borthwick	Grewcock	Thomas	Scayesbrook	Lyle
Balshaw/2dg	Dalzell	Emms	Long	Mallett	Gabey	Grewcock	Thomas	Scayesbrook	Lyle
Balshaw	Cooper	Barnes	Regan	Emms	Borthwick	Grewcock	Scayesbrook	Gabey	Lyle
Balshaw	Cooper	Barnes	Regan	Emms	Borthwick	Grewcock	Scayesbrook	Gabey	Lyle
Barklay/c	Dalzell	Barnes	Regan	Emms	Borthwick	Grewcock	G Thomas	N Thomas(c/t)	Lyle
Barklay/2p	Cooper	Barnes	Regan(d/t)	Emms	Borthwick	Grewcock	G Thomas/t	N Thomas	Lyle
Catt	Williams	Barnes	Long	Mallett	Borthwick	Grewcock	Thomas	Thomas	Lyle
Catt	Williams	Barnes	Long	Mallett	Borthwick	Grewcock	Thomas	Thomas	Lyle
Catt/t	Williams	Barnes	Regan	Emms	Grewcock	Borthwick	Thomas/t	Gabey	Lyle
Catt	Williams	Barnes	Regan	Emms	Borthwick	Grewcock	Thomas	Gabey	Lyle
Catt	Williams	Barnes	Long	Mallett	Borthwick	Grewcock	Thomas	Gabey/t	Thomas
Catt	Williams	Barnes	Long	Emms	Borthwick	Grewcock	Thomas	Gabey	Thomas
Catt	Williams	Barnes	Long	Emms	Borthwick	Grewcock	Thomas/t	Gabey	Thomas
Catt/dg	Williams	Barnes	Regan	Mallett	Borthwick	Grewcock	Thomas	Scayesbrook	Gabey

REPLACEMENTS: a - Kevin Dalzell. b - Tom Voyce. c - Gareth Delve. d - Andrew Long.

WHEN	Total	First Half	Second Half	1/4	2/4	3/4	4/4
The POINTS were scored	311	157	154	66	91	60	94
The POINTS were conceded	524	238	286	111	127	131	155
The TRIES were scored	21	5	16	2	3	7	9
The TRIES were conceded	47	17	30	6	11	13	17

HOW the TRIES were scored

Total	Backs	Forwards	F Back	Wing	Centre	H Back	F Row	Lock	B Row	Pen. Try
21	16	5	2	3	5	6	1	-	4	-

HOW the TRIES were conceded

Total	Backs	Forwards	F Back	Wing	Centre	H Back	F Row	Lock	B Row	Pen. Try
47	33	13	4	15	10	4	4	2	7	1

BATH RUGBY

LEAGUE STATISTICS

compiled by Stephen McCormack

SEASON	Division	P	W	D	L	F	A	Pts Diff	Lge Pts	Lge Pos	Most Points		Most Tries	
92-93	1	12	11	0	1	355	97	258	22	1	122	Jon Webb	7	Stuart Barnes
93-94	1	18	17	0	1	431	181	250	34	1	178	Jon Callard	5	Mike Catt & Ben Clarke
94-95	1	18	12	3	3	373	245	128	27	2	150	Jon Callard	5	Adedayo Adebayo
95-96	1	18	15	1	2	575	276	299	31	1	236	Jon Callard	9	Jeremy Guscott
96-97	1	22	15	1	6	863	411	452	31	2	224	Jon Callard	16	Adedayo Adebayo
97-98	P1	22	13	0	9	575	455	120	26	3	183	Jon Callard	9	Andy Nicol
98-99	P1	26	15	0	11	698	574	124	30	6	294	Mike Catt	14	Jeremy Guscott
99-00	P1	22	15	2	5	690	425	265	43	2	184	Jon Preston	15	Iain Balshaw
00-01	P1	22	14	0	8	680	430	250	70	3	172	Jon Preston	9	Tom Voyce
01-02	P	22	7	0	15	311	524	-213	28	11	129	Oliver Barkley	2	by 5 players

BIGGEST MARGINS

Home Win	77pts - 84-7 v Sale 26.4.97
Away Win	56pts - 68-12 v Rotherham 14.4.01
Home Defeat	18pts - 11-29 v 30.03.02
	9-27 v Bath 09.03.02
Away Defeat	56pts - 12-68 v Gloucester 04.05.02

MOST POINTS

Scored at Home	84 v Sale 26.4.97
Scored Away	68 v Rotherham 14.4.01
Conceded at Home	40 v Wasps 14.9.96
Conceded Away	68 v Gloucester 04.05.02

MOST CONSECUTIVE

Appearances	50 Tony Swift 9.9.89-25.9.93
Matches scoring Tries	6 Andy Nicol, Adedayo Adebayo
Matches scoring points	15 Jon Callard
Victories	15
Defeats	6 (2)

MOST TRIES

Scored in a match	14 v Bedford 13.1.90 v Sale 26.4.97
Conceded in a match	7 v London Irish 17.4.99

MOST APPEARANCES

by a forward	157 (9) Martin Haag
by a back	142 (5) Adedayo Adebayo

	MOST IN A SEASON		MOST IN A CAREER		MOST IN A MATCH		
Points	294	MikeCatt 98-99	1177	Jon Callard 89-00	26	Stuart Barnes	v W. Hartlepool 27.3.93 (A)
						Mike Catt	v Sale 26.4.97 (H)
							v London Scot 15.5.99 (H)
Tries	16	Adedayo Adebayo 96-97	67	Jeremy Guscott 85-99	4	Jeremy Guscott	v Bedford 13.1.90 (H)
						Jeremy Guscott	v London Scot 15.5.99 (H)
						Tony Swift	v Bedford 13.1.90 (H)
Conversions	51	Jon Callard 96-97	186	Jon Callard 89-00	10	Stuart Barnes	v Bedford 13.1.90 (H)
Penalties	53	Mike Catt 99-99	228	Jon Callard 89-00	6	Jon Callard	v Harlequins 6.4.96 (H)
						Mike Catt	v Richmond 13.3.99 (A)
						Jon Preston	v Bristol 25.03.00 (H)
Drop Goals	3	Iain Balshaw 01-02	9	Stuart Barnes 87-94	2	Iain B alshaw	v Lon Irish 10.04.02 (A)

OVERALL PLAYING RECORD

	P	W	D	L	F	A	Pts Diff
Home	33	21	0	12	737	350	387
Away	37	28	0	9	490	290	200
Neutral	10	10	0	0	226	115	111
Total	80	59	0	21	1433	755	698

SEASON BY SEASON

Season	Result
1971-72	1R
1972-73	1R
1973-74	2R
1974-75	QF
1975-76	1R
1976-77	1R
1977-78	1R
1978-79	1R
1979-80	QF
1980-81	4R
1981-82	3R
1982-83	DNQ
1983-84	Won
1984-85	Won
1985-86	Won
1986-87	Won
1987-88	QF
1988-89	Won
1989-90	Won
1990-91	3R
1991-92	Won
1992-93	3R
1993-94	Won
1994-95	Won
1995-96	Won
1996-97	6R
1997-98	5R
1998-99	4R
1999-2000	4R
2000-01	4R
2001-02	6R

BATH
RFU SENIOR CUP
STATISTICS
compiled by Stephen McCormack

TEAM RECORDS

Highest Score
82 v Oxford 88/89
Biggest Winning Margin
73 (82-9) v Oxford 88/89
Highest Score Against
39 v Leicester 96/97
Biggest Losing Margin
24 (27-3) v Wilmslow 73/74

INDIVIDUAL RECORDS

Most Points in a match

Most Tries in a match
4 more than once
Most Conversions in a match

Most Penalties in a match
6 Jon Pretson v Gloucester 00/01
Most Drop Goals in a match
3 Mike Catt v Orrell 94/95

EUROPEAN COMPETITIONS
STATISTICS *compiled by Stephen McCormack*

TEAM RECORDS

Highest Score
56-15 v Padova 1999/00
Biggest Winning Margin
41 Pts 56-15 v Padova 1999/00
Highest Score Against
31-9 v Munster 2000/01
Biggest Losing Margin
22 Pts 31-9 v Munster 2000/01

INDIVIDUAL RECORDS

Most Points in a match
33 Mike Catt v B Treviso 96/97
Most Tries in a match
4 Mike Catt v B Treviso 96/97
Most Conversions in a match
7 Jon Callard v Edinburgh 96/97
Most Penalties in a match
6 Jon Callard v Toulouse 99/00
6 Jon Preston v Castres 00/01
Most Drop Goals in a match
1 Matt Perry v Swanseas 99/00

CAREER RECORDS

Most Appearances:
28: Mike Catt.
25: Matt Perry.
20: Dan Lyle.
19: Mark Regan, Martin Haag.

Most Points:
216: Jonathan Callard.
103: Matt Perry.
97: Jon Preston.
78: Mike Catt

Most Tries:
9: Mike Catt.
7: Tom Voyce.
6: Adedayo Adebayo.

SEASON BY SEASON

Season		Result
1996-97	C	QF
1997-98	C	Won
1998-99	-	D N Play
1999-00	C	Gp Stage
2000-01	C	Gp Stage
2001-02	C	Gp Stage

OVERALL PLAYING RECORD

	P	W	D	L	F	A	Pts Diff
Home	16	15	0	1	462	236	226
Away	16	9	0	7	366	297	69
Neutral	1	1	0	0	19	18	1
Total	33	25	0	8	847	551	296

BATH RUGBY

Founded: 1865

Colours: Blue with black and white

Change colours: Black with white and blue

Website: www.bathrugby.com

GROUND The Recreation Ground, Bath. BA2 6PW.
Telephone: 01225 325200 Fax: 01225 325201
e-mail: enquiries@bathrugby.com
Capacity:7,622 + 560 in corporate boxes (8,182)
Seated: (covered) 2,044 (uncovered) 3,696 Standing: 1,868

Directions: Follow signs to Bath City Centre and then signs to the Recreation Ground.
Nearest Railway Station: Bath Spa (BR). From station walk up Manvers St. towards centre of town.
Turn right into North Parade & left down steps.

Car Parking: None on ground, unlimited `Park & Ride'.

Admission Matchdays: Variable depending upon fixture Ticket Office: 01225 460588
Season Tickets: From £85 Junior to £385 covered seating email: tickets@bathrugby.com

Club Shop: 1 Argyle Street, Bath BA2 4BA Tel: 01225 311950.

Clubhouse: Matchdays 12-11 Snacks & bar meals are available.
Functions: Capacity 250-300
Clubhouse Manager: Dean Quinton 01225 469230 email: clubhouse@bathrugby.com

PROGRAMME Size: A5 Pages: 56 Price: £2.50 Editor: Jennie McMahon 01225 325200
Advertising Rates Colour (Rates excl. VAT) Page £2,000 1/2 page £1,250

BRISTOL SHOGUNS

Chairman & Chief Executive	Malcolm Pearce
Commercial Director	Mike Turner
Operations Director	David Winnie
Registered Office	Bristol Rugby Ltd., Unit 4, Eastgate Office Centre, Eastgate Road, Bristol BS5 6XX Tel: 0117 311 1561 Fax: 0117 311 1460
Head Coach	Peter Thorburn
Marketing & Media Manager	Justin Hopwood Tel: 0117 311 1480 Mobile: 0797 1155112 Fax: 0117 311 1462 Email: jhopwood@bristolshoguns.co.uk

The 2001/02 season gave the supporters of Bristol Shoguns a Twickenham final, security of a five-year £2 million sponsorship deal and the opportunity to watch some of the most exciting rugby in the Zurich Premiership.

The Club had a new name, Bristol Shoguns, thanks to the record breaking sponsorship package with motoring giants Mitsubishi Motors. The team also saw the arrival of some of the game's most promising young talent in the form of Phil Christophers and Andrew Higgins, as well as securing the signatures of England international prop, Julian White and double world cup winning centre, Jason Little.

Despite a mixed start, supporters at the Memorial Stadium witnessed some breathtaking rugby during the second half of the season. With the Shoguns finishing the season with the most bonus points in the Zurich Premiership and with three players in the top try scorers chart.

Highlights on the playing side included victories over Bath, Northampton Saints, Leicester Tigers and NEC Harlequins. However, the pinnacle of the season was reached after two superb victories over Leicester and Northampton in the quarter-final and semi-finals respectively of the Zurich Championship.

Bristol Shoguns reached Twickenham for the first time in 14 years and narrowly lost out to West Country rivals Gloucester in a tense end of season contest that also saw the Shoguns U21s compete in their respective Championship final as a curtain raiser. However, reaching the final secured a place for the first team in the Heineken Cup for the 2002/03 season.

With a Twickenham final and Heineken Cup qualification secured, the team captain Jason Little called time on his impressive career. The double world cup winner's departure was soon followed by Dean Ryan's transfer to Gloucester, with the former England number eight being replaced by former All Black selector Peter Thorburn, who joined the club in the Spring.

Off the field, attendance figures increased by more than 20 per cent and sponsorship grew on the back of the record breaking official main sponsor agreement with Mitsubishi Motors. The 2001/02 season saw demand outstrip supply of the corporate boxes. Record interest in the home fixture against Bath saw more than 900 corporate hospitality tickets sold for the West Country derby in November.

With the expected new signings strengthening the squad and the Shoguns U21s on a high after picking up their third consecutive league trophy in 2002, everyone involved with Bristol Shoguns is looking forward to the 2002/03 season.

BRISTOL

Comp.	Date	H/A	Opponents	Result & Score	Att	15	14	13	12	11
ZP	18-05	A	Leicester Tigers	W 27-13	4771	Best	Rees/t	Williams/t	Little	Christophers
ZP	02-09	H	Sale	L 25-35	4020	Carrington	Rees	Higgins	Little/t	Christophers
ZP	08-09	A	Harlequins	W 38-32	5220	Carrington	Rees	Higgins	Little/2t	Christophers
ZP	16-09	H	London Irish	D 19-19	3900	Best	Rees/t	Christophers	Little	Brown/t
ZP	23-09	H	Leeds Tykes	W 34-29	3632	Carrington	Rees	Christophers/t	Little	Brown
ZP	14-10	A	Newcastle Falcons	L 20-37		Carrington/t	Rees	Higgins	Little/t	Christophers
ZP	21-10	H	London Wasps*	W 43-22	4147	Carrington	Rees	Contepomi/2t3cp	Little	Christophers
ZP	10-11	A	Gloucester	L 17-51	8431	Carrington	Best	Rees/t	Little	Brown
ZP	18-11	H	Bath	W 31-17	10021	Carrington	Nabaro	Rees	Little	Brown/t
ZP	25-11	A	Northampton Saints	W 23-20	7873	Carrington(e/t)	Rees	Christophers	Little	Nabaro
ZP	02-12	H	Saracens	L 22-25	4450	Best	Rees	Christophers	Little	Nabaro
ZP	08-12	A	Leicester Tigers	L 19-26	15519	Best/c	Rees	Christophers	Little	Brown
ZP	29-12	A	Bath	L 9-15	8200	Carrington	Rees	Higgins	Little	Christophers
ZP	10-02	A	London Wasps	L 16-34	5425	Williams	Daniel	Christophers/t	Little	Brown
ZP	24-02	H	Newcastle Falcons	W 33-17	5021	Williams/t	Daniel	Higgins	Little	Christophers/t
ZP	10-03	A	Leeds Tykes	L 6-24	2034	Williams	Daniel	Higgins	Little	Christophers
ZP	16-03	A	London Irish	L 13-24	12873	Williams	Rees/t	Higgins	Little	Christophers
ZP	31-03	H	Harlequins	W 43-27	5618	Williams(e/t)	Rees	Higgins/t	Little	Christophers/2t
ZP	13-04	A	Sale	L 47-53	3609	Best/t	Rees/t	Higgins	Little/t	Christophers
ZP	21-04	H	Gloucester	L 40-41	7066	Best/t	Rees	Williams/t	Contepomi/t4c4p	Christophers/t
ZP	05-05	H	Leicester Tigers	W 38-21	6566	Best	Rees	Higgins/t	Little/t	Christophers/t
ZP	08-05	H	Northampton Saints	L 27-37	4002	Best	Daniel	Rees/t	Little	Christophers
ZP	12-05	A	Saracens	W 28-26	9726	Best/t	Cadwallader/t	Williams	Little(b/p)	Daniel/t
ES	30-09	A	Bourgoin	W 34-28	4000	Carrington/t	Rees/2t	Little/t	Contepomi	Christophers
ES	07-10	H	Neath	W 10-6	3006	Carrington	Rees	Higgins	Little	Christophers
ES	28-10	N	Viadana	W 42-16	1100	Carrington/t	Rees/2t	Christophers/t	Higgins	Brown
ES	04-11	H	Viadana	W 31-15	2543	Carrington	Rees/t	Higgins	Little	Brown/t
ES	05-01	A	Neath	L 29-33	4500	Carrington	Nabaro	Higgins/t	Little	Christophers
ES	13-01	H	Bourgoin	W 43-17	2695	Christophers/t	Nabaro	Higgins/t	Little/t	Brown
ES	25-01	A	Sale	L 20-25	3607	Carrington	Nabaro	Higgins	Little	Christophers/t
PGC	16-12	H	Gloucester	L 23-37	5363	Best/t	Rees/t	Christophers	Little	Brown
ZPO	18-05	A	Leicester Tigers	W 27-13	4771	Best	Rees/t	Williams/t	Little	Christophers
ZPO	01-06	H	Northampton	W 32-24	5292	Best	Carrington	Rees	Little	Christophers
ZPO	08-06	N	Gloucester	L 23-28	28500	Best	Williams	Rees	Little	Christophers

** after opponents name indicates a penalty try. Brackets after a player's name indicates he was replaced. eg (a) means he was replaced by replacement code "a" and so on. / after a player or replacement name is followed by any scores he made - eg /t, /c, /p, /dg or any combination of these*

EVER PRESENT

Most Appearances:
- 21: Alex Brown (1), Jason Little.
- 19: Phil Christophers (1), Neil McCarthy (1), Ben Sturnham (1)..

PLAYERS USED

32 plus one as a replacement only.

MOST POINTS

Pts	Player	T	C	P	DG
221	F Contepomi	9	25	40	2
130	S Drahm	1	16	30	1
35	P Christophers	7	-	-	-
30	J Little	6	-	-	-
27	L Best	5	1	-	-

MATCH FACTS

10	9	1	2	3	4	5	6	7	8
Contepomi/3cpdg	Pichot	Crompton	McCarthy	Bergamaschi	Sturnham	Brown	Short	Lipman/t	rownrigg
Drahm/c6p	Pichot	Johnstone	Nelson	White	Archer	Brown	Salter	Short	Sturnham
Drahm/3c4p	Pichot	Johnstone	McCarthy	White	Archer	Brown	Brownrigg(a/t)	Short	Sturnham/t
Drahm/2p(b/p)	Pichot	Johnstone	McCarthy	White	Archer	Brown	Brownrigg	Short	Sturnham
Contepomi/2t2c5p	Pichot	Johnstone	McCarthy	White	Sheridan	Brown	Salter	Short	Sturnham
Drahm/2c2p	Pichot	Payne	McCarthy	Crompton	Archer	Brown	Salter	Vander	Sturnham
Drahm/c3pdg(c/t)	Pichot	Johnstone	McCarthy	Crompton	Archer	Brown	Salter	Vander	Sturnham
Drahm/2cp	Van Zyl	Johnstone	McCarthy	White	Archer	Brown	Salter	Short	Sturnham(d/t)
Drahm/2c4p	Van Zyl	Johnstone	McCarthy/t	Crompton	Archer/t	Brown	Short	Vander	Salter
Contepomi/t2c3p	Pichot	Johnstone	McCarthy	White	Archer	Brown	Short	Vander	Sturnham
Drahm/c5p	Van Zyl	Johnstone	McCarthy	White	Sheridan	Brown	Short	Vander/t	Sturnham
Contepomi/t3pdg	Pichot	Johnstone	Nelson	White	Sheridan	Brown	Short	Vander	Sturnham
Contepomi/3p	Pichot	Johnstone	McCarthy	White	Archer	Brown	Short	Vander	Sturnham
Contepomi/c3p	Blake	Johnstone	McCarthy	Crompton	Sheridan	Brown	Salter	Short	Sturnham
Drahm/2c3p	Blake	Johnstone	McCarthy	White/t	Archer	Sheridan	Salter	Vander/t	Brown
Contepomi/pdg	Blake	Johnstone	McCarthy	White	Sturnham	Brown	Sheridan	Vander	Salter
Contepomi/c2p	Blake	Johnstone	McCarthy	White	Sheridan	Brown	Short	Lipman	Salter
Contepomi/t5cp	Pichot	Johnstone	McCarthy	White	Archer	Brown	Sheridan/t	Lipman	Sturnham
Contepomi/3c4p(f/t2c)	Pichot	Crompton	McCarthy	White	Archer	Brown	Sheridan	Lipman/t	Sturnham
Drahm	Pichot	Johnstone	McCarthy	White	Sheridan	Brown	Short	Lipman	Sturnham
Contepomi/t3c4p	Pichot	Crompton	McCarthy	White	Archer	Brown	Short	Lipman	Sturnham
Contepomi/c4p	Pichot/tdg	Crompton	McCarthy	White	Archer	Brown	Sheridan	Lipman	Sturnham
Carrington/2c2p	Pichot	Payne	Nelson	White	Archer	Sturnham	Morgan	Short	Brownrigg
Drahm/4c2p	Pichot	Johnstone	Nelson	White	Sturnham	Brown	Brownrigg	Short	Salter
Drahm/tcp	Pichot	Johnstone	McCarthy	White	Archer	Brown	Salter	Vander	Sturnham
Contepomi/4c3p	Pichot	Johnstone	Nelson	White	Sheridan	Brown	Short	Vander/t	Sturnham
Contepomi/2c4p	Blake	Crompton	Nelson	White	Sheridan	Archer	Short	Lipman(g/t)	Salter
Contepomi/2c5p	Pichot	Johnstone	McCarthy	White	Archer	Brown/t	Salter	Short	Sturnham
Drahm/t5cp	Blake	Johnstone	McCarthy	White	Archer/2t	Brown	Brownrigg	Short	Salter
Contepomi/t2c2p	Pichot	Johnstone	McCarthy	White	Archer	Brown	Sheridan	Short	Salter
Contepomi/2c3p	Pichot	Johnstone	Nelson	Crompton	Sturnham	Brown	Short	Vander	Brownrigg
Contepomi/3cpdg	Pichot	Crompton	McCarthy	Bergamaschi	Sturnham	Brown	Short	Lipman/t	Brownrigg
Contepomi/2/2c6p	Pichot	Crompton	McCarthy	Bergamaschi	Archer	Brown	Short	Lipman	Sturnham
Contepomi/2c3p	Pichot/t	Crompton(h/t)	McCarthy	White	Archer	Brown	Short	Lipman	Sturnham

REPLACEMENTS: a - Matt Salter. b - Felipe Contepomi. c - Luke Nabaro. d - Andrew Sheridan. e - Lee Best. f - Shane Drahm. g - Adam Vander. h - Paul Johnstone

WHEN	Total	First Half	Second Half	1/4	2/4	3/4	4/4
The POINTS were scored	591	289	302	116	173	162	140
The POINTS were conceded	632	280	352	105	175	112	240
The TRIES were scored	55	23	32	8	15	16	16
The TRIES were conceded	66	26	40	9	17	11	29

HOW the TRIES were scored

Total	Backs	Forwards	F Back	Wing	Centre	H Back	F Row	Lock	B Row	Pen. Try
55	44	10	7	12	17	8	2	2	6	1

HOW the TRIES were conceded

Total	Backs	Forwards	F Back	Wing	Centre	H Back	F Row	Lock	B Row	Pen. Try
66	40	25	7	9	16	8	5	3	17	1

BRISTOL

LEAGUE STATISTICS
compiled by Stephen McCormack

SEASON	Division	P	W	D	L	F	A	Pts Diff	Lge Pts	Lge Pos	Most Points	Most Tries
92-93	1	12	6	0	6	148	169	-21	12	6	68 Mark Tainton	3 Derek Eves
93-94	1	18	10	0	8	331	276	55	20	4	161 Mark Tainton	8 A Saveriamutto
94-95	1	18	7	0	11	301	353	-52	14	6	196 Mark Tainton	6 Derek Eves
95-96	1	18	8	0	10	329	421	-92	16	6	120 Mark Tainton	4 Martin Corry
96-97	1	22	8	1	13	432	625	-193	17	9	178 Paul Burke	10 David Tiueti
97-98	P1	22	2	0	20	351	733	-382	4	12r	163 Paul Burke	7 David Tiueti
98-99	P2	26	22	0	4	848	418	430	44	1p	164 Paul Hull	13 A Larkin & L Nabaro
99-00	P1	22	12	1	9	632	602	30	34	6	178 Henry Honiball	9 Spencer Brown
00-01	P1	22	9	1	12	443	492	-49	44	11	168 Felipe Contepomi	5 Jamie Mayer
01-02	P	22	9	1	12	591	632	-41	50	8	221 Felipe Contepomi	9 Felipe Contepomi

BIGGEST MARGINS

Home Win	41pts - 55-14 v Fylde 12.9.98	
Away Win	38pts - 57-19 v Bedford 28.4.00	
Home Defeat	42pts	8-50 v Newcastle 27.12.97
Away Defeat	76pts	0-76 v Sale 9.11.97

MOST CONSECUTIVE

Appearances	81 Derek Eves 11.3.88 - 4.3.95
Matches scoring Tries	4 Luke Nabaro
Matches scoring points	31 Mark Tainton
Victories	8
Defeats	12

MOST POINTS

Scored at Home	58 v Moseley 22.11.98
Scored Away	57 v Bedford 28.4.00
Conceded at Home	50 v Newcastle 27.12.97
Conceded Away	76 v Bath 30.10.96 v Sale 9.11.97

MOST TRIES

Scored in a match	10 v Rugby 28.3.92
Conceded in a match	12 v Sale 9.11.97 (A)

MOST APPEARANCES

by a forward	107(1) Dave Hinkins
by a back	146 (4) Paul Hull

	MOST IN A SEASON	MOST IN A CAREER	MOST IN A MATCH
Points	221 Felipe Contepomi 01-02	637 Mark Tainton 87-97	31 Felipe Contepomi v North'ton 16.4.01 (H)
Tries	13 Adam Larkin 98-99 Luke Nabaro 98-99	28 Paul Hull 87-99	5 Luke Nabaro v Blackheath 13.3.99 (H)
Conversions	35 Paul Hull 98-99	62 Mark Tainton 87-97	5 Jon Webb v Sale 24.10.87 (H) Henry Honiball v Sale 13.11.99 (A)
Penalties	56 Mark Tainton 94-95	165 Mark Tainton 87-97	7 Mark Tainton v Leicester 5.11.94 (H)
Drop Goals	3 Simon Hogg 88-89 Arwel Thomas 95-96	6 Mark Tainton 87-97	2 Simon Hogg v Leicester 9.3.91 (H)

BRISTOL SHOGUNS RFU SENIOR CUP STATISTICS

compiled by Stephen McCormack

OVERALL PLAYING RECORD

	P	W	D	L	F	A	Pts Diff
Home	36	24	0	12	795	426	369
Away	35	22	0	13	655	408	247
Neutral	5	1	0	4	105	131	-26
Total	76	47	0	29	1555	965	590

SEASON BY SEASON

Season	Result
1971-72	2R
1972-73	Runners up
1973-74	2R
1974-75	2R
1975-76	QF
1976-77	2R
1977-78	QF
1978-79	DNQ
1979-80	2R
1980-81	4R
1981-82	4R
1982-83	**Winners**
1983-84	Runners up
1984-85	3R
1985-86	3R
1986-87	QF
1987-88	Runners up
1988-89	QF
1989-90	QF
1990-91	4R
1991-92	QF
1992-93	3R
1993-94	5R
1994-95	5R
1995-96	QF
1996-97	6R
1997-98	4R
1998-99	4R
1999-2000	SF
2000-01	5R
2001-02	6R

TEAM RECORDS

Highest Score
60 v Blackheath 96/97
Biggest Winning Margin
55 (55-0) v Sandal 98/99
Highest Score Against
43 v Leicester 84/85 & London Irish 98/99
Biggest Losing Margin
39 (43-4) v Leicester 84/85

INDIVIDUAL RECORDS

Most Points in a match
22 Felipe Contepomi 00/01
Most Tries in a match

Most Conversions in a match

Most Penalties in a match

Most Drop Goals in a match

EUROPEAN COMPETITIONS

STATISTICS *compiled by Stephen McCormack*

TEAM RECORDS

Highest Score
61 v Parma 00/01
Biggest Winning Margin
48 (53-5) v
Highest Score Against
51 v
Biggest Losing Margin
28 (7-35) v

INDIVIDUAL RECORDS

Most Points in a match
31 Steven Vile v Mont de Marsan 00/01
31 Felipe Contepomi v Parma 00/01
Most Tries in a match
2
Most Conversions in a match
7 Felipe Contepomi v Parma 00/01
Most Penalties in a match
9 Steven Vile v Mont de Marsan 00/01
Most Drop Goals in a match
1 Paul Burke v Narbonne 96/97

CAREER RECORDS

Most Appearances
18: Craig Short
16: Paul Johnstone
13: Kristyan Fulman
Most Points
123: Felipe Contepomi
109: Paul Burke
99: Steven Vile
Most Tries
6:Adam Vander, David Rees.
4: Barry Williams, Tevita Tuieti, Sean Marsden.

SEASON BY SEASON

Season		Result
1996-97	S	2nd Round
1997-98	S	1st Round
1998-99	-	2nd Round
1999-00	S	3rd Round
2000-01	S	2nd Round
2001-02	S	QF

OVERALL PLAYING RECORD

	P	W	D	L	F	A	Pts Diff
Home	15	11	1	3	482	277	205
Away	17	6	0	11	393	465	-172
Neutral	-	-	-	-	-	-	-
Total	32	17	0	14	875	742	33

BRISTOL SHOGUNS

FACT FILE

Founded: 1888

Colours: Dark blue with a broad white band on the front
Change colours: White shirt with red and blue shoulders

GROUND

Address: Memorial Stadium, Filton Avenue, Horfield, Bristol. BS7 0AQ

Tel: 0117 908 5500 Fax: 0117 907 4682 Website: www.bristolshoguns.co.uk
Capacity: 11,700 Seated: 2,840 Standing: 8,860

Directions: M4 to junction 19, M32 to junction 2, then join B4469 towards Horfield. Turn left at 2nd set of traffic lights after `Brunel Ford' and bus garage (on the right) into Filton Ave. Ground is on the left.

Nearest Railway Station: Bristol Parkway or Bristol Temple Meads.

Car Parking: Very limited at the ground. Plenty of street parking nearby

Admission:

Season tickets: Centenary and West Stand £180
West Enclosure, Centenary Terrace and Clubhouse Terrace £135 (concession £85)
South Stand and Family Enclosure £110 (U16 £20)
Family ticket in Centenary Stand £450 Family ticket in South Stand or Family Enclosure £205

Match day: Centenary and West Stand £18
West Enclosure, Centenary Terrace and Clubhouse Terrace £14 (concession £10)
South Stand and Family Enclosure £14 (U16 £2)
Family ticket in Centenary Stand £54 Family ticket in South Stand or Family Enclosure £30

Shoguns Shop: Monday - Friday 9.30 - 5.00, Saturday 10 - 3 & matchdays from noon

Clubhouse: Snacks & bar meals available. Contact: Robert Laurence
Tel: 0117 909 6648. Mob: 07831 463437 Fax: 0117 908 5530
Corprate Hospitality: John Reid Mobile: 0797 1155187 Tel: 0117 311 1464 Fax: 0117 311 1462

PROGRAMME

Justin Hopwood, Marketing & Media Manager, Bristol Shoguns, Unit 4, Eastgate Office Centre, Eastgate Road, Bristol, BS5 6XX
Tel: 0117 311 1480; Fax: 0117 311 1462; Mobile: 0797 1155112; Email: jhopwood@bristolshoguns.co.uk

GLOUCESTER RFC

Club Chairman	Tom Walkinshaw
Managing Director	Ken Nottage
Company Secretary	Doug Wadley
Director of Rugby	Nigel Melville
Coach	Dean Ryan
Commercial Officer	Karen Ellis
Media & Marketing Exec.	James Bennett (Mob: 07989 582111)

c/o Gloucester Rugby Club,
Kingsholm,
Kingsholm Road,
Gloucester GL1 3AX
Tel: 01452 381087
Ticket Office: 01452 381087
Fax: 01452 383321

On the whole, Gloucester enjoyed a very satisfying end to the 2001/02 season. After finishing third in the Zurich Premiership, behind perennial Champions Leicester Tigers and the League's surprise package Sale Sharks, on the 8th June they played Bristol Shoguns in the Zurich Championship final.

After destroying Newcastle at home and Sale Sharks away in the previous rounds, the stage was set for Gloucester to take on Bristol in a true West Country showdown between the leagues oldest teams. Although not a great playing spectacle, as the occasion and long season perhaps got to a few players, it was still a pulsating match and with twenty-three points from the best buy of the season, Ludovic Mercier, and a try from man of the match Jake Boer Gloucester won the day 28-23.

Gloucester's form throughout the season and particularly in the lead up to this season's climax was again excellent but perhaps they have still not fulfilled their potential. At Kingsholm, the Cherry and Whites were almost unbeatable, almost, because they did suffer one defeat at home to the Premiership Champions Leicester. It was, however, Gloucester's away form that prevented them from challenging the Tigers more strongly.

In European competition Gloucester swept all before them in the pool stages, and on a cold, wet, windy night they won a tricky Anglo-Welsh fixture against Ebbw Vale in the Parker Pen Shield Quarter-Final. Unfortunately they failed at the penultimate hurdle as they lost to the Sale Sharks in a nail-biting Semi-Final, that the Cheshire side won by a solitary point.

Lessons were learned and towards the end of the season, under the guidance of new director of rugby, Nigel Melville, Gloucester began to raise their standards and tread new ground with away wins against Bristol and Leeds. Finally they had exorcised the demons that had plagued them away from home and with a full pre-season under his belt, Melville, along with new coaching team Dean Ryan, Paul Turner and defensive coach Dave Ellis, will expect to raise the standards once more and mount a serious challenge to the Tigers next season.

Picture by "Bruce Seabrook/Gloucestershire Picture Agency"

E-mail: gpa@gloucestershirepictureagency.co.uk

www.gloucestershirepictureagency.co.uk

GLOUCESTER

Comp.	Date	H/A	Opponents	Result & Score	Att	15	14	13	12	11
ZP	01-09	H	Northampton Saints	W 22-9	8682	Catling	O'Leary	Ewens	Stoica	Albanese
ZP	08-09	A	Saracens	L 30-34	7262	Catling	O'Leary/t	Ewens	Stoica	Albanese
ZP	15-09	H	Leicester Tigers	L 18-40	9729	Stoica	O'Leary	Ewens	Fanolua	Albanese
ZP	22-09	A	Sale	W 44-21	4682	Stoica	O'Leary	Ewens	Fanolua/t	Simpson Daniel
ZP	13-10	H	Harlequins*	W 33-7		Catling	O'Leary	Ewens	Todd	Albanese/t
ZP	21-10	A	London Irish	L 15-19	5937	Catling	O'Leary	Ewens	Todd	Frape
ZP	10-11	H	Bristol	W 51-17	8431	Catling/t	O'Leary	Fanolua(d/t)	Paul/c	Ewens
ZP	18-11	A	Newcastle Falcons	L 16-18	5576	Todd	O'Leary	Fanolua	Paul	Ewens
ZP	23-11	H	London Wasps*	W 43-13	10171	Todd	O'Leary	Fanolua	Paul/c2p	Albanese
ZP	01-12	H	Leeds Tykes	W 58-17	7516	Todd	O'Leary/t(g/t)	Ewens/t	Paul/tc	Simpson Daniel/2
ZP	08-12	A	Bath	L 9-12	8200	Todd	O'Leary	Ewens	Paul	Albanese
ZP	29-12	H	Newcastle Falcons	W 29-25	11000	O'Leary/t	Ewens	Fanolua/t	Todd	Albanese
ZP	09-02	H	London Irish	W 29-22	10112	O'Leary	Fanolua/t	Paul	Todd	Albanese
ZP	23-02	A	Harlequins	W 18-6	8000	O'Leary	Fanolua	Paul	Todd	Albanese/t
ZP	09-03	H	Sale	W 42-14	9461	O'Leary	Albanese	Paul	Todd	Fanolua(d/t)
ZP	16-03	A	Leicester Tigers	L 10-27	16250	O'Leary	Albanese	Paul	Todd	Fanolua
ZP	30-03	H	Saracens	W 36-13	9236	Catling	O'Leary	Paul/c	Todd/t	Fanolua/t
ZP	10-04	A	London Wasps	L 9-44	5769	O'Leary	Albanese	Fanolua	Todd	Beim
ZP	13-04	A	Northampton Saints	L 21-58	9138	Catling	O'Leary	Simpson Daniel	Fanolua	Beim
ZP	21-04	A	Bristol	W 41-40	7066	Catling	O'Leary	Simpson Daniel	Fanolua	Beim
ZP	04-05	H	Bath	W 68-12	11000	Paul/t	Albanese	Fanolua/2t	Todd/t	Simpson Daniel/3
ZP	12-05	A	Leeds Tykes	W 50-17	4144	Paul	Albanese(i/t)	Fanolua	Todd	Simpson Daniel/2
ES	29-09	H	La Rochelle	W 34-15		Stoica/t	O'Leary(m/t)	Fanolua	Todd	Simpson Daniel
ES	06-10	N	Gran Parma Rugby	W 48-5		Stoica/t	Simpson Daniel/2t	Ewens	Todd	Albanese
ES	27-10	H	Caerphilly	W 98-0	7336	Goodridge/t	O'Leary/t	Fanolua/t	Paul/t10cp	Simpson Daniel/2
ES	04-11	N	Caerphilly	W 47-16	3500	Goodridge(m/t)	Todd/t	Fanolua	Paul	Simpson Daniel
ES	05-01	N	Gran Parma Rugby	W 99-0	6567	Goodridge	O'Leary/5t	Ewens/t	Fanolua/t	Albanese/t(k/t)
ES	12-01	N	La Rochelle	W 36-12	5000	Mercier/2c3p2dg	O'Leary/t	Fanolua	Todd	Ewens
ES	25-01	H	Ebbw Vale	W 46-11	6816	O'Leary/t	Simpson Daniel/t	Fanolua	Todd	Albanese
ES sf	28-04	N	Sale	L 27-28	5785	Catling	O'Leary	Fanolua/2t	Todd	Simpson Daniel
PGC	16-12	A	Bristol	W 37-23	5363	Goodridge	Frape(g/t)	Fanolua/t	Todd	Simpson Daniel
PGC	20-01	A	London Irish	L 10-25	8076	Mercier/cp	O'Leary	Ewens	Fanolua	Simpson Daniel
ZPO	18-05	H	Newcastle Falcons	W 60-9	5776	Paul/t2c	O'Leary/t	Fanolua/t	Todd/t	Simpson Daniel
ZPO	02-06	A	Sale	W 33-11	4298	Paul	O'Leary	Fanolua	Todd	Beim/t
ZPO	08-06	N	Bristol	W 28-23	28500					

** after opponents name indicates a penalty try. Brackets after a player's name indicates he was replaced. eg (a) means he was replaced by replacement code "a" and so on. / after a player or replacement name is followed by any scores he made - eg /t, /c, /p, /dg or any combination of these*

EVER PRESENT None

Most Appearances:
21: Ludovic Mercier.
20: Daren O'Leary(1), Jake Boer(1).
19: Junior Paramore(2), Rob Fidler(2)

PLAYERS USED

30 plus three as a replacement

MOST POINTS

Pts	Player	T	C	P	DG
334	L Mercier	2	48	64	12
45	J Paramore	9	-	-	-
45	J Simpson Daniel	9	-	-	-
38	H Paul	2	5	6	-
30	T Fanolua	6	-	-	-

MATCH FACTS

10	9	1	2	3	4	5	6	7	8
Mercier/c5p	Yachvili	Pucciarello	Fortey	Collazo	Fidler	Eustace	Boer	Hazell	Paramore/t
Mercier/c6p	Yachvili	Pucciarello	Fortey(a/t)	Collazo	Fidler	Eustace	Boer	Hazell	Paramore
Mercier/6p	Yachvili	Woodman	Azam	Vickery	Fidler	Eustace	Boer	Hazell	Paramore
Mercier/3c3p3dg	Yachvili/t	Woodman/t	Azam	Collazo(b/t)	Fidler	Pearce	Boer	Eustace	Paramore
Mercier/3c3pdg	Yachvili	Vickery	Azam	Collazo	Fidler	Pearce	Eustace	Hazell	Boer(c/t)
Mercier/5p	Yachvili	Woodman	Azam	Collazo	Fidler	Pearce	Eustace	Hazell	Paramore
Mercier/5c3p	Yachvili(e/t)	Woodman	Fortey/t	Pucciarello	Fidler	Cornwell	Boer	Hazell/t	Paramore/t
Mercier/c3p	Gomersall/t	Woodman	Fortey	Pucciarello	Fidler	Cornwell	Boer	Eustace	Paramore
Mercier/3cp2dg	Gomersall	Collazo	Azam/2t	Pucciarello	Fidler	Pearce	Eustace	Hazell	Boer/t
Mercier/t5c2p	Yachvili	Vickery	Fortey	Pucciarello	Cornwell	Pearce	Boer(f/t)	Sewabu	Paramore
Mercier/p2dg	Gomersall	Collazo	Fortey	Vickery	Fidler	Cornwell	Boer	Hazell	Paramore
Paul/c4p	Yachvili	Woodman	Azam	Vickery	Eustace/t	Cornwell	Forrester	Hazell	Boer
Mercier/2c5p	Gomersall	Collazo	Azam/t	Pucciarello	Fidler	Cornwell	Boer	Forrester	Paramore
Mercier/c2p	Gomersall	Pucciarello	Azam/t	Vickery	Fidler	Cornwell	Boer	Forrester	Paramore
Mercier/4c3p	Gomersall/t	Collazo	Azam	Vickery(b/t)	Fidler	Cornwell	Boer	Forrester/t	Paramore/t
Mercier/tcp	Gomersall	Collazo	Azam	Deacon	Fidler	Cornwell	Boer	Forrester	Paramore
Mercier/2c5p	Gomersall/t	Woodman	Azam	Pucciarello	Fidler	Cornwell	Boer	Forrester	Paramore
Mercier/3p	Gomersall	Collazo	Fortey	Deacon	Fidler	Cornwell	Forrester	Boer	Paramore
Mercier/c2pdg	Gomersall	Collazo	Azam	Pucciarello	Fidler	Cornwell	Forrester	Boer(h/t)	Paramore/t
Mercier/2c2p2dg	Gomersall/t	Woodman	Azam	Vickery/t	Pearce	Cornwell	Forrester	Sewabu/t	Paramore/2t
Mercier/7c2pdg	Gomersall	Collazo/t	Azam	Pucciarello	Fidler	Cornwell	Forrester	Boer	Paramore/t
Mercier/6cp	Gomersall	Woodman/t	Fortey	Pucciarello	Pearce	Fidler	Forrester/t	Boer	Paramore/t(h/t)
Mercier/2c4pdg	Yachvili	Vickery	Fortey	Pucciarello	Fidler	Pearce	Sewabu	Eustace	Paramore/t
Mercier/4c2p	Yachvili(e/2c)	Woodman	Azam/t	Collazo	Pearce	Cornwell	Eustace	Forrester/2t	Paramore
Gomersall	Stuart-Smith	Woodman	Azam	Pucciarello/t	Cornwell/t	Pearce	Sewabu/2t	Forrester/3t	Boer/2t
Mercier/5c4p	Stuart-Smith(j/t)	Collazo	Fortey/t	Vickery	Fidler	Cornwell	Forrester	Hazell	Paramore/t
Paul/t12c	Stuart-Smith/t	Woodman	Fortey	Collazo	Fidler	Pearce	Sewabu/2t	Forrester/t	Paramore/t
Paul/c	Yachvili	Collazo	Fortey/t	Vickery	Fidler/t	Cornwell	Eustace	Hazell	Paramore
Mercier/4c6p	Gomersall	Collazo	Fortey	Pucciarello	Eustace	Cornwell	Boer/t(l/t)	Hazell	Paramore
Mercier/3cpdg	Gomersall	Woodman	Azam	Vickery	Cornwell	Pearce	Forrester/t	Sewabu	Paramore
Paul/3c2p	Yachvili	Woodman	Fortey	Deacon	Cornwell	Eustace	Sewabu	Forrester/3t	Caillet
Paul	Gomersall/t	Pucciarello	Fortey	Deacon	Pearce	Fidler	Boer	Forrester	Caillet
Mercier/t4cp	Gomersall	Collazo	Azam	Vickery/t	Fidler	Pearce	Forrester/t	Boer	Paramore/t
Mercier/3c3pdg	Gomersall/t	Collazo	Azam	Vickery	Pearce	Fidler	Sewabu/t	Boer	Paramore

REPLACEMENTS: a- Olivier Azam b - Federico Pucciarello c - Jumior Paramore d - James Simpson-Daniel e - Andy Gomersall f - Adam Eustace g - Marcel Garvey. h - Kolino Sewabu. i - Daren O'Leary. j - Dmitri Yachvili k - Andy Hazell l - James Forrester. m - Joe Ewena.

WHEN	Total	First Half	Second Half	1/4	2/4	3/4	4/4
The POINTS were scored	692	337	355	150	187	151	204
The POINTS were conceded	485	250	235	136	114	92	143
The TRIES were scored	**68**	**29**	**39**	**10**	**19**	**17**	**22**
The TRIES were conceded	**45**	**16**	**29**	**7**	**9**	**11**	**18**

HOW the TRIES were scored

Total	Backs	Forwards	F Back	Wing	Centre	H Back	F Row	Lock	B Row	Pen. Try
68	36	30	3	16	9	8	12	1	17	2

HOW the TRIES were conceded

Total	Backs	Forwards	F Back	Wing	Centre	H Back	F Row	Lock	B Row	Pen. Try
45	28	15	5	7	11	5	5	2	8	1

GLOUCESTER

LEAGUE STATISTICS

compiled by Stephen McCormack

SEASON	Division	P	W	D	L	F	A	Pts Diff	Lge Pts	Lge Pos		Most Points		Most Tries
92-93	1	12	6	0	6	173	151	22	12	5	71	Tim Smith	3	Tim Smith & Derek Morgan
93-94	1	18	6	2	10	247	356	-109	14	8	82	Tim Smith	3	Paul Holford & Bruce Fenley
94-95	1	18	6	1	11	269	336	-67	13	7	85	Mark Mapletoft	8	Paul Holford
95-96	1	18	6	0	12	275	370	-95	12	8	79	Tim Smith	5	Paul Holford
96-97	1	22	11	1	10	476	589	-113	23	6	269	Mark Mapletoft	7	Mike Lloyd
97-98	P1	22	11	1	10	512	528	-16	23	7	275	Mark Mapletoft	8	Terry Fanolua
98-99	P1	26	9	1	16	554	643	-89	19	10	198	Mark Mapletoft	8	C Catling & P St Andre
99-00	P1	22	15	0	7	628	490	138	40	3	282	Simon Mannix	9	C Catling & E Moncrieff
00-01	P1	22	10	0	12	473	526	-53	48	7	187	Simon Mannix	6	Jason Little
01-02	P	22	14	0	8	692	485	207	68	3	334	Ludovic Mercier	9	Junior Paramore & James Simpson-Daniel

BIGGEST MARGINS

Home Win	56pts - 68-12 v Bath 04.05.02
Away Win	46pts - 49-3 v Orrell 16.11.96
Home Defeat	24pts - 11-35 v Northampton 11.3.00
Away Defeat	56pts - 19-75 v Harlequins 31.8.96

MOST CONSECUTIVE

Appearances	47 Dave Sims 11.4.92-25.3.95
Matches scoring Tries	4 Phillipe St Andre
Matches scoring points	48 Mark Mapletoft
Victories	8
Defeats	7

MOST POINTS

Scored at Home	68 v Bath 04.05.02
Scored Away	50 v Leeds 12.05.02
Conceded at Home	45 v Bath 21.9.96
Conceded Away	75 v Harlequins 31.8.96

MOST TRIES

Scored in a match	11 v Sale 16.4.88
Conceded in a match	11 v Harlequins 31.8.96 v Bath 30.4.97

MOST APPEARANCES

by a forward	130 Dave Sims
by a back	104(2) Chris Catling

	MOST IN A SEASON	MOST IN A CAREER	MOST IN A MATCH
Points	334 Ludovic Mercier 01-02	848 Mark Mapletoft 94-99	28 Simon Mannix v Northampton 16.5.99 (H)
Tries	9 Elton Moncrieff 99-00 Chris Catling 99-00 Junior Paramore 01-02 James SImpson-Daniel 01-02	24 Chris Catling 96-00	4 Elton Moncrieff v Bedford 15.5.00 (H)
Conversions	42 Ludovic Mercier 01-02	90 Mark Mapletoft 94-99	7 Simon Mannix v Bedford 16.5.00 (H) Ludovic Mercier v Bath 04.05.02 (H)
Penalties	48 Ludovic Mercier 01-02	183 Mark Mapletoft 94-99	9 Simon Mannix v Harlequins 23.9.00 (H)
Drop Goals	12 Ludovic Mercier 01-02	12 Martin Kimber 94-96 Ludovic Mercier 01-02	3 Ludovic Mercier v Sale 22.9.01 (A)

OVERALL PLAYING RECORD

	P	W	D	L	F	A	Pts Diff
Home	42	29	0	13	950	394	556
Away	43	30	0	13	734	541	193
Neutral	4	2	1	1	41	72	-31
Total	89	61	1	27	1725	1007	718

SEASON BY SEASON

1971-72	Won
1972-73	2R
1973-74	2R
1974-75	2R
1975-76	2R
1976-77	QF
1977-78	**Winners**
1978-79	1R
1979-80	QF
1980-81	QF
1981-82	Shared
1982-83	3R
1983-84	DNQ
1984-85	SF
1985-86	QF
1986-87	QF
1987-88	4R
1988-89	SF
1989-90	Runners-up
1990-91	4R
1991-92	SF
1992-93	3R
1993-94	QF
1994-95	4R
1995-96	SF
1996-97	SF
1997-98	5R
1998-99	SF
1999-2000	QF
2000-01	5R
2001-02	QF

GLOUCESTER RFU SENIOR CUP

STATISTICS

compiled by Stephen McCormack

TEAM RECORDS

Highest Score

87 v Exeter 85/86 (H)

Biggest Winning Margin

84 Pts - 87-3 v Exeter 85/86 (H)

Highest Score Against

35 v Wasps 98/99 (A)

Biggest Losing Margin

19 Pts v Northampton 97/98 (A)

INDIVIDUAL RECORDS

Most Points in a match

Most Tries in a match

Most Conversions in a match

Most Penalties in a match

6 Mark Mapletoft v Wasps 98/99

Most Drop Goals in a match

EUROPEAN COMPETITIONS

STATISTICS *compiled by Stephen McCormack*

TEAM RECORDS

Highest Score

99 v Gran Palma Rugby 01/02

Biggest Winning Margin

99 (99-0) v Gran Palma Rubgy 01/02

Highest Score Against

62 v Swansea 96/97

Biggest Losing Margin

50 (62-12) v Swansea 96/97

INDIVIDUAL RECORDS

Most Points in a match

34 Mark Mapletoft v Ebbw Vale 96/97

Most Tries in a match

5 Daren O'Leary v Gran Palma Rugby 01/02

Most Conversions in a match

12 Henry Paul v Gran Palma Rugby 01/02

Most Penalties in a match

6 Ludovic Mercier v Ebbw Vale 01/02

Most Drop Goals in a match

2 Ludovic Mercier v La Rochelle 01/02

CAREER RECORDS

Most Appearances
26: Terry Fanolua
21: Phil Vickery, Rob Fidler
18: Mark Cornwall
Most Points
129: Simon Mannix
124: Mark Mapletoft
112: Ludovic Mercier
Most Tries
8: James Forrester, Daren O'Leary.
6: Joe Ewens, Terry Fanolua

SEASON BY SEASON

1996-97	S	Gp Stage
1997-98	S	QF
1998-99	S	D N Play
1999-00	S	Gp Stage
2000-01	C	SF
2001-02	S	SF

OVERALL PLAYING RECORD

	P	W	D	L	F	A	Pts Diff
Home	18	15	1	2	698	234	464
Away	14	7	1	6	409	377	32
Neutral	2	0	0	2	42	47	-5
Total	34	22	2	10	1149	658	491

GLOUCESTER

FACT FILE

Founded: 1873
Nickname: Cherry & whites
Colours: Cherry & white hoops.
Change colours: Blue and red halves.

GROUND

Address: Kingsholm, Gloucester. GL1 3AX.
Tel: 01452 381087 Ticket Hotline: 01452 422422 Fax: 01452 383321
Website: www.gloucesterrugbyclub.com email: postbox@gloucesterrugbyclub.com
Capacity: 10,800 Seated:1,498 Standing: Covered 4,350 Uncovered 4,622

Directions: From M5 junction 11 or 11A follow signs for City Centre and then Kingsholm.
Nearest Railway Station: Gloucester. About a 5 minute walk from the ground. Follow signs

Car Parking: 250 spaces at ground, 1,000 at cattle market 5 mins walk

Admission: Season tickets Premier Grandstand: £330, concessions £270, u16 £165
Grandstand: £270, concessions £210, u16 £135 Ground: £140, concessions £70, u16 £40
Matchday Grandstand: Adults £22; no concessions
Ground: Adults £16 (£14) Concessions £9 (37); u16 £4 (£3)
Figures in brackets are for tickets purchased by 5pm Thursday before Saturday matchday.

Club Shop: 10-4 & matchdays. Contact John Hudson 01452 522978.

Clubhouse: Mon-Sat 6.30-11, Sat matchdays 11-11. Snacks & bar meals available
Function room: Available for hire, capacity 150.

PROGRAMME Size: B5 **Pages:** 48 **Price:** £2
Editor: James Bennett 07989 582111; 01452 381087
Advertising Rates Contact Dunwoody Sports, Newbury 01635 35599

L-R Back Row: Carl Houston, Olivier Azam, Jon Goodridge, Jake Boer, Kolinio Sewabu, Patrice Collazo, Cristian Stoica, Federico Pucciariello, Tom Beim, Duncan Murray, Ludovic Mercier. **Middle**: Laurent Seigne (Ass coach), Pete Glanville (team manager), Andy Keast (ass coach), Simon Mannix, Daren O'Leary, Josh Frape, Rob Fidler, James Forrester, Ed Pearce, Adam Eustace, Mark Cornwell, Nick Cox, Andy Deacon, Andy Gomarsall, Jean-Pierre Darnaud (Physio), Ed Archer (Fitness coach), Philippe Saint-Andre (Director of Rugby), Bernard Faure (Fitness coach). **Front**: Diego Albanese, Terry Fanolua, Chris Catling, Junior Paramore, Phil Vickery, Robert Todd, Joe Ewens, Andy Hazell, Chris Fortey, Trevor Woodman **On ground:** James Simpson-Daniel, Marcel Garvey, Dimitri Yachvili.
Picture by "Bruce Seabrook/Gloucestershire Picture Agency"
Gloucestershire Picture Agency (E-mail: gpa@gloucestershirepictureagency.co.uk www.gloucestershirepictureagency.co.uk)

LEEDS TYKES

Chief Executive	Gary Hetherington	c/o Leeds Rugby Academy, Tel: 0113 239 9172 Savins Mill Way, Kirkstall, Leeds LS3 3BW Fax: 0113 239 9199
Director of Rugby	Phil Davies	c/o Leeds Rugby Academy as above Tel: 0113 239 9173
Club Administrator	Mike Bidgood	c/o Leeds RUFC, The Pavilion as above 01423 734953 (H) 0113 278 6181 X 242 (B), 0113 275 4284 (Fax) 07710 342054 (Mobile) E-Mail: mike.bidgood @ leedsrugby.co.uk
Managing Director	David Howes	c/o Leeds RUFC, The Pavilion as above
Fixtures Secretary	Les Jackson	4 Gledhow Wood Avenue, Leeds. LS8 1NY 0113 266 5544 (H,B & Fax) 07989 878523 (Mobile)

The Tykes fledgling season in the Zurich Premiership was always going to be a difficult one but Phil Davies, men acquitted themselves in fine form at Headingley claiming the scalps of Bath, Saracens, Leicester, Harlequins and Bristol as well as being unbeaten in the Parker Pen Shield also at Headingley.

The season could not have started brighter for the Tykes with victory over Bath at Headingley on a memorable day. Cameron Mather scored the only try of the game at the start of the second half and some stout defence secured the victory.

The following week, Phil Davies men grabbed two bonus points at Bristol with Dan Scarbrough scoring his first of 17 tries. The former Wakefield player had a sensational first season at Leeds scoring some sensational tries along the way and earning a place in the England A and Sevens squad.

The best run of the season came in October when Leeds won three out of four games, with wins against Beziers and Pontypridd in the Europe and the downing of Saracens.

However, perhaps the most memorable victory of the season came on 11th November when the Tykes defeated European and Premiership Champions Leicester at Headingley. Not only did they win but secured a bonus point in an incredible display of attacking rugby against the odds.

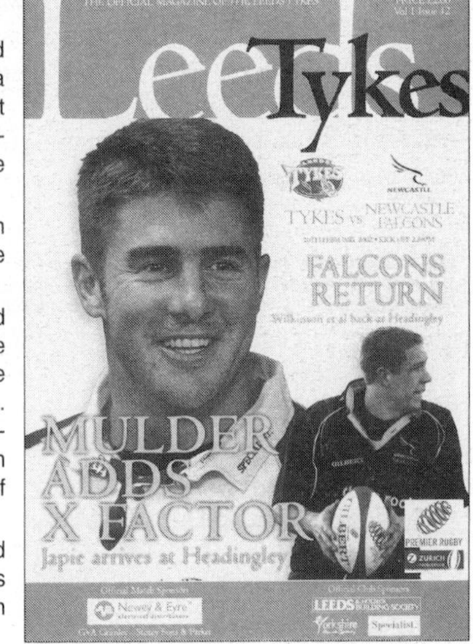

The Christmas and New Year period was one of mixed fortune with victories over Harlequins and Parma at home and a historic win at Beziers, a ground that the home side had not lost at for two seasons. However, it was the disappointing and ultimately crucial loses to Gloucester, Sale and Wasps that were telling.

December also saw the arrival of Springbok Braam van Straaten, who was joined in January by World Cup winner Japie Mulder.

The New Year brought with it a sporadic fixture list that did not ease the situation, with little chance for momentum. The Tykes did manage their first win away from home in the league with victory at Vicarage Road, with Mulder scoring two tries. Things looked to be on the up as Bristol were beaten the following week at Headingley however the massive blow of losing Tom Palmer with a broken leg on England A duty was a cruel turn of fate.

Defeats followed at Leicester, Northampton, Bath and Harlequins however survival was always the primary aim of this first season and the Tykes secured their place in the Zurich Premiership and earned many plaudits along the way.

LEEDS TYKES

Comp.	Date	H/A	Opponents	Result & Score	Att	15	14	13	12	11
ZP	02-09	H	Bath	W 10-6	5181	Benson/cp	Scarborough	Mayer	Woof	Emmerson
ZP	09-09	A	London Irish	L 14-42	4219	Benson/2c	Scarborough	Woof/t	Davies	Emmerson
ZP	16-09	H	Northampton Saints	L 6-26	4080	Scarborough	Rogers	Mayer	Woof	Emmerson
ZP	23-09	A	Bristol	L 29-34	3632	Benson/t	Bartolucci	Mayer	Woof	Emmerson(a/t)
ZP	14-10	H	Saracens	W 27-14	3328	Benson	Hall	Woof	Davies	Scarborough/t
ZP	21-10	A	Newcastle Falcons	L 8-19	4248	Benson	Hall	Woof	Davies	Scarborough
ZP	11-11	H	Leicester Tigers	W 37-16	7162	Benson/4c2p	Scarborough/t	Davies	Mackay	Emmerson/t
ZP	18-11	A	London Wasps	L 14-64	3507	Benson	Scarborough	Davies	Mackay	Emmerson
ZP	25-11	H	Sale	L 20-47	3489	Scarborough	Bartolucci	Woof/t	Mackay/t	Emmerson
ZP	01-12	A	Gloucester	L 17-58	7516	Benson/2cp	Scarborough	Woof	Davies	Emmerson/t
ZP	09-12	H	Harlequins	W 23-18	3401	Benson	Scarborough/2t	Woof	Van Straaten/2c3p	Emmerson
ZP	30-12	H	London Wasps	L 18-28	5166	Benson	Scarborough	Woof	Van Straaten/6p	Emmerson
ZP	10-02	H	Newcastle Falcons	L 9-19	4195	Scarborough	Hall	Davies	Mulder	Emmerson
ZP	24-02	A	Saracens	W 37-15	4325	Scarborough	Hall/t	Woof	Mulder/2t	Emmerson
ZP	10-03	H	Bristol	W 24-6	2034	Scarborough/t	Hall	Woof	Mulder	Emmerson/t
ZP	16-03	A	Northampton Saints	L 14-34	8366	Scarborough/2t	Hall	Woof	Mulder	Emmerson
ZP	31-03	H	London Irish	L 24-29	3392	Benson	Scarborough/2t	Mulder	Van Straaten/3cp	Woof
ZP	13-04	A	Bath	L 12-23	8129	Benson	Scarborough	Mulder	Van Straaten/4p	Woof
ZP	19-04	A	Leicester Tigers	L 10-31		Scarborough/t	Bartolucci	Woof	Mulder	Emmerson
ZP	03-05	A	Harlequins	L 16-40	7255	Benson	Scarborough	Davies	Mulder	Woof
ZP	08-05	A	Sale	L 20-35	3871	Scarborough	Bartolucci	Mulder/t	Van Straaten/2c2p	Hall/t
ZP	12-05	H	Gloucester	L 17-50	4144	Scarborough/t	Bartolucci	Mulder	Van Straaten/cp(d/c)	Hall/t
ES	29-09	A	Parma	L 10-41		Rogers	Hall	Davies	Stanger	Scarborough
ES	07-10	H	Beziers	W 48-17	2229	Benson	Hall/2t	Davies/t	Woof	Scarborough/t
ES	28-10	N	Pontypridd	W 30-27	2642	Scarborough	Hall	Mayer	Stanger	Woof
ES	03-11	A	Pontypridd	L 16-28	4200	Scarborough	Hall	Mayer/t	Mackay	Woof
ES	05-01	N	Beziers	W 26-25	3500	Benson/c3p	Scarborough/t	Davies	Mayer/t	Woof
ES	13-01	N	Parma	W 58-16	1431	Benson/7c3p	Scarborough/2t	Davies	Mayer/3t	Mackay
PGC	15-12	A	Orrell	W 31-22	1300	Benson	Scarborough	Woof/2t	Mackay	Emmerson
PGC	20-01	H	Newcastle Falcons	L 24-41	4183	Benson	Scarborough/t	Mayer/t	Van Straaten/c4p	Emmerson

** after opponents name indicates a penalty try. Brackets after a player's name indicates he was replaced. eg (a) means he was replaced by replacement code "a" and so on. / after a player or replacement name is followed by any scores he made - eg /t, /c, /p, /dg or any combination of these*

EVER PRESENT Mike Shelley.

Most Appearances:
22: Mike Shelley.
21: Danny Scarborough(1).
19: Chris Murphy(1).
17: Scot Benton, Shaun Woof.

PLAYERS USED

33 plus one as a replacement

MOST POINTS

Pts	Player	T	C	P	DG
132	B van Straaten	-	15	33	1
60	D Scarborough	12	-	-	-
51	D Parks	1	8	7	3
43	J Benson	1	10	6	-

MATCH FACTS

10	9	1	2	3	4	5	6	7	8
Bachop	Benton	Shelley	Holt	Wring	Murphy	Palmer	Mather/t	Ponton	Feau'nati
Bachop	Benton	Shelley	Holt	Wring	Murphy	Palmer	Mather/t	Ponton	Feau'nati
Benson/2p	Benton	Shelley	Holt	Wring	Murphy	Palmer	Mather	Ponton	Hogg
Parks/3cp	Benton	Shelley	Rawlinson	Fullman	Murphy/t	Palmer	Hogg	Mather/t	Feau'nati
Parks/c3p2dg	Benton	Shelley	Holt	Kerr	Murphy	Palmer	Mather	Hyde	Hogg/t
Parks/p	Benton	Shelley	Holt	Kerr	C Murphy(b/t)	Murphy	Mather	Ponton	Hogg
Bachop(c/dg)	Benton	Shelley	Holt	Kerr/t	Murphy	Palmer/t	Mather	Hyde	Feau'nati
Parks/t2c	O'Reilly	Shelley	Holt	Kerr	C Murphy(b/t)	Palmer	Mather	Hyde	Hogg
Parks/2c2p	O'Reilly	Shelley	Holt	Fullman	Murphy	Palmer	Mather	Ponton	Feau'nati
Bachop/t	O'Reilly	Shelley	Holt	Kerr	Murphy	Palmer	Hogg	Mather	Feau'nati
Bachop	Kendra	Shelley	Rawlinson	Kerr	Murphy	Palmer	Hogg	Hyde	Feau'nati
Bachop	Kendra	Shelley	Holt	Kerr	Murphy	Palmer	Hogg	Hyde	Feau'nati
Van Straaten/3p	Benton	Shelley	Rawlinson	Kerr	Murphy	Palmer	Hogg	Hyde	Feau'nati
Van Straaten/2c6p	Benton	Shelley	Rawlinson	Kerr	Murphy	Palmer	Mather	Hyde	Feau'nati
Van Straaten/c4p	Benton	Shelley	Rawlinson	Kerr	Murphy	Palmer	Mather	Hyde	Feau'nati
Van Straaten/2c	Benton	Shelley	Rawlinson	Kerr	Murphy	Palmer	Mather	Ponton	Feau'nati
Bachop	Benton/t	Shelley	Rawlinson	Fullman	Murphy	Murphy	Mather	Hyde	Hogg
Bachop	Benton	Shelley	Rawlinson	Kerr	Jones	Murphy	Mather	Hyde	Feau'nati
Van Straaten/cp	Benton	Wring	Luffman	Shelley	Hogg	Murphy	Hyde	Ponton	Feau'nati
Van Straaten/c2pdg	Benton/t	Shelley	Holt	Kerr	Murphy	Murphy	Mather	Hyde	Feau'nati
Bachop	Benton	Wring	Holt	Shelley	Murphy	Murphy	Hyde	Ponton	Hogg
Bachop	Benton	Wring	Holt	Shelley	Murphy	Murphy	Hyde	Ponton	Hogg
Parks/cp	O'Reilly	O'Keefe	Luffman/t	Fullman	Murphy	Jones	Hogg	Hyde	Clarke
Parks/3c3pdg	Benton/t	Shelley	Holt/t	Kerr	Murphy	Palmer	Mather	Hogg	Hyde
Parks/t3c3p	O'Reilly(e/t)	O'Keefe	Luffman	Fullman	Murphy	Jones	Clarke(f/t)	Ponton	Feau'nati
Benson/c3p	Benton	Shelley	Rawlinson	Fullman	Murphy	Palmer	Hogg	Mather	Feau'nati
Bachop	O'Reilly	Fullman	Luffman	Wring/t	Murphy	Jones	Hogg	Mather	Feau'nati
Bachop/t	O'Reilly(e/t)	O'Keefe	Luffman	Fullman	Murphy	Jones	Hogg	Hyde	Feau'nati
Van Straaten/4cp	Kendra	Shelley	Holt	Fullman	Jones/t	Palmer	Hogg	Mather/t	Clarke
Bachop	Benton	Wring	Luffman	Fullman	Jones	Palmer	Hogg	Hyde	Feau'nati

REPLACEMENTS: a - Danny Scarborough. b - Eddie Jones. c - Dan Parks. d - Jon Benson. e - Scot Benton. f - Carl Hogg.

WHEN	Total	First Half	Second Half	1/4	2/4	3/4	4/4
The POINTS were scored	406	188	218	99	89	87	131
The POINTS were conceded	654	330	324	136	194	149	175
The TRIES were scored	38	13	25	6	7	9	16
The TRIES were conceded	68	29	39	9	20	15	24

HOW the TRIES were scored

Total	Backs	Forwards	F Back	Wing	Centre	H Back	F Row	Lock	B Row	Pen. Try
38	29	9	6	13	6	4	1	4	4	-

HOW the TRIES were conceded

Total	Backs	Forwards	F Back	Wing	Centre	H Back	F Row	Lock	B Row	Pen. Try
68	47	21	2	23	14	8	8	2	11	-

LEEDS TYKES

LEAGUE STATISTICS

compiled by Stephen McCormack

SEASON	Division	P	W	D	L	F	A	Pts Diff	Lge Pts	Lge Pos	Most Points	Most Tries
92-93	3	11	7	0	4	228	220	8	14		45 Ben Lloyd	7 Chris Thornton
93-94	4	18	7	0	11	243	318	-75	14		97 David Breakwell	3 Penalty Tries
94-95	4	18	8	0	10	335	291	44	16		83 Ralph Bennett	6 Phil Griffin & Chris Thornton
95-96	4	18	9	1	8	312	347	-35	19		67 Colin Stephens	6 Chris Thornton
96-97	3	30	24	0	6	1209	432	777	48		307 Gerry Ainscough	16 Mark Appleson
97-98	JN1	26	21	1	4	858	407	451	43		322 Sateki Tuipulotu	7 Simon Middleton
98-99	P2	26	16	0	10	713	367	336	28*	6	250 Sateki Tuipulotu	10 Simon Middleton Jonathan Scales
99-00	P2	26	22	0	4	794	269	525	44	2	190 Jon Benson	14 Matt Oliver
00-01	N1	26	24	0	2	1032	407	625	116	1p	337 Richard Le Bas	19 Graham Mackay
01-02	P	22	6	0	16	406	654	-248	28	12	132 Braam van Straatan	12 D Scarborough

BIGGEST MARGINS

Home Win	81pts - 84-3 v Walsall 1.3.97
Away Win	75pts - 84-9 v Clifton 12.4.97
Home Defeat	33pts - 17-50 v Gloucester 12.5.02
Away Defeat	50pts - 14-64 v Wasps 18.11.01

MOST CONSECUTIVE

Appearances	65 Sateki Tuipulotu 7.9.96 - 3.1.99
Matches scoring Tries	7 Simon Middleton
Matches scoring points	46 Sateki Tuipulotu
Victories	11 (twice)
Defeats	7

MOST POINTS

Scored at Home	84 v Walsall 1.3.97
Scored Away	84 v Clifton 12.4.97
Conceded at Home	26 v Liverpool St. Helens 25.3.94
Conceded Away	35 v Liverpool St Helens 15.10.93

MOST TRIES

Scored in a match	14 v Redruth 9.1.96 (H) v Walsall 1.3.97 (H)
Conceded in a match	8 v Gloucester 1.12.01 (H)

MOST APPEARANCES

by a forward	118(4) Mike Shelley
by a back	76 (1) Sateki Tuipulotu

	MOST IN A SEASON	MOST IN A CAREER	MOST IN A MATCH	
Points	337 Richard Le Bas 00-01	769 Sateki Tuipulotu 96-99	27 Gerry Ainscough	v Rosslyn Park 14.9.96(H) v Walsall 1.3.97 (H)
Tries	19 Graham Mackay 00-01	29 Sateki Tupulotu 96-99	5 Simon Middleton	v Otley 24.1.98 (H)
Conversions	72 Richard Le Bas 00-01	135 Sateki Tuipulotu 96-98	9 Gerry Ainscough	v Clifton 7.12.96 (H)
Penalties	53 Sateki Tuipulotu 98-99	118 Sateki Tuipulotu 96-98	7 Sateki Tuipulotu Jon Benson	v Coventry 3.1.99 (A) v Manchester 8.4.00 (A)
Drop Goals	5 Colin Stephens 96-97	13 Colin Stephens 95-98	2 Dan Eddie Colin Stephens	v Broughton Park 19.2.94 v Exeter 9.9.95 (H) v Lon. Welsh 19.10.96 (H)

OVERALL PLAYING RECORD (As Leeds)

	P	W	D	L	F	A	Pts Diff
Home	10	6	0	4	363	141	222
Away	11	5	0	6	245	316	-71
Neutral	-	-	-	-	-	-	-
Total	21	11	-	10	608	457	151

From 71-72 until 91-92 the figure on the left shows **Headingley RFC** and that on the right **Roundhay RFC**

SEASON BY SEASON

1971-72	1R	DNQ
1972-73	DNQ	DNQ
1973-74	1R	1R
1974-75	DNQ	DNQ
1975-76	1R	QF
1976-77	DNQ	DNQ
1977-78	DNQ	DNQ
1978-79	DNQ	DNQ
1979-80	DNQ	DNQ
1980-81	DNQ	3R
1981-82	DNQ	2R
1982-83	DNQ	DNQ
1983-84	3R	DNQ
1984-85	3R	DNQ
1985-86	3R	DNQ
1986-87	DNQ	DNQ
1987-88	3R	DNQ
1988-89	2R	DNQ
1989-90	4R	1R
1990-91	2R	1R
1991-92	2R	1R
1992-93	2R	
1993-94	2R	
1994-95	2R	
1995-96	5R	
1996-97	5R	
1997-98	2R	
1998-99	5R	
1999-00	4R	
2000-01	4R	
2001-02	QF	

LEEDS TYKES RFU SENIOR CUP

STATISTICS

compiled by Stephen McCormack

TEAM RECORDS

Highest Score
100 v Morley 21.10.00
Biggest Winning Margin
100 (100-0) v Morley 21.10.00
Highest Score Against
73 v Northampton 4.11.00
Biggest Losing Margin
49 (49-0) v Leicester 30.02.99

INDIVIDUAL RECORDS

Most Points in a match
35 Richard Le Bas v Morley 21.10.00
Most Tries in a match
5 Wendall Sailor v Rugby
Most Conversions in a match
10 Richard Le Bas v Morley 21.10.00
Most Penalties in a match
4 Braam van Straatan v Newcastle 20.01.02
Most Drop Goals in a match

EUROPEAN COMPETITIONS

STATISTICS *compiled by Stephen McCormack*

TEAM RECORDS

Highest Score
58 v Parma 13.01.02
Biggest Winning Margin
42 (58-16) v Parma 13.01.02
Highest Score Against
41 v Parma 29.09.01
Biggest Losing Margin
31 (41-10) v Parma 29.09.01

INDIVIDUAL RECORDS

Most Points in a match
23 Jon Benson v Parma 13.01.02 (H)
Most Tries in a match
3 Jamie Mayer v Parma 13.01.2002 (H)
Most Conversions in a match
7 Jon Benson v Parma 13.01.2002 (H)
Most Penalties in a match
3 by J Benson (3), D Parkes (2)
Most Drop Goals in a match
1 Dan Parks v Beziers 7.10.01 (H)

CAREER RECORDS

Most Appearances:
6: Danny Scarborough.
5: Carl Hogg (1),
Kristyan Fullman (1).

Most Points:
45: Jon Benson.
43: Dan Parks.
25: Jamie Mayer.

Most Tries:
5: Jamie Mayer.
4: Danny Scarbrough.
3: Scot Benton.
2: Chris Hall.

SEASON BY SEASON

1996-97	-	DNQ
1997-98	-	DNQ
1998-99	-	DNQ
1999-00	-	DNQ
2000-01	-	DNQ
2001-02	S	Gp Stage

OVERALL PLAYING RECORD

	P	W	D	L	F	A	Pts Diff
Home	3	3	0	0	136	60	76
Away	3	1	0	2	52	94	-42
Neutral	-	-	-	-	-	-	-
Total	6	4	0	2	188	154	34

LEEDS TYKES

Founded: 1991
Colours: Royal blue, black, gold & white
Change colours: Maroon and white
Nickname: Tykes
Web site: www.leedsrugby.com

GROUND

Address: Headingley Stadium, St Michaels Lane, Headingley, Leeds. LS6 3BR
Tel: 0113 278 6181 Fax: 0113 275 4284 e-mail: mike.bidgood@leedsrugby.co.uk
Capacity: 23,000 Seated: 9,000 Standing: Covered 11,000, Uncovered 3,000

Directions: Travel Information from M1 and M62
Take M621 - Leave at junction 2, signposted Headingley Stadium. Follow the A643 (A58) Wetherby road - at the next roundabout take the City Centre/Wetherby A58 exit. Almost immediately, bear left to Ilkley (A65) and the airport. At the lights (TGI Friday is on the left), turn left into Kirkstall Road A65. Go straight on for about .75 mile (Yorkshire Television is on the right). There is a sign at the traffic lights showing "Headingley 1.5 miles." Stay in the right-hand lane. Turn right and go up the hill to another set of lights at the crossroads. Carry on up Cardigan Road (Co-op is on the left). After the pedestrian lights & bus stop turn left into St Michael's Lane, signposted Headingley Stadium. The Ground is on your right-hand side.

Car Parking: 390 at ground £3

Admission:

Main Stand Season	Adult £195	OAP/Students £120	Children £40
Main Stand Match Day	Adult £17	OAP/Students £14	Children £11
Ground Match Day	Adult £11	OAP/Student £8	Children £6

Club Shop: Open 9-5 Mon-Fri + Matchdays. Tel 0113 274 0460

Clubhouse: Open during normal licensing hours. Snacks, bar meals & restaurant.

Functions: Capacity 1,200 - contact Leeds RUFC

PROGRAMME Full colour Size: A5 Pages: 36 + cover Price: £2
Editor: Phil Daly 0113 278 6181 x246 (B); 0113 230 7617 (F); 07775 946935 (Mobile)

ADVERTISING RATES: Page £1000; 1/2 page £500; 1/4 page £300

L-R Back row: Steve Carter, (head of athletic performance) Jon Benson, Martin O'Keefe, Eddie Jones,Tony Stanger, Cameron Mather, Tom Palmer, Chris Murphy, Phil Murphy, Justin Wring, Tristan Davies, Chris Hall, Simon Middleton (backs coach)
Middle: John Carey, (equipment manager), Chips Browning (medical staff), Dan Scarborough, Matt Holt, Rob Rawlinson, Ian Clarke, Isaac Feaunati, James Ponton, Dan Hyde, John O'Reilly, Dan Rogers, Martin Higgins (physio.), Mike Lampkowski (team manager)
Front: Gavin Kerr, Jamie Mayer, Scott Benton, Mike Shelley, Carl Hogg (captain), Phil Davies (director of rugby), Steve Bachop (asst. coach), Mark Luffman, Richard le Bas, Shaun Woof. **Photo:** Simon Wilkinson (01943 436649)

LEICESTER TIGERS

Chairman	Peter Tom	Leicester Football Club plc,
Chief Executive	Peter Wheeler	Aylestone Road,
Managing Director	David Clayton	Leicester LE2 7TR
Company Secretary	Mary Ford	Tel: 0116 254 1607
Director of Rugby	Dean Richards	Fax: 0116 285 4766
Communications Manager	Sam Rossiter-Stead	0116 2171284 07967 339001 email: srs@tigers.co.uk

Leicester Tigers finished last season as the top club in Europe once again, after winning their fourth successive Premiership title and clinching the Heineken Cup to be crowned back-to-back European Champions. Following an impressive season, Tigers lifted Europe's most prestigious trophy in May at the Millennium Stadium, Cardiff, beating Munster in a nail-biting final. The club is looking forward to an equally successful season this year.

Director of Rugby, Dean Richards will be once again at the helm alongside his coaching team of John Wells, Rod Kafer, Andy Key and Phil Larder. A million pound refurbishment to the club's existing training facilities at Oval Park shows Tigers' commitment to player development as they look to stay one step ahead of the rest.

Tigers' ongoing success is attributed to their ability to pick and develop home-grown talent, as well as signing more experienced players from further afield to boost their awesome squad. New signings last year came in the form of All Black legend Josh Kronfeld and Australia's Rod Kafer. Kafer joined the team as player-coach and, despite injury, Kronfeld had a positive impact on the team and looks to come back stronger this year.

The talent in the Tigers set-up has been recognised this season with over 40 players receiving international caps at various levels. An outstanding season from Lewis Moody saw him named as England's Young Player of the Year and other successes for the youngsters included 19-year-old scrum half Harry Ellis' match-winning try in the Heineken Cup semi-final against Llanelli.

Support for the Tigers continues to rise with Welford Road achieving an average attendance of 15,400 and the stadium reaching its 16,250 capacity on six occasions last season. The club also remains clear at the top of the Premiership table for season ticket sales smashing the two million pound barrier in mid-July and beating last year's figure of 11,500.

Finishing last season with a 300+ points difference in the Zurich Premiership, the Tigers are strong contenders for the title this year. New signings during the off-season include France's Franck Tournaire and Ireland's Tom Tierney who have added to the strength of the squad. This season, Leicester Tigers look forward to yet more silverware in the Welford Road cabinet.

LEICESTER TIGERS

Comp.	Date	H/A	Opponents	Result & Score	Att	15	14	13	12	11
ZP	02-09	A	Newcastle Falcons	L 16-19		Stimpson	Murphy	Smith	Kafer	Tuilagi/t
ZP	08-09	H	London Wasps	W 45-15	13837	Stimpson/2t2p	Murphy/2t	Gelderbloom/t	Kafer	Tuilagi
ZP	15-09	A	Gloucester	W 40-18	9729	Stimpson/4c2p	Murphy/t	Gelderbloom	Kafer	Tuilagi(a/t)
ZP	22-09	H	Bath	W 48-9	15145	Stimpson/t4c5p	Booth/t	Gelderbloom	Kafer	Tuilagi
ZP	13-10	A	Northampton Saints	W 21-11	11750	Stimpson/cp	Booth/dg	Gelderbloom	Kafer/t	Smith
ZP	20-10	H	Saracens	W 36-10	13762	Stimpson/2c3p	Booth/2t	Gelderbloom	Kafer/t	Smith
ZP	11-11	A	Leeds Tykes	L 16-37	7162	Stimpson/c3p	Booth	Smith	Gelderbloom	Naylor
ZP	17-11	A	Sale	W 37-3	5429	Murphy/2t	Booth/t	Lloyd	Kafer	Tuilagi
ZP	23-11	H	Harlequins	W 23-18	16017	Stimpson/2t2c3p	Murphy	Lloyd	Kafer	Booth
ZP	02-12	A	London Irish	W 30-15	11124	Stimpson/3c3p	Murphy	Lloyd/t	Kafer	Booth
ZP	08-12	H	Bristol	W 26-19	15519	Stimpson/c3p(b/cp)	Murphy	Lloyd	Kafer	Booth/t
ZP	22-12	A	Harlequins	W 38-21	9000	Stimpson/c	Murphy/t4cp	Smith	Kafer	Tuilagi
ZP	27-12	H	Sale	W 33-10	16250	Murphy/tc	Healey	Lloyd/t	Kafer	Booth/tdg
ZP	09-02	A	Saracens	W 48-7	9347	Murphy/t	Booth/t	Smith/t	Kafer/t	Tuilagi/t
ZP	23-02	H	Northampton Saints	W 17-6	16251	Healey	Booth	Smith	Kafer	Tuilagi
ZP	09-03	A	Bath	W 27-9	8200	Stimpson/c5p	Booth	Smith/t	Kafer	Tuilagi
ZP	16-03	H	Gloucester	W 27-10	16250	Stimpson/3c2p	Booth	Smith	Kafer	Tuilagi
ZP	31-03	A	London Wasps	L 24-36	9621	Stimpson/c4p	Booth/t	Gelderbloom	Kafer	Tuilagi/t
ZP	13-04	H	Newcastle Falcons	W 20-12	16250	Stimpson/5p	Booth	Lloyd	Kafer	Tuilagi/t
ZP	19-04	H	Leeds Tykes	W 31-10		Stimpson/4cp	Murphy	Smith/t	Gelderbloom	Lloyd
ZP	05-05	A	Bristol	L 21-38	6566	Murphy/t	Smith	Lloyd	Gelderbloom/t	Booth
ZP	12-05	H	London Irish*	W 34-16	16000	Stimpson/cp	Lloyd/2t	Smith	Gelderbloom	Tuilagi
HC	29-09	H	Llanelli	W 12-9	15170	Stimpson/4p	Booth	Gelderbloom	Kafer	Tuilagi
HC	07-10	A	Calvisano	W 37-3		Stimpson/3c2p	Booth	Gelderbloom	Kafer	Tuilagi/t
HC	27-10	A	Perpignan	W 31-30		Stimpson/c7p	Murphy	Gelderbloom	Kafer	Booth/t
HC	03-11	H	Perpignan	W 54-15	15662	Stimpson/t6c4p	Murphy/t	Gelderbloom	Kafer	Booth/t
HC	05-01	H	Calvisano	W 29-7		Murphy/2tc	Booth/t	Lloyd	Kafer	Smith/t
HC	12-01	A	Llanelli	L 12-24		Murphy	Booth	Lloyd	Kafer	Tuilagi
HC	27-01	H	Leinster	W 29-18	16249	Murphy/t2c	Smith	Lloyd/t	Kafer	Tuilagi
HC	28-04	N	Llanelli	W 13-12	29848	Stimpson/c2p	Murphy	Smith	Kafer	Tuilagi
HC-F	25-05	N	Munster	W 15-9	74000	Stimpson/cp	Murphy/t	Smith	Kafer	Tuilagi
PGC	15-12	H	Exeter	W 27-0	5549	Murphy	Booth	Lloyd/t	Gelderbloom	Smith/2tcp
PGC	19-01	A	Harlequins	L 20-22	8900	Murphy	Smith/t	Lloyd	Kafer/t	Tuilagi
ZPO	18-05	H	Bristol	L 13-27	4771	Billig	Lloyd	Smith	Kafer	Tuilagi

** after opponents name indicates a penalty try. Brackets after a player's name indicates he was replaced. eg (a) means he was replaced by replacement code "a" and so on. / after a player or replacement name is followed by any scores he made - eg /t, /c, /p, /dg or any combination of these*

EVER PRESENT None

Most Appearances:
19: Rod Kafer.
17: Tim Stimpson(2).
16: Steve Booth(3), Darren Garforth(1), Ben Kay(2),

PLAYERS USED

34

MOST POINTS

Pts	Player	T	C	P	DG
212	T Stimpson	5	29	43	-
112	A Goode	4	16	15	5
58	G Murphy	9	5	1	-
51	S Booth	9	-	-	2
30	N Back	6	-	-	-

MATCH FACTS

10	9	1	2	3	4	5	6	7	8
Goode/t2p	Ellis	Rowntree	West	Garforth	Deacon	Kay	Moody	Gustard	Johnson
Goode/3cdg	Ellis	Rowntree	West	Garforth	Deacon	Kay/t	Gustard	Moody	Short
Goode/2dg	Ellis	Rowntree	West	Garforth	Deacon	Kay	Gustard	Moody/2t	Short
Goode/t	Healey/t	Rowntree	West	Garforth	Johnson	Kay	Johnson	Moody/t	Short
Goode/dg	Healey/t	Rowntree	West	Garforth	Johnson	Kay	Johnson	Back	Short
Goode/dg	Hamilton	Jelley/t	Chuter	Garforth	Deacon	Kay	Johnson	Kronfeld	Short
Kafer	Hamilton	Jelley	Chuter	Garforth	Manson-Bishop	Deacon	Johnson	Kronfeld/t	Short
Goode/t4c3p	Hamilton	Freshwater	Cockerill	Garforth	Johnson	Deacon	Johnson	Kronfeld	Balding
Goode	Hamilton	Freshwater	Cockerill	Garforth	Manson-Bishop	Deacon	Johnson	Kronfeld	Balding
Healey	Hamilton/t	Rowntree	West	Nebbett	Johnson	Kay	Moody/t	Back	Balding
Healey	Hamilton	Rowntree	West	Nebbett	Johnson	Kay	Moody/t	Back	Balding
Healey/2t	Hamilton	Rowntree	West	Nebbett	Johnson/2t	Kay	Johnson	Back	Corry
Goode/c2p	Ellis	Rowntree	West	Garforth/t	Johnson	Kay	Moody	Kronfeld	Corry
Goode/t5cp	Hamilton	Rowntree	Cockerill	Garforth	Johnson	Kay	Kronfeld	Back/t	Corry
Goode/4p	Ellis	Freshwater/t	Cockerill	Garforth	Deacon	Kay	Moody	Kronfeld	Johnson
Healey	Hamilton	Rowntree	West	Garforth	Deacon/t	Kay	Moody	Kronfeld	Corry
Healey/t	Ellis	Rowntree	West/t	Garforth	Deacon	Kay	Moody	Back/t	Corry
Healey	Hamilton	Rowntree	West	Garforth	Johnson	Kay	Kronfeld	Back	Corry
Goode	Ellis	Freshwater	Cockerill	Garforth	Johnson	Short	Corry	Moody	Balding
Healey	Ellis	Rowntree	West	Nebbett	Johnson	Deacon	Corry	Back/3t	Balding
Goode/2p	Grindal	Freshwater	Cockerill	Nebbett	Deacon	Short	Johnson	Kronfeld/t	Balding
Goode/2c	Healey	Freshwater	West	Nebbett	Johnson	Kay	Moody	Back/t	Corry/t
Goode	Healey	Rowntree	West	Garforth	Johnson	Kay	Moody	Back	Corry
Goode	Ellis/t(c/t)	Rowntree	West	Garforth	Johnson	Deacon	Short	Back/2t	Corry
Goode/dg	Healey	Rowntree	West	Garforth	Deacon	Kay	Moody	Kronfeld	Short
Healey(d/t)	Hamilton	Rowntree	Chuter	Garforth	Deacon	Kay/t	Moody/t	Back	Johnson
Goode/c	Hamilton	Freshwater	Cockerill	Garforth	Johnson	Deacon	Gustard	Kronfeld	Corry/t
Goode/4p	Hamilton	Rowntree	West	Garforth	Johnson	Kay	Johnson	Back	Corry
Healey/t	Hamilton	Rowntree	Cockerill	Garforth	Johnson	Kay	Moody	Back/2t	Corry
Healey	Ellis/t	Rowntree	West	Garforth	Johnson	Kay	Moody	Back	Corry
Healey/t	Hamilton	Rowntree	Cockerill	Garforth	Johnson	Kay	Moody	Back	Corry
Goode/c	Ellis	Freshwater	Cockerill	Nebbett	Manson-Bishop/t	Kay	Johnson	Gustard	Balding
Goode/2c2p	Hamilton	Jelley	West	Nebbett	Deacon	Kay	Corry	Kronfeld	Balding
Goode/tc2p	Healey	Rowntree	West	Nebbett	Deacon	Kay	Moody	Kronfeld	Corry

REPLACEMENTS: a - Steve Booth. b - Andy Goode. c - Austin Healey. d - Olly Smith

WHEN	Total	First Half	Second Half	1/4	2/4	3/4	4/4
The POINTS were scored	658	272	386	119	153	157	229
The POINTS were conceded	349	215	134	123	92	75	59
The TRIES were scored	**72**	**25**	**47**	**9**	**16**	**17**	**30**
The TRIES were conceded	**19**	**11**	**8**	**7**	**4**	**3**	**5**

HOW the TRIES were scored

Total	Backs	Forwards	F Back	Wing	Centre	H Back	F Row	Lock	B Row	Pen. Try
72	49	22	10	19	10	10	4	4	14	1

HOW the TRIES were conceded

Total	Backs	Forwards	F Back	Wing	Centre	H Back	F Row	Lock	B Row	Pen. Try
19	16	2	3	3	3	7	1	1	-	1

LEICESTER TIGERS

LEAGUE STATISTICS

compiled by Stephen McCormack

SEASON	Division	P	W	D	L	F	A	Pts Diff	Lge Pts	Lge Pos	Most Points	Most Tries
92-93	1	12	9	0	3	220	116	104	18	3	106 John Liley	3 Rory Underwood Nigel Richardson
93-94	1	18	14	0	4	425	210	215	28	2	202 Jez Harris	8 Tony Underwood
94-95	1	18	15	1	2	400	239	161	31	1	181 Jez Harris	5 Steve Hackney
95-96	1	18	15	0	3	476	242	234	30	2	272 John Liley	8 Rory Underwood
96-97	1	22	14	1	7	600	395	205	29	4	195 John Liley	9 Penalty Tries
97-98	P1	22	12	2	8	569	449	120	26	4	253 Joel Stransky	9 Will Greenwood
98-99	P1	26	22	0	4	771	423	348	44	1	202 Joel Stransky	16 Neil Back
99-00	P1	22	18	1	3	687	425	262	51	1	321 Tim Stimpson	10 Dave Lougheed
00-01	P1	22	18	1	3	571	346	225	82	1	260 Tim Stimpson	8 Geordan Murphy & Neil Back
01-02	P	22	18	0	4	658	349	309	83	1	212 Tim Stimpson	9 Geordan Murphy & Steve Booth

BIGGEST MARGINS

Home Win	61pts - 66-5 v Newcastle Gosforth 12.3.94
Away Win	49pts - 54-9 v Harlequins 6.5.00
Home Defeat	10pts - 21-31 v Harlequins 26.11.89
Away Defeat	38pts - 9-47 v Bath 12.4.97

MOST CONSECUTIVE

Appearances	32 Darren Garforth 28.3.92-3.4.94
Matches scoring Tries	4 Geordan Murphy
Matches scoring points	24 John Liley
Victories	13
Defeats	3

MOST POINTS

Scored at Home	72 v West Hartlepool 16.5.99
Scored Away	55 v London Irish 17.5.98
Conceded at Home	31 v Harlequins 26.11.89
Conceded Away	47 v Bath 12.4.97

MOST TRIES

Scored in a match	12 v W Hartlepool 16.5.99
Conceded in a match	7 v Bath 11.1.92

MOST APPEARANCES

by a forward	183 (6) Darren Garforth
by a back	100 (2) John Liley & Stuart Potter 100(3)

	MOST IN A SEASON	MOST IN A CAREER	MOST IN A MATCH	
Points	321 Tim Stimpson 99-00	1070 John Liley 88-97	31 John Liley Tim Stimpson	v Rosslyn P. 21.3.92 (H) v Saracens 24.02.01 (H)
Tries	16 Neil Back 98-99	61 Neil Back 91-02	4 Tony Underwood Geordan Murphy	v Newcastle G. 12.3.94 (H) v Saracens 24.02.01 (H)
Conversions	52 Tim Stimpson 99-00	129 John Liley 88-97	7 John Liley Tim Stimpson	v Rosslyn P. 21.3.92 (H) v Harlequins 6.5.00 (A)
Penalties	64 John Liley 95-96	232 John Liley 88-97	8 John Liley Tim Stimpson	v Bristol 28.10.95 (H) v Gloucester 2.12.00 (H)
Drop Goals	13 Jez Harris 94-95	37 Jez Harris 87-95	3 Jez Harris	v Wasps 23.11.91 (H) v Bath 15.4.95 (H)

OVERALL PLAYING RECORD

	P	W	D	L	F	A	Pts Diff
Home	36	32	0	4	1033	364	669
Away	55	39	0	16	1008	635	373
Neutral	10	5	0	5	145	136	9
Total	101	76	0	25	2086	1105	1051

SEASON BY SEASON

Season	Result
1971-72	1R
1972-73	QF
1973-74	1R
1974-75	DNQ
1975-76	1R
1976-77	2R
1977-78	Runners-up
1978-79	**Winners**
1979-80	**Winners**
1980-81	**Winners**
1981-82	SF
1982-83	Runners-up
1983-84	3R
1984-85	QF
1985-86	SF
1986-87	SF
1987-88	4R
1988-89	Runners-up
1989-90	QF
1990-91	4R
1991-92	SF
1992-93	**Winners**
1993-94	Runners-up
1994-95	SF
1995-96	Runners-up
1996-97	**Winners**
1997-98	5R
1998-99	SF
1999-2000	5R
2000-01	SF
2001-02	QF

LEICESTER TIGERS RFU SENIOR CUP

STATISTICS

compiled by Stephen McCormack

TEAM RECORDS

Highest Score
83 v Otley 00/01

Biggest Winning Margin
76 (76-0) v Exeter 92/03

Highest Score Against
47 v London Irish 99/00

Biggest Losing Margin
40 (47-7) v London Irish 99/00

INDIVIDUAL RECORDS

Most Points in a match
28 Jez Harris v Blackheath 94/95

Most Tries in a match
4 Leon Lloyd v Otley 00/01

Most Conversions in a match
7 Joel Stransky v Coventry 97/98

Most Penalties in a match
7 John Liley v Saracens 95/96

Most Drop Goals in a match
2 Joel Stransky v Gloucester 96/97

EUROPEAN COMPETITIONS

STATISTICS *compiled by Stephen McCormack*

TEAM RECORDS

Highest Score
90 v Glasgow 97/98

Biggest Winning Margin
71 (90-19) v Glasgow 97/98

Highest Score Against
38 v Stade Francais 99/00

Biggest Losing Margin
22 (38-16) v Stade Francais 99/00

INDIVIDUAL RECORDS

Most Points in a match
35 Joel Stransky v Glasgow 97/98

Most Tries in a match
4 Michael Horak 97/98

Most Conversions in a match
10 Joel Stransky v Glasgow 97/98

Most Penalties in a match
7 Tim Stimpson v Perpignan 01/02

Most Drop Goals in a match
2 Andy Goode v Pau 00/01

CAREER RECORDS

Most Appearances
33: Graham Rowntree (5)
32: Darren Garforth (1)
31: Martin Johnson

Most Points
310: Tim Stimpson
106: Joel Stransky
65: Neil Back

Most Tries
13: Neil Back
12: Leon Lloyd
11: Austin Healey

SEASON BY SEASON

Season		Result
1996-97	S	Runners up
1997-98	S	Q-F
1998-99	C	D N Play
1999-00	C	Gp stage
2000-01	C	Winners
2001-02	C	Winners

OVERALL PLAYING RECORD

	P	W	D	L	F	A	Pts Diff
Home	19	17	0	2	666	317	349
Away	15	8	0	7	329	315	14
Neutral	5	4	0	1	90	94	-4
Total	39	29	0	10	1085	726	359

LEICESTER TIGERS

FACT FILE

Founded: 1880
Nickname: Tigers
Colours: Dark green with red and white hoops
Change colours: Navy with green and red hoops
Website: www.tigers.co.uk

GROUND Aylestone Road., Leicester. LE2 7TR Web site: http://www.tigers.co.uk
Tel: 0116 254 1607 Fax: 0116 285 4766 e-mail: tigers@tigers.co.uk
Capacity: 16,250 Seated: 12,000 Standing: 4,000

Directions: From M1, junction 21. Along the A5460 into Leicester. At the Post House Hotel traffic lights turn right onto B5418 (Braunstone Lane East). After 1 mile turn left at `T' junction traffic lights onto A426 (Aylestone Road). Ground 2 miles on right.

Nearest Railway Station: Leicester (London Road).
The ground is about 3/4 mile walk along Waterloo Way. (Station Tel. No. 0116 248 1000)

Car Parking: None available at the ground.

Admission :
Season Standing Adults £139, Juniors £59, Concessions £89.
Seated Adults £149-289, Juniors £69-209, Concessions £119-239
Matchday Standing Adults £12-14, Juniors £5, Concessions £10-12.
Seated Adults £14-27, Juniors £6-18, Concessions £12-25

Club Shop: Yes, manager Sarah Watson, 0116 254 0077

Clubhouse: With six bars and food available.
Functions: Various rooms available.
For details contact Joanna Fairey, 0116 254 1607

PROGRAMME
Size: 170mm x 240mm
Pages: 52 Price: £2.50
Editor: Stuart Farmer, Press Off.
01455 895470
ADVERTISING RATES
On application to
Tracey Branson, c/o Leicester FC

HONOURS

Premiership	98-99, 99-2000, 00-01, 01-02
Courage League Div. 1	87-88, 94-95 R-up 93-94, 95-96
Pilkington Cup	92-93, 96-97 R-up 88-89, 93-94, 95-96
John Player Cup	78-79, 79-80, 80-81 R-up 77-78, 82-83
European Cup	00-01, 01-02 R-up 96-97

LONDON IRISH RFC

Media Liaison Officer Patrick Lennon
Tel: 01753 893050
Fax: 01753 893051
email: mail@patricklennon.com

Chief Executive Geoff Huckstep

Player Coach Brendon Venter

Official Photographer Michael Peel
Tel: 020 8949 5082

Sunbury Administration

Tel: 01932 783034
Fax: 01932 784462
email: lisrmanagement@hotmail.com

Exceeding Expectations!

The first national trophy in 104 years, fourth place in the Zurich Premiership, semi-finalists in the Parker Pen Shield, quarter-finalists in the Zurich Championship and qualification for the Heineken European Cup. Not a bad end of season report for a team that had been written off as 'relegation candidates' by the so-called experts at the start of the season.

Not only did the consistency of the team's results surprised many, its attractive style of rugby also delighted and excited the club's supporters and rugby fans in general. The result was a season that exceeded all expectations.

While 'fortress Madejski' was breached on three occasions, the record of eleven victories, three draws and eight defeats in the Premiership speaks for itself. London Irish finished its league season in fourth place in the table, a position that guaranteed a Heineken Cup place.

For many people winning the first national trophy in the history of the club was the highlight of 2001/02 season. On 20th April "headquarters" was a 75,000 sell out for the club's first national final in 22 years. In a first half display that had those privileged to see it purring, Irish established a commanding lead over Northampton. They went on to score two more tries in the second half to win comfortably by 38-7.

A week later Irish faced Pontypridd at the Kassam Stadium, Oxford for a place in the final of the Parker Pen (European) Shield. In reaching the semi-final Irish had travelled to France, Italy and Spain to win their pool stage of the competition. This was followed by a famous away victory over Pau in south-west France in the quarter-final. Pontypridd, like the Exiles, had emerged during the season with a winning formula based on a team ethic. A hard fought, entertaining encounter saw the Exiles lose by 27-33.

In another complement to the talent that has flourished in the squad last season, the selectors of England, Ireland, Wales and Germany picked 14 London Irish players to play at full international, A or under-21 levels during the year.

A sound foundation has been laid, the challenge is to consolidate and move forward in the coming season.

LONDON IRISH

Comp.	Date	H/A	Opponents	Result & Score	Att	15	14	13	12	11
ZP	01-09	A	Harlequins	W 32-21	7287	Horak	Cunningham/t	Bishop	Venter	Sackey
ZP	09-09	H	Leeds Tykes	W 42-14	4219	Horak	Cunningham	Bishop	Venter/t	Sackey
ZP	16-09	A	Bristol	D 19-19	3900	Horak	Cunningham	Bishop/t	Venter	Sackey
ZP	23-09	H	Newcastle Falcons	L 18-22	5419	Horak	Cunningham	Bishop	Venter	Sackey
ZP	14-10	A	London Wasps	W 20-15	5107	Horak	Bishop	Hoadley	Venter	Sackey/t
ZP	21-10	H	Gloucester	W 19-15	5937	Horak	Bishop	Hoadley	Venter	Sackey
ZP	11-11	A	Bath	L 11-19	7656	Horak	Sackey/t	Appleford	Hoadley	Cunningham/2p
ZP	18-11	H	Northampton Saints	W 48-12	5191	Horak	Sackey	Wright/t	Hoadley	Bishop/t
ZP	22-11	A	Saracens	W 55-13	5216	Horak	Bishop/t	Wright/t	Hoadley(c/t)	Sackey/t
ZP	02-12	H	Leicester Tigers	L 15-30	11124	Horak	Sackey	Appleford	Venter	Bishop
ZP	08-12	A	Sale	D 19-19	4775	Horak	Bishop	Appleford	Venter	Sackey
ZP	23-12	H	Saracens*	W 30-23	8246	Horak	Ezulike	Bishop	Appleford	Sackey/t
ZP	29-12	A	Northampton Saints	L 15-24	10332	Horak	Ezulike	Bishop	Appleford	Sackey
ZP	09-02	A	Gloucester	L 22-29	10112	Horak	Bishop	Hoadley	Venter	Sackey
ZP	24-02	H	London Wasps	W 31-17	7848	Horak	Bishop/t	Appleford	Venter	Sackey
ZP	16-03	H	Bristol	W 24-13	12873	Horak	Sackey	Hoadley	Venter	Bishop
ZP	31-03	A	Leeds Tykes	W 29-24	3392	Horak	Sackey/t	Appleford	Venter	Bishop
ZP	10-04	H	Bath	W 31-15	6055	Horak/t	Sackey	Appleford	Venter	Bishop
ZP	14-04	H	Harlequins	D 18-18	6803	Horak/t	Ezulike/t	Appleford	Venter	Bishop
ZP	05-05	H	Sale	L 32-36	6076	Horak/t	Sackey	Appleford	Venter	Bishop/t
ZP	08-05	A	Newcastle Falcons	L 28-33	5218	Horak	Sackey	Appleford	Hoadley	Bishop
ZP	12-05	A	Leicester Tigers*	L 16-34	16000	Horak	Sackey	Appleford	Hoadley	Bishop
ES	29-09	N	Dax	W 29-22	3500	Horak	Hunt	Hoadley/t	Venter/t	Bishop
ES	07-10	H	L'Aquila*	W 48-12	2200	Thrower/2t	Hunt	Wright	Hoadley/2t	Sackey/2t
ES	28-10	N	Valladolid RAC	W 71-5	2800	Thrower	Cunningham/t9cp	Wright/t	Hoadley	Sackey/2t
ES	04-11	H	Valladolid RAC	W 76-10	2414	Thrower/2tc	Cunningham	Wright	Hoadley/2t	Hunt
ES	04-01	N	L'Aquila	W 32-8	400	Thrower/t	Cunningham	Hoadley	Wright	Hunt/t
ES	13-01	H	Dax	D 28-28	3240	Horak	Sackey	Hoadley	Venter	Bishop/t
ES	26-01	N	Pau	W 38-9	8000	Horak	Sackey/t	Appleford	Venter/dg	Bishop
ES	27-04	N	Pontypridd	L 27-33		Horak/t	Sackey	Appleford	Venter	Bishop
PGC	15-12	A	Bath	W 20-12	5332	Horak/t	Ezulike	Bishop/t	Appleford	Sackey
PGC	20-01	H	Gloucester	W 25-10	8076	Horak	Sackey/t	Appleford	Venter	Bishop
PGC	09-03	A	Harlequins	W 32-27	9000	Horak/t	Sackey	Appleford	Venter/t	Bishop
PGC	20-04	N	Northampton Saints	W 38-7	75000	Horak/t	Sackey	Appleford/2t	Venter	Bishop/2t
ZPO	19-05	H	Northampton Saints	L 14-38	3336	Thrower	Ezulike	Hunt	Cannon	Drake

** after opponents name indicates a penalty try. Brackets after a player's name indicates he was replaced. eg (a) means he was replaced by replacement code "a" and so on. / after a player or replacement name is followed by any scores he made - eg /t, /c, /p, /dg or any combination of these*

EVER PRESENT Ryan Strudwick, Michael Horak

Most Appearances:
22: Ryan Strudwick, Michael Horak.
21: Paul Sackey, Justin Bishop.
20: Barry Everitt(1), Chris Sheasby.

PLAYERS USED

30 plus four as a replacement

MOST POINTS

Pts	Player	T	C	P	DG
343	B Everitt	2	30	83	8
25	P Sackey	5	-	-	-
25	J Bishop	5	-	-	-
20	C Sheasby	4	-	-	-
20	M Worsley	4	-	-	-

MATCH FACTS

10	9	1	2	3	4	5	6	7	8
Everitt/2c5pdg	Edwards	Worsley/t	Drotske	Halford	Strudwick	Fahrenson	Cockle	Dawson	Sheasby
Everitt/3c7p	Edwards	Hatley	Kirke	Hardwick	Strudwick	Fahrenson	Cockle(a/t)	Dawson	Sheasby/t
Everitt/c4p	Edwards	Worsley	Drotske	Halford	Strudwick	Fahrenson	Cockle	Dawson	Sheasby
Everitt/5pdg	Edwards	Hatley	Kirke	Hardwick	Strudwick	Fahrenson	Cockle	Danagher	Sheasby
Everitt/4pdg	Edwards	Worsley	Drotske	Halford	Strudwick	Fahrenson	Cockle	Danagher	Sheasby
Everitt/c4p	Edwards	Hatley	Kirke	Hardwick	Strudwick	Williams	Cockle/t	Danagher	Sheasby
Brown	Edwards	Worsley	Drotske	Halford	Strudwick	Williams	Halvey	Danagher	Sheasby
Everitt/5cp	Edwards/t	Hatley/t	Kirke	Hardwick	Strudwick/t	Williams	Halvey	Danagher/t	Sheasby(b/t)
Everitt/t4c4p	Edwards	Worsley	Drotske/t	Halford	Strudwick	Williams	Halvey	Dawson	Sheasby/t
Everitt/5p	Edwards	Hatley	Kirke	Hardwick	Strudwick	Williams	Halvey	Dawson	Sheasby
Everitt/c4p	Edwards	Worsley	Drotske	Halford	Strudwick/t	Williams	Halvey	Dawson	Sheasby
Everitt/3c3p	Edwards	Worsley	Drotske	Hardwick	Strudwick	Williams	Danagher	Dawson	Sheasby
Everitt/4pdg	Edwards	Hatley	Kirke	Hardwick	Strudwick	Williams	Danagher	Dawson	Sheasby
Everitt/2p2dg	Martens	Worsley/t	Kirke	Hardwick	Strudwick	Williams	Gustard	Danagher	Sheasby/t
Everitt/2c3pdg	Martens/t	Worsley/t	Drotske	Halford	Strudwick	Williams	Gustard	Danagher	Sheasby
Everitt/c4p	Martens	Worsley	Drotske	Hardwick	Strudwick	Williams	Gustard/2t	Danagher	Sheasby
Everitt/tc3pdg	Martens	Worsley/t	Kirke	Hardwick	Strudwick	Williams	Gustard	Danagher	Sheasby
Everitt/c8p	Martens	Worsley	Drotske	Hardwick	Strudwick	Williams	Gustard	Danagher	Sheasby
Brown/cp(d/p)	Edwards	Hatley	Kirke	Halford	Delaney	Williams	Gustard	Danagher	Strudwick
Everitt/3c2p	Edwards	Hatley	Drotske	Hardwick	Strudwick	Fahrenson(f/t)	Gustard	Danagher(g/t)	Sheasby
Everitt/c7p	Edwards	Hatley	Kirke	Halford	Strudwick	Fahrenson	Halvey	Pfister	Sheasby/t
Everitt/c3p	Edwards	Hatley	Drotske	Hardwick	Delaney	Fahrenson	Halvey	Pfister	Strudwick
Everitt/2c5p	Edwards	Worsley	Drotske	Halford	Strudwick	Fahrenson	Cockle	Danagher	Sheasby
Brown/5cp	Barrett	Hatley	Flavin	Hardwick	Delaney	Williams	Halvey	Danagher	Bates
Brown	Turvey(i/t)	Worsley/t	Drotske	Halford	Delaney	Williams	Halvey/3t	Dawson	Danagher(h/t)
Everitt/t7c	Barrett/2t	Hatley	Flavin	Hardwick/t	Delaney	Fahrenson	Cockle/t	Dawson	Danagher/3t
Brown/3c2p	Barrett/t	Worsley	Drotske	Halford	Delaney	Fahrenson	Cockle	Danagher/t	Bates
Everitt/c7p	Barrett	Worsley	Kirke	Halford	Strudwick	Williams	Danagher	Dawson	Sheasby
Everitt/3pdg(j/2c3p)	Martens	Worsley	Kirke	Halford	Strudwick	Williams	Cockle	Danagher/t	Sheasby
Everitt/3c2p	Martens	Hatley	Kirke/t	Halford	Strudwick	Williams	Halvey/t	Danagher	Sheasby
Everitt/cp	Edwards	Hatley(k/t)	Kirke	Hardwick	Strudwick	Williams	Bates	Dawson	Danagher
Everitt/c5pdg	Martens	Worsley	Kirke	Hardwick	Strudwick	Williams	Cockle	Danagher	Sheasby
Everitt/2c6p	Martens	Hardwick	Kirke	Halford	Strudwick	Williams	Halvey	Danagher	Sheasby
Everitt/5cp	Martens	Worsley	Drotske	Hardwick	Strudwick	Williams	Halvey	Danagher	Sheasby
Brown/2c	Barrett/t	Wheatley	Flavin	Halford	Delaney	Burke	Gustard	Pfister/t	Cockle

REPLACEMENTS: a - Richard Bates. b - Kieron Dawson. c - Ed Thrower. d - Jeff Fahrenson. e - Barry Everitt. f - Eddie Halvey. g - Glen Delaney. h - James Cockle. i - Keith Barrett. j - James Brown. k - Michael Worsley.

WHEN	Total	First Half	Second Half	1/4	2/4	3/4	4/4
The POINTS were scored	574	319	255	128	191	105	150
The POINTS were conceded	465	232	233	106	126	105	128
The TRIES were scored	46	20	26	7	13	8	18
The TRIES were conceded	37	18	19	7	11	7	12

HOW the TRIES were scored

Total	Backs	Forwards	F Back	Wing	Centre	H Back	F Row	Lock	B Row	Pen. Try
46	23	21	3	11	5	4	6	4	11	2

HOW the TRIES were conceded

Total	Backs	Forwards	F Back	Wing	Centre	H Back	F Row	Lock	B Row	Pen. Try
37	26	10	2	11	10	3	3	1	6	1

LONDON IRISH

LEAGUE STATISTICS
compiled by Stephen McCormack

SEASON	Division	P	W	D	L	F	A	Pts Diff	Lge Pts	Lge Pos	Most Points		Most Tries	
92-93	1	12	6	0	6	175	223	-48	12	7	111	Michael Corcoran	3	Simon Geoghegan
93-94	1	18	4	0	17	217	391	-174	8	9r	75	Michael Corcoran	5	Simon Geoghegan
94-95	2	18	9	0	9	363	381	-18	18	5	164	Michael Corcoran	6	Rob Henderson
95-96	2	18	15	0	3	583	405	178	30	2p	301	Michael Corcoran	10	Conor O'Shea
96-97	1	22	6	0	16	502	749	-247	12	10	189	David Humphreys	8	Conor O'Shea
97-98	P1	22	6	0	16	457	673	-216	12	11	237	Niall Woods	8	Conor O'Shea Niall Woods
98-99	P1	26	15	0	11	703	607	96	30	7	215	Niall Woods	12	Niall Woods
99-00	P1	22	9	1	12	613	616	-3	25	8	324	Jarod Cunningham	10	Conor O'Shea
00-01	P1	22	10	1	11	476	576	-100	45	8	182	Barry Everitt	8	Paul Sackey
01-02	P	22	11	3	8	574	465	109	57	4	343	Barry Everitt	6	Paul Sackey Justin Bishop

BIGGEST MARGINS

Home Win	48pts - 62-14 v Harlequins 25.4.98 56-8 v Newcastle 2.10.99
Away Win	42pts - 55-13 v Saracens 22.11.01
Home Defeat	48pts - 16-64 v Bath 11.3.00
Away Defeat	59pts - 7-66 v Harlequins 14.9.96

MOST CONSECUTIVE

Appearances	29 Rob Henderson
Matches scoring Tries	4 Rob Saunders
Matches scoring points	24 Michael Corcoran
Victories	8
Defeats	7

MOST POINTS

Scored at Home	62 v Harlequins 25.4.98
Scored Away	55 v Saracens 22.11.01
Conceded at Home	65 v Northampton 9.9.95
Conceded Away	66 v Harlequins 14.9.96

MOST TRIES

Scored in a match	8 v Moseley 30.9.95 (H) v Harlequins 25.4.98 (H)
Conceded in a match	11 v Harlequins 14.9.96 (A)

MOST APPEARANCES

by a forward	96 (1) Gary Halpin
by a back	138(3) Justin Bishop

	MOST IN A SEASON	MOST IN A CAREER	MOST IN A MATCH	
Points	343 Barry Everitt 01-02	744 Michael Corcoran 89-98	32 Niall Woods	v Harlequins 25.4.98 (H)
Tries	12 Niall Woods 98-99	55 Conor O'Shea 95-01	4 Niall Woods	v Northampton 5.1.99 (A)
Conversions	46 Jarod Cunningham 99-00	65 Michael Corcoran 89-98	8 Niall Woods	v Harlequins 25.4.98 (H)
Penalties	83 Barry Everitt 01-02	169 Michael Corcoran 89-98	8 Jarod Cunningham Barry Everitt	v Bristol 10.9.00 (H) v Bath 10.04.02 (H)
Drop Goals	8 Barry Everitt 01-02	10 Brian Mullen 88-92	2 Ralph Kuhn Brian Mullen Ian Aitchison Paul Burke Barry Everitt	v Lon. Scottish 14.1.89 (A) v Richmond 8.4.89 (A) v Plymouth 13.1.90 (H) v Bristol 24.1.92 (H) v Gloucester 9.2.02 (A)

LONDON IRISH RFU SENIOR CUP

STATISTICS

compiled by Stephen McCormack

OVERALL PLAYING RECORD

	P	W	D	L	F	A	Pts Diff
Home	29	17	0	12	476	407	69
Away	31	18	0	13	566	529	37
Neutral	3	1	0	2	64	52	12
Total	63	36	0	27	1106	988	118

SEASON BY SEASON

Season	Result
1971-72	1R
1972-73	DNQ
1973-74	DNQ
1974-75	2R
1975-76	2R
1976-77	1R
1977-78	1R
1978-79	2R
1979-80	Runners up
1980-81	4R
1981-82	3R
1982-83	3R
1983-84	4R
1984-85	DNQ
1985-86	1R
1986-87	3R
1987-88	3R
1988-89	4R
1989-90	2R
1990-91	QF
1991-92	3R
1992-93	3R
1993-94	5R
1994-95	5R
1995-96	SF
1996-97	5R
1997-98	QF
1998-99	QF
1999-2000	SF
2000-01	QF
2001-02	**Winners**

TEAM RECORDS

Highest Score
57 v Exeter 00/01

Biggest Winning Margin
45 (57-12) v Exeter 00/01

Highest Score Against
46 v Nottingham 90/91 & Leicester 95/96

Biggest Losing Margin
36 (46-10) v Nottingham 90/91

INDIVIDUAL RECORDS

Most Points in a match
22 Jarod Cunningham v Leicester 99/00

Most Tries in a match

Most Conversions in a match
7 Jarrod Cunningham v Gloucester 99/00

Most Penalties in a match

Most Drop Goals in a match
2 Brian Mullen v Rugby 90/91

EUROPEAN COMPETITIONS

STATISTICS *compiled by Stephen McCormack*

TEAM RECORDS

Highest Score
76 v Valladolid 01/02

Biggest Winning Margin
66 (76-10 & 71-5) v Valladolid 01/02

Highest Score Against
63 v Swansea 96/97

Biggest Losing Margin
26 (32-6) v Begles 96/97

INDIVIDUAL RECORDS

Most Points in a match
26 By three players

Most Tries in a match
3 By four players

Most Conversions in a match
9 Jarrod Cunningham v Valladolid 01/02

Most Penalties in a match
7 By two players
Barry Everitt (x2), Jarrod Cunningham

Most Drop Goals in a match

CAREER RECORDS

Most Appearances
24: Justin Bishop
15: Neil Hatley, Conor O'Shea
14: Kieran Campbell, Kieron Dawson

Most Points
201: Barry Everitt
139: Jarrod Cunningham
95: Conor O'Shea

Most Tries
13: Conor O'Shea
6: Justin Bishop, Declan Danagher, Paul Sackey

SEASON BY SEASON

Season		Result
1996-97	S	Gp Stage
1997-98	S	Gp Stage
1998-99	-	-
1999-00	S	Semi-final
2000-01	S	Gp Stage
2001-02	S	Semi-final

OVERALL PLAYING RECORD

	P	W	D	L	F	A	Pts Diff
Home	14	10	1	3	505	268	237
Away	18	10	0	8	573	451	222
Neutral	1	-	-	1	27	33	-6
Total	33	20	1	12	1105	752	453

LONDON IRISH

FACT FILE

Founded: 1898
Nickname: The Irish
web site: www.london-irish-rugby.com

Colours: Green/white/green
Change colours: Blue/white/blue

GROUND Madejski Stadium, Reading, Berkshire RG2 0FL
Capacity: 25,000 - all covered seating

Directions: The ground is directly next to Junction 11 of the M4
Nearest Railway Station: Reading Central

Car Parking At the stadium

Admission Matchdays: £1-18
Season Tickets Adults £199

Club Shop At the Madejski Stadium

Clubhouse The Avenue, Sunbury-on-Thames

Sunbury Administration
Tel: 01932 783034 Fax: 01932 784462
email: lisrmanagement@hotmail.com

PROGRAMME

Size:A5 Price: £2.50 Pages: 80
Editor: Sian Isaac 01934 783034

Advertising Rates

Colour - Page £2,000 Half £1,200
Spot Colour - Page 1,500 Half £850

LONDON WASPS

Chairman	Chris Wright
Director of Rugby	Warren Gatland
Operations Manager	Gloria Sennitt
Academy Director	Rob Smith
Community Development Manager	Toni Smyth

London Wasps Training Ground, Twyford Ave. Sports Ground, Twyford Ave., Acton, London W3 9QA
Tel: 020 8902 4200 Fax: 020 8900 2659

A season of mixed fortunes, that's how one can describe London's Wasps during 2001/2002. Finishing runners up in the Zurich Premiership the 2001/2002 season looked promising for "The Men in Black" but unfortunately didn't live up to expectations.

With a slow start and a barrage of injuries, the season got a vital boost when former New Zealand Rugby International and Ireland National coach Warren Gatland replaced Nigel Melville as the Director of Rugby. After months of speculation Melville moved to Gloucester and Gatland took over the reigns. The rewards were instant and with his new playing style and return of many player's from injury including captain Lawrence Dallaglio, flyhalf Alex King and flanker Paul Volley, London Wasps climbed off the bottom position in the Zurich Premiership to end mid table, this remarkable turn around included six consecutive wins including a magnificent 34-24 over eventual European Champions Leicester Tigers. Gatland finished the season in charge with his record as played eight, won six and lost two.

As far as players go, "Kinger" proved remarkable with the boot and slotted an astonishing ten-drop goals during the Zurich Premiership season and ended up second on the drop goal table. The 2001/2002 season also saw the conclusion of one of Rugby's greatest players, Ian Jones. The New Zealand lock moved to London Wasps mid season and his vast amount of experience and leadership proved an inspiration for many of the young players. Jones said, " I have thoroughly enjoyed my time with Wasps and what ever happens I will always have a soft spot for the side and look back on my time here with fond memories". Jones eventually hung up his boots at the end of the season.

As far as the Heineken Cup goes, London Wasps failed to reach their true potential as a force in European Rugby. Finishing third in a group that included Treviso, Ulster and Stade Francais unfortunately excluded them from the playoffs.

In the Powergen Cup, the deadly boot of Jonny Wilkinson - who scored all his sides points, gave defending champions Newcastle Falcons a 24-22 fifth round victory and sank any chance of London Wasps reaching the last eight. Wilkinson injury time drop goal secured victory for the Falcons and summed up the London Wasps season, full of missed chances and very unlucky.

2001/2002 season also saw the last game for the next two years played at Loftus Road for the side as this season will see them playing at Adams Park in High Wycombe. The final game was against Northampton Saints, which was an emotional moment for many of the players, staff and officials.

Unfortunately our fate had already been sealed before Gatland took over and will now see "The Men in Black" spend this season contesting the Parker Pen Challenge Cup but with new signings and an array of young talent we look certain to return to the top and London Wasps will continue to be a club and team to be proud of.

LONDON WASPS

Comp.	Date	H/A	Opponents	Result & Score	Att	15	14	13	12	11
ZP	02-09	H	Saracens	W 12-8	5929	Sampson	Lewsey	Waters	Denney	Logan/3p
ZP	08-09	A	Leicester Tigers	L 15-45	13837	Sampson	Lewsey	Waters	Denney	Logan/5p
ZP	16-09	H	Sale	L 21-40	4403	Roiser	Lewsey	Waters/t	Denney	Logan/c3p
ZP	22-09	A	Harlequins	L 13-33		Roiser	Lewsey/t	Waters	Denney	Sampson/p
ZP	14-10	H	London Irish	L 15-20	5107	Lewsey	Sampson	Waters	Denney	Logan/5p
ZP	21-10	A	Bristol	L 22-43	4147	Roiser	Logan/2cp	Waters/t	Denney	Sampson
ZP	11-11	H	Newcastle Falcons	L 30-33	3955	Sampson/dg	Roiser	Waters	Denney	Scrase
ZP	18-11	H	Leeds Tykes	W 64-14	3507	Sampson	Roiser/t	Waters/2t	Denney(a/t)	Logan/2t
ZP	23-11	A	Gloucester	L 13-43	10171	Leek	Roiser	Waters(a/t)	Denney	Logan
ZP	02-12	H	Bath*	W 23-10	6240	Lewsey	Roiser	Waters	Denney	Logan/2p
ZP	08-12	A	Northampton Saints	L 10-23	8833	Lewsey	Roiser	Abbott	Denney/t	Logan
ZP	30-12	A	Leeds Tykes	W 28-18	5166	Lewsey	Roiser	Waters	Denney	Logan
ZP	27-01	A	Newcastle Falcons	W 23-22	4658	Lewsey	Roiser(b/t)	Denney	Waters/t	Logan/c2p
ZP	10-02	H	Bristol	W 34-16	5425	Lewsey	Roiser/t(b/t)	Waters	Abbott	Logan/p
ZP	24-02	A	London Irish	L 17-31	7848	Lewsey	Roiser	Waters	Denney	Logan/t4p
ZP	16-03	A	Sale	L 22-27	5118	Sampson	Offiah	Waters/t	Denney	Rudd
ZP	31-03	H	Leicester Tigers	W 36-24	9621	Lewsey	Roiser	Waters	Abbott	Logan/3p
ZP	10-04	H	Gloucester	W 44-9	5769	Lewsey/t	Roiser	Waters	Abbott/t	Sampson
ZP	14-04	A	Saracens	W 20-14	10431	Lewsey	Sampson	Waters	Abbott	Logan/p
ZP	26-04	H	Harlequins	W 16-6	8388	Lewsey	Roiser/t	Abbott	Denney	Logan/p
ZP	04-05	H	Northampton Saints	W 17-6	6133	Sampson	Roiser	Lewsey	Denney	Logan/p
ZP	12-05	A	Bath	W 24-22	8200	Lewsey	Roiser(b/t)	Abbott	Denney	Sampson/t
HC	30-09	H	Stade Francais	L 19-25	5950	Lewsey/t	Roiser	Waters	Denney	Logan/t3p
HC	05-10	A	Ulster	L 19-42	10000	Lewsey	Scrase	Waters	Denney	Logan/c4p
HC	28-10	H	Benetton Treviso*	W 29-24		Sampson	Roiser	Waters	Denney	Rudd
HC	03-11	A	Benetton Treviso	L 17-32	4000	Sampson	Roiser/t	Waters	Denney	Roberts
HC	06-01	H	Ulster	W 36-32	5959	Leek	Roiser/t	Waters/t	Denney/t	Roberts
HC	12-01	A	Stade Francais	L 0-31		Logan	Roiser	Waters	Denney	Roberts
PGC	16-12	A	Newcastle Falcons	L 22-24	4100	Lewsey	Waters/t	Abbott	Denney	Logan/2p
ZPO	19-05	A	Sale	L 27-43	3283	Sampson/t	Roberts	Abbott	Denney	Offiah/2t

** after opponents name indicates a penalty try. Brackets after a player's name indicates he was replaced. eg (a) means he was replaced by replacement code "a" and so on. / after a player or replacement name is followed by any scores he made - eg /t, /c, /p, /dg or any combination of these*

EVER PRESENT None

Most Appearances:
21: Craig Dowd, Simon Shaw.
20: Martyn Wood(1), Will Green(2).
19: Joe Worlsey.

PLAYERS USED

30 plus four as a replacement

MOST POINTS

Pts	Player	T	C	P	DG
183	A King	-	24	36	9
121	K Logan	3	5	32	-
30	F Waters	6	-	-	-
20	C Dowd	4	-	-	-

MATCH FACTS

10	9	1	2	3	4	5	6	7	8
Leek/dg	Wood	Molloy	Leota	Dowd	Beardshaw	Shaw	Birkett	Volley	Worsley
Leek	Wood	Molloy	Leota	Dowd	Shaw	Beardshaw	Jenkins	Allen	Worsley
Leek	Wood	Green	Leota	Dowd/t	Beardshaw	Shaw	Jenkins	Allen	Worsley
Leek/cp	Friday	Green	Greening	Dowd	Beardshaw	Shaw	Jenkins	Allen	Worsley
King	Wood	Dowd	Leota	Green	Shaw	Jones	Lock	Jenkins	Worsley
King	Wood	Green	Leota	Dowd/t	Beardshaw	Jones	Jenkins	Lock	Worsley/t
King/9p	Wood	Dowd	Greening	Green	Shaw	Jones	Jenkins	Allen	Lock
King/7c4pdg	Wood	Dowd	Greening/t	Green	Shaw	Jones	Jenkins	Volley	Lock
King/cpdg	Wood	Dowd	Greening	Green	Shaw	Jones	Jenkins	Volley	Lock
King/2cp	Wood	Dowd	Greening	Green	Shaw	Jones	Jenkins	Worsley/t	Lock
King/cp	Wood	Dowd	Greening	Green	Shaw	Jones	Jenkins	Worsley	Lock
King/2c2pdg	Friday	Dowd/2t	Leota	Green	Shaw	Jones	Worsley	Volley	Lock/t
Leek	Wood	Dowd	Leota/t	Green	Jones	Shaw	Lock	Volley	Worsley
Leek/t3c	Wood	Dowd	Leota/t	Green	Shaw	Jones	Lock	Volley/t	Worsley
Leek	Wood	Dowd	Leota	Green	Shaw	Jones	Lock	Volley	Worsley
King/c4pdg	Wood	McKenzie	Leota	Green	Shaw	Jones	Lock	Volley	Worsley
King/7p2dg	Wood	Dowd	Leota	Green	Shaw	Jones	Worsley	Volley	Dallaglio
King/4c2pdg	Wood/t	Dowd	Leota/t	Green	Shaw	Jones	Worsley	Volley	Dallaglio
King/2cp	Wood	Dowd	Greening	Green	Shaw	Jones/t	Worsley/t	Volley	Dallaglio
King/c2dg	Wood	Dowd	Leota	Green	Shaw	Jones	Lock	Worsley	Dallaglio
King/3p	Wood	Dowd	Leota	Green	Shaw/t	Jones	Worsley	Volley	Dallaglio
King/3cp	Wood	Dowd	Leota	Green/t	Shaw	Jones	Lock	Worsley	Dallaglio
Leek	Friday	Molloy	Greening	Dowd	Shaw	Jones	Lock	Jenkins	Worsley
King	Friday	Dowd	Greening	Green/t	Shaw	Jones	Lock	Jenkins	Worsley
King/2c5p	Wood	Dowd	Leota	Green	Beardshaw	Jones	Lock	Jenkins	Worsley/t
Leek/4p	Wood	Dowd	Leota	Green	Shaw	Jones	Jenkins	Allen	Lock
King/3c5p	Wood	Dowd	Leota	Green	Shaw	Jones	Beardshaw	Volley	Lock
Leek	Wood	Dowd	Leota	Green	Beardshaw	Jones	Volley	Lock	Worsley
King/pdg	Friday	Dowd	Leota	Green	Beardshaw	Jones	Worsley	Volley/t	Lock
Lewsey/t	Wood	Dowd	Leota	Green	Shaw	Jones	Worsley	Greening/2cp	Lock

REPLACEMENTS: a - Stuart Abbott. b - Martin Offiah

WHEN	Total	First Half	Second Half	1/4	2/4	3/4	4/4
The POINTS were scored	519	252	267	99	153	110	157
The POINTS were conceded	507	228	279	119	109	112	167
The TRIES were scored	42	15	27	6	9	11	16
The TRIES were conceded	41	10	31	4	6	12	17

HOW the TRIES were scored

Total	Backs	Forwards	F Back	Wing	Centre	H Back	F Row	Lock	B Row	Pen. Try
41	24	16	1	11	10	2	9	2	5	1

HOW the TRIES were conceded

Total	Backs	Forwards	F Back	Wing	Centre	H Back	F Row	Lock	B Row	Pen. Try
41	27	12	4	11	7	5	5	3	4	2

LONDON WASPS

LEAGUE STATISTICS

compiled by Stephen McCormack

SEASON	Division	P	W	D	L	F	A	Pts Diff	Lge Pts	Lge Pos		Most Points		Most Tries
92-93	1	12	11	0	1	186	118	68	22	2	54	Alan Buzza	4	Phil Hopley & Chris Oti
93-94	1	18	10	1	7	362	340	22	21	3	159	Rob Andrew	5	Damian Hopley
94-95	1	18	13	0	5	470	313	157	26	3	135	Rob Andrew	7	Phil Hopley
95-96	1	18	11	0	7	439	322	117	22	4	91	Guy Gregory	8	Shane Roiser
96-97	1	22	18	1	3	685	406	279	37	1	291	Gareth Rees	11	Kenny Logan
97-98	P1	22	8	1	13	490	609	-119	17	9	253	Gareth Rees	5	Mike Friday & Penalty Tries
98-99	P1	26	15	1	10	717	506	211	31	5	263	Kenny Logan	8	Kenny Logan
99-00	P1	22	11	1	10	640	661	-21	31	7	136	Kenny Logan	9	Josh Lewsey
00-01	P1	22	16	0	6	663	428	235	74	2	282	Kenny Logan	11	Paul Sampson
01-02	P	22	12	0	10	519	507	12	54	7	183	Alex King	6	Fraser Waters

BIGGEST MARGINS

Home Win	57pts - 62-5 v Orrell 22.3.97
Away Win	31pts - 57-26 v Harlequins 17.9.94
Home Defeat	31pts - 3-34 v Harlequins 9.3.96
Away Defeat	32pts - 6-38 v Leicester 12.10.93

MOST CONSECUTIVE

Appearances	36 Richard Kinsey 29.2.92-30.4.94
Matches scoring Tries	4 Kenny Logan
Matches scoring points	25 Gareth Rees
Victories	9
Defeats	6

MOST POINTS

Scored at Home	65 v Orrell 22.3.97
Scored Away	57 v Harlequins 17.9.94
Conceded at Home	34 v Harlequins 9.3.96
Conceded Away	45 v London Irish 17.5.00/ v Leices

MOST TRIES

Scored in a match	9 v Coventry 13.4.88 (H); v Bedford 12.3.90 (A); v Liverpool St H 20.4.91; v Orrell 2.3.97 (H) & v Bedford 26.3.00 (H)
Conceded in a match	6 - v Orrell 30.4.94/v Lon Irish17.5.00/ v Leics 9.9.01

MOST APPEARANCES

by a forward	149 (5) Lawrence Dallaglio
by a back	118(2) Shane Rosier

	MOST IN A SEASON		MOST IN A CAREER		MOST IN A MATCH		
Points	291	Gareth Rees 96-97	879	Kenny Logan 96-02	29	Alex King	v Leeds Tykes 18.11.01 (H)
Tries	11	Kenny Logan 96-97 Paul Sampson 00-01	43	Kenny Logan 96-02	5	Kenny Logan	v Orrell 22.3.97 (H)
Conversions	47	Kenny Logan 00-01	82	Rob Andrew 87-96	8	Alex King	v Bedford 26.3.00 (H)
Penalties	62	Gareth Rees 96-97	161	Rob Andrew 87-96	9	Alex King	v Newcastle 11.11.01 (H)
Drop Goals	9	Alex King 01-02	11	Rob Andrew 87-96	2	Jon Ufton Rob Andrew Guy Gregory	v Saracens 23.9.95 (H) v Sale 30.9.95 (A) v Leicester 6.4.96 (A)

LONDON WASPS RFU SENIOR CUP

STATISTICS

compiled by Stephen McCormack

OVERALL PLAYING RECORD

	P	W	D	L	F	A	Pts Diff
Home	31	23	0	8	693	374	319
Away	35	23	0	12	750	444	306
Neutral	7	3	0	4	162	201	-39
Total	73	29	0	24	1605	1019	586

SEASON BY SEASON

Season	Result
1971-72	DNQ
1972-73	DNQ
1973-74	DNQ
1974-75	1R
1975-76	1R
1976-77	DNQ
1977-78	1R
1978-79	SF
1979-80	1R
1980-81	3R
1981-82	3R
1982-83	4R
1983-84	QF
1984-85	4R
1985-86	Runners up
1986-87	Runners up
1987-88	SF
1988-89	QF
1989-90	3R
1990-91	QF
1991-92	4R
1992-93	SF
1993-94	4R
1994-95	Runners up
1995-96	QF
1996-97	6R
1997-98	Runners up
1998-99	**Winners**
1999-2000	**Winners**
2000-01	4R
2001-02	6R

TEAM RECORDS

Highest Score

84 v Rugby Lions 96/97

Biggest Winning Margin

76 (84-8) v Rugby Lions 96/97

Highest Score Against

48 v Saracens 97/98

Biggest Losing Margin

36 (43-7) v Leicester 78/79

INDIVIDUAL RECORDS

Most Points in a match

26 Kenny Logan v Newcastle 99/00

Most Tries in a match

3 on more than one occasion

Most Conversions in a match

7 on more than one occasion

Most Penalties in a match

Most Drop Goals in a match

3 Rob Andrew v Leicester 94-95

EUROPEAN COMPETITIONS

STATISTICS *compiled by Stephen McCormack*

TEAM RECORDS

Highest Score

77-17 v Toulouse 96/97

Biggest Winning Margin

60 Pts 77-27 v Toulouse 96/97

Highest Score Against

54-28 v Swansea 00/01

Biggest Losing Margin

31 Pts 0-31 v Stade Francais 00/01

INDIVIDUAL RECORDS

Most Points in a match

27 Jon Ufton v Toulouse 96/97

Most Tries in a match

3 Kenny Logan v Ulster 97/98

Most Conversions in a match

6 Jon Ufton v Toulouse 96/97

Most Penalties in a match

8 Gareth Rees v Cardiff 96/97

Most Drop Goals in a match

1 Alex King (twice)

CAREER RECORDS

Most Appearances

24: W Green, Shane Roiser.
23: Alex King
21: Lawrence Dallaglio,
Kenny Logan

Most Points:

232: Kenny Logan (13t,22c,41p,-)
130: Gareth Rees (-,20c,30p,-)
100: Alex King (7t,7c,15p,2dg)

Most Tries:

13: Kenny Logan
8: Shane Roiser
7: Alex King, Joe Worsley

SEASON BY SEASON

Season		Result
1996-97	C	Gp Stage
1997-98	C	Q-Finals
1998-99	-	D N Play
1999-00	C	Q-Finals
2000-01	C	Gp Stage
2001-02	C	Gp Stage

OVERALL PLAYING RECORD

	P	W	D	L	F	A	Pts Diff
Home	15	11	0	4	537	290	247
Away	15	7	0	8	360	420	-60
Neutral	-	-	-	-	-	-	-
Total	30	18	0	12	897	710	187

LONDON WASPS

FACT FILE

Founded: 1867
Nickname: Wasps
Web site: wasps.co.uk

Colours: Black and gold
Change colours: Gold and black

Ground Address: Adams Park, High Wycombe
Directions: From London, join M25 and head for J16 M25/M40. Join M40 and head to J4/A404 High Wycombe. At Junction 4 take slip road and turn right, over the motorway and then take first exit for A4010 (John Hall Way). Follow this road crossing 3 mini roundabouts until the road becomes New Road. Keep on New Road until next mini roundabout take left turn onto Lane End Road. Cross next mini roundabout onto Hillbottom Road, this will take you on to Adams Park.

Training Ground: Twyford Avenue Sports Ground, Twyford Avenue, Acton, London W3 9QA
Tel: 020 8902 4200 Fax: 020 8900 2659 Ticket Hotline: 01494 769 471

Directions:
From North: At bottom of M1 join A406 West (North Circular Road). At junction with A4020 (Uxbridge Road) at Ealing Common, turn left. Twyford Avenue is approx half a mile on left (opposite Tesco / Garage). The training ground is second on the right.
From East: Through City on A40 to junction with A406 at Hangar Lane. A406 southbound to junction with A4020 (Uxbridge Road). Twyford Avenue is approx half a mile on left (opposite Tesco / Garage). The training ground is second on the right.
From South: A205 (South Circular Road) over Kew Bridge onto A406 (North Circular Road). Follow A406 to junction with A4020 (Uxbridge Road) at Ealing Common and turn right/ Twyford Avenue is approx half a mile on left (opposite Tesco / Garage). The training ground is second on the right.
From West: A40 (Western Avenue) to junction with A406 (North Circular Road) at Hangar Lane. A406 Southbound to junction with A4020 (Uxbridge Road). Turn left and Twyford Avenue is approx half a mile on left (opposite Tesco / Garage). The training ground is second on the right.

Club Shop: 0208 993 8298
PROGRAMME Size: B5 Pages: 48 Price: £2
Editor: Phil Harris
Advertising PIA Sport Tel: 01625 35546 Fax: 01635 845811

NEC HARLEQUIN FC

Stoop Memorial Ground, Langhorn Drive, Twickenham TW2 7SX.
Tel: 0208 410 6000 Fax: 0208 410 6001

		Telephone	e-mail
Chairman	Christopher Haines		
Chief Executive	Mark Evans	020 8410 6036	marke@quins.co.uk
Managing Director	Tony Copsey	020 8410 6037 07990 571810	tonyc@quins.co.uk
Team Manager	Mike Scott	01252 311311 07774 651330	mikes@harlequins.fsnetco.uk
Press Officer	Nick Melton	020 8410 6045 07990 571807	nickm@quins.co.uk

NEC Harlequins had another disappointing Zurich Premiership campaign, winning only five of their 22 matches and finishing in ninth place. A run of eight consecutive defeats in the league, meant Quins spent the latter half of the season fighting off the prospect of relegation. However, the club recorded two excellent home victories over Newcastle Falcons (33-19) and Leeds Tykes (40-16) which helped them to move away from the bottom of the pile.

Despite their league form, Quins once again showed their liking for cup rugby. By defeating Sale Sharks 32-25 at Heywood Road in the 6th Round of the Powergen Cup, Quins were rewarded a home tie against Leicester Tigers in the quarterfinals. Two late penalties from Paul Burke, the second from well inside his own half, gave Quins a memorable 22-20 victory and a place in the last four, where they faced London Irish.

By scoring 27 unanswered points, Quins staged a remarkable comeback to lead the Exiles 27-26 at the Stoop with just 10 minutes left to play. Barry Everitt then denied Quins a second Twickenham final appearance in two seasons as two late penalties from the fly half meant Irish were the winners of a remarkable game by 32-27.

On their return to the Heineken Cup, Quins failed to reach the knockout stages of the competition. After a 30-24 victory away at Bridgend, the club suffered four defeats on the trot in both the home and away legs against Munster and Castres. By defeating Bridgend 29-25 at the Stoop, ensured Quins did not finish bottom of their pool.

However, the season did see exciting young players make a name for themselves. Just four weeks after making his First XV debut for Quins, scrum half Nick Duncombe made his international debut for England against Scotland in the Calcutta Cup at Murrayfield (2nd February 2002). Duncombe, along with Ben Gollings, were regular members of the England 7's squad throughout the season, while centre Chris Bell captained the England U19 side.

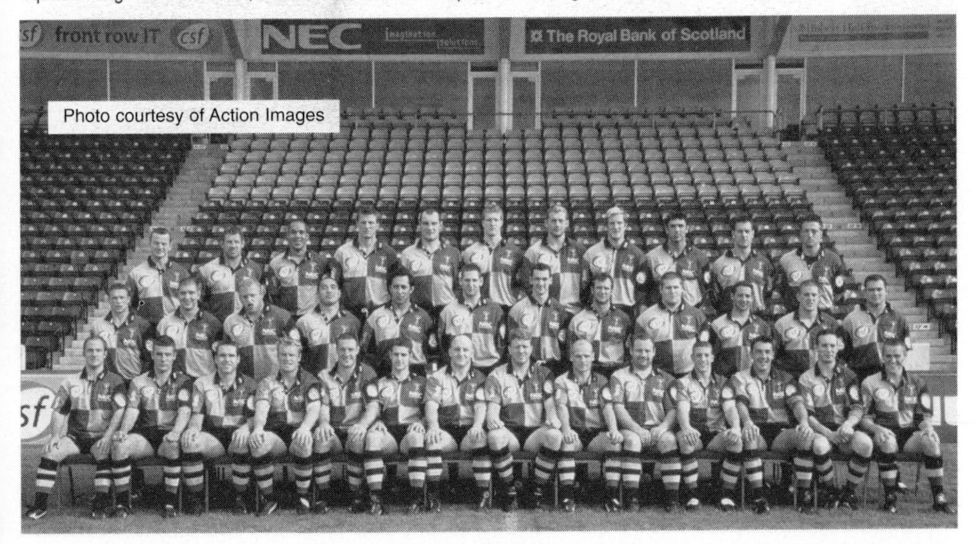

Photo courtesy of Action Images

HARLEQUINS

Comp.	Date	H/A	Opponents	Result & Score	Att	15	14	13	12	11
ZP	01-09	H	London Irish	L 21-32	7287	Gollings	Moore	Burrows	Greenstock	Luger
ZP	08-09	H	Bristol	L 32-38	5220	Gollings	Moore	Burrows	Greenstock/t	Luger/t
ZP	16-09	A	Newcastle Falcons	D 6-6	5551	Gollings	Moore	Burrows	Bell	Luger
ZP	22-09	H	London Wasps	W 33-13		Mapletoft/t	Moore/t	Greenstock	Bell	Luger
ZP	13-10	A	Gloucester	L 7-33		O'Neill	Moore	Greenwood/t	Greenstock	Luger
ZP	20-10	H	Bath	W 15-8	5328	Mapletoft/p	Moore	Burrows	Greenstock	Jewell
ZP	09-11	A	Northampton Saints	D 13-13	8667	Mapletoft	Moore	Burrows	Greenstock	Gollings/t
ZP	16-11	H	Saracens	W 43-6	6450	Mapletoft	Moore/t	Burrows	Bell	Gollings
ZP	23-11	A	Leicester Tigers	L 18-23	16017	Mapletoft	Moore	Burrows	Bell	Gollings
ZP	01-12	H	Sale	L 16-23	5841	Williams	Moore	Greenwood	Burrows	Luger
ZP	09-12	A	Leeds Tykes	L 18-23	3401	Williams	Moore	Greenwood	Burrows	Luger/2t
ZP	22-12	H	Leicester Tigers	L 21-38	9000	O'Neill	Moore	Greenwood	Bell	Luger
ZP	30-12	A	Saracens	L 25-39	13257	O'Neill	Moore	Greenwood/t	Greenstock	Luger
ZP	26-01	H	Northampton Saints	L 16-24	5882	Sleman	Moore	Greenstock	Bell/t	Jewell
ZP	09-02	A	Bath	L 9-18	8200	Sleman	Moore	Greenwood	Burrows	Jewell
ZP	23-02	H	Gloucester	L 6-18	8000	Sleman	Gollings	Greenwood	Burrows	Luger
ZP	16-03	H	Newcastle Falcons	W 33-19	6525	Gollings	Jewell	Greenwood	Bell/t	Moore
ZP	31-03	A	Bristol*	L 27-43	5618	Gollings	Jewell	Greenwood	Greenstock/2t	Luger
ZP	14-04	A	London Irish	D 18-18	6803	Gollings/dg	Jewell	Greenwood	Bell	Luger
ZP	26-04	A	London Wasps	L 6-16	8388	Gollings	Jewell	Greenwood	Bell	Moore
ZP	03-05	H	Leeds Tykes	W 40-16	7255	Gollings	Jewell	Greenwood/t	Greenstock/t	Moore/t
ZP	12-05	A	Sale	L 11-40	5678	Gollings	Jewell	Bell	Greenstock	Moore/t
HC	29-09	A	Bridgend	W 30-24	4000	Mapletoft	Moore	Greenwood	Bell	Luger/t
HC	06-10	H	Munster	L 8-24	9000	Mapletoft	Moore	Greenwood	Greenstock	Luger/t
HC	28-10	H	Castres	L 17-39		O'Neill	Moore	Greenwood	Greenstock	Luger/t
HC	03-11	A	Castres	L 18-24	5000	O'Neill	Moore	Greenwood/t	Greenstock	Luger
HC	05-01	A	Munster	L 17-51		Sleman	Moore	Greenwood	Burrows	Luger
HC	12-01	H	Bridgend	W 29-25	4152	Sleman/t	Moore/t	Burrows	Bell/t	Jewell/t
PGC	15-12	A	Sale	D 22-22		O'Neill	Moore/t	Greenwood	Bell	Luger
PGC	19-01	H	Leicester Tigers	W 22-20	8900	Sleman	Moore	Greenwood	Burrows/t	Jewell
PGC	09-03	H	London Irish	L 27-32	9000	Sleman	Jewell	Greenwood	Burrows	Luger

** after opponents name indicates a penalty try. Brackets after a player's name indicates he was replaced. eg (a) means he was replaced by replacement code "a" and so on. / after a player or replacement name is followed by any scores he made - eg /t, /c, /p, /dg or any combination of these*

EVER PRESENT None

Most Appearances:
20: Paul Burke.
19: Matt Moore.
18: Jason Leonard.
17: Roy Winters(2), Steve White-Cooper, Garrick Morgan (3)

PLAYERS USED

34 plus two as replacement only

MOST POINTS

Pts	Player	T	C	P	DG
258	P Burke	3	21	62	5
20	N Greenstock	4	-	-	-
20	M Moore	4	-	-	-
15	K Wood	3	-	-	-
15	D Sleman	-	-	3	2
15	D Luger	3	-	-	-
15	W Greenwood	3	-	-	-

MATCH FACTS

10	9	1	2	3	4	5	6	7	8
Burke/7p	Powell	Leonard	Fuga	Dawson	Morgan	White-Cooper	Winters	Sanderson	Diprose
Burke/t3c2p	Bemand/t	Leonard	Wood	Olver	Morgan	Davison	Winters	Sanderson	Diprose
Burke/pdg	Bemand	Leonard	Wood	Olver	Morgan	Davison	White-Cooper	Tamarua	Winters
Burke/c7p	Bemand	Leonard	Rodham	Olver	Morgan	White-Cooper	Winters	Tamarua	Diprose
Mapletoft/c	Bemand	Leonard	Fuga	Olver	Morgan	White-Cooper	Sanderson	Tamarua	Diprose
Burke/4p	Bemand	Olver	Fuga	Dawson	Morgan	White-Cooper	Sanderson	Tamarua	Diprose
Burke/c2p	Powell	Starr	Tiatia	Olver	Morgan	Davison	White-Cooper	Sanderson	Winters
Burke/t4c5p	Powell	Starr	Tiatia	Olver/t	Morgan	Davison	White-Cooper	Tamarua/t	Winters
Burke/5pdg	Powell	Starr	Tiatia	Olver	Morgan	Codling	White-Cooper	Tamarua	Winters
Burke/c3p	Bemand	Leonard/t	Tiatia	Olver	Codling	Davison	Winters	Tamarua	Diprose
Burke/c2p	Bemand	Starr	Wood	Leonard	Codling	Davison	Winters	Tamarua	Diprose
Burke/tc3p	Powell(a/t)	Starr	Fuga	Leonard	Morgan	Codling	Winters	Tamarua	Diprose
Burke/c5pdg	Powell	Starr	Rodham	Leonard	Morgan	Codling	Winters	Tamarua	Diprose
Burke/c3p	Duncombe	Leonard	Rodham	Olver	Morgan	Davison	White-Cooper	Tamarua	Diprose
Burke/2pdg	Duncombe	Leonard	Tiatia	Olver	Morgan	White-Cooper	Winters	Sherriff	Diprose
Burke/2p	Duncombe	Leonard	Tiatia	Dawson	Morgan	Codling	White-Cooper	Sanderson	Diprose
Burke/2c3p	Duncombe	Leonard	Wood	Olver/t	Codling	White-Cooper/t	Winters	Tamarua	Diprose
Burke/2cp	Duncombe	Leonard	Wood/t	Olver	Codling	White-Cooper	Winters	Tiatia	Diprose
Burke/2p(b/p2dg)	Powell	Leonard	Wood	Olver	Morgan	Codling	White-Cooper	Tiatia	Winters
Sleman/2p	Powell	Leonard	Wood	Olver	Morgan	Codling	White-Cooper	Tiatia	Winters
Burke/3c2pdg	Powell	Leonard	Wood/2t	Olver	Morgan	Codling	White-Cooper	Tiatia	Diprose
Burke/p(c/p)	Powell	Leonard	Tiatia	Douglas	Codling	Davison	Winters	White-Cooper	Diprose
Burke/t3c3p	Bemand	Starr	Wood	Olver	Morgan	White-Cooper	Winters	Tamarua/t	Diprose
Burke/p	Bemand	Leonard	Wood	Olver	Morgan	White-Cooper	Winters	Tamarua	Diprose
Mapletoft/2cp	Bemand	Leonard	Wood	Dawson	Morgan	White-Cooper/t	Sanderson	Tamarua	Diprose
Sleman/c2p	Powell	Starr	Wood/t	Leonard	Davison	Morgan	White-Cooper	Sanderson	Winters
Burke/2cp	Duncombe	Starr	Rodham	Dawson	Morgan	Davison	White-Cooper	Tamarua	Diprose/2t
Mapletoft/3p	Bemand	Starr	Rodham	Olver	Morgan	Codling	White-Cooper	Alesbrook	Diprose
Burke/c4pdg	Powell	Starr	Wood	Leonard	Morgan	Codling	Winters	Tamarua	Diprose
Burke/c5p	Duncombe	Leonard	Fuga	Olver	Morgan	Davison	White-Cooper	Tamarua	Diprose
Burke/3c2p	Duncombe	Leonard	Tiatia/t	Olver	Codling/t	White-Cooper	Winters	Sanderson	Diprose/t

REPLACEMENTS: a - Scott Bemand b - Dave Sleman. c - Mark Mapletoft.

WHEN	Total	First Half	Second Half	1/4	2/4	3/4	4/4
The POINTS were scored	434	226	208	118	108	107	101
The POINTS were conceded	507	238	269	130	108	134	135
The TRIES were scored	33	14	19	5	9	8	11
The TRIES were conceded	52	21	31	11	10	16	15

HOW the TRIES were scored

Total	Backs	Forwards	F Back	Wing	Centre	H Back	F Row	Lock	B Row	Pen. Try
32	23	9	1	8	9	5	6	1	2	1

HOW the TRIES were conceded

Total	Backs	Forwards	F Back	Wing	Centre	H Back	F Row	Lock	B Row	Pen. Try
52	37	14	6	15	7	9	5	2	7	1

HARLEQUINS

LEAGUE STATISTICS
compiled by Stephen McCormack

SEASON	Division	P	W	D	L	F	A	Pts Diff	Lge Pts	Lge Pos	Most Points		Most Tries
92-93	1	12	5	1	6	197	187	10	11	8	57	Sturat Thresher	3 by 4 players
93-94	1	18	8	0	10	333	287	46	16	6	143	Kent Bray	11 Daren O'Leary
94-95	1	18	6	1	11	275	348	-73	13	8	103	Paul Challinor	4 Peter Mensah
95-96	1	18	13	0	5	524	314	210	26	3	112	Paul Challinor	14 Daren O'Leary
96-97	1	22	15	0	7	745	416	329	30	3	176	Thierry Lacroix	15 Daren O'Leary
97-98	P1	22	8	0	14	516	645	-129	16	10	109	Thierry Lacroix	9 Daren O'Leary
98-99	P1	26	16	1	9	690	653	37	33	4	331	John Schuster	11 Dan Luger
99-00	P1	22	7	0	15	441	687	-246	28	10	84	Rob Liley	7 Brandon Daniel
00-01	P1	22	7	0	15	440	538	-98	38	11	133	Paul Burke	7 Will Greenwood
01-02	P	22	5	3	14	434	507	-73	35	9	258	Paul Burke	4 Nick Greenstock & Matt Moore

BIGGEST MARGINS

Home Win	71pts - 89-18 v Orrell 5.10.96
Away Win	70pts - 91-21 v W. Hartlepool 23.3.96
Home Defeat	49pts - 5-54 v Leicester 6.5.00
Away Defeat	58pts - 19-77 v Bath 29.4.00

MOST CONSECUTIVE

Appearances	42 Andy Mullins 16.11.91-30.4.94
Matches scoring Tries	5 Daren O'Leary
Matches scoring points	21 JohnSchuster
Victories	6 (twice)
Defeats	8

MOST POINTS

Scored at Home	89 v Orrell 5.10.96
Scored Away	91 v West Hartlepool 23.3.96
Conceded at Home	57 v Wasps 17.9.94
Conceded Away	77 v Bath 29.4.00

MOST TRIES

Scored in a match	14 v W. Hartlepool 23.3.96
Conceded in a match	10 v Bath 29.4.00

MOST APPEARANCES

by a forward	118 (2) Andy Mullins
by a back	124(5) Daren O'Leary

	MOST IN A SEASON	MOST IN A CAREER	MOST IN A MATCH	
Points	331 John Schuster 98-99	431 David Pears 89-96	28 John Schuster	v Bath 21.11.98 (H)
Tries	15 Daren O'Leary 96-97	65 Daren O'Leary 93-01	4 Daren O'Leary	v Gloucester 31.8.96 (H)
Conversions	36 John Schuster 98-99	57 David Pears 89-96	9 Paul Challinor	v W Hartlepool 23.3.96 (A)
Penalties	77 John Schuster 98-99	92 Paul Burke 00-02	7 David Pears Paul Burke Paul Burke	v Rosslyn Park 7.12.91 (A) v Wasps 22.9.01 (H) v Lon Irish 1.9.01 (H)
Drop Goals	7 David Pears 95-96	14 David Pears 89-96	3 David Pears	v Wasps 16.9.95 (H)

OVERALL PLAYING RECORD

	P	W	D	L	F	A	Pts Diff
Home	48	36	0	12	1191	585	606
Away	38	26	0	12	774	561	213
Neutral	5	2	0	3	108	103	5
Total	91	64	0	27	2073	1249	824

SEASON BY SEASON

Season	Result
1971-72	QF
1972-73	1R
1973-74	1R
1974-75	DNQ
1975-76	DNQ
1976-77	1R
1977-78	SF
1978-79	2R
1979-80	SF
1980-81	3R
1981-82	QF
1982-83	QF
1983-84	SF
1984-85	QF
1985-86	QF
1986-87	4R
1987-88	**Winners**
1988-89	SF
1989-90	3R
1990-91	**Winners**
1991-92	Runners up
1992-93	Runners up
1993-94	SF
1994-95	SF
1995-96	QF
1996-97	SF
1997-98	4R
1998-99	QF
1999-00	QF
2000-01	Runners up
2001-02	SF

HARLEQUINS RFU SENIOR CUP

STATISTICS

compiled by Stephen McCormack

TEAM RECORDS

Highest Score

88 v Thurrock 99/00

Biggest Winning Margin

88 (88-0) v Thurrock

Highest Score Against

45 v London Welsh 72/73

Biggest Losing Margin

33 (45-12) v London Welsh 72/73

INDIVIDUAL RECORDS

Most Points in a match

22 Paul Burke v Newcastle 24.02.

Most Tries in a match

Most Conversions in a match

7 Rob Liley v Thurrock 99/00

Most Penalties in a match

Most Drop Goals in a match

EUROPEAN COMPETITIONS

STATISTICS *compiled by Stephen McCormack*

TEAM RECORDS

Highest Score

56 v Caledonia 96/97

Biggest Winning Margin

45 (55-10) v Perigueux 00/01

Highest Score Against

51 v Toulouse 97/98 & Munster 01/02

Biggest Losing Margin

41 (51-10) v Toulouse 97/98

INDIVIDUAL RECORDS

Most Points in a match

27 Paul Burke v Narbonne 00-01

Most Tries in a match

3 Jim Staples v Caledonia 96/97

Jamie Williams Neath 96/97

Most Conversions in a match

4 Will Carling v Caledonia 96/97

Most Penalties in a match

7 Thierry Lacroix v Bourgoin 97/98

Most Drop Goals in a match

2 Gareth Rees v Cardiff 99/00

CAREER RECORDS

Most Appearances

26: Jason Leonard

21: Keith Wood, Daren O'Leary

17: Gareth Llewellyn

Most Points

92: Paul Burke

91: Thierry Lacroix

55: Jamie Williams, Daren O'Leary

Most Tries

11: Jamie Williams, Daren O'Leary

6: Will Greenwood

5: Keith Wood

SEASON BY SEASON

Season		Result
1996-97	C	QF
1997-98	C	QF
1998-99	–	–
1999-00	C	Gp Stage
2000-01	S	Winners
2001-02	C	Gp Stage

OVERALL PLAYING RECORD

	P	W	D	L	F	A	Pts Diff
Home	14	9	0	5	417	325	92
Away	17	7	1	9	372	422	-50
Neutral	2	2	0	0	59	45	14
Total	33	18	1	14	848	792	56

HARLEQUINS

FACT FILE

Founded: 1866
Nickname: Quins
Web site: www.quins.co.uk

Colours: Light blue, magenta, chocolate, french grey, light green & black
Change colours: None

GROUND Stoop Memorial Ground, Langhorn Drive, Twickenham. TW2 7SX
Tel: 020 8410 6000 Fax: 020 8410 6001
e-mail: mail@quins.co.uk Advance Ticket Line: 020 8410 6010
Capacity: 8,500 Seated Covered: 4,600 Uncovered: 2,850 Standing uncovered: 1,050

Directions: Langhorn Drive is off the westbound carriageway of theA316 Chertsey Road, 450 yards west of RFU roundabout. No entry for vehicles from Craneford Way
Nearest Railway Station: Twickenham (BR). 12 minutes walk, proceed towards RFU ground, turn left into Court Way, then left into Craneford Way. The ground is at the far end.

Car Parking: Limited amount available @ £5

Admission: Season Tickets (all seated) each price band reflects different seating areas
£399* / 275* / 220*§ / 125 / 75@ @ Under16s concession £25
* includes membership § OAPs/Young Adult (16-23) concession £159
Matchday: Adults £25 - 8 OAPs & Students £10 - 5 Under16s £5/2

Club Shop: Mon-Sat 10-4. Closed Wednesday. Contact Angela Lambert 020 8410 6056
Mail order 07000 478467

Clubhouse: Matchdays 12-late, Evening games 18.30-23.00. Colours restuarant. Snacks & light meals available.
Functions: 500-600 seated, 1000 buffet, 2000 bar.
Contact Crown Catering 020 8410 6052 / 6054

PROGRAMME Size: 170 x 245mm Pages: 56 Price: £2.50
Editor: Nick Melton 020 8410 6045

Advertising Rates
Contact - Gareth Lloyd 020 8410 6039

NEWCASTLE FALCONS

Vice President	Harry Sharp
Chairman	Dave Thompson
Director	John Gray
Managing Director	John Parkinson
Director of Rugby	Rob Andrew
Communications & Media Manager	Kath Charlton Tel: 0191 214 2806 Mob.: 07764 933310
E-mail:	kath.charlton@newcastle-falcons.co.uk
Head of Marketing	Mick Hogan Mobile - 07808 572989
1st Team Coach	Steve Bates

c/o Newcastle R.F.C.
Kingston Park,
Brunton Road,
Kenton Bank Foot,
Newcastle upon Tyne NE13 8AF
Tel: 0191 214 5588
Fax: 0191 286 0824
e-mail:
commercial@newcastle-falcons.co.uk

Newcastle Falcons have had a mixed season in terms of results but there have definitely been more ups than downs and they move into the 2002/03 season with high expectations.

The 2001/2002 campaign provided many memorable games: The opening match saw the Falcons beat triple champions Leicester Tigers 19-16 in front of a packed Kingston Park stadium. The Falcons first taste of the Heineken Cup was as tough as expected. Drawn in a strong group, huge lessons were learnt against Leinster and Newport culminating in a fabulous performance against Toulouse at home. The European experience was hugely beneficial and wetted the appetite for the competition in future seasons. Therefore it was bitterly disappointing not to qualify for next year's tournament at the end of the season. Another good Cup run led us to Northampton in the semi-finals where we met an inform Saints side. A strong end of season saw sound wins over Saracens, Bath and London Irish. The better weather seeming to suit the style of play adopted.

The infamous 'Young Guns' are developing well, led by England fly half Jonny Wilkinson, with others following in his footsteps such as Dave Walder, Tom May and Hugh Vyvyan who were all involved in the England summer tour to Argentina. Jamie Noon & Michael Stephenson were also part of the victorious England Sevens squad in Hong Kong this year.

Five extremely important and influential players departed the club at the end of last season: Inga Tuigamala and Pat Lam who have both retired from playing rugby and Gary Armstrong, Doddie Weir and George Graham who have joined the new Scottish Borders team. This will see the youngsters handed even more responsibility for the forthcoming season.

The 'Young Guns' have demonstrated great ability and commitment and, alongside the experience of Stuart Grimes, Marius Hurter and Steve Brotherstone, will prove very dangerous in the future.

Off the field the Falcons are trying to develop as fast as the team is on it. The Secretary of State recently approved the planning application to develop Kingston Park stadium.

The next few years will see massive developments at Kingston Park; not only will there be a stadium that the growing number of rugby fans in the North East deserve but also the playing & training facilities will be up there with the best in Europe.

A new stadium, an exciting group of players and an ever-growing group of loyal supporters, the future looks bright for Newcastle Falcons.

NEWCASTLE FALCONS

Comp.	Date	H/A	Opponents	Result & Score	Att	15	14	13	12	11
ZP	02-09	H	Leicester Tigers	W 19-16		Walder/t	Botham	Noon	May	Tuigamala
ZP	08-09	A	Sale	L 11-37	4865	Walder/p	Botham	Noon	May	Tuigamala
ZP	16-09	H	Harlequins	D 6-6	5551	Walder	Stephenson	Noon	May	Tuigamala
ZP	23-09	A	London Irish	W 22-18	5419	Walder	Botham	Noon	May/t	Stephenson
ZP	14-10	H	Bristol	W 37-20		Walder	Stephenson	Noon	May/2t	Botham
ZP	21-10	H	Leeds Tykes	W 19-8	4248	Richardson	Botham	Noon	May	Stephenson/t
ZP	11-11	A	London Wasps	W 33-30	3955	Richardson	Botham	Noon/t	May	Stephenson
ZP	18-11	H	Gloucester	W 18-16	5576	Richardson	Tuigamala	Noon	May	Maclure
ZP	25-11	A	Bath	L 9-24	7903	Richardson/p	Botham	Noon	May	Stephenson
ZP	02-12	H	Northampton Saints	L 13-28	5084	Stephenson	Botham	Noon	May/t	Maclure
ZP	09-12	A	Saracens	W 24-19	7294	Walder/dg	Stephenson/t	Noon	May/t	Botham
ZP	29-12	A	Gloucester*	L 25-29	11000	Walder	Maclure	Noon/t	May	Stephenson
ZP	27-01	H	London Wasps	L 22-23	4658	Walder	Maclure	May	Noon	Stephenson
ZP	10-02	A	Leeds Tykes	W 19-9	4195	Richardson	Botham	May	Tuigamala	Maclure
ZP	24-02	A	Bristol	L 17-33	5021	Richardson	Botham	Noon	Tuigamala/t	Stephenson/t
ZP	16-03	A	Harlequins	L 19-33	6525	Richardson	Maclure	Stephenson/t	May	Botham
ZP	31-03	H	Sale	W 30-10	6512	Botham	Stephenson	Noon	May/t	Maclure
ZP	13-04	A	Leicester Tigers	L 12-20	16250	Botham	Stephenson	Noon	May	Maclure
ZP	28-04	H	Bath	W 36-9	5430	Botham	Tuigamala/t	Noon/t	May/t	Stephenson/t
ZP	05-05	H	Saracens	W 47-18	6083	Botham/c	Tuigamala	Noon	May	Stephenson/2
ZP	08-05	H	London Irish	W 33-28	5218	Walder	Stephenson/t	Noon/2t	Tuigamala	Botham
ZP	12-05	A	Northampton Saints	L 19-24	9292	Walder	Stephenson	Noon	May	Botham
HC	29-09	H	Newport	L 21-34	6000	Walder	Botham	Noon	May	Tuigamala
HC	05-10	A	Leinster	L 9-28	7500	Walder	Botham	Tuigamala	May	Maclure
HC	28-10	A	Toulouse	L 13-33	8228	Richardson	Maclure	Noon	May	Tuigamala
HC	03-11	H	Toulouse	W 42-9		Walder	Stephenson/t	Noon	May	Botham
HC	08-01	N	Leinster	L 15-17	1146	Walder	Stephenson	Noon	May/t	Tuigamala/t
HC	11-01	A	Newport	L 17-53		Richardson	Botham	Maclure	Tuigamala	Stephenson
PGC	16-12	H	London Wasps	W 24-22	4100	Walder	Stephenson	Noon	May	Tuigamala
PGC	20-01	A	Leeds Tykes	W 41-24	4183	Walder	Stephenson(b/t)	Noon	May	Maclure
PGC	09-03	A	Northampton Saints	L 7-38	11652	Botham	Stephenson/t	Noon	May	Tuigamala
ZPO	18-05	A	Gloucester	L 9-60	5776	Walder/3p	Botham	Noon	May	Stephenson

** after opponents name indicates a penalty try. Brackets after a player's name indicates he was replaced. eg (a) means he was replaced by replacement code "a" and so on. / after a player or replacement name is followed by any scores he made - eg /t, /c, /p, /dg or any combination of these*

EVER PRESENT None

Most Appearances:
20: Jamie Noon(1), Tom May.
19: Hugh Vyvyan(2).
18: Michael Stephenson, Liam Botham.

PLAYERS USED

30 plus two as a replacement

MOST POINTS

Pts	Player	T	C	P	DG
215	J Wilkinson	2	32	44	3
75	D Walder	2	4	16	3
40	M Stephenson	8	-	-	-
35	T May	7	-	-	-
25	S Grimes	5	-	-	-
25	J Noon	5	-	-	-

MATCH FACTS

10	9	1	2	3	4	5	6	7	8
Wilkinson/c4p	Armstrong	Ward	Howe	Isaacson	Grimes	Vyvyan	Dunbar	Mower	Lam
Wilkinson/p	Armstrong	Ward	Howe	Isaacson	Vyvyan/t	Weir	Dunbar	Devonshire	Lam
Wilkinson/2p	Armstrong	Graham	Howe	Peel	Vyvyan	Grimes	Dunbar	Arnold	Lam
Wilkinson/c5p	Charlton	Ward	Balshan	Peel	Vyvyan	Weir	Taione	Arnold	Dunbar
Wilkinson/4c3p	Charlton	Graham	Makin	Hurter	Vyvyan	Grimes/2t	Taione	Arnold	Lam
Walder/2pdg	Charlton	Ward	Makin	Hurter	Weir	Grimes/t	Taione	Arnold	Lam
Walder/t3c4p	Armstrong	Ward	Makin	Hurter	Vyvyan	Weir/t	Dunbar	Arnold	Lam
Walder/6p	Charlton	Ward	Makin	Hurter	Vyvyan	Weir	Dunbar	Arnold	Lam
Walder/pdg	Armstrong	Peel	Balshan	Hurter	Vyvyan	Weir	Dunbar	Arnold	Lam
Walder/c2p	Charlton	Ward	Makin	Hurter	Vyvyan	Grimes	Taione	Mower	Dunbar
Wilkinson/3c	Charlton	Ward	Makin	Graham/t	Vyvyan	Grimes	Taione	Mower	Lam
Wilkinson/t2c2p	Charlton	Ward	Makin	Graham	Weir	Grimes	Taione	Arnold	Dunbar
Wilkinson/c5p	Armstrong/t	Graham	Balshan	Hurter	Weir	Grimes	Taione	Arnold	Dunbar
Wilkinson/c4p	Charlton	Ward	Brotherstone	Hurter	Vyvyan(a/t)	Weir	Taione	Arnold	Lam
Wilkinson/2cdg	Charlton	Ward	Thompson	Hurter	Vyvyan	Weir	Taione	Arnold	Lam
Wilkinson/c2p2dg	Charlton	Ward	Brotherstone	Peel	Vyvyan	Grimes	Taione	Mower	Arnold
Wilkinson/t3c3p	Charlton	Ward	Brotherstone	Hurter	Vyvyan	Grimes/t	Taione	Arnold	Dunbar
Wilkinson/4p	Charlton	Ward	Brotherstone	Hurter	Vyvyan	Grimes	Taione	Arnold	Dunbar
Wilkinson/4cp	Charlton	Ward	Brotherstone	Hurter	Vyvyan	Grimes	Taione/t	Devonshire	Dunbar
Wilkinson/5c	Charlton/2t	Ward	Brotherstone	Hurter/t	Vyvyan/t	Grimes	Lam	Devonshire	Dunbar/t
Wilkinson/3c4p	Charlton	Graham	Brotherstone	Hurter	Vyvyan	Grimes	Dunbar	Devonshire	Arnold
Wilkinson/c4p	Charlton	Graham	Thompson	Hurter	Vyvyan/t	Grimes	Dunbar	Mower	Arnold
Wilkinson/7p	Armstrong	Ward	Balshan	Isaacson	Vyvyan	Grimes	Taione	Devonshire	Lam
Wilkinson/3p	Charlton	Peel	Makin	Graham	Grimes	Weir	Dunbar	Arnold	Lam
Walder/cpdg	Armstrong	Graham	Makin	Hurter	Vyvyan	Hamilton	Taione/t	Arnold	Dunbar
Wilkinson/3c6pdg	Charlton	Ward	Makin	Hurter	Vyvyan/t	Grimes	Taione/t	Mower	Dunbar
Wilkinson/cp	Charlton	Ward	Balshan	Graham	Vyvyan	Grimes	Dunbar	Devonshire	Lam
Walder/t2cp	Armstrong/t	Peel	Makin	Hurter	Hamilton	Weir	Arnold	Devonshire	Lam
Wilkinson/7pdg	Armstrong	Ward	Makin	Hurter	Vyvyan	Grimes	Taione	Dunbar	Lam
Wilkinson/3c5p	Charlton	Ward	Balshan	Hurter	Vyvyan	Grimes/t	Taione/t	Arnold	Dunbar
Wilkinson/c	Armstrong	Graham	Thompson	Hurter	Vyvyan	Grimes	Taione	Mower	Lam
Wilkinson	Charlton	Graham	Brotherstone	Hurter	Weir	Grimes	Vyvyan	Devonshire	Arnold

REPLACEMENTS: a - Stuart Grimes. b - Va'aiga Tuigamala

WHEN	Total	First Half	Second Half	1/4	2/4	3/4	4/4
The POINTS were scored	490	227	263	108	119	124	139
The POINTS were conceded	458	233	225	108	125	123	102
The TRIES were scored	43	13	30	3	10	14	16
The TRIES were conceded	40	16	24	7	9	13	11

HOW the TRIES were scored

Total	Backs	Forwards	F Back	Wing	Centre	H Back	F Row	Lock	B Row	Pen. Try
43	29	13	1	8	14	6	2	9	2	1

HOW the TRIES were conceded

Total	Backs	Forwards	F Back	Wing	Centre	H Back	F Row	Lock	B Row	Pen. Try
40	27	13	5	9	7	6	4	3	6	-

NEWCASTLE FALCONS

LEAGUE STATISTICS

compiled by Stephen McCormack

SEASON	Division	P	W	D	L	F	A	Pts Diff	Lge Pts	Lge Pos	Most Points		Most Tries	
92-93	2	12	10	0	2	241	106	135	20	1p	136	David Johnson	6	Ross Wilkinson
93-94	1	18	2	1	15	190	483	-293	5	10r	79	David Johnson	4	Ross Wilkinson
94-95	2	18	8	2	8	373	281	92	18	3	193	Simon Mason	8	Tony Penn
95-96	2	18	5	1	12	348	405	-57	11	8	73	Richard Cramb	4	Mike Brummitt & Gary Armstrong
96-97	2	22	19	1	2	1255	346	909	39	2p	297	Rob Andrew	23	John Bentley
97-98	P1	22	19	0	3	645	387	258	38	1	226	Rob Andrew	13	Gary Armstrong
98-99	P1	26	14	0	12	719	639	80	28	8	306	Jonny Wilkinson	12	Gary Armstrong
99-00	P1	22	6	2	14	377	630	-253	19	9	163	Jonny Wilkinson	3	Four players
00-01	P1	22	11	0	11	554	568	-14	57	6	198	Jonny Wilkinson	7	Michael Stephenson Gary Armstrong
01-02	P	22	12	1	9	490	458	32	56	6	215	Jonny Wilkinson	8	Michael Stephenson

BIGGEST MARGINS

Home Win	151pts - 156-5 v Rugby 5.10.96
Away Win	66pts - 75-9 v Moseley 19.10.96
Home Defeat	43pts - 9-52 v Northampton 21.10.95
Away Defeat	61pts - 5-66 v Leicester 12.3.94

MOST CONSECUTIVE

Appearances	44 Neil Frankland 13.1.90-2.10.93
Matches scoring Tries	8 Gary Armstrong
Matches scoring points	22 Rob Andrew
Victories	6
Defeats	12

MOST POINTS

Scored at Home	156 v Rugby 5.10.96
Scored Away	75 v Moseley 19.10.96
Conceded at Home	52 v Northampton 21.10.95
Conceded Away	66 v Leicester 12.3.94

MOST TRIES

Scored in a match	24 v Rugby 5.10.96 (H)
Conceded in a match	10 v Leicester 12.3.94

MOST APPEARANCES

by a forward	164 (7) Richard Arnold
by a back	106 (7) Gary Armstrong

	MOST IN A SEASON	MOST IN A CAREER	MOST IN A MATCH	
Points	306 Jonny Wilkinson 98-99	882 Jonny Wilkinson 97-02	36 Rob Andrew	v Rugby 5.10.96 (H)
Tries	23 John Bentley 96-97	60 Gary Armstrong 95-02	5 Pat Lam	v Rotherham 4.5.97 (H)
Conversions	95 Rob Andrew 96-97	152 Rob Andrew 95-99	18 Rob Andrew	v Rugby 5.10.96 (H)
Penalties	53 Jonny Wilkinson 98-99	173 Jonny Wilkinson 97-02	6 David Johnson Rob Andrew Jonny Wilkinson Dave Walder	v Morlet 11.1.92 (H) v Richmond 26.10.97 (H) four times in 2000/01 v Gloucester 18.11.01(H)
Drop Goals	4 David Johnson 87-88	10 David Johnson 87-94	2 David Johnson Jonny Wilkinson	v Bedford 5.12.87 (A) v Harlequins 16.3.02 (A)

OVERALL PLAYING RECORD

	P	W	D	L	F	A	Pts Diff
Home	38	27	-	11	808	494	314
Away	40	25	-	15	653	534	119
Neutral	5	3	-	2	114	101	13
Total	83	55	-	28	1575	1129	446

SEASON BY SEASON

1971-72	1R
1972-73	1R
1973-74	2R
1974-75	QF
1975-76	Winners
1976-77	Winners
1977-78	2r
1978-79	SF
1979-80	QF
1980-81	Runners up
1981-82	QF
1982-83	3R
1983-84	3R
1984-85	3R
1985-86	3R
1986-87	4R
1987-88	4R
1988-89	3R
1989-90	4R
1990-91	4R
1991-92	QF
1992-93	QF
1993-94	5R
1994-95	4R
1995-96	5R
1996-97	QF
1997-98	QF
1998-99	Runners up
1999-2000	5R
2000-01	Winners
2001-02	SF

NEWCASTLE RFU SENIOR CUP

STATISTICS

compiled by Stephen McCormack

TEAM RECORDS

Highest Score
53 v Bridgwater 93/94
Biggest Winning Margin
52 (52-0) v Ruislip 91/92
Highest Score Against
58 v Wasps 94/95
Biggest Losing Margin
46 (12-58) v Wasps 94/95

INDIVIDUAL RECORDS

Most Points in a match
23 Jonny Wilkinson Lon Irish 00/01
Most Tries in a match

Most Conversions in a match
7 David Johnson v Ruislip 91-92
Most Penalties in a match
6 on more than one occasion
Most Drop Goals in a match
2 David Johnson v Blackheath 90/91

EUROPEAN COMPETITIONS

STATISTICS *compiled by Stephen McCormack*

TEAM RECORDS

Highest Score
99 v Cross Keys 00/01
Biggest Winning Margin
91 (99-8) v Cross Keys 00/01
Highest Score Against
53 v Newport 01/02
Biggest Losing Margin
37 (53-17) v Newport 01/02

INDIVIDUAL RECORDS

Most Points in a match
29 David Walder v Cross Keys 00/01
Most Tries in a match
3 by three players
Most Conversions in a match
12 David Walder v Cross Keys 00/01
Most Penalties in a match
7 Jonny Wilkinson 99/00
Most Drop Goals in a match
-1 by Jonny Wilkinson & David Walder

CAREER RECORDS

Most Appearances
23: Dodie Weir
22: Richard Arnold
17: Gary Armstrong, Inga Tuigamala
Most Points
207: Jonny Wilkinson
128: David Walder
102: Tim Stimpson

Most Tries
9: Inga Tuigamala
6: Tim Stimpson

SEASON BY SEASON

1996-97	-	D N Q
1997-98	S	S-Final
1998-99	-	D N Play
1999-00	S	Q-Final
2000-01	S	S-Final
2001-02	C	Gp Stage

OVERALL PLAYING RECORD

	P	W	D	L	F	A	Pts Diff
Home	14	12	0	2	645	190	455
Away	14	6	0	8	304	342	-38
Neutral	1	0	0	1	12	17	-5
Total	29	18	0	11	961	549	412

NEWCASTLE FALCONS

FACT FILE

Founded: 1877
Nickname: The Falcons
Web site: www.newcastle-falcons.co.uk

Colours: Black with gold trim
Change colours: Gold with black trim

GROUND

Address: Kingston Park, Brunton Road, Kenton Bank Foot, Newcastle upon Tyne NE13 AF
Tel: 0191 214 5588 Fax: 0191 271 5213
Capacity: 7,500 Seated: 2,500

Directions: Travelling from North or South on the City by-pass (A1 Western by-pass) take the Newcastle Airport sign and then follow signs for Kingston Park (Rugby Ground) - approx 1 mile.
Nearest Railway Station: Newcastle Central then Metro to Kingston Park (Green Line)

Car Parking: 600 spaces at ground

Admission: Season Standing, Adults £110, Concessions £55, Family (2A & 2C): £290.
Seated, Adults £200,Concessions £100, Family: £520
Matchday Standing, Adults £10, Concessions £5, Family: £30.
Seated, Adults £15,Concessions £8, Family: £46.

Club Shop: Yes, at Kingston Park
Clubhouse: At Kingston Park, open normal licensing hours
4 inside bar facilities, including corporate facilities,
1 outside bar facility and snack bars.
Functions: Capacity 200 - contact Karen Errington 0191 214 2811

PROGRAMME
Size: B2 Pages: 64 Price: £2.50
Editor: Richard Woollam 0191 214 2808

Advertising Rates Negotiable
Contact Martin Hutton Business Development 0191 214 2830

NORTHAMPTON SAINTS

Franklin's Gardens,
Weedon Road,
St. James',
Northampton NN5 5BG

Tel: 01604 751543
Fax: 01604 599110
e-mail: clubinfo@northamptonsaints.co.uk

Chairman	Keith Barwell
Commercial Director	Allan Robson
Communications Manager	Caroline Moore (nee Hayden)
Operations Director	John Steele
Rugby Administrator	Ros Hargreaves
Head Coach	Wayne Smith

One of the most important aspects for players and supporters alike for the 2002/03 season will the completion of the new-look Franklin's Gardens. The first phase of the redevelopment of the ground was finished in time for Saints' Midlands derby against Leicester Tigers on October 13, 2001. The Tetley's Stand and South Stand have housed the driest and most comfortable supporters for the past season and they have shown their appreciation by getting behind the players – even through the lean times. When the team first ran out in front of those two new stands, it took their breath away. When the West Stand is completed in time for the 2002/03 campaign, they will be greeted by a horseshoe shaped stadium full of 13,500 supporters in black, green and gold – quite a home advantage.

The new Fortress Franklin's will also contain state-of-the-art facilities to benefit the players, such as new home and away changing rooms and a rehabilitation and treatment room. It will also house a new media centre, which will keep me, and hopefully, the reporters, very happy.

There will also be a new man in charge of the entire facility to ensure the best use is made of it. However, it will be a face the rugby community will be familiar with. Former director of rugby John Steele, who guided Saints to three cup finals, including the victorious Heineken Cup win in 2000, has been invited to sit on the club's board as its new operations director. His experience as a chartered surveyor will put him in good stead to take on the responsibility of such a valuable asset as Franklin's Gardens.

Head coach Wayne Smith will also be given the opportunity to start a season from scratch. Since his arrival at the club in December last year, he has turned the team's fortunes around. The one-time relegation candidates ended up fifth in the Zurich Premiership following a Powergen Cup final.

So, the infrastructure is well and truly in place for Saints to try to fulfill their ambitions this season. At the time of writing, the player 'ins' and 'outs' of the season had not been finalised, but some familiar faces will still be running out in black, green and gold next season. The experience of skipper Budge Pountney, Matt Dawson, Ben Cohen, Tom Smith, Jon Phillips, Nick Beal, John Leslie, Peter Jorgensen and Matt Stewart will be vital to Saints' campaign, as will be the slightly more youthful talent of Dan Richmond, Robbie Morris, James Brooks and Mark Tucker. New faces among the squad will be Spanish wing Oriol Ripol and Wales lock/back row Steve Williams, as well as a return to his roots from lock Simon Hepher. Players that will no longer be in action for Saints this season will be Craig Moir, Olivier Brouzet, Andy Rennick, Luca Martin, Simon Webster and Steve Brotherstone.

Caroline Hayden

NORTHAMPTON SAINTS

Comp.	Date	H/A	Opponents	Result & Score	Att	15	14	13	12	11
ZP	01-09	A	Gloucester	L 9-22	8682	Beal	Moir	Jorgensen	Leslie	Cohen
ZP	08-09	H	Bath	W 26-7	10241	Grayson/2c3pdg	Beal	Jorgensen/t	Leslie	Cohen
ZP	16-09	A	Leeds Tykes	W 26-6	4080	Grayson/2c4p	Beal	Jorgensen	Leslie	Cohen/t
ZP	23-09	A	Saracens	L 20-25	8527	Grayson/2c2p	Beal	Martin	Tucker	Cohen/t
ZP	13-10	H	Leicester Tigers	L 11-21	11750	Grayson/2p	Moir	Jorgensen	Leslie/t	Cohen
ZP	20-10	A	Sale	L 14-34	3612	Tucker/3p	Martin	Jorgensen	Leslie	Cohen/t
ZP	09-11	H	Harlequins	D 13-13	8667	Shaw	Moir	Jorgensen	Tucker	Beal
ZP	18-11	A	London Irish	L 12-48	5191	Shaw/t	Moir	Jorgensen/t	Tucker/c	Beal
ZP	25-11	H	Bristol	L 20-23	7873	Shaw	Moir	Jorgensen	Tucker/p	Beal
ZP	02-12	A	Newcastle Falcons	W 28-13	5084	Grayson/4c	Beal	Jorgensen(b/t)	Leslie	Cohen/2t
ZP	08-12	H	London Wasps	W 23-10	8833	Grayson/5p	Beal	Jorgensen	Leslie	Cohen
ZP	29-12	H	London Irish	W 24-15	10332	Beal	Moir	Jorgensen/t	Tucker	Cohen
ZP	26-01	A	Harlequins	W 24-16	5882	Beal	Moir	Jorgensen	Leslie	Cohen/t
ZP	09-02	H	Sale	L 10-20	9589	Beal/p	Moir	Jorgensen	Leslie	Cohen
ZP	23-02	A	Leicester Tigers	L 6-17	16251	Beal/p	Moir	Jorgensen	Leslie	Cohen
ZP	16-03	H	Leeds Tykes	W 34-14	8366	Beal/t	Moir	Jorgensen/t	Leslie/t	Cohen
ZP	30-03	A	Bath	W 29-11	8200	Beal	Brooks/t	Jorgensen/t	Leslie	Tucker
ZP	13-04	H	Gloucester	W 58-21	9138	Beal/t	Brooks	Jorgensen/t	Leslie	Cohen/t
ZP	27-04	H	Saracens	W 52-27	8479	Beal/t	Brooks	Jorgensen	Leslie/t	Cohen/t
ZP	04-05	A	London Wasps	L 6-17	6133	Beal	Moir	Tucker	Leslie	Cohen
ZP	08-05	A	Bristol	W 37-27	4002	Shaw/t	Brooks	Jorgensen	Tucker	Beal
ZP	12-05	H	Newcastle Falcons	W 24-19	9292	Shaw	Brooks	Jorgensen	Leslie	Cohen
HC	28-09	A	Cardiff	L 17-25	10200	Grayson/p(e/t2c)	Beal	Tucker	Leslie	Cohen
HC	07-10	H	Glasgow Caledonians	W 30-9	7433	Tucker/t	Moir(f/t)	Jorgensen	Leslie	Cohen
HC	27-10	H	Montferrand	L 15-21		Cohen	Martin	Jorgensen	Leslie	Webster
HC	04-11	A	Montferrand	L 17-50	10146	Shaw/t	Martin	Jorgensen	Leslie	Cohen
HC	04-01	A	Glasgow Caledonians	L 27-31		Beal	Moir	Jorgensen	Tucker	Cohen/t
HC	12-01	H	Cardiff*	W 26-15	9700	Beal	Moir	Jorgensen	Leslie	Cohen/t
PGC	15-12	H	Birmingham & Solihull	W 32-19	5046	Shaw	Moir	Cohen/3t	Tucker	Beal
PGC	19-01	A	Saracens*	W 30-28	7617	Beal/tdg	Moir	Jorgensen	Leslie	Cohen
PGC	09-03	H	Newcastle Falcons	W 38-7	11652	Beal	Moir/t	Jorgensen/2t	Leslie	Cohen
PGC	20-04	N	London Irish	L 7-38	75000	Beal	Moir	Jorgensen	Leslie	Cohen/t
ZPO	19-05	A	London Irish*	W 38-14	3336	Shaw	Moir	Tucker	Leslie	Beal/2t
ZPO	01-06	A	Bristol	L 24-32	5292	Beal	Brooks	Tucker	Leslie	Moir

** after opponents name indicates a penalty try. Brackets after a player's name indicates he was replaced. eg (a) means he was replaced by replacement code "a" and so on. / after a player or replacement name is followed by any scores he made - eg /t, /c, /p, /dg or any combination of these*

EVER PRESENT None

Most Appearances:
20: Peter Jorgensen.
19: Nick Beal(1), Oliver Brouzet(1).

PLAYERS USED

33 plus four as a replacement.

MOST POINTS

Pts	Player	T	C	P	DG
238	P Grayson	1	31	55	2
40	B Cohen	8	-	-	-
30	P Jorgensen	6	-	-	-
23	J Brooks	4	-	-	1
21	N Beal	3	-	2	-

MATCH FACTS

10	9	1	2	3	4	5	6	7	8
Grayson/3p	Malone	Smith	Thompson	Stewart	Phillips	Brouzet	Blowers	Pountney	Soden
Brooks	Dawson	Smith	Thompson	Stewart	Phillips	Brouzet	Rennick	Pountney/t	Seely
Brooks/t	Malone	Smith	Brotherstone	Budgen	Newman	Brouzet	Blowers	Pountney	Seely
Hepher	Malone	Todd	Thompson/t	Budgen	Newman	Phillips	Rennick	Blowers	Seely
Brooks	Dawson	Smith	Thompson	Stewart	Newman	Brouzet	Blowers	Pountney	Seely
Brooks	Howard	Smith	Thompson	Stewart	Newman	Brouzet	Blowers	Pountney	Seely
Hepher/tc2p	Dawson	Todd	Thompson	Sturgess	Phillips	Hunter	Rennick	Blowers	Soden
Hepher	Malone	Morris	Brotherstone	Budgen	Hunter	Brouzet	Rennick	Blowers	Soden
Brooks(a/4p)	Malone	Morris	Thompson	Budgen	Phillips	Brouzet	Rennick	Blowers	Soden/t
Brooks/t	Malone	Smith	Thompson	Stewart	Phillips	Brouzet	Rennick	Blowers	Hunter
Brooks/tdg	Malone	Smith	Thompson	Stewart	Phillips	Brouzet	Rennick	Pountney	Hunter
Grayson/c4p	Dawson	Smith	Thompson	Stewart	Phillips	Brouzet	Blowers	Pountney/t	Hunter
Grayson/c3pdg	Brooks	Smith/t	Thompson	Stewart	Brouzet	Ackerman	Hunter	Pountney	Seely
Hepher/c	Brooks	Smith/t	Thompson	Stewart	Ackerman	Brouzet	Rennick	Blowers	Soden
Grayson/p	Dawson	Smith	Thompson	Stewart	Ackerman	Phillips	Blowers	Pountney	Seely
Grayson/4c2p	Dawson	Smith	Richmond/t	Morris	Ackerman	Brouzet	Blowers	Pountney	Seely
Grayson/c4p	Dawson	Smith	Thompson(c/t)	Stewart	Phillips	Brouzet	Blowers	Pountney	Seely
Grayson/6c2p	Dawson	Smith/t	Thompson/t	Morris	Phillips/t	Brouzet	Rennick/t	Pountney/t	Blowers
Grayson/5c4p	Malone	Smith	Richmond/t	Morris	Phillips	Brouzet	Soden/t	Pountney	Seely(d/t)
Grayson/2p	Dawson	Smith	Thompson	Morris	Phillips	Brouzet	Hunter	Pountney	Soden
Grayson/2c6p	Malone	Morris	Richmond	Stewart	Phillips	Brouzet	Blowers/t	Pountney/t	Soden
Grayson/tc4p	Dawson	Smith	Thompson	Stewart	Phillips	Brouzet	Blowers	Pountney	Soden/t
Brooks	Dawson	Smith	Thompson	Stewart	Newman	Phillips	Blowers	Pountney	Seely/t
Hepher(g/t)	Dawson/2c2p	Smith	Thompson	Stewart	Phillips	Hunter	Blowers	Pountney/t	Seely
Hepher/5p	Vass	Smith	Thompson	Stewart	Newman	Phillips	Soden	Blowers	Hunter
Hepher/2cp	Vass	Smith	Thompson	Stewart/t	Newman	Phillips	Rennick	Blowers	Hunter
Grayson/c4pdg	Dawson	Todd	Brotherstone	Stewart	Phillips	Brouzet	Rennick	Pountney	Blowers/t
Grayson/2c3pdg	Brooks	Smith	Thompson	Stewart	Phillips	Hunter	Rennick	Pountney	Blowers
Hepher/c(a/cp)	Dawson	Todd	Richmond	Budgen/t(h/t)	Newman	Phillips	Rennick	Pountney	Hunter
Grayson/3c2p	Brooks	Smith	Thompson/t	Stewart	Phillips	Brouzet	Soden	Pountney	Blowers
Grayson/2c3p	Dawson	Morris	Richmond	Stewart	Ackerman	Brouzet	Blowers	Pountney	Seely/2t
Grayson/c	Dawson	Smith	Thompson	Stewart	Ackerman	Brouzet	Blowers	Pountney	Seely
Grayson/3c4p	Dawson	Smith	Thompson	Morris	Phillips	Brouzet	Blowers	Pountney/t	Soden
Grayson/3p	Malone	Stewart	Thompson	Morris	Phillips	Brouzet	Blowers/2t	Pountney	Seely/t

REPLACEMENTS: a - Paul Grayson. b - Mark Tucker. c - Dan Richmond. d - Rob Hunter. e - Ali Hepher. f - Luca Martin. g - James Brooks. h - Mattie Stewart.

WHEN

	Total	First Half	Second Half	1/4	2/4	3/4	4/4
The POINTS were scored	506	231	275	105	126	123	152
The POINTS were conceded	426	242	184	68	174	88	96
The TRIES were scored	48	22	26	7	15	10	16
The TRIES were conceded	36	17	19	2	15	9	10

HOW the TRIES were scored

Total	Backs	Forwards	F Back	Wing	Centre	H Back	F Row	Lock	B Row	Pen. Try
47	29	18	5	9	10	5	7	1	10	-

HOW the TRIES were conceded

Total	Backs	Forwards	F Back	Wing	Centre	H Back	F Row	Lock	B Row	Pen. Try
36	24	12	3	8	7	6	3	3	6	-

NORTHAMPTON SAINTS

LEAGUE STATISTICS
compiled by Stephen McCormack

SEASON	Division	P	W	D	L	F	A	Pts Diff	Lge Pts	Lge Pos	Most Points		Most Tries	
92-93	1	12	8	0	4	215	150	65	16	4	52	John Steele	6	Harvey Thorneycroft
93-94	1	18	9		0	305	342	-37	18	5	132	Paul Grayson	2	by seven players
94-95	1	18	6	0	12	267	335	-68	12	10r	189	Paul Grayson	3	Grant Seely & Matt Dawson
95-96	2	18	18	0	0	867	203	664	36	1p	215	Paul Grayson	20	Matt Allen
96-97	1	22	10	0	12	515	477	38	20	8	129	Paul Grayson	7	Jonathon Bell
97-98	P1	22	9	1	12	493	472	21	19	8	210	Paul Grayson	7	Matt Allen
98-99	P1	26	19	0	7	754	556	198	38	2	156	Paul Grayson	14	Pat Lam
99-00	P1	22	13	0	9	551	480	71	35	5	99	Ali Hepher	6	Ben Cohen
00-01	P1	22	13	0	9	518	43	55	59	4	219	Paul Grayson	9	Ben Cohen
01-02	P	22	12	1	9	506	426	80	56	5	238	Paul Grayson	8	Ben Cohen

BIGGEST MARGINS

Home Win	64pts - 69-5 v Waterloo 13.4.95
Away Win	66pts - 69-3 v Waterloo 28.10.95
Home Defeat	47pts - 3-50 v Lon. Scottish 3.10.87
Away Defeat	60pts - 0-60 v Orrell 27.10.90

MOST CONSECUTIVE

Appearances	31 Frank Packman
Matches scoring Tries	4 Ian Hunter
Matches scoring points	18 Paul Grayson
Victories	20
Defeats	6

MOST POINTS

Scored at Home	69 v Waterloo 13.4.96
Scored Away	69 v Waterloo 28.10.95
Conceded at Home	50 v Lon. Scottish 3.10.87
Conceded Away	60 v Orrell 27.10.90

MOST TRIES

Scored in a match	11 v Blackheath 14.10.95 v Waterloo 28.10.95 & 13.4.96
Conceded in a match	11 v Orrell 27.10.90

MOST APPEARANCES

by a forward	144 (27) John Phillips
by a back	140 (7) Matt Dawson

	MOST IN A SEASON	MOST IN A CAREER	MOST IN A MATCH	
Points	238 Paul Grayson 00-02	1573 Paul Grayson 93-02	26 Paul Grayson	v Bristol 2.10.93 (A)
Tries	20 Matt Allen 95-96	44 Matt Allen 94-01	4 Craig Moir	v Waterloo 13.4.96 (H)
Conversions	76 Paul Grayson 95-96	221 Paul Grayson 93-02	7 Paul Grayson	v Lon. Irish 9.9.95 (H) v Lon. Scottish 4.11.95 (H) v Lon. Scottish 27.4.96 (A)
			Michael Dods	v Blackheath 14.10.95 (H)
Penalties	58 Paul Grayson 00-01	338 Paul Grayson 93-02	7 Paul Grayson	v Richmond 21.2.98 (H) v Leicester 29.04.00 (A)
Drop Goals	4 Paul Grayson 96-97	15 Paul Grayson 93-00	3 John Steele	v Wasps 23.3.91 (A)

NORTHAMPTON SAINTS RFU SENIOR CUP

STATISTICS

compiled by Stephen McCormack

OVERALL PLAYING RECORD

	P	W	D	L	F	A	Pts Diff
Home	36	26	0	10	871	417	454
Away	34	17	0	17	569	535	34
Neutral	4	1	0	3	67	111	-44
Total	74	44	0	30	1507	1063	444

SEASON BY SEASON

Season	Result
1971-72	1R
1972-73	1R
1973-74	QF
1974-75	1R
1975-76	QF
1976-77	2R
1977-78	QF
1978-79	1R
1979-80	1R
1980-81	1R
1981-82	4R
1982-83	2R
1983-84	4R
1984-85	3R
1985-86	4R
1986-87	DNQ
1987-88	3R
1988-89	3R
1989-90	SF
1990-91	Runners up
1991-92	4R
1992-93	SF
1993-94	5R
1994-95	QF
1995-96	4R
1996-97	QF
1997-98	SF
1998-99	5R
1999-2000	Runners up
2000-01	QF
2001-02	Runners up

TEAM RECORDS

Highest Score
118 v Nuneaton 99/00 (H)
Biggest Winning Margin
115 Pts - 118-3 v Nuneaton 99/00 (H)
Highest Score Against
38 v London Irish 01/02 (N)
Biggest Losing Margin
31 Pts - 7-38 v London Irish 01/02 (N)

INDIVIDUAL RECORDS

Most Points in a match
28 Ali Hepher v Nuneaton 99/00
Most Tries in a match
4 Jon Sleightholme v Nuneaton 99/00
4 Federico Mendez v Nuneaton 99/00
Most Conversions in a match
14 Ali Hepher v Nuneaton 99/00
Most Penalties in a match
6 Paul Grayson Wasps 1999/00
Most Drop Goals in a match
3 John Steele v Saracens 90/91

EUROPEAN COMPETITIONS

STATISTICS *compiled by Stephen McCormack*

TEAM RECORDS

Highest Score
66 v Toulon 97/98
Biggest Winning Margin
59 Pts - v Toulon 66-7 96/97
Highest Score Against
50 v Montferrand 01/02
Biggest Losing Margin
33 Pts 50-17 v Montferrand 01/02

INDIVIDUAL RECORDS

Most Points in a match
29 Ali Hepher v Neath 99/00
Most Tries in a match
3 Harvey Thorneycroft v Orrell 96/97
Most Conversions in a match
8 Paul Grayson v Nice 97-98
Most Penalties in a match
7 Paul Grayson v Toulon 96/97
Most Drop Goals in a match

CAREER RECORDS

Most Appearances:
26: Ben Cohen
25: Matt Allen, Budge Pountney, Mattie Stewart.

Most Points
260: Paul Grayson
126: Matt Dawson
111: Alastair Hepher

Most Tries
13: Ben Cohen
9: Matt Dawson
5: Paul Grayson, Gregor Townsend

SEASON BY SEASON

Season		Result
1996-97	S	Q-Finals
1997-98	S	Gp Stage
1998-99	-	D N Play
1999-00	C	**Winners**
2000-01	C	Gp Stage
2001-02	C	Gp Stage

OVERALL PLAYING RECORD

	P	W	D	L	F	A	Pts Diff
Home	15	11	0	4	451	242	209
Away	16	6	0	10	416	400	16
Neutral	2	1	0	1	40	56	-16
Total	33	18	0	15	907	698	209

NORTHAMPTON SAINTS

FACT FILE

Founded: 1880
Nickname: The Saints
Web site: www.northamptonsaints.co.uk

Colours: Black, green, gold hoops
Change colours: gold

GROUND

Address: Franklin's Gardens, Weedon Road, Northampton NN5 5BG
Tel: 01604 751543 Fax: 01604 599110
Capacity: 13,500 Seated Covered: 11,500. Standing: 2,000

Directions: Take junction 16 from the M1, follow signs to St James and Town Centre, turn right at Ross Road or The Franklin's pub.
Nearest Railway Station: Northampton

Car Parking : 1000 spaces, £3.

Admission:	Season	Matchday
Adults	£170-£410	£15-£30
Concessions	£90-£410	£9-£30
Juniors	£90-£410	£7-£30

Club Shop: Manager Jo Norman 01604 599111

Clubhouse: Matchday 12-11 Bar meals & restaurant available
Functions: Rooms for up to 700,
contact Nicola Clark 01604 751543

PROGRAMME

Size: A5
Pages: 64
Price: £2.50
Editor: Caroline Moore 01604 599125
Advertising Rates
Call Ann Gibbs, 01604 751543 for details

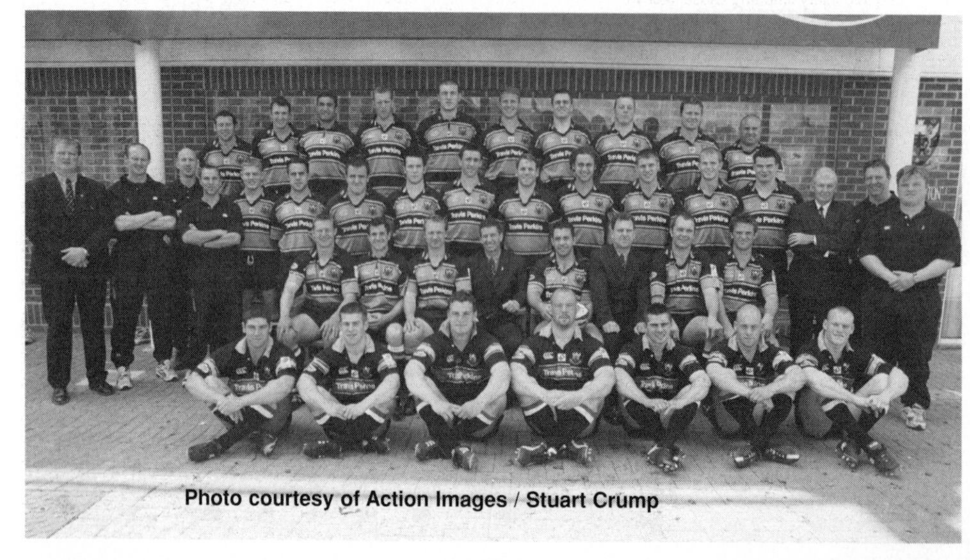

Photo courtesy of Action Images / Stuart Crump

SALE SHARKS

Managing Director	Carl Fox	
Rugby Administrator & Media & PR Manager	Dave Swanton Direct Line: 0161 610 0406 email: dave.swanton@salesharks.co.uk	
Chairman	Brian Kennedy	
President	Sue Gardiner	

c/o Sale Sharks RUFC,
Heywood Road,
Sale M33 3WB
Tel: 0161 283 1861
Fax: 0161 969 4124

Sale Sharks Head Coach Jim Mallinder and Team Manager Steve Diamond took the players to Aldershot Barracks to prepare for the new season and the Commando Training and Bonding certainly paid dividends as the club enjoyed their most successful season ever, finishing second in the Zurich Premiership, winning the Parker Pen Shield and qualifying for the Heineken Cup for the first time.

The Sharks won the first three games of the season, but the club was reeling from the news that Pete Anglesea had been banned for an alleged gouge on a Newcastle player. Club owner Brian Kennedy backed Anglesea to the hilt and Pete had his ban lifted at the end of September. The only game that Anglesea missed was the 93-0 win over RDS Roma in the Parker Pen Shield, when he acted as bottle carrier.

Narrow defeats at Bath and Saracens saw the Sharks drop to seventh place, but wins at Harlequins and Leeds as well as a draw against London Irish saw the Sharks go into Christmas in second place.

January saw the Sharks qualify for the latter stages of the Parker Pen Shield and their unbeaten record in the group stages earned them a home draw with Bristol Shoguns. The Sharks ran out 25-20 winners over Bristol and the reward was a Semi Final game against Gloucester.

After March defeats at Gloucester and Newcastle the Sharks finished the season in 2nd place which was a credit to Jim Mallinder and Steve Diamond's hard work with the players who responded magnificently.

The Parker Pen Shield Semi Final at Northampton against Gloucester was a nail biting encounter to say the least! The Sharks trailed early in the game but came storming back to score 28 points in 33 minutes. The game was balanced on a knife edge going into injury time and Gloucester were awarded a penalty 20 metres out which Mercier managed to miss.

The Parker Pen Shield Final at the Kassam Stadium Oxford saw the Sharks on the back foot early on but the Sharks superiority shone through as Bryan Redpath marshalled his troops and led them to victory 25-22. This victory gave the Sharks their first piece of Major Silverware in their 141 year history.

The club's performances prompted International call ups for Jason Robinson,Mark Cueto,Charlie Hodgson,Bryan Redpath,Mark Giacheri,Peter Anglesea,Alex Sanderson and Iain Fullarton with many more playing their part in the International Programme.

Attendances were up by almost 60% but the Sharks were the second worst supported club in England which prompted owner Brian Kennedy to announce that the club needed to move away from Heywood Road.

Dave Swanton

SALE SHARKS

Comp.	Date	H/A	Opponents	Result & Score	Att	15	14	13	12	11
ZP	02-09	A	Bristol	W 35-25	4020	Robinson	Cueto/t	Shaw	Harris/t	Hanley/t
ZP	08-09	H	Newcastle Falcons	W 37-11	4865	Robinson/t	Cueto	Shaw	Harris	Hanley/t
ZP	16-09	A	London Wasps	W 40-21	4403	Robinson/t	Cueto/t	Shaw	Harris/t	Hanley
ZP	22-09	H	Gloucester	L 21-44	4682	Robinson/t	Davidson	Shaw(b/t)	Harris	Hanley
ZP	13-10	A	Bath	L 17-20	7875	Going	Cueto/2t	Baxendell	Harris	Robinson
ZP	20-10	H	Northampton Saints	W 34-14	3612	Going	Cueto/t	Shaw	Davidson	Hanley/t
ZP	11-11	A	Saracens	L 25-26	6059	Going/t	Cueto	Shaw/t	Deane	Hanley/t
ZP	17-11	H	Leicester Tigers	L 3-37	5429	Going/p	Cueto	Shaw	Deane	Hanley
ZP	25-11	A	Leeds Tykes	W 47-20	3489	Going	Cueto/t	Baxendell	Harris(c/t)	Hanley/2t
ZP	01-12	A	Harlequins	W 23-16	5841	Robinson/t	Cueto	Baxendell	Harris	Hanley/t
ZP	08-12	H	London Irish	D 19-19	4775	Robinson	Cueto	Baxendell	Deane/t	Hanley
ZP	27-12	A	Leicester Tigers	L 10-33	16250	Robinson/t	Cueto	Baxendell	Deane	Elliott
ZP	09-02	A	Northampton Saints	W 20-10	9589	Going	Cueto	Robinson/t	Deane	Hanley
ZP	23-02	H	Bath	W 20-14		Robinson/t	Cueto	Baxendell/tc	Deane	Hanley
ZP	09-03	A	Gloucester	L 14-42	9461	Robinson	Cueto	Shaw	Deane	Hanley
ZP	16-03	H	London Wasps	W 27-22	5118	Robinson	Cueto/t	Deane	Harris	Elliott/t
ZP	31-03	A	Newcastle Falcons	L 10-30	6512	Going	Cueto/t	Deane	Harris	Elliott
ZP	13-04	H	Bristol	W 53-47	3609	Robinson/t	Cueto	Shaw/3t	Deane/t	Hanley
ZP	19-04	H	Saracens	W 23-3	3947	Robinson	Cueto/t	Shaw	Deane	Hanley
ZP	05-05	A	London Irish	W 36-32	6076	Robinson/t	Cueto	Shaw/t	Harris	Hanley
ZP	08-05	H	Leeds Tykes	W 35-20	3871	Robinson	Cueto/2t	Shaw	Deane	Elliott/t
ZP	12-05	H	Harlequins	W 40-11	5678	Robinson	Cueto/2t	Baxendell/t	Deane/t	Elliott
ES	29-09	H	Roma	W 93-0	2807	Going/t	Davidson	Baxendell/t3c	Deane/t	Hanley/2t(f/t)
ES	06-10	N	Narbonne	W 13-10	3500	Going	Cueto	Baxendell	Deane	Davidson
ES	27-10	N	Connacht	W 33-30	1200	Going	Cueto	Shaw	Deane	Hanley
ES	03-11	H	Connacht	W 44-6	2800	Going	Cueto/t	Shaw	Deane/2t	Elliott
ES	08-01	H	Narbonne	W 41-16		Going	Hanley/2t	Shaw/t	Deane	Elliott/t
ES	12-01	N	Roma	W 62-17		Going(f/t)	Hanley/t	Shaw	Deane/2t	Davidson/3c
ES	25-01	H	Bristol	W 25-20	3607	Going/t	Cueto	Robinson	Deane	Hanley/t
ES	28-04	N	Gloucester	W 28-27	5785	Robinson	Cueto/t	Harris/t	Shaw	Hanley/t
ES	26-05	N	Pontypridd	W 25-22	12000	Robinson	Cueto	Shaw/t	Deane(i/t)	Hanley/t
PGC	15-12	H	Harlequins	L 22-32		Robinson	Cueto	Baxendell	Deane/t	Hanley
ZPO	19-05	H	London Wasps	W 43-27	3283	Going	Hanley/2t	Baxendell	Deane	Elliott/t
ZPO	02-06	H	Gloucester	L 11-33	4298	Robinson	Cueto/t	Shaw	Harris	Hanley

** after opponents name indicates a penalty try. Brackets after a player's name indicates he was replaced. eg (a) means he was replaced by replacement code "a" and so on. / after a player or replacement name is followed by any scores he made - eg /t, /c, /p, /dg or any combination of these*

EVER PRESENT Kevin Yates.

Most Appearances:
22: Kevin Yates.
21: Mark Cueto.
20: Iain Fullerton, Stuart Pinkerton, Charlie Hodgson.

PLAYERS USED

32 plus four as replacement only.

MOST POINTS

Pts	Player	T	C	P	DG
273	C Hodgson	7	44	48	2
65	M Cueto	13	-	-	-
45	J Robinson	9	-	-	-
35	S Hanley	7	-	-	-
25	M Shaw	5	-	-	-
25	P Anglesea	5	-	-	-

MATCH FACTS

10	9	1	2	3	4	5	6	7	8
Hodgson/3c3p	Redpath	Yates	Jackman	Turner	Fullerton	Lines	Perelini	Pinkerton/t	Anglesea
Hodgson/t2c2p(b/c)	Redpath	Yates	Titterell	Turner(a/t)	Fullerton	Lines	Perelini	Pinkerton	Anglesea/t
Hodgson/2c6pdg	Redpath	Yates	Titterell	Turner	Fullerton	Lines	Perelini	Pinkerton	Anglesea
Hodgson/c3p	Bramhall	Yates	Titterell	Turner	Fullerton	Lines	Pinkerton	Sanderson	Anglesea
Hodgson/2cp	Redpath	Yates	Titterell	Turner	Fullerton	Giacheri	Perelini	Pinkerton	Anglesea
Hodgson/t4c2p	Redpath	Yates	Titterell	Turner	Fullerton	Lines	Perelini	Anglesea/t	Pinkerton
Hodgson/cp	Bramhall	Yates	Titterell	Turner	Fullerton	Lines	Pinkerton	Sanderson	Anglesea/t
Baxendell	Dickens	Yates	Marais	Turner	Schofield	Lines	Perelini	Pinkerton	Anglesea
Hodgson/2t4c3p	Dickens	Yates	Titterell	Turner	Fullerton	Lines	Sanderson	Pinkerton	Anglesea
Hodgson/2c3p	Dickens	Yates	Marais	Turner	Fullerton	Lines	Perelini	Pinkerton	Anglesea
Hodgson/c4p	Redpath	Yates	Titterell	Turner	Fullerton	Lines	Perelini	Pinkerton	Anglesea
Hodgson/cp	Redpath	Yates	Marais	Turner	Fullerton	Giacheri	Lines	Pinkerton	Sanderson
Hodgson/4pdg	Redpath	Yates	Titterell	Turner	Fullerton	Lines	Davies	Pinkerton	Sanderson
Hodgson/tp	Redpath	Yates	Titterell	Turner	Fullerton	Lines	Jones	Wilks	Sanderson
Going/t3p	Redpath	Yates	Marais	Black	Fullerton	Giacheri	Lines	Wilks	Sanderson
Hodgson/3c2p	Redpath	Yates	Titterell	Turner/t	Fullerton	Lines	Jones	Pinkerton	Perelini
Hodgson	Redpath/t	Yates	Titterell	Black	Fullerton	Giacheri	Jones	Wilks	Pinkerton
Hodgson/4c5p	Redpath	Yates	Titterell	Black	Fullerton	Lines	Jones/t	Pinkerton	Sanderson
Hodgson/2c3p	Redpath	Yates	Titterell	Black	Fullerton	Giacheri(d/t)	Jones	Pinkerton	Sanderson
Hodgson/t4cp	Redpath	Yates	Marais	Turner	Fullerton	Jones/t	Sanderson	Pinkerton	Anglesea/t
Hodgson/3c3p	Redpath/t	Yates	Marais	Stewart	Fullerton	Jones	Sanderson	Pinkerton	Anglesea
Hodgson/t5c	Redpath	Yates	Titterell(e/t)	Turner	Lines	Jones	Sanderson	Pinkerton	Anglesea
Hodgson/7cp(j/t)	Dickens	Black	Titterell(k/t)	Turner	Fullerton	Giacheri	Perelini/3t	Wilks/2t	Pinkerton/t
Hodgson/tc2p	Redpath	Yates	Titterell	Turner	Fullerton	Giacheri	Perelini	Anglesea	Pinkerton
Hodgson/2c3p	Dickens	Yates	Jackman/t	Black	Fullerton	Lines	Anglesea/t	Wilks/t	Pinkerton
Hodgson/t3cp	Bramhall	Black/t	Titterell	Turner	Fullerton	Giacheri	Perelini/t(g/t)	Wilks	Sanderson
Hodgson/3c5p	Dickens	Yates	Titterell	Black	Fullerton	Giacheri	Lines	Wilks	Pinkerton
Baxendell/3c	Dickens	Black(h/t)	Titterell	Turner	Fullerton	Giacheri	Lines/t	Wilks/t	Perelini/2t
Hodgson/2c2p	Redpath/t	Yates	Titterell	Turner	Fullerton	Lines	Perelini	Pinkerton	Sanderson
Hodgson/c2p	Redpath	Yates	Marais/t	Turner	Fullerton	Jones	Sanderson	Pinkerton	Anglesea
Hodgson/2c2p	Redpath	Yates	Marais	Turner	Lines	Jones	Sanderson	Pinkerton	Anglesea
Hodgson/c3p2dg	Redpath	Yates	Titterell	Turner	Fullerton	Lines	Perelini	Wilks	Pinkerton
Hodgson/3c4p	Dickens/t	Black	Marais	Stewart	Lines	Jones	Perelini	Wilks	Sanderson/t
Hodgson/2p	Redpath	Yates	Titterall	Turner	Jones	Lines	Pinkerton	Sanderson	Anglesea

REPLACEMENTS: a - Adam Black. b - Jos Baxendell. c - Mel Deane. d - Pete Anglesea. e - Charl Marais. f - Anthony Elliot. g - Scott Lines. h - Kevin Yates. i - Dan Harris. j - Martin Shaw. k - Bernard Jackman.

WHEN	Total	First Half	Second Half	1/4	2/4	3/4	4/4
The POINTS were scored	589	256	333	117	139	149	184
The POINTS were conceded	517	232	285	87	145	133	152
The TRIES were scored	67	25	42	11	14	18	24
The TRIES were conceded	47	17	30	2	15	14	16

HOW the TRIES were scored

Total	Backs	Forwards	F Back	Wing	Centre	H Back	F Row	Lock	B Row	Pen. Try
67	56	11	9	22	15	10	3	2	6	-

HOW the TRIES were conceded

Total	Backs	Forwards	F Back	Wing	Centre	H Back	F Row	Lock	B Row	Pen. Try
47	32	15	6	9	11	6	7	4	4	-

SALE SHARKS

LEAGUE STATISTICS

compiled by Stephen McCormack

SEASON	Division	P	W	D	L	F	A	Pts Diff	Lge Pts	Lge Pos	Most Points	Most Tries
92-93	2	12	7	1	4	237	102	35	15	5	63 Phil Jee	7 Mark Warr
93-94	2	18	13	2	3	438	160	278	28	1	144 Paul Turner	16 Simon Verbickas
94-95	1	18	7	2	9	327	343	+16	16	4	92 Paul Turner	5 Gareth Stocks & Jim Mallender
95-96	1	18	9	1	8	365	371	-6	19	5	167 Rob Liley	6 Jos Baxendall
96-97	1	22	13	2	7	603	525	78	28	5	150 Simon Mannix	13 Tim Beim
97-98	P1	22	10	22	10	605	558	47	22	6	227 Shane Howarth	14 Tim Beim
98-99	P1	26	9	1	16	604	731	-127	19	11	246 Shane Howarth	12 Steven Hanley
99-00	P1	22	7	0	15	381	633	-252	18	11	101 Nicky Little	6 Steven Hanley
00-01	P1	22	8	1	13	561	622	-61	43	10	163 Nicky Little	10 Steven Hanley
01-02	P	22	14	1	7	589	517	72	69	2	273 Charlie Hodgson	13 Mark Cueto

BIGGEST MARGINS

Home Win	79pts - 88-9 v Otley 12.2.94
Away Win	32pts - 40-8 v Orrell 18.1.97
Home Defeat	46pts - 12-58 v Saracens 29.10.99
Away Defeat	77pts - 7-84 v Bath 26.4.97

MOST CONSECUTIVE

Appearances	39 Phillip Stansfield 22.10.88-14.3.92
Matches scoring Tries	8 Simon Verbickas
Matches scoring points	18 Shane Howarth
Victories	7
Defeats	11

MOST POINTS

Scored at Home	88 v Otley 12.2.94
Scored Away	50 v Bedfordl 14.5.00
Conceded at Home	58 v Saracens 29.10.99
Conceded Away	84 v Bath 26.4.97

MOST TRIES

Scored in a match	14 v Otley 12.2.94 (H)
Conceded in a match	12 v Harlequins 23.4.88 (A) v Bath 24.4.97 (A)

MOST APPEARANCES

by a forward	149 (15)	Dave Baldwin
by a back	169 (2)	Jim Mallinder

	MOST IN A SEASON	MOST IN A CAREER	MOST IN A MATCH	
Points	273 Charlie Hodgson 01-02	473 Shane Howarth 97-99	27 Simon Mannix Charlie Hodgson	v Northampton 9.3.97 (H) v Leeds Tykes 25.11.01
Tries	16 Simon Verbickas 93-94	38 Jim Mallinder 88-00	5 Simon Verbickas	v Otley 12.2.94 (H)
Conversions	44 Charlie Hodgson 01-02	61 Charlie Hodgson 00-02	9 Paul Turner	v Otley 12.2.94 (H)
Penalties	48 Charlie Hodgson 01-02	77 Charlie Hodgson 00-02	7 Simon Mannix Shane Howarth Nicky Little	v Northampton 9.3.97 (H) v Wasps 18.4.98 (H) v Bath 19.8.00 (H)
Drop Goals	4 Paul Turner 95-96	13 Paul Turner 92-96	2 David Pears Paul Turner	v Bedford 22.2.89 (H) v Morley 3.10.92 (H) v Wakefield 9.4.94 (A) v Orrell 6.1.96 (H)

OVERALL PLAYING RECORD

	P	W	D	L	F	A	Pts Diff
Home	34	20	0	14	759	569	190
Away	37	23	0	14	619	454	165
Neutral	1	0	0	1	3	9	-6
Total	72	43	0	29	1381	1032	349

SEASON BY SEASON

Season	Result
1971-72	DNQ
1972-73	SF
1973-74	QF
1974-75	2R
1975-76	SF
1976-77	1R
1977-78	1R
1978-79	1R
1979-80	DNQ
1980-81	QF
1981-82	QF
1982-83	4R
1983-84	3R
1984-85	QF
1985-86	3R
1986-87	3R
1987-88	QF
1988-89	2R
1989-90	4R
1990-91	3R
1991-92	4R
1992-93	3R
1993-94	QF
1994-95	QF
1995-96	4R
1996-97	Runners up
1997-98	SF
1998-99	4R
1999-2000	5R
2000-01	SF
2001-02	6R

SALE SHARKS RFU SENIOR CUP

STATISTICS

compiled by Stephen McCormack

TEAM RECORDS

Highest Score

59 v Waterloo 00/01 (H)

Biggest Winning Margin

51 pts - 58-7 v Otley 93/94 (A)

Highest Score Against

42 v Rosslyn Park 73/74 (H)

Biggest Losing Margin

30 Pts - 12-42 v Rosslyn Park 73/74 (H)

INDIVIDUAL RECORDS

Most Points in a match

19 Charlie Hodgson v Waterloo 00/01

Most Tries in a match

3 Steve Hanley v Waterloo 00/01

3 Jim Mallinder v Newbury 97/98

Most Conversions in a match

8 Charlie Hodgson v Waterloo 00/01

Most Penalties in a match

Most Drop Goals in a match

EUROPEAN COMPETITIONS

STATISTICS *compiled by Stephen McCormack*

TEAM RECORDS

Highest Score

93-0 v Roma 01/02

Biggest Winning Margin

93 (93-0) v 01/02

Highest Score Against

53 v

Biggest Losing Margin

35 (44-9) v

INDIVIDUAL RECORDS

Most Points in a match

24 Charlie Hodgson v Caerphilly 00/01

Most Tries in a match

3 by three player: John Fowler, Matt Moore, Apollo Perelini.

Most Conversions in a match

7 Simon Mannix & Charlie Hodgson

Most Penalties in a match

7 Nikki Little v Agen 00/01

Most Drop Goals in a match

CAREER RECORDS

Most Appearances

16: Jos Baxendell
15: Pete Anglesea, Jim Mallinder
14: Matt Moore

Most Points

154: Nikki Little
146: Charlie Hodgson
83: Shane Howarth

Most Tries

11: Matt Moore
9: Steven Hanley
6: Mel Deane, Anthony Elliot, Apollo Perelini, Richard Wilks, Guy Manson-Bishop.

SEASON BY SEASON

Season		Result
1996-97	S	Gp Stage
1997-98	S	Gp Stage
1998-99	-	D N Play
1999-00	S	Gp Stage
2000-01	S	Gp Stage
2001-02	S	**Winners**

OVERALL PLAYING RECORD

	P	W	D	L	F	A	Pts Diff
Home	16	13	0	3	640	309	331
Away	14	5	0	9	327	378	-51
Neutral	2	2	-	-	53	49	4
Total	30	18	0	12	967	687	280

SALE SHARKS

FACT FILE

Founded: 1861

Colours: Royal blue shirt with navy band
Change colours: Black with green band

Web site: www.salesharks.com

GROUND

Address: Heywood Road, Sale, Cheshire M33 3WB
Tel: 0161 283 1861 Fax: 0161 969 4124 email: enquiries@salesharks.co.uk
Capacity: 5,678 Seated: 3,132 Standing: 2,546

Directions: M6 J19, take A556/A56 for approx 8 miles. Turn right into Marsland Rd and Heywood Rd is on the right after 800m. M60 J6, take A6144. Old Hall Rd/Marsland Rd, Heywood Rd on left after 1.5 miles from J6.
Nearest Railway Station: Brooklands Metrolink, left out of station into Marsland Rd. & Heywood Rd is 200m on the right.

Car Parking: None on ground, 100 spaces nearby

Admission:

		Adults	Concessions	Juniors	Family
Season	Seated	£197	£128	£85	£500
	Standing	£152	£89	£35	£400
Matchday	Seated	£20	£15	£10	£50
	Standing	£15	£ 10	£5	£40

Club Shop: 12-5 matchdays, 9-5 weekdays.
0161 610 0407

Clubhouse: Mon-Fri 7-11, Sat 11-11, Sun 12-3
Matchdays 12-11.
Snacks available Functions: Up to 150
Contact Tracy Grady on 0161 610 0409

MATCHDAY MAGAZINE

Size: B5 Pages: 40 full colour

SARACENS FC

Club Office
Rigby House,
34 The Parade, High St.,
Watford WD17 1EA

Tel: 01923 475222
Fax: 01923 475275

Chief Executive	Peter Deakin
Managing Director	Tim Lawler
Commercial Director	Tom Hill
Brand & Media Director	Robin Bye
Marketing Manager	Anne-Louise Harvey
Media Manager	Matt Jones Mob: 07713 684429 Tel: 01923 204616; Fax: 01923 475275 email: mattjones@saracens.net
Head Coach	Wayne Shelford

The 2001-2002 campaign is one that all Saracens, players and supporters alike, will want to forget.

Going into the season without experienced front row cover meant that Sean Phillips (20) and Luke Harbut (21) were saddled with the responsibility, and well as they played stamina told in the end and the Sarries pack was found wanting.

A narrow defeat at London Wasps was not the best start, but League wins over Gloucester (H), Bath (A) and Northampton and two wins in the Shield brought us back on course.

The implosion really started when the pack were taken apart at Leeds followed by further losses against Leicester, Harlequins, London Irish (twice) and Newcastle before Christmas with only narrow victories over Sale and Harlequins at home and Bristol away to give their loyal supporters any cheer.

Saracens managed only one more League win, at home to Bath, and ended the season with seven straight defeats to leave them perilously close to relegation, while Pontypridd knocked them out of the Shield and a home defeat by Northampton put them out of the Powergen Cup.

The busiest physios in London were at Saracens' training ground, with up to half the squad carrying injuries and some like Thomas Castaignede, Jannie De Beer, Kris Chesney, Ben Cole, Ben Johnston, Romain Megallan and Tom Shanklin out for half the season or more.

On the plus side is the return of chief executive Peter Deakin at the end of the season and new signings Christian Califano, John Marsters, Andy Goode, Craig Quinnell and Morgan Williams.

Everyone is looking forward to the return to full fitness of Castaignede and Tim Horan, while the coaching will be in the more than capable hands of Wayne Shelford.

Off the field Saracens continue to set the standards with the sport in the community programme still setting the pace and cashback at record levels and, despite the poor form on the field, the average home attendance was nearly 8500.

One wish for the coming season - to see Castaignede and Horan play together for the first time.

Bill Edwards

Photo: Action Images / Brandon Malone

SARACENS

Comp.	Date	H/A	Opponents	Result & Score	Att	15	14	13	12	11
ZP	02-09	A	London Wasps	L 8-12	5929	Winnan	Sparg	Shanklin	Sorrell	O'Mahony
ZP	08-09	H	Gloucester	W 34-30	7262	Winnan	Shanklin	Horan/t	Sorrell	O'Mahony
ZP	15-09	A	Bath	W 27-20	7968	Winnan	Shanklin(a/t)	Horan/t	Sorrell	O'Mahony
ZP	23-09	H	Northampton Saints	W 25-20	8527	Winnan	Sparg	Horan	Sorrell	O'Mahony/t
ZP	14-10	A	Leeds Tykes	L 14-27	3328	Winnan/t	Sparg	Arasa	Sorrell	O'Mahony
ZP	20-10	A	Leicester Tigers	L 10-36	13762	Winnan	Sparg	Horan	Sorrell	O'Mahony
ZP	11-11	H	Sale	W 26-25	6059	Winnan	Haughten	Horan/t	Sorrell	O'Mahony/t
ZP	16-11	A	Harlequins	L 6-43	6450	Winnan	Haughten	Shanklin	Sorrell	O'Mahony
ZP	22-11	H	London Irish	L 13-55	5216	Winnan	Sparg	Johnston	Sorrell	O'Mahony
ZP	02-12	A	Bristol	W 25-22	4450	Winnan/t	Sparg	Johnston	Sorrell	O'Mahony
ZP	09-12	H	Newcastle Falcons	L 19-24	7294	Winnan	Sparg	Johnston/t	Sorrell	O'Mahony
ZP	23-12	A	London Irish	L 23-30	8246	Sparg	Johnston	Horan	Sorrell	O'Mahony/t
ZP	30-12	H	Harlequins	W 39-25	13257	Winnan/t	Arasa	Sorrell	Horan/t	O'Mahony
ZP	09-02	H	Leicester Tigers	L 7-48	9347	Winnan	Shanklin	Horan	Sorrell	O'Mahony
ZP	24-02	H	Leeds Tykes	L 15-37	4325	Winnan	Johnston	Sorrell	Horan	Arasa
ZP	17-03	H	Bath	W 33-11	10828	Winnan	Arasa/t	Shanklin	Sorrell/3c3p	O'Mahony
ZP	30-03	A	Gloucester	L 13-36	9236	Sparg	Johnston	Shanklin	Sorrell/c2p	Arasa/t
ZP	14-04	H	London Wasps	L 14-20	10431	Winnan	Johnston/t	Shanklin	Sorrell/3p	O'Mahony
ZP	19-04	A	Sale	L 3-23	3947	Winnan	Johnston	Sorrell/p	Horan	O'Mahony
ZP	27-04	A	Northampton Saints	L 27-52	8479	Winnan	Sparg	Sorrell	Johnston	Shanklin/2t
ZP	05-05	A	Newcastle Falcons	L 18-47	6083	Winnan	Johnston/t	Shanklin	Sorrell	O'Mahony
ZP	12-05	H	Bristol	L 26-28	9726	Winnan	Johnston	Shanklin/t	Sorrell	O'Mahony
ES	29-09	H	Begles-Bordeaux	W 34-14		Winnan	Sparg	Horan	Sorrell	O'Mahony/t
ES	06-10	N	Dinamo Bucharest	W 75-12		Sparg/2t	Haughten/2t	Horan(d/t)	Sorrell/2tc	O'Mahony/2t
ES	28-10	H	Bologna*	W 113-3	5473	Sparg(c/t)	Haughten/2t	Horan/t	Sorrell	O'Mahony/4t
ES	04-11	N	Bologna	W 75-10	1200	Sparg	Haughten/2t	Horan	Sorrell/t	O'Mahony/t
ES	06-01	H	Dinamo Bucharest	W 113-3	3582	Winnan/6c	Arasa	Sorrell/c(h/3t)	Horan/t	O'Mahony/t
ES	12-01	N	Begles-Bordeaux	W 25-24		Winnan/t	Johnston/t	Sorrell	Horan/t	O'Mahony
ES	27-01	H	Pontypridd	L 15-17	4604	Horan	Arasa	Shanklin	Sorrell	O'Mahony
PGC	16-12	H	Rotherham	W 43-17	2403	Winnan/t	Sparg	Johnston	Sorrell	O'Mahony
PGC	19-01	H	Northampton Saints	L 28-30	7617	Winnan	Shanklin(d/t)	Sorrell	Horan	O'Mahony

** after opponents name indicates a penalty try. Brackets after a player's name indicates he was replaced. eg (a) means he was replaced by replacement code "a" and so on. / after a player or replacement name is followed by any scores he made - eg /t, /c, /p, /dg or any combination of these*

EVER PRESENT Kevin Sorrell.

Most Appearances:
22: Kevin Sorrell.
20: Adrian WInnan, Anthony Roques.
16: Abdelatif Benazzi(1).

PLAYERS USED

31 plus four as a replacement

MOST POINTS

Pts	Player	T	C	P	DG
194	L Smith	1	12	53	2
35	K Sorrell	-	4	9	-
34	J De Beer	1	7	5	-
23	T Horan	4	-	-	1

MATCH FACTS

10	9	1	2	3	4	5	6	7	8
Smith/p	Bracken	Harbut	Cairns	Magellan	Benazzi	Murray	Hill/t	Roques	Cole
Smith/c9p	Bracken	Harbut	Russell	Phillips	Benazzi	Murray	Hill	Roques	Cole
Smith/c5p	Bracken	Harbut	Russell	Phillips	Benazzi	Murray	Hill	Roques	Cole
Smith/c5pdg	Walshe	Harbut	Russell	Phillips	Benazzi	Roche	Hill	Roques	Cole
Smith/3p	Bracken	Harbut	Russell	Phillips	Benazzi	Murray	Benazzi	Cheeseborough	Hill
De Beer/tcp	Walshe	Harbut	Russell	Phillips	Benazzi	Roche	Cheeseborough	Roques	Cole
Smith/2c4p	Walshe	Flatman	Cairns	Phillips	Benazzi	Hooper	Cheeseborough	Roques	Roche
Smith/2p	Walshe	Flatman	Cairns	Phillips	Benazzi	Roche	Cheeseborough	Roques	Cole
Smith/c2p	Walshe	Harbut/t	Cairns	Phillips	Benazzi	Hooper	Roche	Roques	Cole
Smith/c6p	Bracken	Harbut	Cairns	Phillips	Benazzi	Murray	Roche	Roques	Cole
Smith/c4p	Bracken	Harbut	Cairns	Phillips	Benazzi	Murray	Hill	Roche	Cole
De Beer/2c3p	Bracken	Flatman/t	Russell	Durant	Benazzi	Roche	Hill	Roques	Cole
De Beer/3cp	Bracken/t	Flatman	Russell/t	Durant	Benazzi	Murray	Hill	Roques/t	Cole/t
De Beer/c	Walshe/t	Flatman	Russell	Durant	Benazzi	Murray	Chesney	Roques	Hill
Smith/5p	Bracken	Flatman	Russell	Durant	Benazzi	Murray	Chesney	Roques	Hill
Horan/dg	Bracken/t	Flatman	Russell	Durant	Benazzi	Murray	Chesney/t	Roques	Hill
Horan	Bracken	Flatman	Russell	Durant	Benazzi	Murray	Chesney	Roques	Hill
Horan	Bracken	Harbut	Cairns	Flatman	Benazzi	Murray	Chesney	Roques	Russell
Smith	Walshe	Russell	Cairns	Flatman	Benazzi	Murray	Chesney	Roques	Hill
Smith/c2p(b/2c)	Walshe	Harbut/t	Cairns	Durant	Benazzi	Roche	Chesney	Roques	Russell
Smith/c2p	Bracken	Harbut	Russell	Flatman	Hooper	Roche	Chesney/t	Roques	Russell
Smith/t2c3pdg	Bracken	Russell	Cairns	Flatman	Benazzi	Murray	Hill	Roques	Russell
Smith/2t4c2p	Walshe	Harbut/t	Russell	Flatman	Benazzi	Roche	Cheeseborough	Hill	Cole
Smith/7c	Bracken	Harbut	Cairns	Phillips	Benazzi/t(e/t)	Murray	Cheeseborough	Hill	Cole/2c
De Beer/t13c	Walshe/t	Flatman/t	Cairns/3t	Phillips	Hooper	Benazzi	Cheeseborough	Roques/2t	Roche
Smith/10c	Walshe	Flatman	Cairns/2t	Harbut/t	Benazzi	Hooper	Cheeseborough	Roques/t	Roche
Smith/t7c	Walshe/2t	Harbut(f/t)	Russell/2t	Phillips	Murray	Benazzi(e/2t)	Cheeseborough	Roques/t(g/t)	Cole/2t
Smith/2c2p	Bracken	Flatman	Russell	Phillips	Murray	Benazzi	Roques	Cole	Hill
De Beer/5p	Bracken	Flatman	Russell	Durant	Hooper	Murray	Chesney	Roques	Hill
De Beer/2t5cp	Bracken/t	Flatman	Russell/t	Durant	Benazzi	Cheeseborough	Hill	Roques/t	Cole
De Beer/c6pdg	Bracken	Flatman	Russell	Durant	Roche	Murray	Chesney	Roques	Hill

REPLACEMENTS: a - Brett Sprag. b - Thomas Castaignede. c - Adrian Winnan. d - Gerard Arasa. e - Kieran Roche. f - David Flatman. g - Matt Cairns. h - Tom Shanklin

WHEN	Total	First Half	Second Half	1/4	2/4	3/4	4/4
The POINTS were scored	425	246	179	131	115	77	102
The POINTS were conceded	671	282	389	127	155	158	231
The TRIES were scored	33	16	17	7	9	6	11
The TRIES were conceded	68	22	46	10	12	17	29

HOW the TRIES were scored

Total	Backs	Forwards	F Back	Wing	Centre	H Back	F Row	Lock	B Row	Pen. Try
33	24	9	3	10	6	5	4	-	5	-

HOW the TRIES were conceded

Total	Backs	Forwards	F Back	Wing	Centre	H Back	F Row	Lock	B Row	Pen. Try
68	45	22	4	22	13	6	8	4	10	1

SARACENS

LEAGUE STATISTICS
compiled by Stephen McCormack

SEASON	Division	P	W	D	L	F	A	Pts Diff	Lge Pts	Lge Pos		Most Points		Most Tries
92-93	1	12	3	0	9	137	180	-43	6	11	43	Ben Rudling	3	Daren O'Leary & Barry Crawley
93-94	2	18	11	1	6	299	238	61	23	3	149	Andy Tunningley	5	Richard Hill & Andy Tunningley
94-95	2	18	15	1	2	389	213	176	31	1	162	Andy Tunningley	7	John Green
95-96	1	18	5	0	13	284	451	-167	10	9	126	Andy Lee	4	Peter Harries
96-97	1	22	12	1	9	568	449	119	25	7	125	Michael Lynagh	9	Richard Wallace
97-98	P1	22	18	1	3	584	484	100	37	2	279	Michael Lynagh	8	Richard Wallace
98-99	P1	26	16	1	9	748	583	165	33	3	318	Gavin Johnson	12	Brandon Daniel
99-00	P1	22	14	0	8	729	514	215	37	4	280	Thierry Lacroix	12	Ryan Constable
00-01	P1	22	12	0	10	589	501	88	58	5	133	T Castaignede	6	Dan Luger
01-02	P	22	7	0	15	425	671	-246	34	10	194	Luke Smith	4	Tim Horan

BIGGEST MARGINS

Home Win	49pts - 55-6 v Newcastle 17.10.99
Away Win	46pts - 58-12 v Sale 29.10.99
Home Defeat	43pts - 6-49 v Bath 27.4.91
Away Defeat	49pts - 3-52 v Sale 18.9.93

MOST POINTS

Scored at Home	56 v Sale 12.3.00
Scored Away	58 v Sale 29.10.99
Conceded at Home	49 v Bath 27.4.91
Conceded Away	52 v Sale 18.9.93

MOST CONSECUTIVE

Appearances	68 Brian Davies
Matches scoring Tries	6 Dave McLagen
Matches scoring points	20 Michael Lynagh/Thierry Lacroix
Victories	17
Defeats	7

MOST TRIES

Scored in a match	9 v Gosforth 22.4.89
	v Bedford 16.04.00
Conceded in a match	9 v Sale 18.9.93

MOST APPEARANCES

by a forward	165(2) Tony Diprose
by a back	106 John Buckton

	MOST IN A SEASON	MOST IN A CAREER	MOST IN A MATCH	
Points	318 Gavin Johnson 98-99	462 Andy Tunningley 90-97	30 Ryan Constable	v Bedford 16.4.00 (A)
Tries	12 Brandon Daniel 98-99 Ryan Constable 99-00	30 Tony Diprose 94-00	6 Ryan Constable	v Bedford 16.4.00 (A)
Conversions	52 Gavin Johnson 98-99	53 Michael Lynagh 96-98	6 Gavin Johnson Thierry Lacroix	v Lon Scot 26.9.98 (A) v Newcastle 17.10.99 (H) v Sale 29.10.99 (A) v Bedford 16.04.00 (A)
Penalties	58 Michael Lynagh 97-98 Gavin Johnson 98-99	92 Andy Tunningley 90-97	9 Thierry Lacroix Luke Smith	v Wasps 27.11.99 (H) v Gloucester 8.9.01 (H)
Drop Goals	6 Andy Lee 94-95	16 Andy Lee 89-95	2 Andy Lee Ben Rudling Gareth Hughes	v Wasps 22.2.92 (A) v Lon. Scottish 5.11.94 (H) v W. Hartlepool 14.10.95 (H) v Lon. Irish 11.4.92 (H) v Bath 24.4.93 (H)

OVERALL PLAYING RECORD

	P	W	D	L	F	A	Pts Diff
Home	26	18	0	8	485	315	170
Away	34	15	0	19	673	532	141
Neutral	1	1	0	0	48	18	30
Total	61	34	0	27	1206	865	341

SEASON BY SEASON

Season	Result
1971-72	2R
1972-73	1R
1973-74	2R
1974-75	DNQ
1975-76	1R
1976-77	SF
1977-78	1R
1978-79	DNQ
1979-80	DNQ
1980-81	3R
1981-82	2R
1982-83	3R
1983-84	1R
1984-85	4R
1985-86	4R
1986-87	3R
1987-88	4R
1988-89	3R
1989-90	4R
1990-91	4R
1991-92	4R
1992-93	4R
1993-94	QF
1994-95	4R
1995-96	5R
1996-97	QF
1997-98	Winners
1998-99	QF
1999-2000	5R
2000-01	QF
2001-02	QF

SARACENS RFU SENIOR CUP

STATISTICS

compiled by Stephen McCormack

TEAM RECORDS

Highest Score
76 v Morley 98/99

Biggest Winning Margin
68 (76-8) v Morley 98/99

Highest Score Against
41 v Leicester 00/01

Biggest Losing Margin
26 (33-7) v London Welsh 71/72

INDIVIDUAL RECORDS

Most Points in a match
21 Gavin Johnson v Morley 98/99

Most Tries in a match
3 Brandon Daniel v Morley 98/99

Most Conversions in a match
8 Gavin Johnson v Morley 98/99

Most Penalties in a match

Most Drop Goals in a match

EUROPEAN COMPETITIONS

STATISTICS *compiled by Stephen McCormack*

TEAM RECORDS

Highest Score
113 v Bologna & D Bucharest 01/02

Biggest Winning Margin
110 (113-3) Bologna & D Bucharest 01/02

Highest Score Against
35 v Munster 99/00

Biggest Losing Margin
14 (18-32) v Castres 97-98

INDIVIDUAL RECORDS

Most Points in a match
31 Jannie de Beer v Bologna

Most Tries in a match
4 Darragh O'Mahony v Bologna

Most Conversions in a match
13 Jannie de Beer v Bologna

Most Penalties in a match
6 Andy Lee v Narbonne 97/98

Most Drop Goals in a match
1 Thomas Castaignede (twice)

CAREER RECORDS

Most Appearances
22: Kevin Sorrell
18: Richard Hill
17: Tony Diprose

Most Points
87: Luke Smith
64: Michael Lynagn
63: Thomas Castaignede
62: Thierry Lacroix

Most Tries
12: Darragh O'Mahony
8: Kevin Sorrell
7: Richard Hill

SEASON BY SEASON

Season		Result
1996-97	S	DNP
1997-98	S	Gp Stage
1998-99	C	DNP
1999-00	C	Gp Stage
2000-01	C	Gp Stage
2001-02	C	Q-final

OVERALL PLAYING RECORD

	P	W	D	L	F	A	Pts Diff
Home	13	10	0	3	663	277	386
Away	12	8	0	4	372	233	139
Neutral	-	-	-	-	-	-	-
Total	25	18	0	7	1035	510	525

SARACENS

Founded: 1876
Nickname: Sarries
Colours: Black, with red shoulders/black/red
Change colours: Black, red and white
Web site: www.saracens.com

ADDRESSES

Ground: Vicarage Road Stadium, Vicarage Road, Watford. WD1 8ER
Capacity: 22,000 - all covered seating

Club Office: Rigby House, 34 The Parade, High St., Watford WD17 1EA
Tel: 01923 475222 Fax: 01923 475275 e-mail: general@saracens.net

Training Ground: Bramley Sports Ground, Chase Side, London N14 4A

Ground Directions: M1, junct. 6.
Follow signs for Watford town centre, then signs for Watford Hospital next to ground

Nearest Railway Station: Watford Junction, 15-20 mins walk

Underground Watford Metropolitan station, 10-15 mins walk

Car Parking: No public parking available at the ground.
There are several multi-storey car parks nearby.

Admission: (all covered seating)

	Adults	Concesions
Season	£99-499	£25-£65
Matchday	£10-35	£5

Club Shop: Mon-Sat 9-5, Matchday 11-5.
Contact 01923 229859

Clubhouse: Bramley Sports Ground,
Chase Side, London N14 4AB.
Snacks & restaurant available.
Functions: Contact Beeton Rumford Catering

PROGRAMME Size: B5
Pages: 64
Price: £2.50
Editor: Robin Bye
Advertising: Contact Commercial Department

RECORDS SECTION

DIVISION ONE
(CURRENTLY ZURICH PREMIERSHIP)

THE LAST TEN YEARS — DIVISION ONE

1992-93
Champions **Bath** | *Runners-up* Wasps | *Relegated* Saracens, Lon. Scottish, West Hartlepool, Rugb

Most
Penalties: 31 Michael Corcoran (Lon. Irish)
Points: 122 Jon Webb (Bath)
Conversions: 19 Jon Webb (Bath)
Tries: 7 Stuart Barnes (Bath)
D.Gs: 6 Paul Burke (Lon. Irish)

1993-94
Champions **Bath** | *Runners-up* Leicester | *Relegated* London Irish, Newcastle Gosforth

Most
Penalties: 41 Jez Harris (Leicester)
Points: 202 Jez Harris (Leicester)
Conversions: 25 Jonathon Callard (Bath)
Tries: 11 Daren O'Leary (Harlequins)
D.Gs: 11 Jez Harris (Leicester)

1994-95
Champions **Leicester** | *Runners-up* Bath | *Relegated* Northampton

Most
Penalties: 56 Mark Tainton (Bristol)
Points: 196 Mark Tainton (Bristol)
Conversions: 19 Rob Andrew (Wasps)
Tries: 8 Paul Holford (Gloucester)
D.Gs: 13 Jez Harris (Leicester)

1995-96
Champions **Bath** | *Runners-up* Leicester | *Relegated*

Most
Penalties: 64 John Liley (Leicester)
Points: 272 John Liley (Leicester)
Conversions: 43 Jonathon Callard (Bath)
Tries: 14 Daren O'Leary (Harlequins)
D.Gs: 7 David Pears (Harlequins)

1996-97
Champions **Wasps** | *Runners-up* Bath | *Relegated* Orrell, West Hartlepool

Most
Penalties: 62 Gareth Rees (Wasps)
Points: 291 Gareth Rees (Wasps)
Conversions: 51 Jonathon Callard (Bath)
Tries: 16 Adedayo Adebayo (Bath)
D.Gs: 6 Alex King (Wasps)

1997-98
Champions **Newcastle** | *Runners-up* Saracens | *Relegated* Bristol (play-off)

Most
Penalties: 58 Mark Mapletoft (Gloucester)
Points: 279 Michael Lynagh (Saracens)
Conversions: 44 Rob Andrew (Newcastle)
Tries: 17 Dominic Chapman (Richmond)
D.Gs: 4 David Humphreys (Lon. Irish)

1998-99
Champions **Leicester** | *Runners-up* Northampton | *Relegated* West Hartlepool

Most
Penalties: 77 John Schuster (Harlequins)
Points: 331 John Schuster (Harlequins)
Conversions: 52 Gavin Johnson (Saracens)
Tries: 16 Neil Back (Leicester)
D.Gs: 6 Jannie de Beer (Lon. Scottish)

99-2000
Champions **Leicester** | *Runners-up* Bath | *Relegated* Bedford

Most
Penalties: 66 Jarrod Cunningham (Lon. Irish)
Points: 324 Jarrod Cunningham (Lon. Irish)
Conversions: 52 Tim Stimpson (Leicester)
Tries: 15 Ian Balshaw (Bath)
D.Gs: 5 Alex King (Wasps)

2000-01
Champions **Leicester** | *Runners-up* London Wasps | *Relegated* Rotherham

Most
Penalties: 58 Paul Grayson (Northampton)
Points: 282 Kenny Logan (Lon. Wasps)
Conversions: 47 Kenny Logan (Lon. Wasps)
Tries: 11 Paul Sampson (Lon. Wasps)
D.Gs: 3 Jonny Wilkinson (Newcastle)

2001-02
Champions **Leicester** | *Runners-up* Sale | *Relegated*

Most
Penalties: 83 Barry Everitt (Lon. Irish)
Points: 343 Barry Everitt (Lon. Irish)
Conversions: 48 Ludovic Mercier (Gloucester)
Tries: 13 Mark Cueto (Sale)
D.Gs: 12 Ludovic Mercier (Gloucester)

ALL TIME RECORDS — TEAM RECORDS — DIVISION ONE

Highest score:	**106**	Bedford 12 Richmond 106. 16.5.99
Highest aggregate:	**118**	As above
Highest score by a losing side:	**41**	London Irish 52 W Hartlepool 41. 28.12.96
Highest scoring draw:	**38**	Bath 38 v Sale 38 27.4.96
Most consecutive wins:	**17**	Bath 1993-94 through 1994-95
Most consecutive defeats:	**18**	West Hartlepool 1995-96
Most points for in a season:	**863**	Bath 1996-97
Least points for in a season:	**70**	Bedford 1989-90
Most points against in a season:	**1007**	West Hartlepool 1998-99
Least points against in a season:	**95**	Orrell 1991-92
Most tries for in a season:	**116**	Bath 1996-97
Most tries against in a season:	**134**	W Hartlepool 1998-99
Least tries for in a season:	**8**	Waterloo 1988-89
Least tries against in a season:	**6**	Bath 1988-89, Wasps 1992-93
Most conversions for in a season:	**77**	Bath 1996-97
Most conversions against in a season:	**69**	Orrell 1996-97
Least conversions for in a season:		
Least conversions against in a season:		
Most penalties for in a season:	**87**	Harlequins 1998-99
Most penalties against in a season:	**73**	Sale 1998-99
Least penalties for in a season:	**7**	Bedford 1989-90
Least penalties against in a season:	**11**	Harlequins 1987-88
Most drop goals for in a season:	**13**	Leicester 1994-95 & Harlequins 1995-96
Most drop goals against in a season:	**8**	Wasps 1993-94 & 1995-96

ALL TIME RECORDS — INDIVIDUAL RECORDS — DIVISION ONE

Most points in a season:	**331**	John Schuster (Harlequins) 1998-99
Most tries in a season:	**17**	Dominic Chapman (Richmond) 1997-98
Most conversions in a season:	**52**	Gavin Johnson (Saracens) 1998-99 & Tim Stimpson (Leicester) 1990-00
Most penalties in a season:	**77**	John Schuster (Harlequins) 1998-99
Most drop goals in a season:	**13**	Jez Harris (Leicester) 1994-95
Most points in a match:	**32**	Niall Woods, *London Irish* v Harlequins 25.4.98
Most tries in a match:	**6**	Ryan Constable,Bedford v *Saracens* 16.4.00
Most conversions in a match:	**13**	Rich Butland, Bedford v *Richmond* 16.5.99
Most penalties in a match:	**9**	Thierry Lacroix, *Saracens* v Wasps 7.11.99
Most drop goals in a match:	**3**	John Steele, *Northampton* v Wasps 23.3.91 Jez Harris, *Leicester* v Wasps 23.11.91 David Pears, *Harlequins* v Wasps 16.9.95 Matthew McCarthy, *Orrell* v W Hartlepool 7.12.96

ALL TIME RECORDS MOST POINTS IN A SEASON DIVISION ONE

Points	Player	Club	Season	Tries	Cons.	Pens.	D.G.
343	Barry Everitt	London Irish	2001-02	2	30	83	8
334	Ludovic Mercier	Gloucester	2001-02	2	48	64	12
331	John Schuster	Harlequins	1998-99	5	36	77	1
324	Jarrod Cunningham	London Irish	99-2000	6	46	66	
321	Tim Stimpson	Leicester	99-2000	5	52	63	1
318	Gavin Johnson	Saracens	1998-99	8	52	58	
306	Jonny Wilkinson	Newcastle	1998-99	9	51	53	
294	Mike Catt	Bath	1998-99	7	50	53	
291	Gareth Rees	Wasps	1996-97	3	45	62	
282	Simon Mannix	Gloucester	99-2000	3	36	62	3
282	Kenny Logan	London Wasps	2000-01	10	47	46	-
280	Thierry Lacroix	Saracens	99-2000	3	47	55	2
279	Michael Lynagh	Saracens	1997-98	5	37	58	2
275	Mark Mapletoft	Gloucester	1997-98	5	35	58	2
273	Charles Hodgson	Sale	2001-02	7	44	48	2
272	John Liley	Leicester	1995-96	5	26	64	1
269	Mark Mapletoft	Gloucester	1996-97	6	25	58	5
263	Kenny Logan	Wasps	1998-99	8	35	51	
260	Tim Stimpson	Leicester	2000-01	7	27	57	-
258	Paul Burke	Harlequins	2001-02	3	21	62	5
253	Joel Stransky	Leicester	1997-98	5	39	47	3
253	Gareth Rees	Wasps	1997-98	1	34	57	3
246	Shane Howarth	Sale	1998-99	9	42	37	
240	Steven Vile	W Hartlepool	1998-99	5	28	52	1
238	Paul Grayson	Northampton	2001-02	1	31	55	2
237	Niall Woods	London Irish	1997-98	8	34	43	
236	Jonathan Callard	Bath	1995-96	3	43	45	
226	Rob Andrew	Newcastle	1997-98	6	44	35	1
224	Jonathan Callard	Bath	1996-97	4	51	34	
224	Shane Howarth	Sale	1997-98	4	39	41	1
221	Felipe Contepomi	Bristol	2001-02	9	25	40	2
219	Paul Grayson	Northampton	2000-01	1	20	58	-
215	Niall Woods	London Irish	1998-99	12	25	35	
215	Jonny Wilkinson	Newcastle	2001-02	2	32	44	3
212	Tim Stimpson	Leicester	2001-02	5	29	43	-
210	Paul Grayson	Northampton	1997-98	4	23	45	3
203	Earl Va'a	Richmond	1998-99	8	32	33	
202	Jez Harris	Leicester	1993-94	2	18	41	11
202	Joel Stransky	Leicester	1998-99	7	34	33	-
198	Mark Mapletoft	Gloucester	1998-99	6	21	41	1
198	Jonny Wilkinson	Newcastle	2000-01	2	34	37	3
196	Mark Tainton	Bristol	1994-95	-	11	56	2
195	John Liley	Leicester	1996-97	3	24	44	
194	Luke Smith	Saracens	2001-02	1	12	53	2
189	Paul Grayson	Northampton	1994-95	1	11	52	2
189	David Humphreys	London Irish	1996-97	4	20	40	3
184	Jon Preston	Bath	99-2000	1	34	32	
183	Jon Callard	Bath	1997-98	1	32	38	
183	Alex King	Wasps	2001-02	-	24	36	9
182	Barry Everitt	London Irish	2000-01	1	15	49	-
181	Jez Harris	Leicester	1994-95	-	11	40	13
178	Jonathan Callard	Bath	1993-94	4	25	36	
178	Paul Burke	Bristol	1996-97	2	27	38	
178	Henry Honiball	Bristol	99-2000	4	34	29	1
176	Thierry Lacroix	Harlequins	1996-97	2	29	33	3
172	Jon Preston	Bath	2000-01	-	23	42	-

ALL TIME RECORDS — MOST POINTS IN A MATCH — DIVISION ONE

Points	Player	Match	Date
32	Niall Woods	London Irish v Harlequins	25.04.98
31	John Liley	Leicester v Rosslyn Park	21.03.92
	David Walder	Newcastle v Saracens	26.11.00
	Tim Stimpson	Leicester v Saracens	24.02.01
	Felipe Contepomi	Bristol v Northampton	16.04.01
30	Steven Vile	West Hartlepool v Richmond	17.04.99
	Ryan Constable	Saracens v Bedford	16.04.00
29	Thomas Castaignede	Saracens v Rotherham	24.09.00
	Kenny Logan	London Wasps v Sale	14.04.01
	Jonny Wilkinson	Newcastle v London Wasps	23.09.00
	Alex King	London Wasps v Leeds Tykes	18.11.01
	Contepomi, Felipe	Bristol v Leeds Tykes	23.09.01
	Luke Smith	Saracens v Gloucester	08.09.01
28	Martin Strett	Orrell v Rosslyn Park	28.04.90
	John Liley	Leicester v Bristol	28.10.95
	Gavin Johnson	Saracens v London Scottish	26.09.98
	John Schuster	Harlequins v Bath	21.11.98
	Steven Vile	West Hartlepool v Gloucester	14.03.99
	Simon Mannix	Gloucester v Northampton	16.05.99
	Kenny Logan	London Wasps v Rotherham	01.04.01
	Paul Burke	Harlequins v Saracens	16.11.01
	Tim Stimpson	Leicester Tigers v Bath	22.09.01
27	David Pears	Harlequins v Bedford	14.10.89
	Mark Mapletoft	Gloucester v Leicester	01.02.98
	Niall Woods	London Irish v Northampton	05.01.99
	Thierry Lacroix	Saracens v Wasps	07.11.99
	Simon Mannix	Gloucester v Harlequins	23.09.00
	Jarrod Cunningham	London Irish v Bristol	10.09.00
	Alex King	London Wasps v Leicester Tigers	31.03.02
	Charles Hodgson	Leeds Tykes v Sale	25.11.01
	Alex King	London Wasps v Newcastle Falcons	11.11.01
	Barry Everitt	London Irish v Leeds Tykes	09.09.01
26	John Liley	Leicester v Bedford	23.09.89
	Stuart Barnes	Bath v West Hartlepool	27.03.93
	Paul Grayson	Northampton v Bristol	02.10.93
	Mark Tainton	Bristol v Leicester	05.12.94
	Andy Lee	Saracens v West Hartlepool	14.10.95
	Paul Challinor	Harlequins v West Hartlepool	23.03.96
	Rob Liley	Leicester v London Irish	31.10.96
	John Stabler	West Hartlepool v London Irish	28.12.96
	Simon Mannix	Sale v Northampton	09.03.97
	Mike Catt	Bath v Sale	26.04.97
	Paul Grayson	Northampton v London Irish	13.12.97
	Thierry Lacroix	Harlequins v Wasps	13.12.97
	Kenny Logan	Wasps v London Irish	19.09.98
	Mike Catt	Bath v London Scottish	15.05.99
	Rich Butland	Richmond v Bedford	16.05.99
	Jarrod Cunningham	London Irish v Newcastle	02.10.00
	Thierry Lacroix	Saracens v Leicester	05.12.99
	Kenny Logan	Wasps v Saracens	13.02.00
	Jonny Wilkinson	Newcastle v Gloucester	30.04.00
	Tim Stimpson	Leicester v Gloucester	02.12.01
	Niki Little	Sale v Bristol	06.09.00
	Barry Everitt	London Irish v Bath	10.04.02

MOST TRIES IN A MATCH

6	Ryan Constable	Saracens v Bedford	16.04.00
5	Kenny Logan	Wasps v Orrel	22.03.97
4	Gary Hartley	Nottingham v Bedford	18.11.89
	Tony Swift	Bath v Bedford	13.01.90
	Jeremy Guscott	Bath v Bedford	13.01.90
	Paul Hamer	Orrell v Rugby	13.03.93
	Tony Underwood	Leicester v Newcastle Gosforth	12.03.94
	Daren O'Leary	Harlequins v Gloucester	31.08.96
	Tom Beim	Sale v Bristol	09.11.97
	Niall Woods	London Irish v Northampton	05.01.99
	Elton Moncrieff	Gloucester v Bedford	06.05.00
	Geordan Murphy	Leicester v Saracens	24.02.01

3	Peter Shillingford	Moseley v Wasps	05.02.88
	Mark Charles	Leicester v Sale	26.03.88
	Andrew Harriman	Harlequins v Nottingham	01.04.88
	Simon Smith	Wasps v Coventry	13.04.88
	Andrew Harriman	Harlequins v Sale	23.04.88
	Jeremy Guscott	Bath v Moseley	12.11.88
	Mark Bailey	Wasps v Moseley	19.11.88
	John Liley	Leicester v Bedford	23.09.89
	Mike Wedderburn	Harlequins v Bedford	14.10.89
	Mark Bailey	Wasps v Gloucester	14.10.89
	Derrick Morgan	Gloucester v Rosslyn Park	11.11.89
	Jonathan Callard	Bath v Bedford	13.01.90
	Chris Gerard	Leicester v Moseley	13.01.90
	Paul Manley	Orrell v Rosslyn Park	31.03.90
	Dewi Morris	Orrell v Liverpool StH	13.10.90
	Dewi Morris	Orrell v Northampton	27.10.90
	Rory Underwood	Leicester v Northampton	21.01.91
	Andrew Harriman	Harlequins v Bristol	30.03.91
	Will Carling	Harlequins v Bristol	30.03.91
	Graham Childs	Wasps v Liverpool StH	20.04.91
	Rob Andrew	Wasps v Bristol	27.04.91
	Rory Underwood	Leicester v Moseley	27.04.91
	Steve Hackney	Leicester v Lon. Irish	04.01.92
	Tony Swift	Bath v Leicester	11.01.92
	Rory Underwood	Leicester v Rosslyn Park	21.03.92
	Mike Lloyd	Bristol v Rugby	28.03.92
	Martin Pepper	Nottingham v Rosslyn Park	04.04.92
	Chris Oti	Wasps v Bristol	25.04.92
	Stuart Barnes	Bath v W. Hartlepool	27.03.93
	Derek Eves	Bristol v Rugby	22.03.93
	Ian Wynn	Orrell v Wasps	30.04.94
	Simon Morris	Gloucester v W. Hartlepool	17.09.94
	Damian Hopley	Wasps v Sale	15.10.94
	Jeremy Guscott	Bath v Bristol	14.10.95
	Graeme Smith	Orrell v Wasps	28.10.95
	Rob Kitchen	Harlequins v Bristol	06.01.96
	Graeme Smith	Orrell v Saracens	13.01.96
	Aadel Kardooni	Leicester v W. Hartlepool	17.02.96
	Spencer Bromley	Harlequins v Sale	30.03.96
	Aadel Kardooni	Leicester v Sale	17.04.96
	Michael Corcoran	Harlequins v Lon. Irish	14.09.96
	Adedayo Adebayo	Bath v Lon. Irish	05.10.96
	Huw Harries	Harlequins v Orrell	05.10.96
	Mike Lloyd	Gloucester v W. Hartlepool	18.01.97
	Jonathan Sleightholme	Bath v Northampton	19.01.97
	Jonathan Sleightholme	Bath v Lon. Irish	08.03.97
	Domonic Chapman	Harlequins v Orrell	08.03.97
	Nick Walshe	Harlequins v W. Hartlepool	22.03.97
	Tom Beim	Sale v W. Hartlepool	05.04.97
	Andy Nicol	Bath v Gloucester	30.04.97
	Richard Wallace	Saracens v Lon. Irish	30.04.97
	David Rees	Sale v Bristol	09.11.97
	Gary Armstrong	Newcastle v Bristol	27.12.97
	Jim Naylor	Newcastle v Lon. Irish	11.01.98
	Eric Peters	Bath v Gloucester	11.02.98
	Richard Wallace	Saracens v Bristol	14.02.98
	Harvey Thorneycroft	Northampton v Bristol	14.03.98
	Will Greenwood	Leicester v Richmond	28.03.98
	Domonic Chapman	Richmond v Bristol	10.04.98
	Justin Bishop	Lon. Irish v Harlequins	25.04.98
	Chris Catling	Gloucester v Newcastle	17.10.98
	Darragh O'Mahoney	Bedford v Richmond	31.10.98
	Tony Underwood	Newcastle v Saracens	31.10.98
	Pat Lam	Northampton v Sale	2.1.99
	Tony Diprose	Saracens v W. Hartlepool	13.2.99
	Iain Balshaw	Bath v Saracens	28.3.99
	Richard Todd	London Irish v Bath	17.4.99
	Gary Armstrong	Newcastle v Richmond	21.4.99
	Darragh O'Mahoney	Bedford v W. Hartlepool	2.5.99
	Brian Cusack	Richmond v Bedford	16.5.99
	Mel Deane	Richmond v Bedford	16.5.99
	Neil Back	Leicester v W. Hartlepool	16.5.99
	Shaun Berne	Bath v Gloucester	9.10.99
	Josh Lewsey	Wasps v Bedford	23.3.00
	Darragh O'Mahoney	Saracens v Harlequins	24.4.00
	Rob Henderson	Wasps v Sale	30.4.00
	Neil Back	Leicester v Bath	21.5.00
	Frank Schisano	Bristol v Rotherham	02.09.00
	Rob Henderson	London Wasps v Gloucester	17.09.00
	Dan Luger	Saracens v Rotherham	24.09.00
	Steve Hanley	Sale v Harlequins	02.12.00
	Kenny Logan	London Wasps v Rotherham	01.04.01
	Rob Thirlby	Bath v Rotherham	14.03.01
	Tom Voyce	Bath v Rotherham	14.04.01
	Mike Catt	Bath v London Irish	14.03.01
	Daniel Simpson	Gloucester v Bath	04.05.02
	Neil Back	Leicester v Leeds	19.04.02
	Martin Shaw	Sale v Bristol	13.04.02

Club	SEASONS									
	92-93	93-94	94-95	95-96	96-97	97-98	98-99	99-00	00-01	01-02
Bath	1	1	2	1	2	3	6	2	3	11
Bedford	-	-	-	-	-	-	13	12	-	-
Bristol	6	4	6	6	9	12	-	6	9	8
Gloucester	5	8	7	8	6	7	10	3	7	3
Harlequins	8	6	8	3	3	10	4	10	11	9
Leeds Tykes	-	-	-	-	-	-	-	-	-	12
Leicester	3	2	1	2	4	4	1	1	1	1
London Irish	7	9	-	-	10	-	7	8	8	4
London Scottish	10	-	-	-	-	-	12	-	-	-
Moseley	-	-	-	-	-	-	-	-	-	-
Newcastle	-	10	-	-	-	1	8	9	6	6
Northampton	4	5	10	-	8	8	2	5	4	5
Orrell	9	7	5	7	12	-	-	-	-	-
Richmond	-	-	-	-	-	5	9	-	-	-
Rosslyn Park	-	-	-	-	-	-	-	-	-	-
Rotherham	-	-	-	-	-	-	-	-	12	-
Rugby	13	-	-	-	-	-	-	-	-	-
(Manchester) Sale	-	-	4	5	5	6	11	11	10	2
Saracens	11	-	-	9	7	2	3	4	5	10
(London) Wasps	2	3	3	4	1	9	5	7	2	7
West Hartlepool	12	-	9	10	11	-	14	-	-	-

NATIONAL DIVISION
ONE

LEAGUE TABLE

									HOME									AWAY								
														For		Against							For		Against	
	P	W	D	L	F	A	PD	Pts	W	D	L	F	A	Tries	Pens	Tries	Pens	W	D	L	F	A	Tries	Pens	Tries	Pens
Rotherham	26	24	0	2	1009	325	774	120	12	0	1	574	116	82	13	10	14	12	0	1	525	209	77	14	22	21
Worcester	26	23	0	3	941	364	577	108	12	0	1	505	170	71	13	19	16	11	0	2	436	194	61	17	24	18
Exeter	26	19	1	6	707	448	259	92	11	1	1	383	205	45	29	22	22	8	0	5	324	243	42	18	29	19
Coventry	26	16	3	7	730	559	171	82	9	1	3	467	284	62	26	38	18	7	2	4	263	275	27	34	28	26
London Welsh	26	15	0	11	580	557	23	69	9	0	4	303	253	36	27	34	13	6	0	7	277	304	29	32	35	25
Bedford	26	12	3	11	654	600	54	68	11	0	2	357	257	43	27	28	26	1	3	9	297	343	38	18	37	35
Otley	26	11	1	14	601	675	-74	56	7	1	5	343	257	39	36	31	20	4	0	9	258	418	23	34	53	26
Birmingham & Sol	26	10	1	15	432	626	-194	52	6	1	6	258	264	31	21	22	41	4	0	9	174	362	21	13	41	31
Wakefield	26	9	2	15	514	607	-93	47	6	2	5	291	264	31	29	32	24	3	0	10	223	343	23	23	37	36
Rugby Lions	26	9	1	16	518	668	-150	47	6	1	6	297	341	36	24	48	16	3	0	10	221	327	27	18	34	37
Moseley	26	9	1	16	448	695	-247	46	6	0	7	233	339	23	25	43	19	3	1	9	215	356	31	10	44	21
Manchester	26	8	0	18	381	758	-377	36	6	0	7	221	346	22	29	46	21	2	0	11	160	412	15	23	56	21
Henley Hawks	26	6	1	19	449	767	-318	33	4	0	9	260	335	23	38	40	27	2	1	10	189	432	17	24	57	23
Bracknell	26	4	0	22	418	823	-405	26	3	0	10	188	361	16	28	41	29	1	0	12	230	462	23	28	63	26

REVIEW

Rotherham dominated the division from start to finish and ended the season 12 points clear of Worcester. They suffered just two defeats all season, one at home to Exeter and one away to Worcester. They also rattled up 24 bonus points, which was easily the highest total in the division. They had a powerful pack who scored 71 tries against 85 by the backs. Leading the way in the try scorers was Oriol Ripol who scored 14 tries is his limited number of appearances. Amongst the forwards back row man Alfie Tooala scored 13 times, the second best by a forward in the division. Hooker Chris Johnson scored 12 tries in the campaign with 10 of them coming away from Clifton Road.

Worcester were always second best against Rotherham despite beating them early in the season. The Sixways side lost only three times all season but picked up 16 bonus points, eight fewer than Rotherham managed. They did though have some good individual performances with three of their backs featuring in the leading try scorers. Leading the way was their Australian winger Chris Garrard with 25 tries, a new record for the division, Ben Hinshelwood, capped.during the summer by Scotland, was second in the list with 21 whilst Duncan Roke was joint third with 16.

Exeter finished third for the second season running but that was 16 points behind second placed Worcester. They have now finished in the top five for four consecutive seasons showing tremendous consistency but unable to break into serious challenges for promotion. They had an impressive home record losing one and drawing one and picking up 11 victories. Richard Baxter topped the try scorers list with a new club record for tries in a league season with 16 whilst new Australian signing Chris Malone topped the points scoring with 247 the second highest total in the division. Included in that total was a new club record of seven-drop goals in a season.

Coventry finished the season in fourth place in and improved their league position for the third consecutive season, which was helped as they finished the season with six wins and a draw in their last eight league matches. They managed a win and a draw against Exeter who finished a point above them in the table but they managed to lose to the relegated side Bracknell. Winger Kurt Johnson topped the try scorers list for a third consecutive season and now has 40 tries for the club in league rugby. Full back Martyn Davies topped the points scorers for the second consecutive season, a feat only previously achieved at the club by Steve Gough in league rugby.

London Welsh improved a place on the previous season with a fifth place finish in National One. This was an excellent position after they suffered a mid season collapse with just three wins in a ten match run before finding some form. That form saw them end the season with seven wins from their last nine matches. The kicking duties were split between John Ufton and Andy Lee with Ufton topping the points scorers with 133. Matt Vines tops the try scoring list for a second successive season but with just eight compared with his 17 from the previous season.

Bedford finished sixth which was a five place improvement on the previous season and was their first winning season since 1997-98. Away from Boddingtons Road they managed just one league win but did end up drawing three matches. At home though they had a superb record with 11 wins and just two sides leaving with a win, Rotherham and Worcester. In the match at Moseley they scored 45 points and still finished on the losing side as Moseley scored a point more for a 46-45 victory, it was the highest ever score by a losing side in the division. James Pritchard in his first season at the club topped the points scoring, the full back scored 244 points including eight tries. James Shanahan topped the try scoring in his second season at the club with 11 tries, the first player to get into double figures since Rory Underwood in 1998-99.

Otley who the previous season just escaped relegation finished up seventh a five place improvement on that campaign. Their cause was helped by the goal kicking of outside half Simon Binns who scored 283 points to top the points scorers list for the division. It was the second highest total by an Otley player in a league season and was 47% of Otley's total points for the season. The leading try scorer was Mark Kirkby for the third time but with just seven compared to his previous totals of 22 but it did see him become the first Otley player to top 50 tries in league rugby. The Cross Green side did well mid season with five wins from seven matches but after seven defeats in their opening ten matches of the season they did well to finish seventh.

Birmingham & Solihull did well to improve a place on the previous season as they finished in eighth place in the second season at this level. The Bees never managed to win more than two consecutive matches as they struggled to score points. They managed just 432 points, which was the third lowest total in the division with just Bracknell and Manchester scoring fewer points. Dave Knight topped the points scoring with just 102, which was the lowest total since 1995-96 to top the list. In the try scoring stakes it was a different story with Nick Baxter, in his first league campaign for Birmingham, topping the list with 15, the second highest total ever for the Bees in a league season after the 16 scored by Ben Shepherd back in 1997-98.

Wakefield dropped five places on the previous season to end up ninth. For a long time they looked likely to be dragged into the relegation battle but a good run at the end of the season saw things change. They won four and drew one of their last seven matches to pull away and maintain their 12-year stay in the division. Rob Liley t

REVIEW continued

opped the points scoring for a fourth season, spread over both his spells at the club, to equal the record of Mike Jackson. Liley also set a new record for points in a season with 237.

Rugby Lions back in the division after a season out maintained their status with 10th place in the division. The Lions suffered two bad losing runs when they lost six consecutive matches but four wins in five matches mid season saw their league position improve. They then went on one of those six match-losing runs they managed to stay clear of the relegation. Scrum half Phil Read topped the try scorers with 12 tries, only the second Rugby player to get into double figures after Eddie Saunders. Saunders himself was again amongst the tries despite his numerous retirements over recent seasons and went passed the magical 100 try mark in league rugby.

Moseley finished the season in 11th place their worst ever finish in league rugby. Scoring points was their problem and they did not have a consistent goal kicker to rack up the points. The try scoring was led by hooker Richard Protherough who crossed the line seven times and that included a hat trick ˆ a feat not achieved by many hooker in league rugby. Only once all season did they manage to win consecutive league matches.

Manchester seemed to be doing alright when they won away at Bracknell in January and were winning their fourth match in five but after that their season disintegrated. In their remaining 11 matches they managed just one win as they slipped down the table and ended up just three points ahead of Henley Hawks at the end to secure their National One status for a fourth season. They struggled to score points and ended the season as the lowest points scorers in the division with 381, which included 37 tries, which was also the lowest total in the division.

Henley Hawks lost their National One status after a three-year stay. They made a valiant effort to avoid the drop but could not quite manage it. Three successive wins in March lifted their spirits but a defeat at Birmingham & Solihull and a draw at Wakefield left them having to beat Rotherham to survive and that was just too much to ask. Full back Jon Fabian did well in his first season for the club and just failed to become the third Henley player to score 200 points in a season finishing on 199.

Bracknell found the going tough and went down after their first season at this level. They managed just four wins all season and three of those came early in the season in their first eight matches. After that they managed just one win in their next 18 league games and finished seven points adrift of Henley Hawks in the end and 10 points off safety. They again failed to find a regular goal kicker with a number of players sharing the responsibility over the campaign.

Stephen McCormack

2001-02 RECORD REVIEW (Individual Records)

The ALL-TIME RECORDS for MOST POINTS IN A MATCH, MOST POINTS IN A SEASON & MOST TRIES IN A MATCH can be found in the Records Section for this division.

MOST POINTS - IN A MATCH

This record was never seriously challenged in the season just gone. The best effort was 32 points by the prolific Worcester full back Sateki Tuipulotu against Henley Hawks in January. It did though move him into sixth on the all time list. In the same fixture last season he scored 31 points. The next best was 30 points by Rotherham's Italian fly half Ramiro Pez who scored his points in the home win against Coventry. Otley fly half Simon Binns was the only player to score 20 points in a match three times during the season..

EVOLUTION OF RECORD - Points in a match

26	Andy Mitchell	London Scot v North	03.10.87
28	David Johnson	New Gos v Morley	11.01.92
30	Michael Corcoran	L. Irish v Waterloo	23.09.95
42	Jez Harris	Coventry v Nott	05.10.96

MOST POINTS - IN A SEASON

No challenge to the record set last season by Sateki Tuipulotu. The leading scorer was the Otley fly half Simon Binns who scored 283 points and moved into ninth place on the all time list for the division.
It is the second club that Binns has scored 200 points in a season for, back in 1997-98 he scored 244 points for Rotherham.
Both Chris Malone, Exeter, and James Pritchard, Bedford, scored 200 points in their first season of league rugby.

EVOLUTION OF RECORD - Points in a season

75	Andy Finnie	Bedford	1987-88
138	Andy Kennedy	Saracens	1988-89
147	David Johnson	Newcastle Gos	1991-92
172	Guy Gregory	Nottingham	1993-94
213	Mike Jackson	Wakefield	1994-95
310	Michael Corcoran	London Irish	1995-96
324	Simon Mason	Richmond	1996-97
349	Sateki Tuipulotu	Worcester	2000-01

MOST TRIES - IN A MATCH

Hat tricks were up after a drop the previous season to 20 and two of those were five tries in a match which equalled the record for the division. Chris Garrard achieved it first in Worcester's home win against Otley in March before Michael Wood did the same thing as Rotherham thrashed Birmingham & Solihull at home in April. In all Garrard scored three hat tricks during the season, no other player scored more than one.

EVOLUTION OF RECORD - Tries in a match
(Only the first to reach the figure is shown except in last instance)

3	Peter Shillingford	Moseley v Wasps	05.02.88
3	Jerry Macklin	Lon Scot v Northampton	03.10.87
5	Simon Verbickas	Sale v Otley	12.02.94
5	Pat Lam	Newcastle v Rotherham	04.05.97
5	Luke Nabaro	Bristol v Blackheath	13.03.99
5	Chris Garrard	Worcester v Otley	09.03.02
5	Michael Wood	Rotherham v Birm Sol	13.04.02

MOST TRIES - IN A SEASON

Worcester right wing Chris Garrard set a new record for tries in a seasoon with 25, two more than John Bentley scored back in 1996-97 for Newcastle in their Championship season. Garrard who scored five tries against Otley also scored two other hat tricks.
Another Worcester back, Ben Hinshelwood also passed the 20 try mark and moved into joint third on the all time list with 21.

EVOLUTION OF RECORD

10	Dave McLagan	Saracens	1987-88
11	Nick Grecian	Lon. Scottish	1991-92
16	Simon Verbickas	Sale	1993-94
20	Matt Allen	Northampton	1996-97
23	John Bentley	Newcastle	1996-97

ALL-TIME RECORDS

25	Chris Garrard	Worcester	2001-02
23	John Bentley	Newcastle	1996-97
21	Gary Armstrong	Newcastle	1996-97
21	Scott Quinnell	Richmond	1996-97
21	Ben Hinshelwood	Worcester	2001-02
20	Matt Allen	Northampton	1995-96
20	Jim Fallon	Richmond	1996-97
19	Graham Mackay	Leeds Tykes	2000-01
18	Dean Lax	Rotherham	1998-99
18	Dean Lax	Rotherham	1999-00
18	Shaun Woof	Leeds Tykes	2000-01
17	Andy Smallwood	Coventry	1996-97
17	Darragh O'Mahoney	Moseley	1997-98
17	Ben Whetstone	Bedford	1997-98
17	Duncan Roke	Henley Hawks	1999-00
17	Dave Scully	Rotherham	1999-00
17	Matt Vines	London Welsh	2000-01
17	Chris Hall	Leeds Tykes	2000-01
17	Sateki Tuipulotu	Worcester	2000-01

MOST CONVERSIONS - IN A MATCH

This record seems safe for a while yet. The best last season was eight by Link Wilfley, Roherham v Moseley, and Tony Yapp, Worcester v Otley.

EVOLUTION OF RECORD

6	Chris Howard	Rugby v Gosforth	11.11.89
9	David Johnson	New Gos v Morley	11.01.92
9	Guy Gregory	Nott v Morley	24.10.92
9	Paul Turner	Sale v Otley	12.02.94
18	Rob Andrew	Newcastle v Rugby	05.10.96

ALL-TIME RECORDS

18	Rob Andrew	Newcastle v Rugby	05.10.96
13	Jez Harris	Coventry v Nottingham	05.10.96
10	Simon Binns	Rotherham v W Hartlepool	02.10.99
10	Mike Umaga	Rotherham v Waterloo	11.03.00
10	Sam Howard	Exeter v W Hartlepool	06.05.00
9	David Johnson	New Gos v Morley	11.01.92
9	Guy Gregory	Nottingham v Morley	24.10.92
9	Paul Turner	Sale v Otley	12.02.94
9	Richard Le Bas	Leeds Tykes v Orrell	

MOST CONVERSIONS - IN A SEASON

Very little changed here apart from Ramiro Pez moving into the all time list but way down the list with his 60 conversions in Roherham's Championship season.

EVOLUTION OF RECORD

14	Andy Kennedy	Saracens	1988-89
24	Martin Livesey	Richmond	1989-90
31	David Johnson	Newcastle Gosforth	1991-92
76	Paul Grayson	Northampton	1995-96
95	Rob Andrew	Newcastle	1996-97

ALL-TIME RECORDS

95	Rob Andrew	Newcastle	1996-97
83	Simon Mason	Richmond	1996-97
76	Paul Grayson	Northampton	1995-96
72	Richard Le Bas	Leeds Tykes	2000-01
67	Mike Rayer	Bedford	1996-97
65	Mike Rayer	Bedford	1997-98
60	Mike Umaga	Rotherham	1999-00
60	Ramiro Pez	Rotherham	2001-02
57	Sateki Tuipulotu	Worcester	2000-01
55	Sam Howard	Exeter	1999-00
50	Tony Yapp	Worcester	1999-00
48	Jez Harris	Coventry	1996-97
48	Steve Gough	Coventry	1998-99

2001-02 RECORD REVIEW (Individual Records) continued

MOST PENALTIES - IN A MATCH

Marcus Barrow the Manchester full back broke Alastair Kerr's record of eight penalties in a match with a new mark of nine. Barrow did it in the home match against Wakefield at home in December. Apart from the performance by Barrow no other player scored more than six penalties in a match during the season.

EVOLUTION OF RECORD

7	Michael Corcoran	Lon Irish v Lon Scottish	13.01.96
8	Alastair Kerr	Moseley v Waterloo	17.02.96
9	Marcus Barrow	Manchester v Wakefield	20.12.01

ALL-TIME RECORDS

9	Marcus Barrow	Manchester v Wakefield	20.12.01
8	Alastair Kerr	Moseley v Water	17.02.96
7	Michael Corcoran	Lon Irish v Lon Scottish	13.01.96
7	Matt Inman	Rotherham v Richmond	14.09.96
7	Sateki Tuipulotu	Leeds v Coventry	03.01.99
7	Steve Gough	Coventry v Worcester	11.03.00
7	Jon Benson	Leeds v Manchester	08.04.00
7	Richard Le Bas	Leeds Tykes v Manchester	07.10.00

MOST PENALTIES - IN A SEASON

The division's leading points scorer Simon Binns kicked 63 penalties for Otley last season and moved into joint second on the all time list alongside Michael Cochoran but two of the all time record.

EVOLUTION OF RECORD

30	Andy Kennedy	Saracens	1988-89
30	David Johnson	Newcastle	1992-93
43	Guy Gregory	Nottingham	1993-94
57	Mike Jackson	Wakefield	1994-95
63	MIchael Corcoran	London Irish	1995-96
65	Lyndon Griffiths	Waterloo	1997-98

ALL-TIME RECORDS

65	Lyndon Griffiths	Waterloo	1997-98
63	Michael Corcoran	London Irish	1995-96
63	Simon Binns	Otley	2001-02
57	Mike Jackson	Wakefield	1994-95
55	Steve Swindells	Manchester	1999-00
55	Matt Jones	Henley	1999-00
53	Steve Gough	Coventry	1998-99
53	Sateki Tuipulotu	Leeds Tykes	1998-99
51	Bryan Easson	Exeter	1998-99
51	Martyn Davies	Coventry	2000-01
50	Sateki Tuipulotu	Worcester	2000-01
50	Rob Liley	Wakefield	2001-02
48	Steve Swindells	Waterloo	1994-95
48	Richard Le Bas	Leeds Tykes	2000-01
47	John Steele	London Scottish	1996-97
47	John Fabian	Henley Hawks	2001-02

MOST DROP GOALS - IN A MATCH

Exeter fly half Chris Malone now has a share of the record after dropping three goals in his sides surprise win at Rotherham last season.

ALL-TIME RECORDS

3	Martin Livesey	Richmond v Northampton	19.11.8
3	Murray Walker	London Scot v W Hartlepool	23.04.9
3	Chris Malone	Exeter v Rotherham	10.11.

MOST DROP GOALS - IN A SEASON

Exter's Australian fly half Chris Malone moved into fourth place on the all time list after dropping seven goals for his club last season.
Not far behind was the Wakefield player Rob Liley who dropped six goals last seaon.

EVOLUTION OF RECORD

4	Simon Smith	Bedford	1987-8
4	David Johnson	Gosforth	1987-8
8	Jon King	Blackheath	1988-8
9	Guy Gregory	Nottingham	1992-9
9	David Sleman	Orrell	2000-0

ALL-TIME RECORDS

9	Guy Gregory	Nottingham	1992-9
9	David Sleman	Orrell	2000-0
8	Jon King	Blackheath	1988-8
7	Chris Malone	Exeter	2001-0
6	Andy Lee	Saracens	1994-9
6	Rob Liley	Wakefield	2001-0
5	Brian Mullen	London Irish	1990-9
5	Sam Howard	Blackheath	1995-9
5	Guy Gregory	Nottingham	1993-9
5	Murray Walker	London Scot	1993-9
5	Jez Harris	Coventry	1996-9
5	Matt Jones	Moseley	1997-9
5	Sam Howard	Exeter	1999-0

2001-02

NATIONAL LEAGUE ONE

MOST POINTS

POINTS			T	C	P	DG
283	Simon Binns	Otley	5	30	63	3
247	Chris Malone	Exeter	5	45	37	7
244	James Pritchard	Bedford	8	42	40	-
237	Rob Liley	Wakefield	1	32	50	6
223	Martyn Davies	Coventry	5	30	46	-
199	John Fabian	Henley Hawks	2	24	47	-
197	Ramiro Pez	Rotherham	4	60	19	-
141	Marcus Barrow	Manchester	3	12	34	-
133	John Ufton	London Welsh	2	21	27	-
127	Richard Davies	Rugby Lions	4	16	22	3
126	Lee Hinton	Moseley	4	17	24	-
125	Chris Garrard	Worcester	25	-	-	-
118	Tony Yapp	Worcester	5	33	8	1
111	Chris Richards	Rugby Lions	3	18	20	-
108	Sateki Tuipulotu	Worcester	3	30	11	-
107	Ben Hinshelwood	Worcester	21	1	-	-
105	Mike Kenworthy	Bracknell	1	8	28	-

MOST PENALTIES

63	Simon Binns	Otley
50	Rob Liley	Wakefield
47	John Fabian	Henley
46	Martyn Davies	Coventry
37	Chris Malone	Exeter
34	Marcus Barrow	Manchester
28	Mike Kenworthy	Bracknell
27	Jon Ufton	London Welsh
24	Lee Hinton	Moseley
22	Richard Davies	Rugby Lions
21	Andy Lee	London Welsh
20	Chris Richards	Rugby Lions
19	Ramiro Pez	Rotherham
17	David Pears	Bracknell

MOST TRIES

25	Chris Garrard	Worcester
21	Ben Hinshelwood	Worcester
16	Duncan Roke	Worcester
16	Richard Baxter	Exeter
15	Nick Baxter	Birmingham & S
14	Kurt Johnson	Coventry
14	Oriol Ripol	Rotherham
13	Michael Wood	Rotherham
13	Alfie Tooala	Rotherham
12	Chris Johnson	Rotherham
12	Phil Read	Rugby Lions
12	James Shanahan	Bedford
11	Pithan Trethewey	Exeter
10	Jon Koloi	Coventry

MOST CONVERSIONS

60	Ramiro Pez	Rotherham
45	Chris Malone	Exeter
42	James Pritchard	Bedford
33	Tony Yapp	Worcester
32	Rob Liley	Wakefield
32	Link Wilfley	Rotherham
30	Simon Binns	Otley
30	Sateki Tuipulotu	Worcester
30	Martyn Davies	Coventry
25	Craig Chalmers	Worcester
24	John Fabian	Henley Hawks
21	John Ufton	London Welsh
18	Chris Richards	Rubgy Lions
18	Dave Knight	Birmingham & S

MOST DROP GOALS

7	Chris Malone	Exeter
6	Rob Liley	Wakefield
4	Mark Meehan	Bedford
3	Jason Keyter	Rotherham
3	Simon Binns	Otley
3	Richard Davies	Rugby
2	James Shanahan	Bedford
2	Greg McDonald	Moseley
1	Tony Yapp	Worcester
1	David Pears	Bracknell

NATIONAL DIVISION 1

FIXTURES 2002-2003

Away Teams

	HOME TEAMS	Bedford	Birmingham & Solihull	Coventry	Exeter	London Welsh	Manchester	Moseley	Orrell	Otley	Plymouth	Rotherham	Rugby Lions	Wakefield	Worcester	
1	Bedford	X	07.12	12.10	29.03	19.04	23.11	31.08	01.03	02.11	11.01	25.01	28.09	14.09	08.02	1
2	Birmingham & Solihull	26.04	X	11.01	01.03	31.08	29.03	14.09	25.01	08.02	28.09	02.11	23.11	12.10	14.12	2
3	Coventry	22.02	07.09	X	01.02	26.10	05.10	15.03	18.01	21.09	16.11	07.12	19.04	12.04	31.08	3
4	Exeter	16.11	26.10	28.09	X	12.04	15.03	07.12	08.02	12.10	19.04	11.01	14.09	31.08	25.01	4
5	London Welsh	14.12	04.01	01.03	23.11	X	26.04	11.01	02.11	29.03	14.09	28.09	08.02	25.01	12.10	5
6	Manchester	12.04	16.11	08.02	02.11	07.12	X	19.04	12.10	01.03	31.08	14.09	25.01	11.01	28.09	6
7	Moseley	04.01	18.01	02.11	26.04	07.09	14.12	X	29.03	23.11	25.01	08.02	12.10	28.09	01.03	7
8	Orrell	26.10	21.09	14.09	05.10	15.03	22.02	16.11	X	01.02	12.04	19.04	31.08	07.12	11.01	8
9	Otley	15.03	05.10	25.01	22.02	16.11	26.10	12.04	28.09	X	07.12	31.08	11.01	19.04	14.09	9
10	Plymouth	07.09	01.02	29.03	14.12	18.01	04.01	21.09	23.11	26.04	X	12.10	01.03	08.02	02.11	10
11	Rotherham	21.09	15.03	26.04	07.09	01.02	18.01	05.10	14.12	04.01	22.02	X	29.03	26.10	23.11	11
12	Rugby Lions	01.0.2	12.04	14.12	18.01	05.10	21.09	22.02	04.01	07.09	26.10	16.11	X	15.03	26.04	12
13	Wakefield	18.01	22.02	23.11	04.01	21.09	07.09	01.02	26.04	14.12	05.10	01.03	02.11	X	29.03	13
14	Worcester	05.10	19.04	04.01	21.09	22.02	01.02	26.10	07.09	18.01	15.03	12.04	07.12	16.11	X	14

BEDFORD BLUES

Chairman Geoff Irvine

Director of Rugby Colin Jackson

Rugby Administrator Tony Mills

Marketing Manager Margaret Hillson

Bedford Blues
Goldington Road
Beford MK40 3NF
Tel: 01234 347980
Fax: 01234 347511

Bedford supporters and players enjoyed a rather unusual phenomena, a season devoid of relegation stress and a sixth place finish was a big improvement on the previous season's nailbiting eleventh. With about half of the previous season's squad being retained the continuity factor played a big part in the club's better fortune.

Director of Rugby Colin Jackson added a quality goalkicker to the squad in Australian, James Pritchard. Whereas in the previous season games were lost through poor kicking, Pritchard quickly became a crowd favourite with his trusty boot. He scored a mammoth 250 points with eight tries, 42 conversions and 42 penalties.

Also a key factor was the early arrival of South African Andre Fox, who did an excellent job coaching the forwards. The pack generally held its own and developed into a strong scrummaging unit with props Chris Horsman, Matthew Volland and John Brooks outstanding.

The player of the year was Frenchman Fred Fichot. He quickly became a crowd favourite and the back row man started in more games than any other player.

The team was very well captained by scrum half Stephen Bell. He lead by example and was consistently one of our better players. Last season's captain and outstanding player, Ben Whetstone, unfortunately injured a knee so badly in the third game that he missed the rest of the season. He was stranded on 99 tries for the club, but we are all looking forward to the new season and his century.

Highlight of the season was the thrilling 36-27 home win over Exeter. A draw and a win over Coventry were also two very creditable performances. The home form was far superior to away and it took until the 26th January for our first away win against Manchester. Some poor performances against lower teams on the table was the most frustrating aspect of the season for players and supporters alike.

Bedford is one of the best supported clubs in Division One and still boasts a terrific following for away games, while the club, very much aware of developing home grown talent, set up an academy two seasons ago. This academy has finally started to pay dividends with two nineteen year olds, Stephen Gray and Andrew Llewellyn, both having debuts in the First Team.

The club is eagerly awaiting the new season and hopes are high that last season's sixth place can be improved upon. Newly appointed fitness coach, Mark Haw from South Africa, has been contracted to raise fitness levels throughout the club.

L-R - Back Row: Ben Williams, Andrew Llewellyn, Michael Ormesher, Cecil du Plessis, Paul Rollason, Andre Fox, John Brooks, Matt Skillecorn, John Haines. **Middle**: Geoff Irvine (chairman), Mark Gray, Ben Reynolds, Mark Sharp, Leigh Mansell, Matt Cook, Phillip Clarke, James Shanahan, Laurence White, Cameron Thomas, James Ross, David Hankinson, Colin Jackson (director of rugby). **Front**: Rob Crowle (team manager), Fred Fichot, James Hinkins, James Pritchard, Mark Meenan, Matt Volland, John Saunders (president), Ben Whetstone, Chris Bajak, Stephen Bell, Henry Whitford, Stephen Gray, Tabo Huntley (fitness coach)

BEDFORD

Comp.	Date	H/A	Opponents	Result & Score	Att	15	14	13	12	11
N1	01-09	A	Rugby Lions*	D 32-32	620	Pritchard/6cp	Dawson/t	Lincoln	Llewellyn(a/t)	Hinkins
N1	08-09	H	Exeter	W 36-27	1323	Pritchard/2t4cp	Dawson/t	Lincoln	Shanahan	Hinkins
N1	15-09	A	Moseley	L 45-46	702	Pritchard/6cp	Bejak	Whetstone/t	Shanahan	Dawson/2t
N1	22-09	H	Manchester	W 21-10	1477	Pritchard/c3p	Dawson	Whetstone	Shanahan/t	Bejak/t
N1	29-09	A	Birmingham & Solihull	D 19-19		Pritchard/c4p	Bejak	Lincoln	Shanahan	Dawson/t
N1	06-10	H	Henley Hawks	W 44-9	1182	Pritchard/2t4cp	Bejak	Jennings	Shanahan/2t	Lincoln/t
N1	20-10	A	Rotherham	L 13-53		Pritchard/cp	Bejak	Jennings	Alatini	Lincoln
N1	10-11	A	Coventry	D 15-15		Pritchard/cp	Bejak	Jennings	Alatini	Lincoln/t
N1	17-11	H	Worcester	L 11-20	1410	Pritchard/2p	Bejak	Jennings	Alatini/t	Lincoln
N1	24-11	H	London Welsh	W 39-27	956	Pritchard/2t3cp	Bejak/3t	Jennings	Alatini	Lincoln
N1	01-12	A	Otley	L 10-26		Pritchard/cp	Bejak	Jennings	Alatini/t	Lincoln
N1	08-12	H	Bracknell	W 27-10	1301	Pritchard/3c2p	Bejak/t	Jennings	Alatini/t	Lincoln
N1	29-12	A	Wakefield	L 6-18	300	Pritchard/2p	Hinkins	Lincoln	Jennings	Dawson
N1	12-01	A	Exeter	L 13-18	1158	Loxton	Bejak/2t	Martin	Lincoln	Pritchard/p
N1	19-01	H	Moseley	W 36-25	1486	Loxton/2t	Bejak	Martin	Lincoln	Pritchard/2c3p
N1	26-01	A	Manchester	W 24-12	550	Loxton	Bejak	Jennings	Lincoln/2t	Pritchard/2p
N1	02-02	H	Birmingham & Solihull	W 23-10	1272	Loxton	Pritchard/c2p	Jennings	Lincoln	Bejak
N1	09-02	A	Henley Hawks	W 37-25	1200	Pritchard/3c2p	Bejak/t	Jennings	Lincoln	Martin
N1	23-02	H	Rotherham	L 31-36	1908	Pritchard/2c4p	Bejak/t	Jennings	Martin	Lincoln
N1	01-03	H	Rugby Lions*	W 25-15	1482	Pritchard/2c2p	Bejak	Jennings	Llewellyn	Lincoln
N1	09-03	A	London Welsh	L 20-26	1300	Pritchard	Lincoln(a/t)	Jennings	Llewellyn	Dawson
N1	16-03	H	Coventry	W 29-24	1732	Meehan/t2c4p	Hinkins/t	Jennings	Llewellyn	Lincoln
N1	30-03	A	Worcester	L 22-46	2296	Meehan/2c	Hinkins/t	Jennings	Llewellyn	Lincoln
N1	06-04	H	Otley	L 17-22	1315	Meehan/c	Hinkins/t	Jennings	Llewellyn	Lincoln
N1	13-04	A	Bracknell	W 41-7		Pritchard/t4cp	Bejak	Jennings	Shanahan/t	Hinkins/t
N1	27-04	H	Wakefield	L 18-22	1601	Pritchard/c2p	Lincoln	Jennings/t	Shanahan	Hinkins
PGC	13-10	H	Wakefield	L 19-22	1071	Pritchard/2p	Bejak/t	Jennings	Shanahan	Dawson

** after opponents name indicates a penalty try. Brackets after a player's name indicates he was replaced. eg (a) means he was replaced by replacement code "a" and so on. / after a player or replacement name is followed by any scores he made - eg /t, /c, /p, /dg or any combination of these*

EVER PRESENT Fred Fichot

Most Appearances:
26: Fred Fichot.
23: Andre Fox (1), Simon Lincoln (1), James Pritchard (1).

PLAYERS USED

34 plus five as replacement only.

MOST POINTS

Pts	Player	T	C	P	DG
239	J Pritchard	7	42	40	-
66	J Shanahan	12	-	-	2
46	M Meehan	2	6	4	4
45	C Bejak	9	-	-	-
40	F Fichot	8	-	-	-

MATCH FACTS

10	9	1	2	3	4	5	6	7	8
Meehan	Bell	Volland	Thomas/t	Ross	Du Plessis(b/t)	Rollason	Clarke	Fox	Fichot
Meehan	Bell/t	Brooks	Thomas	Horsman	Clarke	Du Plessis	Fox	White	Fichot(c/t)
Meehan	Bell/t	Volland	Thomas	Horsman/t	Du Plessis	Clarke	Fox	White	Fichot/t
Meehan	Bell	Brooks	Thomas	Horsman	Clarke	Du Plessis	Whitford	Cook	Fichot
Meehan	Bell	Brooks	Thomas	Horsman	Du Plessis	Clarke	Fox	Whitford	Fichot
Meehan/dg	Bell	Brooks	Thomas	Horsman/t	Du Plessis	Fox	Whitford	Cook	Fichot
Meehan/dg	Bell	Brooks	Thomas	Horsman/t	Rollason	Fox	Whitford	Cook	Fichot
Meehan	Bell	Volland	Thomas	Horsman	Clarke	Fox	Whitford	Cook/t	Fichot
Meehan	Bell	Brooks	Thomas	Horsman	Clarke	Fox	Whitford	Cook	Fichot
Shanahan/t	Bell	Brooks	Thomas	Horsman	Clarke	Fox	Whitford	Cook	Fichot
Shanahan	Williams	Volland	Brooks	Horsman	Clarke	Fox	Whitford	Cook	Fichot
Shanahan/t	Bell	Brooks	Simmonds	Horsman	Clarke	Fox	Whitford	Cook	Fichot
Shanahan	Bell	Volland	Thomas	Horsman	Clarke	Fox	Whitford	Cook	Fichot
Meehan	Bell	Brooks	Thomas	Volland	Clarke	Rollason	Fox	Whitford	Fichot
Meehan/dg(a/t)	Bell	Brooks	Thomas	Volland	Clarke	Rollason/t	Fox	Whitford	Fichot
Hepher/p	Bell	Volland	Thomas	Horsman/t	Rollason	Clarke	Fox	Whitford	Fichot
Hepher	Bell	Volland	Thomas	Horsman	Clarke	Rollason	Fichot/3t	White	Seely
Shanahan/t	Bell	Brooks	Thomas	Horsman	Clarke	Rollason	Fichot	White/t	Seely/2t
Shanahan	Bell	Volland	Thomas	Horsman	Clarke	Rollason	Fichot/t	White	Fox/t
Shanahan	Bell/t	Volland	Thomas	Horsman	Fox	Rollason	Whitford	White(c/t)	Fichot
Meehan/tcdg	Gray	Brooks	Thomas	Horsman	Clarke	Rollason	Fichot/t	White	Fox
Shanahan/dg	Gray	Volland	Thomas	Horsman	Fox	Rollason	Whitford	White	Fichot
Shanahan/dg	Gray	Ross/t	Gunnell	Volland	Fox	Rollason	Whitford	White	Fichot/t
Shanahan/2t	Gray	Volland	Gunnell	Horsman	Clarke	Rollason	Fichot	Cook	Fox
Meehan	Bell	Volland	Thomas/t	Horsman	Quigley	Rollason	Fichot/t	White	Fox/t
Meehan	Bell	Ross	Thomas	Volland	Quigley	Clarke	Fichot	White/t	Fox
Meehan/dg	Bell	Brooks	Thomas	Horsman	Du Plessis	Fox	Whitford/t	Cook	Fichot

REPLACEMENTS: a - James Shanahan. b - Duncan White. c - Matthew Cook.

WHEN	Total	First Half	Second Half	1/4	2/4	3/4	4/4
The POINTS were scored	654	318	336	124	194	140	196
The POINTS were conceded	600	266	334	130	136	170	164
The TRIES were scored	81	34	47	9	25	18	29
The TRIES were conceded	65	29	36	13	16	19	17

HOW the TRIES were scored

Total	Backs	Forwards	F Back	Wing	Centre	H Back	F Row	Lock	B Row	Pen. Try
81	53	26	10	21	12	10	7	2	17	2

HOW the TRIES were conceded

Total	Backs	Forwards	F Back	Wing	Centre	H Back	F Row	Lock	B Row	Pen. Try
65	30	33	5	10	8	7	7	6	20	2

BEDFORD

LEAGUE STATISTICS
compiled by Stephen McCormack

SEASON	Division	P	W	D	L	F	A	Pts Diff	Lge Pts	Lge Pos	Most Points	Most Tries
92-93	2	12	6	2	4	185	186	3	14	7r	75 Andy Finnie	3 Mark Rennell
93-94	3	18	12	0	6	332	260	72	24	3	172 Andy Finnie	8 Vince Turner
94-95	3	18	13	1	4	421	250	172	27	1p	228 Andy Finnie	6 Ben Whetstone
95-96	2	18	5	1	12	289	520	-231	11	10	85 Andy Finnie	8 Matt Oliver
96-97	2	22	15	0	7	720	482	238	30	4	238 Mike Rayer	13 Ben Whetstone
97-98	P2	22	20	0	2	791	365	426	40	1p	289 Mike Rayer	17 Ben Whetstone
98-99	P1	26	6	0	20	541	840	-299	12	13	134 Sam Howard	12 Rory Underwood
99-00	P1	22	1	0	21	396	802	-406	3	12	70 Andy Gomersall	9 Paul Sackey
00-01	N1	26	9	1	16	463	616	-153	47	11	99 Ben Whetstone	9 James Hinkins
01-02	N1	26	12	3	11	654	600	54	68	6	239 James Pritchard	12 James Shanahan

BIGGEST MARGINS

Home Win	55pts - 64-9 v Moseley 2.11.96
Away Win	60pts - 67-7 v Fylde 27.12.97
Home Defeat	94pts - 106-12 v Richmond 16.5.99
Away Defeat	76pts - 0-76 v Bath 13.1.90

MOST CONSECUTIVE

Appearances	46 Paul Alston 19.9.92-12.4.95
Matches scoring Tries	6 Ben Whetstone & Martin Offiah
Matches scoring points	36 Andy Finnie
Victories	18
Defeats	15

MOST POINTS

Scored at Home	72 v Blackheath 22.2.97 & 25.4.98
Scored Away	67 v Fylde 27.12.97
Conceded at Home	106 v Richmond 16.5.99
Conceded Away	76 v Bath 13.1.90

MOST TRIES

Scored in a match	11 v Blackheath 22.2.97
Conceded in a match	16 v Richmond 16.5.99 (H)

MOST APPEARANCES

by a forward	97 Mark Upex
by a back	132 Ben Whetstone

	MOST IN A SEASON	MOST IN A CAREER	MOST IN A MATCH
Points	289 Mike Rayer 97-98	867 Andy Finnie 87-96	25 Andy Finnie v Coventry 27.3.93 (H)
Tries	17 Ben Whetstone 96-97	57 Ben Whetstone 92-02	4 Jason Forsterv Fylde 17.1.98
Conversions	67 Mike Rayer 96-97	127 Mike Rayer 96-98	8 Mike Rayer v Coventry 8.11.97 (H)
Penalties	56 Andy Finnie 94-95	203 Andy Finnie 87-96	7 Andy Finnie v Coventry 27.4.94 (H)
Drop Goals	5 Tony Yapp 98-99	22 Andy Finnie 87-96	2 Andy Finnie v Coventry 27.3.94 (H) v Clifton 14.1.95 (A)

OVERALL PLAYING RECORD

	P	W	D	L	F	A	Pts Diff
Home	31	16	0	15	588	460	128
Away	21	6	0	15	346	400	-54
Neutral	1	1	0	0	28	12	16
Total	53	23	0	30	962	872	90

SEASON BY SEASON

1971-72	2R
1972-73	1R
1973-74	DNQ
1974-75	**Winners**
1975-76	1R
1976-77	QF
1977-78	1R
1978-79	QF
1979-80	2R
1980-81	3R
1981-82	3R
1982-83	4R
1983-84	3R
1984-85	3R
1985-86	2R
1986-87	3R
1987-88	3R
1988-89	3R
1989-90	3R
1990-91	2R
1991-92	3R
1992-93	3R
1993-94	2R
1994-95	4R
1995-96	5R
1996-97	5R
1997-98	4R
1998-99	4R
1999-2000	4R
2000-01	4R
2001-02	3R

BEDFORD RFU SENIOR CUP

STATISTICS

compiled by Stephen McCormack

TEAM RECORDS

Highest Score
76 v Staines 97/98

Biggest Winning Margin
60 (66-6) v Bournemouth 74/75
60 (76-16) v Staines 97/98

Highest Score Against
54 v Saracens 00/01

Biggest Losing Margin
37 (37-0) v Bristol 96/97

INDIVIDUAL RECORDS

Most Points in a match
26 Heinz Pfluger v Staines 97/98

Most Tries in a match
3 Alastair Murdoch v Staines 97/98

Most Conversions in a match
8 Heinz Pfluger v Staines 97/98

Most Penalties in a match
TBA

Most Drop Goals in a match
TBA

EUROPEAN COMPETITIONS

STATISTICS *compiled by Stephen McCormack*

TEAM RECORDS

Highest Score
33 v Rovigo 99/00

Biggest Winning Margin
10 (28-18) v Newport 99/00

Highest Score Against
60 v Castres 99/00 (H)

Biggest Losing Margin
50 (56-6) v Castres 99/00 (A)

INDIVIDUAL RECORDS

Most Points in a match
18 Scott Stewart v Newport 99/00

Most Tries in a match
1 on numerous occasions 99/00

Most Conversions in a match
2 Scott Stewart (2) 99/00

Most Penalties in a match
3 Scott Stewart v Newport 99/00

Most Drop Goals in a match
1 Scott Stewart v Castres 99/00

CAREER RECORDS

Most Appearances:
5: Dan Harris, Roy WInters.

Most Points:
34: Scott Stewart (1t,4c,6p, 1dg)
11: Chris Richards (1c,3p)

Most Tries
2: Alastair McLean, Nick Broughton.

SEASON BY SEASON

1996-97	-	-
1997-98	-	-
1998-99	-	-
1999-00	S	Gp Stage
2000-01	-	-
2001-02	-	-

OVERALL PLAYING RECORD

	P	W	D	L	F	A	Pts Diff
Home	3	1	0	2	63	98	-35
Away	3	1	0	2	58	125	-67
Neutral	-	-	-	-	-	-	-
Total	6	2	0	4	121	223	-102

BEDFORD

FACT FILE

Founded: 1886
Nickname: The Blues
Web Site: www.bedfordrugby.co.uk

Colours: Oxford and Cambridge blue.
Change colours: Cambridge and Oxford blue.

GROUND

Address: Goldington Road, Bedford. MK40 3NF.
Tel: 01234 347980 Fax: 01234 347511 e-mail: info@bedford.rugby.co.uk
Capacity: 6,200 Seated: 800 (covered) 400 (uncovered) Standing: 5,000

Directions: From M1 - J13 onto A421. On edge of Bedford join Southern releif road, signed Cambridge. At r'about at end of relief road, turn left to Bedford Town Centre. Ground approx. 4 miles on right.

From A1 - Join A421 just south of St. Neots. After 8 miles this road takes you on to Goldington Road, into Bedford and ground is on the right.

Nearest Railway Station: Bedford, Midland Road - one mile from the ground.

Car Parking: For hospitality only at ground, but plenty around the ground.

Admission: Match-day admission £15 stand, £10 ground, concessions available
Season Tickets £225 stand, £150 ground, concessions available

Club Shop: Open 9-5 Tues, Wed, Friday & matchdays.

Clubhouse: Open 6.30 - 11pm Tues - Fri and 12.30-11pm on matchdays. Saturday lunches served.

Fred Fichot - Player of the Year - in action

PROGRAMME
Size: A5 Pages: 24
Price: £2.00
Editor: c/o Tony Mills

ADVERTISING RATES
Contact Tony Mills 01234 347980

BIRMINGHAM & SOLIHULL RFC

Chairman	
Club Secretary	Tony Moir
Rugby Administrator	Phil Maynard
Commercial Manager	Rod Williams

All correspondence to:

Birmingham & Solihull RFC
Sharmans Cross Road
Solihull B91 1RQ

Tel. 0121 705 0409
Fax. 0121 705 8253
Website: www.beesrugby.com

The second season for The Bees in National Division One proved to be one of consolidation. Two of the toughest opponents in the league lived up to their reputations in the early part of the season, with Coventry narrowly beating The Bees in their first home fixture, followed by a veritable hammering away the following week to Worcester. However, with that out of the way, the side got to grips with the league and the position of The Bees improved dramatically.

Combined with a strengthening in the league, The Bees turned in a strong performance in the PowerGen Cup. After early successes against Preston Grasshoppers and Henley Hawks, for the second year running The Bees were drawn away at Northampton Saints. Unlike the previous season where the Saints dominated, with 22 minutes to go the scoreline read Saints 12, Bees 19! It took a brace of tries from Saints Ben Cohen, combined with the kicking of Paul Grayson to pull the Saints back from the brink, with the final scoreline reading Saints 32 Bees 19.

Birmingham & Solihull finished 8th in the league, 3 places higher than local rivals, Moseley. Overall, the club was pleased with its performance in the league, showing that the club is worthy of its place in National Divison One. This has provided a base for the future, with the club now laying down plans for future stadium and ground development. Combined with a change of faces in both the coaching and non-playing aspects of the club in the off-season, the future development and growth of Birmingham & Solihull looks bright.

BIRMINGHAM & SOLIHULL

Comp.	Date	H/A	Opponents	Result & Score	Att	15	14	13	12	11
N1	01-09	H	Coventry	L 17-21		Knight/t2cp	Roach	Irwin	Van Deventer	Baxter/t
N1	08-09	A	Worcester	L 3-53	2123	Smallwood	Roach	Van Deventer	Roberts	Baxter
N1	15-09	H	Otley	W 41-16	500	Knight/t5cp	Van Deventer	Irwin/t	Roberts	Baxter/t
N1	22-09	A	Bracknell	W 19-12		Knight/c3p	Smallwood	Irwin	Roberts	Baxter
N1	29-09	H	Bedford	D 19-19		Knight/c4p	Smallwood	Read/t	Roberts	Baxter
N1	06-10	A	Rugby Lions	W 22-6		Knight/2c	Hyslop	Irwin	Roberts	Baxter/2t
N1	20-10	H	Exeter	L 22-26		Knight/t2cp	Smallwood	Minshull	Roberts	Baxter/t
N1	27-10	A	Moseley	W 15-6	717	Knight	Van Deventer/t	Irwin	Roberts	Baxter
N1	10-11	H	Manchester	W 27-8		Knight/c	Van Deventer/t	Irwin	Roberts/t	Baxter/3t
N1	17-11	H	Wakefield	L 18-22		Knight	Van Deventer/t	Irwin	Roberts	Baxter/t
N1	01-12	A	Henley Hawks	W 26-20	300	Knight	Van Deventer/t	Irwin/t	Roberts	Baxter
N1	08-12	H	Rotherham	L 16-56		Knight/t	Van Deventer	Read	Irwin	Baxter/t
N1	29-12	A	London Welsh	L 25-28	930	Knight	Hyslop	Minshull	Roberts(c/t)	Baxter/t
N1	12-01	H	Worcester	L 13-30		Knight	Smallwood/2t	Hyslop	Roberts	Baxter
N1	19-01	A	Otley	L 3-18		Knight	Smallwood	Hyslop	Roberts	Baxter
N1	26-01	H	Bracknell	W 10-3		Knight	Smallwood	Hyslop	Roberts	Baxter/t
N1	02-02	A	Bedford	L 10-23	1272	Knight	Smallwood	Read	Minshull	Baxter
N1	09-02	H	Rugby Lions	W 13-11		Knight	Smallwood	Read	Roberts	Baxter/t
N1	17-02	A	Coventry	L 13-46	924	Knight/t	Smallwood	Hyslop	Minshull	Baxter/t
N1	23-02	A	Exeter	L 10-35	935	Gallagher/tcp	Smallwood	Hyslop	Roberts	Baxter
N1	09-03	H	Moseley	W 14-10		Knight(a/2p)	Hyslop	Read	Minshull	Baxter
N1	16-03	A	Manchester	L 11-16	567	Gallagher/2p	Read	Minshull	Hyslop	Baxter
N1	30-03	A	Wakefield	L 17-26	250	Knight/2c	Smallwood/t	Hyslop/t	Minshull	Baxter
N1	06-04	H	Henley Hawks	W 22-9		Knight/2cp	Smallwood/t	Read(e/t)	Hyslop/t	Baxter
N1	13-04	A	Rotherham	L 0-73	1500	Glackin	Smallwood	Hyslop	Roberts	Baxter
N1	27-04	H	London Welsh	L 26-33	500	Knight/t	Smallwood/t	Hyslop	Roberts	Baxter/t
PGC	13-10	A	Preston Grasshoppers	W 59-15	210	Knight/t4c	Van Deventer	Minshull	Roberts/2t	Baxter
PGC	03-11	H	Wakefield	W 35-6		Knight/t2c2p	Roach	Irwin/2t	Roberts	Baxter
PGC	24-11	H	Henley Hawks*	W 35-22		Knight	Van Deventer	Irwin	Roberts	Baxter
PGC	15-12	A	Northampton Saints	L 19-32	5046	Knight	Hyslop	Read	Minshull	Baxter/t
PGS	24-03	A	Rotherham	L 10-57	2000	Knight	Smallwood/t	Hyslop	Minshull	Baxter

** after opponents name indicates a penalty try. Brackets after a player's name indicates he was replaced. eg (a) means he was replaced by replacement code "a" and so on. / after a player or replacement name is followed by any scores he made - eg /t, /c, /p, /dg or any combination of these*

EVER PRESENT Nick Baxter.

Most Appearances:
26: Nick Baxter.
23: Ed Orgee (1), Dave Knight.
20: Julian Hyde (3).

PLAYERS USED

31 plus eight as a replacement only

MOST POINTS

Pts	Player	T	C	P	DG
102	D Knight	6	18	12	-
75	N Baxter	15	-	-	-
60	M Gallagher	1	5	15	-
34	L Criscuolo	-	5	4	4
30	A Smallwood	6	-	-	-

MATCH FACTS

10	9	1	2	3	4	5	6	7	8
Knight	Cattle	Lewis	Houston	Bullock	Hyde	Underhill	Brookes	Fakatou	Orgee
Knight/p	Cattle	Lewis	Hubbleday	Bullock	Hyde	Fletcher	Salisbury	Fakatou	Orgee
Criscuolo/dg	Knight/t	Lewis	Fortey	Bullock	Fletcher	Underhill	Brookes	Fakatou/t	Orgee
Criscuolo/dg	Knight	Lewis	Fortey	Bullock/t	Hyde	Underhill	Brookes	Fakatou	Orgee
Criscuolo	Cattle	Lewis	Fortey	Bullock	Hyde	Fletcher	Orgee	Fakatou	Brookes
Criscuolo/dg	Knight	Fortey	Hubbleday	Bullock	Hyde	Underhill	Orgee/t	Fakatou	Brookes
Criscuolo	Knight	Fortey	Hubbleday	Bullock	Hyde/t	Fletcher	Orgee	Fakatou	Brookes
Criscuolo/cp	Knight	Lewis	Hubbleday	Bullock	Fletcher	Underhill	Orgee	Jordan	Brookes/t
Criscuolo	Knight	Fortey	Hubbleday	Bullock	Hyde	Underhill	Orgee	Jordan	Fakatou
Criscuolo/c2p	Knight	Lewis	Clark	Fortey	Hyde	Fletcher	Orgee	Jordan	Fakatou
Criscuolo/2c(a/c)	Knight(b/t)	Lewis	Hubbleday	Bullock	Fletcher	Underhill	Orgee/t	Jordan	Fakatou
Gallagher/2p	Cattle	Fortey	Hubbleday	Bullock	Hyde	Fletcher	Orgee	Jordan	Brookes
Gallagher/cp	Cattle	Fortey/t	Hubbleday	Bullock	Hyde/t	Fletcher	Orgee	Jordan	Fakatou
Gallagher/p	Cattle	Lewis	Hubbleday	Bullock	Hyde	Underhill	Orgee	Jordan	Fakatou
Gallagher/p	Cattle	Lewis	Houston	Fortey	Fletcher	Underhill	Orgee	Jordan	Brookes
Criscuolo/c(a/p)	Knight	Lewis	Hubbleday	Fortey	Hyde	Fletcher	Orgee	Jordan	Brookes
Gallagher/cp	Knight	Lewis	Hubbleday	Fortey	Hyde	Underhill	Orgee	Jordan	Brookes(d/t)
Gallagher/c2p	Cattle	Lewis	Houston	Fortey	Hyde	Fletcher	Orgee	Fakatou	Manson-Bishop
Criscuolo/p	Knight	Lewis	Houston	Fortey	Manson-Bishop	Fletcher	Fakatou	Jordan	Brookes
Criscuolo	Cattle	Lewis	Hubbleday	Fortey	Hyde	Underhill	Fakatou	Jordan	Manson-Bishop
Criscuolo/dg	Knight	Fortey	Hubbleday	Bullock	Hyde	Underhill	Orgee	Jordan/t	Hensley
Criscuolo	Cattle	Lewis	Hubbleday	Bullock	Manson-Bishop/t	Underhill	Orgee	Fakatou	Hensley
Gallagher/p	Cattle	Lewis	Hubbleday	Bullock	Hyde	Manson-Bishop	Orgee	Fakatou	Brookes
Knight	Cattle	Lewis	Hubbleday	Bullock	Hyde	Manson-Bishop	Orgee	Brookes	Hensley
Gallagher	Cattle	Fortey	Hubbleday	Bullock	Hyde	Manson-Bishop	Fakatou	Jordan	Hensley
Knight/c3p	Cattle	Fortey	Hubbleday	Bullock	Hyde	Fletcher	Orgee	Jordan	Hensley
Gallagher(f/3c)	Knight/2t	Lewis	Houston/t	Fortey/t	Fletcher	Underhill	Fakatou/2t	Jordan	Orgee
Gallagher/t	Cattle	Lewis	Clark	Fortey	Fletcher	Underhill	Orgee	Jordan/t	Fakatou
Gallagher/3c3p	Cattle/2t	Fortey/t	Clark	Bullock	Hyde	Underhill	Orgee	Fakatou	Brookes
Criscuolo/2p2dg(a/c)	Knight	Lewis	Hubbleday	Bullock	Hyde	Underhill	Orgee	Jordan	Fakatou
Gallagher/cp	Knight	Evans	Hubbleday	Bullock	Manson-Bishop	Hyde	Orgee	Fakatou	Hensley

REPLACEMENTS: a - Matt Gallagher. b - Gavin Cattle. c - Andy Smallwood. d - Rob Salisbury. e - Martin Roberts. f - Luis Criscuolo.

WHEN	Total	First Half	Second Half	1/4	2/4	3/4	4/4
The POINTS were scored	432	258	174	102	141	72	117
The POINTS were conceded	626	320	306	159	161	138	168
The TRIES were scored	52	30	22	15	15	8	14
The TRIES were conceded	63	26	37	13	13	15	22

HOW the TRIES were scored

Total	Backs	Forwards	F Back	Wing	Centre	H Back	F Row	Lock	B Row	Pen. Try
52	41	11	7	25	7	2	2	3	6	-

HOW the TRIES were conceded

Total	Backs	Forwards	F Back	Wing	Centre	H Back	F Row	Lock	B Row	Pen. Try
63	37	26	5	20	6	6	4	3	19	-

BIRMINGHAM & SOLIHULL

LEAGUE STATISTICS
compiled by Stephen McCormack

SEASON	Division	P	W	D	L	F	A	Pts Diff	Lge Pts	Lge Pos		Coach		Captain
92-93	Mid1	13	11	1	1	250	107	143	23	1p				
93-94	D5N	12	5	0	7	128	162	-34	10	9		M Swan		G Smith
94-95	D5N	12	5	0	7	167	226	-59	10	10		N Hurton		S Taylor
												Most Points		**Most Tries**
95-96	D5N	12	8	1	3	202	160	42	17	3	92	Jonathon Smart	3	Richard Packer
96-97	D4N	26	19	0	7	746	391	355	38	2	271	Jonathon Smart	10	David Cox
97-98	N2N	26	23	0	3	805	334	471	46	1p	296	Matt Birch	16	Ben Shepherd
98-99	JN1	26	9	0	17	422	523	101	18	11	170	Matt Birch	6	3 players
99-00	JN1	26	21	1	4	659	346	313	43	2p	166	Jon anthan Smart	14	Paul Lydster
00-01	N1	26	7	5	14	427	481	-54	48	9	176	Steve Gough	6	Chris Budgen
01-02	N1	26	10	1	15	432	626	-194	52	8	102	Dave Knight	15	Nick Baxter

BIGGEST MARGINS

Home Win	46pts - 54-8 v Winnington Park 25.10.97
Away Win	62pts - 72-10 v Aspatria 30.8.97
Home Defeat	47pts - 3-50 v Wakefield 31.10.87
Away Defeat	79pts - 0-79 v Roundhay 26.11.88

MOST POINTS

Scored at Home	55 v Stoke on Trent 21.9.96
Scored Away	72 v Aspatria 30.8.97
Conceded at Home	50 v Wakefield 31.10.87
Conceded Away	79 v Roundhay 26.11.88

MOST CONSECUTIVE

Appearances	
Matches scoring Tries	
Matches scoring points	
Victories	9
Defeats	13

MOST TRIES

Scored in a match	11 v Aspatria 30.8.97
Conceded in a match	? v Roundhay 26.11.88

MOST APPEARANCES

by a forward	**123** (3)	Julian Hyde
by a back	**81** (2)	Ben Shepherd

	MOST IN A SEASON	MOST IN A CAREER	MOST IN A MATCH	
Points	296 Matt Birch 97-98	529 Jonathan Smart 96-00	25 Steve Gough	v Leeds 9.9.00
Tries	16 Ben Shepherd 97-98	31 Ben Shepherd 97-01	4 Steve Chapman	v Hinckley 31.1.98
Conversions	58 Matt Birch 97-98	88 Matt Birch 97-99	7 Matt Birch	v Aspatria 30.8.97
Penalties	55 Matt Birch 97-98	90 Matt Birch 97-99	6 Matt Birch Steve Gough	v Hinckley 8.11.97 v Leeds 9.9.00
Drop Goals	4 Luis Criscuolo 01-02	4 Luis Criscuolo 01-02	1 Luis Criscuolo (4 times) Jonathon Smart (3 times) Steve Gough (twice) Peter Glackin	

OVERALL PLAYING RECORD
(as Birmingham & Solihull)

	P	W	D	L	F	A	Pts Diff
Home	13	11	0	2	297	180	117
Away	10	3	0	7	171	216	-45
Neutral	-	-	-	-	-	-	-
Total	23	14	0	9	468	396	72

From 71-72 until 88-89 the figure on the left shows **Birmingam RFC** and that on the right **Solihull RUFC**

SEASON BY SEASON

Season		
1971-72	1R	DNQ
1972-73	DNQ	DNQ
1973-74	DNQ	DNQ
1974-75	DNQ	1R
1975-76	DNQ	DNQ
1976-77	1R	1R
1977-78	DNQ	DNQ
1978-79	DNQ	DNQ
1979-80	DNQ	DNQ
1980-81	1R	DNQ
1981-82	DNQ	DNQ
1982-83	2R	DNQ
1983-84	DNQ	1R
1984-85	DNQ	DNQ
1985-86	DNQ	DNQ
1986-87	1R	2R
1987-88	DNQ	DNQ
1988-89	DNQ	DNQ
1989-90	DNQ	
1990-91	DNQ	
1991-92	DNQ	
1992-93	DNQ	
1993-94	4R	
1994-95	1R	
1995-96	2R	
1996-97	2R	
1997-98	2R	
1998-99	2R	
99-2000	5R	
2000-01	5R	
2001-02	6R	

BIRMINGHAM & SOLHULL RFU SENIOR CUP
STATISTICS

compiled by Stephen McCormack

TEAM RECORDS

Highest Score
59 v Preston 01/02

Biggest Winning Margin
44 (59-15) v Preston 01/02

Highest Score Against
47 v Northampton 00/01

Biggest Losing Margin
33 v Northampton 01/02

INDIVIDUAL RECORDS

Most Points in a match
TBA

Most Tries in a match
2 on more than one occasion

Most Conversions in a match

Most Penalties in a match

Most Drop Goals in a match

Mudlarks - The Bees' forwards well in control during their February encounter with Exeter.
Photo: Nigel Chanter (01392 467261)

BIRMINGHAM & SOLIHULL

FACT FILE

Founded: 1989 (Birmingham RFC & Solihull RUFC merged)
Nickname: The Bees
Colours: Black & gold with thin red & white bands in top half and on arms
Change colours: Black & white with gold arms and thin red stripe detail

GROUND

Address: Sharmans Cross Road, Solihull.
Tel: 0121 705 0409 email: beesrfc@btinternet.com Web site: www.beesrugby.com
Capacity: 3,000 Seated: None Standing: 3,000

Directions: From Solihull centre take Streetsbrook Road, through the traffic llights, over hump-back bridge. Second left into Sharmans Cross Road and the ground is 300 yards on the left.
Nearest Railway Station: Solihull

Car Parking: Minimal spaces available at the ground.

Admission
Season tickets Adults £100, OAPs £75
Matchday Adults £10, Concessions £6

Clubhouse: Open Sat. 12-11pm, Sun 10-3pm,
Tue & Thur 7-11.30pm.
Snacks and bar meals are available.
Functions: Capacity 150
contact Steve Bakewell 0121 705 7995

Club Shop: Open on match days.

Training Nights: Tuesday and Thursday.

PROGRAMME Size: A5
Pages: 48
Price: Included with entry
Editorial Contact Rod Williams 0121 705 0409
Advertising Rates
Contact Commercial Department 0121 705 0409

COVENTRY FC

President	Brian Holt	Coventry F.C. Ltd., Barkers Butts Lane, Coundon, Coventry CV6 1DU Tel: 02476 601174 Fax: 02476 601194
Chairman	Keith Fairbrother	as above
General Manager	Ian Carvell	as above
Assistant to G.M. / Commercial Manager	Maria Stubbs	as above
New Business Manager	Brian Underwood	as above

A fourth position finish in National Division One was certainly viewed by the club as an improvement on twelve months earlier but even so there was also a feeling of what might have been, given that at times the squad was not blessed with absolute consistency.

Overall though the squad performed well producing some notable results, the absolute highlight being a first ever win at Worcester and a fully merited draw against Exeter at the County Ground. Conversely there was evidence of the very disappointing defeat at subsequently relegated Bracknell and the drawn match at Wakefield, who at the time were seeking a first win of the season.

Player wise, the Bracknell setback also saw the club debut as a replacement of former All Black skipper Zinzan Brooke. It proved to be an inspired piece of recruitment by Chairman Keith Fairbrother, as `Zinnie' quickly became a Coundon Road favourite being named Supporters' Player of the Season. The additional piece of good news for the club came after the season's end when it was announced that Brooke had agreed to another season with the 'Blue & Whites'.

Club skipper for the past season was second row forward Mark Tinnock who made 27 appearances. Top overall of the appearance list was Tongan flanker Jon Koloi, who made a big impression with his powerful running, whilst three players recorded 28 appearances - hooker Trent McMurray on his return after a season away at Birmingham Solihull, prop Rich Siviter and another Tongan Elisi Vunipola at fly half.

Although missing a number of matches with niggling injuries, fullback Martyn Davies again headed the points scoring with 236 in all matches and top try scorer was again winger Kurt Johnson with fifteen in all matches followed by John Koloi twelve and centre threequarter Simon Brocklehurst with ten.

Season 2002/03 will clearly be very competitive again in National Division One not least because of Rotherham's remaining presence, and it should also prove to be a personal landmark for long serving hooker Dave Addleton. At the beginning of the season, Dave will require just seven more games to join the elite band who have made 300 appearances overall for the club.

JOHN BUTLER

Former All Black skipper, Zinzan Brooke seen here breaking from the back of a scrum in the match against Exeter.
'Zinnie" won the Supporters' Player of the Season award.

Photo: Nigel Chanter
Tel: 01392 467261

COVENTRY

Comp.	Date	H/A	Opponents	Result & Score	Att	15	14	13	12	11
N3 N	01-09	A	Birmingham & Solihull	W 21-17		Davies/6p(a/p)	Johnson	Trueman	Martin	Daniel
N3 N	08-09	H	Henley Hawks	W 24-8		Davies/p	Johnson/t	Davies	Curtis	McLean
N3 N	15-09	A	Rotherham	L 9-55		Mitchell/3p	Johnson	Martin	Brocklehurst	Daniel
N3 N	22-09	H	London Welsh	L 19-23	1100	Trueman	Johnson/t	Martin	Davies	McLean
N3 N	29-09	A	Wakefield	D 20-20	350	Mitchell/cp	Johnson	Davies	Curtis	McLean(b/t)
N3 N	06-10	A	Worcester	W 31-22		Davies/2c4p	Johnson/t	Brocklehurst/t	Martin	Trueman
N3 N	20-10	H	Otley	W 47-41	1150	Davies/4c3p	Johnson/t	Brocklehurst/t	Martin	Trueman/t
N3 N	27-10	A	Bracknell	L 8-9	400	Davies/p	Johnson	Brocklehurst	Martin	McLean
N3 N	10-11	H	Bedford	D 15-15		Davies/4p	Johnson	Davies	Curtis	Daniel
N3 N	17-11	A	Rugby Lions	W 27-22	836	Mitchell/c5p	Daniel/t	Brocklehurst	Curtis	Trueman
N3 N	01-12	H	Exeter	W 16-15	2000	Davies/t2p	Johnson	Brocklehurst	Martin	Daniel/t
N3 N	08-12	A	Moseley	W 25-6	726	Davies/2c2p	Johnson/t	Brocklehurst	Curtis	Daniel/t
N3 N	29-12	H	Manchester	W 47-13	1576	Davies/3c2p	Johnson/2t	Brocklehurst/t	Curtis/t	Daniel/t
N3 N	12-01	A	Henley Hawks	W 22-18	700	Davies/c5p	McLean	Brocklehurst	Curtis(c/t)	Worthington
N3 N	19-01	H	Rotherham	L 28-41	4132	Davies/t2c3p	Johnson	Brocklehurst/t	Curtis	McLean
N3 N	26-01	A	London Welsh	L 5-19	700	Davies	Johnson/t	Brocklehurst	Martin	McLean
N3 N	02-02	H	Wakefield	W 37-19	2043	Davies/3c2p	Johnson/2t	Brocklehurst/t	Martin/t	Worthington
N3 N	09-02	H	Worcester	L 26-33	3475	Davies/2c4p	Johnson	Brocklehurst	Martin	Worthington
N3 N	17-02	H	Birmingham & Solihull	W 46-13	924	Davies/4c2p(a/tc)	Johnson	Brocklehurst	Curtis	McLean/t
N3 N	23-02	A	Otley	W 22-11		Davies(a/2cp)	Johnson	Brocklehurst	Martin	McLean
N3 N	09-03	H	Bracknell	W 63-14	1923	Davies/2t4c	Johnson/t	Martin/t	Curtis	McLean/t
N3 N	16-03	A	Bedford	L 24-29	1732	Davies/t2c	Johnson/t	Mitchell	Martin	McLean
N3 N	30-03	H	Rugby Lions	W 47-25	2195	Davies(a/4c3p)	Johnson/t	Brocklehurst	Martin/2t	McLean/t
N3 N	06-04	A	Exeter	D 23-23	952	Davies/2p(a/tc)	Johnson	Brocklehurst	Martin	McLean/t
N3 N	13-04	H	Moseley	W 52-24	2200	Mitchell/t6c	Johnson/t	Brocklehurst	Martin/t	McLean
N3 N	27-04	A	Manchester	W 26-24	674	Davies/c3p	Worthington/t	Brocklehurst/t	Martin	Curtis
PGC	13-10	A	Sedgley Park	W 40-22	550	Davies/2p	Johnson	Brocklehurst/t	Martin/2c	Trueman(f/t)
PGC	03.11	A	Rotherham	L 27-51		Davies/3c2p	Johnson/t	Brocklehurst/t	Curtis/t	Daniel

** after opponents name indicates a penalty try. Brackets after a player's name indicates he was replaced. eg (a) means he was replaced by replacement code "a" and so on. / after a player or replacement name is followed by any scores he made - eg /t, /c, /p, /dg or any combination of these*

EVER PRESENT Jon Koloi.

Most Appearances:
26: Jon Koloi.
23: Kurt Johnson, Elisi Vunipola (1), Mark Tinnock.

PLAYERS USED

30 plus four as replacement only

MOST POINTS

Pts	Player	T	C	P	DG
223	Martyn Davies	5	30	46	-
89	A Mitchell	3	16	14	-
70	K Johnson	14	-	-	-
50	J Koloi	10	-	-	-
35	S Brocklehurst	7	-	-	-
35	E Vunipola	5	5	-	-

MATCH FACTS

10	9	1	2	3	4	5	6	7	8
unipola	Handley	Mika	Addleton	Graham	Hurrell	Tinnock	Crofts	Koloi	Horrobin
unipola/3c	Dawson	Siviter	McMurray	Graham	McGowan	Tinnock	Brady	Koloi/2t	Horrobin
unipola	Dawson	Mika	Addleton	Graham	Tinnock	Hurrell	Brady	Koloi	Horrobin
unipola/t2c	Handley	Mika	McMurray	Graham	McGowan	Tinnock/t	Crofts	Koloi	Horrobin
unipola/t	Dawson	Mika	Addleton	Revan	Tinnock	McGowan	Crofts	Koloi/t	Horrobin
unipola	Handley	Siviter	Addleton	Revan	Hurrell	Tinnock	Crofts	Horrobin	Koloi/t
unipola	Dawson	Mika	Addleton	Revan	Hurrell	Tinnock/t	Brady	Koloi/2t	Horrobin
unipola	Dawson/t	Mika	Addleton	Graham	McGowan	Tinnock	Brady	Koloi	Horrobin
artin/dg	Dawson	Siviter	Addleton	Graham	McGowan	Hurrell	Crofts	Koloi	Horrobin
artin	Handley	Mika	McMurray	Revan	Tinnock/t	Griffiths	Crofts	Koloi	Horrobin
unipola	Dawson	Mika	Addleton	Revan	Griffiths	Tinnock	Horrobin	Koloi	Brooke
unipola	Handley	Hadfield	Addleton	Graham	Griffiths	Tinnock	Horrobin	Koloi/t	Brooke
unipola	Dawson	Siviter	Addleton	Graham	Hurrell	Tinnock	Crofts/t	Koloi	Brooke
unipola	Handley	Mika	McMurray	Graham	Griffiths	Tinnock	Crofts	Koloi	Brooke
unipola	Dawson	Mika	Addleton	Graham	Hurrell	Tinnock/t	Horrobin	Koloi	Brady
unipola	Handley	Siviter	McMurray	Graham	McGowan	Tinnock	Crofts	Koloi	Brady
Mitchell	Handley	Siviter	McMurray	Graham	Hurrell	Tinnock	Crofts/t	Koloi	Brady
Vunipola	Dawson	Mika	Addleton	Graham	Hurrell/t	Tinnock	Brady	Koloi	Horrobin/t
Vunipola	Handley	Mika	Addleton/t	Revan	Hurrell	Crofts/t	Brady/t	Koloi	Brooke/t
Vunipola	Dawson	Siviter(d/t)	McMurray	Graham	Hurrell/t	Crofts	Horrobin	Koloi	Brooke/t
Vunipola/t	Dawson/t	Siviter	Addleton	Revan	Hurrell	Tinnock/t	Crofts/t	Koloi/t	Brooke/t
Vunipola	Dawson	Mika	Addleton	Revan	Hurrell/t	Tinnock	Crofts	Koloi	Brady/t
Vunipola/t	Dawson/t	Siviter	Addleton	Graham	Griffiths	Tinnock	Brady	Koloi	Brooke
Vunipola	Dawson	Mika	Addleton	Revan	McGowan	Tinnock	Crofts	Koloi/t	Brooke
Vunipola/t(e/t)	Dawson	Mika	Addleton	Revan	Crofts/t	Tinnock	Brady/t	Koloi/t	Brooke
Vunipola	Dawson	Mika	Addleton	Revan	Griffiths	Tinnock/t	Koloi	Crofts	Brooke
Vunipola/t	Dawson/t	Siviter	Addleton	Revan	Hurrell	Tinnock	Brady	Koloi/2t	Horrobin
Vunipola	Handley	Siviter	Addleton	Revan	Griffiths	Tinnock	Horrobin	Koloi	Brooke

REPLACEMENTS: a - Allan Mitchell. b - Simon Brocklehurst. c - Simon Martin. d - Mike Mika. e - Martin Worthington. f - Mike Davies.

WHEN	Total	First Half	Second Half	1/4	2/4	3/4	4/4
The POINTS were scored	730	363	367	195	168	176	191
The POINTS were conceded	559	262	297	115	147	125	172
The TRIES were scored	89	41	48	24	17	21	27
The TRIES were conceded	66	28	38	12	16	17	21

HOW the TRIES were scored

Total	Backs	Forwards	F Back	Wing	Centre	H Back	F Row	Lock	B Row	Pen. Try
89	56	33	8	27	13	8	2	11	20	-

HOW the TRIES were conceded

Total	Backs	Forwards	F Back	Wing	Centre	H Back	F Row	Lock	B Row	Pen. Try
66	40	26	9	16	6	9	8	3	15	-

COVENTRY

LEAGUE STATISTICS
compiled by Stephen McCormack

SEASON	Division	P	W	D	L	F	A	Pts Diff	Lge Pts	Lge Pos	Most Points	Most Tries
92-93	2	12	3	0	9	192	236	-44	6	11r	53 Richard Angell	4 Barry Evans
93-94	3	18	14	0	4	406	259	197	28	1p	151 Richard Angell	9 Doug Woodman
94-95	2	18	2	0	16	213	436	-223	4	10r	90 Richard Angell	5 Mark Douglas
95-96	3	18	15	0	3	524	264	260	30	1p	84 Craig Quick	11 Julian Horrobin
96-97	2	22	16	1	5	738	394	344	33	3	236 Jez Harris	17 Andy Smallwood
97-98	P2	22	11	1	10	444	532	-88	23	7	133 Jez Harris	6 Julian Horrobin
98-99	P2	26	14	0	12	662	552	110	34	7	305 Steve Gough	15 Andy Smallwood
99-00	P2	26	15	0	11	714	589	125	30	6	266 Steve Gough	12 Andy Smallwood Kurt Johnson
00-01	N1	26	14	0	12	565	604	-39	66	5	239 Martyn Davies	14 Kurt Johnson
01-02	N1	26	16	3	7	730	559	171	82	4	223 Martyn Davies	14 Kurt Johnson

BIGGEST MARGINS

Home Win	80pts - 102-22 v Nottingham 5.10.96
Away Win	58pts - 61-3 v Rugby 14.9.96
Home Defeat	39pts - 6-45 v Rotherham 15.04.00
Away Defeat	60pts - 8-68 v Leeds Tykes 04.03.01

MOST CONSECUTIVE

Appearances	35 Richard Angell & Warwick Bullock
Matches scoring Tries	4 Andy Smallwood
Matches scoring points	11 Jez Harris
Victories	9
Defeats	13

MOST POINTS

Scored at Home	102 v Nottingham 5.10.96
Scored Away	61 v Rugby 14.9.96
Conceded at Home	45 v Rotherham 15.04.00
Conceded Away	68 v Leeds Tykes 03.04.01

MOST TRIES

Scored in a match	14 v Nottingham 5.10.96
Conceded in a match	12 v Leeds Tykes 03.04.01

MOST APPEARANCES

by a forward	183 (18) Dave Addleton
by a back	123 (5) Andy Smallwood

	MOST IN A SEASON	MOST IN A CAREER	MOST IN A MATCH	
Points	305 SteveGough 98-99	571 Steve Gough 98-00	42 Jez Harris	v Nottingham 5.10.96 (H)
Tries	17 Andy Smallwood 96-97	53 Andy Smallwood 96-01	4 Andy Smallwood	v Wakefield 8.5.99 (H)
Conversions	48 Jez Harris 96-97 Steve Gough 98-99	95 Steve Gough 98-00	13 Jez Harris	v Nottingham 5.10.96 (H)
Penalties	53 Steve Gough 98-99	102 Steve Gough 98-00	7 Steve Gough	v Worcester 11.02.00 (H)
Drop Goals	5 Jez Harris 96-97	10 Mark Lakey 87-95	2 Mark Lakey Jez Harris	v Moseley 3.4.93 (H) v Lon. Irish 8.10.94 (H) v Wakefield 21.9.96 (H)

OVERALL PLAYING RECORD

	P	W	D	L	F	A	Pts Diff
Home	38	25	0	13	841	567	274
Away	38	24	0	14	774	427	347
Neutral	2	2	0	0	53	21	32
Total	78	51	0	27	1668	1015	653

SEASON BY SEASON

Season	Result
1971-72	SF
1972-73	Winners
1973-74	Winners
1974-75	SF
1975-76	2R
1976-77	1R
1977-78	SF
1978-79	2R
1979-80	2R
1980-81	4R
1981-82	SF
1982-83	SF
1983-84	QF
1984-85	SF
1985-86	3R
1986-87	QF
1987-88	4R
1988-89	2R
1989-90	2R
1990-91	3R
1991-92	3R
1992-93	3R
1993-94	4R
1994-95	4R
1995-96	5R
1996-97	6R
1997-98	4R
1998-99	3R
1999-2000	5R
2000-01	4R
2001-02	4R

COVENTRY
RFU SENIOR CUP
STATISTICS
compiled by Stephen McCormack

TEAM RECORDS

Highest Score
83 v Sheffield 97/98

Biggest Winning Margin
62 Pts - 83-19 v Sheffield 97/98

Highest Score Against
51 v Rotherham 01/02

Biggest Losing Margin
38 Pts - 7-45 v Fylde 94/95

INDIVIDUAL RECORDS

Most Points in a match
29 Jez Harris v Kendal 96/97

Most Tries in a match
4 Andy McAdam v Sheffield 97/98

Most Conversions in a match
9 Jez Harris v Kendal 96/97

Most Penalties in a match

Most Drop Goals in a match

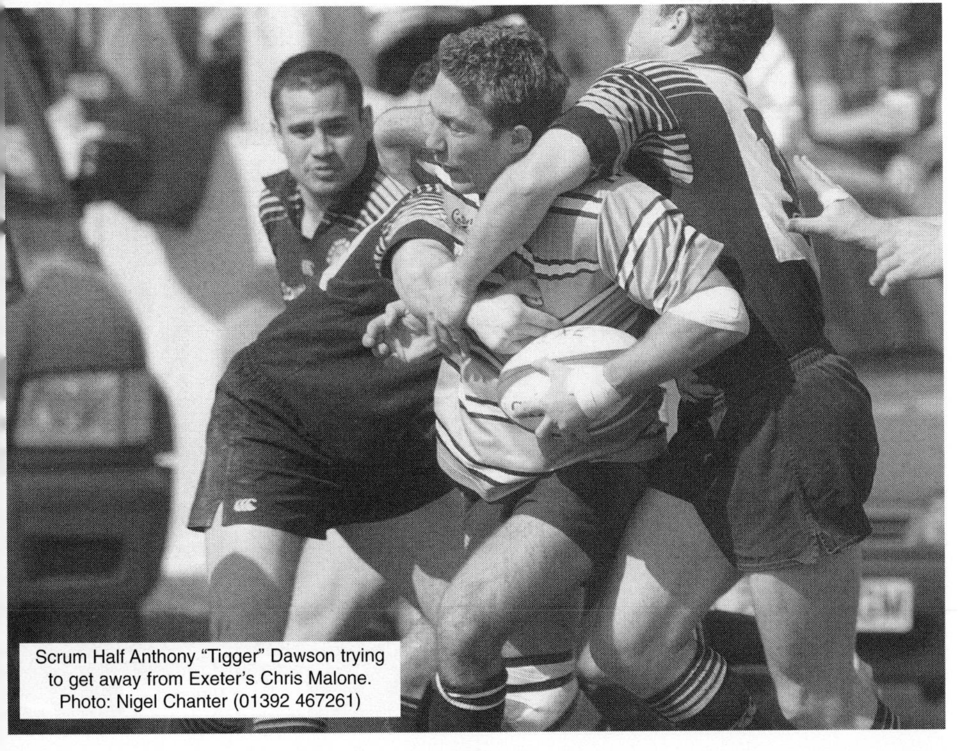

Scrum Half Anthony "Tigger" Dawson trying to get away from Exeter's Chris Malone. Photo: Nigel Chanter (01392 467261)

COVENTRY

FACT FILE

Founded: 1874
Nickname: Cov

Colours: Navy blue with white hoops
Change colours: Red & white

GROUND

Address: Barker Butts Lane, Coundon Road, Coventry. CV6 1DU.
Tel: 02476 601174 Fax: 02476 601194
Capacity: 9,900 Seated: 900 Standing - Covered: 4,000 Uncovered: 5,000

Directions: From ring road take the A414 to Birmingham, turn right at traffic lights and follow road across railway lights. Coming into Coventry on the A45pick up A414 turn left at Hollyhead P.H. right at traffic lights ground on right. Nearest Railway Station: Coventry

Car Parking: None

Admission: Standing/Seated
Season - £90/110 OAPs £55/65 u16 £25/30 17-20 £45/55
Matchday - To be announced

Club Shop: Open matchdays from 1 - 5.30pm.

Clubhouse: Open matchdays Noon - 11pm (except during match) & training eves, Mon & Wed.. Snacks available. Function facilities with a capacity of 200

Training Nights: Tuesday & Thursday

PROGRAMME
Size: A5 Pages: 32 Price: £1.00
Editor: Paul Ingleston

ADVERTISING RATES
Full page £1000 1/2 page £600 1/4 page £400

Sam Viggers

EXETER CHIEFS

President	Dick Manley	
Managing Director	Tony Rowe	
Chairman	Kieron Northcott	
Director of Rugby	Ian Bremner	07710 901809
Press Officer	Neil Devons	01752 691386 (Phone/Fax)
Match Secretary	Roy Huxtable	01392 277385 (H & Fax)
Fixture Secretary	Terry Davies	01803 406566

c/o Exeter RFC,
The County Ground,
Church Road,
Exeter,
Devon EX2 9BQ
Tel: 01392 278759
Fax: 01392 427582
e-mail: exeterrugby@aol.com

A second successive third place in the division once again confirmed Exeter Chiefs' status as the country's leading semi-professional club in a season which added consistency to improving performances.

An early season loss away to Bedford Blues was the only blemish for the opening three months of the season which also saw one of the great upsets of recent years when the Chiefs ambushed Rotherham at Clifton Lane to inflict the only home defeat of the Champions' season.

December saw a change in fortunes with a one-point defeat at Coventry and an unexpected rout at Otley, but the month wasn't a total loss after a thrilling win over Worcester at the County Ground.

The Chiefs were to lose on only three more occasions - away to Worcester, against Rotherham in the season's only home defeat and an unexpected away loss at Henley. Nevertheless, the club improved their away record immensely with no side managing the double over the Chiefs, while the Westcountrymen won home and away against Bracknell, Rugby, Wakefield, Moseley, Manchester, Birmingham/Solihull and London Welsh as well as a hard fought draw against Coventry.

Influential Australian outside half Chris Malone finished as top point scorer for the season before departing for Bath while No.8 Richard Baxter achieved a club record of 16 tries. The long standing club captain, Rob Baxter also achieved the landmark of completing 200 national league appearances for the Chiefs.

The Chiefs also had a memorable cup run with wins over Launceston, London Welsh and Manchester before losing a spirited tie against Leicester at Welford Road. However, qualification for the Powergen Challenge Shield saw a 51-0 semi-final whitewash of Orrell followed by a defeat at Twickenham against Rotherham after leading in the final with only minutes to go.

The 2001/02 season will also be remembered for the 10 Chiefs players who wore England representative shirts in various competitions, for the announcement of an imaginative redevelopment plan for the County Ground aimed at providing a 10,000 capacity stadium within three years and for Exeter Rugby Club being appointed as the administrative headquarters for the RFU's South West Rugby Academy.

EXETER

Comp.	Date	H/A	Opponents	Result & Score	Att	15	14	13	12	11
N1	01-09	H	Bracknell	W 33-30		Howard	Wall	Oliver	Greenaway/2c3p	Trethewey/t
N1	08-09	A	Bedford	L 27-36	1323	Howard	Wall	Oliver	Greenaway/2cp	Trethewey
N1	15-09	H	Rugby Lions*	W 20-15	810	Hill	Wall	Oliver	Greenaway/2c2p	Trethewey
N1	22-09	H	Wakefield	W 39-3	640	Hill/c	Wall	Oliver	Greenaway/t3c2p	Trethewey
N1	29-09	A	Moseley	W 21-6		Hill	Wall	Oliver/t	Greenaway/2p(b/cp)	Trethewey
N1	06-10	H	Manchester	W 16-3	640	Hill	Wall	Oliver	Ward	Trethewey
N1	20-10	A	Birmingham & Solihull	W 26-22		Greenaway	Wall/t	Oliver	Ward	Trethewey
N1	10-11	A	Rotherham	W 19-13		Hill	Wall	Oliver	Ward	Trethewey
N1	17-11	H	London Welsh*	W 52-22	822	Hill	Wall(c/t)	Ward/t	Meinung	Trethewey
N1	01-12	A	Coventry	L 15-16	2000	Hill	Marsden	Ward	Meinung	Trethewey
N1	08-12	H	Worcester	W 21-10	1520	Hill	Wall	Marsden	Ward	Trethewey/
N1	29-12	A	Otley	L 5-26		Hill	Wall	Marsden	Ward/t	Webber
N1	12-01	H	Bedford	W 18-13	1158	Howard	Wall	Marsden	Ward	Kelly
N1	19-01	A	Rugby Lions	W 34-10	420	Howard	Wall	Marsden	Ward	Kelly
N1	26-01	A	Wakefield	W 27-15	300	Howard	Trethewey/t	Marsden	Thompson	Kelly/t
N1	02-02	H	Moseley	W 28-7	750	Howard	Trethewey/t	Marsden	Ward/t	Kelly
N1	16-02	H	Henley Hawks	W 43-23	487	Howard	Trethewey	Marsden	Ward	Kelly(d/t)
N1	23-02	H	Birmingham & Solihull	W 35-10	935	Howard(d/t)	Kelly	Cox/t	Ward	Trethewey/t
N1	02-03	A	Bracknell	W 27-6		Howard	Kelly	Oliver	Ward	Trethewey/t
N1	09-03	A	Henley Hawks	L 19-28	550	Howard/t	Wall	Oliver	Ward	Trethewey/t
N1	16-03	H	Rotherham*	L 23-32	1530	Howard	Kelly	Oliver	Ward	Trethewey
N1	23-03	A	Manchester	W 53-5	250	Howard(c/t)	Wall	Oliver	Ward	Trethewey/t
N1	30-03	A	London Welsh*	W 34-19	1020	Marsden	Wall	Oliver	Ward/t	Trethewey/2
N1	06-04	H	Coventry	D 23-23	952	Marsden	Trethewey	Webber/t	Ward	Wall/t
N1	13-04	A	Worcester	L 17-41	2721	Howard	Trethewey	Oliver	Ward	Kelly
N1	27-04	H	Otley	W 32-14	738	Howard	Wall	Oliver	Ward	Trethewey/t
PGC	13-10	N	Launceston	W 40-26		Hill	Wall/t	Oliver/t	Ward	Trethewey
PGC	03-11	H	London Welsh	W 30-3		Hill	Wall	Oliver/t	Ward/2t	Trethewey
PGC	24-11	A	Manchester	W 30-20	350	Hill	Marsden/t	Ward	Meinung	Trethewey
PGC	15-12	A	Leicester Tigers	L 0-27	5549	Hill	Wall	Marsden	Ward	Trethewey
PGS	20-03	H	Orrell	W 51-0		Howard	Wall	Oliver	Ward/t	Trethewey/t
PGS	20-04	N	Rotherham	L 26-35		Howard	Trethewey	Oliver/t	Ward/t	Wall

** after opponents name indicates a penalty try. Brackets after a player's name indicates he was replaced. eg (a) means he was replaced by replacement code "a" and so on. / after a player or replacement name is followed by any scores he made - eg /t, /c, /p, /dg or any combination of these*

EVER PRESENT One- Richard Baxter.

Most Appearances:
26: Richard Baxter.
25: Rob Baxter, Blair Foote, Stephen Ward.
24: Gary Willis.
23: Pithan Trethewey.

PLAYERS USED

32 plus three as replacement only

MOST POINTS

Pts	Player	T	C	P	DG
247	C Malone	5	45	37	7
80	Richard Baxter	18	-	-	-
55	P Trethewey	11	-	-	-
53	P Greenaway	1	9	10	-
35	R John	7	-	-	-

MATCH FACTS

10	9	1	2	3	4	5	6	7	8
Ward	Sanders	Porte(a/t)	Brooking	Sluman	Reed	Baxter	Willis/t	Foote/t	Baxter
Ward	Sanders	Porte	Clark	Sluman	Reed/t	Baxter	Willis/t	Foote	Baxter/2t
Ward	Sanders/t	Porte	Clark	Sluman	Reed	Baxter	Willis	Foote	Baxter
Ward	John/t	Porte(a/t)	Clark	Sluman	Reed/t	Baxter	Willis	Foote/t	Baxter
Ward	John	Porte	Clark	Sluman/t	Reed	Baxter	Willis	Foote	Baxter
Malone/c3p	John	Porte/t	Clark	Sluman	Reed	Baxter	Willis	Foote	Baxter
Malone/6pdg	Sanders	Porte	Clark	Sluman	Brown	Baxter	Willis	Foote	Baxter
Malone/cp3dg	Sanders	Porte	Brooking	Sluman	Brown	Baxter	Willis	Foote	Baxter/t
Malone/7cdg	Sanders/t	Porte/t	Brooking	Sluman	Brown	Baxter	Willis/t	Foote/t	Baxter
Malone/tcp	John	Porte	Brooking	Sluman/t	Brown	Baxter	Willis	Foote	Baxter
Malone/c3p	John	Porte/t	Brooking	Sluman	Brown	Baxter	Willis	Foote	Baxter
Malone	John	Porte	Clark	Sluman	Brown	Baxter	Brown	Foote	Baxter
Malone/5pdg	Sanders	Hobson	Brooking	Sluman	Brown	Baxter	Willis	Foote	Baxter
Malone/3cp	Sanders/t	Hobson/t	Brooking	Sluman	Brown	Baxter	Willis	Foote	Baxter/3t
Malone/2cp	Sanders	Hobson	Brooking	Sluman	Brown	Baxter	Willis	Foote/t	Baxter/t
Malone/t4c	Sanders	Ozdemir	Brooking	Sluman	Brown	Baxter	Willis/t	Foote	Baxter
Malone/t2c3p	Sanders(e/t)	Ozdemir	Brooking	Sluman	Brown	Baxter	Willis/t	Foote	Baxter/2t
Malone/2c2p	John	Porte/t	Brooking	Sluman	Brown	Baxter	Willis	Hanson	Baxter/t
Malone/2cp	John	Porte	Brooking/t	Ozdemir	Brown	Baxter	Willis	Foote	Baxter/2t
Malone/2c	John/t	Porte	Brooking	Hobson	Harris	Baxter	Willis	Foote	Baxter
Malone/t2c3p	John	Ozdemir	Brooking	Porte	Harris	Baxter	Willis	Foote	Baxter
Malone/5cp	John/t	Ozdemir	Brooking	Sluman/t	Harris(f/t)	Baxter	Willis	Foote/2t	Baxter/t
Malone/3cp	John	Ozdemir	Brooking	Sluman	Harris	Baxter	Willis	Foote	Baxter/t
Malone/2c2pdg	John	Ozdemir	Brooking	Sluman	Harris	Baxter	Willis	Foote	Baxter
Malone/t2cp	Sanders	Ozdemir	Clark	Porte	Brown	Baxter	Kenil	Foote	Baxter/t
Malone/2cp	John/3t	Ozdemir	Brooking	Sluman	Brown	Harris	Willis	Foote	Baxter/t
Malone/2cp(g/t)	Sanders/t	Porte	Clark/t	Sluman	Baxter	Brown	Foote	Willis/t	Baxter/t
Malone/2c2p	Sanders	Porte/t	Clark	Sluman	Reed	Baxter	Willis	Foote	Baxter
Malone/3c3p	Sanders	Porte/t	Brooking	Sluman	Reed	Baxter	Willis	Foote	Baxter/t
Malone	John	Porte	Brooking	Sluman	Brown	Harris	Willis	Foote	Baxter
Malone/5c2p	Sanders(e/t)	Ozdemir	Brooking	Sluman	Harris	Baxter	Willis/t	Foote/t	Baxter/t
Malone/2c3pdg	John	Ozdemir	Brooking	Sluman	Brown	Baxter	Willis	Foote	Baxter

REPLACEMENTS: a - Altan Ozdemir. b - Chris Malone. c - Sean Marsden. d - Chris Wall. e - Richard John. f - Dorian Kenil. g - Philip Greenaway. h - Lee Webber.

WHEN	Total	First Half	Second Half	1/4	2/4	3/4	4/4
The POINTS were scored	707	349	358	178	171	181	177
The POINTS were conceded	448	212	236	99	113	85	151
The TRIES were scored	87	41	46	21	20	23	23
The TRIES were conceded	51	21	30	10	11	10	20

HOW the TRIES were scored

Total	Backs	Forwards	F Back	Wing	Centre	H Back	F Row	Lock	B Row	Pen. Try
87	42	41	3	16	8	15	11	3	27	4

HOW the TRIES were conceded

Total	Backs	Forwards	F Back	Wing	Centre	H Back	F Row	Lock	B Row	Pen. Try
51	37	11	10	15	7	5	1	3	7	3

EXETER CHIEFS

LEAGUE STATISTICS

compiled by Stephen McCormack

SEASON	Division	P	W	D	L	F	A	Pts Diff	Lge Pts	Lge Pos		Most Points		Most Tries
92-93	3	11	8	1	2	247	169	78	17	3	122	Andy Green	5	Andy Maunder
93-94	3	18	9	1	8	308	271	39	19	6	125	Andy Green	5	Andy Maunder
94-95	3	18	3	1	14	153	319	-166	7	10r	35	Ian Stewart	3	Mark Chatterton
95-96	4	18	14	0	4	448	230	218	28	1p	191	Andy Green	8	Andy Maunder
96-97	3	30	25	0	5	923	443	480	50	1p	300	Andy Green	15	Mark Woodman
97-98	P2	22	6	0	16	334	553	-219	12	11	174	John Fabian	6	James Alvis
98-99	P2	26	14	1	11	591	598	-7	29	5	241	Bryan Easson	9	Mark Woodman
99-00	P2	26	19	0	7	742	466	276	38	4	312	Sam Howard	10	Andrew Beattie
00-01	N1	26	14	0	12	677	563	114	71	3	131	Jon Hill	8	Martin Ridley & To'o Vaega
01-02	N1	26	19	1	6	707	448	259	92	3	247	Chris Malone	16	Richard Baxter

BIGGEST MARGINS

Home Win	81pts - 81-0 v W Hartlepool 6.5.00
Away Win	57pts - 60-3 v Clifton 22.3.97
Home Defeat	34pts - 0-34 v Rotherham 22.1.00
Away Defeat	50pts - 13-63 v Leeds Tykes 16.12.00

MOST POINTS

Scored at Home	81 v W Hartlepool 6.5.00
Scored Away	60 v Clifton 22.3.97
Conceded at Home	34 v Rotherham 22.1.00
Conceded Away	63 v Leeds Tykes 16.12.00

MOST CONSECUTIVE

Appearances	88	Andy Maunder 12.9.87- 17.9.94
Matches scoring Tries	3	By six players
Matches scoring points	32	Andy Green
Victories	14	
Defeats	8	

MOST TRIES

Scored in a match	11 v W Hartlepool 6.5.00 (H)
Conceded in a match	10 v Leeds Tykes 16.12.00 (A)

MOST APPEARANCES

by a forward	154 (11) Phil Sluman
by a back	142 (4) Andy Maunder

	MOST IN A SEASON		MOST IN A CAREER		MOST IN A MATCH		
Points	312	Sam Howard 99-00	1085	Andy Green 87-97	31	Sam Howard	v W Hartlepool 6.5.00 (H)
Tries	16	Richard Baxter 01-02	41	Andy Maunder 87-98	4	Simon Dovell John Fabian	v Havant 21.12.96 (H) v Waterloo 17.10.98 (H)
Conversions	58	Andy Green 96-97	140	Andy Green 87-97	10	Sam Howard	v W Hartlepool 6.5.00 (H)
Penalties	54	Sam Howard 99-00	213	Andy Green 87-97	7	Andy Green	v Fylde 5.4.97 (H)
Drop Goals	7	Chris Malone 01-02	22	Andy Green 87-97	2	Andy Green	v Sheffield 23.4.88 (H)

OVERALL PLAYING RECORD

	P	W	D	L	F	A	Pts Diff
Home	30	19	0	11	579	396	183
Away	29	16	0	13	414	501	-87
Neutral	-	-	-	-	-	-	-
Total	59	35	0	24	993	897	96

SEASON BY SEASON

1971-72	2R
1972-73	2R
1973-74	DNQ
1974-75	DNQ
1975-76	DNQ
1976-77	1R
1977-78	2R
1978-79	2R
1979-80	1R
1980-81	4R
1981-82	4R
1982-83	1R
1983-84	DNQ
1984-85	DNQ
1985-86	DNQ
1986-87	2R
1987-88	DNQ
1988-89	3R
1989-90	4R
1990-91	3R
1991-92	2R
1992-93	QF
1993-94	1R
1994-95	QF
1995-96	4R
1996-97	3R
1997-98	4R
1998-99	5R
1999-2000	4R
2000-01	4R
2001-02	5R

EXETER
RFU SENIOR CUP
STATISTICS
compiled by Stephen McCormack

TEAM RECORDS

Highest Score
81 v Whitchurch 98/99

Biggest Winning Margin
70 (81-11) v Whitchurch 98/99

Highest Score Against
76 v Leicester 92/93

Biggest Losing Margin
76 (0-76) v Leicester 92/93

INDIVIDUAL RECORDS

Most Points in a match

Most Tries in a match

Most Conversions in a match

Most Penalties in a match

Most Drop Goals in a match

Steven Ward leads this attack on the Otley defence. Photo courtesy of Nigel Chanter (01392 467261)

EXETER CHIEFS

FACT FILE

Founded: 1872
Nickname: The Chiefs
Web site: exeterchiefs.com

Colours: All black with Cambridge blue trim
Change colours: Cambridge blue/black

GROUND

Address: The County Ground, Church Road, St. Thomas, Exeter. EX2 9BQ.
Tel: 01392 278759 Fax: 01392 427582 e-mail: exeterrugby@aol.com
Capacity: 5,200 Seated: 700 Standing: Covered 500, Uncovered 4,000

Directions: M5 junction 31 follow A377 via A30 to city centre. Continueuntil you reach the turning for B3212 for Moreton Hampstead, turn into CowickStreet, pass under railway bridge. Turn left into Cecil Road at traffic lights, then right into Church Road and into ground
Nearest Railway Station: Exeter(St. Davids), then taxi to ground (appr 2miles)

Car Parking: None at ground.

Admission: Season tickets **Standing** Adults £90, OAPs £75 **Seated** Adults £120, OAPs £110
Matchdays **Standing** Adults £9, OAPs £7 **Seated** £13 (no concessions)
Under 16 admitted free to ground with paying adult/member

Club Shop: Open matchdays & training nights
Manager Angela Abbot 01392 278759.

Clubhouse: Open matchdays 12-11. Training nights 6-11 Snacks and bar meals available
Functions: Capacity 160/60, contact Mr J Davey or Mrs M Boxall

Training Nights: Tuesday and Thursday.

PROGRAMME Size: B6 Pages: 32
Editor: Neil Devons 01752 691386

Advertising Rates
Prices on apllication.
Contact - Eddie Trick,
MPW Limited 01392 424122

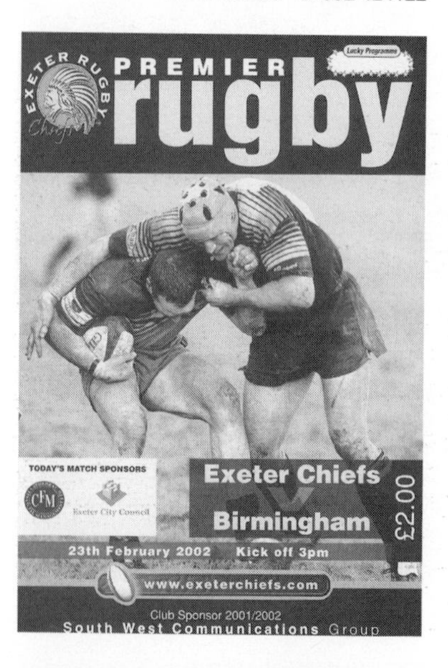

Ian Sanders, Chiefs' scrum half, gets the ball away against Rotherham Photo courtesy of Nigel Chanter

LONDON WELSH RFC

President	S J Dawes OBE
Chairman	David Hammond
Club Secretary	Tudor Roberts
General Manager	Ron Holley
Coach	Adrian Davies
Press Officer	Allan Price
Academy Director	Martin Jones

c/o London Welsh RFC,
Old Deer Park,
Kew Road,
Richmond,
Surrey TW9 2AZ
Tel: 0208 940 2368
Fax: 0208 940 1106

For London Welsh it was a fine season on many fronts. In a year dominated by the professional elites of Rotherham and Worcester, fifth place was a worthy record, while the Druids (the club's second team) won all but one of their 24 games. The Academy played with distinction against top professional clubs in Wales, the Ladies reached the National Cup Final (Southern area) and the social side of London Welsh rugby flourished as never before. With gates up, membership stable and new players flocking to the club, there was a rip roaring spirit at Old Deer Park.

At their best the Welsh were a very good side, playing especially well in hugely competitive and entertaining games at Rotherham and Worcester, and returning with well won bonus points, and there was also a splendid double over Coventry. But for lapses against Moseley (twice) and at Manchester, the Welsh might well have finished fourth themselves. As it was there was still much to admire, with the players responding well to the leadership provided by coach Adrian Davies and captain Matt Fitzgerald, who will both hold the reins agan this season.

John Ufton, who joined the Welsh from Wasps, led the scoring with 136 points in all games, followed by Andy Lee (104). Matt Vines again led the try-scorers, with eight of his ten touchdowns coming in seventeen league games. Prop Steve Pope and flanker Florent Rossigneux won Player of the Year awards. Amongst several honours, winger James Strong, recruited from Newport's Academy, played for Wales at U21 level and Sevens, as well as the Barbarians. Steve Pope, Chris Ritchie and Alex Birkby all played for the National Divisions against the touring Australians and South Africans, and Luke Jones (the former captain who is to retire), Gregg Botterman and Andy Lee were selected by English Counties for the tour of Chile.

All in all a season of genuine progress.

Back row: Richard Elliott, Geraint John, Ed Thorpe, Steve Halsey, Andy Johnson, Paul Carr, Colin Langley, Luke Jones, Morgan Davis, Darren Bowles, Adam Jones, Ken O'Connell, Lee Davies. **Middle**: Adrian Davies (Coaching Director), Al Golding (Fitness), Murray Heckett (Fitness), Steve Pope, Richard Mahony, Richard Griffith, Chad Eagle, Chris Ritchie, David Price, Adam Kelly, Gavin Foreman, John Swords, Nick Huggett, Eirion Morgans (Kit), Nikki Oxford (Physio), Ron Holley (General Manager), Rhian Goodman (Physio), Janice Evans (Admin), Peter Price (Kit), Morlais Evans (Admin). **Front**: Richard Liddington, Alex Birkby, Tom Lewsey, Dave Ramsey, Florent Rossigneux, Matt Fitzgerald, (Captain), Gregg Botterman, Jon Ufton, Adam Bidwell, Matt Vines, Peter Shaw. Absent (10 games or more): Andy Lee, Steve Ravenscroft, James Strong.

LONDON WELSH

Comp.	Date	H/A	Opponents	Result & Score	Att	15	14	13	12	11
N1	01-09	A	Henley Hawks	W 24-9	1150	Vines	Strong/t	Bidwell	Ravenscroft	Green
N1	09-09	H	Rotherham	L 6-28	1200	Mardon	Strong	Bidwell	Ravenscroft	Green
N1	15-09	A	Wakefield	W 21-18	350	Mardon	Strong	Bidwell	Ravenscroft	Shaw
N1	22-09	A	Coventry	W 23-19	1100	Mardon	Strong	Bidwell	Ravenscroft	Shaw
N1	29-09	H	Worcester	L 3-21		Davies	Jones	Bidwell	Ravenscroft	Shaw
N1	06-10	A	Otley	L 9-32		Mardon	Shaw	Bidwell	Davies	Ufton
N1	20-10	H	Bracknell*	W 44-20	730	Vines/t	Strong/t	Bidwell	Lewsey	Shaw
N1	11-11	H	Rugby Lions	W 37-15	730	Vines/3t	Strong	Ufton/4c3p	Lewsey	Shaw
N1	17-11	A	Exeter	L 22-52	822	Vines	Strong	Foreman/t	Lewsey	Shaw/t
N1	24-11	A	Bedford*	L 27-39	956	Vines	Strong	Foreman	Ravenscroft	Ufton/c5p
N1	01-12	H	Moseley*	L 18-29		Vines	Jones	Ufton/c2p	Ravenscroft	Bidwell
N1	08-12	A	Manchester	L 11-12	425	Vines	Shaw	Ufton/2p	Ravenscroft	Foreman
N1	29-12	H	Birmingham & Solihull	W 28-25	930	Vines	Strong/t	Ufton/2c3p	Ravenscroft	Shaw
N1	12-01	A	Rotherham*	L 21-28		Vines	Strong	Clappison	Ravenscroft	Shaw/t
N1	19-01	H	Wakefield	W 16-8	750	Vines(c/t)	Strong	Foreman	Ravenscroft	Shaw
N1	26-01	H	Coventry	W 19-5	700	Ufton/2c	Strong	Foreman	Bidwell/t	Shaw
N1	02-02	A	Worcester	L 6-10		Ufton/2p	Shaw	Foreman	Bidwell	Swords
N1	09-02	H	Otley	W 34-15	650	Ufton/2c	Swords/t	Foreman	Bidwell/2t	Shaw
N1	23-02	A	Bracknell	W 24-22	600	Ufton/c4p	Strong	Bidwell	Ravenscroft	Shaw/t
N1	02-03	H	Henley Hawks	W 33-20	400	Ufton/2p	Strong	Foreman	Ravenscroft	Shaw
N1	09-03	H	Bedford	W 26-20	1300	Vines/t	Strong	John	Ravenscroft	Shaw
N1	16-03	A	Rugby Lions	W 41-20	475	Ufton/2c	Strong/t	John	Bidwell/t	Shaw(h/t)
N1	30-03	H	Exeter*	L 19-34	1020	Ufton/t2c	Strong	John	Bidwell	Shaw(i/t)
N1	06-04	A	Moseley	L 15-17	400	Davies	Foreman	John	Bidwell	Vines/t
N1	13-04	H	Manchester	W 20-13	900	Ufton/cp	John/t	Bidwell	Ravenscroft	Swords
N1	27-04	A	Birmingham & Solihull	W 33-26	500	Ufton/3c3p	Vines/t	John	Ravenscroft	Swords
PGC	13.10	A	London Nigerians	W 43-8	400	Vines/2t	Jones	Ufton	Bidwell/t	Shaw
PGC	03-11	A	Exeter	L 3-30		Vines	Jones	Ufton/p	Bidwell	Shaw

** after opponents name indicates a penalty try. Brackets after a player's name indicates he was replaced. eg (a) means he was replaced by replacement code "a" and so on. / after a player or replacement name is followed by any scores he made - eg /t, /c, /p, /dg or any combination of these*

EVER PRESENT None

Most Appearances:
24: Florent Rossingneux.
23: Paul Carr (2).
22: Stephen Pope.

PLAYERS USED

38 plus six as a replacement only.

MOST POINTS

Pts	Player	T	C	P	DG
133	J Ufton	2	21	27	-
102	A Lee	3	12	21	-
40	M Vines	8	-	-	-
39	R Mahoney	2	4	7	-
30	F Rossinguex	6	-	-	-
25	C Ritchie	5	-	-	-

MATCH FACTS

10	9	1	2	3	4	5	6	7	8
Mahony/c3p(a/p)	Birkby/t	Pope	Ritchie	Brannighan	Eagle	Carr	Griffiths	Rossingneux	Fitzgerald
Mahony(a/2p)	Birkby	Brannighan	Ritchie	Kelly	Eagle	Carr	Griffiths	Rossingneux	Fitzgerald
Clappison/2p(a/cp)	Birkby	Liddington	Ritchie/t	Kelly	Eagle	Carr	Griffiths	Rossingneux/t	Fitzgerald
Lee/2c3p	Lewsey	Pope	Ritchie	Kelly	Langley	Carr	Griffiths	Rossingneux/t	Fitzgerald/t
Lee/p	Lewsey	Pope	Ritchie	Kelly	Eagle	Carr	O'Connell	Rossingneux	Fitzgerald
Lee/3p	Lewsey	Pope	Ritchie	Kelly	Eagle	Carr	Griffiths	Rossingneux	Fitzgerald
Lee/t3c6p	Birkby	Pope	Ritchie	Kelly	Eagle	Carr	Rossingneux	Jones	Griffiths
Davies	Birkby	Pope/t	Ritchie	Kelly	Langley	Carr	Rossingneux	Jones	Ramsey
Davies/2cp	Birkby	Pope	Ritchie	Kelly	Langley	Carr	O'Connell	Rossingneux/t	Ramsey
Davies(b/t)	Birkby	Pope	Ritchie	Liddington	Langley	Carr	Jones	Rossingneux	Ramsey
Lee	Birkby/t	Liddington	Ritchie	Kelly	Eagle	Carr	O'Connell	Rossingneux	Ramsey
Davis(a/t)	Birkby	Pope	Ritchie	Kelly	Eagle	Carr	O'Connell	Rossingneux	Ramsey
Lee/t	Birkby/t	Pope	Ritchie	Kelly	Eagle	Carr	O'Connell	Rossingneux	Ramsey
Lee/3c	Birkby	Pope	Botterman/t	Kelly	Eagle	Johnson	O'Connell	Rossingneux	Ramsey
Lee/c3p	Birkby	Pope	Ritchie	Kelly	Eagle	Johnson	O'Connell	Rossingneux	Ramsey
Lee	Lewsey/t	Pope	Ritchie/t	Liddington	Carr	Johnson	Ramsey	Rossingneux	Fitzgerald
Mahony	Lewsey	Pope	Ritchie	Liddington	Carr	Johnson	Ramsey	Rossingneux	Fitzgerald
Mahony/t	Lewsey	Pope	Ritchie/2t	Liddington	Pain	Carr	Ramsey	Rossingneux	Fitzgerald
Mahony	Lewsey	Pope	Ritchie	Liddington	Johnson(d/t)	Carr	Ramsey	Jones	Fitzgerald
Mahony/t2cp	Birkby	Pope	Botterman(e/t)	Liddington	Carr	Johnson	O'Connell	Rossingneux(f/t)	Fitzgerald/t
Mahony/c3p	Lewsey	Pope	Ritchie(g/t)	Kelly	Eagle	Carr	O'Connell	Rossingneux/t	Fitzgerald
Lee/c	Lewsey	Pope	Botterman/t	Kelly	Eagle	Halsey(d/t)	Jones	Rossingneux/t(f/t)	Fitzgerald
Lee	Lewsey	Pope	Botterman	Kelly	Eagle	Carr	Ramsey	Rossingneux	Fitzgerald
Lee/cp	Lewsey	Liddington	Botterman	Kelly	Eagle	Carr	Thorpe/t	Ramsey	Fitzgerald
Davies/t	Birkby	Pope	Botterman/t	Kelly	Eagle	Carr	Ramsey	Rossingneux	Fitzgerald
Davies/p	Lewsey	Pope	Botterman	Kelly	Eagle	Carr	Griffiths	Rossingneux/t	Fitzgerald/t
Davies/4c	Lewsey	Pope	Botterman	Liddington	Eagle	Johnson/t	Bowles/2t	L Jones	Griffiths/t
Lee	Birkby	Pope	Ritchie	Kelly	Eagle	Carr	Rossingneux	Jones	Griffiths

REPLACEMENTS: a - Andy Lee. b - Tom Lewsey. c - Jon Ufton. d - Ben Pain. e - Chris Ritchie. f - Ed Thorpe. g - Greg Botterman. h - Matt Vines. i - John Swords.

WHEN	Total	First Half	Second Half	1/4	2/4	3/4	4/4
The POINTS were scored	580	301	279	148	153	83	196
The POINTS were conceded	557	285	272	159	126	124	148
The TRIES were scored	65	28	37	14	14	9	28
The TRIES were conceded	69	34	35	19	15	15	20

HOW the TRIES were scored

Total	Backs	Forwards	F Back	Wing	Centre	H Back	F Row	Lock	B Row	Pen. Try
65	36	24	7	13	5	11	10	2	12	5

HOW the TRIES were conceded

Total	Backs	Forwards	F Back	Wing	Centre	H Back	F Row	Lock	B Row	Pen. Try
69	45	21	5	22	12	6	5	7	9	3

LONDON WELSH

LEAGUE STATISTICS
compiled by Stephen McCormack

SEASON	Division	P	W	D	L	F	A	Pts Diff	Lge Pts	Lge Pos	Most Points		Most Tries	
92-93	D4S	12	10	0	2	353	170	183	20		111	Mike hamlin	6	Andy Tucker & Mickey Bell
93-94	D4S	12	5	3	4	216	140	76	13		41	David Shufflebotham	6	Peter Walters
94-95	D4S	12	10	2	0	409	126	283	22		109	Craig Raymond	7	Colin Charvis & David Lubliner
95-96	4	18	12	0	6	424	269	155	24		204	Craig Raymond	9	David Lubliner
96-97	3	30	12	0	18	634	777	-143	24		300	Craig Raymond	13	Tom Lewsey
97-98	N1	26	21	1	4	848	478	370	43		264	Craig Raymond	17	Scott Roskell
98-99	P2	26	17	0	9	662	552	110	34	4	99	Andy Lee	15	Andy Currier
99-00	P2	26	16	0	10	712	476	236	32	5	198	Andy Lee	14	Simon Frost
00-01	N1	26	13	0	13	525	616	-91	64	6	179	Andy Lee	17	Matt Vines
01-02	N1	26	15	0	11	580	557	23	69	5	133	Jon Ufton	8	Matt Vines

BIGGEST MARGINS

Home Win	81pts - 88-7 v Sudbury 25.3.95
Away Win	43pts - 49-6 v Sidcup 16.11.91
Home Defeat	25pts - 3-28 v Lydney 18.11.90
Away Defeat	44pts - 19-63 v Coventry 10.10.98

MOST CONSECUTIVE

Appearances	33 Graeme Peacock
Matches scoring Tries	5 Mickey Bell (x2), Adam Jones & Andy Currier
Matches scoring points	23 Craig Raymond
Victories	10
Defeats	6

MOST POINTS

Scored at Home	88 v Sudbury 25.3.95
Scored Away	49 v Sidcup 16.11.91
Conceded at Home	36 v Exeter 22.2.97
Conceded Away	63 v Coventry 10.10.98

MOST TRIES

Scored in a match	12 v Sudbury 25.3.95 (H)
Conceded in a match	8 v Wharfedale 15.2.97 (A) v Harrogate 1.3.97 (A) v Coventry 10.10.98 (A)

MOST APPEARANCES

by a forward	113 (5) Graeme Peacock
by a back	101 (10) Peter Shaw

	MOST IN A SEASON	MOST IN A CAREER	MOST IN A MATCH	
Points	300 Craig Raymond	916 Craig Raymond 94-99	30 Andy Lee	v Rugby 18.12.99 (H)
Tries	17 Scott Roskell 97-98 Matt Vines 00-01	36 Andy Currier 97-00	4 Mickey Bell David Lubliner Lennie Woodard	v N. Walsham 13.10.90 (H) v Sudbury 25.3.95 (H) v Blackheath 17.4.99 (H)
Conversions	64 Craig Raymond 97-98	160 Craig Raymond 94-98	8 Craig Raymond Andy Lee	v Wharfedale 21.3.98 (H) v Blackheath 17.4.99 (H) v Rugby Lions 18.2.99 (H)
Penalties	57 Craig Raymond 96-97	148 Craig Raymond 94-98	6 Craig Raymond	v Lydney 9.11.96 (H) v Clifton 28.12.96 (H) v Rosslyn Park 18.2.97 (H)
Drop Goals	7 Craig Raymond 96-97	14 Craig Raymond 94-98	2 Craig Raymond	v Exeter 27.4.96 (A) v Liverpool St H 31.8.96 (A)

LONDON WELSH
RFU SENIOR CUP
STATISTICS
compiled by Stephen McCormack

OVERALL PLAYING RECORD

	P	W	D	L	F	A	Pts Diff
Home	40	26	0	14	815	540	275
Away	34	20	0	14	542	468	74
Neutral	1	0	0	1	15	24	-9
Total	75	46	0	29	1372	1032	340

SEASON BY SEASON

Season	Round
1971-72	QF
1972-73	SF
1973-74	1R
1974-75	1R
1975-76	QF
1976-77	SF
1977-78	2R
1978-79	QF
1979-80	2R
1980-81	DNQ
1981-82	4R
1982-83	QF
1983-84	4R
1984-85	Runners -up
1985-86	QF
1986-87	4R
1987-88	3R
1988-89	2R
1989-90	3R
1990-91	3R
1991-92	DNQ
1992-93	3R
1993-94	3R
1994-95	2R
1995-96	4R
1996-97	3R
1997-98	3R
1998-99	4R
1999-2000	QF
2000-01	5R
2001-02	4R

TEAM RECORDS

Highest Score
65 v Clifton 97/98

Biggest Winning Margin
48 Pts - 65-17 v Clifton

Highest Score Against
43 v Headingley 89/90

Biggest Losing Margin
40 Pts - 43-3 v Headingley 89/90

INDIVIDUAL RECORDS

Most Points in a match

Most Tries in a match

Most Conversions in a match

Most Penalties in a match

Most Drop Goals in a match

Matt Fitzgerald, who will stay as captain for the coming season, is seen here powering over for the decisive try in Welsh's 23-19 win at Coventry.

LONDON WELSH

FACT FILE

Founded: 1885
Nickname: The Welsh
Web site: www.london.welsh.co.uk

Colours: Scarlet & black hoops
Change colours: Black

GROUND **Address:** Old Deer Park, Kew Road, Richmond, Surrey TW9 2AZ
Tel: 0208 940 2368 **Fax:** 0208 940 1106 **e-mail:** rugby@lon/welsh.co.uk
Capacity: 4,500 Covered Seating: 1,000 Uncovered Standing: 3,500

Directions: Half mile north of Richmond BR station into Kew Road. Ground on left before Kew Gardens
Nearest Railway Station: Richmond (BR & Underground)

Car Parking: 200, public car park close by.

Admission:
Membership Only: £30
Season Tickets
Ground - Adult £100, OAPs £50,
Family £180 (2 adults & children u16)
Granstand - Adult £100, OAPs £60
Matchday Tickets
£10 - concessions half-price

Club Shop: Yes open matchdays

Clubhouse: Three bars, open during normal licensing hours.
Snacks & bar meals available.
Functions: Capacity 300

Training Nights: Tuesday, Wednesday & Thursday

PROGRAMME Size: A5 Pages: 40 Price: £2
Editor: Paul Beken 0208 643 2456
Advertising - Contact Ron Holley

MANCHESTER RUGBY CLUB

President	Russ Jenkins	**Fixtures Secretary**	Ian Geary (1st & 2nd XV)
Chairman	Alan Hanson	**Press Officer**	Mike Bradley
C.E.O.	Alan Hanson	**Director of Rugby**	Ian Geary
Finance Director	tbc	**Club Manager**	Colin Garner
Secretary	Aileen Scoltock	**Academy Director**	tbc

All correspondence: c/o Manchester Rugby Club, Grove Park, Grove Lane, Cheadle Hulme, Cheshire SK8 7NB
Tel: 0161 485 3733 Fax: 0161 485 1115 e-mail: rugby@manchester-rugby.co.uk

Jekyll and Hyde performances provided Manchester spectators with a season of high points and low points. A fine early season performance in a `friendly' fixture against Premiership neighbours Sale Sharks saw Manchester lose by a closes margin but spectators were filled with great expectations for the season. Early season wins against Bracknell and Rugby Lions fuelled these expectations, but home defeats by Moseley, Henley and Exeter Chiefs brought both players and spectators back to earth. Injuries to first choice players like Danny Collins, Gareth Gerrard and Gary Longhorn did not help Manchester's cause. Exeter Chiefs became Manchester's bogey team by beating them twice in the League and Round Four of the National Cup.

The season ebbed and flowed with Manchester producing some scintillating rugby, but complementing that from time to time with below par performances. After a winter of discontent, Manchester found itself close to the relegation zone but improved performances towards the end of the season augured well for the future.

The club provided no less than five players to the Cheshire side who, at the end of the season, lost the County Championship to Gloucestershire. Manchester also provided Lancashire and the English Counties XV with the try scoring No 8 in Dave Muckalt, Manchester's Captain.

The club continues to go from strength to strength as a traditional rugby club, providing teams from seven years to nineteen years, a Ladies Team and four amateur sides, the top one of which, the Wanderers, just failed to win the Lancashire Plate.

The New Look Manchester Squad for the 2002-2003 season has Ian Geary as Director of Rugby, Dave Baldwin (ex Sale and England) as Head Coach and Jos Baxendell (Sale) as his assistant. New players James Carew (Waikato), David Jessiman (Brisbane), Peter Carpenter (Papakarua), Isaac Richmond (Bay of Plenty), Alex Alesbrook and Steve Perry (Harlequins), Andy Whittle and Steve Davidson (Sale), Liam Wordley and Matt Lewis (U.W.I.C.) along with Ricky Pellow (Worcester) should strengthen the Manchester Team.

MANCHESTER

Comp.	Date	H/A	Opponents	Result & Score	Att	15	14	13	12	11
N1	01-09	A	Worcester	L 11-45		Graham/t	Greenlees	Hughes	Leuila	Lucas
N1	08-09	A	Otley	W 21-8		Graham	Greenlees	Hughes	Leuila	Lucas
N1	15-09	H	Bracknell	W 28-13	750	Graham	Greenlees/4t	Hughes	Leuila	Cooper
N1	22-09	A	Bedford	L 10-21	1477	Graham	Greenlees	Hughes	Leuila	Cooper
N1	29-09	H	Rugby Lions	W 22-14	685	Graham(b/t)	Greenlees	Hughes	Leuila	Cooper
N1	06-10	A	Exeter	L 3-16	640	Barrow	Graham	Hughes	Leuila	Gross
N1	20-10	H	Moseley	L 6-15	465	Graham	Greenlees	Hughes	Leuila	Gross
N1	10-11	A	Birmingham & Solihull	L 8-27		Graham	Gross	Hughes	Leuila	Barrow/p
N1	17-11	H	Henley Hawks	L 25-26	400	Graham	Gross	Hughes	Gregory	Leuila/t
N1	01-12	A	Rotherham	L 10-55		Barrow/cp	Leuila	Hughes	Langhorn	Lomax
N1	08-12	H	London Welsh	W 12-11	425	Barrow/4p	Leuila	Hughes	Langhorn	Lomax
N1	15-12	H	Wakefield	W 27-16	381	Barrow/9p	Leuila	Hughes	Langhorn	Lomax
N1	29-12	A	Coventry	L 13-47	1576	Barrow/c2p	Leuila	Graham	Hughes	Lomax
N1	12-01	H	Otley	W 20-3	485	Barrow/2c2p	Leuila	Hughes	Graham/t	Lomax
N1	19-01	A	Bracknell	W 22-15		Barrow/tc5p	Leuila	Graham	Hughes	Lomax
N1	26-01	H	Bedford	L 12-24	550	Barrow/c	Leuila	Graham	Hughes	Baker
N1	02-02	A	Rugby Lions	L 13-25	300	Barrow/p	Baker	Graham	Hughes	Leuila
N1	16-02	H	Worcester	L 17-62	255	Graham	Mill/t	Smith	Hughes	Baker
N1	23-02	A	Moseley	L 6-32	359	Barrow/2p	Leuila	Gregory	Hughes	Graham
N1	09-03	A	Wakefield	L 10-56	350	Barrow/cp	Baker	Graham	Hughes/t	Leuila
N1	16-03	H	Birmingham & Solihull	W 16-11	567	Barrow/tc3p	Graham	Gerrard	Hughes	Long
N1	23-03	H	Exeter	L 5-53	250	Devlin	Long	Hughes	Gerrard	Graham
N1	30-03	A	Henley Hawks	L 20-45	850	Graham/t	Long/t	Hughes	Gerrard	Cooper
N1	06-04	H	Rotherham	L 7-72	828	Graham	Cooper/t	Hughes	Gerrard(e/c)	Long
N1	13-04	A	London Welsh	L 13-20	900	Barrow/c2p	Cooper	Devlin	Gerrard	Long
N1	27-04	H	Coventry	L 24-26	674	Barrow/3cp	Cooper	Devlin/t	Gerrard	Long/t
PGC	13-10	A	Kendal	W 16-6		Graham	Greenlees	Hughes	Leuila	Gross
PGC	03-11	N	Darlington MP	W 39-27		Graham/2t	Harris/3cp	Hughes/t	Leuila	Barrow
PGC	24-11	H	Exeter	L 20-30	350	Barrow/cp	Gross/t	Hughes	Langhorn/t	Leuila

** after opponents name indicates a penalty try. Brackets after a player's name indicates he was replaced. eg (a) means he was replaced by replacement code "a" and so on. / after a player or replacement name is followed by any scores he made - eg /t, /c, /p, /dg or any combination of these*

EVER PRESENT

None.

Most Appearances:
24: Richard Hughes (1).
21: James Batt, Philip Graham (1), Dave Muckalt (1), Paul White.

PLAYERS USED

41 plus one as a replacement

MOST POINTS

Pts	Player	T	C	P	DG
141	M Barrow	3	12	34	-
37	A Kahn	1	4	8	-
34	L Griffiths	-	2	10	-
30	D Muckalt	6	-	-	-
20	J Greenlees	4	-	-	-

MATCH FACTS

10	9	1	2	3	4	5	6	7	8
Griffiths/p(a/p)	Morris	Batt	Armstrong	Davies	White	Bradshaw	Manley	Morris	Muckalt
Kahn/tc3p	Morris	Batt	Armstrong	Davies	White	Bradshaw	Otuvaka	White	Muckalt/t
Kahn/p	Morris	Batt	Armstrong	Davies	White/t	Bradshaw	Manley	Morris	Muckalt
Kahn/cp	Morris	Batt	Armstrong	Davies	White	Bradshaw	Manley	Morris	Muckalt/t
Griffiths/c5p	Morris	Batt	Armstrong	Davies	White	Bradshaw	Manley	Morris	Muckalt
Kahn/p	Morris	Batt	Armstrong	Davies	White	Bradshaw	Manley	Otuvaka	Muckalt
Griffiths/2p	Baker	Batt	Armstrong	Davies	White	Norris	Manley	Morris	Muckalt
Kahn	Thompson	Batt	Armstrong	Kelly	White	Gunson	Otuvaka	White/t	Muckalt
Kahn/c(c/c2p)	Thompson/t	Batt	Armstrong	Bieniasz	White	Gunson	Otuvaka	White	Muckalt/t
Kahn	Thompson	Kelly	Hewson	Bieniasz	White	Gunson	Otuvaka/t	White	Muckalt
Kahn	Morris(d/t)	Batt	Armstrong	Bieniasz	White	Gunson	Otuvaka	White	Muckalt
Kahn	Thompson	Kelly	Armstrong	Bieniasz	White	Bradshaw	Otuvaka	Morris	Muckalt
Kahn	Morris	Kelly	Armstrong	Bieniasz	White	Gunson	Manley	Morris	Lacey
Kahn	Morris	Batt/t	Armstrong	Bieniasz	White	Bradshaw	Otuvaka	Muckalt	Lacey
Kahn	Morris	Batt	Hewson	Bieniasz	White	Bradshaw	Otuvaka	White	Lacey
Kahn	Morris/t	Batt	Hewson	Bieniasz	White	Bradshaw	Muckalt/t	White	Lacey
Leyden	Thompson/t	Batt	Armstrong	Bieniasz	Norris	Bradshaw	Muckalt/t	White	Lacey
Leyden/tc	Thompson	Kelly	Whitfield	Davies	Lund	Norris	Muckalt	Collins/t	Lacey
Kahn	Thompson	Batt	Whitfield	Davies	Lund	Norris	Muckalt	Collins	Lacey
Kahn	Morris	Batt	Hewson	Davies	White	Norris	Manley	Muckalt	Lacey
Kahn	Baker	Batt	Armstrong	Davies	Norris	White	Morris	Collins	Muckalt
Leyden	Baker	Batt	Armstrong	Davies	Norris	Bradshaw	Morris	Collins/t	White
Kahn/cp	Morris	Batt	Hewson	Davies	White	Norris	Otuvaka/t	Collins	Lacey
Kahn	Morris	Batt	Hewson	Davies	Norris	Bradshaw	Otuvaka	Collins	Lacey
Kahn	Baker	Batt	Hewson	Davies	White	Norris	Lacey/t	Collins	Muckalt
Kahn	Baker	Davies	Hewson	Bieniasz	Norris	White	Lacey	Collins	Muckalt/t
Kahn/2p	Thompson	Batt	Hewson	Davies	White	Bradshaw	Otuvaka	Morris	Muckalt/2t
Kahn/t	Thompson	Batt/t	Armstrong/t	Kelly	White	Norris	Otuvaka	White	Muckalt
Kahn	Thompson	Kelly	Hewson	Bieniasz(f/t)	Norris	Gunson	Otuvaka	White	Muckalt

REPLACEMENTS: a - Andrew Kahn. b - Marcus Barrow. c - Lyndon Griffiths. d - Jimmy Thompson. e - Matthew Leyden. f - Ian Davies

WHEN	Total	First Half	Second Half	1/4	2/4	3/4	4/4
The POINTS were scored	381	192	189	71	121	57	132
The POINTS were conceded	758	378	380	195	183	186	194
The TRIES were scored	37	18	19	5	13	4	15
The TRIES were conceded	102	49	53	26	23	24	29

HOW the TRIES were scored

Total	Backs	Forwards	F Back	Wing	Centre	H Back	F Row	Lock	B Row	Pen. Try
37	23	14	4	10	3	6	1	1	12	-

HOW the TRIES were conceded

Total	Backs	Forwards	F Back	Wing	Centre	H Back	F Row	Lock	B Row	Pen. Try
102	70	31	7	34	21	8	7	7	17	1

MANCHESTER

LEAGUE STATISTICS

compiled by Stephen McCormack

SEASON	Division	P	W	D	L	F	A	Pts Diff	Lge Pts	Lge Pos		Coach		Captain
92-93	N- N2	12	10	0	2	302	103	199	20	1p				
93-94	N- N1	12	8	0	4	208	159	49	16	4				
94-95	N- N1	12	7	3	2	217	166	51	17	3				
95-96	N- N1	12	10	1	1	362	124	238	21	1p				A Hanson
												Most Points		Most Tries
96-97	D4N	26	17	1	8	795	504	291	35	4	251	Steve Swindells	15	Tim Burgon Glen Pearson
97-98	N2N	26	21	2	3	1029	472	557	44	2p	398	Steve Swindells	21	Matt Hoskin
98-99	JN1	26	20	1	5	758	372	386	41	2	365	Steve Swindells	11	Tim Burgon
99-00	P2	26	11	0	15	513	617	-104	22	8	237	Steve Swindells	6	Matt Kirke
00-01	N1	26	12	0	14	471	549	-78	53	8	162	Steve Swindells	7	Stuart Williams
01-02	N1	26	8	0	18	381	758	-377	36	12	141	Marcus Barrow	6	Dave Muckalt

BIGGEST MARGINS

Home Win	89pts - 101-12 v Nuneaton 25.4.98
Away Win	37pts - 56-13 v Hinckley 22.11.97
Home Defeat	65pts - 7-72 v Rotherham 6.04.02
Away Defeat	46pts - 10-56 v Wakefield 9.3.02

MOST CONSECUTIVE

Appearances	
Matches scoring Tries	6 Tim Burgon
Matches scoring points	
Victories	9
Defeats	7

MOST POINTS

Scored at Home	101 v Nuneaton 25.04.98
Scored Away	62 v Aspatria 11.10.97
Conceded at Home	72 v Rotherham6.04.02
Conceded Away	56 v Wakefield 9.3.02

MOST TRIES

Scored in a match	15 v Nuneaton 25.4.98
Conceded in a match	12 v Rotherham 6.4.02

MOST APPEARANCES

by a forward	88(16) Luke Hewson
by a back	109 Steve Swindells

	MOST IN A SEASON	MOST IN A CAREER	MOST IN A MATCH
Points	398 Steve Swindells 97-98	1413 Steve Swindells 96-01	28 Steve Swindells v Hereford 22.3.97 (H)
Tries	21 Matt Hoskin 97-98	46 Tim Burgon 96-01	5 Matt Hoskin v Camberley
Conversions	91 Steve Swindells 97-98	242 Steve Swindells 96-01	10 Steve Swindells v Nuneaton 25.4.98 (H)
Penalties	70 Steve Swindells 98-99	267 Steve Swindells 96-01	9 Marcus Barrow v Wakefield 15.12.01 (H)
Drop Goals	3 Rod Ellis 98-99 & 99-00	6 Rod Ellis 96-00	2 Rod Ellis v Orrell 2.10.99 (H)

OVERALL PLAYING RECORD

	P	W	D	L	F	A	Pts Diff
Home	11	6	0	5	232	202	30
Away	11	8	0	3	282	247	35
Neutral	-	-	-	-	-	-	-
Total	22	14	0	8	514	449	65

SEASON BY SEASON

Season	Result
1971-72	DNQ
1972-73	DNQ
1973-74	DNQ
1974-75	DNQ
1975-76	DNQ
1976-77	DNQ
1977-78	DNQ
1978-79	DNQ
1979-80	DNQ
1980-81	DNQ
1981-82	DNQ
1982-83	DNQ
1983-84	DNQ
1984-85	DNQ
1985-86	DNQ
1986-87	DNQ
1987-88	DNQ
1988-89	DNQ
1989-90	DNQ
1990-91	DNQ
1991-92	4R
1992-93	DNQ
1993-94	DNQ
1994-95	DNQ
1995-96	1R
1996-97	2R
1997-98	4R
1998-99	2R
1999-2000	QF
2000-01	5R
2001-02	5R

MANCHESTER RFU SENIOR CUP

STATISTICS

compiled by Stephen McCormack

TEAM RECORDS

Highest Score
50 v Nottingham 99/00

Biggest Winning Margin
33 (50-17) v Nottingham 99/00

Highest Score Against
62 v Wasps 99/00

Biggest Losing Margin
59 (62-3) v Wasps 99/00

INDIVIDUAL RECORDS

Most Points in a match

Most Tries in a match

Most Conversions in a match

Most Penalties in a match

Most Drop Goals in a match

Photo courtesy of Peter Barton (0161 969 0508)

MANCHESTER

FACT FILE

Founded: 1860

Colours: Red shirt with blue & white pinstripe hoops/blue/red
Change colours: Navy shirt with red & white pinstripe hoops

GROUND

Address: Grove Park, Grove Lane, Cheadle Hulme, Cheshire. SK8 7NB.
Tel: 0161 485 3733 Fax: 0161 485 1115
e-mail: rugby@manchester-rugby.co.uk Website: www.manchester-rugby.co.uk
Capacity: 4,750 Seated: 250 Standing - Covered: 750 Uncovered: 3,750

Directions: Exit Junct. 3 from M60 and head south on A34 (Wilmslow) for 2.5 miles to second roundabout. Exit left (B5095) and club is 400 metres on the right.
From South: M56, Manchester Airport to A34, Wilmslow to B5095, Bramhall, club is about a mile.
Nearest Railway Station: Cheadle Hulme.

Car Parking: 200 spaces available within the ground.

Admission: Match day Members & OAPs £5.00. Non Members £8 u-16: Free
Season Ticket: £80 includes membership or £50 non membership

Club Shop: Yes. Manager - Colin Garner

Clubhouse: Has three bars and food is available. Functions: up to 160 for a seated meal. 0161 485 3733

Training Nights: Tuesday and Thursday 7pm

Marcus Barrow in action.
Photo courtesy of Peter Barton (0161 969 0508)

PROGRAMME

Size: A5
Pages: 48
Price: Free with entry
Editor: Mike Bradley
Advertising Rates- Mono
Special location - Page £250
Page £200 1/2 page £125 1/4 page £70

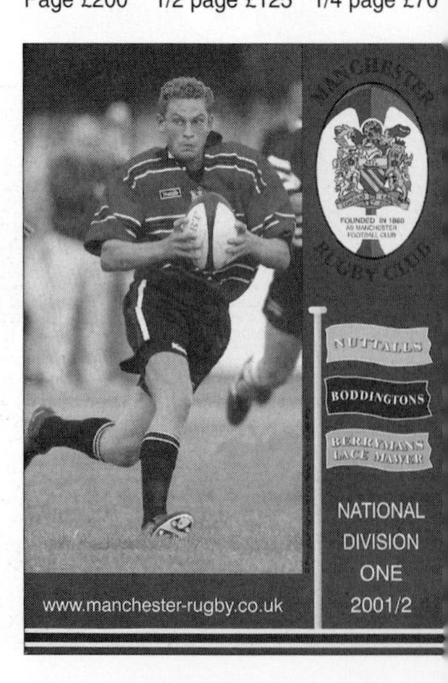

MOSELEY FC

Director	Dave Warren	W 0121 440 3443
Secretary	Tony Kenny	
Chairman of Playing	John Beale	H 0121 608 0858
Subscriptions / International tickets	Mary Bucknall	10 Fittersmill Close, Edgbaston, Birmingham, B5 7QB
Commercial Manager	Greville Edwards	27/29 High Street, Droitwich, Worcestershire, WR9 8RJ 01905 7751

Moseley FC, Charles W Gillett Centre, 998 Bristol Rd., Selly Oak, Birmingham B29 6LE
Tel: 0121 415 2207 Fax: 0121 415 2388 email: moseleyfc@csi.com
Web site: http://uk.geocities.com/moseleyfan

Moseley has found itself (like most 1st Division sides) as a feeder for the Premiership clubs and consequently has lost a number of young professionals over the last three seasons.

The beginning of last season was no different with Scott Beamon and Andy Hall moving to greener pastures and so Moseley's season can be viewed as one of consolidation and frustration.

Moseley beat all but one of the teams outside the top four this season, but only recorded two double wins - against Manchester and London Welsh. Unfortunately Moseley's inconsistency led them to play extremely well against top teams and then lose badly to sides much further down the league.

Hopefully this can be put down to inexperience and as the team matures they will become more consistent in their performances.

On a positive note Moseley's pack developed considerably during the season and became their most potent weapon. This was shown in the try tally and end-of-season awards with hooker Richard Protherough ending the season top try scorer and Player of the Year, with second row Richard Stott being voted Supporters' Player of the Year.

MOSELEY

Comp.	Date	H/A	Opponents	Result & Score	Att	15	14	13	12	11
N3 N	01-09	H	Otley	L 16-39	250	Cook	Hinton/c3p	Eason	Brading	Gregory
N3 N	08-09	A	Bracknell	L 11-20		Cook	Martin	Eason	Binns	Colvin
N3 N	15-09	H	Bedford	W 46-45	702	Hinton/4c6p	Martin	Binns	Brading/t	Colvin
N3 N	22-09	A	Rugby Lions*	L 19-28		Cook	Gray	Eason	Brading	Gregory
N3 N	29-09	H	Exeter	L 6-21		Hinton/2p	Gray	Eason	Brading	Gregory
N3 N	06-10	H	Wakefield	W 31-23		Hinton/2t2c3p	Gregory/t	Cook	Brading	Sleight
N3 N	20-10	A	Manchester	W 15-6	465	Cook	Gregory	Dineen/t	Brading	Colvin
N3 N	27-10	H	Birmingham & Solihull	L 6-15	717	Cook	Gregory	Dineen	Eason	Colvin
N3 N	10-11	A	Henley Hawks	W 29-24		Hinton	Colvin/t	Dineen	Martin	Gregory
N3 N	17-11	H	Rotherham	L 3-47	490	Cook	Colvin	Dineen	Martin	Gregory
N3 N	01-12	A	London Welsh	W 29-18		Hinton/3cp	Gregory/3t	Martin/t	Brading	Colvin
N3 N	08-12	H	Coventry	L 6-25	726	Hinton/p	Colvin	Martin	Brading	Gregory
N3 N	29-12	A	Worcester	L 12-33	3223	Hinton/c	Colvin	Dineen/t	Brading	Gregory
N3 N	12-01	H	Bracknell	W 25-23		Hinton/t2c2p	Martin	Dineen	Cook	Gray
N3 N	19-01	A	Bedford	L 25-36	1486	Hinton(b/cp)	Martin/t	Cook	Brading	Gregory/2t
N3 N	02-02	A	Exeter	L 7-28	750	Dineen	Martin	Cook	Brading	Mousford/t
N3 N	09-02	A	Wakefield	L 15-17	350	Dineen	Colvin	Cook/t	Brading	Martin
N3 N	23-02	H	Manchester	W 32-6	359	Binns/t	Mousford/t	Dineen	Martin/t	Colvin
N3 N	02-03	A	Otley	D 19-19		Binns	Mousford/t	Dineen/t	Martin/t	Colvin
N3 N	09-03	A	Birmingham & Solihull	L 10-14		Binns	Mousford	Dineen/t	Martin	Hinton/cp
N3 N	16-03	H	Henley Hawks	L 21-26	300	Hinton/3c	Colvin	Martin	Cook	Mousford
N3 N	23-03	H	Rugby Lions	W 17-12	150	Hinton/3p(c/dg)	Martin	Dineen	Brading	Mousford
N3 N	30-03	A	Rotherham	L 0-61	2000	Cook	Colvin	Dineen	Binns	Martin
N3 N	06-04	H	London Welsh	W 17-15	400	Cook/t	Colvin	Dineen	Binns	Mousford/t
N3 N	13-04	A	Coventry	L 24-52	2200	Martin/t	Mousford	Dineen	Binns	Colvin
N3 N	27-04	H	Worcester	L 7-42	1529	Martin	Colvin	Brading	Binns	Mousford
PGC	13-10	N	North Walsham	W 25-17	350	Hinton/tp	Sleight	Cook	Brading	Colvin/2t
PGC	03-11	H	Worcester	L 3-50	1200	Cook	Sleight	Gray	Colvin	Gregory

** after opponents name indicates a penalty try. Brackets after a player's name indicates he was replaced. eg (a) means he was replaced by replacement code "a" and so on. / after a player or replacement name is followed by any scores he made - eg /t, /c, /p, /dg or any combination of these*

EVER PRESENT None

Most Appearances:
22: Richard Protherough (3), Richard Stott (2).
20: Richard Ward, Ian Patten (4).

PLAYERS USED

32 plus six as a replacement

MOST POINTS

Pts	Player	T	C	P	DG
126	L Hinton	4	17	24	-
59	G McDonald	-	13	9	2
35	R Protherough	7	-	-	-
30	G Gregory	6	-	-	-
25	R Martin	5	-	-	-

MATCH FACTS

10	9	1	2	3	4	5	6	7	8
Binns	Becconsall	Long	Protherough	Mackinnon	Hadley	Ward	White/t	Renwick	Stott
Hinton/t2p	Powell	Long	Protherough	Sigley	Hadley	Stott	White	Renwick	Hunt
McDOnald	Becconsall	Long	Protherough/t	Sigley	Hadley	Mitchell	White/t	Renwick/t	Patten
McDOnald/2c	Becconsall/t	Long	Protherough	Sigley	Hadley	Mitchell	Evans	Renwick	Patten/t
McDOnald	Becconsall	Sigley	Caves	Sigley	Hadley	Mitchell	White	Renwick	Patten
McDOnald/dg	Powell	Sigley	Protherough	Sigley	Mitchell	Stott	White	Renwick	Patten
McDOnald/cp	Powell	Long	Protherough	Sigley	Stott	Mitchell	White	Evans(a/t)	Patten
Brading	Powell	Long	Protherough	Sigley/2p	Ward	Stott	White	Evans	Patten
McDOnald/c4p	Becconsall	Long	Protherough/t	Sigley	Ward	Stott	White	Hunt	Patten/t
McDOnald/dg	Powell	Long	Caves	Sigley	Ward	Mitchell	White	Hunt	Patten
McDOnald	Powell	Long	Protherough	Buxton	Stott	Ward	White	Hunt	Patten
McDOnald/p	Powell	Long	Protherough	Buxton	Stott	Ward	White	Hunt	Patten
McDOnald	Powell	Long	Protherough	Buxton	Ward	Stott	White	Hunt/t	Evans
McDOnald	Powell	Long	Protherough/t	Buxton	Ward	Stott/t	Hunt	Renwick	Evans
Binns	Powell	Long/t	Protherough	Buxton	Ward	Stott	Hunt	Renwick	Evans
Binns/c	Powell	Long	Protherough	Buxton	Stott	Ward	Hunt	Renwick	Evans
Binns	Powell	Long	Protherough	Buxton	Ward/t	Stott	White	Renwick	Patten/t
McDOnald/3c2p	Powell	Long	Protherough/t	Buxton	Ward	Stott	White	Renwick	Patten
McDOnald/2c	Powell	Long	Protherough	Buxton	Ward	Stott	White	Renwick	Patten
McDOnald	Powell	Long	Caves	Buxton	Ward	Stott	White	Renwick	Patten
Binns	Becconsall	Long	Protherough/3t	Buxton	Stott	Ward	White	Renwick	Patten
Binns	Powell	Sigley	Protherough	Buxton	Stott	Ward	White/t	Renwick	Patten
Nutt	Becconsall	Sigley	Caves	Buxton	Stott	Ward	Hunt	Renwick	Patten
McDOnald/c	Becconsall	Sigley/t	Protherough	Buxton	Ward	Stott	White	Hunt	Patten
McDOnald/2c	Becconsall	Sigley	Protherough	Buxton	Ward	Stott	Renwick/t	Hunt/t	Patten/t
McDOnald(c/c)	Becconsall(d/t)	Sigley	Protherough	Buxton	Stott	Ward	Hunt	Renwick	Patten
McDOnald/c	Powell	Sigley	Protherough/t	Sigley	Stott	Withers	White	Renwick	Patten
Dineen	Becconsall	Long	Caves	Sigley/p	Mitchell	Ward	Stott	Renwick	Hunt

REPLACEMENTS: a - David Hunt. b - Greg McDOnald. c - Stephen Nutt. d - Steve Powell.

WHEN	Total	First Half	Second Half	1/4	2/4	3/4	4/4
The POINTS were scored	448	187	261	117	70	134	127
The POINTS were conceded	695	385	310	157	228	147	163
The TRIES were scored	54	21	33	15	6	17	16
The TRIES were conceded	87	48	39	21	27	17	22

HOW the TRIES were scored

Total	Backs	Forwards	F Back	Wing	Centre	H Back	F Row	Lock	B Row	Pen. Try
54	30	23	6	12	9	3	9	2	12	1

HOW the TRIES were conceded

Total	Backs	Forwards	F Back	Wing	Centre	H Back	F Row	Lock	B Row	Pen. Try
87	53	33	9	21	9	14	8	9	16	1

MOSELEY

LEAGUE STATISTICS
compiled by Stephen McCormack

SEASON	Division	P	W	D	L	F	A	Pts Diff	Lge Pts	Lge Pos	Most Points		Most Tries	
92-93	2	12	6	2	4	184	150	34	14		40	Bob Massey	3	Nick Parry & Bob Massey
93-94	2	18	9	1	8	266	220	46	19		83	Simon Hodgkinson	5	Mark Linett
94-95	2	18	8	1	9	299	303	-4	17		156	Simon Hodgkinson	2	by 6 players
95-96	2	18	7	0	11	327	447	-120	14		172	Alastair Kerr	7	Alastair Kerr
96-97	2	22	9	0	13	492	741	-249	18		177	Richard Le Bas	15	Darragh O'Mahoney
97-98	P2	22	11	1	10	478	421	57	23		178	Matt Jones	17	Darragh O'Mahoney
98-99	P2	26	10	0	16	498	633	-135	20	10	85	Andy Binns	9	Marcus Cook
99-00	P2	26	14	0	12	595	526	69	28	7	116	Owen Doyle	11	Peter Buckton
00-01	N1	26	9	2	15	497	646	-149	47	10	181	Ben Harvey	6	Andy Gray & Rod Martin
01-02	N1	26	9	1	16	448	695	-247	46	11	126	Lee Hinton	7	R Protherough

BIGGEST MARGINS

Home Win	35pts - 44-9 v Fylde 25.4.98
Away Win	29pts - 42-13 v Wakefield 29.03.97
Home Defeat	72pts - 15-87 v Richmond 5.10.96
Away Defeat	69pts - 19-88 v Newcastle 22.3.97

MOST CONSECUTIVE

Appearances	32 Mark Linnett 3.11.92 - 1.10.94
Matches scoring Tries	5 Darragh O'Mahoney
Matches scoring points	11 Carl Arntzen
Victories	5
Defeats	8

MOST POINTS

Scored at Home	48 v Rotherham 26.4.97
Scored Away	46 v Coventry 19.12.98 v Waterloo 09.09.00
Conceded at Home	87 v Richmond 5.10.96
Conceded Away	88 v Newcastle 22.3.97

MOST TRIES

Scored in a match	9 v Sale 4.4.92
Conceded in a match	14 v Richmond 5.10.96 (H) v Newcastle 22.3.97 (A)

MOST APPEARANCES

by a forward	90(17) Neil Mitchell
by a back	111 (4) Rob Martin

	MOST IN A SEASON	MOST IN A CAREER	MOST IN A MATCH	
Points	181 Ben Harvey 00-01	364 Alastair Kerr 91-96	27 Simon Hodgkinson	v Lon. Irish 8.4.95 (H)
Tries	17 Darragh O'Mahoney 97-98	32 Darragh O'Mahoney 95-98	3 Peter Shillingford Dave Spiller Darragh O'Mahoney Peter Buckton R Protherough	v Wasps 5.2.88 (H) v Sale 4.4.92 (H) v Nottingham 2.2.97 (A) v Waterloo 14.2.98 (A) v Fylde 25.4.98 (H) v Coventry 18.03.00 (A) v Henley 16.3.02 (H)
Conversions	27 Richard Le Bas 96-97	38 Alastair Kerr 91-96	6 Richard Le Bas	v Rotherham 26.4.97 (H)
Penalties	41 Simon Hodgkinson 94-95 Ben Harvey 00-01	61 Alastair Kerr 91-96	8 Alastair Kerr	v Waterloo 17.2.96 (H)
Drop Goals	5 Matt Jones 97-98	5 Alastair Kerr 91-96 Matt Jones 97-98	2 Alastair Kerr A Houston Matt Jones	v Plymouth 21.12.92 (H) v Blackheath 14.1.95 v Orrell 25.10.97 (H)

MOSELEY
RFU SENIOR CUP
STATISTICS
compiled by Stephen McCormack

OVERALL PLAYING RECORD

	P	W	D	L	F	A	Pts Diff
Home	42	30	0	12	847	546	301
Away	26	13	0	13	292	373	-81
Neutral	3	0	1	2	30	44	-14
Total	71	43	1	27	1169	963	206

SEASON BY SEASON

1971-72	Runners-up
1972-73	2R
1973-74	2R
1974-75	QF
1975-76	2R
1976-77	QF
1977-78	2R
1978-79	Runners-up
1979-80	2R
1980-81	SF
1981-82	Shared Cup
1982-83	3R
1983-84	4R
1984-85	4R
1985-86	4R
1986-87	QF
1987-88	SF
1988-89	3R
1989-90	SF
1990-91	QF
1991-92	2R
1992-93	QF
1993-94	QF
1994-95	4R
1995-96	4R
1996-97	5R
1997-98	6R
1998-99	4R
1999-2000	4R
2000-01	3R
2001-02	4R

TEAM RECORDS

Highest Score
79 v Liverpool St H 97/98
Biggest Winning Margin
69 Pts - 79-10 v Liverpool St H 97/98
Highest Score Against
41 v Newcastle 99/00
Biggest Losing Margin
34 Pts - 41-8 v Newcastle 99/00

INDIVIDUAL RECORDS

Most Points in a match
24 John Liley v Liverpool St H 97/98
Most Tries in a match
3
Most Conversions in a match
8 John Liley v Liverpool St H 97/98
Most Penalties in a match

Most Drop Goals in a match

Good Moseley defence and cover keeping Exeter at bay.

Photo: Nigel Chanter (01392 46726)

MOSELEY

FACT FILE

Founded: 1873
Nickname: Mose

Colours: Red with black hoops/black/red & black hoops
Change colours: Light grey & navy blue hoops

OFFICE
Address: Moseley FC, Charles W Gillett Centre, 998 Bristol Rd., Selly Oak, Birmingham B29 6LE
Tel: 0121 415 2207 Fax: 0121 415 2388 email: moseleyfc@csi.com

GROUND
Address: The University of Birmingham, Bristol Road, Egbaston, Birmingham B15 2TT
Tel: 0121 449 2149
Capacity: 4,600 Seating: Covered: 600 Standing: Uncovered : 4,000

Directions: From the NW or SE along the M6 - Jct 6 (signed Birmingham Central) to A38 (M). At end of motorway keep to the right, over a flyover, through 3 underpasses to join the A38, Bristol Road.
The University is on the right 2.5 miles from the City Centre.
From the SW - leave M5 at Jct 4 (signed Birmingham SW) to join A38.
The University is on the left of the A38 Bristol Road approx. 8 miles from the motorway.
From the M40 and M42 - it is easiest to turn south on the M42 and leave at Jct 1 to join the A38 and then drive north to the Campus.
Nearest Railway Station: University Station or Main-line: Birmingham New Street,

Car Parking: 1000 spaces (350 covered) at ground

Admission:
Season
Adult £100 Oap's £65 Students £25 Family £150
Matchday
Adult £9 Oap's £6 Students £3 u16 Free

Club Shop: Jan Webster Sports,
University of Birmingham
0121 414 3344

Clubhouse: Normal Licensing hours,
Cafeteria/Restaurant
Functions: Rooms available for hire,
contact Club for details

Training Nights: Tuesday & Thursday

PROGRAMME Size: B4 Pages: 32
Price: £1.50
Editor: Peter Woodroofe
Advertising Rates
Greville Edwards Sports Promotion & Sponsorship

ORRELL RUFC

Chairman	Maurice Lindsay	e-mail: m.lindsay@jjbstadium.co.uk
Finance Director	Nigel Hansford	e-mail: n.hansford@jjbstadium.co.uk
Director of Rugby	Maurice Lindsay	e-mail: m.lindsay@jjbstadium.co.uk
Head Coach	Ross Reynolds	e-mail: r.reynolds@jjbstadium.co.uk
Colts & Juniors	Paul Liptrot	c/o Orrell RUFC
Sales Manager	Adrian Blackburn	e-mail: a.blackburn@jjbstadium.co.uk
Chief Administrator	Wendy Hamer	e-mail: w.hamer@jjbstadium.co.uk

C/o Orrell RUFC, The JJB Stadium, Loire Drive, Wigan. WN5 0UH
Tel: 01942 774000 Fax: 01942 214880

Media Liaison	Geoff Lightfoot Media	01744 603199 (Tel & Fax) 0378 006567 (Mobile) e-mail: gcl@rapid.co.uk

From relegation at the end of the previous season and almost total despair in July, when no more than four players reported for pre-season training, to the euphoria of lifting the National Division Two trophy after a 66-15 victory away at Nottingham in the final match of the season, Orrell are once again ready to reclaim a place in the upper echelons of the game.

With the real possibilty of not having enough players to start the season the Orrell directors decided that something had to be done. Wigan Warriors Chairman Maurice Lindsay and business tycoon David Whelan, the owner of the JJB Sports empire, had already been making noises about forming a rugby union side. Contact was made and the rest is now history but Orrell still had the problem of preparing a side to open their campaign at newly promoted Stourbridge.

Most of the players who had been looking elsewhere were persuaded to stay and Phil Jones, who has just completed his first season in the game by playing for the full England side against the Barbarians at Twickenham, was recruited from the Warriors.

Orrell lost that opening game and although they beat Preston Grasshoppers at Edge Hall Road the following week they went down again away at Newbury. However the management was never less than confident that they could still achieve their target of an immediate return to National One.

Wade Kelly an outstanding centre from Australia, Nick Easter a No 8 from Rosslyn Park, Tonga Lea'aetoa a prop with Super 12 experience and Wes Davies swelled the ranks and Orrell started a winning sequence which was to be broken just once before the end of the season.

Now that they have returned to National One they have gone full time with the Premiership their next target. Most of last season's squad have been re-signed and has been strengthened by the signing of Samoan scrum half Stephen So'oialo, hooker Mike Howe from Newcastle and Steve Barretto a prop from Leinster. Others are expected before the new campaign starts.

Orrell captain and Scotland centre, Andy Craig, with the National Two trophy after the win at Nottingham.

ORRELL

Comp.	Date	H/A	Opponents	Result & Score	Att	15	14	13	12	11
N2	01-09	A	Stourbridge	L 18-21	700	Jones/c2p	Horrocks	Welding	Wynn	Kerfoot/2t
N2	08-09	H	Preston Grasshoppers	W 28-16	800	Welding	Beauchamp	Craig	Wynn/t	Kerfoot/t
N2	15-09	A	Newbury	L 24-26		Welding	Beauchamp	Craig	Wynn/t	Kerfoot
N2	22-09	H	Waterloo	W 51-18		Welding	Beauchamp/t	Craig/t	Kelly/t	Kerfoot
N2	06-10	A	Fylde	W 28-13		Welding	Beauchamp	Craig/t	Kelly	Kerfoot/t
N2	20-10	H	Wharfedale	W 44-16		Davies	Welding/t	Craig/2t	Kelly(a/t)	Kerfoot/t
N2	27-10	A	Sedgley Park	L 12-25		Welding	Beauchamp	Craig	Wynn	Kerfoot
N2	10-11	H	Rosslyn Park	W 25-8		Welding/t2c2p	Yates	Craig	Wynn/t	Kerfoot/t
N2	17-11	A	Kendal	W 41-18		Welding/t	Wynn/t	Craig/2t	Kelly	Kerfoot
N2	01-12	H	Stourbridge	W 43-16	600	Welding/t	Nicholson	Craig	Wynn	Kerfoot/2t
N2	08-12	H	Esher	W 41-7	800	Welding/2cp(b/t)	Wynn/t	Craig	Barrow/t	Kerfoot/3t
N2	29-12	H	Nottingham	W 52-5		Davies/t	Craig	Barrow	Connelly	Kerfoot/t
N2	12-01	H	Kendal	W 29-9		Welding	Davies	Connelly	Kelly/t	Craig
N2	19-01	A	Rosslyn Park	W 31-11		Davies/t	Craig	Connelly/3t	Kelly	Kerfoot
N2	26-01	H	Sedgley Park	W 43-16	1000	Welding/t	Davies/t	Connelly/t	Kelly	Craig
N2	02-02	A	Wharfedale	W 18-8		Welding	Davies/2t	Connelly/t	Kelly	Craig
N2	09-02	H	Fylde	W 46-6	800	Davies/3t	Wynn	Craig/t	Kelly	Kerfoot
N2	16-02	A	Plymouth Albion	W 20-14	2042	Davies	Welding	Connelly	Kelly	Craig/t
N2	23-02	A	Waterloo	W 27-16		Davies	Welding/t	Craig/t	Kelly	Kerfoot
N2	02-03	H	Harrogate	W 40-24	700	Davies/t	Welding	Craig/t	Kelly/2t	Kerfoot
N2	09-03	H	Newbury	W 57-7	700	Welding/t	Wynn	Craig/2t	Kelly/t	Kerfoot/t
N2	16-03	A	Preston Grasshoppers	W 67-8		Davies	Welding/t	Craig/3t	Kelly	Kerfoot/3t
N2	30-03	A	Harrogate	W 29-21	722	Davies/t	Welding	Craig	Kelly	Kerfoot/t
N2	06-04	H	Plymouth Albion	W 37-13	1300	Davies/t	Welding/2t	Craig	Kelly/t	Kerfoot/t
N2	13-04	A	Esher	W 45-12		Davies/t	Welding	Craig/3t	Kelly	Kerfoot
N2	20-04	A	Nottingham	W 66-15	546	Davies/t	Welding/2t8c	Craig/t	Wynn	Kerfoot/t
PGC	29-09	H	Scunthorpe	W 83-8	500	Welding/2t	Beauchamp/2t	Craig/3t	Kelly	Kerfoot/2t
PGC	13-10	A	Rosslyn Park	W 40-32		Davies/2t	Welding	Craig	Kelly	Kerfoot/t
PGC	03-11	H	Fylde	W 37-9		Welding/2cp	Yates	Craig/t	Kelly	Kerfoot/2t
PGC	24-11	A	Newbury	W 30-25		Welding	Newton	Craig/2t	Wynn/t	Kerfoot
PGC	15-12	H	Leeds Tykes	L 22-31	1300	Welding/c4p	Davies	Craig	Connelly/t	Kerfoot
PGS	20-03	A	Exeter	L 0-51		Davies	Riley	Yates	Ince	O'Connor

** after opponents name indicates a penalty try. Brackets after a player's name indicates he was replaced. eg (a) means he was replaced by replacement code "a" and so on. / after a player or replacement name is followed by any scores he made - eg /t, /c, /p, /dg or any combination of these*

EVER PRESENT Chris Bentley.

Most Appearances:
26: Chris Bentley.
25: Andy Craig, Mark Lloyd, Alastair Livesey (1).
23: Charles Cusani, Richard Welding (1).

PLAYERS USED

33 plus three as a replacement

MOST POINTS

Pts	Player	T	C	P	DG
343	P Jones	15	59	50	-
95	A Craig	19	-	-	-
95	N Kerfoot	19	-	-	-
93	R Welding	12	12	3	-
65	W Davies	13	-	-	-

MATCH FACTS

10	9	1	2	3	4	5	6	7	8
Broxson	Wood	Winstanley	Moffatt	Livesey	Bentley	Cusani	Monaghan	Lloyd	Scorvill
Jones/t2c3p	Wood	Winstanley	Moffatt	Livesey	Bentley	Cusani	Riley	Lloyd	Bennett
Jones/tc4p	Wood	Winstanley	Moffatt	Livesey	Bentley	Cusani	Riley	Lloyd	Bennett
Jones/2t5c2p	Broxson	Winstanley	Giles	Livesey/t	Bentley	Cusani	Bennett	Lloyd/t	Monaghan
Jones/t2c3p	Broxson	Winstanley	Moffatt	Livesey	Bentley	Cusani	Bennett	Lloyd	Monaghan
Jones/3cp	Broxson	Livesey/t	Giles	Laa'atoa	Bentley	Cusani	Bennett/t	Lloyd	Easter
Jones/4p	Broxson	Winstanley	Giles	Laa'atoa	Cusani	Bentley	Bennett	Lloyd	Monaghan
Broxson	Newton	Livesey	Moffatt	Laa'atoa	Bentley	Monaghan	Bennett	Lloyd	Easter
Jones/3c5p	Broxson	Livesey	Moffatt	Laa'atoa	Bentley	Cusani	Bennett	Lloyd	Easter
Jones/2c3p	Newton	Livesey/t	Moffatt	Laa'atoa	Bentley	Cusani	Bennett	Lloyd/t	Easter/t
Kelly	Newton	Livesey	Moffatt	Laa'atoa	Bentley	Cusani	Bennett/t	Lloyd	Easter
Broxson/3c2p	Newton	Livesey	Moffatt	Cundick	Bentley	Cusani/t	Bennett/t	Lloyd/2t	Easter/2t
Jones/3cp	Newton	Livesey	Moffatt(c/t)	Laa'atoa	Bentley	Cusani	Bennett/t	Lloyd	Easter/t
Jones/4cp	Wood	Laa'atoa	Giles	Cundick	Bentley	Cusani	Monaghan	Lloyd	Easter
Jones/2t5cp	Wood	Livesey	Moffatt	Laa'atoa	Bentley	Cusani	Bennett	Lloyd/t	Easter
Jones/p	Wood	Livesey	Moffatt	Laa'atoa	Bentley	Cusani	Bennett	Lloyd	Easter
Jones/3t4cp	Wood	Livesey	Livesey	Laa'atoa	Bentley	Cusani	Bennett	Carroll	Easter
Jones/tcp	Wood	Livesey	Moffatt(d/t)	Laa'atoa	Bentley	Cusani	Bennett	Lloyd	Easter
Jones/c5p	Wood	Livesey	Pearson	Laa'atoa	Bentley	Cusani	Carroll	Lloyd	Easter
Jones/3c3p	Wood	Livesey	Moffatt	Laa'atoa	Bentley	Cusani	Monaghan	Lloyd	Easter/t
Jones/t6c	Newton/t	Livesey	Moffatt	Laa'atoa	Bentley	Cusani	Monaghan	Lloyd/t	Easter/t
Jones/2t6c	Newton	Livesey	Pearson/t	Laa'atoa	Bentley	Cusani	Monaghan	Lloyd	Easter/t
Jones/c4p	Wood	Livesey	Moffatt	Laa'atoa	Bentley	Cusani	Bennett	Lloyd	Easter/t
Jones/3c2p	Newton	Livesey	Pearson	O'Connor	Bentley	Monaghan	Bennett	Lloyd	Easter
Jones/t3c3p	Wood	Livesey	Pearson	O'Connor	Bentley	Monaghan	Riley(e/t)	Lloyd	Bennett
Kelly/2t	Wood	Livesey/t	Pearson/t	Giles	Bentley	Cusani	Bennett	Lloyd/t	Monaghan
Jones/2t10cp	Broxson	Winstanley	Giles	Livesey	Bentley	Cusani(e/t)	Carroll	Lloyd	Monaghan
Jones/t3c3p	Broxson	Winstanley	Giles	Laa'atoa	Bentley	Cusani	Bennett/t	Carroll	Monaghan
Broxson/t	Newton	Livesey/t	Moffatt	Laa'atoa	Bentley	Cusani/t	Bennett	Lloyd	Monaghan
Jones/2c2p	Broxson	Winstanley	Moffatt	Laa'atoa	Bentley	Cusani	Bennett/t	Carroll	Monaghan
Broxson/dg	Newton	Livesey	Moffatt	Laa'atoa	Bentley	Cusani	Bennett	Lloyd	Monaghan
Pearson	Kelly	Kendrick	Kerfoot	Millachip	Newton	Nicholson	Barrow	Verbickas	Carroll

REPLACEMENTS: a - Paul Newton. b - John Broxson. c - David Giles. d - Chris Pearson. e - Anton Cramant

WHERE	Total	Home	Away
The POINTS were scored	962	536	426
The POINTS were conceded	369	208	161
The TRIES were scored	129	76	53
The TRIES were conceded	36	21	15

HOW the TRIES were scored

Total	Backs	Forwards	F Back	Wing	Centre	H Back	F Row	Lock	B Row	Pen. Try
129	100	29	15	34	33	18	8	1	20	-

HOW the TRIES were conceded

Total	Backs	Forwards	F Back	Wing	Centre	H Back	F Row	Lock	B Row	Pen. Try
36	28	7	4	9	11	4	1	3	3	1

ORRELL

LEAGUE STATISTICS

compiled by Stephen McCormack

SEASON	Division	P	W	D	L	F	A	Pts Diff	Lge Pts	Lge Pos	Most Points		Most Tries	
92-93	1	12	5	0	7	175	183	-8	10		63	Gerry Ainscough	6	Dewi Morris
93-94	1	18	8	0	10	327	302	25	16		84	Simon Langford	8	James Naylor
94-95	1	18	6	3	9	256	326	-70	15		81	Simon Langford	7	Ian Wynn
95-96	1	18	7	0	11	323	477	-154	14		166	Simon Mason	10	Graeme Smith
96-97	1	22	3	0	19	352	886	-534	6		116	Matthew McCarthy	5	Jim Naylor
97-98	P2	22	12	0	10	533	400	133	24		165	Simon Verbickas	12	Simon Verbickas
98-99	P2	26	12	0	14	566	483	83	24	8	224	SimonVerbickas	13	Simon Verbickas
99-00	P2	26	7	0	19	388	682	-294	14	11	146	David Sleman	7	Rob Hitchmough & Alex Bennett
00-01	N1	26	8	1	17	437	661	-224	46	13r	179	David Sleman	9	Andy Craig
01-02	N2	26	23	0	3	962	369	593	46	1p	343	Phil Jones	19	Andy Craig & Neil Kerfoot

MOST POINTS

Scored at Home	66 v Rugby 13.3.93
Scored Away	67 v Preston 16.3.02
Conceded at Home	56 v Bath 31.8.96 v Harlequins 8.3.97
Conceded Away	89 v Harlequins 5.10.96

MOST CONSECUTIVE

Appearances	39 David Southern 26.9.87 - 17.11.90
Matches scoring Tries	4 Neil Kerfoot, Andy Craig, Wes Davies & Nick Easter
Matches scoring points	17 Martin Strett
Victories	19
Defeats	11

BIGGEST MARGINS

Home Win	66pts - 66-0 v Rugby 13.3.93
Away Win	59pts - 67-8 v Preston 16.3.02
Home Defeat	43pts - 13-56 v Bath 31.8.96
Away Defeat	71pts - 18-89 v Harlequins 5.10.96

MOST TRIES

Scored in a match	11	v Rugby 13.3.93 (H) v Northampton 27.10.90 (H) v Rosslyn P. 28.4.90 (H)
Conceded in a match	14	v Harlequins 5.10.96 (A)

MOST APPEARANCES

by a forward	151 (2) Charles Cusani
by a back	96 (5) SteveTabener

	MOST IN A SEASON		MOST IN A CAREER		MOST IN A MATCH		
Points	343	Phil Jones 01-02	389	Simon Verbickas 97-99	29	Simon Verbickas	v Wakefield 25.4.98 (H)
Tries	19	Andy Craig 01-02 Neil Kerfoot 01/02	28	Andy Craig 00-02	4	Paul Hamer	v Rugby 13.3.94 (H)
Conversions	59	Phil Jones 01-02	59	Phil Jones 01-02	8	Martin Strett Richard Welding	v Rosslyn P. 28.4.90 (H) v Nottingham 20.4.02 (A)
Penalties	50	Phil Jones 01-02	71	Gerry Ainscough 87-95	6	Martin Strett Matthew McCarthy	v Gloucester 28.3.92 (H) v Lon. Irish 22.2.97 (H)
Drop Goals	9	David Sleman 96-97	13	David Sleman 99-01	3	Matthew McCarthy	v W. Hartlepool 7.12.97(H)

ORRELL
RFU SENIOR CUP
STATISTICS
compiled by Stephen McCormack

OVERALL PLAYING RECORD

	P	W	D	L	F	A	Pts Diff
Home	35	18	0	17	740	524	216
Away	21	12	0	9	346	311	35
Neutral	-	-	-	-	-	-	-
Total	56	30	0	26	1086	835	251

SEASON BY SEASON

Season	Result
1971-72	DNQ
1972-73	QF
1973-74	SF
1974-75	DNQ
1975-76	1R
1976-77	DNQ
1977-78	DNQ
1978-79	1R
1979-80	1R
1980-81	4R
1981-82	3R
1982-83	4R
1983-84	4R
1984-85	DNQ
1985-86	3R
1986-87	SF
1987-88	3R
1988-89	3R
1989-90	4R
1990-91	SF
1991-92	QF
1992-93	4R
1993-94	SF
1994-95	5R
1995-96	4R
1996-97	6R
1997-98	3R
1998-99	4R
1999-2000	5R
2000-01	3R
2001-02	6R

TEAM RECORDS

Highest Score
83 v Scunthorpe 01/02
Biggest Winning Margin
75 (83-8) v Scunthorpe 01/02
Highest Score Against
57 v Sale 96/97
Biggest Losing Margin
57 (57-0) v Sale 96/97

INDIVIDUAL RECORDS

Most Points in a match
33 Phil Jones v Scunthorpe 01/02
Most Tries in a match
3 Andy Craig v Scunthorpe 01/02
Most Conversions in a match
10 Phil Jones v Scunthorpe 01/02
Most Penalties in a match

Most Drop Goals in a match

EUROPEAN COMPETITIONS
STATISTICS *compiled by Stephen McCormack*

SEASON BY SEASON

Season	S	Gp Stage
1996-97	S	Gp Stage
1997-98	-	-
1998-99	-	-
1999-00	-	-
2000-01	-	-
2001-02	-	-

OVERALL PLAYING RECORD

	P	W	D	L	F	A	Pts Diff
Home	3	2	0	1	97	82	15
Away	2	0	0	2	25	91	-66
Neutral	-	-	-	-	-	-	-
Total	5	2	0	3	122	173	-51

TEAM RECORDS

Highest Score
42 v Padova 96/97

Biggest Winning Margin
17 (52-25) v Padova 96/97

Highest Score Against
61 v Northampton 96/97

Biggest Losing Margin
54 (61-7) v Northampton 96/97

ORRELL

FACT FILE

Founded: 1927
Colours: Amber & black
Change colours: Red

GROUND

Address: Edgehall Road, Orrell, Wigan, Lancs. WN5 8TL.
Tel: 01695 623193 / 01695 632114 Fax: 01695 632116
Capacity: 6,000 Seated: Covered 1,000 Standing: Covered 2,000, Uncovered 3,000

Directions: Ground is about 2 miles from M6 junct. 26. Left at traffic lights at end of slip road, then left at lights at the Stag Inn. After about 400 yds. left again at lights & after another 400 yds. left again at lights which take you into Edgehall Road.
Nearest Railway Station: Orrell

Car Parking: 250 spaces at the ground, 250 nearby

Admission: to be announced

Club Shop: Yes
Clubhouse: Open normal licensing hours. Snacks, bar meals & restaurant available
Functions: Contact Steve Moores (Operations Manager) on 01695 632114

Training Nights: Tuesday and Thursday.

PROGRAMME (full colour) Size: A5 Pages: 40 Price: £2.00
Editorial: Geoff Lightfoot Media 01744 603199 (Tel & Fax) e-mail: gcl@rapid.co.uk

ADVERTISING RATES - Contact Adrian Blackburn on 01942 774000

England 'A' and sevens outside half Phil Jones in action for Orrell.

OTLEY RUFC

President	Eric Bryden	Manor Heath, Burley-in-Wharfedale, Ilkley LS29 7HH 01943 863848 (H)
Chairman	Paul Jaques	Springsyde, Birdcage Walk, Otley. LS21 3HB 01943 462714 (H), 01943 467866 (B)
Club Secretary	Marc Lawrence	16 Bankfield Terrace, Baildon, Shipley BD17 7HZ 01274 593535 (H)
Director of Rugby	Mike Wright	Cherry Tree Cottage, Dacre, Harrogate HG3 4ES 01423 780216 (H)
Fixture Secretary	Ronnie Franks	38 Ings Lane, Guiseley, Leeds LS20 8DA 01943 877086
Press Officer	John C Finch	9 Glen Mount, Menston, Ilkley. LS29 6DJ 01943872491 (H)

Having survived by the closest margin last season Otley consolidated their position in League 2 becoming the highest members run club in the RFU, finishing in seventh place. In doing so they completed doubles over Bedford, Bracknell and Henley although they did succumb to the Hawks in the Cup. There were, unfortunately, two doubles conceded, not surprisingly, to Rotherham and Worcester.

The arrival of Simon Binns and Phil Greaves from Rotherham enabled the team to produce the open football which had taken then up through the leagues and the former, voted club player of the year, was the Division's top points scorer with a total of 283 which consisted of five tries, 30 conversions, 63 penalties and three drop goals. Both players turned out for the League team against the two touring sides last summer, being responsible for all the points in the first game.

Twenty-one players shared 62 tries, winger Mark Kirkby claiming seven and he and scrum-half Andy Brown were chosen for the English Counties summer tour to Chile whilst the only ever present out of the 35 who shared selection was James Tiffany who joined from Leeds. James began by filling an early season void in the second row before appearing in every spot in the back row. Ian Carroll, needing just eleven more league appearances to reach the 200 mark for Otley, again had an outstanding season in the second row and every encouragement will be made to get him on the pitch in September.

Coach Peter Clegg, although not always ecstatic with his team's performance, was mostly upbeat about their general play and feels that with a little fine tuning they will once again be a force to be reckoned with.

Meanwhile the Second, Third and Fourth teams had great success and, with the numerous under age teams producing many boys and girls for the county sides, this all helped to make the club a happy corner of Yorkshire.

JOHN C. FINCH

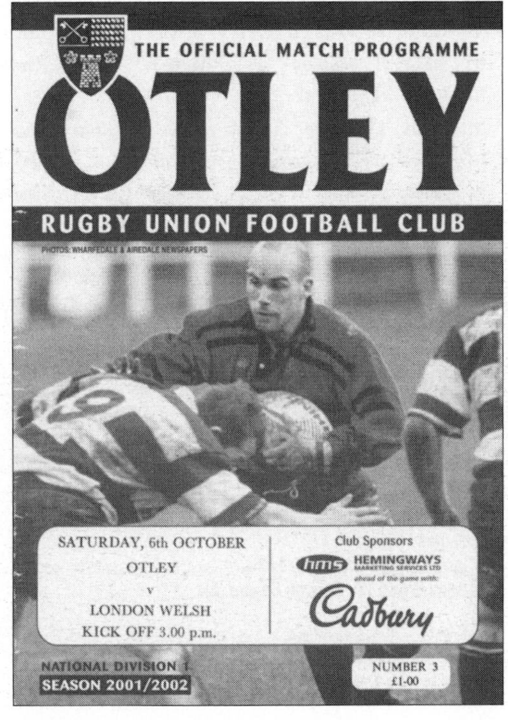

OTLEY

Comp.	Date	H/A	Opponents	Result & Score	Att	15	14	13	12	11
N1	01-09	A	Moseley	W 39-16	250	Shuttleworth	Kirkby/t	Greaves	Whatmuff	Smith
N1	08-09	H	Manchester	L 8-21		Shuttleworth	Kirkby	Greaves	Whatmuff	Gardner
N1	15-09	A	Birmingham & Solihull	L 16-41	500	Foster	Smith	Greaves	Whatmuff	Kirkby
N1	22-09	H	Henley Hawks	W 55-13		Shuttleworth	Smith/t	Greaves/t	Malherbe/2t	Walker/t
N1	29-09	A	Rotherham	L 6-55		Shuttleworth	Smith	Malherbe	Greaves	Walker
N1	06-10	H	London Welsh	W 32-9		Shuttleworth	Smith(b/t)	Malherbe/t	Greaves/t	Walker
N1	20-10	A	Coventry	L 41-47	1150	Shuttleworth/t	Smith	Malherbe	Greaves	Kirkby
N1	27-10	H	Worcester	L 23-40		Foster/p(b/t)	Smith/c	Whatmuff	Billington	Walker/t
N1	10-11	A	Wakefield	L 22-29	300	Shuttleworth	Smith	Malherbe	Greaves/t	Kirkby
N1	17-11	A	Bracknell	W 25-19		Shuttleworth	Whatmuff	Greaves/t	Malherbe/dg	Kirkby
N1	01-12	H	Bedford	W 26-10		Shuttleworth	Whatmuff	Malherbe	Greaves	Kirkby
N1	08-12	A	Rugby Lions	L 19-25	500	Shuttleworth/2t	Whatmuff	Malherbe	Greaves	Kirkby
N1	29-12	H	Exeter	W 26-5		Shuttleworth	Smith	Whatmuff	Greaves/t	Kirkby/t
N1	12-01	A	Manchester	L 3-20	485	Shuttleworth	Smith	Whatmuff	Greaves	Kirkby
N1	19-01	H	Birmingham & Solihull	W 18-3		Shuttleworth	Smith	Whatmuff	Billington	Kirkby/t
N1	26-01	A	Henley Hawks	W 22-12	350	Shuttleworth	Smith	Whatmuff	Greaves	Walker
N1	02-02	H	Rotherham	L 9-18		Shuttleworth	Smith	Greaves	Whatmuff	Kirkby
N1	09-02	A	London Welsh	L 15-34	650	Shuttleworth	Smith	Whatmuff/t	Greaves	Kirkby
N1	23-02	H	Coventry	L 11-22		Shuttleworth	Smith	Whatmuff	Billington	Kirkby/t
N1	02-03	H	Moseley	D 19-19		Shuttleworth(c/t)	Darby/t	Whatmuff	Greaves	Kirkby
N1	09-03	A	Worcester	L 14-71	1750	Duckett	Darby(d/t)	Whatmuff	Greaves	Kirkby
N1	16-03	H	Wakefield	W 45-33		Shuttleworth/t	Darby/t	Whatmuff	Greaves/t	Kirkby
N1	31-03	H	Bracknell	W 39-28	550	Shuttleworth/t2c2p	Darby/2t	Billington	Greaves	Kirkby
N1	06-04	A	Bedford	W 22-17	1315	Duckett	Darby/t	Billington	Gardner	Kirkby
N1	13-04	H	Rugby Lions	L 32-36		Shuttleworth	Darby/t	Billington/t	Gardner	Kirkby/t
N1	27-04	A	Exeter	L 14-32	738	Shuttleworth	Darby	Whatmuff	Greaves	Kirkby
PGC	03-11	A	Henley Hawks	L 30-48	300	Shuttleworth/2c	Smith	Whatmuff/t	Greaves/t	Kirkby

** after opponents name indicates a penalty try. Brackets after a player's name indicates he was replaced. eg (a) means he was replaced by replacement code "a" and so on. / after a player or replacement name is followed by any scores he made - eg /t, /c, /p, /dg or any combination of these*

EVER PRESENT None

Most Appearances:
25: James Tiffany (1).
24: Ian Shuttleworth, Simon Binns.
22: Andy Brown (3), Duncan Sayers (2).

PLAYERS USED

29 plus five as a replacement.

MOST POINTS

Pts	Player	T	C	P	DG
283	S Binns	5	30	63	3
55	I Shuttleworth	6	2	6	1
35	M Kikrby	7	-	-	-
30	W Darby	6	-	-	-
30	P Greaves	6	-	-	-

MATCH FACTS

10	9	1	2	3	4	5	6	7	8
Binns/4cpdg	Brown/2t	Pogson	Sayers	Kelly	Tiffany/t	Williams/t	Griffin	Bland	Burke
Binns/p	Brown	Kelly	Sayers	Pogson	Tiffany	Williams/t	Griffin	Bland	Spence
Binns/c3p	Brown	Kelly	Sayers	Hall	Carroll	Curtis	Griffin/t	Bland	Tiffany
Binns/c6p	Brown	Kelly/t	Sayers	Hall	Curtis	Williams	Tiffany(a/t)	Bland	Burke
Binns/2p	Brown	Kelly	Sayers	Hall	Carroll	Curtis	Griffin	Tiffany	Burke
Binns/t3c2p	Brown	Pogson	Sayers	Hall	Carroll	Curtis	Griffin	Tiffany	Burke
Binns/t5c2p	Brown	Kelly/t	Sayers	Hall	Carroll	Curtis/t	Griffin	Tiffany/t	Burke
Shuttleworth/p	Brown/t	Kelly	Sayers	Hall	Williams	Curtis	Griffin	Tiffany	Boyle
Binns/c5p	Brown	Kelly	Hepafila	Hall	Curtis	Williams	Griffin	Tiffany	Burke
Binns/c5p	Brown	Kelly	Sayers	Pogson	Williams	Curtis	Tiffany	Bland	Griffin
Binns/c3p	Brown	Kelly	Sayers	Hall	Williams	Curtis	Tiffany/t	Bland	Burke/2t
Binns/3p	Brown	Kelly	Sayers	Hall	Carroll	Williams	Boyle	Tiffany	Burke
Binns/tc3p	Brown	Pogson	Sayers	Hall	Carroll	Williams	Burke	Tiffany	Griffin
Binns/p	Brown	Pogson	Sayers	Hall	Carroll	Williams	Tiffany	Bland	Griffin
Binns/cpdg	Brown/t	Kelly	Hepafila	Hall	Carroll	Williams	Griffin	Tiffany	Burke
Binns/tc5p	Wright	Kelly	Sayers	Hall	Carroll	Curtis	Burke	Tiffany	Griffin
Binns/3p	Brown	Kelly	Sayers	Pogson	Carroll	Williams	Burke	Tiffany	Griffin
Binns/cp	Brown	Kelly	Sayers	Pogson	Carroll	Williams	Burke/t	Tiffany	Griffin
Binns/2p	Wright	Kelly	Sayers	Hall	Carroll	Williams	Burke	Tiffany	Griffin
Binns/3p	Brown	Pogson	Sayers	Hall	Carroll	Curtis	Williams	Bland	Griffin
Binns/2c	Wright	Pogson	Hepafila	Hall	Carroll/t	Williams	Tiffany	Bland	Griffin
Binns/t4c4p	Brown	Kelly	Sayers	Pogson	Carroll	Williams	Tiffany	Bland/t	Griffin
Binns/2c	Wright	Kelly	Sayers	Pogson	Carroll/t(a/t)	Williams	Burke	Bland	Tiffany
Shuttleworth/t3pdg	Brown	Kelly	Hepafila	Pogson	Williams	Curtis	Burke	Bland	Tiffany
Binns/c4pdg	Brown	Kelly	Sayers	Hall	Carroll	Curtis	Burke	Bland	Tiffany
Binns/3p	Brown	Kelly	Sayers	Pogson	Curtis/t	Williams	Burke	Bland	Tiffany
Binns/c2pdg	Wright/t	Kelly	Hepafila	Hall	Williams	Curtis	Boyle	Tiffany	Griffin

REPLACEMENTS: a - Andy Boyle. b - Mark Kirkby. c - Simon SMith. d - Tim Foster.

WHEN	Total	First Half	Second Half	1/4	2/4	3/4	4/4
The POINTS were scored	601	297	304	129	168	138	166
The POINTS were conceded	675	349	326	197	152	184	142
The TRIES were scored	62	28	34	11	17	13	21
The TRIES were conceded	84	41	43	22	19	23	20

HOW the TRIES were scored

Total	Backs	Forwards	F Back	Wing	Centre	H Back	F Row	Lock	B Row	Pen. Try
62	44	18	7	16	11	10	2	8	8	-

HOW the TRIES were conceded

Total	Backs	Forwards	F Back	Wing	Centre	H Back	F Row	Lock	B Row	Pen. Try
84	56	27	4	25	16	11	8	5	14	1

OTLEY

LEAGUE STATISTICS

compiled by Stephen McCormack

SEASON	Division	P	W	D	L	F	A	Pts Diff	Lge Pts	Lge Pos		Most Points		Most Tries
92-93	3	11	8	1	2	274	118	156	17		121	Peter Rutledge	6	Glyn Melville & Mark Farrar
93-94	2	18	4	1	13	235	449	-214	9		119	Peter Rutledge	7	Sean Atkinson
94-95	3	18	9	0	9	278	258	20	18		167	Peter Rutledge	6	Peter Rutledge
95-96	3	18	6	1	11	278	441	-163	13		147	Peter Rutledge	3	John Hall & Jon Flint
96-97	3	30	13	0	17	720	766	-46	26		287	Peter Rutledge	22	Mark Kirby
97-98	JN1	26	10	1	15	447	679	-232	21		150	Peter Rutledge	7	Wayne Hartley Chris Thornton
98-99	JN1	26	15	1	10	508	416	92	31		138	Dan Clappison	15	Lafaele Filipo
99-00	JN1	26	22	1	3	817	399	418	45	1p	262	Dan Clappison	22	Mark Kirkby
00-01	N1	26	9	1	16	455	630	-175	46	12	13	Dan Clappison	8	Andy Brown
01-02	N1	26	11	1	14	601	675	-74	56	7	283	Simon Binns	7	Mark Kirkby

BIGGEST MARGINS

Home Win	100pts - 103-3 v Blackheath 04.12.99
Away Win	47pts - 55-8 v Blackheath 15.04.00
Home Defeat	61pts - 7-68 v Worcester 21.2.98
Away Defeat	79pts - 9-88 v Sale 12.2.94

MOST CONSECUTIVE

Appearances	41 Richard Petyt 11.11.91 - 30.4.94
Matches scoring Tries	5 Glyn Melville
Matches scoring points	18 Peter Rutledge
Victories	9
Defeats	7

MOST POINTS

Scored at Home	103 v Blackheath 04.12.99
Scored Away	55 v Blackheath 15.04.00
Conceded at Home	68 v Worcester 21.2.98
Conceded Away	88 v Sale 12.2.94

MOST TRIES

Scored in a match	16 v Blackheath 04.12.99 (H)
Conceded in a match	14 v Sale 12.2.94 (A)

MOST APPEARANCES

by a forward	168(8) Steve Rice
by a back	127(12) Mark Billington

	MOST IN A SEASON	MOST IN A CAREER	MOST IN A MATCH
Points	287 Peter Rutledge 96-97	991 Peter Rutledge 92-98	25 Mark Kirkby v Redruth 8.2.97 Simon Binns v Wakefield 16.3.02 (H)
Tries	22 Mark Kirkby 96-97 & 99-00	51 Mark Kirkby 96-02	5 Mark Kirkby v Redruth 8.2.97 (A)
Conversions	56 Peter Rutledge 96-97	125 Peter Rutledge 92-98	10 Dan Clappison v Blackheath 04.12.99 (H)
Penalties	63 Simon Binns 01-02	207 Peter Rutledge 92-98	6 Peter Rutledge v Harrogate 29.10.94 (A) Simon Binns v Henley 22.9.01 (H)
Drop Goals	7 Richard Petyt 93-94	10 Richard Petyt 91-94	2 Richard Peyt v Nottingham 11.9.93 (A) Dan Clappison v Birmingham & Sol 11.12.99 (

OVERALL PLAYING RECORD

	P	W	D	L	F	A	Pts Diff
Home	10	5	0	5	207	243	-36
Away	11	4	0	7	267	230	37
Neutral	-	-	-	-	-	-	-
Total	21	9	-	12	474	473	1

SEASON BY SEASON

1971-72	DNQ
1972-73	DNQ
1973-74	DNQ
1974-75	DNQ
1975-76	DNQ
1976-77	DNQ
1977-78	DNQ
1978-79	DNQ
1979-80	DNQ
1980-81	DNQ
1981-82	DNQ
1982-83	DNQ
1983-84	DNQ
1984-85	DNQ
1985-86	DNQ
1986-87	DNQ
1987-88	DNQ
1988-89	DNQ
1989-90	2R
1990-91	DNQ
1991-92	1R
1992-93	2R
1993-94	5R
1994-95	2R
1995-96	3R
1996-97	4R
1997-98	3R
1998-99	2R
1999-2000	3R
2000-01	4R
2001-02	4R

OTLEY
RFU SENIOR CUP
STATISTICS
compiled by Stephen McCormack

TEAM RECORDS

Highest Score
76 v Whitchurch 99/00
Biggest Winning Margin
76 (76-0) v Whitchurch 99/00
Highest Score Against
83 v Leicester 00/01
Biggest Losing Margin
72 (83-11) v Leicester 00/01

INDIVIDUAL RECORDS

Most Points in a match
21 Dan Clappison v Whitchurch 99/00
Most Tries in a match

Most Conversions in a match
8 Dan Clappison v Whitchurch 99/00
Most Penalties in a match

Most Drop Goals in a match

FACT FILE

Founded: 1865

Colours : Black with irregular white hoops
Change colours: Red with irreguaIr white hoops

GROUND

Address: Cross Green, Otley. LS21 1HE
Tel: 01943 850142 Fax: 01943 461180
Capacity: 7,000 Seated: 499 Standing: 6,501

Directions: Left hand side of Pool Road, leading to Harrogate, 1/2 mile fromtown centre.
Nearest Railway Station: Leeds BR

Car Parking: 100 on ground

Admission: Season Adults Patrons £80, Members £70, Children/OAPs £35
Matchday Adults Standing £8, Children/OAPs £4;
Seated Adults £9,Children/OAPs £5

Club Shop: Yes, matchdays & Sunday lunchtime

Clubhouse: Normal licensing hours, three bars with snacks available
Functions: Capacity 130 seated Contact Peter Longstaffe 01943 - 461180 or 850142

Training Nights: Tuesdays & Thursdays

PROGRAMME Size: A5 Price: £1 Pages: 28 + cover Editor: Peter Thompson 0113 284 2134

Advertising Rates
Mono - Full page £200 Half page £120 Qtr page £60

PLYMOUTH ALBION RFC

Director of Rugby	Graham Dawe	c/o Plymouth Albion RFC, Beacon Park, Plymouth PL2 3JP 01752 777454 (Club), 01752 793273 (Fax)
Press Officer	Paddy Marsh	Hardwick Farmhouse, Drunken Bridge Hill, Plymouth PL7 1UG 01752 343631 (H), 01752 773187 (B), 01752 771522 (Fax)
Club Secretary	Michelle Chapman	c/o Plymouth Albion RFC, Beacon Park, Plymouth PL2 3JP 01752 777454 (Club), 01752 793273 (Fax)
Fixtures Secretary	Terry Brown	30 Abbots Park, Cornwood, nr Plymouth 01752 837742 (H), 01752 777454 (B), 01752 793273 (Fax)

Plymouth Albion's resurgence under the astute leadership of Graham Dawe continued when the club gained their second successive promotion, which returned them to a status they held a decade ago.

Albion led the table all season, but finished runners up to Orrell who won the title with a slightly better points difference after completing the double over Dawe's side.

Plymouth's only other league defeat came at the hands of Wharfedale, who ended a National League record of 41 successive victories with an inspired performance in the Dales.

Albion started the season with wins against fellow Division Two newcomers Sedgley Park and Stourbridge. An injury time winner against Rosslyn Park showed the team had the character and determination to have a successful season.

A disappointing performance at Rosslyn Park saw Albion depart from the National knock out cup at the first hurdle, but this was the spark which resulted in the club winning its first eleven league games.

In the run up to Christmas Albion faced three consecutive trips up north, the last of which was the loss at Wharfedale, but victory at Esher the following Saturday started another run that was ended when Orrell became the first side for over two years to win a league game at Beacon Park.

Despite being pipped for the title Albion will enter life in National Division 1 full of optimism and eagerly looking forward to the two local derbies with Exeter.

Many records fell during the season which also saw Dawe join the select band of players to complete 200 league games. Fullback Chris Atkinson who rejoined the club in mid season passed 1000 National League points, while No 8 Dan Ward-Smith's 24 tries saw him pass his own club record.

Albion finished the season unsure where they would be playing home matches come September. With Beacon Park being sold for housing development the two options are Devonport Services' ground at the Rectory or a new multi sport facility at Brickfields.

PADDY MARSH

Picture courtesy of the Evening Herald, Plymouth

PLYMOUTH ALBION

Comp.	Date	H/A	Opponents	Result & Score	Att	15	14	13	12	11
N2	01-09	H	Sedgley Park	W 34-13	1600	Proctor	Thompson/t	Fisilau	Thompson(a/c)	Matchett
N2	08-09	A	Stourbridge	W 34-10	650	Proctor	Thompson	Fisilau	Thompson/2t	Matchett
N2	15-09	H	Rosslyn Park	W 19-15		Proctor/t	Thompson	Bunny	Thompson/t	Matchett
N2	22-09	A	Preston Grasshoppers	W 36-22	330	Proctor	Thompson/t	Bunny/t	Thompson	Matchett
N2	06-10	H	Kendal	W 57-12		Proctor	Thompson/c	Bunny/2t	Thompson/t	Matchett/t
N2	20-10	A	Newbury	W 40-12		Proctor	Thompson/t	Bunny	Thompson	Matchett
N2	27-10	H	Nottingham	W 46-12		Proctor	Thompson/2t	Bunny	Thompson/t	Matchett/t
N2	10-11	A	Waterloo*	W 37-0		Proctor(b/c)	Thompson	Bunny/t	Thompson	Matchett/t
N2	17-11	H	Harrogate	W 57-3	1500	Proctor	Thompson/t	Bunny/3t	Thompson	Matchett
N2	24-11	A	Fylde	W 20-0		Proctor/t	Williams/t	Bunny	Thompson	Matchett
N2	01-12	A	Sedgley Park	W 32-13	500	Proctor	Thompson	Bunny/t	Thompson/t	Matchett
N2	08-12	A	Wharfedale	L 20-28		Proctor	Thompson/t	Bunny	Thompson	Matchett
N2	22-12	A	Esher	W 22-15		Proctor	Williams	Bunny	Thompson/t	Matchett
N2	05-01	H	Fylde	W 28-5	2100	Atkinson/2c3p	Williams	Bunny(d/t)	Thompson	Matchett
N2	12-01	A	Harrogate	W 21-15	570	Atkinson/c2p	Thompson	Thompson	Fisilau	Matchett/t
N2	19-01	H	Waterloo	W 43-15	1205	Atkinson/5cp	Proctor	Thompson	Farley/t	Matchett
N2	26-01	A	Nottingham	W 26-13	342	Atkinson/3c	Proctor	Bunny	Thompson/t	Matchett
N2	02-02	H	Newbury*	W 57-10	1080	Atkinson/6c	Proctor	Bunny/t	Thompson	Matchett
N2	09-02	A	Kendal*	W 7-0		Atkinson/c	Williams	Fisilau	Thompson	Matchett
N2	16-02	H	Orrell	L 14-20	2042	Proctor	Williams	Bunny/t	Thompson	Matchett
N2	23-02	H	Preston Grasshoppers	W 66-12	1200	Atkinson/8c	Williams	Bunny	Thompson/t	Matchett/t
N2	09-03	A	Rosslyn Park	W 41-13		Atkinson/3c5p	Williams/t	Sykes	Thompson(f/t)	Matchett
N2	16-03	H	Stourbridge	W 23-16	1550	Atkinson/cp	Williams/t	Sykes	Bunny	Matchett
N2	30-03	H	Esher	W 57-0		Atkinson/7cdg	Williams/t	Sykes/t	Bunny/t	Matchett
N2	06-04	A	Orrell	L 13-37	1300	Thompson	Williams	Bunny	Sykes	Matchett
N2	13-04	H	Wharfedale	W 45-3	1800	Thompson	Sykes/2t	Bunny	Fisilau	Matchett
PGC	29-09	A	Rosslyn Park	L 6-15		Proctor	Thompson	Bunny	Fisilau	Matchett

** after opponents name indicates a penalty try. Brackets after a player's name indicates he was replaced. eg (a) means he was replaced by replacement code "a" and so on. / after a player or replacement name is followed by any scores he made - eg /t, /c, /p, /dg or any combination of these*

EVER PRESENT

Tom Barlow, Andy Matchett, Danny Thomas, Dan Ward-Smith.

Most Appearances:

26: Tom Barlow, Andy Matchett, Danny Thomas, Dan Ward-Smith.

25: William James, Wayne Reed, Graham Dawe.

PLAYERS USED

26 plus seven as a replacement

MOST POINTS

Pts	Player	T	C	P	DG
211	T Barlow	10	40	23	4
115	D Ward-Smith	23	-	-	-
113	C Atkinson	-	37	12	1
60	G Bunny	12	-	-	-
50	W James	10	-	-	-

MATCH FACTS

10	9	1	2	3	4	5	6	7	8
Barlow/2t3c2p	Williams	Paver	Dawe	Reed	Perry	James	Ward-Smith/t	Thomas	Luxton
Barlow/4cpdg	Williams	Paver	Dawe	Reed	Perry	James	Ward-Smith	Thomas	Luxton/2t
Barlow/2c	Williams	Paver	Dawe	Reed	James	Perry	Ward-Smith/t	Thomas	Luxton
Barlow/2c3pdg	Williams	Paver/t	Dawe	Reed	James	Luxton	Burnett	Thomas/t	Ward-Smith
Barlow/6cp	Cane	Mathias	Dawe/2t	Reed	James	Luxton	Searle/t	Thomas	Ward-Smith/t
Barlow/t3c3p	Cane/t	Mathias	Dawe	Reed	James	Luxton/t	Searle	Thomas	Ward-Smith/t
Barlow/3c	Cane/t	Mathias	Dawe	Reed	James	Luxton	Searle	Thomas/t	Ward-Smith/2t
Barlow/2c2p	Cane	Paver	Dawe	Reed	James	Luxton	Searle	Thomas/t	Ward-Smith/t
Barlow/3c2p	Cane	Paver	Dawe	Reed	James	Luxton/t	Searle	Thomas/t	Ward-Smith/3t
Barlow/cp	Cane	Risdon	Dawe	Reed	James	Luxton	Hart	Thomas	Ward-Smith/t
Barlow/3c2p	Cane	Risdon	Dawe	Reed	James	Perry	Luxton	Thomas/t	Ward-Smith/t
Barlow/cp	Cane	Risdon(c/t)	Dawe	Reed	James	Perry	Luxton	Thomas	Ward-Smith/t
Barlow/2cp	Cane	Risdon	Dawe	Reed	James/t	Luxton	Hart	Thomas	Ward-Smith/t
Barlow	Cane	Paver	Dawe	Reed	James/t	Perry/t	Hart	Thomas	Ward-Smith
Barlow/dg	Cane	Paver	Dawe	Reed	James	Perry	Hart	Thomas	Ward-Smith/t
Barlow/t	Williams/t	Paver	Dawe	Reed	James/2t	Perry	Hart	Thomas	Ward-Smith/t
Barlow	Williams	Paver	Dawe	Reed/t	James	Perry/t	Hart	Thomas	Ward-Smith/t
Barlow	Williams	Paver/t	Dawe	Reed	James/t	Perry/t	Hart/t	Thomas	Ward-Smith/3t
Barlow	Cane	Paver	Dawe	Reed	Luxton	Perry	Searle	Thomas	Ward-Smith
Barlow/3p	Cane	Paver	Dawe	Reed	James	Perry	Searle	Thomas	Ward-Smith
Barlow/t	Cane/t	Paver	Dawe	Risdon	James/3t	Perry	Searle/t(e/t)	Thomas	Ward-Smith/t
Barlow	Cane	Risdon	Dawe/t	Reed	James	Perry/t	Hart	Thomas	Ward-Smith
Barlow/dg	Cane	Risdon	Dawe	Reed	James	Perry	Hart/t	Thomas	Ward-Smith/t
Barlow/t	Cane	Risdon	Dawe	Reed	James/2t	Perry	Hart/t	Thomas	Ward-Smith(e/t)
Barlow/2tp	Cane	Risdon	Dawe	Reed	James	Perry	Hart	Thomas	Ward-Smith
Barlow/2t5c	Cane	Risdon	Harper/t	Reed	James	Perry	Hart	Thomas/t	Ward-Smith/t
Barlow/2p	Williams	Paver	Owen	Reed	James	Lockley	Burnett	Searle	Luxton

REPLACEMENTS: a - Lee Thomas. b - Puil Williams. c - Alan Paver. d - Tom Farley. e - Elliot Bunny. f - Brett Luxton.

WHERE	Total	Home	Away
The POINTS were scored	895	546	349
The POINTS were conceded	314	178	136
The TRIES were scored	123	79	44
The TRIES were conceded	34	19	15

HOW the TRIES were scored

Total	Backs	Forwards	F Back	Wing	Centre	H Back	F Row	Lock	B Row	Pen. Try
123	58	62	2	18	24	14	8	16	38	3

HOW the TRIES were conceded

Total	Backs	Forwards	F Back	Wing	Centre	H Back	F Row	Lock	B Row	Pen. Try
34	26	8	5	11	7	3	4	2	2	-

PLYMOUTH ALBION

LEAGUE STATISTICS

compiled by Stephen McCormack

SEASON	Division	P	W	D	L	F	A	Pts Diff	Lge Pts	Lge Pos	Most Points	Most Tries
92-93	D3	11	0	0	11	130	305	-175	0	12r	26 Martin Thompson	3 Mark Haimes
93-94	D4	18	9	0	9	286	416	-130	18	4	90 Martin Thompson	5 Roger Bailey
94-95	D4	18	4	2	12	324	381	-57	10	8	129 Martin Thompson	6 Steve Walklin
95-96	D4	18	4	0	14	268	545	-277	8	10	61 Mark Slade	6 Steve Walklin
96-97	D4S	26	13	3	10	709	591	118	29	6	131 Martin Thompson	12 Steve Walklin
97-98	N2S	26	6	0	20	472	756	-284	12	13	131 Martin Thompson	15 Steve Walklin
98-99	N2S	26	7	1	18	457	666	-209	15	12	89 Richard Thompson	6 Richard Thompson, Martin Ridley & Roger Thompson
99-00	N2S	26	17	2	7	664	382	282	36	4	260 Chris Atkinson	15 Steve Walklin
00-01	N3S	26	26	0	0	910	240	670	52	1p	255 Tom Barlow	20 Dan Ward-Smith
01-02	N2	26	23	0	3	895	314	581	46	2p	211 Tom Barlow	23 Dan Ward-Smith

MOST POINTS

Scored at Home	73 v Charlton Park 29.03.97
Scored Away	46 v Birmingham 17.10.87
Conceded at Home	64 v Bracknell 03.04.99
Conceded Away	70 v Esher 07.02.98

MOST CONSECUTIVE

Appearances	43 Kevin Turton 12.09.87 - 23.03.91	
Matches scoring Tries	9	Dan Ward Smith
Matches scoring points	19	Chris Atkinson
Victories	41	
Defeats	8	

BIGGEST MARGINS

Home Win	66pts	72-6 v Basingstoke 23.12.00
Away Win	43pts	46-3 v Birmingham 17.10.87
Home Defeat	52pts	12-64 v Bracknell 03.04.99
Away Defeat	70pts	0-70 v Esher 07.02.98

MOST TRIES

Scored in a match	11 v Charlton Park 29.03.97 11 v Basingstoke 23.12.00
Conceded in a match	10 v Esher 07.02.98

MOST APPEARANCES

by a forward:	93 (5) Ian Goldsmith
by a back:	164 (4) Richard Thompson

	MOST IN A SEASON	MOST IN A CAREER	MOST IN A MATCH
Points	260 Chris Atkinson 1999-00	566 Martin Thompson 1989-99	25 Domonic Cundy v Met Police 26.11.88 (H) Nick Burt v Charlton Park 29.03.97 (H)
Tries	23 Dan Ward-Smith 2001-02	77 Steve Walklin 1987-00	4 Steve Walklin v Birmingham 17.10.87 (A) Ian Russell v Fylde 31.10.87 (A)
Conversions	42 Tom Barlow 2000-01	103 Chris Atkinson 99-02	8 Dominic Cundy v Met Police 26.11.88 (H) Chris Atkinson v Preston 23.2.02
Penalties	59 Chris Atkinson 1999-00	93 Martin Thompson 89-99	6 Mark Slade v Bedford 14.12.91 (H)
Drop Goals	5 Tom Barlow 2000-01	16 Martin Thompson 89-99	3 Mark Slade v Liverpool St H 09.02.96 (H)

PLYMOUTH ALBION RFU SENIOR CUP

STATISTICS

compiled by Stephen McCormack

OVERALL PLAYING RECORD

	P	W	D	L	F	A	Pts Diff
Home	16	7	0	9	401	277	124
Away	18	4	0	14	174	334	-160
Neutral	-	-	-	-	-	-	-
Total	34	11	-	23	575	611	-36

SEASON BY SEASON

Season	Result
1971-72	1R
1972-73	DNQ
1973-74	DNQ
1974-75	1R
1975-76	1R
1976-77	DNQ
1977-78	DNQ
1978-79	1R
1979-80	DNQ
1980-81	DNQ
1981-82	DNQ
1982-83	3R
1983-84	4R
1984-85	3R
1985-86	3R
1986-87	DNQ
1987-88	QF
1988-89	3R
1989-90	3R
1990-91	2R
1991-92	2R
1992-93	2R
1993-94	3R
1994-95	2R
1995-96	2R
1996-97	2R
1997-98	1R
1998-99	2R
1999-2000	1R
2000-01	4R
2001-02	2R

TEAM RECORDS

Highest Score
60 v Stoke OB 88/89

Biggest Winning Margin
57 (60-3) v Stoke OB

Highest Score Against
49 v Rosslyn Park 92/93

Biggest Losing Margin
46 (49-3) v Rosslyn Park 92/93

INDIVIDUAL RECORDS

Most Points in a match

Most Tries in a match

Most Conversions in a match

Most Penalties in a match

Most Drop Goals in a match

Plymouth Albion celebrate after their victory over Esher guaranteed them promotion to National Div 1.
Photo: Nigel Chanter (01392 467261)

PLYMOUTH ALBION

FACT FILE

Founded: 1876
Nickname: Albion
Colours: White with broad cherry band edged with green.
Change colours: Red.

GROUND

Address: Beacon Park, Beacon Park Road, Plymouth, PL2 3JP
Tel: 01752 777454 Fax 01752 777454
Capacity: 3,000 Seated: 500 Standing: 2,500

Directions: On approaching Plymouth follow signs for Plymouth Argyle FC. 200 yards past Safeway Superstore at 3rd traffic lights turn right, turn left at Cherry Tree Pub into Langstone Rd, ground 500yards on right.
Nearest Railway Station: Plymouth North Road

Car Parking: 50 within ground

Admission: Matchday - Seated Adults £8 Children/OAPs £4.
Ground Adults £6, Children/OAPs £3 -members £1 reduction into ground.

Clubhouse: Normal licensing hours. Snacks & bar meals available
Functions: Capacity 120, contact Squash Club 01752 777454

Club Shop: Open matchdays only. Other times from bar staff Manager Vince Jones

Training Nights: Tuesday & Thursday

PROGRAMME
Size: A5 Price: £1.50
Pages: 36 + cover
Editor: Peter Harrison 01503 230216

ADVERTISING RATES
Colour
Full page £750, Half £350, Qtr £250
No mono

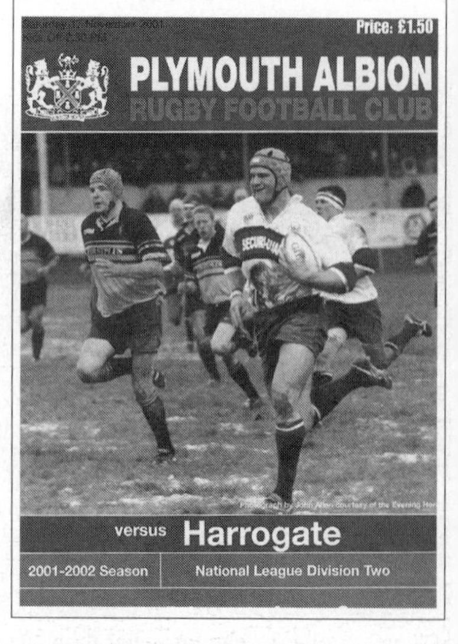

Picture courtesy of the Evening Herald, Plymouth

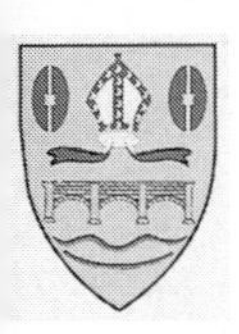

ROTHERHAM RUFC

Chief Executive	Jim Kilfoyle	c/o Rotherham RUFC
Chairman	Martin Jenkinson	c/o Rotherham RUFC
Coach	Mike Schmid	c/o Rotherham RUFC
Backs Coach	Mike Umaga	c/o Rotherham RUFC
Operations Manager	Wilf Duke	c/o Rotherham RUFC 07887 775622 (Mob)

Rotherham RUFC, Clifton Lane Sports Ground, Badsley Moor Lane, Rotherham. S65 2AA.
Tel: 01709 370763 Fax: 01709 370802

Rotherham's season began in difficult fashion at Wakefield and London Welsh - two opponents who always pose problems for Rotherham. However with two wins under their belt together with maximum bonus points Rotherham made their best start ever in this league. The first half of the season was a series of very good wins, home and away, with their only setbacks being a narrow defeat against old rivals Worcester (away 19-26) and Exeter (home 13-19). Both defeats were hard fought campaigns against good sides, but they were seen as opportunities lost and they were stung into reflective analysis. In this half of the season, a good Cup run with victories at home against Rugby Lions and Coventry and comfortable revenge at Worcester ended at Saracens against the best side that the Watford club put out all season.

The recruitment of stand-off Ramiro Pez, centre John Cannon and back row Alfie Tooala added kicking accuracy and running power to an already formidable squad. However the late arrival of Oriol Ripol, a Spanish wing, was to add a cutting edge that no-one had anticipated.

The rest of the season was to be a series of wins, varying from the comfortable to the exciting. Coventry (away 41-26), Worcester (home 18-8), Otley (away 18-9), Bedford (away 36-31) and Exeter (away 32-23) ensured that the character, skills and resilience of the squad were well tested, and, when injuries had depleted an already small squad, Mario Pereyra and Eric Peters were added to it to bring their experience at the end of the season. 300 points in the last five games and an exciting Powergen Shield victory against a brave Exeter side at Twickenham made it a memorable and record-breaking season, only for the dark shadow of non-promotion to emerge after the season ended.

ROTHERHAM

Comp.	Date	H/A	Opponents	Result & Score	Att	15	14	13	12	11
N1	01-09	A	Wakefield	W 34-22	1100	Massey/t	Keyter	Cannon/t	Umaga/t	Dixon
N1	09-09	A	London Welsh	W 28-6	1200	Umaga	Keyter	Cannon	Northey(a/t)	Massey
N1	15-09	H	Coventry	W 55-9		Umaga/t	Keyter	Cannon/t	Shepherd	Massey
N1	22-09	A	Worcester	L 18-20	4800	Umaga/t	Keyter	Cannon/t	Shepherd	Massey
N1	29-09	H	Otley	W 55-6		Umaga	Keyter/t	Cannon	Shepherd	Massey/2t
N1	06-10	A	Bracknell	W 42-10		Umaga	Keyter	Cannon/t	Shepherd	Massey
N1	20-10	H	Bedford	W 53-13		Massey	Keyter/dg	Cannon	Shepherd(f/t)	Dixon
N1	10-11	H	Exeter	L 13-19		Umaga	Keyter/dg	Cannon	Shepherd/t	Massey
N1	17-11	A	Moseley	W 47-3	490	Massey/2t	Keyter/t	Cannon(h/t)	Northey	Wood
N1	01-12	H	Manchester	W 55-10		Umaga/4c	Dixon	Cannon/t	Northey/t	Wood/t
N1	08-12	A	Birmingham & Solihull	W 56-16		Umaga/t	Ripol/t	Keyter	Northey	Wood(j/t)
N1	29-12	H	Henley Hawks	W 48-6		Massey/t	Ripol/3t	Keyter	Umaga	Wood/t
N1	12-01	H	London Welsh	W 28-21		Massey	Ripol/t	Umaga	Shepherd	Wood/t
N1	19-01	A	Coventry	W 41-28	4132	Massey	Ripol/2t	Cannon	Shepherd	Wood
N1	26-01	H	Worcester	W 18-8	2500	Massey	Ripol/2t	Umaga	Shepherd	Wood
N1	02-02	A	Otley	W 18-9		Massey	Keyter	Umaga/t	Shepherd	Wood
N1	09-02	H	Bracknell	W 55-8	1500	Massey	Keyter/t	Cannon/t	Northey	Ripol/2t(n/3t)
N1	15-02	A	Rugby Lions	W 47-14	300	Massey/t	Dixon	Umaga	Shepherd/t	Wood
N1	23-02	A	Bedford*	W 36-31	1908	Massey	Ripol	Cannon/t	Shepherd	Wood/t
N1	02-03	H	Wakefield	W 30-8	1200	Massey	Keyter/dg	Umaga	Shepherd	Wood/t
N1	09-03	H	Rugby Lions	W 30-8	1500	Massey	Keyter/t	Cannon	Northey	Wood/t
N1	16-03	A	Exeter*	W 32-23	1530	Massey	Ripol	Umaga	Shepherd	Wood
N1	30-03	H	Moseley	W 61-0	2000	Umaga	Ripol/t	Keyter/t	Northey	Wood/t
N1	06-04	A	Manchester	W 72-7	828	Umaga/t	Keyter/2t	Cannon	Shepherd/2t	Wood/t
N1	13-04	H	Birmingham & Solihull	W 73-0	1500	Massey/t	Dixon	Keyter	Shepherd	Wood/5t
N1	27-04	A	Henley Hawks*	W 54-20	1325	Umaga/t2c	Ripol/t	Keyter	Northey/t	Dixon
PGC	13-10	H	Rugby Lions	W 48-3		Massey/t	Keyter	Cannon/2t	Shepherd/t	Dixon/t
PGC	24-11	A	Worcester	W 26-19	1610	Umaga	Cannon	Keyter	Shepherd	Wood/2t
PGC	16-12	A	Saracens	L 17-43	2403	Massey	Ripol	Keyter	Cannon	Wood/t
PGS	24-03	H	Birmingham & Solihull	W 57-10	2000	Umaga/2c	Ripol	Keyter/t	Shepherd	Wood
PGS	20-04	N	Exeter	W 35-26		Massey	Ripol	Keyter	Shepherd/t	Wood

** after opponents name indicates a penalty try. Brackets after a player's name indicates he was replaced. eg (a) means he was replaced by replacement code "a" and so on. / after a player or replacement name is followed by any scores he made - eg /t, /c, /p, /dg or any combination of these*

EVER PRESENT None

Most Appearances:

21: Simon Bunting (3), Leon Greef, Glen Kenworthy (2), Peter Massey (3).

PLAYERS USED

29 plus two as a replacement

MOST POINTS

Pts	Player	T	C	P	DG
197	R Pez	4	60	19	-
97	L Wilfley	3	32	6	-
70	O Ripol	14	-	-	-
65	A Tooala	13	-	-	-
65	M Wood	13	-	-	-
60	C Johnson	12	-	-	-

MATCH FACTS

10	9	1	2	3	4	5	6	7	8
Pez/3cp	Harrison	Thorp	Johnson/t	Bunting	Greef/t	Kenworthy	Earnshaw	Spence	Schmid
Pez/3c	Harrison(b/c)	Thorp/2t	Johnson	Bunting	Parr(c/t)	Kenworthy	Greef	Earnshaw	Schmid
Pez/2t7c2p	Harrison	Thorp	Johnson(d/t)	Bunting(e/t)	Cook	Kenworthy	Greef	Spence	Schmid/t
Pez/c2p	Harrison	Thorp	Johnson	Bunting	Cook	Kenworthy	Greef	Spence	Schmid
Pez/7c2p	Harrison	Thorp/t	Johnson	Bunting/t	Cook	Parr/t	Greef	Earnshaw	Schmid/t
Pez/6c	Harrison	Thorp	Johnson/t	Bunting	Cook	Kenworthy	Schmid/t	Earnshaw/3t	Tooala
Pez/2c	Scully/4cp	Thorp	Johnson	Bunting/t	Cook	Kenworthy/t	Greef/2t(g/t)	Earnshaw	Schmid/t
Scully/cp	Harrison	Bunting	Toews	Bone	Cook	Kenworthy	Greef	Spence	Schmid
Pez/5c	Scully/c	Bunting	Toews	Bone	Parr/2t	Cook	Greef	Earnshaw	Schmid/t
Pez/2cp	Scully/t	Thorp	Toews	Bunting	Cook(i/t)	Kenworthy	Schmid/t	Spence	Tooala/2t
Pez/4cp	Harrison/t	Thorp	Toews	Bunting	Parr	Kenworthy/t	Greef/t	Spence/2t	Tooala/t
Wilfley/4c	Scully	Thorp	Toews/t	Bunting	Parr	Kenworthy	Greef	Spence	Tooala/2t
Wilfley/3c(k/c)	Scully/t	Thorp	Toews	Bone	Parr	Kenworthy	Greef/t	Spence	Tooala
Pez/2p	Harrison	Thorp	Toews(l/3t)	Bunting	Cook	Kenworthy	Greef	Earnshaw/2t	Schmid
Pez/c2p	Harrison	Thorp	Johnson	Bunting	Cook	Kenworthy	Greef	Earnshaw	Schmid
Wilfley/c2p	Harrison	Bunting	Johnson/t	Cundick	Cook	Kenworthy	Spence	Earnshaw	Tooala
Pez/t4c(m/c)	Harrison/t	Bunting	Johnson	Bone	Parr	Cook	Greef	Earnshaw	Tooala
Wilfley/5c	Scully/c	Toews	Johnson/2t	Bone	Kenworthy	Cook	Greef/2t	Earnshaw	Tooala/t
Pez/2c4p	Scully	Bunting	Toews	Bone(l/t)	Kenworthy	Cook	Greef	Earnshaw	Tooala
Wilfley/2cp	Scully	Toews	Johnson	Bone	Parr	Kenworthy	Greef/t	Earnshaw/t	Tooala/t
Pez	Harrison/t	Toews	Johnson/t	Bunting	Parr	Cook	Greef/t	Earnshaw	Tooala/t
Pez/3c2p	Scully	Bunting	Johnson/t	Pereyra	Kenworthy	Cook	Greef	Earnshaw	Tooala/t(o/t)
Wilfley/t8c	Scully/t	Toews	Johnson/t	Bunting	Cook	Kenworthy/t	Schmid	Earnshaw	Tooala/2t
Wilfley/t6c	Scully/t	Toews	Johnson	Pereyra	Cook	Parr	Peters/t	Spence/t	Greef
Wilfley/t3c3p(k/4c)	Scully(p/t)	Bunting	Toews	Pereyra	Cook/t	Kenworthy	Greef(o/t)	Earnshaw	Tooala
Pez/t5c	Harrison	Cundick	Toews	Pereyra	Parr	Kenworthy	Peters	Spence/2t	Tooala/t
Pez/t5cp	Scully	Thorp	Toews	Gravil	Cook	Kenworthy	Spence/t	Earnshaw	Schmid
Pez/c3p	Scully	Bunting	Toews	Bone	Cook	Parr/t	Greef	Earnshaw	Tooala
Pez/3pdg	Harrison	Thorp	Toews	Bunting	Parr	Kenworthy	Greef	Spence	Tooala
Wilfley/t5cp	Harrison(b/t)	Bunting	Johnson/t	Pereyra	Parr	Kenworthy/t	Schmid/t	Earnshaw/t	Tooala/t
Wilfley/3p(k/2c4p)	Scully(p/t)	Bunting	Johnson	Pereyra	Cook	Kenworthy	Peters	Earnshaw	Tooala

REPLACEMENTS: a - Jonathan Shpherd. b - Dave Scully. c - Dan Cook. d - Harry Toews. e - Jason Cundick. f - Andy Northey. g - Alfie Tooala. h - Oriol Ripol. i - Howard Parr. j - Peter Massey. k - Ramiro Pez. l - Chris Johnson. m - Mike Umaga. n - Stuart Dixon. o - Mike Schmid. p - Charlie Harrison

WHEN	Total	First Half	Second Half	1/4	2/4	3/4	4/4
The POINTS were scored	1099	497	602	228	269	272	330
The POINTS were conceded	325	191	134	71	120	47	87
The TRIES were scored	159	72	87	33	39	38	49
The TRIES were conceded	32	13	19	4	9	5	14

HOW the TRIES were scored

Total	Backs	Forwards	F Back	Wing	Centre	H Back	F Row	Lock	B Row	Pen. Try
159	85	71	11	40	19	15	20	10	41	3

HOW the TRIES were conceded

Total	Backs	Forwards	F Back	Wing	Centre	H Back	F Row	Lock	B Row	Pen. Try
32	19	11	2	12	3	2	4	1	6	2

ROTHERHAM

LEAGUE STATISTICS
compiled by Stephen McCormack

SEASON	Division	P	W	D	L	F	A	Pts Diff	Lge Pts	Lge Pos	Most Points	Most Tries
92-93	D4N	12	10	1	1	259	123	136	21		50 Steve Worrall	8 Andy Challinor
93-94	D5N	12	10	1	1	335	142	193	21		118 Kevin Plant	8 John Dudley
94-95	4	18	17	0	1	576	267	309	34		202 Kevin Plant	8 John Dudley & Paul Scott
95-96	3	18	12	0	6	384	368	16	24		155 Kevin Plant	5 Paul Scott, Richard Selkirk & Richard Heaselgrave
96-97	2	22	11	0	11	525	661	-136	22		92 Dean Lax	13 Guy Easterby
97-98	P2	22	14	0	8	566	386	180	28		244 Simon Binns	12 Greg Austin
98-99	P2	26	22	0	4	756	336	420	44	2	144 Doug Trivella	18 Dean Lax
99-00	P2	26	24	0	2	1045	267	778	48	1	251 Mike Umaga	18 Dean Lax
00-01	P1	22	2	0	20	335	813	-478	12	12r	139 Mike Umaga	3 James Naylor & Mike Umaga
01-02	N1	26	24	0	2	1099	325	774	120	1	197 Ramiro Pez	14 Oriol Ripol

BIGGEST MARGINS

Home Win	85pts - 93-8 v W Hartlepool 2.10.99
Away Win	65pts - 72-7 v Manchester 6.42.02
Home Defeat	56pts - 12-68 v Bath 14.04.01
Away Defeat	55pts - 3-58 v London Wasps 01.04.01

MOST CONSECUTIVE

Appearances	89 Richard Selkirk 12.9.87-1.4.94
Matches scoring Tries	5 Dean Lax & Dave Scully
Matches scoring points	14 Kevin Plant (twice)
Victories	22
Defeats	8

MOST POINTS

Scored at Home	93 v W Hartlepool 2.10.99
Scored Away	72 v Manchester 6.4.02
Conceded at Home	68 v Bath 14.4.01
Conceded Away	61 v Newcastle 4.5.97

MOST TRIES

Scored in a match	13 v W Hartlepool 2.10.99
Conceded in a match	11 v Newcastle 4.5.97 (A)

MOST APPEARANCES

by a forward	165 (26) John Dudley
by a back	99 (1) Paul Scott

	MOST IN A SEASON	MOST IN A CAREER	MOST IN A MATCH	
Points	249 Mike Umaga 99-00	922 Kevin Plant 87-96	41 Simon Binns	v W Hartlepool 2.10.99 (H)
Tries	18 Dean Lax 98-99 & 99-00	42 Paul Scott 87-96	6 Paul Scott	v Westoe 8.4.89 (A)
Conversions	60 Ramiro Pez 01-02	141 Kevin Plant 87-96	10 Simon Binns	v W Hartlepool 12.10.99 (H)
Penalties	41 Kevin Plant 90-91 Simon Binns 97-98	182 Kevin Plant 87-96	6 David Francis Dean Lax	v Keighley 8.4.89 (H) v Lon. Scottish 2.11.96 (H)
Drop Goals	5 Kevin Plant 95-96	17 Kevin Plant 87-96	2 Kevin Plant	v Coventry 28.10.95

OVERALL PLAYING RECORD

	P	W	D	L	F	A	Pts Diff
Home	11	6	0	5	357	255	102
Away	9	4	0	5	156	202	-46
Neutral	-	-	-	-	-	-	-
Total	20	10	0	10	513	457	56

SEASON BY SEASON

1971-72	DNQ
1972-73	DNQ
1973-74	DNQ
1974-75	DNQ
1975-76	DNQ
1976-77	DNQ
1977-78	DNQ
1978-79	DNQ
1979-80	DNQ
1980-81	DNQ
1981-82	DNQ
1982-83	DNQ
1983-84	DNQ
1984-85	DNQ
1985-86	DNQ
1986-87	DNQ
1987-88	DNQ
1988-89	DNQ
1989-90	2R
1990-91	DNQ
1991-92	DNQ
1992-93	DNQ
1993-94	1R
1994-95	4R
1995-96	2R
1996-97	6R
1997-98	5R
1998-99	4R
1999-00	3R
2000-01	5R
2001-02	5R

ROTHERHAM
RFU SENIOR CUP
STATISTICS
compiled by Stephen McCormack

TEAM RECORDS

Highest Score
67 v Launceston 97/98
Biggest Winning Margin
52 (67-15) v Launceston 97/98
Highest Score Against
43 v Sale 89/90 & Saracens 01/02
Biggest Losing Margin
33 (43-10) v Sale

INDIVIDUAL RECORDS

Most Points in a match

Most Tries in a match

Most Conversions in a match

Most Penalties in a match

Most Drop Goals in a match

EUROPEAN COMPETITIONS
STATISTICS *compiled by Stephen McCormack*

TEAM RECORDS

Highest Score
35 v Grenoble 00/01
Biggest Winning Margin
30 (35-5) v Grenoble 00/01
Highest Score Against
61 v Bridgend 00/01
Biggest Losing Margin
54 (61-8) v Bridgend 00/01

INDIVIDUAL RECORDS

Most Points in a match
25 Mike Umaga v Grenoble 00/01
Most Tries in a match
2 Mike Umaga v Grenoble 00/01
Most Conversions in a match
3 Mike Umaga v Grenoble 00/01
Most Penalties in a match
4 Mike Umaga v Perpignan 00/01
Most Drop Goals in a match
-

CAREER RECORDS

Most Points:
56: Mike Umaga.
18: Dave Scully

Most Tries:
3: Mike Umaga
2: Martin Dawson

SEASON BY SEASON

1996-97	-	-
1997-98	-	-
1998-99	-	-
1999-00	-	-
2000-01	S	Gp Stage
2001-02	-	-

OVERALL PLAYING RECORD

	P	W	D	L	F	A	Pts Diff
Home	3	2	0	1	73	44	29
Away	3	2	0	1	49	92	-43
Neutral	-	-	-	-	-	-	-
Total	6	4	0	2	122	136	-14

ROTHERHAM

FACT FILE

Founded: 1923
Nickname: Roth

Colours: Burgundy, navy, white bands
Change colours: Red with navy/white shoulders

GROUNDS All home matches (02-03) will be played at Rotherham United Football Club

Address: Millmoor Ground, Rotherham, S60 1HR
Tel: 01709 512434

Directions:
From **NORTH:** Exit M1 at Junction 34 following Rotherham (A6019) signs to traffic lights and turn right. Ground is 1/4 mile on the right over the railway bridge.
From **SOUTH & WEST:** Exit M1 at junction 33 turn right flollowing Rotherham signs. Left at roundabout and right at next roundabout. Follow duel carriageway to next roundabout and go straight on. Turn left at next roundabout. Ground is 1/4 on the left.
From **THE EAST:** Take A630 into Rotherham following Sheffield signs. At 1st roundabout go straight on down Fitzwilliam Road at 2nd roundabout go straight on down inner bypass Centenary Way at 3rd r'about take 2nd left, at 4th r'about turn right onto Masborough Street then left into Milmoor Lane.

Address: Clifton Lane Sports Ground, Badsley Moor Lane, Rotherham. S65 2AA.
Tel: 01709 370763 Fax: 01709 370802

Directions: M1 Jnc 33. Follow Rotherway for half mile to r'about. Take 2nd exit signed Bawtry. Traffic lights straight on up hill to r'about. Exit 1st left, follow road into town centre. Ground approx 1 mile on right. M18 Jnc 1. follow signs Rotherham. After 2 miles at 2nd r'about (Brecks Hotel) fork right. At next r'about (Stag Inn) 2nd exit. Follow road into town centre. Ground approx 1 mile on right.
Nearest Railway Station: Rotherham

Car Parking: 20 on ground, 1,000 No Charge nearby.

Admission: Season
Adults Standing: £120
Seated: £160
Matchday
Standing: Adult £10
OAPs £8 Children £1
Seated: Adult £13
OAPs £11 Children £4

Club Shop: Yes

Clubhouse: Normal Licensing Hours, snacks available
Functions: Capacity 100
Contact Peter Hudson (Clubhouse manager) at club.

PROGRAMME Size: A5 Pages: 48 Price: £4
Editor: C Middleton 01709 532186
ADVERTISING RATES
Full page £599
1/2 page £399
1/4 page £299

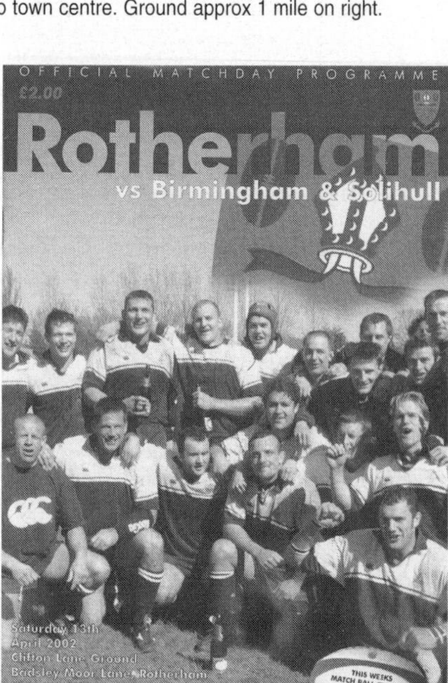

RUGBY FC

Rugby FC,
Webb Ellis Road,
Rugby,
Warwickshire CV22 7AU
Tel: 01788 334466
Fax: 01788 334888
e-mail:
mal@therugbyfootballclub.com

Chairman	David Owen	c/o Rugby FC	
Chief Executive/ Secretary	"Mal" Malik	c/o Rugby FC	01788 334466 Fax: 01788 334887
Director of Rugby	"Mal" Malik	as above	
Directors	Eddie Saunders Mike Tarrant	c/o Rugby FC c/o Rugby FC	01788 334466 01788 334466
General Manager & Fixtures Secretary		c/o Rugby FC	01788 334885
Director of Coaching	TBA		
Marketing	Linda Dainty	c/o Rugby FC	01788 334466
Clubhouse Manager	Tracy Garrett	c/o Rugby FC	01788 334885

Having bounced back into National Division One, the Lions' target was a top six finish. The principal reasons for failing to achieve this were injuries to key players in pre-season training and the loss, in late September, of the club's influential coach, Paul Turner. It was anticipated that Rugby's young lightweight pack, coached by Leicester hooker Richard Cockerill, would come under pressure but, with a good set of backs spinning the ball wide would, it was hoped, compensate for this shortcoming.

The season started well with two wins, a draw and one close defeat at Exeter before an ominous run of seven lost league games, the first of them coinciding with Turner's departure for Gloucester. They included a shock defeat at Henley that provided the Hawks with their first league victory of the season. With ex-England Sevens coach Adrian Thompson taking charge, Rugby's fortunes picked up again as they won a home game against Otley in December, followed by good away victories at Bracknell and Wakefield and some of Rugby's youngsters had now begun to establish themselves. After two wins and two losses, defeat at Bedford, in a game they should have won, saw the departure of coach Thompson. This event was followed by five more lost games that included another shocker, this time against Moseley at Bournbrook. The season's end was, however, a happy one with a superlative win at Otley and a big home defeat of Bracknell.

Wing/scrum half Phil Reed was top try scorer and the supporter's Player of the Season but numerous other team members, including Richard Davies, Chris Richards, Pete Roberts, Chris Jones, Will Pilkington, Tristan Prosser-Shaw (Players' Player of the Year), Fa'atoto Moananu and Tim Stannard were nominated as Webby `Man of the Match' during the season.

Evergreen Eddie Saunders (nine games/six tries) who reached 103 league and 250 club tries, remains officially retired.

Tristan Prosser-Shaw after receiving the Players' Player of the Year award.

RUGBY LIONS

Comp.	Date	H/A	Opponents	Result & Score	Att	15	14	13	12	11
N1	01-09	H	Bedford	D 32-32	620	Roberts	Saunders	Potter	Hyde/t	Ogilvie-Bull/t
N1	08-09	H	Wakefield	W 18-6		Roberts	Read	Potter	Hyde	Moananu/t
N1	15-09	A	Exeter	L 15-20	810	Roberts/t	Read	Potter	Hyde	Moananu
N1	22-09	H	Moseley	W 28-19		Moananu	Read/t	Potter	Tassell	Ogilvie-Bull
N1	29-09	A	Manchester*	L 14-22	685	Moananu	Read	Potter	Tassell	Ogilvie-Bull
N1	06-10	H	Birmingham & Solihull	L 6-22		Richards	Read	Potter	Tassell	Moananu
N1	20-10	A	Henley Hawks	L 12-15	300	Stewart	Moananu(a/t)	Roberts	Tassell	Read
N1	11-11	A	London Welsh	L 15-37	730	Stewart	Moananu	Potter(b/t)	Ogilvie-Bull	Read
N1	17-11	H	Coventry	L 22-27	836	Moananu/t	Read	Stewart	Ogilvie-Bull	Saunders
N1	01-12	A	Worcester	L 5-30		Richards	Saunders	Potter	Ogilvie-Bull	Read/t
N1	08-12	H	Otley	W 25-19	500	Richards/2c2p	Saunders	Moananu	Davies	Read/t
N1	29-12	A	Bracknell	W 35-23	475	Richards/3c3p	Roberts/t	Davies	Ogilvie-Bull	Read/t
N1	12-01	A	Wakefield	W 18-16	300	Richards/c2p	Roberts/t	Ogilvie-Bull	Steyn	Read
N1	19-01	H	Exeter	L 10-34	420	Richards/cp	Roberts	Potter	Steyn(d/t)	Read
N1	02-02	H	Manchester	W 25-13	300	Richards/cp	Roberts/t	Newmarch	Potter	Read/t
N1	09-02	A	Birmingham & Solihull	L 11-13		Richards/2p	Roberts/t	Potter	Newmarch	Read
N1	15-02	H	Rotherham	L 14-47	300	Davies/2c	Roberts	Newmarch	Potter	Read/t
N1	23-02	H	Henley Hawks	W 25-13		Davies/t2p	Roberts/t	Newmarch	Potter	Read
N1	01-03	A	Bedford	L 15-25	1482	Davies	Roberts	Potter	Ogilvie-Bull	Read/t
N1	09-03	A	Rotherham	L 8-30	1500	Davies	Roberts/t	Ogilvie-Bull	Moananu	Read
N1	16-03	H	London Welsh	L 20-41	475	Davies	Roberts	Ogilvie-Bull	Moananu/t	Read/t
N1	23-03	A	Moseley	L 12-17	150	Davies/4p	Roberts	Steyn	Potter	Read
N1	30-03	A	Coventry	L 25-47	2195	Davies/2c	Saunders/t	Potter	Steyn(b/t)	Moananu
N1	06-04	H	Worcester	L 23-41	700	Richards/c2p	Saunders/t	Tassell(d/t)	Steyn	Roberts
N1	13-04	A	Otley	W 36-32		Richards/4cp	Saunders/2t	Potter	Steyn	Roberts/t
N1	27-04	H	Bracknell	W 49-27		Moananu/2t	Saunders/2t	Tassell	Potter	Roberts
PGC	13-10	A	Rotherham	L 3-48		Stewart	Hands	Hyde	Talbot	Moananu

** after opponents name indicates a penalty try. Brackets after a player's name indicates he was replaced. eg (a) means he was replaced by replacement code "a" and so on. / after a player or replacement name is followed by any scores he made - eg /t, /c, /p, /dg or any combination of these*

EVER PRESENT

Richard Davies, Tristan Prosser

Most Appearances:
26: Richard Davies, Tristan Prosser.
25: Phil Read. 24: Chris Jones.

PLAYERS USED

37 plus five as a replacement

MOST POINTS

Pts	Player	T	C	P	DG
127	R Davies	4	16	22	3
111	C Richards	3	18	20	-
60	P Read	12	-	-	-
40	P ROberts	8	-	-	-
30	E Saunders	6	-	-	-
30	T Prosser	6	-	-	-

MATCH FACTS

10	9	1	2	3	4	5	6	7	8
Davies/c5p	Walsh	Buxton	Brittin	Smith	Smith	Jones	Prosser	Pilkington	Tovo/t
Davies/c2p	Walsh	Greenbury	Brittin	Williams	Collier	Jones	Prosser/t	Pilkington	Smith
Davies/tcp	Walsh	Greenbury	Kuisiuk	Smith	Collier	Jones	Prosser	Lewitt	Smith
Davies/t2c2pdg	Walsh	Buxton	Brittin/t	Mee	Collier	Jones	Prosser	Pilkington	Smith
Davies/2c	Walsh	Buxton	Brittin	Woolrich/t	Collier	Jones	Lewitt	Pilkington	Prosser
Davies/2p	Walsh	Williams	Brittin	Woolrich	Collier	Jones	Prosser	Lewitt	Stannard
Davies/c	Walsh	Shadbolt	Brittin	Woolrich	Collier	Jones	Prosser	Lewitt	Tovo/t
Davies/cp	Bainbridge-Kay	Woolrich	Brittin	Smith	Collier/t	Jones	Prosser	Pilkington	Smith
Davies/2p2dg	Walsh	Shadbolt	Gladstone	Mee	Collier	Jones	Prosser/t	Lewitt	Smith
Davies	Walsh	Woolrich	Gladstone	Smith	Stannard	Jones	Tovo	Prosser	Smith
Jones	Walsh	Woolrich	Brittin	Mee	Collier/t	Jones	Prosser/t	Lewitt	Smith
Jones	Walsh	Woolrich	Brittin	Greenbury	Collier	Jones	Prosser/t	Tovo/t	Smith
Davies	Walsh	Woolrich	Brittin	Greenbury	Field(c/t)	Jones	Prosser	Lewitt	Smith
Davies	Walsh	Woolrich	Brittin	Greenbury	Stannard	Jones	Prosser	Lewitt	Tovo
Davies	Walsh	Greenbury	Gladstone	Smith	Collier	Jones	Prosser/t	Tovo/t	Stannard
Davies	Walsh	Shadbolt	Gladstone	Smith	Collier	Jones	Prosser	Pilkington	Stannard
Steyn	Edwards/t	Greenbury	Gladstone	Smith	Collier	Jones	Prosser	Tovo	Stannard
Steyn(a/t2c)	Edwards	Greenbury	Brittin	Smith	Stannard	Jones	Prosser	Lewitt	Gladstone
Richards/tcp	Edwards	Shadbolt	Brittin	Greenbury	Collier	Jones	Prosser	Pilkington	Stannard
Richards/p	Walsh	Greenbury	Brittin	Smith	Collier	Jones	Prosser	Pilkington	Stannard
Richards/2c2p	Walsh	Woolrich	Brittin	Smith	Collier	Jones	Prosser	Lewitt	Stannard
Jones	Walsh	Smith	Brittin	Mee	Smith	Jones	Prosser	Pilkington	Stannard
Richards/2p	Read/t	Woolrich	Kuisiuk	Smith	Stannard	Jones	Pilkington	Lewitt	Prosser
Davies	Read/t	Greenbury	Kuisiuk	Mee	Collier	Stannard	Pilkington	Lewitt	Prosser
Davies	Read/t	Greenbury	Kuisiuk	Smith	Collier	Jones	Prosser/t	Lewitt	Stannard
Davies/t3cp	Read/t	Greenbury	Kuisiuk	Carson	Stannard	Jones	Prosser	Pilkington	Tovo
Jones/p	Read	Shadbolt	Kuisiuk	Smith	Stannard	Thompson	Lewitt	Pilkington	Prosser

REPLACEMENTS: a - Chris Richards. b - Matt Tassell. c - Paul Thompson. d - James Ogilvie-Bull.

WHEN	Total	First Half	Second Half	1/4	2/4	3/4	4/4
The POINTS were scored	518	268	250	142	126	101	149
The POINTS were conceded	668	364	304	160	204	121	183
The TRIES were scored	63	29	34	15	14	11	23
The TRIES were conceded	82	42	40	19	23	16	24

HOW the TRIES were scored

Total	Backs	Forwards	F Back	Wing	Centre	H Back	F Row	Lock	B Row	Pen. Try
63	47	15	5	24	8	10	2	3	10	1

HOW the TRIES were conceded

Total	Backs	Forwards	F Back	Wing	Centre	H Back	F Row	Lock	B Row	Pen. Try
82	47	31	8	20	8	11	11	4	16	4

RUGBY LIONS

LEAGUE STATISTICS

compiled by Stephen McCormack

SEASON	Division	P	W	D	L	F	A	Pts Diff	Lge Pts	Lge Pos		Most Points		Most Tries
92-93	1	12	1	0	11	104	368	-264	2		26	Mark Mapletoft	3	Eddie Saunders
93-94	2	18	5	1	12	186	302	-116	11		115	Mark Mapletoft	5	Mark Mapletoft
94-95	3	18	11	0	7	355	271	84	22		131	Jim Quantrill	8	David Bishop
95-96	3	18	12	1	5	395	284	111	25		183	Jim Quantrill	8	Eddie Saunders
96-97	2	22	3	0	19	317	1060	-743	6		72	Jim Quantrill	8	Eddie Saunders
97-98	JN1	26	21	0	5	733	405	328	42		171	Jim Quantrill	11	Eddie Saunders
98-99	P2	26	9	0	17	425	660	-235	18	11	189	Martyn Davies	7	Eddie Saunders
99-00	P2	26	6	1	19	408	905	-497	13	13r	179	Martyn Davies	6	Oscar Wingham
00-01	N2	*25	19	2	4	888	320	568	40	2p	120	Jaques Steyn	16	Eddie Saunders
01-02	N1	26	9	1	16	518	668	-150	47	10	127	Richard Davies	12	Phil Read

BIGGEST MARGINS

Home Win	69pts - 69-0 v W Hartlepool 10.02.01
Away Win	57pts - 69-12 v Camberley 21.4.01
Home Defeat	62pts - 8-70 v Newcastle 8.2.97
Away Defeat	151pts - 5-156 v Newcastle 5.10.96

MOST CONSECUTIVE

Appearances	42 Steve Smith 11.4.92-14.1.95
Matches scoring Tries	5 Eddie Saunders
Matches scoring points	19 Chris Howard
Victories	8
Defeats	12

MOST POINTS

Scored at Home	80 v Camberley 2.12.00
Scored Away	69 v Camberley 21.4.01
Conceded at Home	72 v Richmond 22.3.97
Conceded Away	156 v Newcastle 5.10.96

MOST TRIES

Scored in a match	11 v Morley 25.10.97 (H)
Conceded in a match	24 v Newcastle 5.10.96 (A)

MOST APPEARANCES

by a forward	148 (9)Trevor Revan
by a back	219 (1)Eddie Saunders

	MOST IN A SEASON	MOST IN A CAREER	MOST IN A MATCH	
Points	189 Martyn Davies 98-99	559 Jim Quantrill 93-98	28 Jaques Steyn	v Camberley 2.12.00 (H)
Tries	16 Eddie Saunders 00-01	103 Eddie Saunders 87-01	3 Chris Howard	v Vale of Lune 10.9.88 (H)
			Eddie Saunders	v Bedford 12.4.95 (A)
				v Rotherham 23.9.95 (H)
				v Moseley 12.10.96 (H)
Conversions	36 Paul Turner 00-01	84 Jim Quantrill 93-98	9 Jaques Steyn	V Camberley 21.12.00 (H)
Penalties	42 Jim Quantrill 95-96	109 Jim Quantrill 93-98	7 Denzil Evans	v Richmond 15.10.94 (H)
Drop Goals	4 Richard Pell 87-88	14 Richard Pell 87-95	2 Richard Davies	v Coventry 17.11.01 (H)

OVERALL PLAYING RECORD

	P	W	D	L	F	A	Pts Diff
Home	17	10	0	7	315	256	59
Away	17	8	0	9	334	442	-108
Neutral	-	-	-	-	-	-	-
Total	34	18	0	16	649	698	-49

SEASON BY SEASON

Season	Result
1971-72	1R
1972-73	DNQ
1973-74	DNQ
1974-75	DNQ
1975-76	DNQ
1976-77	DNQ
1977-78	DNQ
1978-79	1R
1979-80	DNQ
1980-81	DNQ
1981-82	DNQ
1982-83	DNQ
1983-84	DNQ
1984-85	DNQ
1985-86	DNQ
1986-87	3R
1987-88	DNQ
1988-89	3R
1989-90	3R
1990-91	4R
1991-92	3R
1992-93	4R
1993-94	4R
1994-95	4R
1995-96	4R
1996-97	5R
1997-98	5R
1998-99	3R
1999-2000	4R
2000-01	4R
2001-02	3R

RUGBY LIONS RFU SENIOR CUP

STATISTICS

compiled by Stephen McCormack

TEAM RECORDS

Highest Score

48 v Liverpool St Helens 00/01

Biggest Winning Margin

46 (46-0) v Vagabonds 97/98

Highest Score Against

84 v Wasps 96/97

Biggest Losing Margin

76 (84-8) v Wasps 96/97

INDIVIDUAL RECORDS

Most Points in a match

Most Tries in a match

Most Conversions in a match

Most Penalties in a match

Most Drop Goals in a match

Lions' centre looking for a way through against Exeter.

Photo courtesy of Nigel Chanter (01392 467261)

RUGBY LIONS

FACT FILE

Founded: 1873
Nickname: The Lions
Web sites: www.the rugbylions.com
www.the rugbyfootballclub.com

Club Colours: Black shirt with red trim/black/black with red trim
Change colours: Red shirt with black trim/black/black with red trim

GROUND

Address: Webb Ellis Road, Rugby. CV22 7AU
Tel: 01788 334466 Fax: 01788 334888 email: mal@therugbyfootballclub.com
Capacity: 3,396 Seated: 240 Standing: Covered 600; Uncovered 2,556

Directions: Second turn right, half mile south west of town centre on A4071,Bilton Road.
From NW: M6 Jnc 1 A426 Rugby A4071 From NE: M1 Jnc 20 A426 Rugby A4071
From SE: M1 Jnc 17/M45/A4071 towards Rugby.
Nearest Railway Station: Rugby - recommend taxi 2 miles to ground

Car Parking: Available at ground

Admission: Season: V.P. £80 OAPs £45 u16 Free
Matchday: Adults £8 OAPs £5

Club Shop: Matchday 12-5, Mon-Fri 9-5 or by appointment.

Clubhouse: Matchdays 12-late & training nights
Functions: Capacity 120-200

Training Nights: Monday, Tuesday & Thursday evenings 6pm

PROGRAMME

Size: B4 Pages: 30 Price: £1.50
Editor: Dennis Keen

Advertising Rates:
Contact Linda Dainty 01788 34882

Lineout action from Lions' visit to Exeter.
Photo courtesy of Nigel Chanter (01392 467261)

WAKEFIELD RFC

President	D Beaumont	c/o Wakefield RFC, as below
Chairman	G Marshall	c/o Wakefield RFC, as below
Club Secretary	R Parkinson	c/o Wakefield RFC, College Grove, Eastmoor Rd., Wakefield WF1 3RR Tel: 01924 374801 Fax: 01924 290069
Director of Rugby	Roger Burman / Darryl Shelford - c/o Wakefield RFC as above	

"B" for Victory!

At 3pm on September 1st we little realised what a huge impact on our season the letter "B" was to have.

Having lost players of the calibre and experience of Carl Houston, Paul Rees, Alex Birkby, Danny Scarborough, Richard Hurton and others, it promised to be a difficult season despite the recruitment of players such as James Tapster, Dominic Castle, Richard Wigham and Phil Maddick. All are young and promising, though inexperienced at this level of play.

Experienced full back Phil Belgion also joined the club but later had to leave because of work commitments (an occupational hazard with part time players!). Newly relegated Rotherham, our visitors for the first game, were put down as an away banker but the truth was a long way short of that. Their 34-22 win included 3 converted tries in 10 minutes midway through the second half. In fact neither Rotherham nor Worcester managed more than 39 points against us. The last 8 games however produced 7 defeats and a draw. The draw – at home with Coventry – saw the visitors snatch a late result in injury time. Even more sickening was when London Welch snatched a 19-18 victory, again at home in injury time.

The final position of 9th was due to 3 doubles – Bedford (also won there in the Cup), Bracknell and Birmingham Solihull (but away in the Cup). The other 3 victories were home games against Otley, Mosely and Manchester. "B" was very kind to us in terms of victories.

After Christmas came the other significant input of the letter "B", when the Super League champions, Bradford Bulls, bought out the controlling interest in Wakefield. Whilst still early days in the relationship, their undoubted expertise is already beginning to have an effect. Nobody can predict the future but with The Bulls behind us, and if we can overcome what might be a difficult first season together, then maybe it really will be "B" for Victory.

Richard Hughes proving to be a bit of a handful for Exeter's Phil Sluman & Neil Clark.
Photo courtesy of Nigel Chanter (01392 467261)

WAKEFIELD

Comp.	Date	H/A	Opponents	Result & Score	Att	15	14	13	12	11
N1	01-09	H	Rotherham	L 22-34	1100	Belgian	Edwards	Summers	Winney	Metcalfe/2t
N1	08-09	A	Rugby Lions	L 6-18		Belgian	Edwards	Summers	Winney	Metcalfe
N1	15-09	H	London Welsh	L 18-21	350	Belgian	Tapster	Summers	Callaghan	Edwards
N1	22-09	A	Exeter	L 3-39	640	Cawthorne	Tapster	Winney	Callaghan	Edwards
N1	29-09	H	Coventry	D 20-20	350	Belgian	Tapster	Edwards	Winney	Callaghan
N1	06-10	A	Moseley	L 23-31		Belgian/t	Emmerson	Edwards	Winney	Tapster
N1	20-10	H	Worcester	L 8-39	350	Belgian/p	Tapster/t	Edwards	Callaghan	Sodje
N1	10-11	H	Otley	W 29-22	300	Liley/c4p	Feeley/t	Edwards/t	Callaghan	Tapster
N1	17-11	A	Birmingham & Solihull	W 22-18		Liley/c5p	Feeley	Edwards	Callaghan	Tapster
N1	01-12	H	Bracknell	W 33-22	300	Liley/2c2p	Feeley	Edwards/t	Callaghan	Tapster/t
N1	08-12	A	Henley Hawks	L 13-20	550	Liley/c2p	Feeley	Edwards	Callaghan	Tapster
N1	15-12	A	Manchester	L 16-27	381	Liley/c3p	Feeley	Edwards	Callaghan	Tapster/t
N1	29-12	H	Bedford	W 18-6	300	Winney	Tapster	Edwards	Callaghan	Feeley
N1	12-01	H	Rugby Lions	L 16-18	300	Winney	Tapster	Edwards	Callaghan	Feeley
N1	19-01	A	London Welsh	L 8-16	750	Winney	Feeley	Edwards	Callaghan	Tapster
N1	26-01	H	Exeter	L 15-27	300	Winney	Tapster	Metcalfe	Callaghan	Feeley/t
N1	02-02	A	Coventry	L 19-37	2043	Winney	Feeley(a/t)	Edwards	Callaghan	Tapster
N1	09-02	H	Moseley	W 17-15	350	Winney	Tapster/t	Edwards	Callaghan	Johnson/t
N1	23-02	A	Worcester	L 8-36	1811	Winney	Feeley/t	Wilkinson	Callaghan	Tapster
N1	02-03	A	Rotherham	L 8-30	1200	Winney	Feeley	Cawthorne	Parker	Tapster
N1	09-03	H	Manchester	W 56-10	350	Winney/t	Feeley/2t	Cawthorne/t	Callaghan/t	Tapster/t(c/t)
N1	16-03	A	Otley	L 33-45		Winney	Feeley/t	Cawthorne/t	Callaghan/t	Tapster
N1	30-03	H	Birmingham & Solihull	W 26-17	250	Winney	Feeley	Cawthorne	Callaghan	Tapster/t
N1	06-04	A	Bracknell*	W 42-8		Winney	Feeley	Cawthorne	Callaghan/t	Tapster
N1	13-04	H	Henley Hawks	D 13-13	250	Winney	Feeley	Cawthorne	Callaghan	Tapster
N1	27-04	A	Bedford	W 22-18	1601	Maddick	Feeley	Cawthorne	Callaghan	Tapster
PGC	13-10	A	Bedford	W 22-19	1071	Belgian/c	Sodje	Edwards	Winney	Tapster/t
PGC	03-11	A	Birmingham & Solihull	L 6-35		Belgian	Tapster	Edwards	Winney/dg	Feeley

** after opponents name indicates a penalty try. Brackets after a player's name indicates he was replaced. eg (a) means he was replaced by replacement code "a" and so on. / after a player or replacement name is followed by any scores he made - eg /t, /c, /p, /dg or any combination of these*

EVER PRESENT One

Most Appearances:

- 26: Nick Lloyd.
- 25: Jon Skurr.
- 24: Sam Blythe (2), Rob Liley, James Tapster (1), Ross Winney (2).

PLAYERS USED

36 plus two as a replacement

MOST POINTS

Pts	Player	T	C	P	DG
237	R Liley	1	32	50	6
30	J Tapster	6	-	-	-
30	J Feeley	6	-	-	-
28	S Blythe	5	-	-	1
25	N Lloyd	5	-	-	-
25	G Wilson	5	-	-	-

MATCH FACTS

10	9	1	2	3	4	5	6	7	8
Liley/2cp	Castle	Lloyd	Blythe/t	Bijl	Hughes	Manuel	Skurr	Hamilton	Wilson
Liley/2p	Castle	Lloyd	Blythe	Bijl	Hughes	Manuel	Skurr	Hamilton	Wilson
Liley/5p	Castle	Lloyd	Blythe/dg	Bijl	Watson	Manuel	Hughes	Hobson	Skurr
Liley/p	Castle	Lloyd	Blythe	Bijl	Watson	Manuel	Hughes	Hobson	Skurr
Liley/4pdg	Castle	Lloyd	Blythe	Bijl	Hughes	Manuel	Fletcher	Hobson	Skurr/t
Liley/c2p	Kendra	Lloyd	Blythe/t	Bijl	Hughes	Manuel/t	Fletcher	Wigham	Skurr
Winney	Kendra	Lloyd	Blythe	Bijl	Schofield	Manuel	Skurr	Wigham	Fletcher
Winney	Kendra	Lloyd	Blythe	Bijl	Hughes	Watson	Skurr	Wigham	Sowerby/t
Winney	Castle	Lloyd	Blythe/t	Bijl	Hughes	Watson	Skurr	Wigham	Sowerby
Winney/dg	Castle	Lloyd/t	Blythe/t	Bijl	Hughes	Watson	Skurr	Wigham	Wilson
Winney	Castle	Lloyd/t	Blythe	Bijl	Hughes	Watson	Skurr	Wigham	Wilson
Winney	Castle	Lloyd	Blythe	Bijl	Hughes	Schofield	Skurr	Wigham	Wilson
Liley/c2p	Castle	Lloyd/t	Blythe	Bijl	Hughes	Schofield	Skurr	Wigham	Wilson/t
Liley/t2p	Castle	Lloyd/t	Blythe	Bijl	Hughes	Schofield	Fletcher	Wigham	Wilson
Cawthorne/p	Castle	Lloyd	Blythe	Bijl	Hughes	Schofield/t	Skurr	Wigham	Wilson
Liley/cp	Castle	Lloyd	Blythe	Harper	Watson	Schofield/t	Skurr	Wigham	Wilson
Liley/2c	Castle(b/t)	Lloyd	Blythe	Harper	Watson/t	Schofield	Skurr	Sowerby	Fletcher
Liley/2cp	Cawthorne	Lloyd	Worsley	Harper	Manuel	Schofield	Skurr	Sowerby	Wilson
Liley/p	Cawthorne	Lloyd	Worsley	Hanson	Manuel	Schofield	Skurr	Sowerby	Wilson
Liley/p	Mee	Lloyd	Blythe	Harper	Manuel	Schofield	Skurr	Wigham	Wilson/t
Liley/5c2p	Mee	Lloyd	Blythe	Bijl	Manuel	Schofield	Skurr	Wigham/t	Wilson
Liley/4c	Mee	Lloyd/t	Blythe	Bijl	Manuel/t	Schofield	Skurr	Wigham	Wilson
Liley/2c3pdg	Mee	Lloyd	Blythe	Hanson	Manuel	Schofield	Skurr	Wigham	Wilson/t
Liley/4c2pdg	Mee/t	Lloyd	Blythe	Hanson	Manuel	Schofield	Skurr	Wigham	Wilson/2t
Liley/cpdg	Mee	Lloyd	Blythe/t	Hanson	Watson	Schofield	Skurr	Wigham	Wilson
Liley/c3p2dg	Mee	Lloyd	Blythe	Bijl	Manuel	Schofield/t	Skurr	Sowerby	Wilson
Liley/5p	Kendra	Lloyd	Blythe	Hanson	Schofield	Manuel	Skurr	Wigham	Fletcher
Liley/p	Kendra	Lloyd	Blythe	Bijl	Schofield	Watson	Skurr	Wigham	Hughes

REPLACEMENTS: a - Will Johnson. b - Mike Cawthorn. c - Alex Wilkinson

WHEN	Total	First Half	Second Half	1/4	2/4	3/4	4/4
The POINTS were scored	514	232	282	109	123	128	154
The POINTS were conceded	607	314	293	153	161	119	174
The TRIES were scored	54	20	34	9	11	15	19
The TRIES were conceded	69	33	36	15	18	14	22

HOW the TRIES were scored

Total	Backs	Forwards	F Back	Wing	Centre	H Back	F Row	Lock	B Row	Pen. Try
54	29	24	2	17	7	3	10	6	8	1

HOW the TRIES were conceded

Total	Backs	Forwards	F Back	Wing	Centre	H Back	F Row	Lock	B Row	Pen. Try
69	45	24	8	16	16	5	4	4	16	-

WAKEFIELD

LEAGUE STATISTICS
compiled by Stephen McCormack

SEASON	Division	P	W	D	L	F	A	Pts Diff	Lge Pts	Lge Pos	Most Points	Most Tries
92-93	2	12	8	1	3	186	123	63	17		101 Rob Liley	7 Jon Sleightholme
93-94	2	18	8	3	7	347	240	107	19		90 Mike Jackson	12 Jon Sleightholme
94-95	2	18	12	1	5	354	261	93	25		213 Mike Jackson	7 Richard Thompson
95-96	2	18	8	0	10	328	331	-3	16		177 Mike Jackson	7 Dave Scully
96-97	2	22	11	0	11	504	557	-53	22		199 Mike jackson	9 Dave Scully
97-98	P2	22	6	0	16	382	556	-174	12		141 Greg Miller	6 Dave Scully
98-99	P2	26	6	0	20	469	812	-343	12		76 Phil Ure	10 Ian Breheny
99-00	P2	26	10	0	16	547	638	-91	20	10	93 Tom Rhodes	9 Danny Scarborough
00-01	N1	26	15	0	11	568	503	65	70	4	111 Rob Liley	10 Carl Houston
01-02	N1	26	9	2	15	514	607	-93	47	9	237 Rob Liley	6 James Tapster 6 Jon Feeley

BIGGEST MARGINS

Home Win	70pts - 70-0 v MetropolitanPolice 24.9.88
Away Win	47pts - 50-3 v Birmingham 31.10.87
Home Defeat	69pts - 15-84 v Worcester 16.10.99
Away Defeat	48pts - 19-67 v Worcester 17.4.99

MOST CONSECUTIVE

Appearances	49 Dave Scully
Matches scoring Tries	4 Leroy McKenzie
Matches scoring points	21 Mike Jackson
Victories	10
Defeats	7

MOST POINTS

Scored at Home	70 v Metropolitan Police 24.9.88
Scored Away	50 v Birmingham 31.01.87
Conceded at Home	84 v Worcester 16.10.99
Conceded Away	67 v Worcester 17.4.99

MOST TRIES

Scored in a match	14 v Metropolitan Police 24.9.88
Conceded in a match	13 v Worcester 16.10.99

MOST APPEARANCES

by a forward	139(9) Rod Latham
by a back	160 (1) Dave Scully

	MOST IN A SEASON	MOST IN A CAREER	MOST IN A MATCH	
Points	237 Rob Liley 01-02	707 Mike Jackson 93-98	23 Rob Liley	v Rugby 11.9.93 (H)
Tries	12 Jon Sleightholme 93-94	52 Dave Scully 87-98	4 Ian Breheny	v Moseley 24.4.99 (H)
Conversions	33 Mike Jackson 96-97	82 Mike Jackson 93-98	7 Ray Adamson	v Birmingham 31.10.87 (A)
Penalties	57 Mike Jackson 94-95	165 Mike Jackson 93-98	6 Ray Adamson Mike Jackson Greg Miller	v Vale of Lune 27.2.88 (H) v Nottingham 1.10.94 (A) v Lon. Irish 22.10.94 (H) v Blackheath 18.4.98 (H)
Drop Goals	6 Rob Liley 01-02	9 Rob Liley 97-02	1 by 8 players	on 20 occasions incl Greg Miller(x3) Rob Liley(x9) Steve Townend(x2)

OVERALL PLAYING RECORD

	P	W	D	L	F	A	Pts Diff
Home							
Away							
Neutral							
Total							

SEASON BY SEASON

Season	Result
1971-72	DNQ
1972-73	DNQ
1973-74	DNQ
1974-75	DNQ
1975-76	SF
1976-77	1R
1977-78	2R
1978-79	1R
1979-80	DNQ
1980-81	DNQ
1981-82	DNQ
1982-83	4R
1983-84	DNQ
1984-85	3R
1985-86	4R
1986-87	3R
1987-88	3R
1988-89	QF
1989-90	4R
1990-91	2R
1991-92	2R
1992-93	4R
1993-94	4R
1994-95	QF
1995-96	5R
1996-97	QF
1997-98	4R
1998-99	3R
1999-2000	3R
2000-01	5R
2001-02	

WAKEFIELD RFU SENIOR CUP

STATISTICS

compiled by Stephen McCormack

TEAM RECORDS

Highest Score

53 v Morley 97/98

Biggest Winning Margin

39 Pts - 53-14 v Morley 97/98

Highest Score Against

47 v Harlequins 92/93

Biggest Losing Margin

29 Pts - 47-18 v Harlequins 92/93

INDIVIDUAL RECORDS

Most Points in a match

18 Greg Miller v Morley 97/98

Most Tries in a match

Most Conversions in a match

6 Greg Miller v Morley 97/98

Most Penalties in a match

Most Drop Goals in a match

Outside half Rob Liley gets Wakefield on the move against Exeter.
Photo courtesy of Nigel Chanter (01392 467261)

WAKEFIELD

FACT FILE

Founded: 1901
Nickname: Field

Colours: Black with 2 gold bands on rt sleeve/black/black
Change colours: Gold with irregular black hoops/black/black

GROUND

Address: College Grove, Eastmoor Road, Wakefield. WF1 3RR
Tel: 01924 374801 Fax: 01924 290069
Capacity: 2,450 Seated: 450 Standing: 2,000

Directions: From M1 Jnc 41, A650 into Wakefield City Centre, turn left at Queen Elizabeth Grammar School onto Westfield Road, ground in front 250 yards
From M62 Jnc 30, A642 into Wakefield, turn right at traffic lights immediately after Hospital onto Eastmoor Road, ground 300 yards on left
Nearest Railway Station: Wakefield Westgate

Car Parking: No parking in ground, 200 spaces nearby £1

Admission: Season Standing Adult £85
OAP £50, Children (12-17) £15
Family (2 adults & children) £150
Matchday Seated Adults £9, OAP £5 Children u12 £3
Standing Adult £8, OAP £4 Children u12 £2

Club Shop: Yes; Manager George Stephens via club

Clubhouse: Open during normal Licensing Hours. Three bars with snacks & bar meals available
Functions: Contact John Scones via club.
Also Hospitality lounge seating 72

Training Nights: Tuesday & Thursday

PROGRAMME Size: B5 Pages: 30
Price: £1

Advertising Rates
Colour: Page £350
1/2 page £200
Mono: Page £300
1/2 page £175
1/4 page £100

WORCESTER RFC

Sixways, Pershore Lane, Hindlip, Worcester, WR3 8ZE
Tel: 01905 454183 Fax: 01905 459302

Chairman	Cecil Duckworth	01905 459300	louiseb@wrfc.co.uk
Chief Executive	Chris Laidlaw	01905 459319	chrisl@wrfc.co.uk
Director of Rugby	John Brain	01905 459339	johnb@wrfc.co.uk
Academy Manager	Nigel Redman	01905 459338	nigelr@wrfc.co.uk
Operations Manager	Mike Robins	01905 459324	miker@wrfc.co.uk
Commercial Manager	Kathy Leather	01905 459326	kathyl@wrfc.co.uk
Club President	Roger Phillips		r_phillips@btopenworld.com
Club Hon Secretary	Adrian Harling		adrian@lawach.freeserve.co.uk

A fine start to the 2001/2002 season saw big wins over Manchester and Birmingham & Solihull. This form, however, did not continue, as the team seemed to lose some direction, and despite a hard fought victory over main promotion rivals Rotherham, bonus points were regularly dropped. The low points of the first half of the season were the shock loss to Coventry at Sixways and defeat at Exeter.

The Christmas break brought coaching changes as Steve Townend departed to make way for Andy Keast and a rejuvenated Worcester began to show their true capabilities. The pack continued to dominate possession and the newly confident back line turned on the style. Despite defeat at Rotherham the bonus points came at every following game bar the home encounter against London Welsh played in monsoon conditions.

The Coventry loss was avenged at Coundon Road and a heavy defeat of Manchester in the postponed fixture showed the new determination in the Worcester squad. The influence of Craig Chalmers, the pace of Chris Garrard combined with the evasive running of Duncan Roke tore defences apart. The fact that 3 of National 1's top 4 try scorers are based at Sixways gives an indication of how the performances changed in 2002.

The greatest satisfaction for the fans came in two matches. The win over Exeter at home was possibly the best Worcester performance of the season. Scoring in the opening minutes, a feast of running rugby saw no answers from an outplayed Exeter despite injuries to Chalmers and Richard Smith.

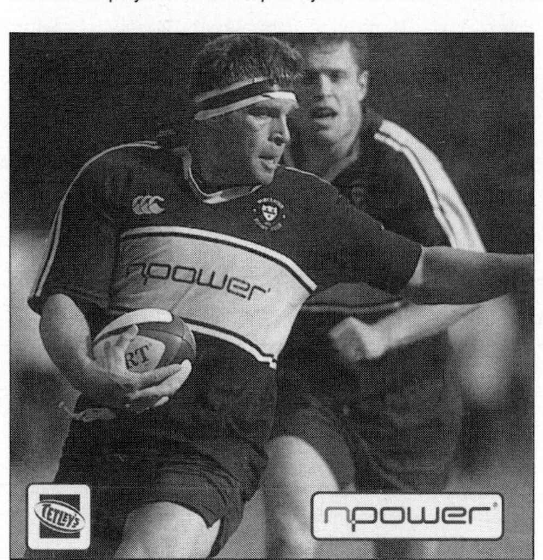

Jim Jenner, Player of the Year.

The Moseley jinx was finally broken at Bournbrook. Worcester had so far failed in every season to get the better of Moseley in an away league game. Two successive Cup wins had done nothing to ease the memories of defeats at The Reddings and Bournbrook. This though was to be Worcester's year and the season ended as it had begun, the pace and power was just too much for the University based opposition as the try count mounted.

The end of season party back at Sixways saw a celebration, not of promotion, but of a team re-born.

WORCESTER

Comp.	Date	H/A	Opponents	Result & Score	Att	15	14	13	12	11
N1	01-09	H	Manchester	W 45-11		Tuipulotu/6cp	Garrard/4t	Hinshelwood	Yates	Stanley/t
N1	08-09	H	Birmingham & Solihull	W 53-3	2123	Tuipulotu/4c2p	Garrard/t	Hinshelwood/2t	Yates/t	Stanley/2t
N1	15-09	A	Henley Hawks	W 31-0	950	Hinshelwood	Garrard/t	Truman	Yates	Wilks
N1	22-09	H	Rotherham	W 20-18	4800	Tuipulotu/2cp	Garrard/t	Hinshelwood/t	Yates	Stanley
N1	29-09	A	London Welsh	W 21-3		Tuipulotu/c(b/t)	Garrard	Hinshelwood/t	Yates	Stanley
N1	06-10	H	Coventry	L 22-31		Tuipulotu/2cp	Garrard/t	Hinshelwood	Yates/t	Stanley
N1	20-10	A	Wakefield	W 39-8	350	Hinshelwood/2t	Garrard	Roke/2t	Yates	Stanley/t
N1	27-10	A	Otley	W 40-23		Hinshelwood/t	Garrard/t	Barrow	Yates	Stanley/t
N1	11-11	H	Bracknell	W 32-6		Hinshelwood	Garrard	Roke/t	Yates/t	Stanley
N1	17-11	A	Bedford	W 20-11	1410	Hinshelwood/2t	Garrard	Roke	Yates	Stanley
N1	01-12	H	Rugby Lions	W 30-5		Hinshelwood	Garrard	Roke/t	Yates	Stanley/t
N1	08-12	A	Exeter	L 10-21	1520	Hinshelwood	Tuipulotu/cp	Roke	Yates	Stanley
N1	29-12	H	Moseley	W 33-12	3223	Tuipulotu/4c	Garrard/t	Hinshelwood	Yates	Murdoch/t
N1	12-01	A	Birmingham & Solihull	W 30-13		Tuipulotu/3c3p	Garrard	Hinshelwood	Yates/t	Murdoch
N1	19-01	H	Henley Hawks	W 66-17		Roke	Tuipulotu/3t7cp	Hinshelwood/2t	Yates	Murdoch/2t
N1	26-01	A	Rotherham	L 8-18	2500	Roke	Tuipulotu/p	Hinshelwood	Truman	Murdoch
N1	02-02	H	London Welsh	W 10-6		Roke	Tuipulotu	Hinshelwood	Truman	Garrard
N1	09-02	A	Coventry	W 33-26	3475	Roke/2t	Murdoch	Hinshelwood	Yates	Garrard/t
N1	16-02	A	Manchester	W 62-17	255	Roke/t	Murdoch/t	Hinshelwood/t	Yates/2t	Garrard/2t
N1	23-02	H	Wakefield	W 36-8	1811	Roke/t	Stanley	Hinshelwood/2t	Murdoch	Garrard/t
N1	09-03	H	Otley*	W 71-14	1750	Roke/t	Murdoch	Hinshelwood/t	Yates/t	Garrard/5t
N1	16-03	A	Bracknell	W 59-24		Roke/3t	Barrow	Hinshelwood/2t	Yates	Garrard/t
N1	30-03	H	Bedford	W 46-22	2296	Roke/t	Murdoch	Hinshelwood/t	Yates(h/t)	Garrard/t
N1	06-04	A	Rugby Lions	W 41-23	700	Roke	Murdoch/t	Hinshelwood/tc	Yates	Garrard/t
N1	13-04	H	Exeter	W 41-17	2721	Roke/t	Murdoch	Hinshelwood/t	Truman	Garrard/3t
N1	27-04	A	Moseley	W 42-7	1529	Roke/t	Murdoch	Hinshelwood/t	Truman/t(j/t)	Garrard
PGC	13-10	A	Lydney	W 45-0	987	Stanley/t	Tuipulotu/2c2p	Hinshelwood	Roke/2t	Murdoch
PGC	03-11	A	Moseley	W 50-3	1200	Hinshelwood/2tc	Stanley	Yates/t	Roke	Garrard/t
PGC	24-11	H	Rotherham	L 19-26	1610	Stanley	Garrard	Roke	Hinshelwood	Murdoch

** after opponents name indicates a penalty try. Brackets after a player's name indicates he was replaced. eg (a) means he was replaced by replacement code "a" and so on. / after a player or replacement name is followed by any scores he made - eg /t, /c, /p, /dg or any combination of these*

EVER PRESENT

One

Most Appearances:
26: B Hinshelwood.
24: Will Morgan (1), Richard Smith (1).
23: Chris Garrard.
22: Jim Jenner (3), Tony WIndo (1).

PLAYERS USED

32 plus four as a replacement

MOST POINTS

Pts	Player	T	C	P	DG
125	C Garrard	25	-	-	-
118	T Yapp	5	33	8	1
108	S Tuipulotu	3	30	11	-
107	B Hinshelwood	21	1	-	-
81	C Chalmers	2	25	7	-
80	D Roke	18	-	-	-

MATCH FACTS

10	9	1	2	3	4	5	6	7	8
Yapp	Smith	Windo	Hall	Lyman	Morgan	Zaltman	Clarke	Jones/t	Jenner
Chalmers/2c	Smith	Windo/t	Ross	Lyman	Zaltman	Morgan	Clarke	Jones	Jenner
Yapp/t2c4p	Smith	Windo	Ross	Lyman	Sims	Morgan	Clarke	Jones/t	Jenner
Chalmers(a/dg)	Smith	Windo	Ross	Moreno	Zaltman	Morgan	Clarke	Jones	Jenner
Yapp/2c	Smith	Windo	Ross	Moreno	Zaltman	Morgan/t	Clarke	Jones	Jenner
Yapp	Smith	Windo	Ross	Moreno	Zaltman	Morgan/t	Evans	Jones	Clarke
Chalmers/2c	Smith	Windo	Ross/t	Moreno	Zaltman	Morgan	Clarke	Jones	Jenner/t
Chalmers/3c3p	Smith	Windo	Ross	Moreno	Zaltman	Morgan	Clarke/t	Carter	Jenner/t
Vile/3c2p	Smith	Davies	Hall(c/t)	Moreno	Zaltman	Morgan	Clarke	Carter	Jenner/t
Vile/2c2p	Smith	Windo	Ross	Lyman	Zaltman	Morgan	Evans	Jones	Jenner
Yapp/2c3p(d/c)	Moncrieff	Windo	Hall(c/t)	Moreno	Sims	Zaltman	Clarke	Jones	Jenner
Chalmers	Moncrieff(f/t)	Davies	Ross	Moreno	Morgan	Zaltman	Evans	Jones	Jenner
Chalmers/t	Smith	Davies	Ross	Moreno	Morgan	Soper	Carter/t	Jones	Clarke(g/t)
Chalmers	Smith	Davies	Ross	Moreno	Morgan	Soper	Carter	Jones	Clarke/2t
Chalmers(a/2c)	Smith/t	Windo	Ross	Moreno	Zaltman	Morgan	Evans	Nias	Jenner/t
Chalmers	Smith	Windo	Ross/t	Moreno	Zaltman	Morgan	Evans	Nias	Jenner
Chalmers	Smith	Windo	Ross	Lyman	Sims	Morgan/t	Evans	Nias	Jenner/t
Chalmers/t2c3p	Smith	Windo	Ross	Moreno	Zaltman	Morgan	Evans	Jones	Jenner
Chalmers/5c(a/c)	Smith/t	Windo	Hall	Lyman	Sims	Morgan/t	Evans	Jones/t	Jenner
Chalmers/3c	Smith/t	Windo	Hall	Lyman	Sims	Morgan	Evans	Jones	Jenner/t
Yapp/t8c	Smith	Windo	Ross	Lyman	Sims	Soper	Mason/t	Jones	Jenner
Yapp/t7c	Smith	Windo/t	Ross	Lyman	Morgan/t	Sims	Mason	Jones	Evans
Chalmers/c(a/t2c)	Smith/t	Windo	Hall	Lyman	Zaltman	Morgan/2t	Evans	Jones	Jenner
Yapp(d/2c)	Smith/t	Windo	Hall/t	Lyman/t	Zaltman	Morgan(i/t)	Evans	Jones	Jenner
Chalmers/4cp(a/t)	Smith	Windo	Hall	Lyman	Zaltman	Morgan	Evans	Nias	Jenner
Yapp/t6c	Smith	Windo	Hall	Lyman	Zaltman/t	Morgan	Evans	Nias	Jenner
Yapp/3t	Smith/t	Windo	Ross	Moreno	Sims	Morgan	Evans	Jones	Clarke
Chalmers(e/5cp)	Smith	Davies/2t	Hall/t	Lyman	Zaltman	Sims	Evans	Carter	Jenner
Vile/c4p	Moncrieff	Windo	Hall	Lyman	Zaltman	Morgan	Evans	Jones	Jenner/t

REPLACEMENTS: a - Tony Yapp. b - Duncan Roke. c - Joe Ross. d - Craig Chalmers. e - Steven Vile. f - Richard Smith. g - Jim Jenner. h - Gary Truman. i - Dave Sims. j - Chris Yates.

WHEN	Total	First Half	Second Half	1/4	2/4	3/4	4/4
The POINTS were scored	941	514	427	261	253	173	254
The POINTS were conceded	364	166	198	76	90	86	112
The TRIES were scored	132	72	60	36	36	24	36
The TRIES were conceded	43	16	27	7	9	10	17

HOW the TRIES were scored

Total	Backs	Forwards	F Back	Wing	Centre	H Back	F Row	Lock	B Row	Pen. Try
132	99	32	17	39	30	13	8	9	15	1

HOW the TRIES were conceded

Total	Backs	Forwards	F Back	Wing	Centre	H Back	F Row	Lock	B Row	Pen. Try
43	29	14	3	15	6	5	3	2	9	-

WORCESTER

LEAGUE STATISTICS

compiled by Stephen McCormack

SEASON	Division	P	W	D	L	F	A	Pts Diff	Lge Pts	Lge Pos		Coach		Captain
92-93	Mid. 2	11	9	0	2	188	89	99	18	2p				
93-94	Mid. 1	12	8	0	4	234	104	130	16	2				
94-95	Mid. 1	12	11	1	0	278	82	196	23	1p		P Maynard		N Stoodley
												Most Points		**Most Tries**
95-96	D5N	12	9	0	3	317	187	130	18	2	50	Spencer Bradley	10	Spencer Bradley
96-97	D4N	26	23	3	0	830	375	455	49	1p	242	Tim Smith	18	Nick Baxter
97-98	JN1	26	24	0	2	1001	331	670	48	1p	221	Richard Le Bas	29	Nick Baxter
98-99	P2	26	18	0	8	716	409	307	34*	3	162	Richard Le Bas	13	Nick Baxter
99-00	P2	26	19	0	7	865	450	415	38	3	229	Tony Yapp	13	Nick Baxter
00-01	N1	26	23	1	2	844	387	457	112	2	349	Sateki Tuipulotu	17	Sateki Tuipulotu
01-02	N1	26	23	0	3	941	364	577	108	2	125	Chris Garrard	25	Chris Garrard

BIGGEST MARGINS

Home Win	68pts - 78-10 v Waterloo 20.11.99
Away Win	69pts - 84-15 v Wakefield 16.10.99
Home Defeat	15pts - 13-28 v Lon. Welsh 25.10.97
Away Defeat	42pts - 0-42 v Rotherham 8.4.00

MOST CONSECUTIVE

Appearances	24 Duncan Hughes
Matches scoring Tries	9 Nick Baxter
Matches scoring points	17 Tim Smith
Victories	18
Defeats	1

MOST POINTS

Scored at Home	78 v Liverpool St Helens 21.3.98 v Waterloo 20.11.99
Scored Away	84 v Wakefield 16.10.99
Conceded at Home	32 v Orrell 4.12.99 v Wakefield 26.2.00
Conceded Away	42 v Rotherham 8.4.00

MOST TRIES

Scored in a match	13 v Wakefield 16.10.99 (A)
Conceded in a match	6 v Rotherham 8.4.00 (A)

MOST APPEARANCES

by a forward	100(21) Neil Lyman
by a back	94(7) Nick Baxter

	MOST IN A SEASON	MOST IN A CAREER	MOST IN A MATCH
Points	349 Sateki Tuipulotu 00-01	457 Sateki Tuipulotu 00-02	31 Sateki Tuipulotu v Henley 20.1.01
Tries	29 Nick Baxter 97-98	88 Nick Baxter 95-01	6 Nick Baxter v Otley 21.2.98 (A)
Conversions	61 Tim Smith 96-97	87 Sateki Tuipulotu 00-02	9 Richard Le Bas v Liverpool St H 21.3.98 (H) Tony Yapp v Waterloo20.11.99 (H)
Penalties	50 Sateki Tuipulotu 00-01	61 Sateki Tuipulotu 00-02	5 Tim Smith v Leeds 27.12.97 (A)
Drop Goals	2 Rich Wylde 95-96 Gareth Hughes 96-97	2 Rich Wylde 95-98 Gareth Hughes 96-97 Greg Harwood 95-98	1 By six players - Ulan Richards, Richard Wylde (2), Greg Harwood (2), Gareth Hughes (2), Richard LeBas, Tony Yapp

OVERALL PLAYING RECORD

	P	W	D	L	F	A	Pts Diff
Home	10	6	0	4	207	149	58
Away	14	9	0	5	413	247	166
Neutral	-	-	-	-	-	-	-
Total	24	15	0	9	620	396	224

SEASON BY SEASON

1971-72	DNQ
1972-73	DNQ
1973-74	DNQ
1974-75	DNQ
1975-76	DNQ
1976-77	DNQ
1977-78	DNQ
1978-79	DNQ
1979-80	DNQ
1980-81	DNQ
1981-82	DNQ
1982-83	2R
1983-84	DNQ
1984-85	DNQ
1985-86	DNQ

1986-87	DNQ
1987-88	DNQ
1988-89	DNQ
1989-90	DNQ
1990-91	DNQ
1991-92	DNQ
1992-93	2R
1993-94	DNQ
1994-95	DNQ
1995-96	4R
1996-97	2R
1997-98	5R
1998-99	4R
1999-2000	4R
2000-01	5R
2001-02	5R

WORCESTER
RFU SENIOR CUP
STATISTICS
compiled by Stephen McCormack

TEAM RECORDS

Highest Score
76 v Tynedale 00/01
Biggest Winning Margin
64 (76-12) v Tynedale
Highest Score Against
42 v Saracens 00/01
Biggest Losing Margin
29 (42-13) v Saracens 00/01

INDIVIDUAL RECORDS

Most Points in a match
36 Sateki Tuipulotu v Tynedale 00/01
Most Tries in a match
4 Sateki Tuipulotu v Tynedale 00/01
Most Conversions in a match
8 Sateki Tuipulotu v Tynedale 00/01
Most Penalties in a match

Most Drop Goals in a match

L-R - Back Row: Chris Garrard, Ben Clarke, Christian Evans, Martin Morgan, Lee Soper, Dave Sims, Dan Zaltsman, Chris Yates, George Davies, Winston Stanley, Tom Warren.
MiddleRow: Peter Finch (Fitness Coach), Alessandro Moreno, Tony Windo, Andy Collins, Richard Nias, Duncan Roke, Dave Fryday, Greg Meredith, Richard Smith, Dan Cullen, Ollie Smith, Steve Townsend (Asst. Coach), John Brain (Head Coach)
Front: Ricky Pellow, Elton Moncrief, Nathan Carter, Chris Hall, Alistair Murdoch, Tony Yapp, Kinesley Jones (Capt.) Jim Jenner, Gary Truman, Scott Barrow, Joe Ross, Craig Chalmers.

WORCESTER

FACT FILE

Founded: 1871
Nickname: 'Warriors'
Website: www.wrfc.co.uk

Colours: Old gold and navy
Change colours: White, red and green

GROUND

Address: Sixways, Pershore Lane, Hindlip, Worcester. WR3 8ZE
Tel: 01905 454183 Fax: 01905 459352 email: rugby@wrfc.co.uk
Capacity: 5,000 Seated: 3,700 (covered) 1,000 (uncovered) Standing: 300

Directions: M5 junction 6 (Worcester North) and follow the signs for Worcester Rugby Centre. Take B4538 to Droitwich and the ground is 300 yards on the left.
For Parking: M5 junction 6 and follow AA signs for Park And Walk at Shire Business Park.
Car Parking: Limited parking on site @£5
Nearest Railway Station: Worcester Shrub Hill and taxi or Worcester Foregate Street and bus link from Crowngate Bus Station.

Admission: Season From £96 (Adults)
Matchday Adults £8, £10, £12 - Child discounts available.
Contact Maxine James, Ticket Office manager on 01905 459325

Club Shop: Open Tue., Thur. & Fri. 9-3.30; Sat. 11-3 or 11-6 (1st XV matchdays) & Sun. 9.30-1.30
Contact Jane Fudger, Retail Manager, on 01905 459308.

Clubhouse: Open matchdays 12- late, eveing games 6-11pm.
Snacks, light meals and silver service catering available.
Wide range of hospitality and catering facilities for groups up to 300 available throughout the week. Contact Kathy Leather on 01905 459326

PROGRAMME Size: B5
Pages: 64
Price: £2

Editorial and Advertising Rates contact Mike Robins on 01905 459324

The programme cover shows Worcester's Player of the Year, Jim Jenner, in action

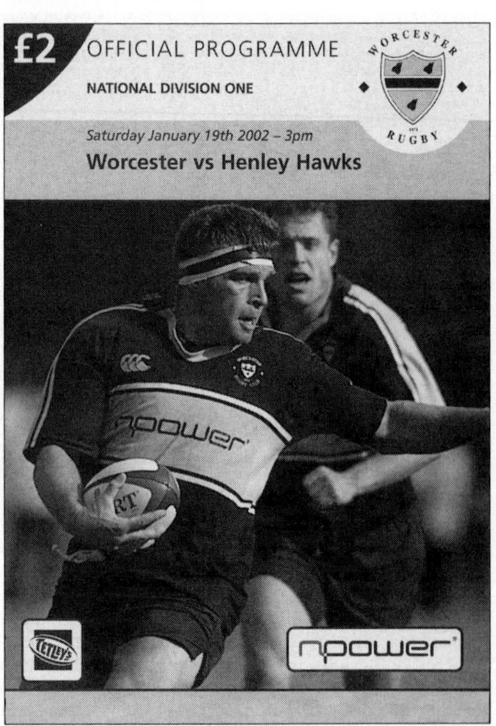

RECORDS SECTION

DIVISION TWO
(CURRENTLY NATIONAL LEAGUE ONE)

THE LAST TEN YEARS DIVISION TWO

1992-93
Champions Newcastle Gosforth
Runners-up Waterloo
Relegated Bedford, Rosslyn Park, Richmond, Blackheath, Coventry, Fylde & Morley.
Most
Points: 136 David Johnson (Newcastle Gosforth)
Tries: 8 Martin Kelly (Broughton Park)
Penalties: 16 David Johnson (Newcastle Gosforth)
Conversions: 30 David Johnson (Newcastle Gosforth)
D.Gs: 9 Guy Gregory (Nottingham)

1993-94
Champions Sale
Runners-up West Hartlepool
Relegated Rugby, Otley
Most
Points: 172 Guy Gregory (Nottingham)
Tries: 16 Simon Verbickas (Sale)
Penalties: 29 Paul Turner (Sale)
Conversions: 43 Guy Gregory (Nottingham)
D.Gs: 5 Guy Gregory (Nottingham)
Murray Walker (London Scottish)

1994-95
Champions Saracens
Runners-up Wakefield
Relegated Fylde, Coventry
Most
Points: 213 Mike Jackson (Wakefield)
Tries: 8 Tony Penn (Newcastle Gosforth)
Penalties: 21 Simon Mason (Newcastle Gosforth)
Andy Tunningley (Saracens)
Conversions: 57 Mike Jackson (Wakefield)
D.Gs: 6 Andy Lee (Saracens)

1995-96
Champions Northampton
Runners-up London Irish
Relegated No relegation
Most
Points: 301 Michael Corcoran (London Irish)
Tries: 20 Matt Allen (Northampton)
Penalties: 76 Paul Grayson (Northampton)
Conversions: 63 Michael Corcoran (London Irish)
D.Gs: 5 Sam Howard (Blackheath)

1996-97
Champions Richmond
Runners-up Newcastle
Relegated Rugby, Nottingham
Most
Points: 334 Simon Mason (Richmond)
Tries: 23 John Bentley (Newcastle)
Penalties: 47 John Steele (London Scottish)
Conversions: 95 Rob Andrew (Newcastle)
D.Gs: 5 Jez Harris (Coventry)

1997-98
Champions Bedford
Runners-up West Hartlepool
Relegated No relegation
Most
Points: 289 Mike Rayer (Bedford)
Tries: 29 Darragh O'Mahoney (Moseley)
Ben Whetstone (Bedford)
Penalties: 66 Lyndon Griffiths (Waterloo)
Conversions: 65 Mike Rayer (Bedford)
D.Gs: 5 Matt Jones (Moseley)

1998-99
Champions Bristol
Runners-up Rotherham
Relegated Blackheath, Fylde
Most
Points: 305 Steve Gough (Coventry)
Tries: 18 Dean Lax (Rotherham)
Penalties: 53 Steve Gough (Coventry)
Conversions: 48 Steve Gough (Coventry)
D.Gs: 3 by 4 players

1999-00
Champions Rotherham
Runners-up Leeds Tykes
Relegated Rugby Lions, West Hartlepool
Most
Points: 312 Sam Howard (Exeter)
Tries: 18 Dean Lax (Rotherham)
Penalties: 55 Matt Jones (Henley) &
Steve Swindells (Manchester)
Conversions: 60 Mike Umaga (Rotherham)
D.Gs: 5 Sam Howard (Exeter)

2000-01
Champions Leeds Tykes
Runners-up Worcester
Relegated Orrell, Waterloo
Most
Points: 349 Sateki Tuipulotu (Worcester)
Tries: 19 Graham Mackay (Leeds Tykes)
Penalties: 51 Martyn Davies (Coventry)
Conversions: 72 Richard Le Bas (Leeds Tykes)
D.Gs: 9 David Sleman (Orrell)

2001-02
Champions Rotherham
Runners-up Worcester
Relegated Henley Hawks, Bracknell
Most
Points: 283 Simon Binns (Otley)
Tries: 25 Chris Garrard (Worcester)
Penalties: 63 Simon Binns (Otley)
Conversions: 60 Ramiro Pez (Rotherham)
D.Gs: 7 Chris Malone (Exeter

ALL TIME RECORDS TEAM RECORDS DIVISION TWO

Highest score:	**156**	Newcastle 156 Rugby 5. 5.10.96
Highest aggregate:	**161**	As above
Highest score by a losing side:	**36**	Moseley 36 Blackheath 51. 27.4.96
Highest scoring draw:	**24**	London Scottish v London Welsh 13.4.88
		Nottingham v Newcastle Gosforth 13.1.96
Most consecutive wins:	**22**	Rotherham 1999-00
Most consecutive defeats:	**14**	West Hartlepool 1999-00
Most points for in a season:	**1255**	Newcastle 1996-97
Least points for in a season:	**81**	Northampton 1987-88
Most points against in a season:	**1114**	West Hartlepool 1999-00
Least points against in a season:	**80**	Saracens 1989-90
Most tries for in a season:	**189**	Newcastle 1996-97
Most tries against in a season:	**151**	West Hartlepool 1999-00
Least tries for in a season:	**7**	Morley 1992-93
Least tries against in a season:	**5**	Sale 1992-93
Most conversions for in a season:	**119**	Newcastle 1996-97
Most conversions against in a season:	**101**	Orrell 1996-97
Most penalties for in a season:	**66**	Waterloo 1997-98
Most penalties against in a season:	**54**	London Scottish 1996-97
Least penalties for in a season:	**6**	Gosforth 1987-88
Least penalties against in a season:	**8**	Saracens 1987-88, Sale 1990-91
Most drop goals for in a season:	**11**	London Scottish 1994-95
Most drop goals against in a season:	**12**	London Irish 1994-95

ALL TIME RECORDS INDIVIDUAL RECORDS DIVISION TWO

Most points in a season:	**334**	Simon Mason (Richmond) 1996-97
Most tries in a season:	**23**	John Bentley (Newcastle) 1996-97
Most conversions in a season:	**95**	Rob Andrew (Newcastle) 1996-97
Most penalties in a season:	**66**	Lyndon Griffiths (Waterloo) 1997-98
Most drop goals in a season:	**8**	Guy Gregory (Nottingham) 1992-93
Most points in a match:	**42**	Jez Harris, *Coventry* v Nottingham 5.10.96
Most tries in a match:	**5**	Simon Verbickas, *Sale* v Otley 12.2.94
		Pat Lam, *Newcastle* v Rotherham 4.5.97
		Luke Nabaro, *Bristol* v Blackheath 13.3.99
Most conversions in a match:	**18**	Rob Andrew, *Newcastle* v Rugby 5.10.96
Most penalties in a match:	**8**	Alastair Kerr, *Moseley* v Waterloo 17.2.96
Most drop goals in a match:	**3**	Martin Livesey, Richmond v Northampton 19.11.88
		Murray Walker, Lon. Scottish v W. Hartlepool 23.4.94

ALL TIME RECORDS MOST POINTS IN A SEASON DIVISION TWO

Points	Player	Club	Season	Tries	Cons.	Pens.	D.G.
349	Sateki Tuopulotu	Worcester	2000-01	17	57	50	-
333	Richard Le Bas	Leeds Tykes	2000-01	9	72	48	-
324	Simon Mason	Richmond	1996-97	10	83	36	
312	Sam Howard	Exeter	99-2000	5	55	54	5
310	Michael Corcoran	London Irish	1995-96	8	36	63	
305	Steve Gough	Coventry	1998-99	10	48	53	0
297	Rob Andrew	Newcastle	1996-97	7	95	23	1
289	Mike Rayer	Bedford	1997-98	6	65	43	
283	Simon Binns	Otley	2001-02	5	30	63	3
266	Steve Gough	Coventry	99-2000	5	47	49	-
261	Lyndon Griffiths	Waterloo	1997-98	1	29	66	
256	John Steele	Northampton	1996-97	5	39	47	4
251	Mike Umaga	Rotherham	99-2000	5	60	33	-
250	Sateki Tuipulotu	Leeds Tykes	1998-99	3	38	53	-
247	Chris Malone	Exeter	2001-02	5	45	37	7
244	Simon Binns	Rotherham	1997-98	8	39	41	1
241	Steven Vile	West Hartlepool	1997-98	8	33	43	2
241	Bryan Easson	Exeter	1998-99	2	39	51	-
239	Martyn Davies	Coventry	2000-01	4	33	51	-
239	James Pritchard	Bedford	2001-02	7	42	40	-
238	Mike Rayer	Bedford	1996-97	7	67	23	
237	Steve Swindells	Manchester	99-2000	2	31	55	-
237	Rob Liley	Wakefield	2001-02	1	32	50	6
236	Jez Harris	Coventry	1996-97	4	48	35	5
236	Matt Jones	Henley Hawks	99-2000	1	30	55	1
229	Tony Yapp	Worcester	99-2000	6	50	33	-
224	Simon Verbickas	Orrell	1998-99	13	30	33	-
223	Martyn Davies	Coventry	2001-02	5	30	46	-
218	Paul Grayson	Northampton	1995-96	3	76	14	3
213	Mike Jackson	Wakefield	1994-95	2	16	57	
201	Lyndon Griffiths	Waterloo	99-2000	-	33	45	-
199	Mike Jackson	Wakefield	1996-97	5	33	35	1
199	John Fabian	Henley Hawks	2001-02	2	24	47	-
198	Lyndon Griffiths	Waterloo	1998-99	2	25	46	-
198	Andy Lee	London Welsh	99-2000	2	46	32	-
197	Ramiro Pez	Rotherham	2001-02	4	60	19	-
193	Simon Mason	Newcastle	1994-95	1	21	45	2
190	Jon Benson	Leeds Tykes	99-2000	4	40	40	-
190	Philip Belgian	Waterloo	2000-01	5	21	41	-
189	Martyn Davies	Rugby Lions	1998-99	4	23	41	-
181	Ben Harvey	Moseley	2000-01	2	21	41	2
179	Martyn Davies	Rugby Lions	99-2000	1	21	42	2
179	David Sleman	Orrell	2000-01	8	17	26	9
179	Andy Lee	London Welsh	2000-01	2	23	41	-
178	Matt Jones	Moseley	1997-98	3	26	32	5
177	Mike Jackson	Wakefield	1995-96	2	19	43	
177	Richard Le Bas	Moseley	1996-97	3	27	36	
176	Steve Gough	Birmingham & Sol	2000-01	2	17	42	2
174	Jon Fabian	Exeter	1997-98	2	16	44	
172	Alastair Kerr	Moseley	1995-96	7	13	36	2
171	Guy Gregory	Nottingham	1993-94	1	11	43	5
171	Matt Jones	Henley Hawks	2000-01	-	21	42	1
165	Simon Verbickas	Orrell	1997-98	12	24	19	
164	Michael Corcoran	London Irish	1994-95	3	16	38	1
164	Paul Hull	Bristol	1998-99	5	35	23	-

ALL TIME RECORDS MOST POINTS IN A MATCH DIVISION TWO

Points	Player	Match	Date
42	Jez Harris	Coventry v Nottingham	05.10.96
41	Simon Binns	Rotherham v West Hartlepool	02.10.99
36	Rob Andrew	Newcastle v Rugby	05.10.96
34	Steve Gough	Coventry v London Welsh	10.10.98
33	Mike Umaga	Rotherham v Waterloo	11.03.00
32	Sateki Tuipulotu	Worcester v Hanley Hawks	19.01.02
31	Sam Howard	Exeter v West Hartlepool	06.05.00
	Sateki Tuipulotu	Worcester v Henley Hawks	20.01.01
30	Michael Corcoran	London Irish v Waterloo	23.09.95
	John Steele	London Scottish v Rugby	29.03.97
	Andy Lee	London Welsh v Rugby	08.12.99
	Ramiro Pez	Rotherham v Coventry	15.09.01
29	Simon Mason	Richmond v Rotherham	14.09.96
	Simon Verbickas	Orrell v Wakefield	25.04.98
	Tony Yapp	Worcester v Wakefield	16.10.99
	Andy Lee	London Welsh v Bracknell	20.10.01
28	David Johnson	Newcastle Gosforth v Morley	11.01.92
	David Johnson	Newcastle Gosforth v Liverpool StH	29.02.93
27	Simon Hodgkinson	Moseley v London Irish	08.04.95
	Simon Verbickas	Orrell v Waterloo	08.05.99
	Marcus Barrow	Manchester v Wakefield	15.12.01
26	Andy Mitchell	London Scottish v Northampton	03.10.87
	Michael Corcoran	London Irish v Bedford	21.10.95
	Michael Corcoran	London Irish v Blackheath	28.10.95
	Steven Vile	West Hartlepool v Fylde	14.02.98
	Jon Benson	Leeds Tykes v Manchester	05.04.00
	Richard Le Bas	Leeds v Orrell	17.03.01
	Lee Hinton	Moseley v Bedford	15.09.01
25	Chris Howard	Rugby v Newcastle Gosforth	11.11.89
	Andy Finnie	Bedford v Coventry	27.03.93
	Guy Gregory	Nottingham v Otley	11.09.93
	Simon Verbickas	Sale v Otley	12.02.94
	John Steele	London Scottish v Bedford	14.10.95
	Simon Mason	Richmond v Nottingham	16.11.96
	Pat Lam	Newcastle v Rotherham	04.05.97
	Richard Le Bas	Worcester v Exeter	10.10.98
	Steve Swindells	Manchester v Exeter	09.10.99
	Steve Gough	Coventry v Worcester	11.03.00
	RIchard Le Bas	Leeds v Birmingham & Solihull	09.09.00
	Steve Gough	Birmingham & Solihull v Leeds Tykes	09.09.00
	Sateki Tuipulotu	Worcester v Manchester	23.09.00
	Chris Garrard	Worcester v Otley	09.03.02
	Simon Binns	Otley v Wakefield	16.03.02
	Michael Wood	Rotherham v Birmingham & Solihull	13.04.02
24	Simon Irving	Headingley v London Scottish	12.11.88
	Andy Kennedy	Saracens v Nottingham	12.11.88
	Nick Grecian	London Scottish v Blackheath	16.11.91
	Alastair Kerr	Moseley v Waterloo	17.02.96
	Simon Mason	Richmond v London Scottish	12.10.96
	Jez Harris	Coventry v London Scottish	19.10.96
	Simon Mason	Richmond v Rugby	22.03.97
	Steve Gough	Coventry v Fylde	26.09.98
	Steve Gough	Coventry v Rugby	29.04.00
	Matt Jones	Henley v Rugby	15.01.00
	Steve Swindells	Manchester v Moseley	14.10.00

ALL TIME RECORDS — MOST TRIES IN A MATCH — DIVISION TWO

5

Simon Verbickas	Sale v Otley	12.02.94
Pat Lam	Newcastle v Rotherham	04.05.97
Luke Nabaro	Bristol v Blackheath	13.03.99
Chris Garrard	Worcester v Otley	09.03.02
Michael Wood	Rotherham v Birmingham & S.	13.04.02

4

Craig Moir	Northampton v Waterloo	13.04.96
Gary Armstrong	Newcastle v Nottingham	14.09.96
Scott Quinnell	Richmond v Waterloo	02.11.96
John Bentley	Newcastle v Wakefield	08.03.97
John Clarke	Blackheath v Fylde	20.09.97
Jason Foster	Bedford v Fylde	17.01.98
Ben Wade	Rotherham v Exeter	25.04.98
John Fabian	Exeter v Waterloo	17.10.98
Lennie Woodward	Lon. Welsh v Fylde	12.12.98
Jonathon Scales	Leeds Tykes v Exeter	07.02.99
Dean Lax	Rotherham v Orrell	13.02.99
Ian Breheny	Wakefield v Moseley	24.04.99
Andy Smallwood	Coventry v Wakefield	08.05.99
Andy Currier	London Welsh v Waterloo	06.10.99
Chris Garrard	Worcester v Manchester	01.09.01
Jamie Greenlees	Manchester v Bracknell	15.09.01

3

Jerry Macklin	Lon. Scottish v Northampton	03.10.87
Orsen Blewitt	Northampton v Bedford	21.11.87
John Roberts	Headingley v Northampton	16.04.88
Pete Rowland	Coventry v Lon. Irish	10.09.88
Dave Kennell	Headingley v Gosforth	14.01.89
Laurie Smith	Saracens v Gosforth	22.04.89
Nigel Saunders	Plymouth v Blackheath	14.10.89
Graham Robbins	Coventry v Waterloo	13.01.90
Rob Saunders	Lon. Irish v Rugby	13.10.90
Jonathan Wrigley	W Hartlepool v Moseley	14.12.91
Peter Walton	Newcastle G. v Blackheath	14.12.91
Jon Sleightholme	Wakefield v Blackheath	04.01.92
Gary Clark	Newcastle G. v Liverpool StH	29.02.92
Richard Arnold	Newcastle G. v Liverpool StH	29.02.92
Dave Spiller	Moseley v Sale	04.04.92
Richard Gee	Coventry v Moseley	19.09.92
Malcolm Walker	Nottingham v Moseley	24.10.92
Mark Warr	Sale v Otley	12.02.94
Matt Allen	Northampton v Lon. Irish	09.09.95
Conor O'Shea	Lon. Irish v Moseley	30.09.95
Gregor Townsend	Northampton v Blackheath	14.10.95
Grant Seeley	Northampton v Blackheath	14.10.95
Matt Allen	Northampton v Newcastle G.	21.10.95
Matt Allen	Northampton v Waterloo	28.10.95
Gregor Townsend	Northampton v Lon. Scottish	04.11.95
Gregor Townsend	Northampton v Lon. Irish	11.11.95
Gary Armstrong	Newcastle G. v Waterloo	30.03.96
Alan Royer	Nottingham v Moseley	30.03.96
Matt Allen	Northampton v Lon. Scottish	27.04.96
Mitch Hoare	Blackheath v Rotherham	07.09.96
Scott Quinnell	Richmond v Rotherham	14.09.96
Andy McAdam	Coventry v Nottingham	05.10.96
Derek Eves	Coventry v Nottingham	05.10.96
Jim Fallon	Richmond v Moseley	05.10.96
Scott Quinnell	Richmond v Moseley	05.10.96
Gary Armstrong	Newcastle v Rugby	05.10.96
Ross Nesdale	Newcastle v Rugby	05.10.96
George Graham	Newcastle v Rugby	05.10.96
Dean Ryan	Newcastle v Rugby	05.10.96
Eddie Saunders	Rugby v Moseley	12.10.96
Jim Fallon	Richmond v Rugby	19.10.96
John Bentley	Newcastle v Moseley	19.10.96
Andy McAdam	Coventry v Lon. Irish	19.10.96
Steve Wichary	Lon. Scottish v Moseley	26.10.96
Craig Quinnell	Richmond v Waterloo	02.11.96
Tim Stimpson	Newcastle v Lon. Scottish	16.11.96
Darragh O'Mahoney	Moseley v Nottingham	02.02.97
John Bentley	Newcastle v Rugby	08.02.97
Julian Horrobin	Coventry v Blackheath	08.03.97
Steve Bates	Newcastle v Nottingham	16.03.97
John Bentley	Newcastle v Moseley	22.03.97
Va'aiga Tuigamala	Newcastle v Moseley	22.03.97
Scott Quinnell	Richmond v Rugby	22.03.97
Matt Griffiths	Blackheath v Waterloo	19.04.97
Jason Hall	Nottingham v Rugby	19.04.97
Jim Fallon	Richmond v Wakefield	19.04.97
Ronnie Eriksson	Lon. Scottish v Fylde	30.08.97
Cunan Sharman	Lon. Scottish v Bedford	20.09.97
Nigel Heslop	Orrell v Fylde	04.10.97
Ben Whetstone	Bedford v Coventry	08.11.97
Jason Forster	Bedford v Fylde	27.12.97
Simon Verbickas	Orrell v Coventry	24.01.98
Darragh O'Mahoney	Moseley v Waterloo	14.02.98
Jason Minshull	Coventry v Waterloo	07.03.98
Julian Horrobin	Coventry v West Hartlepool	28.03.98
Darragh O'Mahoney	Moseley v Fylde	25.04.98
Richard Stone	Bedford v Blackheath	25.04.98
Simon Verbickas	Orrell v Wakefield	25.04.98
Rob Myler	Worcester v Wakefield	12.09.98
Wayne Kilford	Coventry v Fylde	26.09.98
Adam Larkin	Bristol v Blackheath	03.10.98
Steve Gough	Coventry v L. Welsh	10.10.98
Mike White	Lon. Welsh v Wakefield	17.10.98
Andy Currier	Lon. Welsh v Exeter	21.11.98
Wendal Sailor	Leeds Tykes v Fylde	17.01.99
Ben Wade	Rotherham v Leeds Tykes	23.01.99
Richard baxter	Exeter v Fylde	23.01.99
Andy Currier	Lon. Welsh v Coventry	27.02.99
Karl Johnson	Orrell v Bristol	27.02.99
Luke Nabaro	Bristol v Rugby Lions	03.04.99
Neil Marden	Lon. Welsh v Blackheath	17.04.99
Lennie Woodward	Lon. Welsh v Blackheath	17.04.99
Nick Baxter	Worcester v Wakefield	17.04.99
Dean Lax	Rotherham v Waterloo	24.04.99
Matt Walker	Rotherham v Worcester	01.05.99
Wayne Reed	Exeter v Orrell	01.05.99
Simon Verbickas	Orrell v Waterloo	08.05.99
Simon Binns	Rotherham v W. Hartlepool	02.10.99
Howard Parr	Rotherham v W. Hartlepool	02.10.99
Nigel Cane	Coventry v W. Hartlepool	16.10.99
Martin Dawson	Rotherham v Orrell	23.10.99
Duncan Roke	Henley v Moseley	20.11.99
Jim Jenner	Worcester v Watreloo	20.11.99
Dave Scully	Rotherham v Exeter	22.01.00
Carl Houston	Wakefield v Manchester	12.02.00
Matt Sims	Coventry v W. Hartlepool	19.02.00
Simon Frost	London Welsh v Waterloo	19.02.00
Doug Trivela	Rotherham v Waterloo	11.03.00
Peter Buckton	Moseley v Coventry	18.03.00
Nick Drake	London Welsh v Manchester	19.03.00
Simon Frost	London Welsh v Wakefield	15.04.00
Kurt Johnson	Coventry v Henley	22.04.00
Andy Beattie	Exeter v W. Hartlepool	06.05.00
Richard Le Bas	Leeds v Wakefield	19.11.00
Alastair McLean	Worcester v London Welsh	25.11.00
Matt Vines	London Welsh v Orrell	02.12.00
Scott Benton	Leeds v Waterloo	06.01.01
Sateki Tuipulotu	Worcester v Henley Hawks	20.01.01
Kurt Johnson	Coventry v Bedford	27.01.01
Shaun Woof	Leeds v Bedford	10.02.01
Danny Scarbrough	Wakefield v Bedford	24.02.01
Chris Hall	Leeds v Manchester	24.02.01
Spencer Bromley	Worcester v Bedford	10.03.01
Chris Hall	Leeds v Moseley	10.03.01

TEN YEAR RECORDS DIVISION TWO

SEASONS

Club	92-93	93-94	94-95	95-96	96-97	97-98	98-99	99-00	00-01	01-02
Bedford	7	-	-	10	4	1	-	-	11	6
Birmingham Solihull	-	-	-	-	-	-	-	-	9	8
Bracknell	-	-	-	-	-	-	-	-	-	14
Blackheath	10	-	-	7	10	9	13	-	-	-
Bristol	-	-	-	-	-	-	1	-	-	-
Coventry	11	-	10	-	3	7	7	6	5	4
Exeter	-	-	-	-	-	11	5	4	3	3
Fylde	12	-	9	-	-	12	14	-	-	-
Gosforth/Newcastle	1	-	3	8	2	-	-	-	-	-
Henley Hawks	-	-	-	-	-	-	-	9	7	13
Leeds (Tykes)	-	-	-	-	-	-	6	2	1	-
Liverpool St. Helens	-	-	-	-	-	-	-	-	-	-
London Irish	-	-	5	2	-	-	-	-	-	-
London Scottish	-	8	4	3	5	3	-	-	-	-
London Welsh	-	-	-	-	-	-	4	5	6	5
Manchester	-	-	-	-	-	-	-	8	8	12
Morley	13	-	-	-	-	-	-	-	-	-
Moseley	6	5	6	6	8	6	10	7	10	11
Northampton	-	-	-	1	-	-	-	-	-	-
Nottingham	4	6	7	9	12	-	-	-	-	-
Orrell	-	-	-	-	-	5	8	11	13	-
Otley	-	10	-	-	-	-	-	-	12	7
Plymouth Albion	-	-	-	-	-	-	-	-	-	-
Richmond	9	-	-	-	1	-	-	-	-	-
Rosslyn Park	8	-	-	-	-	-	-	-	-	-
Rotherham	-	-	-	-	7	4	2	1	-	1
Rugby (Lions)	-	9	-	-	11	-	11	13	-	10
Sale	5	1	-	-	-	-	-	-	-	-
Saracens	-	3	1	-	-	-	-	-	-	-
Wakefield	3	4	2	4	6	10	12	10	4	9
Waterloo	2	7	8	5	9	8	9	12	14	-
West Hartlepool	-	2	-	-	-	2	-	14	-	-
Worcester	-	-	-	-	-	-	3	3	2	2

MOST TRIES IN A MATCH cont.

Carl Houston	Wakefield v London Welsh	10.03.01
Steve Bachop	Leeds v Orrell	17.03.01
Sateki Tuipulotu	Worcester v Manchester	17.03.01
Graham Mackay	Leeds London Welsh	21.04.01
Russell Earnshaw	Bracknell v Rotherham	06.10.01
Nick Baxter	Birmingham & S v Manchester	10.11.01
Matt Vines	London Welsh v Rugby Lions	11.11.01
Chris Bejak	Bedford v London Welsh	24.11.01
Geoff Gregory	London Welsh v Moseley	01.12.01
Oriol Ripol	Rotherham v Henley Hawks	29.12.01
Sateki Tuipulotu	Worcester v Henley Hawks	19.01.02
Richard Baxter	Rugby Lions v Exeter	19.01.02
Chris Johnson	Coventry v Rotherham	19.01.02
Fred Fichot	Bedford v Birmingham & S	02.02.02
Stuart Dixon	Rotherham v Bracknell	09.02.02
Richard Protherough	Moseley v Henley Hawks	16.03.02
Duncan Roke	Bracknell v Worcester	16.03.02
Sam Nowak	Bracknell v Worcester	16.03.02
Chris Garrard	Worcester v Exeter	13.04.02
Richard John	Exeter v Otley	27.04.02

Exeter's Piran Tretheway crashes into Coventry's Tigger Dawson and Elisi Vinupola.

Photo courtesy of Nigel Chanter (01392 467261)

Exeter's Chris Malone escapes the grip of the Rotherham defence to score.

Photo courtesy of Nigel Chanter (01392 467261)

PLAYERS SECTION

Premiership and National One clubs

This season we introduce a players section.
This gives details of all league matches, National Cup matches and European games played by players who qualify.
The European section is complete and the league appearance section is fairly comprehensive but the National Cup appearances needs some work.
We hope to have it complete and up to date for the next edition.
To qualify a player has to have been on the pitch in 15 matches in the league for their club last season.
This has seen a number of players omitted so next season we will adjust that figure.

Just to confuse, you will see that some Wt. & Ht.measurements are metric and some are Imperial
Conversions factors cms divded by 2.54 for inches
kg multiply by 2.2 for lbs.

NAME		D.o.B.	Birthplace Club	Ht. Position	Wt.		Apps	Pts	T	P	C	DG
Stuart	Abbott	03.06.78	SouthAfrica	183cm	87kg							
			Leicester	Center		NL	2(0)	-	-	-	-	-
			LondonWasps	Center		NL	7(9)	15	3	-	-	-
						NC	1(0)	-	-	-	-	-
Dave	Addleton	30.03.65	England	5 9	14 2							
			Coventry	Hooker		NL	44(17)	30	6	-	-	-
						NC	5(0)	10	2	-	-	-
Peter	Anglesea	30.10.71	England	191cm	104kg							
			Orrell	Flanker		NL	21(1)	15	3	-	-	-
						ES	1(0)	-	-	-	-	-
			Sale	Flanker		NL	76(7)	45	9	-	-	-
						NC	5(1)	-	-	-	-	-
						ES	15(2)	25	5	-	-	-
Gerald	Arasa	21.12.80	*	176cm	85kg							
			Saracens	RightWing		NL	10(15)	30	6	-	-	-
						NC	2(2)	10	2	-	-	-
						ES	2(3)	10	2	-	-	-
						EC	0(1)	-	-	-	-	-
Gareth	Archer	15.12.74	England	198cm	114kg							
			Bristol	Lock		NL	59(1)	10	2	-	-	-
						NC	5(0)	-	-	-	-	-
						ES	9(0)	10	2	-	-	-
			Newcastle	Lock		NL	61(1)	30	6	-	-	-
						NC	7(0)	-	-	-	-	-
						ES	7(0)	10	2	-	-	-
Gary	Armstrong	30.09.66	Scotland	173cm	86kg							
			Newcastle	ScrumHalf		NL	105(17)	314	60	4	2	-
						NC	17(1)	5	1	-	-	-
						ES	14(0)	15	3	-	-	-
						EC	3(2)	5	1	-	-	-
Mike	Armstrong	27.06.71	England	5 10	15"							
			Manchester	Hooker		NL	28(32)	5	1	-	-	-
						NC	1(4)	5	1	-	-	-
Richard	Arnold	16.08.69		193cm	100kg							
			Newcastle	O'sideFlanker		NL	166(8)	69	15	-	-	-
						NC	13(3)	-	-	-	-	-
						ES	19(0)	10	2	-	-	-
						EC	3(2)	-	-	-	-	-

Oliver	Azam	21.10.74	France	185cm	115kg							
			Gloucester	Hooker		NL	28(9)	30	6	-	-	-
						ES	3(1)	5	1	-	-	-
						EC	8(0)	-	-	-	-	-
Simon	Baker	01.02.75	England	5 7	13'							
			Manchester	ScrumHalf		NL	12(37)	-	-	-	-	-
						NC	0(5)	-	-	-	-	-
Iain	Balshaw	18.03.79	England	186cm	83kg							
			Bath	RightWing		NL	76(9)	186	35	1	-	3
						NC	4(2)	-	-	-	-	-
						EC	18(1)	22	4	1	-	-
Oliver	Barklay	28.11.81	England	178cm	83kg							
			Bath	OutsideHalf		NL	19(2)	129	2	7	35	-
						NC	0(1)	-	-	-	-	-
						EC	5(2)	30	-	3	8	-
Tom	Barlow	28.09.77	England	6 0	13 10							
			Leicester	RightWing		NL	3(0)	5	1	-	-	-
						EC	3(0)	5	1	-	-	-
			PlymouthAlbion	OutsideHalf		NL	51(0)	466	22	82	55	9
						NC	3(0)	19	-	2	5	-
David	Barnes	12.07.76	England	183cm	112kg							
			Bath	Prop		NL	32(12)	-	-	-	-	-
						NC	1(0)	-	-	-	-	-
						EC	10(2)	5	1	-	-	-
			Harlequins	Prop		NL	22(9)	5	1	-	-	-
						NC	4(0)	-	-	-	-	-
						EC	2(0)	-	-	-	-	-
			Newcastle	Prop		NL	0(1)	-	-	-	-	-
						NC	1(0)	-	-	-	-	-
						ES	0(1)	-	-	-	-	-
			WestHartlepool	Prop		NL	9(1)	5	1	-	-	-
Marcus	Barrow	05.12.78	England	6 0	13 10							
			Manchester	FullBack		NL	23(9)	158	3	13	39	-
						NC	2(0)	5	-	1	1	-
James	Batt	13.05.75	England	6 1	17 4							
			Manchester	Prop		NL	55(2)	30	6	-	-	-
						NC	8(0)	10	2	-	-	-
			Sale	Prop		NL	0(1)	-	-	-	-	-
Jos	Baxendell	03.12.72	England	183cm	89kg							
			Sale	Center		NL	143(11)	129	25	2	-	-
						NC	12(1)	5	1	-	-	-
						ES	16(3)	32	4	6	-	-
Nick	Baxter	13.04.73	England	6 0	14 7							
			Birmingham&S.	LeftWing		NL	26(0)	75	15	-	-	-
						NC	4(0)	5	1	-	-	-
			Worcester	LeftWing		NL	94(9)	440	88	-	-	-
						NC	2(1)	-	-	-	-	-
Rob	Baxter	10.03.71	England	196cm	108kg							
			Exeter	Lock		NL	205(0)	55	11	-	-	-
						NC	8(0)	5	1	-	-	-
Richard	Baxter	23.06.78	England	193cm	108kg							
			Exeter	BlindsideFlanker		NL	??(12)	??	31	-	-	-
						NC	8(1)	10	2	-	-	-
Nick	Beal	02.12.70	England	188cm	95kg							
			Northampton	FullBack		NL	134(1)	212	29	11	14	1
						NC	10(0)	18	3	-	-	1
						ES	8(1)	20	4	-	-	-
						EC	11(0)	5	1	-	-	-
Joe	Beardshaw	30.10.76	England	196cm	109kg							
			Bedford	Lock		NL	3(1)	-	-	-	-	-
			LondonWasps	Lock		NL	15(32)	5	1	-	-	-
						NC	2(0)	-	-	-	-	-
						EC	4(7)	-	-	-	-	-
Gary	Becconsall		England	0cm	0kg							
			Leicester	ScrumHalf		NL	1(1)	-	-	-	-	-
			Moseley	ScrumHalf		NL	10(9)	5	1	-	-	-
						NC	1(1)	-	-	-	-	-
			RugbyLions	ScrumHalf		NL	16(2)	30	6	-	-	-
						NC	3(0)	-	-	-	-	-

Chris	Bejak	01.07.74	England	178cm	100kg							
			Bedford	RightWing		NL	34(10)	75	15	-	-	-
						NC	2(0)	10	2	-	-	-
Stephen	Bell	21.03.76	Ireland	183cm	85kg							
			Bedford	ScrumHalf		NL	21(0)	15	3	-	-	-
						NC	1(0)	-	-	-	-	-
			Ulster	ScrumHalf								
						EC	1(2)	-	-	-	-	-
Chris	Bell	07.07.83	England	188cm	95kg							
			Harlequins	Center		NL	10(10)	10	2	-	-	-
						NC	1(2)	-	-	-	-	-
						EC	2(0)	5	1	-	-	-
			PlymouthAlbion	Center		NL	6(0)	5	1	-	-	-
Scott	Bemand	21.09.78	England	180cm	88kg							
			Harlequins	ScrumHalf		NL	7(8)	10	2	-	-	-
						NC	0(2)	-	-	-	-	-
						EC	4(1)	-	-	-	-	-
			Moseley	ScrumHalf		NL	15(13)	10	2	-	-	-
						NC	1(0)	-	-	-	-	-
Abdelatif	Benazzi	20.08.68	France	198cm	110kg							
			Saracens	Lock		NL	16(2)	-	-	-	-	-
						NC	1(0)	-	-	-	-	-
						ES	3(0)	-	-	-	-	-
Agen	Lock											
						ES	1(1)	5	1	-	-	-
Alex	Bennett	18.01.75	Wales	0cm	0kg							
			Orrell	Flanker		NL	48(5)	80	16	-	-	-
						NC	6(0)	15	3	-	-	-
						ES	2(0)	-	-	-	-	-
			Saracens	Flanker		NL	8(2)	-	-	-	-	-
						NC	1(1)	5	1	-	-	-
						ES	2(0)	-	-	-	-	-
			Llanelli	Flanker								
			Brive	Flanker		ES	0(1)	-	-	-	-	-
Jon	Benson	11.01.76	England	0cm	87kg							
			LeedsTykes	FullBack		NL	52(16)	264	4	65	38	-
						NC	6(1)	43	-	17	3	-
						ES	4(1)	45	-	9	9	-
			WestHartlepool	OutsideHalf		NL	15(5)	41	3	7	4	-
						NC	2(0)	-	-	-	-	-
Chris	Bentley	25.04.79	England	0cm	0kg							
			Orrell	Lock		NL	68(1)	10	2	-	-	-
						NC	9(0)	-	-	-	-	-
Scott	Benton	08.09.74	England	0cm	90kg							
			Gloucester	ScrumHalf		NL	50(3)	40	8	-	-	-
						NC	4(1)	5	1	-	-	-
						ES	4(1)	5	1	-	-	-
			LeedsTykes	ScrumHalf		NL	68(0)	130	26	-	-	-
						NC	4(1)	25	5	-	-	-
						ES	2(2)	15	3	-	-	-
			Morley	Scrumhalf		NL	18	30	6	-	-	-
Lee	Best	16.10.78	England	191cm	102kg							
			Bristol	FullBack		NL	39(6)	47	9	1	-	-
						NC	6(0)	10	2	-	-	-
						ES	1(3)	-	-	-	-	-
			Richmond	FullBack		NL	5(2)	15	3	-	-	-
						NC	1(0)	-	-	-	-	-
Adam	Bidwell	15.07.75	England	6 2	15 8							
			LondonWelsh	Center		NL	34(3)	28	5	-	-	1
						NC	3(0)	-	-	-	-	-
Robert	Bieniasz	10.08.79	England	6 1	17 0							
			Manchester	Prop		NL	14(27)	-	-	-	-	-
						NC	1(1)	-	-	-	-	-
Rueban	Bijl	22.10.77	England	0cm	0kg							
			LondonScottish	Prop		NL	0(1)	-	-	-	-	-
			Wakefield	Prop		NL	37(30)	10	2	-	-	-
						NC	1(3)	-	-	-	-	-

Simon	Binns	20.09.74	England	181cm	92kg							
			LondonScottish	OutsideHalf		NL	12(5)	-	-	-	-	-
						NC	0(1)	-	-	-	-	-
			Otley	OutsideHalf		NL	24(0)	283	5	30	63	3
						NC	1(0)	11	-	1	2	1
			Rotherham	OutsideHalf		NL	39(0)	172	12	26	16	4
						NC	1(0)	8	-	1	2	-
Andy	Binns	29.06.76	England	0cm	0kg							
			Moseley	Center		NL	54(0)	93	6	12	13	-
						NC	2(0)	-	-	-	-	-
Alex	Birkby	21.07.77	England	5 9	14 0							
			LondonWelsh	ScrumHalf		NL	14(10)	15	3	-	-	-
						NC	1(0)	-	-	-	-	-
			Wakefield	ScrumHalf		NL	64(7)	80	10	6	6	-
						NC	3(0)	-	-	-	-	-
Justin	Bishop	08.11.74	Ireland	186cm	87kg							
			LondonIrish	RightWing		NL	139(4)	155	31	-	-	-
						NC	15(1)	25	5	-	-	-
						ES	24(3)	30	6	-	-	-
Adam	Black	24.05.75	England	188cm	121kg							
			Bedford	Prop		NL	14(3)	5	1	-	-	-
						NC	1(0)	-	-	-	-	-
						ES	4(0)	-	-	-	-	-
			LondonWasps	Prop		NL	7(8)	5	1	-	-	-
						NC	1(2)	-	-	-	-	-
						EC	0(2)	-	-	-	-	-
			Sale	Prop		NL	18(24)	10	2	-	-	-
						NC	3(2)	5	1	-	-	-
						ES	9(6)	5	1	-	-	-
Ross	Blake	29.12.79	England	5 9	12 8							
			Bristol	Scrum Half		NL	5(18)	-	-	-	-	-
						NC	0(2)	-	-	-	-	-
						ES	2(2)	-	-	-	-	-
Adrian	Blowers	27.03.75	NewZealand	193cm	110kg							
			Northampton	Flanker		NL	31(0)	10	2	-	-	-
						NC	6(0)	-	-	-	-	-
						EC	6(0)	5	1	-	-	-
			Wellington	Flanker								
Sam	Blythe		England	0cm	0kg							
			Wakefield	Hooker		NL	43(24)	28	5	-	-	1
						NC	4(2)	-	-	-	-	-
Jake	Boer	01.11.75	SouthAfrica	188cm	104kg							
			Gloucester	O'sideFlanker		NL	37(3)	10	2	-	-	-
						NC	3(0)	-	-	-	-	-
						ES	2(3)	15	3	-	-	-
						EC	5(0)	-	-	-	-	-
			LondonIrish	BlindsideFlanker		NL	33(1)	15	3	-	-	-
						NC	7(0)	5	1	-	-	-
						ES	4(1)	5	1	-	-	-
Steve	Booth		England	0cm	0kg							
			Leicester	FullBack		NL	19(7)	81	12	3	3	2
						NC	1(1)	-	-	-	-	-
						EC	6(1)	15	3	-	-	-
Steve	Borthwick	12.10.79	England	199cm	101kg							
			Bath	Lock		NL	76(2)	-	-	-	-	-
						NC	4(0)	-	-	-	-	-
						EC	19(0)	5	1	-	-	-
Liam	Botham	26.08.77	England	182cm	96kg							
			Newcastle	RightWing		NL	33(0)	17	3	1	-	-
						NC	4(0)	10	2	-	-	-
						ES	7(0)	20	4	-	-	-
						EC	4(0)	-	-	-	-	-
			WestHartlepool	Center		NL	11(1)	10	2	-	-	-
Gregg	Botterman	03.03.68	England	6 1	15 7							
			LondonWelsh	Hooker		NL	32(39)	25	5	-	-	-
						NC	5(2)	5	1	-	-	-
			Saracens	Hooker		NL	88(10)	25	5	-	-	-
						NC	3(3)	5	1	-	-	-
						ES	4(1)	-	-	-	-	-

Andy	Boyle		England	0cm	0kg							
			Otley	No.8		NL	2(14)	10	2	-	-	-
						NC	1(0)	-	-	-	-	-
			Harrogate	No.8		NL	3(2)	-	-	-	-	-
Simon	Brading	03.07.79	England	0cm	0kg							
			Moseley	Center		NL	57(9)	35	7	-	-	-
						NC	3(0)	5	1	-	-	-
Richard	Bradshaw	24.01.78	England	6 7	17 7							
			Manchester	Lock		NL	36(20)	10	2	-	-	-
						NC	5(1)	-	-	-	-	-
Shaun	Brady		England	6 1	108kg							
			Coventry	Flanker		NL	16(18)	20	4	-	-	-
						NC	1(1)	-	-	-	-	-
			RugbyLions	Flanker		NL	8(3)	-	-	-	-	-
						NC	0(1)	-	-	-	-	-
Simon	Brocklehurst	-	England	5 11	85kg							
			Coventry	Centre		NL	19(2)	35	7	-	-	-
						NC	2(0)	10	2	-	-	-
			RugbyLions	Center		NL	1(5)	-	-	-	-	-
Mike	Brookes		England	0cm	0kg							
			Birmingham&S.	Flanker		NL	46(12)	30	6	-	-	-
						NC	4(5)	-	-	-	-	-
			Moseley	Flanker		NL	0(1)	-	-	-	-	-
Keith	Brooking	07.05.73	England	180cm	102kg							
			Exeter	Hooker		NL	61(14)	20	4	-	-	-
						NC	6(0)	-	-	-	-	-
John	Brooks	11.11.77	England	178cm	108kg							
			Bedford	Prop		NL	27(18)	-	-	-	-	-
						NC	2(1)	5	1	-	-	-
James	Brooks	06.03.80	England	178cm	84kg							
			Northampton	OutsideHalf		NL	16(8)	28	5	-	-	1
						NC	1(2)	-	-	-	-	-
						EC	2(3)	5	1	-	-	-
Steve	Brotherstone	16.03.71	Scotland	183cm	108kg							
			Newcastle	Hooker		NL	7(1)	-	-	-	-	-
			Northampton	Hooker		NL	12(12)	-	-	-	-	-
						NC	1(1)	-	-	-	-	-
						EC	6(5)	-	-	-	-	-
Olivier	Brouzet	22.11.72	France	201cm	117kg							
			Northampton	Lock		NL	35(2)	-	-	-	-	-
						NC	3(0)	-	-	-	-	-
						EC	5(0)	5	1	-	-	-
Alex	Brown	17.05.79	Englnad	201cm	111kg							
			Bristol	Lock		NL	38(4)	5	1	-	-	-
						NC	4(0)	-	-	-	-	-
						ES	11(1)	5	1	-	-	-
Andy	Brown		England	5 9	13 0							
			Otley	ScrumHalf		NL	120(11)	140	28	-	-	-
						NC	3(0)	10	2	-	-	-
Ian	Brown	09.03.78	England	193cm	108kg							
			Exeter	Lock		NL	27(11)	5	1	-	-	-
						NC	2(3)	-	-	-	-	-
John	Broxson	05.10.80	England	0cm	0kg							
			Orrell	Scrum Half		NL	18(22)	26	2	5	2	-
						NC	5(0)	8	1	-	-	1
Warwick	Bullock	09.02.70	England	0cm	0kg							
			Birmingham&S.	Prop		NL	54(11)	30	6	-	-	-
						NC	4(5)	-	-	-	-	-
			Gloucester	Prop								
						ES	1(0)	-	-	-	-	-
Glenn	Bunny	12.12.75	Other	6 0	14 3							
			PlymouthAlbion	Center		NL	20(1)	60	12	-	-	-
						NC	1(0)	-	-	-	-	-
Simon	Bunting	17.09.70	England	188cm	114kg							
			Rotherham	Prop		NL	134(17)	30	6	-	-	-
						NC	4(1)	5	1	-	-	-
						ES	2(2)	-	-	-	-	-

Paul	Burke	01.05.73	Ireland	173cm	85kg							
			Bristol	OutsideHalf		NL	34(2)	331	4	49	69	2
						NC	1(0)	12	-	-	4	-
						ES	9(0)	109	2	12	24	1
			Harlequins	OutsideHalf		NL	36(1)	391	3	38	92	8
						NC	4(0)	68	1	6	16	1
						ES	4(1)	62	-	7	15	1
						EC	3(1)	30	1	5	5	-
Jonathan	Burke	01.12.71	England	6 6	17 0							
			Otley	No.8		NL	139(9)	80	16	-	-	-
						NC	2(0)	-	-	-	-	-
Ben	Buxton	09.11.79	England	188cm	107kg							
			Moseley	Prop		NL	16(0)	-	-	-		
	-	-	RugbyLions	Prop		NL	3(1)	-	-	-	-	-
						NC	0(1)	-	-	-	-	-
Matthew	Cairns	31.03.79		178cm	95kg							
			Saracens	Hooker		NL	18(31)	5	1	-	-	-
						NC	1(4)	-	-	-	-	-
						ES	3(3)	30	6	-	-	-
						EC	0(6)	-	-	-	-	-
Aaron	Callaghan	13.03.72	England	0cm	0kg							
			Wakefield	Center		NL	57(8)	25	5	-	-	-
						NC	1(2)	-	-	-	-	-
Nigel	Cane	19.09.77	England	6 0	13 7							
			Coventry	ScrumHalf		NL	5(9)	20	4	-	-	-
						NC	0(1)	-	-	-	-	-
			Gloucester	ScrumHalf		NL	0(1)	-	-	-	-	-
						NC	2(0)	-	-	-	-	-
			PlymouthAlbion	ScrumHalf		NL	45(1)	55	11	-	-	-
						NC	2(1)	2	-	1	-	-
Jon	Cannon		Canada	0cm	0kg							
			Rotherham	Center		NL	15(1)	35	7	-	-	-
						NC	4(0)	15	3	-	-	-
Paul	Carr	25.03.68	England	6 5	15 0							
			LondonWelsh	Lock		NL	70(13)	10	2	-	-	-
						NC	2(1)	5	1	-	-	-
			Richmond	Lock		NL	65(1)	5	1	-	-	-
						NC	0(1)	-	-	-	-	-
						ES	0(1)	-	-	-	-	-
			Fylde	Lock		NL	35	-	-	-	-	-
Matt	Carrington	26.08.76	NewZealand	181cm	86kg							
			Bristol	FullBack		NL	10(6)	15	1	2	2	-
						NC	0(1)	-	-	-	-	-
						ES	6(0)	10	2	-	-	-
Ian	Carroll		England	6 5	17 7							
			Otley	Lock		NL	79(12)	30	6	-	-	-
						NC	3(0)	5	1	-	-	-
Nathan	Carter	22.06.72	England	6 0	16 0							
			Gloucester	Flanker		NL	59(3)	25	5	-	-	-
						NC	7(0)	-	-	-	-	-
						ES	9(0)	-	-	-	-	-
			Worcester	Flanker		NL	44(24)	20	4	-	-	-
						NC	6(2)	-	-	-	-	-
Gavin	Cattle	05.04.80	England	0cm	0kg							
			Birmingham&S.	ScrumHalf		NL	21(28)	10	2	-	-	-
						NC	2(2)	10	2	-	-	-
Andy	Caves	21.05.82		0cm	0kg							
			Moseley	O'sideFlanker		NL	4(26)	-	-	-	-	-
						NC	1(0)	-	-	-	-	-
Mike	Cawthorne	15.05.72	England	0cm	0kg							
			LeedsTykes	FullBack		NL	20(15)	32	5	2	1	-
						NC	1(1)	-	-	-	-	-
			Wakefield	FullBack		NL	23(16)	40	7	1	1	-
						NC	1(0)	-	-	-	-	-
Craig	Chalmers		Scotland	0cm	0kg							
			Harlequins	OutsideHalf		NL	4(8)	4	-	2	-	-
						NC	2(0)	7	-	2	1	-
						ES	1(0)	17	1	-	3	1
			Worcester	OutsideHalf		NL	15(3)	81	2	25	7	-
						NC	1(0)	-	-	-	-	-

Hall	Charlton	25.10.79	England	180cm	89kg							
			Newcastle	ScrumHalf		NL	26(17)	20	4	-	-	-
						NC	2(5)	-	-	-	-	-
						ES	5(1)	10	2	-	-	-
						EC	3(2)	-	-	-	-	-
Phil	Christophers		England	0cm	0kg							
			Bristol	Center		NL	19(1)	35	7	-	-	-
						NC	1(0)	-	-	-	-	-
						ES	6(0)	15	3	-	-	-
			Brive	Center								
						ES	3(0)	20	4	-	-	-
Neil	Clark	08.10.80	England	177cm	96kg							
			Exeter	Hooker		NL	17(40)	5	1	-	-	-
						NC	2(4)	5	1	-	-	-
Phillip	Clarke	19.07.77	England	204cm	114kg							
			Bedford	Lock		NL	36(5)	5	1	-	-	-
						NC	1(0)	-	-	-	-	-
Richard	Cockerill	16.12.70	England	178cm	108kg							
			Leicester	Hooker		NL	77(30)	25	5	-	-	-
						NC	7(4)	5	1	-	-	-
						EC	19(13)	20	4	-	-	-
Alex	Codling	25.09.73	England	198cm	116kg							
			Bedford	Lock		NL	4(1)	-	-	-	-	-
			Harlequins	Lock		NL	20(14)	-	-	-	-	-
						NC	4(2)	5	1	-	-	-
						ES	0(4)	-	-	-	-	-
						EC	1(3)	-	-	-	-	-
			Richmond	Lock		NL	3(13)	-	-	-	-	-
						NC	2(1)	-	-	-	-	-
						ES	3(2)	-	-	-	-	-
Ben	Cohen	14.09.78	England	188cm	100kg							
			Northampton	RightWing		NL	75(6)	135	27	-	-	-
						NC	14(0)	55	11	-	-	-
						ES	5(0)	15	3	-	-	-
						EC	21(0)	50	10	-	-	-
Ben	Cole	31.08.75	England	191cm	97kg							
			Saracens	O'sideFlanker		NL	24(25)	25	5	-	-	-
						NC	1(4)	10	2	-	-	-
						ES	4(0)	14	2	2	-	-
						EC	1(1)	-	-	-	-	-
Patrice	Collazo	27.03.74	France	0cm	0kg							
			Gloucester	Prop		NL	13(8)	5	1	-	-	-
						NC	0(1)	-	-	-	-	-
						ES	5(1)	-	-	-	-	-
			StadeFrancais	Prop								
						EC	1(3)	5	1	-	-	-
Tim	Collier	27.10.77	England	0cm	0kg							
			Harlequins	Lock		NL	7(6)	-	-	-	-	-
			RugbyLions	Lock		NL	44(2)	65	13	-	-	-
						NC	2(1)	10	2	-	-	-
			West Hartlepool	Lock		NL	3(0)	-	-	-	-	-
Carl	Colvin	18.01.81	England	0cm	0kg							
			Moseley	FullBack		NL	17(3)	5	1	-	-	-
						NC	2(0)	10	2	-	-	-
Felipe	Contepomi	20.08.77	Argentina	0cm	0kg							
			Bristol	OutsideHalf		NL	25(3)	389	13	42	78	2
						NC	2(0)	35	1	3	7	1
						ES	9(1)	123	2	19	25	-
Dan	Cook	10.09.74	England	204cm	111kg							
			Rotherham	Lock		NL	45(24)	25	5	-	-	-
						NC	5(0)	-	-	-	-	-
						ES	2(2)	-	-	-	-	-
Marcus	Cook	14.07.73	England	0cm	0kg							
			Moseley	FullBack		NL	50(6)	65	13	-	-	-
						NC	5(0)	15	3	-	-	-
Matthew	Cook	17.05.78	England	198cm	99kg							
			Bedford	O'sideFlanker		NL	12(20)	25	5	-	-	-
						NC	1(1)	-	-	-	-	-

Mark	Cornwell	22.02.73	England	201cm	114kg							
			Gloucester	Lock		NL	51(28)	15	3	-	-	-
						NC	8(2)	20	4	-	-	-
						ES	17(2)	10	2	-	-	-
						EC	1(3)	-	-	-	-	-
Andy	Craig	16.03.76	Scotland	0cm	0kg							
			Orrell	Center		NL	44(2)	140	28	-	-	-
						NC	6(0)	40	8	-	-	-
Luis	Criscuolo	-	Argentina	0cm	0kg							
			Birmingham&S.	OutsideHalf		NL	14(1)	34	-	5	4	4
						NC	1(3)	18	-	3	2	2
Alex	Crockett	08.07.79	England	0cm	0kg							
			Bath	Center		NL	4(12)	-	-	-	-	-
						EC	0(3)	-	-	-	-	-
Lee	Crofts	07.09.68	England	6 4	17 7							
			Coventry	BlindsideFlanker		NL	136(18)	125	25	-	-	-
						NC	5(1)	10	2	-	-	-
Darren	Crompton	12.09.72	England	188cm	114kg							
				Bath	Prop	NL	5(1)	-	-	-	-	-
				Bristol	Prop	NL	33(14)	5	1	-	-	-
						NC	2(1)	-	-	-	-	-
						ES	8(6)	-	-	-	-	-
				Richmond	Prop	NL	33(7)	-	-	-	-	-
						NC	4(1)	-	-	-	-	-
						ES	2(1)	-	-	-	-	-
Mark	Cueto	26.12.79	England	182cm	93kg							
			Sale	RightWing		NL	21(0)	65	13	-	-	-
						NC	1(0)	-	-	-	-	-
						ES	6(0)	10	2	-	-	-
Jason	Cundick	09.09.73	England	6 0	17 0							
			Orrell	Prop		NL	51(7)	-	-	-	-	-
						NC	3(0)	-	-	-	-	-
			Rotherham	Prop		NL	2(12)	5	1	-	-	-
						NC	0(1)	-	-	-	-	-
Peter	Curtis		England	0cm	0kg							
			Otley	Lock		NL	56(10)	25	5	-	-	-
						NC	4(0)	-	-	-	-	-
Mick	Curtis	27.06.72	England	5 11	16 0							
			Coventry	Center		NL	39(20)	20	4	-	-	-
						NC	6(1)	5	1	-	-	-
Charles	Cusani	22.10.65	England	6 6	17 6							
			Orrell	Lock		NL	72(3)	5	1	-	-	-
						NC	7(1)	10	2	-	-	-
Declan	Danagher	11.01.80	England	190cm	102kg							
			LondonIrish	No.8		NL	19(14)	5	1	-	-	-
						NC	4(0)	-	-	-	-	-
						ES	13(1)	30	6	-	-	-
Simon	Danielle	08.07.79	England	0cm	0kg							
			Bath	Center		NL	15(6)	10	2	-	-	-
						NC	1(0)	-	-	-	-	-
						EC	0(2)	-	-	-	-	-
			Bristol	LeftWing		NL	1(0)	-	-	-	-	-
Martyn	Davies	12.10.73	Wales	0cm	0kg							
			Coventry	FullBack		NL	42(0)	462	9	63	97	-
						NC	4(0)	47	2	5	9	-
			RugbyLions	FullBack		NL	54(0)	468	5	-	-	-
						NC	1(0)	8	-	1	2	-
Ian	Davies		England	0cm	0kg							
			Manchester	Prop		NL	20(10)	-	-	-	-	-
						NC	2(1)	5	1	-	-	-
Gareth	Davies	02.08.73	England	0cm	0kg							
			Fylde	Center		NL	19(1)	10	2	-	-	-
						NC	2(0)	5	1	-	-	-
			Waterloo	Center		NL	67(1)	47	9	1	-	-
						NC	3(0)	10	2	-	-	-
Tristan	Davies	07.10.76	Wales	0cm	95kg							
			LeedsTykes	Center		NL	8(10)	-	-	-	-	-
						NC	0(2)	-	-	-	-	-
						ES	4(2)	5	1	-	-	-
			Neath	Center								

Richard	Davies	-	Other	0cm	0kg							
			RugbyLions	OutsideHalf		NL	26(0)	127	4	16	22	3
						NC	0(1)	-	-	-	-	-
Wes	Davies	-	England	0cm	0kg							
			Orrell	FullBack		NL	15(0)	65	13	-	-	-
						NC	2(0)	10	2	-	-	-
Graham	Dawe	04.09.59	England	5 11	14 0							
			Bath	Hooker		NL	7(0)	-	-	-	-	-
						EC	1(0)	-	-	-	-	-
			PlymouthAlbion	Hooker		NL	49(1)	35	7	-	-	-
						NC	1(3)	-	-	-	-	-
			Sale	Hooker		NL	4(8)	-	-	-	-	-
						NC	1(1)	5	1	-	-	-
						ES	3(1)	-	-	-	-	-
			Bath	Hooker		NL			-	-	-	-
Andy	Dawling	05.11.73	England	178cm	96kg							
			Bracknell	Flanker		NL	11(5)	5	1	-	-	-
			Coventry	Flanker		NL	9(1)	-	-	-	-	-
			Gloucester	Flanker		NL	1(0)	5	1	-	-	-
			Harlequins	Flanker		NL	3(6)	-	-	-	-	-
						NC	0(1)	-	-	-	-	-
						ES	0(2)	-	-	-	-	-
Matt	Dawson	31.10.72	England	178cm	86kg							
			Northampton	ScrumHalf		NL	140(7)	411	32	42	55	1
						NC	14(0)	24	3	3	1	-
						ES	8(0)	30	6	-	-	-
						EC	9(1)	86	3	10	17	-
Anthony	Dawson	29.01.75	England	5 10	11 0							
			Coventry	ScrumHalf		NL	113(14)	85	17	-	-	-
						NC	6(0)	5	1	-	-	-
Louis	Deacon	07.10.80	England	196cm	111kg							
			Leicester	Flanker		NL	20(5)	5	1	-	-	-
						NC	2(1)	-	-	-	-	-
						EC	7(3)	-	-	-	-	-
Mel	Deane	16.01.75		176cm	87kg							
			Richmond	Center		NL	14(7)	20	4	-	-	-
						NC	2(0)	-	-	-	-	-
						ES	1(0)	5	1	-	-	-
			Sale	Center		NL	25(11)	30	6	-	-	-
						NC	4(0)	20	4	-	-	-
						ES	11(2)	30	6	-	-	-
Glenn	Delaney	16.11.73	NewZealand	196cm	115kg							
			Coventry	Lock		NL	24(0)	25	5	-	-	-
						NC	3(0)	10	2	-	-	-
			London Irish	Lock		NL	12(22)	5	1	-	-	-
						NC	2(4)	5	1	-	-	-
						ES	8(3)	5	1	-	-	-
			Nottingham	Lock		NL						
Steve	Dennehy		England	0cm	0kg							
			Waterloo	Prop		NL	59(5)	-	-	-	-	-
						NC	5(0)	-	-	-	-	-
Mark	Denney	25.01.75	England	183cm	100kg							
			Bristol	Center		NL	14(2)	5	1	-	-	-
						ES	5(0)	5	1	-	-	-
			LondonWasps	Center		NL	69(10)	50	10	-	-	-
						NC	6(0)	15	3	-	-	-
						EC	18(1)	15	3	-	-	-
Alan	Dickens	04.02.76	England	0cm	0kg							
			Manchester	ScrumHalf		NL	25(0)	20	4	-	-	-
						NC	2(0)	5	1	-	-	-
			Sale	ScrumHalf		NL	3(15)	-	-	-	-	-
						NC	0(1)	-	-	-	-	-
						ES	4(2)	-	-	-	-	-
			Stourbridge	ScrumHalf								
Paul	Dineen			0cm	0kg							
			Moseley	Center		NL	15(1)	20	4	-	-	-
						NC	1(0)	-	-	-	-	-

Tony	Diprose	22.09.72	England	196cm	111kg							
			Harlequins	No.8		NL	16(4)	-	-	-	-	-
						NC	3(0)	5	1	-	-	-
						EC	5(1)	10	2	-	-	-
			Saracens	No.8		NL	165(13)	170	34	-	-	-
						NC	12(1)	10	2	-	-	-
						ES	5(1)	-	-	-	-	-
						EC	12(0)	10	2	-	-	-
Craig	Dowd	26.10.69	NewZealand	189cm	115kg							
			LondonWasps	Prop		NL	21(0)	20	4	-	-	-
						NC	1(0)	-	-	-	-	-
						EC	6(0)	-	-	-	-	-
			AucklandBlues	Prop								
Shane	Drahm		Australia	0cm	0kg							
			Bristol	OutsideHalf		NL	10(9)	130	1	16	30	1
						NC	0(1)	-	-	-	-	-
						ES	3(0)	42	2	10	4	-
Naka	Drotske	15.03.71	SouthAfrica	182cm	105kg							
			LondonIrish	Hooker		NL	12(9)	5	1	-	-	-
						NC	1(3)	-	-	-	-	-
						ES	3(3)	-	-	-	-	-
			Cats	Hooker								
John	Dudley	16.07.66	England	6 4	18 0							
			Rotherham	Lock		NL	165(26)	236	49	-	-	-
			Harrogate	Lock		NL	42(1)	110	22	-	-	-
Jon	Dunbar		England	0cm	0kg							
			Newcastle	Flanker		NL	16(2)	5	1	-	-	-
						NC	2(0)	-	-	-	-	-
						EC	4(1)	-	-	-	-	-
Chad	Eagle	24.08.71	England	6 5	18 0							
			Bedford	Lock		NL	17(5)	-	-	-	-	-
						ES	3(2)	5	1	-	-	-
			Bristol	Lock		NL	55(2)	20	4	-	-	-
						NC	2(0)	-	-	-	-	-
						ES	11(0)	-	-	-	-	-
			LondonWelsh	Lock		NL	30(5)	15	3	-	-	-
						NC	4(0)	-	-	-	-	-
Russell	Earnshaw	08.03.75	England	194cm	108kg							
			Bath	Flanker		NL	27(10)	40	8	-	-	-
						NC	2(0)	5	1	-	-	-
						EC	5(1)	10	2	-	-	-
			Rotherham	Flanker		NL	21(12)	30	6	-	-	-
						NC	3(1)	-	-	-	-	-
						ES	4(1)	-	-	-	-	-
			WestHartlepool	Flanker		NL	8(0)	15	3	-	-	-
Nick	Easter	-	Other	0cm	0kg							
			Orrell	No.8		NL	18(1)	40	8	-	-	-
			RosslynPark	No.8		NL	4(0)	-	-	-	-	-
						NC	1(1)	5	1	-	-	-
Darran	Edwards	25.03.73	Wales	172cm	80kg							
			LondonIrish	ScrumHalf		NL	17(5)	5	1	-	-	-
						NC	1(2)	-	-	-	-	-
						ES	1(2)	-	-	-	-	-
			LondonWelsh	ScrumHalf		NL	20(0)	5	1	-	-	-
						NC	3(0)	-	-	-	-	-
			Saracens	ScrumHalf		NL	0(1)	-	-	-	-	-
			Newport	ScrumHalf								
						EC	6(0)	-	-	-	-	-
Diccon	Edwards	13.03.73	England	0cm	0kg							
			LeedsTykes	Center		NL	39(3)	40	8	-	-	-
						NC	2(0)	-	-	-	-	-
			Wakefield	Center		NL	26(0)	30	6	-	-	-
						NC	2(0)	-	-	-	-	-
			Leicester	Centre		NL	15(0)	-	-	-	-	-
Harry	Ellis	-	England	0cm	0kg							
			Leicester	ScrumHalf		NL	8(10)	-	-	-	-	-
						NC	1(1)	-	-	-	-	-
						EC	2(6)	10	2	-	-	-

Craig	Emmerson	14.09.71	England	0cm	0kg							
			Gloucester	RightWing		NL	11(2)	-	-	-	-	-
						NC	2(1)	-	-	-	-	-
						ES	1(3)	5	1	-	-	-
			LeedsTykes	LeftWing		NL	73(11)	110	22	-	-	-
						NC	6(1)	5	1	-	-	-
			Wakefield	LeftWing		NL	1(0)	-	-	-	-	-
Simon	Emms	27.01.75	Wales	183cm	111kg							
			Bath	Prop		NL	20(17)	-	-	-	-	-
						NC	1(1)	-	-	-	-	-
						EC	7(2)	-	-	-	-	-
			Bristol	Prop		NL	14(2)	-	-	-	-	-
						NC	1(0)	-	-	-	-	-
Chris	Evans	27.12.70	Wales	6 3	16 7							
			Bristol	Flanker		NL	27(9)	25	5	-	-	-
						NC	1(0)	-	-	-	-	-
						ES	5(2)	5	1	-	-	-
			Worcester	Flanker		NL	36(10)	5	1	-	-	-
						NC	4(0)	-	-	-	-	-
Mark	Evans	-	England	0cm	0kg							
			Moseley	-		NL	7(11)	-	-	-	-	-
						NC	0(1)	-	-	-	-	-
Barry	Everitt	09.03.76	Ireland	175cm	80kg							
			LondonIrish	OutsideHalf		NL	33(2)	525	3	45	132	8
						NC	7(0)	86	-	13	19	1
						ES	11(0)	201	2	28	44	1
Joe	Ewens	16.12.77	England	180cm	90kg							
			Bath	Center		NL	1(2)	-	-	-	-	-
			Bedford	Center		NL	24(4)	50	10	-	-	-
			Gloucester	Center		NL	42(7)	15	3	-	-	-
						NC	6(0)	5	1	-	-	-
						ES	9(2)	25	5	-	-	-
						EC	2(0)	5	1	-	-	-
John	Fabian	-	England	0cm	0kg							
			Exeter	Full Back		NL	48(9)	241	9	-	-	-
						NC	2(0)	-	-	-	-	-
			HenleyHawks	Full Back		NL	21(0)	199	2	24	47	-
						NC	3(0)	37	2	6	5	-
Hesekaia	Fakatou	30.04.72	England	0cm	0kg							
			Birmingham&S.	Flanker		NL	42(6)	30	6	-	-	-
						NC	6(0)	15	3	-	-	-
			LeedsTykes	Flanker		NL	5(5)	-	-	-	-	-
Terry	Fanolua	03.07.74	Samoa	186cm	86kg							
			Gloucester	Center		NL	84(4)	100	19	1	1	-
						NC	9(0)	29	3	4	2	-
						ES	18(1)	78	6	12	8	-
						EC	8(0)	12	-	3	2	-
Isaac	Feau'nati	23.07.73	Fiji	188cm	108kg							
			LeedsTykes	No.8		NL	15(2)	-	-	-	-	-
						NC	1(0)	-	-	-	-	-
						ES	4(0)	-	-	-	-	-
			LondonIrish	No.8		NL	20(6)	30	6	-	-	-
						NC	3(0)	-	-	-	-	-
						ES	1(2)	-	-	-	-	-
			Rotherham	No.8		NL	20(0)	10	2	-	-	-
						NC	2(0)	-	-	-	-	-
						ES	3(2)	5	1	-	-	-
Jon	Feeley	12.04.79	England	0cm	0kg							
			LeedsTykes	RightWing		NL	16(6)	57	11	1	-	-
						NC	0(1)	-	-	-	-	-
			Wakefield	RightWing		NL	24(8)	45	9	-	-	-
						NC	1(0)	-	-	-	-	-
Fred	Fichot	23.01.74	France	193cm	108kg							
			Bedford	No.8		NL	26(0)	40	8	-	-	-
						NC	1(0)	-	-	-	-	-
Rob	Fidler	21.09.74	England	196cm	112kg							
			Gloucester	Lock		NL	116(4)	35	7	-	-	-
						NC	13(0)	-	-	-	-	-
						ES	16(3)	5	1	-	-	-
						EC	6(1)	-	-	-	-	-

Matt	Fitzgerald	07.06.73	England	6 4	17 0							
			LondonWelsh	No.8		NL	37(13)	30	6	-	-	-
						NC	1(0)	-	-	-	-	-
			Richmond	No 8		NL	46	30	6	-	-	-
David	Flatman	21.01.80	England	183cm	111kg							
			Saracens	Prop		NL	50(13)	25	5	-	-	-
						NC	8(0)	10	2	-	-	-
						ES	5(1)	10	2	-	-	-
						EC	11(1)	-	-	-	-	-
Darren	Fletcher	27.07.81	England	0cm	0kg							
			Wakefield	Flanker		NL	5(19)	-	-	-	-	-
						NC	1(0)	-	-	-	-	-
Neil	Fletcher		England	0cm	0kg							
			Birmingham&S.	Lock		NL	15(10)	-	-	-	-	-
						NC	2(1)	-	-	-	-	-
			Leicester	Lock		NL	13(10)	5	1	-	-	-
						NC	1(1)	-	-	-	-	-
						EC	0(1)	-	-	-	-	-
			Sale	Lock		NL	6(1)	-	-	-	-	-
						NC	1(2)	-	-	-	-	-
						ES	1(1)	-	-	-	-	-
Blair	Foote	08.05.73	NewZealand	191cm	96kg							
			Exeter	BlindsideFlanker		NL	56(15)	85	17	-	-	-
						NC	8(0)	-	-	-	-	-
James	Forrester	-	England	0cm	0kg							
			Gloucester	BlindsideFlanker		NL	12(5)	15	3	-	-	-
						NC	2(0)	15	3	-	-	-
						ES	5(2)	40	8	-	-	-
Chris	Fortey	25.08.75	England	180cm	103kg							
			Gloucester	Hooker		NL	49(34)	15	3	-	-	-
						NC	6(3)	5	1	-	-	-
						ES	6(3)	10	2	-	-	-
						EC	0(3)	-	-	-	-	-
Lee	Fortey	25.02.71	England	0cm	0kg							
			Birmingham&S.	Hooker		NL	18(6)	5	1	-	-	-
						NC	3(1)	10	2	-	-	-
			Newport	Hooker								
						EC	0(1)	-	-	-	-	-
Andre	Fox	24.08.71	SouthAfrica	200cm	110kg							
			Bedford	No.8		NL	35(1)	15	3	-	-	-
						NC	1(1)	-	-	-	-	-
Perry	Freshwater	27.07.73	NewZealand	183cm	112kg							
			Coventry	Prop		NL	1(0)	-	-	-	-	-
			Leicester	Prop		NL	16(46)	5	1	-	-	-
						NC	3(3)	20	4	-	-	-
						EC	7(9)	-	-	-	-	-
			RugbyLions	Prop		NL	0(1)	-	-	-	-	-
Mike	Friday	25.03.72	England	173cm	77kg							
			Harlequins	ScrumHalf		NL	0(8)	-	-	-	-	-
						NC	0(2)	-	-	-	-	-
						ES	4(1)	5	1	-	-	-
			LondonWasps	ScrumHalf		NL	22(35)	35	7	-	-	-
						NC	6(4)	10	2	-	-	-
						EC	2(2)	-	-	-	-	-
			Blackheath	Scrum half		NL	61(3)	95	19	-	-	-
Tani	Fuga	14.07.73	Samoa	180cm	98kg							
			Harlequins	Hooker		NL	9(21)	-	-	-	-	-
						NC	4(3)	-	-	-	-	-
						ES	2(5)	5	1	-	-	-
						EC	0(2)	-	-	-	-	-
Iain	Fullerton	25.03.76	Scotland	0cm	0kg							
			Sale	Lock		NL	20(0)	-	-	-	-	-
						NC	1(0)	-	-	-	-	-
						ES	8(0)	-	-	-	-	-
			EdinburghReivers		Lock							
						EC	4(0)	-	-	-	-	-

Mark	Gabey	27.07.73		194cm	110kg							
			Bath	Flanker		NL	17(12)	10	2	-	-	-
						NC	1(1)	-	-	-	-	-
						EC	5(3)	5	1	-	-	-
			Bristol	Flanker		NL	20(2)	45	9	-	-	-
						NC	1(0)	-	-	-	-	-
			LondonIrish	Flanker		NL	12(5)	5	1	-	-	-
						NC	2(1)	-	-	-	-	-
						ES	2(2)	5	1	-	-	-
Matt	Gallagher		England	0cm	0kg							
			Birmingham&S.	FullBack		NL	10(10)	60	1	5	15	-
						NC	3(1)	22	1	4	3	-
			Coventry	FullBack		NL	19(7)	69	2	13	10	1
						NC	1(0)	-	-	-	-	-
Darren	Garforth	09.03.66	England	178cm	118kg							
			Leicester	Prop		NL	182(6)	35	7	-	-	-
						NC	11(3)	-	-	-	-	-
						EC	32(1)	5	1	-	-	-
Chris	Garrard	25.09.77	Australia	0cm	0kg							
			Worcester	RightWing		NL	23(0)	125	25	-	-	-
						NC	2(1)	5	1	-	-	-
Glen	Gelderbloom	11.12.69		180cm	85kg							
			Leicester	Center		NL	15(17)	10	2	-	-	-
						NC	2(3)	-	-	-	-	-
						EC	4(4)	-	-	-	-	-
David	Giles		ENgland	0cm	0kg							
			Orrell	Prop		NL	5(14)	5	1	-	-	-
						NC	2(1)	-	-	-	-	-
Fergie	Gladstone	-	England	0cm	0kg							
			RugbyLions	-		NL	6(9)	-	-	-	-	-
Vaughan	Going	26.08.71	New Zealand	178cm	89kg							
			Harlequins	FullBack		NL	0(3)	-	-	-	-	-
			LondonWelsh	LeftWing		NL	23(0)	47	9	1	-	-
						NC	4(0)	28	5	-	-	1
			Sale	FullBack		NL	21(10)	52	8	-	4	-
						NC	3(2)	-	-	-	-	-
						ES	9(2)	15	3	-	-	-
Ben	Gollings	12.05.80	England	173cm	81kg							
			Harlequins	LeftWing		NL	35(6)	77	11	2	5	1
						NC	2(4)	-	-	-	-	-
						ES	4(1)	27	1	8	2	-
						EC	0(2)	-	-	-	-	-
Andy	Gomersall	24.07.74	England	178cm	86kg							
			Bath	ScrumHalf		NL	0(2)	-	-	-	-	-
			Bedford	ScrumHalf		NL	20(0)	70	3	11	11	-
						NC	1(0)	-	-	-	-	-
						ES	3(0)	8	-	1	2	-
			Gloucester	ScrumHalf		NL	29(13)	55	7	1	6	-
						NC	2(2)	5	1	-	-	-
						ES	3(3)	4	-	2	-	-
						EC	3(3)	2	-	1	-	-
			LondonWasps	ScrumHalf		NL	38(8)	30	6	-	-	-
						NC	3(4)	-	-	-	-	-
						EC	8(1)	10	2	-	-	-
Andy	Goode	03.03.80	England	181cm	87kg							
			Leicester	OutsideHalf		NL	32(11)	140	8	17	15	7
						NC	6(0)	40	2	12	2	-
						EC	17(4)	37	1	1	4	6
Steve	Gough	22.04.66	England	0cm	0kg							
			Birmingham&S.	OutsideHalf		NL	18(2)	176	2	17	42	2
						NC	1(0)	7	-	2	1	-
			Coventry	OutsideHalf		NL	48(1)	571	15	-	-	-
						NC	3(0)	25	-	5	5	-
			Fylde	OutsideHalf		NL	128(9)	806	27	7	16	-
						NC	2(1)	30	-	3	8	-
			Preston	OutsideHalf		NL	2(1)	2	-	1	-	-

George	Graham	19.01.66	Scotland	171cm	108kg							
			Newcastle	Prop		NL	52(30)	45	9	-	-	-
						NC	9(4)	5	1	-	-	-
						ES	6(4)	25	5	-	-	-
						EC	3(0)	-	-	-	-	-
Paul	Graham	28.03.67	Wales	0cm	0kg							
			Coventry	Prop		NL	15(7)	-	-	-	-	-
						NC	0(2)	-	-	-	-	-
			Harlequins	Prop		NL	11(2)	-	-	-	-	-
						NC	3(0)	-	-	-	-	-
						EC	4(0)	-	-	-	-	-
			Pontypridd	Prop								
						EC	1(1)	-	-	-	-	-
Phillip	Graham	02.12.76	England	5 10	14 0							
			Manchester	Center		NL	45(1)	40	8	-	-	-
						NC	4(0)	15	3	-	-	-
			Waterloo	FullBack		NL	59(0)	50	10	-	-	-
			Liverpool St H	Centre		NL	29(2)	40	8	-	-	-
Ian	Grainey		England	0cm	0kg							
			Orrell	Flanker		NL	26(11)	-	-	-	-	-
			SedgleyPark	Flanker		NL	5(14)	-	-	-	-	-
						NC	0(2)	-	-	-	-	-
Stephen	Gray			0cm	0kg							
			Bedford	-		NL	4(12)	-	-	-	-	-
						NC	0(1)	-	-	-	-	-
Paul	Grayson	30.05.71	England	180cm	87kg							
			Northampton	OutsideHalf		NL	115(9)	1335	14	125	239	10
						NC	17(1)	185	2	41	28	3
						ES	9(0)	150	5	25	25	-
						EC	9(1)	110	-	7	30	2
			Waterloo	Outside half		NL	10	126	1	8	29	6
			Preston	Outside half		NL	??	265	5	19	62	6
Philip	Greaves	16.02.78	England	183cm	98kg							
			Otley	Center		NL	21(1)	30	6	-	-	-
						NC	1(0)	5	1	-	-	-
			Rotherham	FullBack		NL	22(9)	20	4	-	-	-
						NC	1(0)	-	-	-	-	-
						ES	1(1)	5	1	-	-	-
			WestHartlepool	Center		NL	10(3)	10	2	-	-	-
						NC	0(1)	-	-	-	-	-
Leon	Greef	09.03.75	Zimbabwe	196cm	105kg							
			Rotherham	O'sideFlanker		NL	29(6)	45	9	-	-	-
						NC	3(0)	-	-	-	-	-
						ES	2(1)	-	-	-	-	-
Will	Green	25.10.73	England	178cm	114kg							
			LondonWasps	Prop		NL	126(2)	40	8	-	-	-
						NC	15(0)	15	3	-	-	-
						EC	24(2)	10	2	-	-	-
Phil	Greenbury		England	0cm	0kg							
			Leicester	Prop								
						EC	0(1)	-	-	-	-	-
			RugbyLions	Prop		NL	32(6)	-	-	-	-	-
						NC	3(0)	-	-	-	-	-
Danny	Grewcock	07.11.72	England	198cm	111kg							
			Bath	Lock		NL	17(1)	-	-	-	-	-
						NC	1(0)	-	-	-	-	-
						EC	7(0)	-	-	-	-	-
			Saracens	Lock		NL	60(3)	25	5	-	-	-
						NC	11(0)	10	2	-	-	-
						ES	4(1)	-	-	-	-	-
						EC	11(0)	-	-	-	-	-
			Coventry	Lock		NL	31	15	3	-	-	-
Phil	Griffin	01.01.00	England	0cm	0kg							
			Otley	O'sideFlanker		NL	70(9)	60	12	-	-	-
						NC	4(0)	15	3	-	-	-
			Leeds	Flanker		NL	67(7)	65	13	-	-	-
Stuart	Grimes	04.03.74	Scotland	196cm	108kg							
			Newcastle	Lock		NL	41(8)	45	9	-	-	-
						NC	8(0)	5	1	-	-	-
						ES	8(1)	-	-	-	-	-
						EC	4(0)	-	-	-	-	-

Simon	Halford	26.06.69		188cm	116kg							
			LondonIrish	Prop		NL	33(17)	-	-	-	-	-
						NC	7(4)	-	-	-	-	-
						ES	12(8)	-	-	-	-	-
David	Hall		England	6 1	17 0							
			Otley	Prop		NL	86(14)	30	6	-	-	-
						NC	5(0)	-	-	-	-	-
			Harrogate	Prop		NL	74(2)	10	2	-	-	-
Chris	Hall		England	0cm	0kg							
			Worcester	Hooker		NL	12(29)	15	3	-	-	-
						NC	2(2)	5	1	-	-	-
Eddie	Halvey	11.07.70	Ireland	193cm	103kg							
			LondonIrish	O'sideFlanker		NL	22(13)	20	4	-	-	-
						NC	5(0)	5	1	-	-	-
						ES	4(2)	20	4	-	-	-
Jamie	Hamilton	01.07.70	England	175cm	79kg							
			Leicester	ScrumHalf		NL	47(20)	25	5	-	-	-
						NC	5(3)	10	2	-	-	-
						EC	14(7)	10	2	-	-	-
			London Scot	Scrum half		NL	5(1)	5	1	-	-	-
Tobias	Handley	14.03.76		0cm	0kg							
			Coventry	ScrumHalf		NL	9(15)	-	-	-	-	-
						NC	1(0)	-	-	-	-	-
			W Hartlepool	RightWing		NL	5(8)	5	1	-	-	-
			L'Aquila	ScrumHalf								
						EC	4(0)	-	-	-	-	-
Steve	Hanley	11.06.79	England	193cm	102kg							
			Sale	LeftWing		NL	54(3)	175	35	-	-	-
						NC	5(0)	25	5	-	-	-
						ES	12(3)	45	9	-	-	-
Richard	Hanson		England	0cm	0kg							
			Orrell	Prop		NL	0(1)	-	-	-	-	-
			Preston	Prop		NL	2(0)	-	-	-	-	-
						NC	2(0)	-	-	-	-	-
			Wakefield	Prop		NL	4(13)	-	-	-	-	-
						NC	1(0)	-	-	-	-	-
Luke	Harbut	18.03.80		178cm	108kg							
			Saracens	Prop		NL	14(14)	10	2	-	-	-
						NC	0(1)	-	-	-	-	-
						ES	4(1)	10	2	-	-	-
Rob	Hardwick	29.03.69	England	182cm	117kg							
			LondonIrish	Prop		NL	36(24)	5	1	-	-	-
						NC	7(2)	-	-	-	-	-
						ES	8(2)	5	1	-	-	-
Dan	Harper	09.03.75	England	0cm	0kg							
			Wakefield	Prop		NL	25(17)	10	2	-	-	-
						NC	3(2)	-	-	-	-	-
Adam	Harris	04.07.78	England	198cm	108kg							
			Exeter	Lock		NL	15(19)	-	-	-	-	-
						NC	3(1)	-	-	-	-	-
Charles	Harrison	06.08.75	England	178cm	86kg							
			Bath	ScrumHalf		NL	8(4)	9	1	2	-	-
						NC	0(1)	-	-	-	-	-
						EC	4(2)	2	-	1	-	-
			Bedford	ScrumHalf		NL	17(9)	5	1	-	-	-
						ES	2(1)	-	-	-	-	-
			Rotherham	ScrumHalf		NL	21(21)	20	4	-	-	-
						NC	3(2)	5	1	-	-	-
						ES	1(4)	-	-	-	-	-
Jason	Hart			0cm	0kg							
			PlymouthAlbion	Lock		NL	33(5)	40	8	-	-	-
						NC	3(0)	10	2	-	-	-
Virgil	Hartland		England	0cm	0kg							
			Bedford	Prop		NL	17(8)	-	-	-	-	-
						NC	0(1)	-	-	-	-	-
						ES	3(1)	-	-	-	-	-
			Stourbridge	Prop		NL	25(0)	10	2	-	-	-
						NC	1(0)	-	-	-	-	-
			WestHartlepool	Prop		NL	5(1)	-	-	-	-	-
			Worcester	Prop		NL	4(8)	-	-	-	-	-
						NC	0(1)	-	-	-	-	-

Ben	Harvey	01.01.00	England	0cm	0kg							
			Moseley	OutsideHalf		NL	16(2)	181	2	21	41	2
						NC	1(0)	6	-	-	2	-
			Richmond	ScrumHalf		NL	1(4)	-	-	-	-	-
						NC	0(1)	-	-	-	-	-
			Stourbridge	FullBack		NL	25(0)	298	9	44	55	-
						NC	1(0)	8	-	1	2	-
			Worcester	OutsideHalf		NL	11(16)	129	8	22	15	-
						NC	0(2)	5	-	1	1	-
Carlos	Hassan	02.01.71		183cm	102kg							
			Bristol	Center		NL	5(1)	10	2	-	-	-
						NC	1(0)	-	-	-	-	-
			Rotherham	Center		NL	40(4)	30	6	-	-	-
						NC	3(0)	-	-	-	-	-
						ES	5(1)	-	-	-	-	-
			SedgleyPark	Center		NL	22(1)	15	3	-	-	-
						NC	2(0)	-	-	-	-	-
Neal	Hatley	23.12.69		183cm	116kg							
			Bedford	Prop		NL	9(0)	-	-	-	-	-
						NC	1(0)	-	-	-	-	-
			LondonIrish	Prop		NL	50(31)	25	5	-	-	-
						NC	10(1)	5	1	-	-	-
						ES	15(2)	-	-	-	-	-
Austin	Healey	26.10.73	England	178cm	91kg							
			Leicester	ScrumHalf		NL	96(11)	137	26	2	-	1
						NC	12(0)	10	2	-	-	-
						EC	28(2)	61	11	-	-	2
			Orrell	Scrum half		NL	32(1)	27	4	2	1	-
			Waterloo	Scrum half		NL	20	18	3	-	1	-
Liu	Hepafila			0cm	0kg							
			Otley	Hooker		NL	4(27)	-	-	-	-	-
						NC	1(0)	-	-	-	-	-
Luke	Hewson	06.12.69	England	0cm	0kg							
			Manchester	Hooker		NL	88(16)	25	5	-	-	-
						NC	8(1)	-	-	-	-	-
			Sale	Hooker		NL	10(5)	5	1	-	-	-
						ES	3(1)	-	-	-	-	-
Richard	Hill	23.05.73	England	188cm	102kg							
			Saracens	Flanker		NL	134(3)	135	27	-	-	-
						NC	11(1)	-	-	-	-	-
						ES	7(2)	5	1	-	-	-
						EC	11(0)	30	6	-	-	-
John	Hill	17.07.78	England	175cm	83kg							
			Exeter	FullBack		NL	33(14)	143	4	24	25	-
						NC	6(0)	-	-	-	-	-
James	Hinkins	11.05.77	England	186cm	80kg							
			Bedford	Left wing		NL	25(20)	70	14	-	-	-
						NC	2(0)	5	1	-	-	-
			Moseley	Left wing		NL	33	35	7	-	-	-
Ben	Hinshelwood	22.03.77	Scotland	6 3	15 7							
			Bedford	FullBack		NL	25(1)	36	6	-	2	-
						NC	2(0)	-	-	-	-	-
			Worcester	Center		NL	26(0)	107	21	1	-	-
						NC	3(0)	12	2	1	-	-
Leigh	Hinton	21.02.79	England	0cm	0kg							
			Moseley	LeftWing		NL	32(5)	227	9	31	40	-
						NC	1(1)	8	1	-	1	-
			Worcester	Center		NL	0(1)	-	-	-	-	-
Rob	Hitchmough	17.12.75	England	0cm	0kg							
			Orrell	FullBack		NL	50(8)	88	14	3	4	-
						NC	3(0)	12	2	1	-	-
						ES	2(0)	5	1	-	-	-
			Waterloo	FullBack		NL	30(1)	35	7	-	-	-
						NC	1(0)	-	-	-	-	-
			Wakefield	Full back		NL	13	10	2	-	-	-
Robert	Hoadley	28.03.80	Ireland	185cm	87kg							
			LondonIrish	Center		NL	11(14)	5	1	-	-	-
						NC	0(3)	-	-	-	-	-
						ES	6(0)	25	5	-	-	-
Jason	Hobson	10.02.83	England	180cm	114kg							
			Exeter	Prop		NL	5(14)	10	2	-	-	-
						NC	0(4)	-	-	-	-	-

Charles	Hodgson	12.11.80	England	178cm	81kg							
			Sale	OutsideHalf		NL	31(0)	414	11	61	77	2
						NC	3(0)	49	1	10	6	2
						ES	10(2)	146	4	27	24	-
Carl	Hogg	05.07.69	Scotland	0cm	95kg							
			LeedsTykes	No.8		NL	20(8)	5	1	-	-	-
						NC	2(0)	-	-	-	-	-
						ES	5(1)	5	1	-	-	-
Matt	Holt	30.10.71	Australia	0cm	98kg							
			LeedsTykes	Hooker		NL	13(5)	-	-	-	-	-
						NC	1(1)	-	-	-	-	-
						ES	1(1)	5	1	-	-	-
			Waterloo	Hooker		NL	85(11)	85	17	-	-	-
						NC	3(1)	10	2	-	-	-
Michael	Horak	03.06.77	England	190cm	92kg							
			Bristol	FullBack		NL	3(0)	22	-	5	4	-
			Leicester	FullBack		NL	20(5)	50	8	2	2	-
						NC	2(0)	-	-	-	-	-
						EC	8(0)	25	5	-	-	-
			LondonIrish	FullBack		NL	27(4)	30	6	-	-	-
						NC	5(0)	15	3	-	-	-
						ES	7(2)	15	3	-	-	-
Julian	Horrobin	17.03.69	England	0cm	0kg							
			Bristol	No 8		NI	10	16	4	-	-	-
			Coventry	No.8		NL	152(7)	195	39	-	-	-
						NC	2(2)	5	1	-	-	-
Chris	Horsman	02.02.77	England	188cm	111kg							
			Bath	Prop		NL	11(18)	-	-	-	-	-
						NC	1(0)	-	-	-	-	-
						EC	5(4)	10	2	-	-	-
			Bedford	Prop		NL	21(4)	20	4	-	-	-
						NC	1(0)	-	-	-	-	-
Sam	Howard	31.07.74	England	6 0	13 7							
			Blackheath	Outside half		NL	56(6)	349	6	32	76	9
			Bedford	Outside half		NL	16(3)	134	3	28	20	1
			Exeter	Outside half		NL	64(1)	442	11	69	75	8
						NC	4(0)	36	-	6	8	-
Alan	Hubbleday	24.02.79	England	0cm	0kg							
			Birmingham&S.	Hooker		NL	23(20)	-	-	-	-	-
						NC	2(2)	-	-	-	-	-
			Moseley	Hooker		NL	0(3)	-	-	-	-	-
Richard	Hughes	17.06.76	England	0cm	0kg							
			Wakefield	Lock		NL	53(11)	5	1	-	-	-
						NC	5(0)	-	-	-	-	-
Richard	Hughes	28.01.76	England	5 10	13 7							
			Manchester	Center		NL	47(12)	20	4	-	-	-
						NC	5(1)	5	1	-	-	-
David	Hunt	02.01.80	England	0cm	0kg							
			Moseley	Flanker		NL	14(10)	15	3	-	-	-
						NC	1(1)	-	-	-	-	-
Robert	Hunter	23.05.72	England	194cm	108kg							
			LondonIrish	Flanker		NL	6(9)	-	-	-	-	-
						NC	1(1)	-	-	-	-	-
						ES	1(3)	-	-	-	-	-
			LondonScottish	Flanker		NL	23(1)	20	4	-	-	-
						NC	3(0)	-	-	-	-	-
			Northampton	Flanker		NL	8(17)	5	1	-	-	-
						NC	1(1)	-	-	-	-	-
						EC	5(4)	5	1	-	-	-
Robbie	Hurrell	13.06.77	England	6 7	0kg							
			Coventry	Lock		NL	34(9)	15	3	-	-	-
						NC	3(0)	5	1	-	-	-
			Leicester	Lock								
						NC	1(0)	-	-	-	-	-
Marius	Hurter	08.10.70	SouthAfrica	188cm	121kg							
			Newcastle	Prop		NL	64(3)	10	2	-	-	-
						NC	14(0)	-	-	-	-	-
						ES	9(1)	10	2	-	-	-
						EC	3(1)	-	-	-	-	-

Dan	Hyde	06.01.76	England	0cm	102kg							
			LeedsTykes	Flanker		NL	35(3)	35	7	-	-	-
						NC	3(0)	10	2	-	-	-
						ES	3(2)	-	-	-	-	-
			WestHartlepool	Flanker		NL	8(3)	10	2	-	-	-
Julian	Hyde	22.05.68	England	0cm	0kg							
			Birmingham&S.	Lock		NL	71(3)	25	5	-	-	-
						NC	8(1)	-	-	-	-	-
Ricky	Hyslop	21.03.78	England	0cm	0kg							
			Birmingham&S.	Center		NL	29(4)	15	3	-	-	-
						NC	2(0)	-	-	-	-	-
			Coventry	Center		NL	12(5)	25	5	-	-	-
						NC	1(0)	-	-	-	-	-
Richard	Jackson		England	0cm	0kg							
			Bedford	FullBack		NL	1(4)	-	-	-	-	-
						NC	0(2)	-	-	-	-	-
			Northampton	FullBack		NL	4(4)	5	1	-	-	-
						NC	2(0)	5	1	-	-	-
			RosslynPark	FullBack		NL	14(1)	8	1	-	1	-
						NC	2(0)	-	-	-	-	-
William	James	22.12.76	Wales	6 6	19 2							
			PlymouthAlbion	Lock		NL	25(0)	50	10	-	-	-
						NC	1(0)	-	-	-	-	-
			Pontypridd	Lock								
						EC	1(2)	-	-	-	-	-
Jim	Jenner	27.11.71	England	193cm	109kg							
			Newcastle	No.8		NL	13(7)	10	2	-	-	-
						NC	3(1)	5	1	-	-	-
						ES	4(1)	-	-	-	-	-
			Worcester	No.8		NL	65(8)	120	24	-	-	-
						NC	4(1)	15	3	-	-	-
Ed	Jennings	11.03.79	England	180cm	83kg							
			Bedford	Center		NL	19(1)	5	1	-	-	-
						NC	1(0)	-	-	-	-	-
			Harlequins	Center		NL	2(7)	-	-	-	-	-
						NC	0(3)	-	-	-	-	-
						ES	4(4)	20	1	3	3	-
Richard	John	30.05.74	England	5 10	10 0							
			Exeter	ScrumHalf		NL	81(31)	97	19	1	-	-
						NC	6(3)	-	-	-	-	-
Martin	Johnson	09.03.70	England	198cm	117kg							
			Leicester	Lock		NL	168(5)	40	8	-	-	-
						NC	10(2)	5	1	-	-	-
						EC	31(0)	5	1	-	-	-
Will	Johnson	18.03.74	England	193cm	109kg							
			Leicester	O'sideFlanker		NL	49(19)	5	1	-	-	-
						NC	6(2)	-	-	-	-	-
						EC	11(7)	-	-	-	-	-
Chris	Johnson	23.05.73	England	181cm	103kg							
			Leicester	Hooker		NL		7(1)	5	1	-	-
			Northampton	Hooker		NL	21(13)	10	2	-	-	-
						NC	1(3)	10	2	-	-	-
						ES	4(3)	5	1	-	-	-
						EC	0(2)	-	-	-	-	-
			Rotherham	Hooker		NL	31(8)	65	13	-	-	-
						NC	2(1)	10	2	-	-	-
						ES	5(1)	-	-	-	-	-
Kurt	Johnson	23.06.77	England	5 10	98kg							
			Coventry	RightWing		NL	69(1)	200	40	-	-	-
						NC	7(0)	20	4	-	-	-
			Orrell	RightWing		NL	13(2)	50	10	-	-	-
Andrew	Johnson	29.10.77	England	6 6	16 0							
			Bedford	Lock		NL	1(1)	-	-	-	-	-
						ES	3(1)	-	-	-	-	-
			LondonWelsh	Lock		NL	21(19)	10	2	-	-	-
						NC	1(1)	-	-	-	-	-
Paul	Johnstone	16.10.70	Zimbabwe	180cm	108kg							
			Bristol	Prop		NL	54(3)	40	8	-	-	-
						NC	6(0)	5	1	-	-	-
						ES	16(1)	10	2	-	-	-
			LondonScottish	Prop		NL	25(0)	10	2	-	-	-
						NC	2(0)	5	1	-	-	-

Wayne Morris, Manchester's scrum half, clears his lines. Photo courtesy of Nigel Chanter (01392 467261)

Gloucesters' Andrew Hazell keeps Saracens Adryan Winnan (right) at arms length. ©2001 Gloucestershire Picture Agency
E-mail: gpa@gloucestershirepictureagency.co.uk www.gloucestershirepictureagency.co.uk

Ian	Jones	17.03.67	NewZealand	199cm	104kg							
			Gloucester	Lock		NL	31(1)	15	3	-	-	-
						NC	2(0)	-	-	-	-	-
						ES	2(1)	5	1	-	-	-
						EC	6(0)	-	-	-	-	-
			LondonWasps	Lock		NL	18(0)	5	1	-	-	-
						NC	1(0)	-	-	-	-	-
						EC	6(0)	-	-	-	-	-
Kingsley	Jones	19.06.70	Wales	183cm	100kg							
			Gloucester	O'sideFlanker		NL	35(3)	10	2	-	-	-
						NC	2(0)	-	-	-	-	-
						ES	0(1)	5	1	-	-	-
						EC	7(1)	-	-	-	-	-
			Worcester	Flanker		NL	19(0)	15	3	-	-	-
						NC	2(0)	-	-	-	-	-
Chris	Jones	05.03.80	Other	0cm	0kg							
			RugbyLions	Lock		NL	24(1)	-	-	-	-	-
Phil	Jones		England	0cm	0kg							
			Orrell	FullBack		NL	22(0)	343	15	59	50	-
						NC	3(0)	63	3	15	6	-
Thomas	Jordan	26.05.79	England	0cm	0kg							
			Birmingham&S.	-		NL	18(22)	5	1	-	-	-
						NC	3(3)	5	1	-	-	-
Peter	Jorgensen	30.03.73	Australia	180cm	83kg							
			Northampton	Center		NL	20(0)	30	6	-	-	-
						NC	3(0)	10	2	-	-	-
						EC	5(0)	-	-	-	-	-
Rod	Kafer	25.06.71	Australia	0cm	0kg							
			Leicester	OutsideHalf		NL	19(0)	15	3	-	-	-
						NC	1(1)	5	1	-	-	-
						EC	9(0)	-	-	-	-	-
			ACT	OutsideHalf								
Andrew	Kahn	09.09.78	England	6 1	13 10							
			Manchester	OutsideHalf		NL	21(9)	45	2	4	9	-
						NC	5(0)	11	1	-	2	-
Ben	Kay	14.12.75	England	198cm	112kg							
			Leicester	Lock		NL	47(6)	20	4	-	-	-
						NC	7(0)	-	-	-	-	-
						EC	20(2)	5	1	-	-	-
Ron	Kelly	01.01.00	England	0cm	0kg							
			Otley	Prop		NL	62(10)	47	9	1	-	-
						NC	5(0)	-	-	-	-	-
Steve	Kelly	11.05.72	England	0cm	0kg							
			Manchester	Prop		NL	5(12)	-	-	-	-	-
						NC	2(1)	-	-	-	-	-
			Orrell	Prop		NL	54(19)	25	5	-	-	-
						NC	3(0)	-	-	-	-	-
						ES	1(0)	-	-	-	-	-
Adam	Kelly	06.02.74	England	6 1	18 7							
			LondonWelsh	Prop		NL	21(6)	-	-	-	-	-
						NC	1(1)	-	-	-	-	-
Wade	Kelly		England	0cm	0kg							
			Orrell	Center		NL	19(0)	40	8	-	-	-
						NC	3(0)	-	-	-	-	-
Glen	Kenworthy	15.03.74	England	199cm	111kg							
			Rotherham	Lock		NL	80(4)	25	5	-	-	-
						NC	6(1)	-	-	-	-	-
						ES	5(0)	-	-	-	-	-
Neil	Kerfoot		England	0cm	0kg							
			Orrell	Center		NL	40(13)	110	22	-	-	-
						NC	7(0)	25	5	-	-	-
Gavin	Kerr	03.03.77	Scotland	188cm	109kg							
			LeedsTykes	Prop		NL	21(7)	5	1	-	-	-
						NC	0(1)	-	-	-	-	-
						ES	1(3)	-	-	-	-	-
			Sale	Prop								

Jason	Keyter	20.12.73	England	0cm	0kg							
			Harlequins	RightWing		NL	40(23)	70	14	-	-	-
						NC	5(1)	-	-	-	-	-
						EC	6(0)	5	1	-	-	-
			Rotherham	RightWing		NL	19(6)	44	7	-	-	3
						NC	4(0)	5	1	-	-	-
			Roma	Center								
						EC	6(0)	-	-	-	-	-
Alex	King	17.01.75	England	180cm	87kg							
			LondonWasps	OutsideHalf		NL	103(2)	497	18	61	71	24
						NC	13(0)	43	1	10	3	3
						EC	23(0)	100	7	7	15	2
Mark	Kirkby		England	0cm	0kg							
			Bedford	Left wing		NL	1(0)	-	-	-	-	-
			LeedsTykes	Left wing		NL	7(0)	15	3	-	-	-
			Otley	Right wing		NL	70(4)	175	35	-	-	-
						NC	3(1)	-	-	-	-	-
Richard	Kirke	16.03.71		182cm	105kg							
			LondonIrish	Hooker		NL	59(18)	45	9	-	-	-
						NC	11(1)	10	2	-	-	-
						ES	7(6)	5	1	-	-	-
Paul	Knight	26.03.77	England	178cm	86kg							
			Birmingham&S.	ScrumHalf		NL	15(7)	16	1	1	3	-
						NC	2(2)	10	2	-	-	-
			Sale	ScrumHalf		NL	1(16)	19	2	3	1	-
						NC	0(2)	-	-	-	-	-
						ES	3(2)	15	3	-	-	-
Dave	Knight	19.01.79		0cm	0kg							
			Birmingham&S.	FullBack		NL	33(0)	148	7	28	19	-
						NC	4(0)	28	2	6	2	-
Jon	Koloi			0cm	0kg							
			Coventry	O'sideFlanker		NL	26(0)	50	10	-	-	-
						NC	2(0)	10	2	-	-	-
Marek	Kwisiuk	14.09.78		0cm	0kg							
			Bedford	Hooker		NL	9(2)	5	1	-	-	-
						NC	0(1)	-	-	-	-	-
						ES	3(2)	-	-	-	-	-
			RugbyLions	Hooker		NL	10(13)	-	-	-	-	-
						NC	1(0)	-	-	-	-	-
Tonga	Laa'atoa		Samoa	0cm	0kg							
			Orrell	Prop		NL	17(1)	-	-	-	-	-
						NC	4(0)	-	-	-	-	-
Pat	Lam	29.09.68	Samoa	188cm	105kg							
			Newcastle	No.8		NL	33(10)	45	9	-	-	-
						NC	5(1)	5	1	-	-	-
						ES	7(0)	25	5	-	-	-
						EC	4(1)	-	-	-	-	-
			Northampton	No.8		NL	53(1)	100	20	-	-	-
						NC	7(0)	-	-	-	-	-
						EC	11(0)	5	1	-	-	-
Rhodri	Latham	01.08.69	England	186cm	121kg							
			Rotherham	Prop		NL	3(13)	-	-	-	-	-
						NC	0(1)	-	-	-	-	-
						ES	1(1)	-	-	-	-	-
			SedgleyPark	Prop		NL	15(10)	-	-	-	-	-
						NC	2(0)	-	-	-	-	-
			Wakefield	Prop		NL	134(14)	15	3	-	-	-
						NC	1(0)	-	-	-	-	-
Andy	Lee	10.11.68	England	0cm	0kg							
			LondonWelsh	OutsideHalf		NL	67(17)	578	8	-	-	-
						NC	7(0)	55	-	8	13	-
			Saracens	OutsideHalf		NL	58(9)	290	8	-	-	-
						NC	0(2)	2	-	1	-	-
						ES	2(1)	28	-	2	8	-
Matthew	Leek	25.10.80		176cm	83kg							
			LondonWasps	OutsideHalf		NL	14(19)	45	1	8	7	1
						NC	0(1)	-	-	-	-	-
						EC	5(4)	12	-	-	4	-
			Saracens	OutsideHalf		NL	2(5)	10	-	2	1	1
						NC	0(2)	13	-	2	3	-
						EC	1(1)	6	-	3	-	-

Jason	Leonard	14.08.68	England	178cm	111kg							
			Saracens		Prop	NL	19	4	1	-	-	-
			Harlequins	Prop		NL	155(6)	9	2	-	-	-
						NC	9(1)	-	-	-	-	-
						ES	7(0)	-	-	-	-	-
						EC	19(2)	-	-	-	-	-
Trevor	Leota	08.02.75	Samoa	173cm	110kg							
			LondonWasps	Hooker		NL	65(26)	110	22	-	-	-
						NC	9(2)	10	2	-	-	-
						EC	16(3)	10	2	-	-	-
John	Leslie	25.11.70	Scotland	191cm	92kg							
			Newcastle	Center		NL	10(0)	20	4	-	-	-
						ES	2(0)	-	-	-	-	-
			Northampton	Center		NL	22(1)	25	5	-	-	-
						NC	3(0)	-	-	-	-	-
						EC	5(1)	-	-	-	-	-
Peauafi	Leuila			0cm	0kg							
			Manchester	LeftWing		NL	32(16)	15	3	-	-	-
						NC	3(1)	5	1	-	-	-
Nick	Lewis	12.07.71	England	0cm	0kg							
			Birmingham&S.	Prop		NL	63(14)	5	1	-	-	-
						NC	9(1)	-	-	-	-	-
Ben	Lewitt		England	0cm	0kg							
			Leicester	Flanker		NL	0(2)	-	-	-	-	-
						NC	0(1)	-	-	-	-	-
			RugbyLions	Flanker		NL	13(5)	-	-	-	-	-
						NC	1(0)	-	-	-	-	-
Josh	Lewsey	30.11.76	England	180cm	85kg							
			Bristol	FullBack		NL	22(3)	46	7	1	3	-
						NC	1(0)	-	-	-	-	-
						ES	5(0)	2	-	1	-	-
			LondonWasps	FullBack		NL	71(3)	95	19	-	-	-
						NC	10(0)	10	2	-	-	-
						EC	12(0)	20	4	-	-	-
Tom	Lewsey	03.05.75	England	5 11	13 9							
			LondonWelsh	ScrumHalf		NL	20(27)	15	3	-	-	-
						NC	0(3)	-	-	-	-	-
Richard	Liddington	31.12.78		6 0	18 3							
			LondonWelsh	Prop		NL	16(20)	-	-	-	-	-
						NC	0(1)	-	-	-	-	-
Rob	Liley	03.04.70	England	0cm	0kg							
			Harlequins	OutsideHalf		NL	24(8)	174	5	34	27	-
						NC	4(0)	30	1	11	1	-
						EC	1(4)	15	1	2	2	-
			Leicester	OutsideHalf		NL	11(2)	44	3	7	5	-
						NC	0(1)	-	-	-	-	-
						EC	7(0)	62	1	12	11	-
			Sale	Outside half		NL	25	209	3	28	44	2
			Wakefield	OutsideHalf		NL	64(3)	562	5	80	118	8
						NC	2(0)	18	-	-	6	-
Simon	Lincoln		England	0cm	0kg							
			Bedford	Center		NL	23(3)	20	4	-	-	-
						NC	0(1)	-	-	-	-	-
			BedfordAthletic	Center		NL	22(0)	24	4	2	-	-
						NC	1(0)	-	-	-	-	-
Scott	Lines	28.07.73		196cm	105kg							
			Bristol	Lock		NL	4(0)	5	1	-	-	-
			Sale	Lock		NL	30(10)	5	1	-	-	-
						NC	4(1)	-	-	-	-	-
						ES	11(3)	10	2	-	-	-
Jason	Little	26.08.70	Australia	185cm	92kg							
			Bristol	Center		NL	21(0)	30	6	-	-	-
						NC	1(0)	-	-	-	-	-
						ES	6(0)	10	2	-	-	-
			Gloucester	Center		NL	13(0)	30	6	-	-	-
						EC	8(0)	10	2	-	-	-
Alastair	Livesey		England	0cm	0kg							
			Orrell	Prop		NL	48(13)	25	5	-	-	-
						NC	3(3)	5	1	-	-	-

Andrew	Llewellyn	11.07.82	England	196cm	96kg							
			Bedford	Center		NL	6(10)	-	-	-	-	-
						NC	0(1)	-	-	-	-	-
Nick	Lloyd	12.10.76	England	0cm	0kg							
			Wakefield	Prop		NL	74(0)	55	11	-	-	-
						NC	6(0)	5	1	-	-	-
Mark	Lloyd		England	0cm	0kg							
			Orrell	O'sideFlanker		NL	43(5)	35	7	-	-	-
						NC	4(4)	-	-	-	-	-
Mark	Lock	22.09.72	England	188cm	98kg							
			LondonWasps	O'sideFlanker		NL	16(15)	10	2	-	-	-
						NC	1(0)	-	-	-	-	-
						EC	7(0)	-	-	-	-	-
Kenny	Logan	03.03.72	Scotland	185cm	93kg							
			LondonWasps	LeftWing		NL	94(4)	879	43	107	150	-
						NC	12(1)	118	7	10	21	-
						EC	21(1)	232	13	22	41	-
Andy	Long	02.09.77	England	181cm	99kg							
			Bath	Hooker		NL	36(39)	20	4	-	-	-
						NC	1(3)	-	-	-	-	-
						EC	9(11)	5	1	-	-	-
Matt	Long	25.03.73	England	0cm	0kg							
			Moseley	Prop		NL	49(14)	30	6	-	-	-
						NC	3(1)	5	1	-	-	-
Brett	Luxton	11.07.76	England	0cm	0kg							
			PlymouthAlbion	No.8		NL	14(9)	30	6	-	-	-
						NC	1(0)	-	-	-	-	-
			Launceston	No.8		NL	26(0)	35	7	-	-	-
						NC	3(0)	5	1	-	-	-
Dan	Lyle	28.09.70	UnitedStates	196cm	114kg							
			Bath	No.8		NL	77(4)	70	14	-	-	-
						NC	5(0)	-	-	-	-	-
						EC	20(6)	17	3	1	-	-
Neil	Lyman	06.05.70	England	5 9	18 0							
			Worcester	Prop		NL	65(16)	40	8	-	-	-
						NC	7(0)	-	-	-	-	-
Gareth	Maclure	17.12.79		191cm	96kg							
			Newcastle	LeftWing		NL	15(12)	20	4	-	-	-
						NC	2(1)	-	-	-	-	-
						ES	2(3)	10	2	-	-	-
						EC	3(1)	-	-	-	-	-
			WestHartlepool	RightWing		NL	4(5)	10	2	-	-	-
Chris	Malherbe			0cm	0kg							
			Otley	Center		NL	8(1)	18	3	-	-	1
						NC	0(1)	-	-	-	-	-
			Kendal	Center		NL	13(0)	25	5	-	-	-
John	Mallett	28.05.70	England	188cm	111kg							
			Bath	Prop		NL	90(28)	14	3	-	-	-
						NC	3(3)	-	-	-	-	-
						EC	13(4)	-	-	-	-	-
Dominic	Malone	12.12.74	England	183cm	89kg							
			Northampton	ScrumHalf		NL	38(19)	30	6	-	-	-
						NC	2(4)	-	-	-	-	-
						ES	1(1)	-	-	-	-	-
						EC	6(7)	5	1	-	-	-
Chris	Malone	08.01.78	Australia	182cm	89kg							
			Exeter	OutsideHalf		NL	21(1)	247	5	45	37	7
						NC	4(0)	32	-	7	6	-
Gareth	Manuel		England	0cm	0kg							
			Wakefield	No.8		NL	32(31)	10	2	-	-	-
						NC	1(4)	-	-	-	-	-
Mark	Mapletoft	25.12.71	England	171cm	83kg							
			Rugby	Full back		NL	41	201	6	14	45	3
			Gloucester	FullBack		NL	71(4)	848	19	90	184	7
						NC	7(2)	88	2	6	22	-
						ES	9(0)	128	5	20	19	2
			Harlequins	FullBack		NL	10(14)	13	1	1	2	-
						NC	0(1)	-	-	-	-	-
						EC	4(1)	16	-	2	4	-
			Saracens	FullBack		NL	12(0)	25	2	3	3	-
						NC	1(0)	-	-	-	-	-
						EC	4(0)	33	3	6	2	-

First	Surname	DOB	Country / Club	Height / Position	Weight	Comp	Apps	Pts	T	C	PG	DG
Charl	Marais	02.09.70	South Africa	183cm	105kg							
			Sale	Hooker		NL	6(10)	5	1	-	-	-
						NC	0(1)	-	-	-	-	-
						ES	2(1)	5	1	-	-	-
Sean	Marsden	17.01.80	England	183cm	84kg							
			Bristol	FullBack		NL	9(13)	25	5	-	-	-
						NC	1(1)	5	1	-	-	-
						ES	11(1)	20	4	-	-	-
			Exeter	FullBack		NL	10(6)	10	2	-	-	-
						NC	2(0)	5	1	-	-	-
Hentie	Martens	29.10.71	SouthAfrica	179cm	78kg							
			LondonIrish	ScrumHalf		NL	5(11)	5	1	-	-	-
						NC	3(1)	-	-	-	-	-
						ES	2(0)	-	-	-	-	-
			NatalSharks	ScrumHalf								
Rod	Martin	25.11.75	England	0cm	0kg							
			Moseley	RightWing		NL	111(4)	117	21	3	2	-
						NC	3(1)	7	-	2	1	-
Jon	Martin	12.10.76	England	0cm	0kg							
			Clifton	OutsideHalf		NL	24(0)	228	7	32	41	2
			Newbury	OutsideHalf		NL	22(0)	30	2	4	3	1
						NC	2(1)	-	-	-	-	-
Simon	Martin		England	0cm	0kg							
			Bristol	Center		NL	26(7)	46	6	5	2	-
						NC	2(0)	-	-	-	-	-
						ES	8(0)	5	1	-	-	-
			Clifton	LeftWing		NL	13(1)	5	1	-	-	-
			Coventry	Center		NL	19(7)	33	6	-	-	1
						NC	1(0)	4	-	2	-	-
Peter	Massey	03.03.75	England	180cm	86kg							
			Newcastle	FullBack		NL	22(8)	26	2	2	4	-
						NC	2(1)	-	-	-	-	-
						ES	4(1)	5	1	-	-	-
			Rotherham	Center		NL	24(4)	50	10	-	-	-
						NC	3(0)	5	1	-	-	-
Andy	Matchett	17/08/74	England	6 0	14 0							
			PlymouthAlbion	LeftWing		NL	50(0)	90	18	-	-	-
						NC	3(1)	5	1	-	-	-
Cameron	Mather	02.08.72	Scotland	0cm	0kg							
			LeedsTykes	Flanker		NL	16(5)	15	3	-	-	-
						NC	1(0)	5	1	-	-	-
						ES	3(0)	-	-	-	-	-
			Worcester	Flanker		NL	8(7)	5	1	-	-	-
						NC	1(0)	-	-	-	-	-
			EdinburghReiv	Flanker								
						EC	2(0)	-	-	-	-	-
Tom	May	05.02.79	England	177cm	92kg							
			Newcastle	Center		NL	48(0)	65	13	-	-	-
						NC	10(0)	20	4	-	-	-
						ES	7(2)	15	3	-	-	-
						EC	5(0)	5	1	-	-	-
Neil	McCarthy	29.11.74	England	178cm	102kg							
			Bath	Hooker		NL	1(2)	-	-	-	-	-
			Bristol	Hooker		NL	32(3)	5	1	-	-	-
						NC	2(1)	-	-	-	-	-
						ES	8(4)	-	-	-	-	-
			Gloucester	Hooker		NL	27(15)	5	1	-	-	-
						NC	6(0)	-	-	-	-	-
						ES	10(2)	5	1	-	-	-
Greg	McDonald	06.10.80	England	0cm	0kg							
			Moseley	OutsideHalf		NL	19(8)	64	1	13	9	2
						NC	1(0)	2	-	1	-	-
Louis	McGowan		England	0cm	0kg							
			Coventry	Lock		NL	7(8)	-	-	-	-	-
						NC	0(1)	-	-	-	-	-
			Waterloo	Lock		NL	34(15)	10	2	-	-	-
						NC	2(2)	10	2	-	-	-

Alastair	McLean		England	0cm	0kg							
			Bedford	RightWing		NL	10(2)	15	3	-	-	-
						NC	0(1)	-	-	-	-	-
						ES	4(1)	10	2	-	-	-
			Coventry	RightWing		NL	14(3)	20	4	-	-	-
			Worcester	RightWing		NL	5(3)	20	4	-	-	-
						NC	0(1)	-	-	-	-	-
Trent	McMurray	16.06.71	England	0cm	0kg							
			Birmingham&S.	Hooker		NL	19(2)	5	1	-	-	-
						NC	1(0)	-	-	-	-	-
			Coventry	Hooker		NL	15(29)	20	4	-	-	-
						NC	0(3)	-	-	-	-	-
Mark	Meehan	08.08.80	England	189cm	83kg							
			Bedford	OutsideHalf		NL	17(5)	46	2	6	4	4
						NC	1(0)	3	-	-	-	1
Ludovic	Mercier	01.11.76	France	0cm	0kg							
			Gloucester	OutsideHalf		NL	21(0)	334	2	48	64	12
						NC	1(1)	5	-	1	1	-
						ES	6(0)	112	-	20	20	4
			Aurillac	OutsideHalf								
						ES	2(0)	9	-	3	1	-
Mike	Mika	24.07.68	England	0cm	0kg							
			Coventry	Prop		NL	47(10)	10	2	-	-	-
						NC	4(2)	5	1	-	-	-
Jason	Minshull	20.12.67	England	0cm	0kg							
			Birmingham&S.	Center		NL	7(11)	-	-	-	-	-
						NC	2(1)	-	-	-	-	-
			Coventry	Center		NL	103(9)	74	16	-	-	-
						NC	1(1)	-	-	-	-	-
Neil	Mitchell	22.06.66	England	0cm	0kg							
			Moseley	Lock		NL	50(23)	30	6	-	-	-
						NC	3(1)	-	-	-	-	-
Alan	Mitchell	22.10.74	England	0cm	0kg							
			Coventry	Center		NL	6(12)	89	3	16	14	-
			Walsall	Center		NL	6(3)	-	-	-	-	-
Fa'atoto	Moananu	-	Samoa	0cm	0kg							
			RugbyLions	RightWing		NL	13(2)	25	5	-	-	-
						NC	1(0)	-	-	-	-	-
Alex	Moffatt	01.01.00	England	0cm	0kg							
			Orrell	Hooker		NL	45(23)	5	1	-	-	-
						NC	4(4)	5	1	-	-	-
						ES	1(0)	-	-	-	-	-
Andy	Monighan	-	England	0cm	0kg							
			Orrell	BlindsideFlanker		NL	12(14)	-	-	-	-	-
						NC	5(0)	-	-	-	-	-
Lewis	Moody	12.06.78	England	193cm	101kg							
			Leicester	Flanker		NL	57(21)	45	9	-	-	-
						NC	5(3)	5	1	-	-	-
						EC	12(7)	15	3	-	-	-
Matt	Moore	02.03.76	England	180cm	87kg							
			Harlequins	RightWing		NL	19(2)	20	4	-	-	-
						NC	2(0)	5	1	-	-	-
						EC	6(0)	5	1	-	-	-
			Sale	RightWing		NL	62(2)	100	20	-	-	-
						NC	5(0)	10	2	-	-	-
						ES	14(1)	55	11	-	-	-
Alejandro	Moreno	21.04.73	Italian	0cm	0kg							
			Worcester	Prop		NL	13(9)	-	-	-	-	-
						NC	1(2)	-	-	-	-	-
Garrick	Morgan	25.01.70	Australia	201cm	120kg							
			Harlequins	Lock		NL	77(4)	45	9	-	-	-
						NC	8(3)	-	-	-	-	-
						ES	9(0)	-	-	-	-	-
						EC	11(0)	-	-	-	-	-
Martin	Morgan	22.02.79		0cm	0kg							
			Worcester	Lock		NL	24(1)	35	7	-	-	-
						NC	2(0)	-	-	-	-	-

Andy	Morris	01.09.71	England	183cm	95kg							
			Manchester	Flanker		NL	10(5)	-	-	-	-	-
						NC	1(0)	-	-	-	-	-
			Sale	Flanker		NL	33(19)	10	2	-	-	-
						NC	1(1)	-	-	-	-	-
						ES	10(2)	-	-	-	-	-
Wayne	Morris		England	0cm	0kg							
			Manchester	ScrumHalf		NL	13(4)	5	1	-	-	-
			Waterloo	ScrumHalf		NL	43(8)	15	3	-	-	-
						NC	2(2)	5	1	-	-	-
Dave	Muckalt		England	0cm	0kg							
			HenleyHawks	No.8		NL	19(6)	25	5	-	-	-
						NC	2(0)	-	-	-	-	-
			Manchester	No.8		NL	21(1)	30	6	-	-	-
						NC	3(0)	10	2	-	-	-
			RugbyLions	No.8		NL	18(2)	25	5	-	-	-
						NC	3(0)	5	1	-	-	-
Chris	Murphy	02.02.76	England	201cm	114kg							
			LeedsTykes	Lock		NL	19(1)	5	1	-	-	-
						NC	0(2)	-	-	-	-	-
						ES	2(1)	-	-	-	-	-
			Rotherham	Lock		NL	7(0)	5	1	-	-	-
						NC	1(0)	-	-	-	-	-
						ES	4(0)	-	-	-	-	-
			Sale	Lock		NL	26(12)	5	1	-	-	-
						NC	4(1)	-	-	-	-	-
						ES	3(1)	-	-	-	-	-
			WestHartlepool	Lock		NL	19(0)	-	-	-	-	-
Ricky	Nebbett	16.08.77	England	180cm	108kg							
			Harlequins	Prop		NL	13(6)	5	1	-	-	-
						NC	1(2)	-	-	-	-	-
			Leicester	Prop		NL	16(24)	-	-	-	-	-
						NC	3(2)	-	-	-	-	-
						EC	0(7)	-	-	-	-	-
Saul	Nelson			0cm	0kg							
			Bristol	Flanker		NL	3(20)	-	-	-	-	-
						NC	1(1)	-	-	-	-	-
						ES	3(3)	-	-	-	-	-
Paul	Newton	29.04.78	England	0cm	0kg							
			Orrell	ScrumHalf		NL	52(23)	25	5	-	-	-
						NC	7(1)	5	1	-	-	-
Jamie	Noon	09.05.79	England	177cm	86kg							
			Newcastle	Center		NL	49(7)	45	9	-	-	-
						NC	9(0)	15	3	-	-	-
						ES	11(1)	25	5	-	-	-
						EC	4(0)	-	-	-	-	-
Ed	Norris		England	0cm	0kg							
			Manchester	BlindsideFlanker		NL	13(13)	5	1	-	-	-
						NC	2(1)	-	-	-	-	-
Andrew	Northey	17.02.73	England	183cm	99kg							
			Northampton	Center		NL	30(11)	-	-	-	-	-
						NC	3(4)	5	1	-	-	-
						EC	0(4)	-	-	-	-	-
			Rotherham	Center		NL	21(16)	15	3	-	-	-
						NC	1(4)	-	-	-	-	-
						ES	4(1)	5	1	-	-	-
Daren	O'Leary	27.06.73	England	6 0	13 0							
			Gloucester	Left wing		NL	20(1)	20	4	-	-	-
						NC	1(0)	-	-	-	-	-
						ES	6(0)	40	8	-	-	-
			Harlequins	Right wing		NL	125(2)	339	65	-	-	1
						NC	5(2)	50	10	-	-	-
						ES	6(1)	5	1	-	-	-
						EC	15(1)	50	10	-	-	-
			Saracens	Right wing		NL	10	15	3	-	-	-
Matt	Oliver	30.11.76	England	186cm	87kg							
			Exeter	Centre		NL	15(2)	5	1	-	-	-
						NC	2(0)	10	2	-	-	-
			LeedsTykes	Centre		NL	23(2)	65	13	-	-	-
						NC	4(0)	-	-	-	-	-
			LondonIrish	Centre		NL	7(2)	10	2	-	-	-
						NC	3(0)	10	2	-	-	-
						ES	6(0)	25	5	-	-	-

Adrian	Olver	02.06.69	England	183cm	99kg							
			Bedford	Prop		NL	22(2)	10	2	-	-	-
						NC	1(0)	-	-	-	-	-
						ES	3(0)	5	1	-	-	-
			Harlequins	Prop		NL	25(4)	15	3	-	-	-
						NC	2(0)	-	-	-	-	-
						EC	3(2)	-	-	-	-	-
			Rotherham	Prop		NL	4(2)	-	-	-	-	-
						NC	0(1)	5	1	-	-	-
						ES	1(2)	-	-	-	-	-
			Saracens	Prop		NL	16(19)	10	2	-	-	-
						NC	2(1)	-	-	-	-	-
						ES	3(2)	5	1	-	-	-
Darragh	O'Mahony	18.08.73	Ireland	180cm	82kg							
			Bedford	LeftWing		NL	23(0)	55	11	-	-	-
			Moseley	LeftWing		NL	33	160	32	-	-	-
			Saracens	LeftWing		NL	54(8)	95	19	-	-	-
						NC	7(0)	20	4	-	-	-
						ES	7(0)	45	9	-	-	-
						EC	8(2)	15	3	-	-	-
John	O'Reilly	07.01.76	England	0cm	86kg							
			LeedsTykes	ScrumHalf		NL	3(19)	-	-	-	-	-
						NC	0(2)	-	-	-	-	-
						ES	4(2)	-	-	-	-	-
			Leicester	ScrumHalf		NL	1(3)	-	-	-	-	-
						NC	0(1)	5	1	-	-	-
			Manchester	ScrumHalf		NL	24(1)	10	2	-	-	-
						NC	4(0)	5	1	-	-	-
			Sale	ScrumHalf		NL	4(3)	-	-	-	-	-
						ES	4(0)	-	-	-	-	-
Edward	Orgee	29.02.76	England	0cm	0kg							
			Birmingham&S.	No.8		NL	23(1)	10	2	-	-	-
						NC	4(0)	-	-	-	-	-
			Moseley	Flanker		NL	3(3)	-	-	-	-	-
			Worcester	Flanker		NL	10(8)	-	-	-	-	-
Soakai	Otuvaka	10.05.78	England	0cm	0kg							
			LeedsTykes	BlindsideFlanker		NL	0(1)	-	-	-	-	-
			Manchester	BlindsideFlanker		NL	11(8)	10	2	-	-	-
						NC	3(0)	-	-	-	-	-
			Tynedale	O'sideFlanker		NL	7(0)	5	1	-	-	-
Altan	Ozdemir		England	0cm	0kg							
			Bedford	Prop		NL	6(4)	-	-	-	-	-
			Exeter	Prop		NL	9(12)	10	2	-	-	-
						NC	0(3)	-	-	-	-	-
			Gloucester	Prop								
			Harlequins	Prop		NL	5(2)	-	-	-	-	-
						NC	1(0)	-	-	-	-	-
						EC	1(0)	-	-	-	-	-
			LeedsTykes	Prop		NL	9(25)	5	1	-	-	-
						NC	0(2)	-	-	-	-	-
Tom	Palmer	27.03.79	England	0cm	105kg							
			LeedsTykes	Lock		NL	77(6)	60	12	-	-	-
						NC	6(1)	10	2	-	-	-
						ES	2(4)	-	-	-	-	-
Junior	Paramore	18.11.68	Samoa	188cm	105kg							
			Bedford	No.8		NL	48(0)	90	18	-	-	-
						NC	1(0)	10	2	-	-	-
			Gloucester	BlindsideFlanker		NL	42(4)	55	11	-	-	-
						NC	3(3)	5	1	-	-	-
						ES	7(1)	15	3	-	-	-
						EC	5(0)	-	-	-	-	-
Howard	Parr	01.11.72	England	191cm	111kg							
			Orrell	Flanker								
						ES	1(0)	-	-	-	-	-
			Rotherham	Flanker		NL	35(37)	65	13	-	-	-
						NC	3(3)	10	2	-	-	-
						ES	1(3)	-	-	-	-	-
Ian	Patten	31.05.70	England	6 5	17 0							
			Coventry	No 8		NL	45	50	10	-	-	-
			Moseley	No.8		NL	63(4)	50	10	-	-	-
						NC	4(0)	-	-	-	-	-

Henry	Paul		England	0cm	0kg							
			Bath	Center		NL	3(0)	10	2	-	-	-
						EC	3(1)	5	1	-	-	-
			Gloucester	Center		NL	13(3)	38	2	5	6	-
						NC	2(0)	12	-	3	2	-
						ES	4(2)	59	2	23	1	-
Alan	Paver	28.11.77	England	0cm	0kg							
			PlymouthAlbion	Prop		NL	54(21)	40	8	-	-	-
						NC	3(0)	-	-	-	-	-
Ed	Pearce	02.09.75	*	198cm	123kg							
			Bath	Flanker		NL	2(1)	-	-	-	-	-
			Gloucester	Flanker		NL	46(23)	10	2	-	-	-
						NC	7(4)	-	-	-	-	-
						ES	17(3)	-	-	-	-	-
						EC	0(2)	-	-	-	-	-
Ian	Peel	24.01.76	England	180cm	112kg							
			Newcastle	Prop		NL	36(28)	-	-	-	-	-
						NC	2(7)	-	-	-	-	-
						ES	7(6)	-	-	-	-	-
						EC	2(4)	-	-	-	-	-
Ricky	Pellow	19.02.78	England	5 6	13 0							
			Bath	ScrumHalf		NL	1(5)	-	-	-	-	-
						NC	1(0)	-	-	-	-	-
						EC	4(3)	-	-	-	-	-
			Exeter	ScrumHalf		NC	0(1)	-	-	-	-	-
			Worcester	ScrumHalf		NL	5(30)	10	2	-	-	-
						NC	0(4)	-	-	-	-	-
Andy	Perry	12.07.77	England	0cm	0kg							
			Exeter	Lock		NL	13(17)	5	1	-	-	-
						NC	1(2)	-	-	-	-	-
			PlymouthAlbion	Lock		NL	18(1)	20	4	-	-	-
Ramiro	Pez	06.12.78	Italy	0cm	0kg							
			Rotherham	OutsideHalf		NL	17(4)	197	4	60	19	-
						NC	3(0)	41	1	6	7	1
			Roma	OutsideHalf								
						EC	4(0)	29	1	6	3	1
Jon	Phillips	16.08.72	England	198cm	115kg							
			Northampton	Lock		NL	144(28)	45	9	-	-	-
						NC	12(3)	-	-	-	-	-
						ES	9(0)	-	-	-	-	-
						EC	10(6)	5	1	-	-	-
Agustin	Pichot	22.08.74	Argentina	178cm	79kg							
			Bristol	ScrumHalf		NL	46(0)	38	7	-	-	1
						NC	5(0)	-	-	-	-	-
						ES	12(1)	10	2	-	-	-
			Richmond	ScrumHalf		NL	25(0)	35	7	-	-	-
						NC	3(0)	5	1	-	-	-
						ES	4(0)	10	2	-	-	-
Will	Pilkington		England	0cm	0kg							
			RugbyLions	Flanker		NL	12(8)	-	-	-	-	-
						NC	1(0)	-	-	-	-	-
			Waterloo	Flanker		NL	31(8)	25	5	-	-	-
						NC	1(0)	-	-	-	-	-
Stuart	Pinkerton	25.03.75	Australia	186cm	100kg							
			Sale	BlindsideFlanker		NL	20(0)	5	1	-	-	-
						NC	1(0)	-	-	-	-	-
						ES	7(0)	5	1	-	-	-
Adam	Pogson		England	0cm	0kg							
			Otley	Prop		NL	17(32)	-	-	-	-	-
						NC	0(3)	-	-	-	-	-
Stephen	Pope	24.11.73	England	5 11	18 2							
			LondonWelsh	Prop		NL	40(23)	5	1	-	-	-
						NC	2(1)	-	-	-	-	-
Danny	Porte			0cm	0kg							
			Exeter	Hooker		NL	21(20)	20	4	-	-	-
						NC	4(0)	10	2	-	-	-
			Waterloo	Prop		NL	1(9)	-	-	-	-	-

Stuart	Potter	11.11.67	England	5 11	14 7							
			Nottingham	Centre		NL	30	20	5	-	-	-
			Leicester	Center		NL	100(3)	85	17	-	-	-
						NC	5(0)	5	1	-	-	-
						EC	15(0)	-	-	-	-	-
			RugbyLions	Center		NL	18(2)	-	-	-	-	-
Budge	Pountney	13.11.73	Scotland	183cm	98kg							
			Northampton	O'sideFlanker		NL	129(2)	160	32	-	-	-
						NC	12(0)	15	3	-	-	-
						ES	10(0)	5	1	-	-	-
						EC	15(0)	15	3	-	-	-
Matt	Powell	08.05.78	England	178cm	89kg							
			Harlequins	ScrumHalf		NL	23(15)	-	-	-	-	-
						NC	6(1)	-	-	-	-	-
						ES	9(0)	5	1	-	-	-
						EC	1(4)	-	-	-	-	-
			Saracens	ScrumHalf		NL	5(12)	10	2	-	-	-
						NC	1(0)	5	1	-	-	-
						EC	1(0)	5	1	-	-	-
Steve	Powell	12.04.75	England	0cm	0kg							
			Moseley	ScrumHalf		NL	40(22)	15	3	-	-	-
						NC	2(1)	-	-	-	-	-
			Worcester	ScrumHalf		NL	0(1)	5	1	-	-	-
James	Pritchard	21.07.79	Australia	176cm	80kg							
			Bedford	FullBack		NL	23(1)	244	8	42	40	-
						NC	1(0)	6	-	-	2	-
Nick	Proctor		England	0cm	0kg							
			PlymouthAlbion	Center		NL	23(3)	30	6	-	-	-
						NC	1(0)	-	-	-	-	-
Tristan	Prosser-Shaw		Wales	0cm	0kg							
			RugbyLions	BlindsideFlanker		NL	26(0)	30	6	-	-	-
						NC	1(0)	-	-	-	-	-
Richard	Protherough	09.11.76	England	5 9	14 0							
			Moseley	Hooker		NL	53(16)	50	10	-	-	-
						NC	4(1)	5	1	-	-	-
Federico	Pucciarello	24.06.75		0cm	0kg							
			Gloucester	Prop		NL	12(9)	10	2	-	-	-
						NC	1(1)	-	-	-	-	-
						ES	3(2)	5	1	-	-	-
			Narbonne	Prop								
						ES	3(0)	-	-	-	-	-
Dave	Ramsey	17.02.77	England	6 3	15 7							
			LondonWelsh	O'sideFlanker		NL	17(14)	-	-	-	-	-
						NC	0(1)	-	-	-	-	-
Steve	Ravenscroft	02.11.70	England	5 11	14 2							
			LondonWelsh	Center		NL	37(2)	20	4	-	-	-
						NC	1(0)	-	-	-	-	-
			Saracens	Center		NL	106(9)	75	15	-	-	-
						NC	9(0)	10	2	-	-	-
						ES	3(0)	5	1	-	-	-
Rob	Rawlinson	23.08.76	England	0cm	90kg							
			LeedsTykes	Hooker		NL	22(22)	5	1	-	-	-
						NC	1(1)	-	-	-	-	-
						ES	1(1)	-	-	-	-	-
			Orrell	Hooker		NL	23(12)	-	-	-	-	-
						ES	1(0)	-	-	-	-	-
Phil	Read	01.05.80	England	0cm	0kg							
			RugbyLions	ScrumHalf		NL	25(5)	65	13	-	-	-
						NC	1(0)	-	-	-	-	-
Bryan	Redpath	21.07.71	Scotland	173cm	86kg							
			Sale	ScrumHalf		NL	36(1)	25	5	-	-	-
						NC	3(0)	-	-	-	-	-
						ES	8(2)	5	1	-	-	-
Wayne	Reed	27.10.71	England	0cm	0kg							
			Exeter	Prop		NL	38(5)	25	5	-	-	-
						NC	1(0)	-	-	-	-	-
			PlymouthAlbion	Prop		NL	51(1)	35	7	-	-	-
						NC	4(0)	-	-	-	-	-

David	Rees	15.10.74	England	175cm	83kg							
			Bristol	LeftWing		NL	44(1)	50	10	-	-	-
						NC	4(0)	5	1	-	-	-
						ES	6(1)	30	6	-	-	-
			Sale	LeftWing		NL	42(3)	55	11	-	-	-
						NC	6(0)	-	-	-	-	-
						ES	2(0)	-	-	-	-	-
Paul	Rees	10.04.73	England	0cm	0kg							
			LeedsTykes	Lock		NL	3(8)	5	1	-	-	-
						NC	1(1)	-	-	-	-	-
			Orrell	Lock		NL	18(1)	5	1	-	-	-
						ES	2(0)	-	-	-	-	-
			SedgleyPark	Lock		NL	22(0)	-	-	-	-	-
						NC	2(0)	-	-	-	-	-
			Wakefield	Lock		NL	14(10)	5	1	-	-	-
						NC	2(1)	-	-	-	-	-
Mark	Regan	28.01.72	England	178cm	95kg							
			Bath	Hooker		NL	75(21)	35	7	-	-	-
						NC	4(0)	-	-	-	-	-
						EC	19(7)	-	-	-	-	-
			Bristol	Hooker		NL	51(0)	15	3	-	-	-
						NC	1(0)	-	-	-	-	-
						ES	2(0)	-	-	-	-	-
Shaun	Renwick			0cm	0kg							
			Moseley	O'sideFlanker		NL	18(6)	10	2	-	-	-
						NC	2(0)	-	-	-	-	-
Chris	Richards			0cm	0kg							
			Bedford	FullBack		NL	7(2)	2	-	1	-	-
						NC	1(0)	-	-	-	-	-
						ES	4(0)	11	-	1	3	-
			RugbyLions	FullBack		NL	14(2)	111	3	18	20	-
Dan	Richmond	12.02.79	England	181cm	104kg							
			Northampton	Hooker		NL	5(16)	15	3	-	-	-
						NC	2(3)	-	-	-	-	-
						EC	0(1)	-	-	-	-	-
Peter	Risdon		England	0cm	0kg							
			PlymouthAlbion	Prop		NL	10(8)	-	-	-	-	-
			Launceston	Prop		NL	13(1)	15	3	-	-	-
						NC	3(2)	-	-	-	-	-
Martin	Roberts	26.01.68	England	0cm	0kg							
			Birmingham&S.	Center		NL	51(4)	30	6	-	-	-
						NC	5(0)	10	2	-	-	-
			Gloucester	Center		NL	47(1)	66	3	6	13	-
						NC	3(0)	-	-	-	-	-
						ES	2(0)	-	-	-	-	-
			Moseley	Center		NL	4(0)	5	1	-	-	-
						NC	0(1)	-	-	-	-	-
Peter	Roberts	28.11.74		0cm	0kg							
			RugbyLions	FullBack		NL	18(4)	40	8	-	-	-
Jason	Robinson	30.07.74	England	173cm	83kg							
			Bath	Full back		NL	7(0)	20	4	-	-	-
						EC	5(0)	-	-	-	-	-
			Sale	Right wing		NL	31(0)	80	16	-	-	-
						NC	5(0)	10	2	-	-	-
						ES	3(0)	-	-	-	-	-
Kieran	Roche	03.05.79	Ireland	198cm	107kg							
			Saracens	No.8		NL	15(23)	-	-	-	-	-
						NC	1(3)	-	-	-	-	-
						ES	3(4)	15	3	-	-	-
						EC	0(1)	5	1	-	-	-
Shane	Roiser	07.06.73	England	178cm	89kg							
			LondonWasps	Rightwing		NL	118(13)	175	35	-	-	-
						NC	10(0)	20	4	-	-	-
						EC	24(0)	40	8	-	-	-
Duncan	Roke	05.07.74	England	0cm	0kg							
			HenleyHawks	Center		NL	49(1)	134	22	6	4	-
						NC	3(0)	15	3	-	-	-
			Leicester	Center		NL	0(1)	-	-	-	-	-
			Worcester	Center		NL	17(4)	80	16	-	-	-
						NC	3(0)	10	2	-	-	-

Paul	Rollason		England	0cm	0kg							
			Bedford	Lock		NL	14(11)	5	1	-	-	-
						NC	0(1)	-	-	-	-	-
Anthony	Roques	07.09.78	England	188cm	93kg							
			Saracens	Flanker		NL	34(12)	10	2	-	-	-
						NC	5(0)	20	4	-	-	-
						ES	5(0)	20	4	-	-	-
						EC	1(0)	-	-	-	-	-
James	Ross	08.03.78	NewZealand	189cm	110kg							
			Bedford	Hooker		NL	8(26)	15	3	-	-	-
						NC	0(1)	-	-	-	-	-
Joe	Ross	05.07.75	New Zealand	5 11	16 7							
			Worcester	-		NL	17(9)	20	4	-	-	-
						NC	1(2)	-	-	-	-	-
Florent	Rossingneux	17.02.70	England	6 2	15 10							
			Bedford	Flanker		NL	14(5)	5	1	-	-	-
						NC	1(0)	-	-	-	-	-
						ES	3(1)	5	1	-	-	-
			LondonWasps	Flanker		NL	3(2)	5	1	-	-	-
			LondonWelsh	Flanker		NL	32(9)	30	6	-	-	-
						NC	1(3)	-	-	-	-	-
Graham	Rowntree	18.03.71	England	183cm	108kg							
			Leicester	Prop		NL	96(17)	10	2	-	-	-
						NC	12(0)	-	-	-	-	-
						EC	33(5)	15	3	-	-	-
Robbie	Russell	01.05.76	Scotland	178cm	92kg							
			Saracens	Hooker		NL	28(8)	10	2	-	-	-
						NC	5(0)	-	-	-	-	-
						ES	4(1)	10	2	-	-	-
						EC	6(1)	-	-	-	-	-
Paul	Sackey	08.11.79	England	186cm	86kg							
			Bedford	RightWing		NL	14(3)	45	9	-	-	-
						NC	1(0)	-	-	-	-	-
						ES	3(0)	5	1	-	-	-
			LondonIrish	RightWing		NL	39(1)	65	13	-	-	-
						NC	6(0)	10	2	-	-	-
						ES	8(0)	30	6	-	-	-
Ian	Sanders	22.01.71	England	175cm	85kg							
			Bath	ScrumHalf		NL	30(4)	15	3	-	-	-
						NC	1(0)	-	-	-	-	-
						EC	0(1)	-	-	-	-	-
			Exeter	ScrumHalf		NL	23(13)	20	4	-	-	-
						NC	3(0)	5	1	-	-	-
			Gloucester	ScrumHalf		NL	17(13)	5	1	-	-	-
						NC	4(2)	3	-	-	-	1
						ES	10(1)	5	1	-	-	-
						EC	0(1)	-	-	-	-	-
Alex	Sanderson	07.10.79	England	188cm	100kg							
			Sale	O'sideFlanker		NL	56(8)	30	6	-	-	-
						NC	3(0)	5	1	-	-	-
						ES	8(1)	-	-	-	-	-
Duncan	Sayers		England	0cm	0kg							
			Otley	Hooker		NL	92(8)	15	3	-	-	-
						NC	2(0)	-	-	-	-	-
Danny	Scarborough	16.02.78	England	0cm	84kg							
			LeedsTykes	RightWing		NL	21(1)	60	12	-	-	-
						NC	2(0)	5	1	-	-	-
						ES	6(0)	20	4	-	-	-
			Wakefield	RightWing		NL	43(2)	85	17	-	-	-
						NC	3(0)	-	-	-	-	-
James	Scayesbrook	01.01.89	England	0cm	0kg							
			Bath	Flanker		NL	9(8)	-	-	-	-	-
						NC	1(0)	-	-	-	-	-
Michael	Schmid	28.11.69	Canada	191cm	108kg							
			Rotherham	No.8		NL	90(13)	160	32	-	-	-
						NC	5(2)	5	1	-	-	-
						ES	4(1)	5	1	-	-	-

Dean	Schofield	19.01.79	England	198cm	114kg							
			Sale	Lock		NL	1(0)	-	-	-	-	-
						ES	0(1)	-	-	-	-	-
			Wakefield	Lock		NL	16(1)	15	3	-	-	-
						NC	2(0)	-	-	-	-	-
Brett	Scriven		England	0cm	0kg							
			Stourbridge	No.8		NL	22(7)	20	4	-	-	-
						NC	1(0)	-	-	-	-	-
			Worcester	Flanker		NL	6(4)	10	2	-	-	-
David	Scully	07.08.65	England	173cm	79kg							
			Wakefield	Scrum half		NL	160(1)	298	52			
			Rotherham	ScrumHalf		NL	74(20)	168	27	12	3	-
						NC	5(2)	16	-	2	4	-
						ES	5(1)	18	-	3	4	-
Grant	Seely	17.01.74	England	193cm	111kg							
			Bedford	No.8		NL	2(0)	10	2	-	-	-
			Northampton	Flanker		NL	83(32)	145	29	-	-	-
						NC	9(3)	30	6	-	-	-
						ES	2(0)	10	2	-	-	-
						EC	5(5)	10	2	-	-	-
James	Shanahan	12.02.77	England	194cm	100kg							
			Bedford	OutsideHalf		NL	39(11)	127	18	5	4	5
						NC	3(0)	9	1	2	-	-
Simon	Shaw	01.09.72	England	203cm	127kg							
			Bristol	Lock		NL	56(0)	15	3	-	-	-
						NC	1(0)	-	-	-	-	-
						ES	4(0)	-	-	-	-	-
			LondonWasps	Lock		NL	88(13)	38	7	-	-	1
						NC	10(1)	-	-	-	-	-
						EC	17(3)	10	2	-	-	-
Martin	Shaw	02.09.78	England	183cm	89kg							
			Newcastle	Center		NL	39(7)	40	8	-	-	-
						NC	8(0)	10	2	-	-	-
						ES	9(1)	25	5	-	-	-
			Sale	Center		NL	18(12)	25	5	-	-	-
						NC	3(2)	5	1	-	-	-
						ES	8(1)	15	3	-	-	-
Peter	Shaw	09.11.73	Wales	5 11	13 0							
			LondonWelsh	FullBack		NL	102(10)	115	23	-	-	-
						NC	5(0)	5	1	-	-	-
Chris	Sheasby	30.11.66	England	188cm	104kg							
			Harlequins	No.8		NL	93(10)	69	14	-	-	-
						NC	4(1)	-	-	-	-	-
						EC	1(3)	-	-	-	-	-
			LondonIrish	No.8		NL	37(1)	20	4	-	-	-
						NC	3(1)	-	-	-	-	-
						ES	6(3)	-	-	-	-	-
			LondonWasps	No.8		NL	21(5)	40	8	-	-	-
						NC	2(0)	-	-	-	-	-
						EC	10(0)	25	5	-	-	-
Mike	Shelley	13.03.72	England	0cm	110kg							
			LeedsTykes	Prop		NL	94(2)	55	11	-	-	-
						NC	6(0)	5	1	-	-	-
						ES	2(1)	-	-	-	-	-
Jonathan	Shepherd	31.07.74	England	5 9	13 0							
			Rotherham	Center		NL	49(16)	70	14	-	-	-
						NC	3(2)	10	2	-	-	-
Andrew	Sheridan	01.11.79	England	196cm	130kg							
			Bristol	Lock		NL	22(24)	20	4	-	-	-
						NC	0(3)	5	1	-	-	-
						ES	6(2)	-	-	-	-	-
			Richmond	Lock		NL	3(2)	-	-	-	-	-
						NC	2(0)	5	1	-	-	-
Peter	Short	20.06.79	England	194cm	114kg							
			Leicester	No.8		NL	14(15)	-	-	-	-	-
						NC	1(2)	5	1	-	-	-
						EC	2(5)	-	-	-	-	-
Craig	Short	26.06.75	England	188cm	102kg							
			Bristol	O'sideFlanker		NL	51(24)	15	3	-	-	-
						NC	6(0)	-	-	-	-	-
						ES	18(9)	15	3	-	-	-

Ian	Shuttleworth		England	0cm	0kg							
			Otley	OutsideHalf		NL	42(2)	66	7	5	6	1
						NC	1(0)	4	-	2	-	-
			Wakefield	OutsideHalf		NL	0(1)	3	-	-	1	-
Terry	Sigley	12.01.78	England	0cm	0kg							
			Moseley	Prop		NL	49(11)	36	6	-	2	-
						NC	3(1)	3	-	-	1	-
Rob	Sigley	26.10.76	England	0cm	0kg							
			Moseley	Prop		NL	16(19)	-	-	-	-	-
						NC	1(2)	-	-	-	-	-
			Stourbridge	Prop		NL	8(4)	-	-	-	-	-
John	SimpsonDaniel		England	0cm	0kg							
			Gloucester	O'sideFlanker		NL	8(14)	50	10	-	-	-
						NC	2(0)	-	-	-	-	-
						ES	6(0)	25	5	-	-	-
						EC	1(0)	-	-	-	-	-
Dave	Sims	22.11.69	England	6 6	18 0							
			Bedford	Lock		NL	5(6)	-	-	-	-	-
			Gloucester	Lock		NL	130(8)	38	8	-	-	-
						NC	6(1)	5	1	-	-	-
						ES	6(1)	-	-	-	-	-
			Worcester	Lock		NL	37(23)	25	5	-	-	-
						NC	6(0)	-	-	-	-	-
Richard	Siviter	24.06.79		188cm	109kg							
			Bristol	Prop		NL	0(1)	-	-	-	-	-
						ES	2(1)	-	-	-	-	-
			Coventry	Prop		NL	9(16)	-	-	-	-	-
						NC	2(0)	-	-	-	-	-
Jon	Skurr		England	0cm	0kg							
			Otley	O'sideFlanker		NL	9(12)	25	5	-	-	-
						NC	2(2)	-	-	-	-	-
			Wakefield	O'sideFlanker		NL	25(0)	5	1	-	-	-
						NC	2(0)	-	-	-	-	-
Phil	Sluman	15.03.67	England	6 0	17 0							
			Exeter	Prop		NL	154(11)	59	12	-	-	-
						NC	9(0)	-	-	-	-	-
Andy	Smallwood	13.06.72	England	5 10	13 11							
			Birmingham&S.	LeftWing		NL	15(3)	30	6	-	-	-
						NC	0(1)	-	-	-	-	-
			Nottingham	Left wing		NL	47	60	12	-	-	-
			Coventry	LeftWing		NL	123(5)	265	53	-	-	-
						NC	5(0)	5	1	-	-	-
Oliver	Smith	14.08.82	England	188cm	88kg							
			Leicester	Center		NL	20(6)	20	4	-	-	-
						NC	5(0)	25	4	1	1	-
						EC	5(7)	15	3	-	-	-
Tom	Smith	31.10.71	Scotland	178cm	105kg							
			Northampton	Prop		NL	17(0)	15	3	-	-	-
						NC	2(1)	-	-	-	-	-
						EC	5(0)	-	-	-	-	-
			Brive	Prop		ES	3(0)	-	-	-	-	-
Bennett	Smith		England	0cm	0kg							
			RugbyLions	Prop		NL	25(12)	-	-	-	-	-
						NC	1(3)	-	-	-	-	-
Luke	Smith	09.02.71	SouthAfrica	172cm	80kg							
			Rotherham	OutsideHalf		NL	5(0)	61	-	2	18	1
						NC	2(0)	23	-	4	5	-
			Saracens	OutsideHalf		NL	15(3)	194	1	12	53	2
						NC	0(1)	-	-	-	-	-
						ES	5(0)	87	3	30	4	-
Simon	Smith		England	6 2	15 0							
			Otley	RightWing		NL	105(11)	147	29	1	-	-
						NC	3(0)	10	2	-	-	-
Richard	Smith	06.06.73	Wales	5 10	13 0							
			Bristol	ScrumHalf		NL	2(1)	5	1	-	-	-
			Sale	ScrumHalf		NL	24(8)	40	8	-	-	-
						NC	3(1)	5	1	-	-	-
						ES	3(0)	5	1	-	-	-
			Worcester	ScrumHalf		NL	24(1)	30	6	-	-	-
						NC	2(0)	5	1	-	-	-
			EbbwVale	ScrumHalf		ES	1(1)	-	-	-	-	-

First	Surname	DOB	Country / Club	Height / Position	Weight	Comp	Apps	Pts	T	C	PG	DG
Mark	Soden	10.03.81	England	188cm	104kg							
			Northampton	Prop		NL	11(11)	15	3	-	-	-
						NC	2(2)	-	-	-	-	-
						EC	1(3)	-	-	-	-	-
Kevin	Sorrell	06.03.77	England	183cm	80kg							
			Saracens	Center		NL	76(4)	153	11	10	26	-
						NC	5(2)	-	-	-	-	-
						ES	10(1)	29	5	2	-	-
						EC	12(0)	15	3	-	-	-
Mark	Sowerby	05.09.69	England	0cm	0kg							
			Wakefield	BlindsideFlanker		NL	112(42)	10	2	-	-	-
						NC	3(2)	-	-	-	-	-
Brett	Sparg	21.03.78	Namibia	183cm	81kg							
			Saracens	FullBack		NL	27(15)	10	2	-	-	-
						NC	3(1)	5	1	-	-	-
						ES	4(1)	10	2	-	-	-
						EC	4(1)	5	1	-	-	-
Neil	Spence	30.08.76	England	181cm	95kg							
			Rotherham	O'sideFlanker		NL	83(11)	50	10	-	-	-
						NC	5(2)	5	1	-	-	-
						ES	1(0)	-	-	-	-	-
Tim	Stannard		England	0cm	0kg							
			Lydney	No.8		NL	3(0)	-	-	-	-	-
			RugbyLions	No.8		NL	15(6)	-	-	-	-	-
						NC	1(0)	-	-	-	-	-
Bruce	Starr	05.01.73	Australia	180cm	115kg							
			Harlequins	Prop		NL	22(15)	-	-	-	-	-
						NC	3(5)	-	-	-	-	-
						ES	2(3)	-	-	-	-	-
						EC	4(0)	-	-	-	-	-
Michael	Stephenson	20.09.80	England	182cm	83kg							
			Newcastle	FullBack		NL	38(1)	75	15	-	-	-
						NC	8(1)	5	1	-	-	-
						ES	7(0)	15	3	-	-	-
						EC	3(3)	5	1	-	-	-
Mattie	Stewart	18.05.73	Scotland	180cm	114kg							
			Northampton	Prop		NL	83(8)	5	1	-	-	-
						NC	14(1)	5	1	-	-	-
						ES	7(2)	-	-	-	-	-
						EC	18(1)	5	1	-	-	-
Tim	Stimpson	10.09.73	England	191cm	101kg							
			Leicester	FullBack		NL	76(5)	954	19	122	204	1
						NC	7(0)	55	1	10	10	-
						EC	20(1)	310	4	34	74	-
			Newcastle	FullBack		NL	23(2)	138	14	28	4	-
						NC	2(0)	14	2	2	-	-
						ES	5(0)	102	6	18	12	-
			W Hartlepool	Full back		NL	23	203	7	21	42	2
Richard	Stott	01.09.78	England	0cm	0kg							
			Gloucester	BlindsideFlanker		NL	0(1)	-	-	-	-	-
			Moseley	BlindsideFlanker		NL	33(12)	5	1	-	-	-
						NC	2(1)	-	-	-	-	-
James	Strong	04.03.81	Pontypridd	5 11	12 10							
			LondonWelsh	Right wing		NL	17(0)	20	4	-	-	-
Ryan	Strudwick	03.08.73	Australia	195cm	108kg							
			Harlequins	Lock		NL	4(0)	-	-	-	-	-
			LondonIrish	No.8		NL	75(1)	20	4	-	-	-
						NC	13(0)	5	1	-	-	-
						ES	11(4)	15	3	-	-	-
Ben	Sturnham	06.03.74	England	196cm	111kg							
			Bath	Flanker		NL	21(14)	15	3	-	-	-
						NC	0(1)	-	-	-	-	-
						EC	3(2)	-	-	-	-	-
			Bristol	Flanker		NL	29(9)	10	2	-	-	-
						NC	3(0)	-	-	-	-	-
						ES	9(3)	-	-	-	-	-
			Saracens	Flanker		NL	8(4)	10	2	-	-	-
						NC	3(1)	5	1	-	-	-
						ES	3(2)	10	2	-	-	-

Epeli	Taione	02.03.79	Tonga	193cm	116kg							
			Newcastle	LeftWing		NL	24(5)	5	1	-	-	-
						NC	5(1)	5	1	-	-	-
						ES	5(1)	15	3	-	-	-
						EC	3(1)	10	2	-	-	-
Matt	Tassell	23.12.77	England	0cm	0kg							
			RugbyLions	Center		NL	30(11)	40	8	-	-	-
						NC	2(1)	10	2	-	-	-
Karl	Temmen	23.09.74	England	6 9	19 0							
			Manchester	Lock		NL	26(10)	5	1	-	-	-
						NC	4(1)	-	-	-	-	-
			Waterloo	Lock		NL	15(0)	5	1	-	-	-
						NC	1(0)	-	-	-	-	-
Rob	Thirlby	02.03.79	England	186cm	84kg							
			Bath	Left wing		NL	25(9)	54	8	1	4	-
						NC	0(2)	-	-	-	-	-
						EC	2(3)	-	-	-	-	-
			Saracens	Left wing		NL	21(7)	71	6	13	5	-
						NC	2(1)	2	-	1	-	-
						EC	4(0)	10	2	-	-	-
Gavin	Thomas	22.10.77	Wales	186cm	100kg							
			Bath	Flanker		NL	37(16)	10	2	-	-	-
						NC	2(1)	-	-	-	-	-
						EC	12(4)	15	3	-	-	-
Nathan	Thomas	22.01.76	Wales	191cm	98kg							
			Bath	Flanker		NL	66(23)	30	6	-	-	-
						NC	3(2)	-	-	-	-	-
						EC	14(2)	5	1	-	-	-
Cameron	Thomas	23.06.70	NewZealand	178cm	110kg							
			Bedford	Hooker		NL	37(8)	30	6	-	-	-
						NC	2(0)	5	1	-	-	-
Danny	Thomas	12.05.76	England	5 11	15 0							
			PlymouthAlbion	Flanker		NL	48(0)	45	9	-	-	-
						NC	3(1)	5	1	-	-	-
Steve	Thompson	15.07.78	England	188cm	110kg							
			Northampton	Hooker		NL	39(19)	40	8	-	-	-
						NC	4(3)	5	1	-	-	-
						EC	13(4)	15	3	-	-	-
Richard	Thompson	24.08.73	England	0cm	0kg							
			PlymouthAlbion	FullBack		NL	164(4)	369	48	-	-	-
						NC	4(0)	-	-	-	-	-
Russell	Thompson		New Zealand	0cm	0kg							
			PlymouthAlbion	Center		NL	45(0)	90	18	-	-	-
						NC	3(0)	-	-	-	-	-
James	Thorp	22.05.75	England	183cm	108kg							
			Rotherham	Prop		NL	33(25)	30	6	-	-	-
						NC	4(1)	5	1	-	-	-
						ES	4(2)	-	-	-	-	-
James	Tiffany		England	0cm	0kg							
			LeedsTykes	BlindsideFlanker		NL	1(8)	-	-	-	-	-
			Otley	Lock		NL	25(1)	15	3	-	-	-
						NC	1(0)	-	-	-	-	-
Mike	Tindall	18.10.78	England	188cm	92kg							
			Bath	Center		NL	56(4)	93	18	-	1	-
						NC	2(0)	-	-	-	-	-
						EC	15(0)	12	2	1	-	-
Mark	Tinnock	15.07.68	Soth Africa	6 7	18 2							
			Coventry	Lock		NL	35(0)	40	8	-	-	-
						NC	3(0)	-	-	-	-	-
			Sale	Lock		NL	11(5)	25	5	-	-	-
						ES	2(0)	-	-	-	-	-
Andrew	Titterell	10.01.81	England	176cm	93kg							
			Sale	Hooker		NL	19(11)	5	1	-	-	-
						NC	1(0)	-	-	-	-	-
						ES	7(3)	5	1	-	-	-
			Waterloo	Hooker		NL	0(1)	-	-	-	-	-

Robert	Todd	19.03.71	England	180cm	97kg							
			Gloucester	Center		NL	16(4)	15	3	-	-	-
						NC	1(1)	-	-	-	-	-
						ES	6(0)	5	1	-	-	-
			LondonIrish	Center		NL	25(4)	35	7	-	-	-
						NC	3(1)	-	-	-	-	-
						ES	6(0)	5	1	-	-	-
Harry	Toews			0cm	0kg							
			Leicester	Prop		NL	1(1)	-	-	-	-	-
			Rotherham	Prop		NL	15(13)	10	2	-	-	-
						NC	4(0)	-	-	-	-	-
Alfie	Tooala			0cm	0kg							
			Rotherham	BlindsideFlanker		NL	15(7)	65	13	-	-	-
						NC	2(1)	-	-	-	-	-
Piran	Trethewey	31.12.75	NewZealand	178cm	89kg							
			Exeter	RightWing		NL	24(8)	60	12	-	-	-
						NC	4(0)	-	-	-	-	-
Mark	Tucker	16.03.80	England	188cm	95kg							
			Northampton	Center		NL	19(23)	53	5	5	6	-
						NC	1(6)	-	-	-	-	-
						EC	3(6)	5	1	-	-	-
Inga	Tuigamala	04.09.70	Samoa	180cm	110kg							
			LondonWasps	Center		NL	8(0)	15	3	-	-	-
						EC	4(0)	-	-	-	-	-
			Newcastle	Center		NL	87(16)	172	34	1	-	-
						NC	14(4)	60	12	-	-	-
						ES	16(1)	40	8	-	-	-
						EC	5(1)	5	1	-	-	-
Stuart	Turner	22.03.72	England	183cm	108kg							
			Waterloo	Prop		NL	38	-	-	-	-	-
			Orrell	Prop		NL	53(1)	5	1	-	-	-
						ES	1(0)	-	-	-	-	-
			Rotherham	Prop		NL	38(3)	20	4	-	-	-
						NC	3(0)	-	-	-	-	-
						ES	4(2)	-	-	-	-	-
			Sale	Prop		NL	17(1)	5	1	-	-	-
						NC	1(0)	-	-	-	-	-
						ES	7(0)	-	-	-	-	-
			Worcester	Prop		NL	5(3)	5	1	-	-	-
John	Ufton	31.01.74	England	6 1	14 2							
			LondonWasps	FullBack		NL	32(10)	80	4	12	12	-
						NC	3(0)	5	1	-	-	-
						EC	10(0)	49	1	10	8	-
			LondonWelsh	FullBack		NL	15(2)	133	2	21	27	-
						NC	1(0)	3	-	-	1	-
Mike	Umaga	19.02.68	Samoa	183cm	100kg							
			Rotherham	FullBack		NL	99(3)	516	29	88	65	-
						NC	2(1)	-	-	-	-	-
						ES	4(0)	56	3	4	11	-
Neil	Underhill	23.06.72	England	6 10	17 0							
			Birmingham&S.	Lock		NL	34(23)	-	-	-	-	-
						NC	5(0)	-	-	-	-	-
			RugbyLions	Lock		NL	47(18)	30	6	-	-	-
Brendan	Venter		SouthAfrica	0cm	0kg							
			LondonIrish	Center		NL	51(1)	25	5	-	-	-
						NC	7(0)	15	3	-	-	-
						ES	4(0)	8	1	-	-	1
Matt	Vines	01.05.76	England	6 0	14 7							
			LondonWelsh	FullBack		NL	54(9)	158	30	1	2	-
						NC	4(0)	15	3	-	-	-
Matt	Volland	30.06.74	England	183cm	114kg							
			Bedford	Prop		NL	17(9)	-	-	-	-	-
			Northampton	Prop		NL	54(21)	-	-	-	-	-
						NC	2(3)	-	-	-	-	-
						ES	6(0)	-	-	-	-	-
						EC	0(2)	-	-	-	-	-
Tom	Voyce		England	0cm	0kg							
			Bath	FullBack		NL	30(8)	50	10	-	-	-
						EC	6(3)	35	7	-	-	-

Elisi	Vunipola		Tonga	0cm	0kg							
			Coventry	OutsideHalf		NL	42(1)	60	10	5	-	-
						NC	4(0)	5	1	-	-	-
Hugh	Vyvyan	08.09.76	England	198cm	102kg							
			Newcastle	Lock		NL	45(20)	40	8	-	-	-
						NC	8(3)	5	1	-	-	-
						ES	9(4)	5	1	-	-	-
						EC	4(2)	5	1	-	-	-
David	Walder	07.05.76	England	178cm	83kg							
			Newcastle	OutsideHalf		NL	34(3)	200	7	18	39	4
						NC	5(2)	16	1	4	1	-
						ES	8(3)	108	3	24	15	-
						EC	6(0)	20	1	3	2	1
Chris	Wall	14.02.76	England	182cm	89kg							
			Exeter	RightWing		NL	23(6)	20	4	-	-	-
						NC	4(0)	5	1	-	-	-
Martin	Wallwork	30.03.78	England	5 11	12 0							
			Bedford	ScrumHalf		NL	15(10)	2	-	1	-	-
						NC	1(1)	-	-	-	-	-
			Fylde	ScrumHalf		NL	19(10)	5	1	-	-	-
						NC	1(0)	-	-	-	-	-
			RugbyLions	ScrumHalf		NL	8(3)	5	1	-	-	-
Thomas	Walsh	16.01.78	England	0cm	0kg							
			RugbyLions	ScrumHalf		NL	18(7)	-	-	-	-	-
			CrossKeys	ScrumHalf								
						ES	3(0)	5	1	-	-	-
Nick	Walshe	01.11.73	England	178cm	84kg							
			Rosslyn Park	Scrum half		NL	13(1)	5	1	-	-	-
			Harlequins	ScrumHalf		NL	25(7)	37	7	1	-	-
						NC	1(1)	-	-	-	-	-
						EC	1(3)	5	1	-	-	-
			Saracens	ScrumHalf		NL	29(23)	15	3	-	-	-
						NC	1(4)	6	-	3	-	-
						ES	4(2)	15	3	-	-	-
						EC	5(2)	10	2	-	-	-
Micky	Ward	09.01.79	England	180cm	108kg							
			Newcastle	Prop		NL	28(20)	15	3	-	-	-
						NC	7(2)	-	-	-	-	-
						ES	9(5)	15	3	-	-	-
						EC	3(2)	-	-	-	-	-
Richard	Ward	26.11.70	England	0cm	0kg							
			Bedford	Lock		NL	21(3)	-	-	-	-	-
						NC	2(0)	-	-	-	-	-
			Gloucester	Lock		NL	11(4)	-	-	-	-	-
						NC	0(1)	-	-	-	-	-
						ES	1(2)	-	-	-	-	-
			Moseley	Lock		NL	20(0)	5	1	-	-	-
						NC	1(0)	-	-	-	-	-
Stephen	Ward	16.10.77	England	178cm	83kg							
			Exeter	OutsideHalf		NL	25(0)	20	4	-	-	-
						NC	4(0)	10	2	-	-	-
			Gloucester	Center		NL	1(0)	5	-	1	1	-
			Lydney	Center		NL	14(0)	70	3	5	15	-
			Worcester	OutsideHalf		NL	2(0)	-	-	-	-	-
Dan	Ward-Smith	02.01.78	New Zealand	6 4	17 0							
			PlymouthAlbion	No.8		NL	52(0)	215	43	-	-	-
						NC	3(1)	20	4	-	-	-
Fraser	Waters	31.03.76		183cm	88kg							
			Bath	Centre		NL	0(1)	-	-	-	-	-
			Bristol	Center		NL	16(0)	10	2	-	-	-
			LondonWasps	Centre		NL	60(4)	55	11	-	-	-
						NC	8(0)	5	1	-	-	-
						EC	15(0)	15	3	-	-	-
Mick	Watson	02.08.65	England	0cm	0kg							
			W Hartlepooll	No8		NL	27	25	5	-	-	-
			Harlequins	No.8		NL	5(2)	5	1	-	-	-
						EC	3(1)	5	1	-	-	-
			LondonScottish	Lock		NL	24(0)	10	2	-	-	-
						NC	2(0)	-	-	-	-	-
			Wakefield	Flanker		NL	29(14)	30	6	-	-	-
						NC	4(0)	-	-	-	-	-

Doddie	Weir	04.07.70	Scotland	198cm	109kg							
			Newcastle	Lock		NL	115(13)	65	13	-	-	-
						NC	13(4)	5	1	-	-	-
						ES	21(0)	5	1	-	-	-
						EC	2(3)	-	-	-	-	-
Richard	Welding		England	0cm	0kg							
			Orrell	Center		NL	54(2)	138	20	13	4	-
						NC	5(1)	31	2	3	5	-
Ged	Welsh		England	0cm	0kg							
			Orrell	Flanker		NL	0(2)	-	-	-	-	-
			Preston	Flanker		NL	18(10)	10	2	-	-	-
						NC	2(1)	-	-	-	-	-
Dorian	West	05.10.67	England	181cm	101kg							
			Leicester	Hooker		NL	57(30)	25	5	-	-	-
						NC	8(3)	15	3	-	-	-
						EC	19(4)	10	2	-	-	-
Robert	Whatmuff		England	0cm	0kg							
			Otley	Center		NL	82(8)	95	19	-	-	-
						NC	3(1)	5	1	-	-	-
Julian	White	14.05.73	England	186cm	114kg							
			Bristol	Prop		NL	18(1)	5	1	-	-	-
						ES	7(0)	-	-	-	-	-
			Saracens	Prop		NL	32(5)	15	3	-	-	-
						NC	5(0)	-	-	-	-	-
						EC	6(1)	-	-	-	-	-
Lawrence	White	29.11.77	England	186cm	100kg							
			Bedford	O'sideFlanker		NL	33(10)	20	4	-	-	-
						NC	2(0)	5	1	-	-	-
Paul	White	08.05.70	England	6 4	17 2							
			Manchester	Lock		NL	21(0)	5	1	-	-	-
						NC	1(0)	-	-	-	-	-
			Waterloo	Lock		NL	123(3)	40	8	-	-	-
						NC	4(0)	-	-	-	-	-
Duncan	White	18.09.82	England	0cm	0kg							
			Moseley	BlindsideFlanker		NL	24(10)	20	4	-	-	-
						NC	1(0)	-	-	-	-	-
James	White	04.04.77	England	6 3	14 7							
			Manchester	Flanker		NL	9(7)	5	1	-	-	-
						NC	3(1)	-	-	-	-	-
Steve	White-Cooper	15.07.75	England	193cm	103kg							
			Harlequins	O'sideFlanker		NL	52(7)	15	3	-	-	-
						NC	8(0)	15	3	-	-	-
						ES	8(0)	5	1	-	-	-
						EC	8(3)	5	1	-	-	-
Henry	Whitford	07.03.74	England	191cm	106kg							
			Bedford	BlindsideFlanker		NL	30(10)	5	1	-	-	-
						NC	1(1)	5	1	-	-	-
Richard	Wigham	22.02.79	England	0cm	0kg							
			Wakefield	BlindsideFlanker		NL	18(19)	5	1	-	-	-
						NC	2(2)	-	-	-	-	-
Jonny	Wilkinson	25.05.79	England	178cm	84kg							
			Newcastle	OutsideHalf		NL	78(3)	882	16	128	173	9
						NC	15(0)	190	1	22	46	1
						ES	10(1)	145	3	20	30	-
						EC	4(0)	62	-	4	17	1
Richard	Wilks	08.10.77	England	183cm	99kg							
			Sale	O'sideFlanker		NL	4(32)	-	-	-	-	-
						NC	1(1)	-	-	-	-	-
						ES	8(7)	30	6	-	-	-
Steven	Williams	30.10.70	Wales	195cm	112kg							
			LondonIrish	Lock		NL	24(4)	-	-	-	-	-
						NC	4(2)	5	1	-	-	-
						ES	6(1)	-	-	-	-	-
Paul	Williams		England	6 6	16 3							
			Otley	Lock		NL	86(7)	65	13	-	-	-
						NC	2(0)	-	-	-	-	-
Phil	Williams	29.11.78	England	5 11	12 0							
			PlymouthAlbion	Right wing		NL	24(15)	27	5	1	-	-
						NC	3(0)	-	-	-	-	-

Gary	Willis	07.10.68	Zimbabwe	188cm	96kg							
			Exeter	Flanker		NL	97(3)	80	18	-	-	-
						NC	9(0)	10	2	-	-	-
Glen	Wilson	31.07.76	England	0cm	0kg							
			Wakefield	No.8		NL	112(2)	90	18	-	-	-
						NC	4(1)	-	-	-	-	-
Tony	Windo	30.04.69	England	6 0	17 7							
			Gloucester	Prop		NL	52(3)	20	4	-	-	-
						NC	5(1)	5	1	-	-	-
						ES	9(0)	10	2	-	-	-
			Worcester	Prop		NL	69(5)	40	8	-	-	-
						NC	5(2)	-	-	-	-	-
Adryan	Winnan	28.03.83	England	188cm	91kg							
			Saracens	FullBack		NL	20(0)	15	3	-	-	-
						NC	2(0)	5	1	-	-	-
						ES	3(2)	24	2	7	-	-
Ross	Winney		England	0cm	0kg							
			Wakefield	OutsideHalf		NL	52(20)	160	4	22	30	2
						NC	6(0)	35	-	4	7	2
Roy	Winters	13.12.75	England	194cm	102kg							
			Bedford	BlindsideFlanker		NL	65(9)	40	8	-	-	-
						NC	2(0)	5	1	-	-	-
						ES	5(1)	-	-	-	-	-
			Harlequins	Flanker		NL	27(4)	-	-	-	-	-
						NC	4(0)	-	-	-	-	-
						ES	8(0)	5	1	-	-	-
						EC	3(1)	-	-	-	-	-
Martyn	Wood	25.03.77	England	178cm	85kg							
			LondonWasps	ScrumHalf		NL	71(5)	50	10	-	-	-
						NC	7(2)	-	-	-	-	-
						EC	14(2)	12	2	1	-	-
Michael	Wood	15.07.76	England	181cm	85kg							
			Bath	Right wing		NL	1(0)	-	-	-	-	-
						EC	1(1)	-	-	-	-	-
			Newcastle	Right wing		NL	20(2)	15	3	-	-	-
						NC	2(0)	5	1	-	-	-
						ES	3(0)	5	1	-	-	-
			Rotherham	Right wing		NL	28(5)	75	15	-	-	-
						NC	3(1)	20	4	-	-	-
			WestHartlepool	Right wing		NL	15(0)	15	3	-	-	-
						NC	0(1)	-	-	-	-	-
David	Wood		England	0cm	0kg							
			Orrell	ScrumHalf		NL	15(16)	-	-	-	-	-
						NC	0(5)	-	-	-	-	-
Trevor	Woodman	04.08.76	England	180cm	114kg							
			Gloucester	Prop		NL	55(18)	20	4	-	-	-
						NC	5(0)	-	-	-	-	-
						ES	6(2)	-	-	-	-	-
						EC	3(0)	-	-	-	-	-
Shaun	Woof	06.03.77	England	0cm	93kg							
			Waterloo	Centre		NL	50(3)	80	16	-	-	-
			LeedsTykes	Centre		NL	39(4)	100	20	-	-	-
						NC	3(1)	20	4	-	-	-
						ES	4(0)	-	-	-	-	-
			Worcester	Centre		NL	7(7)	-	-	-	-	-
Tom	Woolrich		England	0cm	0kg							
			RugbyLions	Hooker		NL	14(20)	10	2	-	-	-
						NC	1(3)	-	-	-	-	-
Joe	Worsley	14.06.77	England	196cm	108kg							
			LondonWasps	O'sideFlanker		NL	87(9)	80	16	-	-	-
						NC	10(1)	-	-	-	-	-
						EC	17(4)	35	7	-	-	-
Michael	Worsley	01.12.76	England	185cm	106kg							
			Bristol	Prop		NL	8(0)	-	-	-	-	-
						NC	1(0)	-	-	-	-	-
						ES	2(0)	-	-	-	-	-
			LondonIrish	Prop		NL	38(25)	35	7	-	-	-
						NC	3(5)	5	1	-	-	-
						ES	6(8)	5	1	-	-	-
			Orrell	Prop		NL	17(0)	5	1	-	-	-
						ES	1(0)	-	-	-	-	-

Steve	Worsley		England	0cm	0kg							
			Wakefield	Hooker		NL	2(24)	-	-	-	-	-
						NC	0(2)	-	-	-	-	-
			Waterloo	Hooker		NL	3(6)	-	-	-	-	-
Peter	Wright		England	0cm	0kg							
			Otley	ScrumHalf		NL	14(38)	18	3	-	1	-
						NC	1(3)	5	1	-	-	-
Dmitri	Yachvili	19.09.80	France	183cm	81kg							
			Gloucester	ScrumHalf		NL	9(11)	5	1	-	-	-
						NC	1(1)	-	-	-	-	-
						ES	3(2)	5	1	-	-	-
Tony	Yapp	26.07.77	England	5 10	14 0							
			Bedford	OutsideHalf		NL	22(0)	120	3	15	20	5
			Worcester	OutsideHalf		NL	38(31)	368	12	88	42	2
						NC	3(3)	25	3	2	1	1
Chris	Yates	13.05.71	England	186cm	100kg							
			Gloucester	Center		NL	36(4)	40	8	-	-	-
						NC	2(1)	-	-	-	-	-
						ES	1(3)	-	-	-	-	-
						EC	6(1)	-	-	-	-	-
			Sale	Center		NL	62(7)	101	19	-	-	2
						NC	4(0)	10	2	-	-	-
						ES	5(1)	10	2	-	-	-
			Worcester	Center		NL	21(2)	40	8	-	-	-
						NC	1(0)	5	1	-	-	-
Kevin	Yates	06.11.72	England	180cm	114kg							
			Bath	Prop		NL	21(15)	10	2	-	-	-
						NC	1(1)	-	-	-	-	-
						EC	4(0)	-	-	-	-	-
			Sale	Prop		NL	22(0)	-	-	-	-	-
						NC	1(0)	-	-	-	-	-
						ES	6(2)	5	1	-	-	-
Dan	Zaltman	26.12.75	England	6 6	17 6							
			Bedford	Lock		NL	28(4)	20	4	-	-	-
						NC	1(0)	-	-	-	-	-
			Leicester	Lock		NL	2(1)	-	-	-	-	-
			Coventry	Lock		NL	12	-	-	-	-	-
			Saracens	Lock		NL	0(2)	-	-	-	-	-
			Worcester	Lock		NL	42(2)	15	3	-	-	-
						NC	3(0)	-	-	-	-	-

Otley scrum half Andy Brown gets good quick ball away from the scrum. Photo courtesy of Nigel Chanter (01392 467261)

NATIONAL DIVISION

TWO

2001-02 Season

CLUBS

Division Three Records

LEAGUE TABLE

									HOME									AWAY								
														For		Against							For		Against	
	P	W	D	L	F	A	PD	Pts	W	D	L	F	A	Tries	Pens	Tries	Pens	W	D	L	F	A	Tries	Pens	Tries	Pens
Orrell	26	23	0	3	962	369	593	46	13	0	0	536	161	76	22	15	24	10	0	3	426	208	53	33	21	27
Plymouth Albion	26	23	0	3	895	314	581	46	12	0	1	546	136	79	13	15	14	11	0	2	349	178	44	22	19	19
Sedgley Park	26	20	1	5	684	468	216	41	11	1	1	363	253	44	28	29	21	9	0	4	321	215	38	26	24	22
Harrogate	26	16	1	9	744	556	188	33	9	0	2	428	255	58	19	33	19	7	1	5	316	301	42	16	41	20
Fylde	26	14	0	12	462	549	-87	28	7	0	6	245	244	34	15	24	27	7	0	6	217	305	26	18	36	27
Wharfedale	26	11	2	13	603	638	-35	24	6	2	5	313	257	37	27	31	26	5	0	8	290	381	32	27	50	21
Esher	26	12	0	14	547	587	-40	24	7	0	6	310	255	25	50	30	18	5	0	8	237	332	23	28	38	27
Nottingham	26	12	0	14	539	658	-119	24	7	0	6	298	289	37	23	38	17	5	0	8	241	369	27	33	47	29
Newbury	26	12	0	14	548	723	-175	24	8	0	5	272	302	31	24	35	26	4	0	9	276	421	29	25	57	22
Kendal	26	10	0	16	576	607	-31	20	7	0	6	332	254	41	24	26	28	3	0	10	244	353	22	33	44	25
Stourbridge	26	9	1	16	600	702	-102	19	6	0	7	329	324	36	33	39	21	3	1	9	271	378	29	27	48	23
Rosslyn Park	26	8	1	17	490	605	-115	17	4	0	9	238	312	32	17	34	27	4	1	8	252	293	34	15	34	23
Waterloo	26	4	2	20	476	792	-316	10	3	1	9	232	365	28	18	40	39	1	1	11	244	427	30	20	55	28
Preston G'hoppers	26	4	0	22	401	959	-558	8	2	0	11	235	443	25	27	58	24	2	0	11	166	516	18	18	69	27

REVIEW

Orrell took the National Two title after a fantastic run which saw them win their last 19 league matches and claw back Plymouth's big early season lead. They started the season losing three of their first four away matches whilst at home they were unbeaten all season in the league with 13 consecutive wins. Phil Jones, capped by England A during the season, led the way with a club record 343 points which included an impressive 15 tries. In the try scoring Neil Kerfoot and Andy Craig set a new club record with 19 tries each beating the previous record of 13 set by Simon Verbickas during the 1998-99 season.

Plymouth Albion went up for a second successive season to reach National One for the first time in their history. They got off to a great start and were well clear early on in the season after 11 consecutive wins before coming unstuck at Wharfedale in December. That was their first defeat for 41 league matches dating back to March 2000 when they lost at Westcombe Park. The Wharfedale defeat was their only outside of two losses to the eventual Champions Orrell as Plymouth Albion return to the second tier of English rugby for the first time since 1991-92. No 8 Dan Ward-Smith broke his own club record of 20 tries in a season with a new record total of 23 and becomes the first man to score 20 tries in successive seasons.

Sedgley Park had a fantastic first season in National Two and only the re emergence of Orrell stopped them getting a second successive promotion. Only Plymouth Albion left Park Lane with both points as they won 11 of their 13 home matches in the league, Waterloo managed a draw late in the season. They ended the season strongly with 17 out of 18 points from their last nine league matches but with the top two in even better form third place was easily theirs. Outside half Colin Stephens was again amongst the points and broke his own club record of 235 points in a season with a new total of 244. Rob Moon topped the try scorers with 12 tries and scored over 100 points in the season and extended his all time club record to 540 points but has Colin Stephens closing in on him.

Harrogate recovered well after a stuttering start to the season to finish in fourth place – eight points behind third placed Sedgley but five points clear of Fylde in fifth. They did though end the season with just three defeats in their last 12 league matches. At the start of the season they managed just two wins from seven matches after winning their opening two matches. They lost four times at home in the league, three times to the sides who finished above them and an early season defeat against Rosslyn Park who were to be relegated. Outside half Lee Cholewa topped the points scoring with 289 points – the second highest total for the club in league rugby – for the second season running and in the process set a new record of 68 conversions in a league campaign.

Fylde finished in fifth place which was probably better than their expectations and but for winning matches against Rosslyn Park and Wharfedale, completing the double against both, they could have dropped down the table a few places. They were not the highest scorers in the division far from it with only bottom of the table Preston scoring fewer points. What they did have was a good defence and the ability to win the close matches with seven of their 14 wins by seven points or less. They ended the season with a poor run of form with just two wins in their final seven league matches. Their home win against Fylde was the only match they won against the four teams that finished above them in the league.

Wharfedale equalled last seasons sixth place and maintained their record of finishing in the top ten in each of their six seasons at this level. They had an up and down season on twice managing to win successive matches. Jonathan Davies took over the kicking duties full time and set a new record of 278 points in a league season, a total that included a record 44 conversions. In the try scoring stakes Andrew Hodgson topped the list for a third time in six seasons and extended his club record to 67 since making his debut back in 1996.

Esher finished a highly creditable seventh a one place improvement on the previous season and their highest ever finish in league rugby. It could have been a lot better as they lost their last three matches of the season and managed just three wins in their last nine league matches. Jonathan Gregory was again at the forefront of Esher's efforts with 311 points for the club and in the process passed 1,000 league points for Esher. In three of the last four seasons he has passed 300 points and in the only man in the history of National League rugby to score 300 points in a season three times. The leading try scorer was Spencer Bromley in his first season at the club.

REVIEW continued

Nottingham finished in the top ten for the fist time in four seasons despite starting the season with four successive defeats. Their fortunes changed with the return to the side of Russell Southam who missed the first eight matches of the season. They then went on to win 10 of the next 18 matches and gradually move up the table. Southam ended the season as top points and try scorer with 203 and eight respectively. Southam topped 200 points for the second successive season to equal the club record of Chris Atkinson who achieved this feat in the late 90's.

Newbury finished ninth for the second successive season and maintained their record of finishing in the top ten for each of their five season in this division. Newbury started the season with an indifferent run of just two wins from eight matches and they had to wait till March before they could string together successive league victories. And then managed four wins from their last seven matches to climb to ninth place in the table. Ian Morgan topped the points scorers with 162 points and had the honour of being the most consistent goal kicker in the division. No 8 Craig Davies topped the try scorers after a three year break and took his total for Newbury in the league to 63.

Kendal's second season at this level was a disappointment after the previous season when they finished fourth at their first attempt, this time they had to settle for tenth. They started the season well and eight wins from their first 14 matches they were hovering above half way but things changed from there on. In their final 12 matches they managed just two wins and plummeted down the league table and finished just three points clear of the relegation zone. Mike Scott again topped the points scorers and was just two short of Casey Mee's record of 273 points in a league season as he passed 500 points in his second season at the club. Right winger Jason Balmer was again top of the try scorers with 10, a position he shared with centre Ian Voortman, and has had a share in the leading try scorers list for five successive seasons now.

Stourbridge just managed to keep their National Two league status after a battle with Rosslyn Park to avoid the drop. A convincing win at home to Esher sealed their survival as Park were beaten at Fylde. They got of to a great start with four wins in their first five league matches but a mid season run which saw them pick up just two wins in 12 matches saw them plummet down the league table. Ben Harvey had a great first season for the club and smashed the club record for points in a season with 298, he also finished joint top try scorer with Duncan Hughes who topped the list the previous season. They were involved in an amazing match with Wharfedale at home where they lost 41-42, the second highest score ever by a losing side in the division.

Rosslyn Park nearly managed to stage a late rally and avoid the drop but just failed in the end. It was their home form that was normally reliable, which deserted them as they slipped to eight successive home loses from the start of the season. They did manage to turn it round and managed four wins from their final five matches with just Plymouth leaving with the points. Park again failed to find a reliable goal kicker, which with a lot of the defeats by narrow margins could well have been the difference with staying up. The late season defeat at Fylde sealed their fate and they slipped into the Three South division for the first time ever in league rugby. Despite being relegated they had the seventh best defensive record in the division but it was the points for which was the problem, so after last season losing out on promotion on points difference they slipped to relegation, what a difference 12 months can make.

Waterloo suffered a second successive relegation as they slipped to their lowest ever place in league rugby. In id season they had a run when they managed just one point from 22 and were relegated fairly early by normal standards. They did improve late in the season and got a highly creditable draw at high flying Sedgley Park and a home win against Kendal. They also went close in a number of other matches. With Freeman Payne scoring tries on a regular basis and set a new record of 16, double the previous record, he also took the career record for tries with a new total of 23.

Preston Grasshoppers ended their three-year stay at this level as they finished bottom and returned to Three North. They managed four wins in their first ten matches before going on the worst run in their league history. After beating Rosslyn Park at home in late November they went on to lose their remaining 16 league matches. Full back Chris Glynn did his best to stop the slide and ended the season as leading points and try scorer with 210 and six respectively. In the process he set a new record of 539 points in a league career for Preston set over the last three seasons.

2001-02 RECORD REVIEW
Individual Records

The ALL-TIME RECORDS for MOST POINTS IN A MATCH, MOST POINTS IN A SEASON & MOST TRIES IN A MATCH can be found in the Records Section for this division.

MOST POINTS - IN A MATCH

dy got near Mike Scott's record set during the pre- season. We did though have two players score 30 ; in a match and move into joint third on the all ist. First Colin Stephens scored 30 points for ey Park in the home win against Wharfedale last nber with two tries, four conversions, three penal- nd a drop goal. The second instance was later in eason when Ben Harvey scored 30 points for bridge in the 45-19 win at home to Esher.

.UTION OF RECORD - Points in a match

Steve Burnage	Fylde v Birmingham	07.11.87
Paul Morris	Lydney v Otley	14.09.96
Rob Ashworth	Havant v Clifton	21.09.96
Paul Brett	Liverpool v Redruth	01.02.97
Paul Brett	Liverepool v Clifton	15.02.97
Mike Scott	Kendal v W Hartlepool	27/01/01

MOST POINTS - IN A SEASON

outside half Phil Jones topped the points scorers 343 which puts him into third place on the all time r the division. Esher Full back Jonathan Gregory me the tenth player to top 300 points in a season in ivision and ended up sixth on the all time list.

LUTION OF RECORD - Points in a season

Steve Burnage	Fylde	1987-88
Chris Howard	Rugby	1988-89
Andy Finnie	Bedford	1993-94
Andy Finnie	Bedford	1994-95
Steve Gough	Fylde	1996-97

MOST TRIES - IN A MATCH

The only player to score four tries in a match during last season was the Harrogates Mark Farrar who achieved the feat in the away match at Preston late in the season. In all we had 25 hat tricks and four players did it twice. Andy Craig and Neil Kerfoot of Orrell, Dan Ward-Smith of Plymouth and Carl Burnett of Wharfedale.

EVOLUTION OF RECORD - Tries in a match
(Only the first to reach the figure is shown)

3	Kevin Norris	Plymouth v Sheffield	12.09.87
4	Brendan Hanavan	Fylde v Exeter	03.10.87
5	Mark Kirkby	Otley v Redruth	08.02.97
6	Nick Baxter	Worcester v Otley	21.02.98

MOST TRIES - IN A SEASON

Plymouth No 8 Dan Ward-Smith moved into second place on the all time list for a season with his 23 in his clubs promotion campaign.
Ward-Smith finished four tries clear of the Orrell pair Andy Craig and Neil Kerfoot who now slot into joint seventh on the all time list with 19 tries.

EVOLUTION OF RECORD

10	Brendan Hanavan	Fylde	1987-88
12	Brendan Hanavan	Fylde	1993-94
12	Colin Phillips	Reading	1994-95
22	Mark Kirkby	Otley	1996-97
29	Nick Baxter	Worcester	1997-98

ALL-TIME RECORDS

29	Nick Baxter	Worcester	1997-98
23	Dan Ward-Smith	Plymouth	2001-02
22	Mark Kirkby	Otley	1996-97
22	Mark Kirkby	Otley	1999-00
21	Andrew Hodgson	Wharfedale	1996-97
20	Mark Preston	Fylde	1996-97
19	Andrew Hodgson	Wharfedale	1999-00
19	Andy Craig	Orrell	2001-02
19	Neil Kerfoot	Orrell	2001-02
17	Ben Wade	Morley	1996-97
17	Simon Middleton	Leeds	1997-98
17	Scott Roskell	London Welsh	1997-98
17	Ed Smithies	Harrogate	2000-01
16	Mark Appleson	Leeds	1996-97
16	Jim Jenner	Worcester	1997-98
16	Craig Davies	Newbury	1997-98
16	James Tapster	Harrogate	2000-01
16	Jamie Morley	Nottingham	2000-01
16	James Justice	Rosslyn Park	2000-01
16	Eddie Saunders	Rugby Lions	2000-01
16	John Dudley	Harrogate	2001-02
16	Freeman Payne	Waterloo	2001-0

MOST PENALTIES - IN A MATCH

The record of nine was threatened by the Esher full back Jonathan Gregory who kicked eight as his side beat Preston 43-0 last December.
After that six penalties in a match was the next best effort.

EVOLUTION OF RECORD

6	John Stabler	W Hart v Met Police	06.01.88
7	Andy Finnie	Bedford v Coventry	23.04.94
9	Paul Morris	Lydney v Otley	14.09.96

ALL-TIME RECORDS

9	Paul Morris	Lydney v Otley	14.09.96
9	Rob Ashworth	Havant v Clifton	21.09.96
8	Richard Mills	Walsall v Leeds	12.10.96
8	Jonathan Gregory	Esher v Preston	01.12.01
7	Andy Finnie	Bedford v Coventry	23.04.94
7	Denzil Evans	Rugby v Richmond	15.10.94
7	Phil Belshaw	Reading v Morley	14.10.95
7	Jamie Grayshon	Morley v Rugby	21.10.95
7	Andy Green	Exeter v Fylde	05.04.97
7	Richard Mills	Walsall v Redruth	19.04.97
7	Nat Saumi	Redruth v Clifton	03.05.97
7	Guy Gregory	Camberley v Birm &Solihull	19.12.98
7	Ben Stafford	Camberley v Nottingham	10.10.99

MOST PENALTIES - IN A SEASON

Jonathan Gregory got near to the record and with only 26 league matches compared to the 30 played when Steve Gough set the record it was an excellent effort. Gregory kicked 76 penalties which moved him into third place on the all time list.

EVOLUTION OF RECORD

21	Ray Adamson	Wakefield	1987-88
22	Andy Higgin	Vale of Lune	1989-90
26	Mike Jackson	Fylde	1991-92
31	Andy Green	Exeter	1992-93
45	Andy Finnie	Bedford	1993-94
56	Andy Finnie	Bedford	1994-95
82	Steve Gough	Fylde	1996-97

ALL-TIME RECORDS

82	Steve Gough	Fylde	1996-97
81	Richard Mills	Walsall	1996-97
76	Jonathan Gregory	Esher	2001-02
70	Steve Swindells	Manchester	1998-99
66	Paul Morris	Lydney	1996-97
64	Chris Atkinson	Nottingham	1997-98
64	Chris Atkinson	Nottingham	1998-99
57	Craig Raymond	London Welsh	1996-97
57	Mike Scott	Kendal	2001-02
56	Andy Finnie	Bedford	1994-95
55	Adam Mounsey	Wharfedale	1999-00
55	Ben Harvey	Stourbridge	2001-02

MOST CONVERSIONS - IN A MATC

The record was safe last season with eight being the most scored in a match last season. Plymouth Albion back Chris Atkinson kicked eight against Preston in February. The other occasion was when Orrell clinche the title and Richard Welding, playing instead of Phil Jones who was on England duty, kicked eight against Nottingham in April.

EVOLUTION OF RECORD

9	Steve Burnage	Fylde v Birmingham	07.11
9	Gerry Ainscough	Leeds v Clifton	07.12
12	Paul Brett	Liverpool v Clifton	15.02

ALL-TIME RECORDS

12	Paul Brett	Liverpool v Clifton	15.02
11	Mike Scott	Kendal v W Hartlepool	27.01
10	Dan Clappison	Otley v Blackheath	04.12
10	Chris Glynn	Preston v Camberley	25.03
9	Steve Burnage	Fylde v Birmingham	07.11
9	Gerry Ainscough	Leeds v Clifton	07.12
9	Jason Dance	Reading v Redruth	15.02
9	Jamie Grayshon	Morley v Walsall	17.05
9	Paul Roblin	Rosslyn Pv W Hartlepool	16.12

MOST CONVERSIONS - IN A SEASO

Harrogate fly half Lee Cholewa moved to the top of th list with his 68 conversion during his sides campaign. It was four more than the previous record set by Lond Welsh fly half Craig Raymond back in 1997-98.

ALL-TIME RECORDS

68	Lee Cholewa	Harrogate	2001-
64	Craig Raymond	London Welsh	1997-
63	Ralph Zoing	Harrogate	1996-
61	Jason Dance	Reading	1996-
61	Dan Clappison	Otley	1999-
60	Sateki Tuipulotu	Leeds Tykes	1997-
60	Richard LeBas	Worcester	1997-
60	Steve Swindells	Manchester	1998-
59	Phil Jones	Orrell	2001-
58	Andy Green	Exeter	1996-

MOST DROP GOALS - IN A MATCH

Mike Scott kicked six drop goals during the season bu no player managed more than two in a match.

ALL-TIME RECORD

4	Andy Rimmer	Broughton P v Sheffield	17.11.

2001-02

NATIONAL LEAGUE TWO

MOST POINTS

POINTS			T	C	P	DG
343	Phil Jones	Orrell	15	59	50	-
311	Jonathan Gregory	Esher	5	29	76	-
298	Ben Harvey	Stourbridge	9	44	55	-
289	Lee Cholewa	Harrogate	9	68	35	1
278	Jonathan Davies	Wharfedale	5	44	54	1
271	Mike Scott	Kendal	2	36	57	6
244	Colin Stephens	Sedgley Park	4	37	46	4
211	Tom Barlow	Plymouth A	10	40	23	4
210	Chris Glynn	Preston	6	21	45	1
203	Russell Southam	Nottingham	6	34	35	-
165	Ian Morgan	Newbury	2	31	30	1
160	Tony Handley	Waterloo	2	27	32	-
115	Dan Ward-Smith	Plymouth A	23	-	-	-
113	Chris Atkinson	Plymouth A	-	37	12	1
112	Ben Godfrey	Fylde	8	15	13	1
110	Rob Moon	Sedgley Park	12	13	8	-
95	Neil Kerfoot	Orrell	19	-	-	-
95	Andy Craig	Orrell	10	-	-	-

MOST PENALTIES

76	Jonathan Gregory	Esher
57	Mike Scott	Kendal
55	Ben Harvey	Stourbridge
54	Jonathan Davies	Wharfedale
50	Phil Jones	Orrell
46	Colin Stephens	Sedgley Park
45	Chris Glynn	Preston
35	Lee Cholewa	Harrogate
35	Russell Southam	Nottingham
32	Tony Handley	Waterloo
30	Ian Morgan	Newbury
23	Tom Barlow	Plymouth A
16	Steve Gough	Fylde/Preston
13	Ben Godfrey	Fylde

MOST TRIES

23	Dan Ward-Smith	Plymouth A
19	Neil Kerfoot	Orrell
19	Andy Craig	Orrell
16	John Dudley	Harroagte
16	Freeman Payne	Waterloo
15	Andrew Hodgson	Wharfedale
15	Phil Jones	Orrell
13	Ed Smithies	Harrogate
13	Wes Davies	Orrell
12	Richard Welding	Orrell
12	Rob Moon	Sedgley Park
12	Ross Bullough	Sedgley Park
12	Glenn Bunny	Plymouth A

MOST CONVERSIONS

68	Lee Cholewa	Harrogate
59	Phil Jones	Orrell
44	Ben Harvey	Stourbridge
44	Jonathan Davies	Wharfedale
40	Tom Barlow	Plymouth A
37	Chris Atkinson	Plymouth A
37	Colin Stephens	Sedgley Park
36	Mike Scott	Kendal
34	Russell Southam	Nottingham
31	Ian Morgan	Newbury
29	Jonathan Gregory	Esher
27	Tony Handley	Waterloo
21	Chris Glynn	Preston
15	Ben Godfrey	Fylde

MOST DROP GOALS

6	Mike Scott	Kendal
4	Colin Stephens	Sedgley Park
4	Tom Barlow	Plymouth A
2	James Hendy	Rosslyn Park
1	Duncan Hughes	Stourbridge
1	Ben Godfrey	Fylde
1	Chris Atkinson	Plymouth A
1	Ian Morgan	Newbury
1	Chris Glynn	Preston
1	Lee Cholewa	Harrogate
1	Jonathan Davies	Wharfedale

FIXTURES 2002-2003

Away Teams

	HOME TEAMS	Bracknell	Doncaster	Esher	Fylde	Harrogate	Henley Hawks	Kendal	Launceston	Newbury	Nottingham	Penzance & Newlyn	Sedgley Park	Stourbridge	Wharfedale	
1	Bracknell	XXX	26-10	21-12	07-12	28-09	16-11	18-01	31-08	12-04	01-02	11-01	15-03	14-09	22-02	1
2	Doncaster	08-02	XXX	11-01	25-01	12-04	12-10	15-03	23-11	07-12	01-03	02-11	21-12	31-08	14-09	2
3	Esher	26-04	30-11	XXX	29-03	16-11	14-12	28-09	21-09	22-02	04-01	07-09	01-02	26-10	18-01	3
4	Fylde	04-01	16-11	14-09	XXX	26-10	30-11	26-04	12-04	15-03	18-01	14-12	22-02	28-09	01-02	4
5	Harrogate	01-03	07-09	25-01	08-02	XXX	21-09	14-12	02-11	23-11	29-03	12-10	07-12	11-01	26-04	5
6	Henley Hawks	25-01	22-02	31-08	11-01	15-03	XXX	01-02	07-12	21-12	26-10	23-11	14-09	12-04	28-09	6
7	Kendal	23-11	21-09	01-03	21-12	31-08	02-11	XXX	29-03	08-02	12-10	07-12	11-01	25-01	07-09	7
8	Launceston	14-12	18-01	15-03	07-09	01-02	04-01	14-09	XXX	28-09	30-11	26-04	26-10	22-02	16-11	8
9	Newbury	07-09	04-01	12-10	21-09	18-01	26-04	26-10	01-03	XXX	14-12	29-03	16-11	01-02	30-11	9
10	Nottingham	02-11	28-09	07-12	23-11	14-09	08-02	22-02	11-01	31-08	XXX	25-01	12-04	21-12	15-03	10
11	Penzance & Newlyn	30-11	01-02	12-04	31-08	22-02	18-01	04-01	21-12	14-09	16-11	XXX	28-09	15-03	26-10	11
12	Sedgley Park	21-09	26-04	02-11	12-10	04-01	29-03	30-11	08-02	25-01	07-09	01-03	XXX	23-11	14-12	12
13	Stourbridge	29-03	14-12	08-02	01-03	30-11	07-09	16-11	12-10	02-11	26-04	21-09	18-01	XXX	04-01	13
14	Wharfedale	12-10	29-03	23-11	02-11	21-12	01-03	12-04	25-01	11-01	21-09	08-02	31-08	07-12	XXX	14

BRACKNELL RFC

President	Jonathan Dance	H 01189 700288 M07836 239575 Email Jonathandance@therfu.com
Chairman	Dave Bolton	H 01189 791151 M 07979652342 Email daveb@bis-comm.co.uk
Hon Secretary	Andy Johnson	H 01344 301037 M 07767 657975 Email anrj@btinternet.com
Fixture Secretary	Simon Mitchinson	M 07766 230839 Email simon@fuzzymoon.freeserve.co.uk

Club Offices - Telephone: 01344 420236

Chief Exec.	Ed Trick	M 07970029959 Email Edward.mpw@btopenworld.com
Asst. Chief Exec.	James Sinclair	Email jamessinclair@bracknellrugbyclub.com
Director of Rugby	Bob Crooks	Email Bob.crooks@bracknellrugbyclub.com
Community Project Man.	Jim Kelly	Email jimkelly@bracknellrugbyclub.com

All contacted through c/o Bracknell RFC, Lily Hill Park, Lily Hill Drive, Bracknell, Berks. RG12 2UG
Tel: 01344 424013 Fax: 01344 485268

The coming season is viewed with mixed emotions.

On the one hand we are extremely disappointed to have failed to stay in National Division 1. On the other hand the Club is excited, about the challenge to regain its former status knowing in the coming season we will meet old friends and, clubs we have enjoyed both visiting, and hosting.

After the heady success of achieving four promotions in five seasons, Bracknell's record in National Division 1 in 2001/02 was disappointing. The Club had not prepared itself for the difference in pace and standards between the National 2 and National 1. The tactics that had been successful in gaining those promotions were not successful in this new division although a number of games were desperately close and the Club could well have achieved its ambition of staying up. The Club (in contrast to its previous years) developed a habit of losing games it should have won (e.g. leading 23 – 13 with twenty minutes to go and losing 23 – 25 to the last kick of the game). There were few highlights in a season that yielded only four League wins but the defeat of Coventry in that Clubs first ever match at Bracknell will live in the memory of those who were there.

The experience has caused a re-appraisal of the clubs organisation and structure which has resulted in Ed Trick's appointment as Chief Executive and Bob Crooks being brought in as Director of Rugby following the resignation of Paul Rendall.

The objective in the coming season is to consolidate the clubs infrastructure both on and off the field with a view to progressing to the higher division taken account of the experience of last season and to learn from errors made.

Nick Marsh gets the ball away to Andy Dawling as Exeter's Sam Howard closes in.
Photo courtesy of Nigel Chanter (01392 467261)

BRACKNELL

Comp.	Date	H/A	Opponents	Result & Score	Att	15	14	13	12	11
N3 N	01-09	A	Exeter	L 30-33		Marsh/t	Chapman/t	Nowak	Heke	Spencer
N3 N	08-09	H	Moseley	W 20-11		Kenworthy/t2c2p	Nowak	Marsh	Heke	Chapman
N3 N	15-09	A	Manchester	L 13-28	750	Kenworthy/c2p	Nowak	Boulard	Heke	Chapman
N3 N	22-09	H	Birmingham & Solihull	L 12-19		Marsh	Chapman	Nowak	Heke	Spencer
N3 N	29-09	A	Henley Hawks	W 26-24	1000	Marsh	Spencer	Kenworthy/c	Heke	Chapman
N3 N	06-10	H	Rotherham	L 10-42		Marsh	Chapman	Kenworthy/p(a/c)	Heke	Spencer
N3 N	20-10	A	London Welsh	L 20-44	730	Marsh	Chapman	Boulard	Heke	Nowak
N3 N	27-10	H	Coventry	W 9-8	400	Marsh	Chapman	Boulard	Kenworthy/3p	Nowak
N3 N	11-11	A	Worcester	L 6-32		Costoloe	Chapman	Boulard	Nowak/2p	Nowak/2p
N3 N	17-11	H	Otley	L 19-25		Kenworthy/c4p	Chapman/t	Villamu	Heke	Greenlees
N3 N	01-12	A	Wakefield	L 22-33	300	Kenworthy/c5p	Chapman/t	Heke	Boulard	Greenlees
N3 N	08-12	A	Bedford	L 10-27	1301	Kenworthy/cp	Nowak/t	Boulard	Heke	Greenlees
N3 N	29-12	H	Rugby Lions	L 23-35	475	Barber/t	Chapman	Boulard	Heke	Greenlees
N3 N	12-01	A	Moseley	L 23-25		Barber	Chapman/t	Spencer	Heke	Nowak/c2p
N3 N	19-01	H	Manchester	L 15-22		Barber	Chapman	Spencer	Heke	Drake
N3 N	26-01	A	Birmingham & Solihull	L 3-10		Marsh	Drake	Spencer	Heke	Cannon
N3 N	03-02	H	Henley Hawks	W 13-6	600	Marsh	Chapman	Spencer	Heke	Drake
N3 N	09-02	A	Rotherham	L 8-55	1500	Spencer	Chapman/t	Heke	Cannon/p	Greenlees
N3 N	23-02	H	London Welsh*	L 22-24	600	Marsh	Drake	Vaega	Heke	Chapman
N3 N	02-03	H	Exeter	L 6-27		Marsh	Chapman	Vaega	Heke	Southall
N3 N	09-03	A	Coventry	L 14-63	1923	Marsh	Chapman	Vaega	Heke	Southall/t
N3 N	16-03	H	Worcester	L 24-59		Marsh	Chapman	Vaega	Heke	Southall/c
N3 N	31-03	A	Otley	L 28-39	550	Marsh/t	Greenlees	Vaega	Heke	Chapman/t
N3 N	06-04	H	Wakefield	L 8-42		Marsh	Chapman	Vaega	Nowak	Greenlees
N3 N	13-04	H	Bedford	L 7-41		Marsh	Greenlees(c/c)	Vaega	Heke	Chapman
N3 N	27-04	A	Rugby Lions	L 27-49		Marsh(e/t)	Chapman/2t	Spencer	Heke	Barber/t

** after opponents name indicates a penalty try. Brackets after a player's name indicates he was replaced. eg (a) means he was replaced by replacement code "a" and so on. / after a player or replacement name is followed by any scores he made - eg /t, /c, /p, /dg or any combination of these*

EVER PRESENT None

Most Appearances:
24: Dominic Chapman.
23: Josh Heke.
22: David Jackson (1).
20: Alan Leishman (2)

PLAYERS USED

42 plus six as replacement only.

MOST POINTS

Pts	Player	T	C	P	DG
105	M Kenworthy	1	8	28	-
73	D Pears	1	7	17	1
40	D Chapman	8	-	-	-
32	T Southall	1	6	5	-
25	B Nowak	1	4	4	-

MATCH FACTS

10	9	1	2	3	4	5	6	7	8
Kenworthy/c6p	Wright	Edwards	Alexopoulous	Anstead	Leishman	Parker	Jackson	Dawling	Brewer
Costoloe	Wright	Kelly	Alexopoulous/t	Anstead	Moore	Parker	Jackson	Dawling	Brewer
Costoloe	Pearce	Kelly	Alexopoulous	Anstead	Moore	Rudzski	Jackson/t	Dawling	Brewer
Kenworthy/4p	Wright	Kelly	Alexopoulous	Anstead	Rudzski	Moore	Jackson	Dawling	Sparks
Wright/t	Pearce	Kelly	Alexopoulous/t	Anstead	Rudzski	Moore	Jackson	Cornish	Sparks
Pears/t	Wright	Kelly	Fitzpatrick	Anstead	Rudzski	Moore	Jackson	Cornish	Nowak
Pears/4pdg	Wright	Kelly	Alexopoulous	Anstead	Leishman	Parker	Jackson/t	Dawling	Nowak
Pears	Wright	Kelly	Alexopoulous	Anstead	Leishman	Parker	Jackson	Cornish	Brewer
Pears	Wright	Kelly	Alexopoulous	Anstead	Leishman	Parker	Jackson	Cornish	Brewer
Pears	Shaw	Kelly	Alexopoulous	Anstead	Leishman	Parker	Jackson	Cornish	Nowak
Pears	Shaw	Kelly	Alexopoulous	Anstead	Leishman	Moore	Jackson	Cornish	Smith
Costoloe	Shaw	Kelly	Alexopoulous	Anstead	Leishman	Parker	Jackson	Dawling	Moore
Pears/2c3p	Wright	Kelly	Alexopoulous	Anstead	Leishman	Parker	Jackson	Dawling	Moore/t
Wright/t	Shaw	Kelly/t	Alexopoulous	Mosses	Leishman	Parker	Jackson	Cornish	Brewer
Wright/tp	Shaw/c	Kelly	Alexopoulous/t	Mosses	Leishman	Parker	Jackson	Cornish	Brewer
Pears/p	Wright	Kelly	Alexopoulous	Mosses	Smith	Parker	Blackburn	Dawling	Brewer
Pears/c2p	Wright/t	Kelly	Alexopoulous	Mosses	Leishman	Smith	Jackson	Dawling	Brewer
Costoloe	Wright	Kelly	Bibby	Anstead	Leishman	Parker	Smith	Starling	Moore
Pears/c5p	Wright	Kelly	Bibby	Mosses	Leishman	Parker	Dawling	Starling	Moore
Pears/2p	Wright	Kelly	Bibby	Mosses	Leishman	Moore	Jackson	Dawling	Nowak
Pears/2c	Turvey	Edwards	Bibby	Johnson	Leishman	Moore	Jackson	Cornish(b/t)	Nowak
Pears/c	Turvey	Johnson	Bibby/t	Mosses	Leishman	Blackburn	Jackson	Starling	Nowak/3t
Southall/2c3p	Turvey/t	Johnson	Fitzpatrick	Anstead	Leishman	Blackburn	Jackson	Cornish	Nowak
Southall/p	Turvey	Johnson	Fitzpatrick	Anstead	Leishman	Blackburn	Jackson/t	Starling	Nowak
Wright	Turvey	Johnson(d/t)	Box	Anstead	Leishman	Blackburn	Brewer	Cornish	Nowak
Southall/2cp	Turvey	Johnson	Box	Mosses	Leishman	Blackburn	Jackson	Brewer	Nowak

REPLACEMENTS: a - Ben Nowak. b - Andy Dawling. c - Tim Southall. d - Elliot Strong. e - Jerry Costoloe

WHEN	Total	First Half	Second Half	1/4	2/4	3/4	4/4
The POINTS were scored	418	245	173	123	122	56	117
The POINTS were conceded	823	393	430	184	209	183	247
The TRIES were scored	39	22	17	12	10	4	13
The TRIES were conceded	104	49	55	24	25	23	32

HOW the TRIES were scored

Total	Backs	Forwards	F Back	Wing	Centre	H Back	F Row	Lock	B Row	Pen. Try
39	22	16	5	11	-	6	6	1	9	1

HOW the TRIES were conceded

Total	Backs	Forwards	F Back	Wing	Centre	H Back	F Row	Lock	B Row	Pen. Try
104	67	35	12	29	14	12	10	7	18	2

BRACKNELL

LEAGUE STATISTICS
compiled by Stephen McCormack

SEASON	Division	P	W	D	L	F	A	Pts Diff	Lge Pts	Lge Pos	Coach	Captain
92-93	SWSC	12	8	1	3	198	95	103	17	4		
93-94	SWSC	12	10	0	2	294	90	204	20	2		
94-95	SWSC	12	10	0	2	365	80	285	20	2		
95-96	SWSC	12	11	0	1	409	76	333	22	2		
96-97	SWSC	22	22	0	0	868	201	667	44	1p		
											Most Points	**Most Tries**
97-98	SW1	22	18	2	2	786	271	515	38	1p	293 Carson Russell	20 Alex Poole
98-99	J2S	26	23	1	2	631	317	314	47	1p	216 Carson Russell	8 Howard Lamb & Phil Hopley
99-00	JN1	26	14	0	12	608	408	200	28	7	133 Carson Russell	10 Guy Spencer
00-01	N2	26	22	0	4	752	310	442	44	1p	145 Mike Kenworthy	14 Graham Sparks
01-02	N1	26	4	0	22	418	823	-405	26	14	105 Mike Kenworthy	8 Dominic Chapman

BIGGEST MARGINS

Home Win	76pts - 76-0 v W Hartlepool 14.04.01
Away Win	54pts -64-12 v Plymouth 03.04.99
Home Defeat	35pts -24-59 v Worcester 16.03.02
Away Defeat	36pts - 14-63 v Coventry 9.3.02

MOST POINTS

Scored at Home	76 v W Hartlepool 14.04.01
Scored Away	64 v Plymouth 03.04.99
Conceded at Home	59 v Worcester 16.03.02
Conceded Away	63 v Coventry 9.3.02

MOST CONSECUTIVE

Appearances	17 Nick Robinson
Matches scoring Tries	3 John Clarke
Matches scoring points	19 Carson Russell
Victories	19
Defeats	9

MOST TRIES

Scored in a match	12 v W Hartlepool 14.04.01
Conceded in a match	7 v Rugby Lions 16.12.00

MOST APPEARANCES

by a forward	89 Alan Leishman
by a back	64 Guy Spencer

	MOST IN A SEASON	MOST IN A CAREER	MOST IN A MATCH
Points	216 Carson Russell 98-99	386 Mike Kenworthy 98-02	26 Carson Russell v N Walsham 27.03.99 (H)
Tries	14 Graham Sparkes 00-01	29 Guy Spencer 98-01	3 David Jackson v Bridgwater 06.02.99 (H) Jon Clarke v Plymouth 03.04.99 (A)
Conversions	39 CarsonRussell 98-99	62 Mike Kenworthy 98-02	5 Carson Russell v Plymouth 03.04.99 (A) v Reading 07.11.99 (H)
Penalties	45 Carson Russell 98-99	76 CarsonRussell 98-99	8 Carson Russell v N Walsham 27.03.99 (H)
Drop Goals	1 Michael Kenworthy 98-99/00-01 Carson Russell 98-99 Ben Nowak 00-01 David Pears 01-02	2 Michael Kenworthy 98-01	1 By four players five times

All records relate to National league rugby only.

BRACKNELL
RFU SENIOR CUP
STATISTICS
compiled by Stephen McCormack

OVERALL PLAYING RECORD

	P	W	D	L	F	A	Pts Diff
Home	5	4	0	1	129	49	80
Away	13	8	0	5	332	277	55
Neutral	-	-	-	-	-	-	-
Total	18	12	0	6	461	326	135

SEASON BY SEASON

Season	Result
1971-72	DNQ
1972-73	DNQ
1973-74	DNQ
1974-75	DNQ
1975-76	DNQ
1976-77	DNQ
1977-78	DNQ
1978-79	DNQ
1979-80	DNQ
1980-81	DNQ
1981-82	DNQ
1982-83	DNQ
1983-84	DNQ
1984-85	DNQ
1985-86	DNQ
1986-87	DNQ
1987-88	DNQ
1988-89	DNQ
1989-90	DNQ
1990-91	DNQ
1991-92	DNQ
1992-93	DNQ
1993-94	DNQ
1994-95	DNQ
1995-96	DNQ
1996-97	3R
1997-98	4R
1998-99	4R
1999-2000	4R
2000-01	4R
2001-02	3R

TEAM RECORDS

Highest Score
58 v Haywards Heath 96/97

Biggest Winning Margin
45 (45-0) v Dorchester 00/01

Highest Score Against
34 v W Hartlepool 98/99

Biggest Losing Margin
24 (33-9) v Coventry 99/00

INDIVIDUAL RECORDS

Most Points in a match

Most Tries in a match

Most Conversions in a match

Most Penalties in a match

Most Drop Goals in a match

PLAYERS

	Position	D.o.B.	Apps.	Pts.	T	C	P	DG
Ben Nowak	Centre	29.11.77	61(12)	223	14	29	30	1
Nick Marsh	Full back	27.09.77	25	35	7			
Domonic Chapman	Winger		24	40	8	-	-	-
Guy Spencer	Winger	22.06.67	64	145	29	-	-	-
Josh Heke	Centre	23.06.75	46	15	3	-	-	-
Simon Shaw	Scrum half	21.08.72	53(17)	77	15	1	-	-
Craig Turvey	Scrum half		6	5	1	-	-	-
Tim Southall	Fly half		6(4)	32	1	6	5	-
David Pears	Fly half		13	73	1	7	17	1
Paul Boulard	Centre	09.03.78	26(2)	15	3	-	-	-
Mike Kenworthy	Centre	30.05.67	48(5)	386	11	62	67	2
Jamie Greenlees	Winger		9(1)	-	-	-	-	-
Jim Kelly	Prop	16.02.76	82(7)	5	1	-	-	-
Glynn Mosses	Prop	02.01.61	56(9)	20	4	-	-	-
David Box	Hooker	18.08.80	7	-	-	-	-	-
Greg Anstead	Prop	06.03.75	42(18)	-	-	-	-	-
Dinos Alexopoulos	Hooker		16	15	3	-	-	-
Matt Johnson	Prop		6(4)	-	-	-	-	-
Alan Leishman	Lock	19.04.75	89(1)	15	3	-	-	-
Richard Parker	Lock	03.10.71	58(15)	20	4	-	-	-
Chris Moore	Back row	07.11.68	42(6)	40	8	-	-	-
David Jackson	Back row	24.02.70	88(2)	85	17	-	-	-
Matt Cornish	Back row		11(10)	-	-	-	-	-
Andy Dawling	Back row		11(4)	5	1	-	-	-

BRACKNELL

FACT FILE

Founded: 1955
Web site: www.bracknellrugbyclub.com

Colours: Black with green & yellow hoops/black
Change colours: All black

GROUND

Address: Lily Hill Park, Lily Hill Drive, Bracknell, Berks RG12 2UG
Tel: 01344 424013 Fax: 01344 485268 email: info@Bracknellrugbyclub.com
Capacity: 1,150 1.000 uncovered standing 150 Covered seats hopefully for 2001-02

Directions: **From M4**, J10 - A329(M) Bracknell, B3408 Binfield, follow to A329 Bracknell. Through town towards Ascot, turn left at 'Running Horse' PH r'about, ground at rear.
From M3, J3 - A322 Bracknell - A332 Ascot to Heatherwood Hospital roundabout, A329 Bracknell to 'Running Horse' PH (on Right). Ground at rear.
Nearest Railway Station: Bracknell (approx 1.5 miles), frequent service London & Reading

Car Parking: 70 spaces at ground for permit holders only,
but secure off-site parking about 2 mins away. Please park as signposted.

Admission: Season ticket: £70 (standing)
Matchday: Standing - Adults: £8, Concessions £6 Seated - £11 - incl. programme

Clubhouse: Lounge bar & Players bar.
Snacks & bar meals available.
Functions: Contact Paul Adams (Bar Manager) on 01344 424013

Club Shop: Open on match days
plus Tues, Wed & Thur evenings 7.30 - 9.30

Training Nights: Tuesday & Thursday (1st & 2nd XV squads).
Lower XVs & ladies Wednesday

PROGRAMME Size: A5 Pages: 48 Editor: John Denman
Price: Included with admission
Advertising Rates Contact J Lucas 01252 621143
Per page, per season - Full page £490, Half £275, Qtr £175.

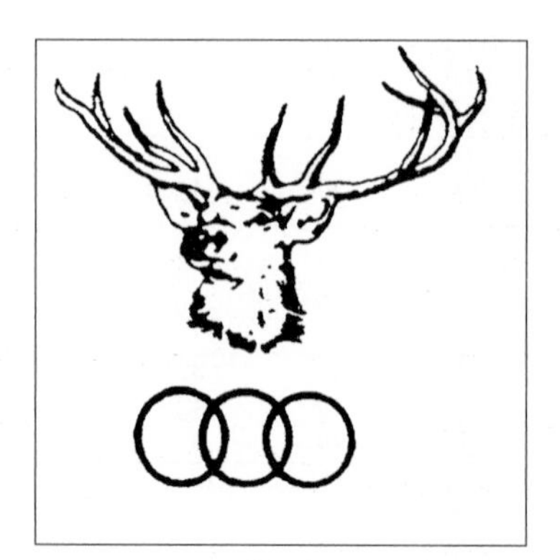

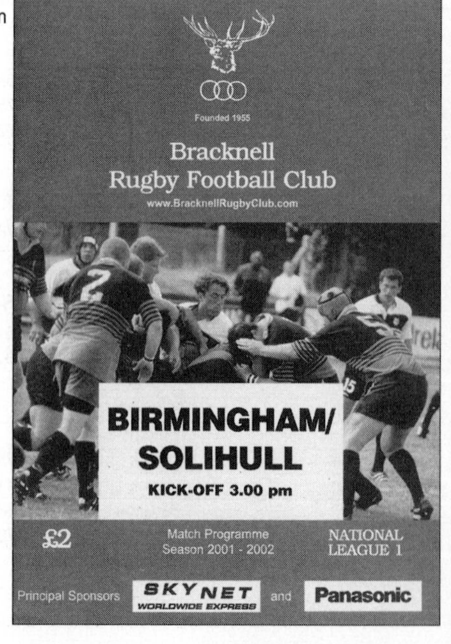

DONCASTER RFC

President	Tony DeMulder	c/o Doncaster RFC
Chief Executive	John Lowe	Doncaster RFC, 01302 831388 or 07977 112706 (M)
Director of Rugby & Fixtures	Derek Eves	Doncaster RFC, 01302 831388 or 07977 432586 (M)
Director of Playing Admin	John Blount	c/o Doncaster RFC, 07808 721807 (M)
Press Officer	Allan MacGregor	c/o Doncaster RFC, 01302 538584 (H/B) or 07703 181872 (M)

After three seasons in Three North, and with the best facilities in the Division, Doncaster won promotion in emphatic style winning 25 of 26 games played and the last 19 in a row. The sole defeat was a 16-0 loss at runners-up Dudley Kingswinford in early November; and it was the 20-8 victory in the return fixture in January (before a noisy 1800 crowd) that really set up the march towards the championship.

A number of league records fell or were matched on the way – the 153 tries and 1074 points scored eclipsed previous records: John Liley's 10 conversions vs West Hartlepool, Matt Donkin's 7 tries vs Whitchurch, and the 19 consecutive wins all matched the previous records. And the overwhelming 95-13 win against West Hartlepool set an all time club record.

All this was achieved with only 25 players starting all season, a testament to the fitness levels and commitment of the playing squad. Under the captaincy of Chris Conway and the Direction of Derek Eves, the philosophy of total rugby was pursued consistently. Conway and Eves both scored 24 tries, and Matt Brain and Matt Donkin 23 each. The usually reliable boot of John Liley kept adding the extras available and he finished the season with 359 points, his best haul of a distinguished career. We expect the current squad, and some useful additions, to be a competitive force in Division Two this coming season.

Youth rugby remains a priority at Doncaster, with the club having the largest junior section in the North. Our Colts were a young group this year but nevertheless won the Yorkshire Merit Table and will be together next season again; and with our under 16s winning the Yorkshire Cup, the pipeline for the future continues to look bright.

We look forward to making new friends this season, and to renewing some old acquaintances.

DONCASTER

Comp.	Date	H/A	Opponents	Result & Score	Att	15	14	13	12	11
N3 N	01-09	A	Sandal	W 71-28		Liley/2t8c	Donkin/t	Brain/t	Mortimore/t	Conway
N3 N	08-09	H	Nuneaton	W 49-13		Liley/c5p(b/tc)	Donkin	Brain/2t	Mortimore	Conway/t
N3 N	22-09	A	Morley	W 41-15		Liley/4cp	Donkin	Brain	Mortimore/t	Conway/t
N3 N	06-10	H	Liverpool St Helens	W 49-22		Liley/5c3p	Donkin/t	Brain/t	Mortimore	Conway/3t
N3 N	20-10	A	Bedford Athletic	W 20-12		Liley/cp	Donkin/t	Brain	Mortimore/t	Conway
N3 N	27-10	H	New Brighton	W 51-10		Liley/t3c5p	Townsley/2t	Donkin	Mortimore	Conway
N3 N	03-11	A	Dudley Kingwinsford	L 0-16	750	Liley	Townsley	Donkin	Mortimore	Conway
N3 N	10-11	H	Whitchurch	W 74-7		Liley/t7c	Townsley	Donkin/7t	Mortimore/2t	Conway
N3 N	17-11	A	Blaydon	W 29-10	300	Liley/2c5p	Townsley	Donkin/t	Mortimore	Conway
N3 N	24-11	H	West Hartlepool	W 95-13		Liley/t10c	Storey/6t	Brain/t	Donkin	Conway/t
N3 N	01-12	H	Sandal	W 70-7		Liley/5c	Storey/2t	Poskitt/2t(c/2t)	Mortimore	Conway/t
N3 N	08-12	A	Darlington MP	W 21-7		Liley/3c	Brain	Poskitt	Mortimore	Conway/t
N3 N	15-12	H	Tynedale	W 40-13		Liley/3c3p	Brain/2t	Poskitt/t	Donkin	Conway
N3 N	22-12	H	Scunthorpe	W 20-13	1000	Liley/cp	Brain	Poskitt	Donkin	Conway
N3 N	12-01	H	Blaydon	W 23-15		Liley/c2p	Brain/2t	Evans	Mortimore	Conway
N3 N	19-01	A	Whitchurch	W 13-0		Liley/c2p	Brain	Evans	Mortimore	Conway/t
N3 N	26-01	H	Dudley Kingwinsford	W 20-8	2000	Liley/2c2p	Donkin	Brain/t	Mortimore	Conway/t
N3 N	02-02	A	New Brighton	W 20-19		Liley/c	Donkin	Brain	Mortimore	Conway/2t
N3 N	09-02	H	Bedford Athletic	W 23-10		Liley/cpdg	Donkin/t	Brain	Mortimore	Conway/t
N3 N	09-03	H	Morley	W 27-13		Liley/2cp	Donkin/t	Brain	Mortimore	Conway/t
N3 N	16-03	A	Nuneaton	W 51-32		Liley/2t5c2p	Donkin/t	Brain/t	Mortimore	Conway/2t
N3 N	23-03	A	West Hartlepool	W 43-6		Liley/4c	Storey	Brain/t	Mortimore	Conway/2t
N3 N	30-03	A	Scunthorpe	W 72-33		Liley/2t8c2p	Donkin/t	Brain/t	Mortimore/t(b/t)	Conway/2t
N3 N	06-04	A	Tynedale	W 33-15	350	Liley/2c3p	Storey/2t	Brain	Donkin/t	Conway
N3 N	13-04	H	Darlington MP	W 86-3		Liley/2t8c	Donkin/t	Brain/2t	Mortimore/3t	Conway/3t
N3 N	27-04	A	Liverpool St Helens	W 33-17		Liley/c2p	Brain	Poskitt/t	Mortimore/2t	Conway/t
PGC	15-09	N	Sandal*	W 41-8		Storey/3c	Manson	Brain	Mortimore/2t	Conway/t
PGC	29-09	A	Kendal	L 17-30		Liley/tc	Manson	Donkin	Mortimore/2t	Conway

** after opponents name indicates a penalty try. Brackets after a player's name indicates he was replaced. eg (a) means he was replaced by replacement code "a" and so on. / after a player or replacement name is followed by any scores he made - eg /t, /c, /p, /dg or any combination of these*

EVER PRESENT

Four

Most Appearances:
26: Gavin Baldwin, Chris Conway, John Liley, Richard White.
25: Andy Fish (1), Derek Eves (1).

PLAYERS USED

25 plus four as a replacement only

MOST POINTS

Pts	Player	T	C	P	DG
359	J Liley	11	89	41	1
120	C Conway	24	-	-	-
120	D Eves	24	-	-	-
85	Matt Brain	17	-	-	-
85	M DOnkin	17	-	-	-
57	J Storey	11	1	-	-

MATCH FACTS

10	9	1	2	3	4	5	6	7	8
Poskitt/t	Townsley	Baldwin	Ward	Fish	Wood	White/t	Jones/t	Senior/t	Eves/2t
Poskitt	Townsley	Baldwin	Ward	Fish	Norris(a/t)	White	Jones/t	Senior	Eves/t
Poskitt/t	Townsley	Baldwin	Ward	Fish	Wood	White/t	Jones	Senior/t	Eves/t
Poskitt	Townsley	Baldwin	Ward	Fish	Wood	White	Jones	Eves/t	Filipo
Poskitt	Lock	Baldwin	Ward	Fish	Wood	White	Jones	Senior	Eves/t
Poskitt	Lock/t	Baldwin	Ward	Fish/t	Wood	White	Jones	Eves/t	Filipo
Poskitt	Lock	Baldwin	Ward	Fish	Wood	White	Jones	Eves	Filipo
Poskitt	Lock	Baldwin	Ward	Fish	Longworth	White	Jones/t	Eves/t	Filipo
Poskitt	Lock	Baldwin	Plevey	Fish	Longworth	White	Jones/t	Eves	Filipo
Niarchos	Townsley/t	Baldwin	Plevey	Fish	Norris	White/2t	Jones/2t	Senior	Eves/t
Niarchos/t	Lock	Baldwin	Ward	Waddington	Longworth	White	Eves/2t	Senior	Filipo/2t
Niarchos	Townsley	Baldwin	Ward	Fish	Longworth	White	Jones	Eves/2t	Filipo
Niarchos	Townsley	Baldwin	Ward	Fish	Longworth	White	Jones	Senior	Eves/2t
Niarchos	Townsley	Baldwin	Ward	Fish	Longworth	White	Jones	Eves/2t	Filipo/t
Niarchos	Greenslade	Baldwin	Plevey	Fish	Longworth	White	Ward	Senior(d/t)	Filipo
Poskitt	Townsley	Baldwin	Plevey	Fish	Longworth	White	Jones	Senior	Eves
Niarchos	Townsley	Baldwin	Ward	Fish	Longworth	White	Jones	Senior	Eves
Poskitt/dg	Townsley	Baldwin	Ward	Fish/t	Longworth	White	Jones	Senior	Eves
Poskitt	Lock	Baldwin	Plevey	Fish	Longworth	White	Jones	Eves/t	Filipo
Poskitt/t	Townsley	Baldwin	Plevey	Fish	Longworth	White	Ward	Senior	Eves/t
Niarchos	Townsley	Baldwin	Ward	Fish	Longworth/t	White	Jones	Senior	Eves
Poskitt	Greenslade	Baldwin	Plevey	Fish	Longworth/t	White	Jones	Eves/3t	Filipo
Poskitt/t	Lock	Baldwin	Ward/t	Fish	Longworth	White	Eves	Senior	Filipo
Poskitt	Lock/t	Baldwin	Plevey	Fish	Longworth	White	Jones	Eves	Filipo
Poskitt	Lock	Baldwin	Ward/2t	Fish	Longworth	White	Jones/t	Senior	Eves
Niarchos	Lock	Baldwin	Ward	Fish	Norris	White	Jones	Senior	Eves/t
Poskitt/t	Greenslade	Martin	Plevey	Fish/t	Wood	White	Jones	Senior	Filipo/t
Poskitt	Townsley	Baldwin	Plevey	Fish	Rutherford	White	Jones	Senior	Filipo

REPLACEMENTS: a - Lafaeli Filipo. b - J Storey. c - Matt Brain. d - D Eves.
Most replacement appearances in the league: 10: Lafaele Filipo, Scott Plevey. 6Jonathan Storey, Jason Niarchos.
Most times replaced: 10: Senior. 9: Rob Ward. 8: Richard Poskitt. 6: Gavin Baldwin

WHERE	Total	Home	Away
The POINTS were scored	1074	627	447
The POINTS were conceded	357	210	147
The TRIES were scored	153	91	62
The TRIES were conceded	48	29	19

HOW the TRIES were scored

Total	Backs	Forwards	F Back	Wing	Centre	H Back	F Row	Lock	B Row	Pen. Try
153	105	48	11	48	38	8	5	2	8	-

HOW the TRIES were conceded

Total	Backs	Forwards	F Back	Wing	Centre	H Back	F Row	Lock	B Row	Pen. Try
48	39	9	9	15	9	6	4	-	5	-

DONCASTER

LEAGUE STATISTICS

compiled by Stephen McCormack

SEASON	Division	P	W	D	L	F	A	Pts Diff	Lge Pts	Lge Pos	Most Points	Most Tries
92-93	North E2	12	11	0	1	294	39	255	22	1p		
93-94	North E1	12	11	0	1	232	70	162	22	1p		
94-95	North 2	12	7	0	5	136	155	-19	14	6		
95-96	North 2	12	4	2	6	183	168	15	10	9		
96-97	North 2	22	22	0	0	690	259	431	44	1p		
97-98	North 1	22	17	2	3	489	285	204	36	2		
98-99	North 1	22	18	1	3	550	214	336	37	1p		
99-00	JN2N	26	12	2	12	656	539	117	26	6	279 John Liley	19 Chris Conway
00-01	N3N	*23	16	0	7	579	352	227	32	4	244 John Liley	13 Derek Eves
01-02	N3N	26	25	0	1	1074	357	717	50	1p	359 John Liley	24 Derek Eves & Chris Conway

BIGGEST MARGINS

Home Win	83 pts	86-3 v Darlington MP 13.4.02
Away Win	43pts	71-28 v Sandal 1.9.01
Home Defeat	17pts	13-30 v Kendal 9.10.99
Away Defeat	45pts	5-50 v Nuneaton 22.1.00

MOST POINTS

Scored at Home	95 v West Hartlepool 24.11.01
Scored Away	72 v Scunthorpe 30.3.02
Conceded at Home	35 v Bedford Ath 25.9.99
Conceded Away	50 v Nuneaton 22.1.00

MOST CONSECUTIVE

Appearances	39 Gavin Baldwin 25.11.00 to date
Matches scoring Tries	8 Chris Conway 19.1.02 - 30.3.02
Matches scoring points	19 John Liley 10.11.01 to date
Victories	19
Defeats	2 five times

MOST TRIES

Scored in a match	15 v W Hartlepool 24.11.01
Conceded in a match	8 v Nuneaton 22.1.00

MOST APPEARANCES

by a forward	71 Gavin Baldwin
by a back	71 Chris Conway

	MOST IN A SEASON	MOST IN A CAREER	MOST IN A MATCH
Points	359 John Liley 01-02	882 John Liley 99-02	32 John Liley v Scunthorpe 30.3.02 (A)
Tries	24 Derek Eves 01-02	52 Chris Conway 99-02	7 Chris Donkin v Whitchurch 10.11.01 (H)
Conversions	89 John Liley 99-02	172 John Liley 99-02	10 John Liley v W Hartlepool 24.11.01 (H)
Penalties	55 John Liley 99-00	135 John Liley 99-02	9 John Liley v Sheffield 4.12.99 (H)
Drop Goals	1 John Liley 01-02	1 John Liley 99-02	1 John Liley v Bedford 9.2.02 (H)

All records relate to National league rugby only.

DONCASTER
RFU SENIOR CUP
STATISTICS
compiled by Stephen McCormack

OVERALL PLAYING RECORD

	P	W	D	L	F	A	Pts Diff
Home	4	3	0	1	150	60	90
Away	6	2	0	4	84	133	-49
Neutral	-	-	-	-	-	-	-
Total	10	5	0	5	234	193	41

SEASON BY SEASON

Season	Result
1971-72	DNQ
1972-73	DNQ
1973-74	DNQ
1974-75	DNQ
1975-76	DNQ
1976-77	DNQ
1977-78	DNQ
1978-79	DNQ
1979-80	DNQ
1980-81	DNQ
1981-82	DNQ
1982-83	DNQ
1983-84	DNQ
1984-85	DNQ
1985-86	DNQ
1986-87	DNQ
1987-88	DNQ
1988-89	DNQ
1989-90	DNQ
1990-91	DNQ
1991-92	DNQ
1992-93	DNQ
1993-94	DNQ
1994-95	DNQ
1995-96	DNQ
1996-97	DNQ
1997-98	4R
1998-99	2R
1999-2000	1R
2000-01	2R
2001-02	2R

TEAM RECORDS

Highest Score
79 v Sandal 01/02

Biggest Winning Margin
71 (79-8) v Sandal 01/02

Highest Score Against
58 v Richmond 97/98

Biggest Losing Margin
50 (58-8) v Richmond 97/98

INDIVIDUAL RECORDS

Most Points in a match

Most Tries in a match

Most Conversions in a match

Most Penalties in a match

Most Drop Goals in a match

PLAYERS DONCASTER

	Position	D.o.B.	Apps.	Pts.	T	C	P	DG
John Liley	Full back	21.08.67	71(2)	892	26	172	235	1
Chris Conway	Winger	11.10.71	71	260	52	-	-	-
Matt Brain	Winger	16.03.67	55(2)	145	29	-	-	-
James Mortimer	Centre	05.10.78	57(3)	115	23	-	-	-
Matt Donkin	Centre	23.11.71	42(1)	110	22	-	-	-
James Storey	Winger	17.07.82	5(6)	68	11	2	3	-
Paul Townsley	Scrum half	27.04.79	31	30	6	-	-	-
Simon Greenslade	Scrum half	05.10.72	35(5)	35	7	-	-	-
Jason Niarchos	Fly half		9(6)	5	1	-	-	-
Gavin Baldwin	Prop	06.12.68	71	-	-	-	-	-
Andy Fish	Prop	15.05.69	64(9)	20	4	-	-	-
Andrew Waddington	Prop	08.06.71	13(12)	-	-	-	-	-
Scott Plevey	Hooker	28.09.68	29(10)	5	1	-	-	-
Rob Ward	Hooker	10.05.76	40(6)	35	7	-	-	-
Richard White	Lock		26	20	4	-	-	-
James Norris	Lock	11.05.76	44(6)	-	-	-	-	-
Geoff Jones	Back row		22(1)	35	7	-	-	-
Derek Eves	Back row	07.01.66	48(1)	185	37	-	-	-
Lafaele Filipo	Back row		13(10)	20	4	-	-	-
Mark Longworth	Lock	06.02.69	49(4)	15	3	-	-	-

DONCASTER

FACT FILE

Founded: 1875

Colours: Navy blue with 2 thin red & white bands
Change colours: Red

GROUND

Address: Castle Park, Armthorpe Road, Doncaster DN2 5QB
Tel: 01302 831388 Fax: 01302 836300 e-mail: coach@drfc.co.uk
Web Site: www.drfc.co.uk
Capacity: 4.252 Seated: 252 Standing: 4,200 (200 covered)

Directions: Leave M18 at junction 4 and follow signs to Doncaster. At 2nd roundabout turn left towards Armthorpe. At next roundabout turn right and the ground is 1.25 miles on the left.
Nearest Railway station: Doncaster

Car Parking: Spaces for 400 cars at the ground

Admission:
Season £45
Matchday Visiting Adults £6; Members £3; Children/OAPs £1

Clubhouse: Open every evening except Sunday
Functions: Yes - Contact club to book

Club Shop: Yes - contact Paul Turton at club.

Training Nights: Monday & Thursday, 7.15pm

PROGRAMME
Size: A5 Price: With admission
Pages: 36 + cover Editor: Allan MacGregor

ADVERTISING RATES
Colour: Full Page £200
Mono: Full Page £160 Half £85

ESHER RFC

Correspondence to: c/o Esher RFC, 369 Molesey Road, Hersham, Surrey KT12 3PF
Tel: 01932 220295 (B)

President Ross Howard

Chairman Tim Bale

Club Secretary Wally Grey

Director of Rugby Hugh McHardy

Rugby Managers John Inverdale, Bob Stratton & David Page

1st XV Manager/ Press Officer NCA Rep. David Page 35 Misty's Field, Walton on Thames, Surrey KT12 2BG
07973 488142 (M) 0870 131 5073 (Fax) email: pageyd14@aol.com

Club Captain: Jan Bonney

Coaches: Peter Winterbottom, Jim Staples, Julian Davies

Fixtures Secretary Simon Gardner 01962 869846 (H) email: gardner_man_services@compuserve.com

Esher enjoyed, if that's the word, the proverbial curate's egg of a season, with some sparkling displays mixed in with some indescribably average ones.

As a consequence, a mid-table position was probably fair for a side that promised much but which ultimately failed to deliver on too many occasions. However, two victories over Rosslyn Park, and a courageous victory away at Kendal stand out among the dozen league successes, and in Chris Finch and Dan Wassell, Esher found two players who made a real difference to the cutting edge in the backs, where captain Jan Bonney had a fine season and full-back Jon Gregory was his usual points machine.

In the pack, various permutations across the eight perhaps gave the team an unsettled look on occasions, but Glyn Dewhurst enjoyed a good first season in the back row, and in Christian Short and Rob Hart, two young second-rows offered heart for the future. Chris Wilkins, as ever, was the rock upon which the pack was based.

Off the pitch, the seemingly never-ending round of legal rows with builders and contractors over the new club-house cast a pall on the first-half of the season. The generosity of spirit shown by all other clubs in the league towards our predicament was truly heart-warming when officials, players and fans could easily, and justifiably, have complained bitterly about the (lack of) facilities they had to contend with.

Thankfully work has been completed, and we can now put the problems of the last 18 months behind us, and focus on matters on the pitch. Hugh McHardy, Peter Winterbottom and Jim Staples will again be the coaching triumverate charged with steering the club through another season. It will be nice to have a year talking about line-outs and miss-moves rather than portacabins and building sub-contractors.

John Inverdale

Scrum half Charlie Mulraine gets good ball away in the match against Plymouth Albion.
Photo courtesy of Nigel Chanter (01392 467261)

ESHER

Comp.	Date	H/A	Opponents	Result & Score	Att	15	14	13	12	11
N2	01-09	A	Preston Grasshoppers	L 21-22	260	Gregory/c3p	Smith	Bonney	Burns/t	Flood
N2	08-09	H	Newbury	W 33-22		Gregory/tc2p	Bromley/2t	Burns	Bonney	Thorneycro*
N2	15-09	A	Waterloo	W 50-15		Gregory/4c4p	Thorneycroft/t	Dixon	Burns	Bromley
N2	22-09	H	Fylde	W 26-3		Gregory/c3p	Burns	Burns	Burns	Bromley/t
N2	06-10	A	Wharfedale	L 13-16		Gregory/c2p	Thorneycroft/t	Cook	Burns	Fisher
N2	20-10	H	Sedgley Park	W 16-14		Gregory/c2p	Cook/t	Bonney	Burns	Bromley
N2	27-10	A	Rosslyn Park	W 17-10		Gregory/4p	Cook	Bonney	Burns	Bromley/t
N2	10-11	H	Kendal	L 22-25		Gregory/c5p	Thorneycroft	Bonney	Burns	Bromley/t
N2	17-11	A	Nottingham	L 6-25	284	Gregory/2p	Cook	Bonney	Burns	Clouston
N2	24-11	H	Harrogate	L 12-24		Gregory/4p	Bonney	Burns	Wassell	Bromley
N2	01-12	H	Preston Grasshoppers	W 43-0		Gregory/2c8p	Thorneycroft	Burns	Wassell/t	Bromley
N2	08-12	A	Orrell	L 7-41	800	Gregory/c	Bonney	Burns	Wassell	Bromley/t
N2	15-12	H	Stourbridge	W 45-17		Gregory/t3c3p	Thorneycroft	Bonney	Wassell	Bromley/3t
N2	22-12	H	Plymouth Albion	L 15-22		Gregory/4p	Thorneycroft	Bonney/dg	Wassell	Cook
N2	12-01	H	Nottingham	L 23-24		Gregory/6p	Thorneycroft	Bonney	Cook	Bromley
N2	19-01	A	Kendal	W 14-12		Gregory/2p	Cook/tp	Bonney	Cook	McKay
N2	26-01	H	Rosslyn Park	W 17-16		Gregory/3p	Thorneycroft	Bonney	Cook	Cook/p
N2	02-02	A	Sedgley Park*	L 16-20		Gregory/c2p	McKay	Bonney	Cook	Cook
N2	09-02	H	Wharfedale	L 13-17		Gregory/tc2p	Thorneycroft	Bonney	Wassell	Cook
N2	16-02	A	Harrogate	L 23-34	263	Gregory/2c3p	Cook	Bonney/t	Wassell/t	Clouston
N2	23-02	A	Fylde	W 27-13		Gregory/t3c2p	Thorneycroft/t	Clouston	Wassell	Cook
N2	09-03	H	Waterloo	W 33-26		Gregory/3c4p	Thorneycroft	Clouston	Wassell	Cook
N2	16-03	A	Newbury*	W 24-22		Gregory/tc3p	Cowell	Bonney	Wassell	Thorneycroft
N2	30-03	A	Plymouth Albion	L 0-57		Gregory	Owen	Bonney	Wassell	Cowell
N2	06-04	A	Stourbridge	L 19-45	300	Gregory/2c	Cowell/2t	Bonney	Wassell/t	Bird
N2	13-04	H	Orrell	L 12-45		Gregory/3p	Cowell	Bonney	Wassell	Thorneycroft
PGC	29-09	N	Launceston	L 10-19	350	Taylor/t	Thorneycroft	Wassell	Bonney	Barnett/t

** after opponents name indicates a penalty try. Brackets after a player's name indicates he was replaced. eg (a) means he was replaced by replacement code "a" and so on. / after a player or replacement name is followed by any scores he made - eg /t, /c, /p, /dg or any combination of these*

EVER PRESENT Jonathan Gregory.

Most Appearances:

26: Jonathan Gregory.
24: Chris Wilkins (1), Duncan Cormack.
22: Jan Bonney.

PLAYERS USED

39 plus six as a replacement

MOST POINTS

Pts	Player	T	C	P	DG
311	J Gregory	5	29	76	-
45	S Bromley	9	-	-	-
20	S Owen	4	-	-	-
19	C Finch	2	-	-	3

MATCH FACTS

10	9	1	2	3	4	5	6	7	8
Stanley	Mulraine	Cormack	Seymour	Smith	Mole	Short	Allison/t	Kronfeld	Wilkins
Stanley	Barr/t	Cormack	Hill	Smith	Mole	Owen/t	Butterworth	Allison	Wilkins
Bonney/t	Mulraine/t	Cormack	Hill	Smith	Mole	Owen/t	Butterworth/t	Bird	Wilkins/t
Stanley/t	Barr/t	Cormack	Hill	Smith	Mole	Short	Owen	Bird	Wilkins
Bonney	Barr	Cormack	Hill	Smith	Mole	Short	Allison	Bird	Wilkins
Stanley/dg	Barr	Cormack	Bennett	Smith	Mole	Morahan	Allison	Owen	Wilkins
Stanley	Barr	Cormack	Hill	Seymour	Mole	Morahan	Allison	Bird	Wilkins
Stanley	Barr	Cormack	Hill	Seymour	Mole	Morahan	Bird	Kronfeld	Wilkins
Stanley	Mulraine	Cormack	Hill	Smith	Mole	Morahan	Bird	Kronfeld	Wilkins
Stanley	Barr	Cormack	Seymour	Smith	Mole	Owen	Butterworth	Bird	Wilkins
Stanley	Barr/t	Cormack	Bennett/t	Seymour	Mole	Owen	Butterworth	Bird	Wilkins
Stanley	Mulraine	Cormack	Bennett	Seymour	Mole	Owen	Butterworth	Mills	Wilkins
Finch	Mulraine	Cormack	Bennett	Seymour	Hart/t	Owen/t	Butterworth	Mills	Wilkins
Finch	Barr	Cormack	Bennett	Seymour	Mole	Owen	Butterworth	Bird	Wilkins
Finch	Barr	Cormack	Bennett	Smith	Mole	Morahan	Butterworth	Bird/t	Wilkins
Finch	Barr	Cormack	Bennett	Seymour	Mole	Owen	Butterworth	Dewhurst	Wilkins
Finch	Barr	Cormack	Seymour/t	Smith	Mole	Owen	Butterworth	Dewhurst	Wilkins
Finch/dg	Barr	Cormack	Bennett	Smith	Mole	Owen	Bird	Dewhurst	Wilkins
Finch	Mulraine	Cormack	Bennett	Seymour	Hart	Owen	Bird	Dewhurst	Butterworth
Finch	Mulraine	Seymour	Bennett	Smith	Short	Hart	Allison	Mills	Butterworth
Finch/t	Mulraine	Cormack	Bennett	Smith	Hart	Finnegan	Owen	Dewhurst	Wilkins
Finch/t	Mulraine	Cormack	Bennett	Smith	Short	Owen/t	Mills	Dewhurst/t	Wilkins
Finch/dg	Mulraine	Cormack	Bennett	Smith	Hart	Owen	Mills	Dewhurst	Wilkins
Finch	Mulraine	Cormack	Bennett	Seymour	Hart	Short	Bird	Mills	Wilkins
Finch	Mulraine	Cormack	Bennett	Seymour	Hart	Short	Butterworth	Dewhurst	Wilkins
Finch/dg	Mulraine	Alexander	Seymour	Smith	Hart	Allison	Butterworth	Dewhurst	Wilkins
Stanley	Mulraine	Cormack	Bennett	Smith	Mole	Short	Owen	Mills	Butterworth

REPLACEMENTS

WHERE	Total	Home	Away
The POINTS were scored	547	310	237
The POINTS were conceded	587	332	255
The TRIES were scored	48	25	23
The TRIES were conceded	68	38	30

HOW the TRIES were scored

Total	Backs	Forwards	F Back	Wing	Centre	H Back	F Row	Lock	B Row	Pen. Try
48	34	12	5	16	5	8	2	5	5	2

HOW the TRIES were conceded

Total	Backs	Forwards	F Back	Wing	Centre	H Back	F Row	Lock	B Row	Pen. Try
68	45	23	4	17	15	7	3	6	14	2

ESHER

LEAGUE STATISTICS

compiled by Stephen McCormack

SEASON	Division	P	W	D	L	F	A	Pts Diff	Lge Pts	Lge Pos	Most Points	Most Tries
92-93	L2S	12	7	0	5	201	189	12	14	3		
93-94	L2S	12	10	2	0	382	95	287	22	1p		
94-95	L1	12	10	0	2	344	132	212	20	2		
95-96	L1	12	9	0	3	280	159	121	18	3		
96-97	L1	13	12	0	1	458	171	287	24	1p		
97-98	N2S	26	18	1	7	651	448	203	37	4	92 Ray Dudman	12 Mark Butterworth
98-99	N2S	26	23	0	3	864	308	566	46	2	303 Jon Gregory	16 Nana Dontah
99-00	N2S	26	23	0	3	1018	356	662	46	1	351 Jon Gregory	15 Michael Corcoran
00-01	N2	26	11	1	14	577	484	93	23	8	260 John Gregory	7 John Gregory
01-02	N2	26	12	0	14	547	587	40	24	7	311 John Gregory	9 Spencer Bromley

BIGGEST MARGINS

Home Win	97pts - 104-7 v Met Police
Away Win	43pts - 56-13 v Norwich
Home Defeat	33pts - 12-45 v Orrell 13.4.02
Away Defeat	57pts -0-57 v Plymouth A 30..3.02

MOST CONSECUTIVE

Appearances	
Matches scoring Tries	
Matches scoring points	
Victories	15
Defeats	4

MOST POINTS

Scored at Home	104 v Met Police
Scored Away	57 v Met Police 14.2.98
Conceded at Home	45 v Orrell 13.4.02
Conceded Away	57 v Plymouth A. 30.03.02

MOST TRIES

Scored in a match	17 v Met Police
Conceded in a match	8 v Plymouth 30.03.02

MOST APPEARANCES

by a forward	**103 (11) Mark Butterworth**
by a back	**98 Jonathon Gregory**

	MOST IN A SEASON	MOST IN A CAREER	MOST IN A MATCH
Points	351 Jon Gregory 1999-00	1233 Jon Gregory 1998-02	34 Michael Corcoran v Cheltenham 13.2.99
Tries	16 Nana Dontah 1998-99	30 Michael Corcoran 1998-00	4 Nana Dontah v Plymouth 10.10.98 (H) Michael Corcoran v Cheltenham 13.2.99(H)
Conversions	78 Jon Gregory 1999-00	205 Jon Gregory 1998-02	8 Jon Gregory v Clifton 2.10.99 (H) v W Hartelpool 8.4.01 (H)
Penalties	76 Jon Gregory 2001-02	227 Jon Gregory 1998-02	8 Jon Gregory v Preston 1.12.01(H)
Drop Goals	3 Richard Bailey 1998-99 Chris Finch 2001-02	3 Richard Bailey 1998-00 Chris Finch 2001-02	1 By nine players

OVERALL PLAYING RECORD

	P	W	D	L	F	A	Pts Diff
Home	11	7	0	4	247	180	67
Away	11	4	0	7	215	245	-30
Neutral	-	-	-	-	-	-	-
Total	22	11	0	11	462	425	37

SEASON BY SEASON

Season	Result
1971-72	DNQ
1972-73	DNQ
1973-74	DNQ
1974-75	DNQ
1975-76	DNQ
1976-77	1R
1977-78	1R
1978-79	1R
1979-80	1R
1980-81	DNQ
1981-82	DNQ
1982-83	DNQ
1983-84	DNQ
1984-85	DNQ
1985-86	DNQ
1986-87	DNQ
1987-88	DNQ
1988-89	DNQ
1989-90	DNQ
1990-91	DNQ
1991-92	DNQ
1992-93	DNQ
1993-94	DNQ
1994-95	2R
1995-96	DNQ
1996-97	4R
1997-98	1R
1998-99	4R
1999-2000	3R
2000-01	4R
2001-02	2R

ESHER

RFU SENIOR CUP

STATISTICS

compiled by Stephen McCormack

TEAM RECORDS

Highest Score

60 v Clifton 98/99

Biggest Winning Margin

57 (60-3) v Clifton 98/99

Highest Score Against

50 v Leeds Tykes 99/00

Biggest Losing Margin

43 (50-7) v Leeds Tykes 99/00

INDIVIDUAL RECORDS

Most Points in a match

25 Jonathan Gregory v Clifton 98/99

Most Tries in a match

2 on numerous occasions

Most Conversions in a match

7 Jonathan Gregory v Clifton 98/99

Most Penalties in a match

5 Jonathan Gregory v Tabard 98/99

Most Drop Goals in a match

-

PLAYERS

	Position	D.o.B.	Apps.	Pts.	T	C	P	DG
Jonathan Gregory	Full back	02.06.73	98	1231	28	205	227	-
Jan Bonney	Centre	27.01.71	69	76	13	-	-	4
Chris Finch	Fly half		14	19	2	-	-	3
Spencer Bromley	Winger	12.12.69	11	45	9	-	-	-
Sean Burns	Centre	10.06.71	32(1)	20	4	-	-	-
Charlie Mulraine	Scrum half	24.12.73	29(8)	15	3	-	-	-
Harvey Thorneycroft	Winger	22.02.69	14	15	3	-	-	-
Billy Stanley	Fly half	27.03.78	30	27	3	-	2	2
Graham Barr	Scrum half	31.05.80	13(3)	15	3	-	-	-
Alan Cook	Winger	26.05.77	17	5	1	-	-	-
Tim Cook	Winger		7	11	1	-	2	-
Dan Wassell	Centre		13	15	3	-	-	-
Duncan Cormack	Prop	03.04.75	44(8)	20	4	-	-	-
Paddy Seymour	Prop	18.07.78	31(11)	10	2	-	-	-
Jeff Smith	Prop	25.03.76	43(17)	15	3	-	-	-
Mark Bennett	Hooker	27.08.73	61(17)	25	5	-	-	-
Rob Hart	Lock	05.03.79	8(1)	5	1	-	-	-
Christian Short	Lock	15.11.79	7(1)	-	-	-	-	-
Peter Mole	Lock	21.02.66	87(14)	30	6	-	-	-
Mark Butterworth	Back row	21.02.73	103(11)	130	26	-	-	-
Chris Wilkins	Back row	03.01.71	50(1)	35	7	-	-	-
Ciaran Bird	Back row	29.11.71	70(10)	115	23	-	-	-
Caleb Kronfeld	Back row	06.01.76	30(14)	50	10	-	-	-

ESHER

FACT FILE

Founded: 1923-24

Colours: Black with amber collar

Change Colours: Amber with black collar

Nickname: The EE's

GROUND

Address: 369 Molesey Road, Hersham, Surrey KT12 3PF
Tel: 01932 220295 (Office), 01932 254627 (Fax), 01932 224834 (Clubhouse)
Web site: http://www.esherrfc.org email: webmaster@esherrfc.org
Capacity: 3,000 Seated: 1,200 Standing: Uncovered 1,800

Directions: M25 Junc 10, A3 to London. After 1 mile left to Walton-on-Thames (A245), after 1/4 mile right at lights into Seven Hills Road (B365).Turn right at r/about into Burwood Road & follow into Hersham Village, bear right into Molesey Road. After the railway bridge (Hersham BR) the ground is 300yds on the left . NB Low bridge at Hersham BR station.
Nearest Railway Station: Hersham (Waterloo-Woking line)

Car Parking: 1,000 on ground

Admission: Season - £50. Matchdays £8 incl. programme Under 16: Free

Clubhouse: Open matchdays & training nights.
Snacks & bar meals available.
Functions room, Business meetings & conferences catered for. From 10-220 people
Sponsors' lounges available on matchdays
Prices on application
contact House & Grounds Manager David Alexander 07773 329047 or bookings@esherrfc.org

Club Shop: Open matchdays & training nights..
See website for stock items

Training Nights: Monday & Thursday 7pm

PROGRAMME

Size: A5 full colour
Price: with admission
Pages: 40+
Editor: David Page 07973 488142
Advertising Rates
Colour - Full page £750, Half £400, Qtr £250
One off match day rates on apllication.
Contact David Alexander 07773 329047
or email: advertising@esherrfc.org

FYLDE RUFC

President	Ron King	27 Evesham Rd., Lytham St. Annes FY8 3ES 01253 780567
Chairman	Malcom Jones	Dibbs Cottage, Brades lane, Freckleton PR4 1HH 01772 634086
Club Secretary	David Walsh	33 Kingsway, Lytham 01253 738452 (H) 01253 739137 (Club Fax) 01253 734733 (Club Tel)
Chairman of Rugby	Tony Todd	c/o Fylde Rugby Club Tel/Fax: 01253 739137
Press Officer	Stewart Brown	179 Hardhorn Road, Poulton-le-Fylde, Lancs. FY6 8ES 01253 883100 (H) 01253 739137 (Fax)
1st Team Manager	Steve Rigby	01257 450580 (H) 01257 450991 (B) 07831 403400 (M)
Coach	Dean Kenny	c/o Fylde Rugby Club 01253 739137 (club) 01942 498480 (B) 07909 981791 (M)
Assistant Coach	Stuart Connell	c/o Fylde Rugby Club 01254 851407 (H) 07977 261302 (M)

This season should be remembered for the fact that Fylde has stopped the sequence of being in the relegation zone for the first time in four years. The club now has a base from which it can launch a push to be in contention for top honours in the league next season. Those supporters who have followed the club this season will know that, with more consistency, at least five more games could have been won. This would have been a fair reflection for the season.

The team has had a combination of experience and youth, which is borne out in the fact that of the 49 players who played first team rugby, 24 were debutants, young players coming up through the ranks. It is imperative that the 2nd XV continues to provide this young talent. Such players include Nick Kenyon, Ben Trend, Tom Kerr, Grant Ferguson, Ben Bullough, Ben James, Ed Scott, Nick Cassidy, Matt Wilkinson, Dave Wiseman, Tim Wyles and Ben and Tom Godfrey. Stuart Connell can take a bow for helping these players to improve.

Fylde's pack was one of the best in the league and continually produced good ball, which was not always used as well as it should have been. The front five, of Matt Filipo, Craig McIntyre, Martin Scott, Alan Yates, Jon Taylor and Dave Baldwin has well over a 1,000 first class games under its belt. Such was their domination that out of the top six try scorers four were forwards, Brent Wilson, Craig McIntyre, Dylan O'Grady and Chris Jones.

FYLDE

Comp.	Date	H/A	Opponents	Result & Score	Att	15	14	13	12	11
N2	01-09	H	Kendal	W 17-14		Trend	Evans	Kenyon	Davies	Godfrey
N2	08-09	A	Nottingham	W 18-16	311	Trend	Godfrey	Evans	Davies	Anderton
N2	15-09	H	Harrogate	W 13-9		Trend	Godfrey	Evans	Davies	Kerr
N2	22-09	A	Esher	L 3-26		Trend	Godfrey	Evans	Wiseman	Kerr
N2	06-10	H	Orrell	L 13-28		Perry	Evans/t	Kenyon	Davies	Godfrey
N2	20-10	A	Stourbridge	W 35-12		Kenyon	Evans	Connell	Davies/t	Kerr
N2	27-10	H	Preston Grasshoppers	L 10-21		Kenyon	Perry	Perry	Davies	Evans
N2	10-11	A	Newbury	W 29-16		Kenyon/3cp	Evans/2t	Hassan	Davies	Perry/t
N2	17-11	H	Waterloo	W 32-15		Kenyon/t2cp	Evans	Hassan	Davies	Trend(b/t)
N2	24-11	H	Plymouth Albion	L 0-20		Kenyon	Kerr	Wiseman	Evans	Perry
N2	01-12	A	Kendal	L 18-27		Kenyon	Godfrey/tc2p	Wiseman/t	Evans	Perry
N2	08-12	H	Sedgley Park	L 19-22	450	Kenyon	Evans	Wiseman	Hassan(d/p)	Godfrey/t2p
N2	15-12	A	Rosslyn Park	W 24-18		Kenyon	Evans	Hassan	Davies	Godfrey/c3pdg
N2	22-12	H	Wharfedale	W 17-13		Kenyon	Evans	Hassan/t	Davies	Godfrey/tc
N2	05-01	A	Plymouth Albion	L 5-28	2100	Kenyon	Evans	Hassan	Davies	Godfrey/t
N2	12-01	A	Waterloo	W 20-10		Kenyon	Evans	Davies	Hassan	Godfrey/cp
N2	19-01	H	Newbury*	W 39-3		Kenyon	Kenyon	Hassan	Davies	Godfrey/3t2c
N2	26-01	A	Preston Grasshoppers*	W 17-5	495	Kenyon	Kenyon	Hassan	Davies	Godfrey/c(d/cp
N2	02-02	H	Stourbridge*	W 33-20		Godfrey/4c	Kenyon	Hassan	Davies/t	Evans
N2	09-02	A	Orrell	L 6-46	800	Kenyon	Kenyon	Hassan	Davies	Godfrey/2p
N2	23-02	H	Esher	L 13-27		Kenyon	Kenyon/t	Hassan	Davies	Godfrey/p
N2	09-03	A	Harrogate	L 0-43	317	Kenyon	Evans	Hassan	Davies	Kenyon
N2	16-03	H	Nottingham	L 13-30	500	Kenyon	Godfrey/c2p	Hassan	Davies	Evans
N2	30-03	A	Wharfedale	W 27-21		Kenyon	Trend	Evans	Hassan	Kenyon
N2	06-04	H	Rosslyn Park	W 26-22	300	Kenyon	Kerr	Kenyon	Wiseman	Godfrey/t3c
N2	13-04	A	Sedgley Park	L 15-37	550	Kenyon	Trend	Kenyon	Evans	Kerr
PGC	13-10	N	Norwich	W 32-0		Godfrey	Trend/t	Kenyon	Connell	Kerr
PGC	03-11	A	Orrell	L 9-37		Kenyon/3p	Evans	Hassan	Davies	Perry

** after opponents name indicates a penalty try. Brackets after a player's name indicates he was replaced. eg (a) means he was replaced by replacement code "a" and so on. / after a player or replacement name is followed by any scores he made - eg /t, /c, /p, /dg or any combination of these*

EVER PRESENT Dave Baldwin

Most Appearances:
26: Dave Baldwin.
25: Alan Yates.
23: Laurence Condon (2), Matt Filipo.
21: Matt Evans, Richard Kenyon (1).

PLAYERS USED

37 plus four as a replacement

MOST POINTS

Pts	Player	T	C	P	DG
112	B Godfrey	8	15	13	1
67	S Gough	1	7	16	-
40	B Wilson	8	-	-	-
35	C McIntyre	7	-	-	-
30	D O'Grady	6	-	-	-

MATCH FACTS

10	9	1	2	3	4	5	6	7	8
Gough/4p	Condon	Filipo	Scott(a/t)	Yates	Taylor	Baldwin	Atkinson	Bradwell	Ferguson
Gough/c2p	Condon	Filipo	Scott/t(a/t)	Yates	Taylor	Baldwin	Atkinson	Lavin	Ferguson
Gough/c2p	Condon	Filipo/t	Scott	Yates	Taylor	Baldwin	Atkinson	Lavin	Ferguson
Gough/p	Condon	Filipo	Scott	Yates	O'Neill	Baldwin	Atkinson	Lavin	Ferguson
Gough/p	Condon	Filipo/t	Scott	Yates	Taylor	Baldwin	Ferguson	Lavin	Wilson
Gough/t3c3p	Tinsdale	Filipo	McIntyre	Yates	Taylor	Baldwin	Jones/t	Lavin	Wilson/t
Gough/cp	Tinsdale	Filipo	McIntyre/t	Yates	Baldwin	Taylor	Jones	Lavin	Wilson
Wallwork	Condon	Cassidy	Scott	Yates	Taylor	Baldwin	Jones	Bradwell	Wilson/t
Wallwork	Condon	Filipo	Scott	Yates	Taylor	Baldwin	Jones/2t	Bradwell(c/t)	Wilson
Wallwork	Condon	Filipo	Scott	Yates	Taylor	Baldwin	O'Grady	Jones	Wilson
Wallwork	Condon	Cassidy	Williams	Yates	O'Neill	Baldwin	O'Grady	Bradwell	Wilson
Wallwork/t	Condon	Filipo	McIntyre	Yates	Taylor	Baldwin	O'Grady	Jones	Wilson
Gough	Condon	Filipo	Scott	Yates	O'Neill	Baldwin	O'Grady	Jones/t	Wilson/t
Gough	Condon	Filipo	Scott	Yates	O'Neill	Baldwin	Ferguson	Lavin	Wilson/t
Gough	Condon	Filipo	Scott	Yates	O'Grady	Baldwin	Tasker	McIntyre	Wilson
Wallwork	Condon/t	Filipo	McIntyre	Yates	O'Neill	Baldwin	Tasker	O'Grady/t	Peters/t
Wallwork	Condon	Filipo	McIntyre/t	Yates	Taylor	Baldwin	Ferguson	O'Grady/2t	Peters
Wallwork	Condon	Filipo	McIntyre	Yates	Taylor	Baldwin/t	Ferguson	O'Grady	Wilson
Wallwork	Condon	Filipo	McIntyre/2t	Yates	Taylor	Baldwin	Ferguson	O'Grady	Wilson/t
Wiseman	Condon	Filipo	McIntyre	Yates	Taylor	Baldwin	Bradwell	O'Grady	Wilson
Wiseman/t	Condon	Filipo	McIntyre	Yates	Taylor	Baldwin	Bradwell	O'Grady	Wilson
Wiseman	Condon	Filipo	Scott	Yates	Atkinson	Baldwin	Tasker	O'Grady	Wilson
Wallwork	Condon	Filipo	McIntyre	Webster	Atkinson	Baldwin	Bradwell	O'Grady/t	Wilson
Moffatt/3c2p	Wallwork	Filipo	McIntyre/t	Yates	Atkinson	Baldwin	Bradwell	Wilson/t	O'Grady/t
Wallwork	Condon/t	Filipo	McIntyre	Yates	Atkinson/t	Baldwin	Bradwell	Wilson/t	O'Grady
Wallwork	Condon/t	Webster/t	McIntyre	Yates	Baldwin	Taylor	Bradwell	O'Grady	Wilson/t
Gough/2cp	Condon/t	Filipo	McIntyre/t	Webster	Taylor	Baldwin	Jones/t	Lavin/t	Wilson
Wallwork	Condon	Cassidy	Scott	Yates	Taylor	Baldwin	Bradwell	Lavin	Wilson

REPLACEMENTS: a - Craig McIntyre. b - David Wiseman. c - Dylan O'Grady. d - Steve Gough.

WHERE	**Total**	**Home**	**Away**
The POINTS were scored	462	245	217
The POINTS were conceded	549	305	244
The TRIES were scored	60	34	26
The TRIES were conceded	60	36	24

HOW the TRIES were scored

Total	Backs	Forwards	F Back	Wing	Centre	H Back	F Row	Lock	B Row	Pen. Try
60	25	32	1	13	5	6	11	2	19	3

HOW the TRIES were conceded

Total	Backs	Forwards	F Back	Wing	Centre	H Back	F Row	Lock	B Row	Pen. Try
60	44	14	9	15	7	13	3	4	7	2

FYLDE

LEAGUE STATISTICS

compiled by Stephen McCormack

SEASON	Division	P	W	D	L	F	A	Pts Diff	Lge Pts	Lge Pos	Most Points	Most Tries
92-93	2	12	0	3	9	108	290	-182	0	12r	40 Mike Jackson	2 Steve Gough & John Nicholson
93-94	3	18	13	0	5	339	219	120	26	2p	109 Andy Parker	12 Brendan Hanavan
94-95	2	18	8	0	10	250	329	-79	16	9r	91 Andy Parker	5 Brendan Hanavan, Steve Gough & Greg Anderton
95-96	3	18	3	1	14	283	448	-165	7	10	138 Steve Gough	5 Greg Anderton
96-97	3	30	24	1	5	813	439	374	49	2p	404 Steve Gough	20 Mark Preston
97-98	P2	22	2	0	20	258	710	-452	4	12	98 Steve Gough	6 Mark Preston
98-99	P2	26	4	1	21	375	805	-430	9	14r	72 Alun Peacock	6 Mark Evans Carl Lavin
99-00	JN1	26	10	1	15	387	485	-98	21	9	194 Nick Booth	6 Richard Kenyon Greg Anderton
00-01	N2	26	11	1	14	377	594	-217	21(-2)	10	84 Ben Godfrey	7 Greg Anderton
01-02	N2	26	14	0	12	462	549	-87	28	5	112 Ben Godfrey	8 Brent Wilson

BIGGEST MARGINS

Home Win	61pts - 68-7 v Birmingham 7.11.87
Away Win	47pts - 60-13 v Havant 15.2.97
Home Defeat	60pts - 7-67 v Bedford 27.12.97
Away Defeat	65pts - 7-72 v Rugby 6.4.01

MOST CONSECUTIVE

Appearances	41 Andy Parker 12.3.94 to date
Matches scoring Tries	4 Greg Anderton
Matches scoring points	20 Steve Burnage
Victories	9
Defeats	7

MOST POINTS

Scored at Home	68 v Birmingham 7.11.87
Scored Away	60 v Havant 15.2.97
Conceded at Home	67 v Bedford 27.12.97
Conceded Away	72 v Wharfedale 23.9.00 & Rugby

MOST TRIES

Scored in a match	10 v Birmingham 7.11.87 (H) v Redruth 9.4.94 (H)
Conceded in a match	10 v West Hartlepool 14.2.98

MOST APPEARANCES

by a forward	168 (9) John Taylor
by a back	148(2) Ian Barclay

	MOST IN A SEASON	MOST IN A CAREER	MOST IN A MATCH	
Points	404 Steve Gough 96-97	739 Steve Gough 92-98	28 Steve Burnage	v Birmingham 7.11.87 (H)
Tries	20 Mark Preston 96-97	41 Brendan Hanavan 87-96	4 Brendan Hanavan	v Exeter 3.10.87 (H) v Birmingham 7.11.87 (H) v Redruth 9.4.94 (H)
Conversions	57 Steve Gough 96-97	85 Steve Gough 92-98	9 Steve Burnage	v Birmingham 7.11.87 (H)
Penalties	82 Steve Gough 96-97	143 Steve Gough 92-98	6 Steve Gough	v Walsall 21.9.96 (H) v Morley 25.1.97 (A)
Drop Goals	5 Ian Barclay 94-95	7 Ian Barclay 87-95	2 Ian Barclay	v Waterloo 25.3.95 (A)

OVERALL PLAYING RECORD

	P	W	D	L	F	A	Pts Diff
Home	20	14	0	6	363	242	121
Away	25	10	0	15	412	533	-121
Neutral	-	-	-	-	-	-	-
Total	45	24	0	21	775	775	0

SEASON BY SEASON

1971-72	DNQ
1972-73	DNQ
1973-74	DNQ
1974-75	DNQ
1975-76	DNQ
1976-77	QF
1977-78	DNQ
1978-79	DNQ
1979-80	1R
1980-81	3R
1981-82	DNQ
1982-83	3R
1983-84	2R
1984-85	DNQ
1985-86	DNQ
1986-87	2R
1987-88	2R
1988-89	2R
1989-90	3R
1990-91	2R
1991-92	3R
1992-93	3R
1993-94	5R
1994-95	5R
1995-96	3R
1996-97	3R
1997-98	5R
1998-99	3R
1999-2000	2R
2000-01	3R
2001-02	4R

FYLDE
RFU SENIOR CUP
STATISTICS
compiled by Stephen McCormack

TEAM RECORDS

Highest Score
48 v Aspatria 97/98
Biggest Winning Margin
43 (48-5) v Aspatria 97/98
Highest Score Against
60 v Bedford Athletic 99/00
Biggest Losing Margin
42 (55-13) v Sale 94/95

INDIVIDUAL RECORDS

Most Points in a match
18 Steve Gough v Aspatria 97/98
Most Tries in a match

Most Conversions in a match
5 Steve Gough v Aspatria 97/98
Most Penalties in a match

Most Drop Goals in a match

PLAYERS FYLDE

	Position	D.o.B.	Apps.	Pts.	T	C	P	DG
Mark Evans	Centre	21.02.75	110(5)	80	16	-	-	-
Richard Kenyon	Fly half	23.02.80	57(14)	83	9	7	8	-
Tom Kerr	Winger		6	-	-	-	-	-
Ben Trend	Winger		7	-	-	-	-	-
Laurence Condon	Scrum half	09.06.72	64(3)	40	8	-	-	-
Ben Godfrey	Centre	08.07.81	36(1)	196	9	26	32	1
Phil Hassan	Centre		15(1)	5	1	-	-	-
Gareth Davies	Centre	02.08.73	19	10	2	-	-	-
Stuart Connell	Centre	17.04.67	80(6)	8	2	-	-	-
David Wiseman	Fly half	20.09.80	38(4)	89	6	7	14	1
Alan Yates	Prop		25	-	-	-	-	-
Martin Scott	Hooker	05.07.67	83(14)	40	8	-	-	-
Matt Filipo	Prop	28.10.71	48	20	4	-	-	-
Mike Bradwell	Back row	04.05.80	18(11)	-	-	-	-	-
Jon Taylor	Lock	05.10.66	185(7)	45	9	-	-	-
Dylan O'Grady	Back row	19.11.71	57(5)	70	14	-	-	-

FYLDE

FACT FILE

Founded: 1919

Colours: Claret, gold and white/white/claret
Change colours: Maroon

GROUND

Address: Woodlands Memorial Ground, Blackpool Road, Ansdell, Lytham St. Annes. FY8 4EL
Tel: 01253 734733 Fax:
Capacity: 5,440 Seated: 440 Standing: 5,000

Directions: From the end of the M55 follow signs for Lytham St. Annes -B5230 then B5261 onto Queensway - ground is three miles on the left opposite Blossoms P.H. and R.C. Church.
Nearest Railway Station: Ansdell & Fairhaven. Left outside station, down the hill away from the sea, along Woodlands Rd to T junction (R.C. Church & Blossoms PH) - ground is opposite to the right.

Car Parking: 150 spaces available F.O.C. at the ground.

Admission: (Standing only)
Matchdays Non members £8, OAPs £4; Members £6, OAPs £5.
Season tickets Members only £60 OAPs £35.

Club Shop: Open matchdays 1-6pm & Sundays 10-Noon.
Contact D Walsh 01253 729253.

Clubhouse: Open matchdays Noon-11, Sun Noon-3, Tue,Thur, Fri 7.30-11pm. 3 bars.
Snacks and bar meals available.
Functions: Approx 400
Contact D Walsh 01253 729253.
Training Nights: Tuesday and Thursday.

PROGRAMME

Size: A5 Pages: 40
Price: Free with admission
Editor: Malcolm Jones, Commercial Manager 01253 739731

ADVERTISING RATES

Full page: Colour £650 Two Tone £450
1/2 page Colour £350 Two Tone £250
1/4 page: Colour £200 Two Tone £150
Back page (teams): Colour £650

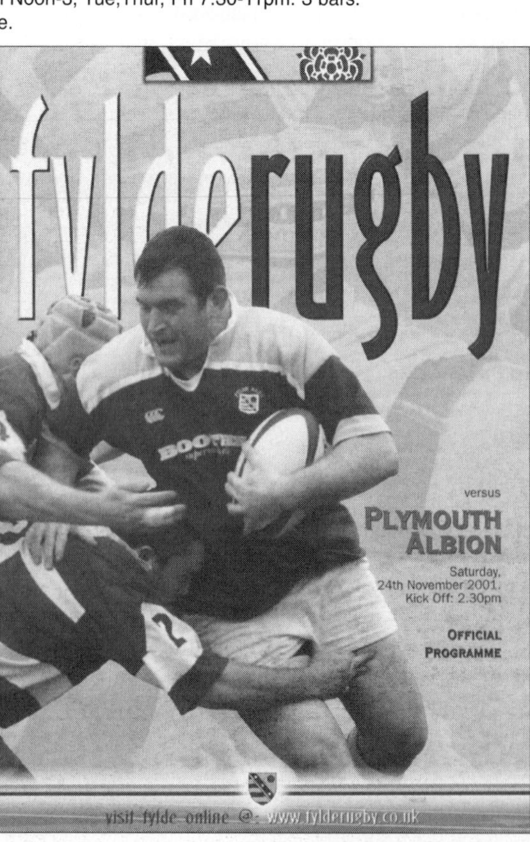

HARROGATE RUFC

President	Roy Guy	4 Southway, Harrogate HG2 0CA 01423 503054
Chairman	Frank Carter	6 Blackthorn Lane, Burn Bridge, Harrogate HG3 1NW 01423 870654
Club Secretary	Ian Gair	Glenshee, Spofforth Lane, Follifoot, Harrogate HG3 7EG 01423 871743
Treasurer	Nic Davies	3 Hereford Road, Harrogate HG1 2NP 01423 522066
Fixtures Secretary	Bill Barrack	15 Eastgate Close, Bramhope, Leeds LS16 9AR 0113 284 2540

Under the captaincy of Rhys Morgan and the coaching of Ralph Zoing and Martin Pepper the 2001/2002 season saw Harrogate reach their highest ever finish in the National League Two (fourth), being separated by Sedgley Park from the powerfully backed sides from Orrell and Plymouth.

League highlights of the season started with a first ever win against Newbury at their home ground, and at Claro Road high scoring and entertaining wins against Waterloo 48-32 and Wharfedale 51-36.

Lows of the season were the losses against Rosslyn Park at home 29-36, and Kendal away 32-14. The long trip to Plymouth in November, where Harrogate played a lot better than the 57-3 score line suggested, was a watershed in the First Team's form and application. From the first weekend in December we played far better at home than away, winning twelve of the remaining seventeen games. Narrow reverses against Orrell, Plymouth and Sedgley Park (all at home), when we led in all three, finally dented our promotion hopes.

Away from the league, the defeat in the first round of the National Cup away at New Brighton was disappointing, but Harrogate went on to win the Yorkshire Cup for the first time in ten years, as two splendid victories were achieved en route against newly promoted Doncaster, and local Nat. 1 team Otley in the semi final. Wharfedale were beaten 24-7 in the final.

Harrogate also provided the entire Yorkshire 7-a-side squad to the Tetley's County 7's competition for the second year in succession. As Northern Champions through the knock out stage, we then beat last year's winners Middlesex in the semi-final and Cornwall 42-26 at Twickenham on finals day to cap a great season.

Next season is looked forward to with relish for all at Claro Road.

DAVE OSWIN

HARROGATE

Comp.	Date	H/A	Opponents	Result & Score	Att	15	14	13	12	11
N2	01-09	A	Newbury	W 38-20		Smithies/2t	Farrar/t	Duncombe	Sarjaent/t	Marr
N2	08-09	H	Waterloo*	W 48-32	487	Smithies	Farrar	Duncombe	Sarjaent	Marr/t
N2	15-09	A	Fylde	L 9-13		Smithies	Farrar	Duncombe	Sarjaent	Marr
N2	22-09	H	Wharfedale	W 51-36		Smithies/2t	Farrar	Duncombe	Sarjaent	Marr/t
N2	06-10	A	Sedgley Park	L 27-33	325	Smithies	Farrar/t	Duncombe	Sarjaent	Shackleton/t
N2	20-10	H	Rosslyn Park	L 29-36		Smithies	Farrar/t	Duncombe	Sarjaent	Marr
N2	27-10	A	Kendal	L 14-32		Smithies	Farrar	Duncombe	Sarjaent	Marr
N2	10-11	H	Nottingham	W 25-16		Smithies/t	Barker	Duncombe	Sarjaent	Marr
N2	17-11	A	Plymouth Albion	L 3-57	1500	Smithies	Barker	Duncombe	Sarjaent	Marr
N2	24-11	A	Esher	W 24-12		Smithies	Clayton/t	Barker/t	Duncombe	Marr
N2	01-12	H	Newbury	W 29-19		Smithies/2t	Clayton	Barker/t	Duncombe/t	Marr
N2	08-12	A	Stourbridge	W 39-21	200	Smithies	Clayton	Barker	Duncombe/t	Marr/t
N2	15-12	H	Preston Grasshoppers	W 53-3	402	Smithies/t	Clayton	Barker/t	Duncombe	Marr
N2	12-01	H	Plymouth Albion	L 15-21	570	Smithies/t	Clayton/t	Barker	Duncombe	Marr
N2	19-01	A	Nottingham*	W 24-5		Smithies	Clayton/t	Barker/t	Duncombe	Marr
N2	26-01	H	Kendal*	W 25-12	493	Smithies	Clayton	Barker	Duncombe	Marr
N2	02-02	A	Rosslyn Park	W 20-17		Smithies/t	Clayton	Barker	Duncombe	Marr
N2	09-02	H	Sedgley Park	L 10-13	487	Smithies	Clayton	Duncombe	Sarjaent	Marr
N2	16-02	H	Esher	W 34-23	263	Smithies	Clayton	Barker	Duncombe	Sarjaent/3t
N2	23-02	A	Wharfedale	D 6-6		Smithies	Clayton	Barker	Duncombe	Sarjaent
N2	02-03	A	Orrell	L 24-40	700	Smithies	Clayton	Barker/t	Duncombe	Sarjaent
N2	09-03	H	Fylde	W 43-0	317	Smithies/t	Clayton	Barker	Duncombe	Sarjaent
N2	16-03	A	Waterloo	W 26-21		Smithies	Clayton/t	Barker	Duncombe	Sarjaent
N2	30-03	H	Orrell	L 21-29	722	Smithies	Marr	Barker	Duncombe/t	Sarjaent
N2	06-04	A	Preston Grasshoppers	W 62-24	95	Smithies/t	Farrar/4t	Duncombe	Sarjaent	Barker/t
N2	13-04	H	Stourbridge	W 45-15	329	Smithies	Farrar	Duncombe/t	Sarjaent(e/t)	Barker
PGC	29-09	A	New Brighton	L 5-13		Smithies	Farrar	Manson	Sarjaent	Marr/t

** after opponents name indicates a penalty try. Brackets after a player's name indicates he was replaced. eg (a) means he was replaced by replacement code "a" and so on. / after a player or replacement name is followed by any scores he made - eg /t, /c, /p, /dg or any combination of these*

EVER PRESENT **3** as below

Most Appearances:
26: Lee Cholewa, Ed Smithies, Richard Melton.

PLAYERS USED

29 plus five as a replacement

MOST POINTS

Pts	Player	T	C	P	DG
284	L Cholewa	7	69	36	1
80	J Dudley	16	-	-	-
65	E SMithies	13	-	-	-
55	R Wade	11	-	-	-
35	M Farrar	7	-	-	-

MATCH FACTS

10	9	1	2	3	4	5	6	7	8
Cholewa/4c	Morgan	Melton	Salkeld	Wilson	Taylor	Clark	Dudley	Worden	Wade/2t
Cholewa/4c	Morgan	Melton/t	Salkeld	Wilson	Taylor	Fforde	Dudley/2t	Worden/t	Wade/2t
Cholewa/3p	Morgan	Melton	Salkeld	Wilson	Taylor	Clark	Dudley	Worden	Wade
Cholewa/t5cpdg	Morgan	Melton	Salkeld/t	Wilson	Taylor	Clark	Dudley/t	Worden	Wade/t
Cholewa/t2cp	Morgan	Melton	Salkeld	Wilson	Taylor	Clark	Dudley/t	Worden	Wade
Cholewa/t3cp	Morgan	Melton	Salkeld	Wilson	Taylor	Clark	Dudley/2t	Worden	Wade
Cholewa/2c	Morgan(a/t)	Melton	Salkeld	Wilson	Taylor	Clark	Dudley	Worden	Slater/t
Cholewa/2c2p	Morgan	Melton	Erven/t	Hardcastle	Dudley/t	Clark	Salkeld	Worden	Cook
Cholewa/p	Morgan	Melton	Erven	Wilson	Taylor	Dudley	Slater	Worden	Cook
Cholewa/2c	Morgan	Melton	Erven	Wilson	Dudley/t	Slater	Horner/t	Worden	Wade
Cholewa/2c	Morgan	Melton	Erven	Wilson	Dudley/t	Slater	Horner	Worden	Wade
Cholewa/t4c2p	Morgan	Melton	Salkeld	Wilson	Dudley/t	Taylor	Worden	Hobson	Wade/t
Cholewa/2t6c2p	Morgan	Melton/t	Salkeld	Wilson	Dudley/t	Taylor	Slater	Hobson	Wade/t
Cholewa/cp	Shackleton	Melton	Salkeld	Wilson	Dudley	Taylor	Slater	Dawson	Wade
Cholewa/2c	Morgan	Melton	Salkeld	Wilson/t	Dudley	Taylor	Horner	Slater	Wade
Cholewa/2c2p	Morgan	Melton	Salkeld	Wilson/t	Dudley	Taylor	Slater	Worden	Wade/t
Cholewa/t2c2p	Morgan	Melton	Salkeld	S Wilson	Dudley	Taylor	Slater	Worden	Wade
Cholewa/cp	Morgan/t	Melton	Salkeld	Wilson	Dudley	Taylor	Worden	Hobson	Wade
Cholewa/4c2p	Morgan	Melton	Salkeld	Wilson	Dudley	Taylor	Worden	Hobson	Cook(b/t)
Cholewa/2p	Morgan	Melton	Salkeld	Wilson	Dudley	Taylor	Slater	Worden	Cook
Cholewa/c4p	Morgan	Melton	Salkeld	Wilson	Dudley/t	Taylor	Cook	Worden	Wade
Cholewa/t2c3p	Morgan	Melton	Salkeld	Wilson	Dudley	Clark	Slater	Worden/2t	Wade/2t
Cholewa/3c	Morgan	Melton	Erven	Wilson	Dudley/2t	Clark	Worden/t	Slater	Wade
Cholewa/c3p	Morgan	Melton	Salkeld	Wilson	Clark	Taylor	Worden	Hobson	Wade(c/t)
Cholewa/7cp	Morgan	Melton	Erven	Wilson	Dudley/t	Clark	Worden	Hobson/t	Cook/t
Cholewa/t6cp	Morgan	Melton	Salkeld	Wilson	Dudley/t	Clark	Cook	Worden/t	Wade(d/t)
Quick	Morgan	Melton	Erven	R Wilson	Taylor	Clark	Dudley	Worden	Wade

REPLACEMENTS: a - Jaime Barker. b - Richard Wade. c - Oliver Cook. d - Steve Hobson. e - Paul Clayton.

WHERE	Total	Home	Away
The POINTS were scored	744	428	316
The POINTS were conceded	556	301	255
The TRIES were scored	100	58	42
The TRIES were conceded	74	41	33

HOW the TRIES were scored

Total	Backs	Forwards	F Back	Wing	Centre	H Back	F Row	Lock	B Row	Pen. Try
100	52	45	12	21	9	10	7	10	28	3

HOW the TRIES were conceded

Total	Backs	Forwards	F Back	Wing	Centre	H Back	F Row	Lock	B Row	Pen. Try
74	43	29	5	16	15	7	6	8	12	2

HARROGATE

LEAGUE STATISTICS

compiled by Stephen McCormack

SEASON	Division	P	W	D	L	F	A	Pts Diff	Lge Pts	Lge Pos	Most Points	Most Tries
92-93	D4N	12	10	1	1	363	115	248	21	1	131 Ralph Zoing	9 Steve Baker Guy Easterby
93-94	4	18	14	2	2	479	219	260	30	2	105 Ralph Zoing	13 Jeremy Hopkinson
94-95	3	18	7	2	9	275	404	-129	16	7	110 Dan Clappison	7 Rob Bell
95-96	3	18	6	3	9	333	387	-54	15	6	215 Ralph Zoing	5 Richard Marcroft
96-97	3	30	18	0	12	832	595	237	36	5	305 Ralph Zoing	13 Rob Bell, Mike Farrar & Kerry Morley
97-98	JN1	26	4	1	21	463	707	-244	9	14	79 Neil James	10 Lee Feurer
98-99	JN1	26	8	2	16	309	461	-152	18	12	61 Ralph Zoing	5 Mark Farrar
99-00	JN1	26	14	1	11	508	449	59	29	6	190 Matt Duncombe	11 Ed Smithies
00-01	N1	26	14	2	10	617	422	195	30	5	161 Lee Cholewa	17 Ed Smithies
01-02	N2	26	16	1	9	744	556	188	33	4	284 Lee Cholewa	16 John Dudley

BIGGEST MARGINS

Home Win	72pts - 79-7 v Clifton 5.4.97
Away Win	56pts - 70-14 v W Hartlepool 13.01.01
Home Defeat	54pts - 12-66 v Leeds 21.3.98
Away Defeat	47pts - 3-50 v Worcester 31.1.98

MOST CONSECUTIVE

Appearances	49 Rob Bell 9.92 -9.9.95
Matches scoring Tries	6 Clive Ware
Matches scoring points	24 Ralph Zoing
Victories	5
Defeats	10

MOST POINTS

Scored at Home	79 v Clifton 5.4.97
Scored Away	70 v W Hartlepool 13.1.01
Conceded at Home	66 v Leeds 21.3.98
Conceded Away	50 v Worcester 31.1.98

MOST TRIES

Scored in a match	14 v Aspatria 30.4.94
Conceded in a match	10 v Leeds 21.3.98 (H)

MOST APPEARANCES

by a forward	184(4) Peter Taylor
by a back	149 (9) Craig Reed

	MOST IN A SEASON	MOST IN A CAREER	MOST IN A MATCH
Points	305 Ralph Zoing 96-97	1086 Ralph Zoing 87-99	27 Ralph Zoing v Fylde 14.10.95 (H)
Tries	17 Ed Smithies 00-01	42 Jeremy Hopkinson 90-98	5 Steve Baker v Lichfield 14.11.92 (H)
Conversions	69 Lee Cholewa 01-02	175 Ralph Zoing 87-99	9 Ralph Zoing v Towcestrians 13.3.93 (H)
Penalties	51 Ralph Zoing 95-96	209 Ralph Zoing 87-99	7 Ralph Zoing v Halifax 18.11.90 (H)
Drop Goals	5 Ralph Zoing 96-97	16 Ralph Zoing 87-99	2 Ralph Zoing v Askeans 20.11.93 (H)

HARROGATE
RFU SENIOR CUP
STATISTICS
compiled by Stephen McCormack

OVERALL PLAYING RECORD

	P	W	D	L	F	A	Pts Diff
Home	14	7	0	7	323	244	79
Away	11	2	0	9	152	178	-26
Neutral	-	-	-	-	-	-	-
Total	25	9	0	16	475	422	53

SEASON BY SEASON

Season	Result
1971-72	DNQ
1972-73	DNQ
1973-74	DNQ
1974-75	DNQ
1975-76	DNQ
1976-77	DNQ
1977-78	DNQ
1978-79	DNQ
1979-80	DNQ
1980-81	DNQ
1981-82	3R
1982-83	3R
1983-84	DNQ
1984-85	DNQ
1985-86	DNQ
1986-87	DNQ
1987-88	DNQ
1988-89	1R
1989-90	3R
1990-91	3R
1991-92	2R
1992-93	2R
1993-94	2R
1994-95	4R
1995-96	2R
1996-97	3R
1997-98	2R
1998-99	3R
1999-2000	2R
2000-01	2R
2001-02	2R

TEAM RECORDS

Highest Score
61 v Nuneaton 91/92

Biggest Winning Margin
57 (61-4) v Nuneaton 91/92

Highest Score Against
42 v Esher 98/99

Biggest Losing Margin
33 (33-0) v Sale 94/95

INDIVIDUAL RECORDS

Most Points in a match

Most Tries in a match

Most Conversions in a match

Most Penalties in a match

Most Drop Goals in a match

PLAYERS

	Position	D.o.B.	Apps.	Pts.	T	C	P	DG
Ed Smithies	Full back	25.05.74	78	195	39	-	-	-
Jeremy Marr	Winger	22.09.72	18(1)	15	3	-	-	-
Graeme Sarjaent	Winger	25.09.75	40(5)	35	7	-	-	-
Jamie Barker	Centre		18(1)	30	6	-	-	-
Matt Duncombe	Centre	27.08.75	73(2)	241	15			
Lee Cholewa	Fly half	12.05.78	51	445	10	100	64	1
Rhys Morgan	Scrum half	30.07.67	88(1)	90	18	-	-	-
Mark Farrar	Winger	27.07.68	109(11)	230	46	-	-	-
Paul Clayton	Winger	31.12.74	33(4)	45	9	-	-	-
Ian Salkeld	Hooker	08.06.71	75	20	4	-	-	-
Richard Melton	Prop		26	10	2	-	-	-
Rob Wilson	Prop	27.08.80	27(14)	-	-	-	-	-
Scott Wilson	Prop	14.01.72	147(9)	20	4	-	-	-
Paul Clark	Lock	30.05.73	55	10	2	-	-	-
Peter Taylor	Lock	13.01.71	187(4)	115	20	-	-	-
John Dudley	Lock	16.07.66	41	110	22	-	-	-
Mike Worden	Back row	26.05.76	77(8)	60	12	-	-	-
Richard Wade	Back row	07.11.76	40(8)	85	17	-	-	-
Steve Hobson	Back row		27(1)	27	3	3	2	-
Chris Horner	Back row		3(4)	5	1	-	-	-
Rijan Slater	Back row	08.01.78	12(1)	5	1	-	-	-

HARROGATE

FACT FILE

Founded: 1871
Nickname: Gate
Web site: harrogaterufc.or.uk

Colours: Red, amber & black
Change colours: Red

GROUND

Address: The County Ground, Claro Road, Harrogate. HG1 4AG.
Tel : 01423 566966 Fax: 01423 509073 E-mail: hrufc@lineone.net
Capacity: 2,999 Seated: 4990 Standing: 2,500

Directions: Claro Road is on the north side of the A59 (York Skipton road), just off the Stray (open grassed area adjacent to the town centre).
Nearest Railway Station: Harrogate, exit to East Parade turn left, right onto Parkview continues into Kingsway & Walkers passage, cross Stray to Claro Rd (10mins).

Car Parking: 400 at the ground, unlimited nearby

Admission **Matchday:** £6

Club Shop: Matchdays only.
Contact Pam Oswin 01423 871905.

Clubhouse: Mon - Fri 7-11, Sat 11-11, Sun 10-2,
bar meals available.
Functions: Up to 120, contact Mick Lancaster at club

Training Nights: Tuesday and Thursday

PROGRAMME Size: A5 Pages: 32 Price: £1
Editor: Stuart Young 01423 500263

ADVERTISING RATES Mono (Contact Club)
Full page £300
1/2 page £160
1/4 page £90

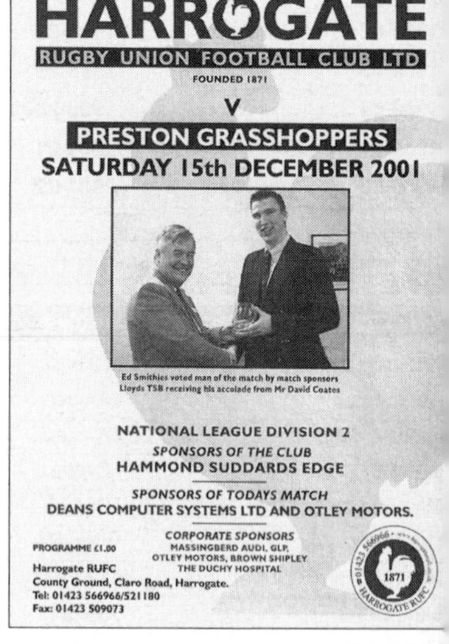

Action from the Wharfedale versus Harrogate match last season.
Photo: Quinn Evans

HENLEY HAWKS

President	Doug Ash	c/o Henley RFC, Dry Leas, Marlow Road, Henley-on-Thames RG9 2JA Tel: 01491 574499 Fax: 01491 412335
Chairman	Graham Horner	c/o Henley RFC, as above
Commercial Director/ General Manager	Martin Unsworth	c/o Henley RFC, as above
Press Officer	Noel Armstead	8 Chiswick Lodge, Liston Rd, Marlow, Bucks SL7 1AG 01628 474398 (B & Fax). e-mail: scoop.hrfc@virgin.net
1st XV Coach	Nigel Dudding	01491 576502 Mobile 07710 110654

For the first time since competitive leagues were introduced Henley Hawks finished in a lower position than they had started the season. They did this with a resounding thump falling from 7th place in National 1 to 13th and with it relegation.

They did not recover from a poor start whereby they lost their first six league matches and, crucially, as it turned out, amongst these was a home defeat, in injury time, to local rivals Bracknell who turned out also to be doomed to relegation.

The loss of five of their more experienced and gifted players viz Duncan Roke (transferred to Worcester),skipper Steve Barnes (cruciate ligament injury),Jerry Sampson and Willie Phillips (both retired) and Matt Jones (unavailable unitl December) proved vital as did the lack of early season fitness. National 1, all agreed, was far more competitive than in previous seasons with more clubs finding funds to engage full time professionals with which the comparatively modestly funded Henley could not compete, which was compounded by the dropping of 'the pilot', Tony Macarthur as Director of Rugby because of financial reasons.

Nevertheless there was a revival in the autumn when four out of five matches were won but two of these were in the Powergen Cup (posthumously named) and co-incided with the return of the 'retired' Willie Phillips.

Unfortunately he could not work his magic for long, despite a total of 8 appearances, and the post-Christmas period saw nine league defeats on the trot. Crucially some of these were lost in the last quarter of the game and against London Welsh at Old Deer Park in time added on for injuries!

The squad was strengthened at the beginning of 2002 with the advent of US Eagles lock Philippe Farner, Michael McNair (Australian Schools) Pete Nicholas, the Oxford University hooker, and the return of Matt Jones and Des Brett, the latter from Cambridge. Although hampered by injuries to Mark Venner and Jones, causing them to miss vital games, the 'great escape' was nearly achieved with three victories, including the important scalp of Exeter Chiefs at Dry Leas, and a draw in the last six games, but that all important additional victory, which would have sealed Manchester's fate, over whom they did the double, eluded them.

With Nigel Dudding, who steered them through their promotion seasons, back as head coach, Jim McKay having left for Birmingham/Solihull, the Hawks are determined to bounce back and with 20 of last year's squad available aim to show that they were too good to be relegated, as they were told so many times by their opponents last season.

HENLEY HAWKS

Comp.	Date	H/A	Opponents	Result & Score	Att	15	14	13	12	11
N1	01-09	H	London Welsh	L 9-24	1150	Barlow	Rowland	Tuivai	Van Zyl	Holloway
N1	08-09	A	Coventry	L 8-24		Barnes	Rowland/t	Osman	Tuivai	Holloway
N1	15-09	H	Worcester	L 0-31	950	Barnes	Rowland	Osman	Tuivai	Holloway
N1	22-09	A	Otley	L 13-55		Barnes/c2p	Rowland	Osman/t	Tuivai	Holloway
N1	29-09	H	Bracknell	L 24-26	1000	Fabian	Rowland/2t	Osman	Van Zyl	Davies
N1	06-10	A	Bedford	L 9-44	1182	Fabian	Holloway	Osman	Van Zyl	Davies
N1	20-10	H	Rugby Lions	W 15-12	300	Fabian/5p	Holloway	Osman	Van Zyl	Davies
N1	10-11	H	Moseley	L 24-29		Fabian/c4p	Rowland	Osman	Van Zyl	Davies
N1	17-11	A	Manchester	W 26-25	400	Fabian/2t2c3p	Rowland	Osman	Van Zyl	Davies
N1	01-12	H	Birmingham & Solihull	L 20-26	300	Fabian/2c2p	Dixon	Osman	Van Zyl	Davies/t
N1	08-12	H	Wakefield	W 20-13	550	Fabian/5p	Rowland	Stebbings	Van Zyl	Davies
N1	29-12	A	Rotherham	L 6-48		Fabian/p	Rowland	Osman	Jones/p	Davies
N1	12-01	H	Coventry	L 18-22	700	Fabian/c2p	Rowland	Osman	Van Zyl	Davies/t
N1	19-01	A	Worcester	L 17-66		Fabian/2cp	Rowland	Osman/t	Jones	McNair/t
N1	26-01	H	Otley	L 12-22	350	Fabian/4p	Rowland	Osman	Van Zyl	Davies
N1	03-02	A	Bracknell	L 6-13	600	Fabian/2p	Rowland	Osman	Van Zyl	Davies
N1	09-02	H	Bedford	L 25-37	1200	Fabian/2c2p	Rowland	Van Zyl/t	Jones	McNair
N1	16-02	A	Exeter	L 23-43	487	Fabian/2c2p	Rowland	Van Zyl/t	Jones/dg	Davies
N1	23-02	A	Rugby Lions	L 13-25		Fabian/c2p	Rowland	Van Zyl	Jones	Davies
N1	02-03	A	London Welsh	L 20-33	400	Fabian/cp	Holloway	Erinlee/t	Van Zyl/t	Davies/t
N1	09-03	H	Exeter*	W 28-19	550	Fabian/2c3p	Holloway	Erinlee/t	Van Zyl	Davies
N1	16-03	A	Moseley	W 26-21	300	Fabian/3c	McNair	Erinlee	Van Zyl	Davies/t
N1	30-03	H	Manchester	W 45-20	850	Fabian/4c3p	McNair	Erinlee/t	Van Zyl/t	Davies/t
N1	06-04	A	Birmingham & Solihull	L 9-22		Fabian/3p	McNair	Erinlee	Van Zyl	Davies
N1	13-04	A	Wakefield	D 13-13	250	Fabian/c2p	McNair	Erinlee/t	Van Zyl	Rowland
N1	27-04	H	Rotherham	L 20-54	1325	McNair	Rowland/t	Erinlee	Van Zyl(b/t)	Davies/t
PGC	13-10	H	Liverpool St Helens	W 54-14		Fabian/t(c/c)	Holloway	Osman	Van Zyl/t	Davies/2t
PGC	03-11	H	Otley	W 48-30	300	Fabian/t5cp	Rowland/t	Osman	Van Zyl/2t	Davies/t
PGC	24-11	A	Birmingham & Solihull	L 22-35		Fabian/c4p	Rowland	Osman	Van Zyl	Davies

** after opponents name indicates a penalty try. Brackets after a player's name indicates he was replaced. eg (a) means he was replaced by replacement code "a" and so on. / after a player or replacement name is followed by any scores he made - eg /t, /c, /p, /dg or any combination of these*

EVER PRESENT None

Most Appearances:
23: James Winterbottom.
21: Ricardo Van Zyl, Jon Fabian.
20: Jeff Atkinson (2).

PLAYERS USED

41 plus six as a replacement

MOST POINTS

Pts	Player	T	C	P	DG
199	J Fabian	2	24	47	-
58	B Reeves	4	1	11	1
30	P Davies	6	-	-	-
20	J Atkinson	4	-	-	-
20	A Erinlee	4	-	-	-
20	B Rowland	4	-	-	-
20	R Van ZYl	4	-	-	-

MATCH FACTS

10	9	1	2	3	4	5	6	7	8
Reeves/3p	Smaje	Hannan	Harbinson	Hall	Moxon	Winterbottom	Street	Venner	Metcalfe
Reeves/p	Smaje	Hannan	Harbinson	Hall	Moxon	Winterbottom	Street	Pegna	Metcalfe
Reeves	Ayers	Hannan	Hall	Brett	Moxon	Tyler	Metcalfe	Pegna	Mortimore
Reeves	Smaje	Hannan	Hall	Brett	Moxon	Pettermerides	Metcalfe	Venner	Mortimore
Reeves/c4p	Ayers	Hannan	Hall	Brett	Sampson	Pettermerides	Metcalfe	Venner	Mortimore
Reeves/3p	Ayers	Hannan	Harbinson	Hall	Winterbottom	Pettermerides	Metcalfe	Venner	Mortimore
Osman	Ayers	Fuller	Phillips	Hall	Pettermerides	Winterbottom	Atkinson	Venner	Mortimore
Reeves	Ayers	Fuller	Phillips	Hall	Pettermerides	Winterbottom	Atkinson/t	Venner	Mortimore/t
Reeves/dg	Ayers	Fuller	Phillips	Hall	Pettermerides	Winterbottom	Atkinson	Venner	Mortimore
Reeves	Ayers	Fuller	Phillips	Hall	Pettermerides	Winterbottom	Atkinson	Venner/t	Mortimore
Jones	Ayers/t	Fuller	Phillips	Hall	Pettermerides	Winterbottom	Atkinson	Venner	Mortimore
Reeves	Ayers	Fuller	Hall	Brett	Pettermerides	Winterbottom	Atkinson	Venner	Mortimore
Jones	Ayers	Fuller	Hall	Brett	Farner	Winterbottom	Atkinson	Venner/t	Mortimore
Reeves	Smye	Hannan	Hall	Brett	Farner	Winterbottom	Atkinson	Venner	Metcalfe
Jones	Ayers	Hannan	Hall	Brett	Farner	Winterbottom	Miall	Atkinson	Fryday
Jones	Smaje	Hannan	Hall	Brett	Farner	Winterbottom	Miall	Atkinson	Fryday
Reeves/t	Ayers	Hannan	Nicholas	Brett	Farner	Winterbottom	Atkinson	Venner/t	Fryday
Reeves/t	Ayers	Fuller	Nicholas	Brett	Farner	Winterbottom	Atkinson	Venner	Fryday
Reeves/t	Ayers	Hannan	Nicholas	Nwume	Farner	Winterbottom	Atkinson	Venner	Fryday
Reeves	Ayers	Hannan	Nicholas	Brett	Farner	Winterbottom	Atkinson	Venner	Mortimore
Reeves	Ayers	Hannan	Hall	Brett	Farner	Winterbottom	Atkinson/t	Venner	Mortimore
Reeves/t	Ayers	Hannan	Nicholas/t	Brett	Winterbottom	Farner	Atkinson/t	Venner	Mortimore
Reeves	Ayers(a/dg)	Hannan	Nicholas	Brett	Farner	Winterbottom/t	Atkinson/t	Venner	Mortimore
Reeves	Smaje	Hannan	Nicholas	Brett	Farner	Winterbottom	Miall	Atkinson	Fryday
Smaje	Ayers	Hannan	Nicholas	Brett	Farner	Winterbottom	Fryday	Atkinson	Mortimore
Jones/cp	Smaje	Hannan	Hall	Brett	Farner	Winterbottom	Fryday	Atkinson	Mortimore
Reeves/4c3p	Ayers/2t	Hall	Phillips	Hannan	Pettermerides	Winterbottom/t	Atkinson	Venner	Mortimore
Reeves	Ayers	Fuller	Phillips	Hall	Pettermerides	Winterbottom	Atkinson	Venner/t	Mortimore/t
Reeves/dg	Ayers	Fuller	Phillips	Hall	Pettermerides	Winterbottom	Metcalfe(d/t)	Atkinson	Mortimore

REPLACEMENTS: a - Dan Smaje. b - Russell Osman. c - Phil Osman. d - Ben Pegna.

WHEN	Total	First Half	Second Half	1/4	2/4	3/4	4/4
The POINTS were scored	449	254	195	111	143	119	76
The POINTS were conceded	767	375	392	183	192	115	277
The TRIES were scored	40	18	22	8	10	15	7
The TRIES were conceded	97	45	52	22	23	12	40

HOW the TRIES were scored

Total	Backs	Forwards	F Back	Wing	Centre	H Back	F Row	Lock	B Row	Pen. Try
40	29	10	2	11	11	5	1	1	8	1

HOW the TRIES were conceded

Total	Backs	Forwards	F Back	Wing	Centre	H Back	F Row	Lock	B Row	Pen. Try
97	61	35	7	27	11	16	11	1	23	1

HENLEY HAWKS

LEAGUE STATISTICS

compiled by Stephen McCormack

SEASON	Division	P	W	D	L	F	A	Pts Diff	Lge Pts	Lge Pos		Coach		Captain
92-93	SW1	12	9	0	3	312	143	169	18	2		C Woodward		
93-94	SW1	12	12	0	0	328	125	203	24	1p		C Woodward		
94-95	D5S	12	5	0	7	190	299	-109	10	9		C Woodward		R Heginbotham
												Most Points		**Most Tries**
95-96	D5S	12	8	0	4	349	192	157	16	3	176	Richard Perkins	10	Richard Perkins
96-97	D4S	26	20	2	4	768	456	312	42	2	140	Matt Maudsley	12	Gavin Sharp Matt Maudsley
97-98	N2S	26	22	0	4	772	384	388	44	2p	204	Nick Buoy	15	Mark Venner
98-99	JN1	26	22	1	3	644	299	345	45	1P	118	Duncan Roke	14	Peter Davies
99-00	P2	26	10	1	15	599	696	-97	21	9	236	Matt Jones	17	Duncan Roke
00-01	N1	26	12	2	12	517	589	-72	62	7	171	Matt Jones	6	Bruce Rowland
01-02	N1	26	15	0	11	580	557	69	5	5	199	John Fabian	6	Peter Davies

BIGGEST MARGINS

Home Win	85pts - 93-8 v Met. Police 28.3.98
Away Win	35pts - 47-12 v Camberley 30.3.96
Home Defeat	36pts - 15-41 v Leeds Tykes 11.3.00
Away Defeat	49pts - 17-66 v Worcester 19.1.02

MOST CONSECUTIVE

Appearances	-
Matches scoring Tries	
Matches scoring points	
Victories	11
Defeats	9

MOST POINTS

Scored at Home	93 v Met. Police 28.3.98
Scored Away	47 v Camberley 30.3.96
Conceded at Home	54 v Rotherham 13.4.02
Conceded Away	66 v Worcester 19.01.02

MOST TRIES

Scored in a match	15 v Met. Police 28.3.98 (H)
Conceded in a match	9 v Worcester 19.1.02 (A)

MOST APPEARANCES

by a forward	139 (13) Willie Phillips
by a back	95 (3) Tom Holloway

	MOST IN A SEASON	MOST IN A CAREER	MOST IN A MATCH
Points	236 Matt Jones 99-00	407 Matt Jones 99-01	34 Chris Spencer v Charlton Park 12.4.97(H)
Tries	17 Duncan Roke 99-00	37 Matt Maudsley 94-99	4 Chris Spencer v Charlton Park 12.4.97 (H)
Conversions	30 Matt Jones 99-00	58 Matt Maudsley 96-00	8 Phil Osman v Met. Police 28.03.98 (H)
Penalties	55 Matt Jones 99-00	97 Matt Jones 99-00	8 Matt Jones v Rugby Lions 15.01.00 (A)
Drop Goals	5 Phil Osman 98-99	8 Phil Osman 97-99	2 Phil Osman v Reading (A)

HENLEY HAWKS
RFU SENIOR CUP
STATISTICS
compiled by Stephen McCormack

OVERALL PLAYING RECORD

	P	W	D	L	F	A	Pts Diff
Home	14	11	0	3	593	205	388
Away	17	7	0	10	327	371	-44
Neutral	-	-	-	-	-	-	-
Total	31	18	0	13	920	576	344

SEASON BY SEASON

Season	Result
1971-72	DNQ
1972-73	DNQ
1973-74	DNQ
1974-75	DNQ
1975-76	DNQ
1976-77	DNQ
1977-78	DNQ
1978-79	DNQ
1979-80	DNQ
1980-81	DNQ
1981-82	DNQ
1982-83	DNQ
1983-84	2R
1984-85	DNQ
1985-86	2R
1986-87	DNQ
1987-88	DNQ
1988-89	DNQ
1989-90	DNQ
1990-91	DNQ
1991-92	DNQ
1992-93	2R
1993-94	4R
1994-95	2R
1995-96	3R
1996-97	3R
1997-98	2R
1998-99	4R
1999-2000	4R
2000-01	3R
2001-02	5R

TEAM RECORDS

Highest Score
100 v Havant 98/99

Biggest Winning Margin
81 (100-19) v Havant 98/99

Highest Score Against
46 v Bristol 93/94

Biggest Losing Margin
40 (46-6) v Bristol 93/94

INDIVIDUAL RECORDS

Most Points in a match

Most Tries in a match

Most Conversions in a match

Most Penalties in a match

Most Drop Goals in a match

PLAYERS

	Position	D.o.B.	Apps.	Pts.	T	C	P	DG
Russell Osman	Centre	17.06.72	44(16)	70	14	-	-	-
John Fabian	Full back		21	199	2	24	47	-
Matt Jones	Fly half		58(4)	418	1	52	99	4
Phil Osman	Fly half	18.12.68	43(5)	131	8	14	13	8
Peter Davies	Winger	01.12.75	62(8)	145	29	-	-	-
Ben Ayers	Scrum half	07.05.74	68(16)	65	13	-	-	-
Liam Smye	Scrum half	18.01.78	24(25)	10	2	-	-	-
Tom Holloway	Winger	16.10.73	33(2)	25	5	-	-	-
Jon Stebbings	Full back	28.10.76	12(11)	70	3			
Ricardo Van Zyl	Centre		35	40	8	-	-	-
Lee Hall	Prop		44(4)	5	1	-	-	-
Willie Phillips	Hooker	16.04.58	139(13)	100	20	-	-	-
Rowan Fuller	Prop		39(28)	5	1	-	-	-
Des Brett	Prop		18(6)	-	-	-	-	-
Colin Hannan	Prop		33(4)	-	-	-	-	-
Jerry Sampson	Lock	04.06.68	121(3)	50	10	-	-	-
James Winterbottom	Lock		69(6)	5	1	-	-	-
Phillipe Farner	Lock		14	-	-	-	-	-
Mark Venner	Back row	14.04.69	120(3)	170	34	-	-	-
Ali Metcalfe	Back row		37(9)	5	1	-	-	-
Jeff Atkinson	Back row		20(2)	20	4	-	-	-

HENLEY HAWKS

FACT FILE

Founded: 1930
Nickname: Hawks

Colours: Gold with navy & dark green hoops
Change colours: Dark green with navy & gold hoops

GROUND

Address: Dry Leas, Marlow Rd, Henley-on-Thames, Oxon RG9 2JA
Tel. 01491 574499 Fax: 01491 412335
Website: www.henleyrugbyclub.org.uk email: admin@henleyrugbyclub.org.uk
Capacity: 3,000 Seated: Covered 120 Standing: Uncovered 2,880

Directions: Centre of Henley follow signs to Marlow, ground on left 100 yards past roundabout
Nearest Railway Station: Henley, follow signs from Town Centre to Marlow - ground 100yds left at start of Marlow Rd. **Car Parking:** 600 at ground

Admission: Season
Standing Adult Members £65, Non-Members £85
Matchday
Standing Adults £8, Seated Adults £11
(Children/OAPs half price)

Clubhouse: Tues, Wed, Thurs eves.
Matchdays incl Sundays.
Snacks & bar meals available.
Functions: Capacity 200

Club Shop: Yes

Training Nights:
Monday, Tuesday, Wednesday, Thursday

PROGRAMME

Size: A5 Pages: 48 Price: £1
Editor: Noel Armstead 01628 474398

ADVERTISING RATES
Inside covers £1000 (colour)
Full page £450 (Mono)
Half page £250 (Mono)

Hawks' centre, Ric Van Zyl, scored seven tries last season.

Photo: John Batty

KENDAL RFC

President	J D Healey	55 Calder Drive, Kendal LA9 6LR. 01539 723913 (H)
Chairman	Ian W Hutton	168 Vicarage Drive, Kendal, Cumbria, LA9 5BX 01539 733152 (H), 01539 733333 (B)
Hon/Match Secretary	Roger Wilson	31 Hills Wood Avenue, Kendal, Cumbria. 01539740449 (H)
Fixture Secretary	Andrew Quarry	07733 111868 (M)
Rugby Manager	Chris Hayton	106 Burneside Road, Kendal, Cumbria LA9 4RT. 01539 724600 (H)
Press Secretary	John Hutton	168 Vicarage Drive, Kendal LA9 5BX 01539 733152(H)

Kendal started the season with great optimism after their successful first season in National Division Two when they finished fourth.

Unfortunately they lost their opening game away at Fylde 17-14, but a very tight home 'derby' game against Wharfedale saw Kendal record the narrowest of victories by 24-23 and give them their first league points.

Kendal's form was mixed and they struggled to find consistency in their performances, however only Orrell managed to beat them on their own soil at Mintbridge before Christmas. Meanwhile they recorded notable away victories at Stourbridge and Esher (through an injury time try), but especially their eight try Christmas feast at Preston on the 22nd December which left them riding high in the league.

The second half of the season saw Kendal really struggle to win a game, a good home performance against Stoubridge in the middle of February secured two vital league points to keep them out of the relegation zone - the last game senior coach Peter Kremer watched before his sad death, after a brave battle against cancer, just days later.

Kendal's determination to avoid relegation really showed in their performance in March against Wharfedale - the most entertaining game of the season - but this time they were on the wrong end of a 22-21 scoreline. League survival was secured with a 48-8 victory over Preston on the 30th March.

KENDAL

Comp.	Date	H/A	Opponents	Result & Score	Att	15	14	13	12	11
N2	01-09	A	Fylde	L 14-17		Dodds	Balmer	Healey	Voortman/t	Woodcock
N2	08-09	H	Wharfedale	W 24-23		Dodds/t	Balmer/t	Healey	Voortman	Woodcock
N2	15-09	A	Sedgley Park	L 12-31	800	Stephens	Balmer	Woodcock	Voortman	Spiby
N2	22-09	H	Rosslyn Park	W 39-9		Stephens	Spiby/t	Healey	Voortman/t	Woodcock
N2	06-10	A	Plymouth Albion	L 12-57		Rose	Balmer	Healey	Voortman	Woodcock
N2	20-10	A	Nottingham	L 20-34		Dodds	Balmer	Healey	Voortman/t	Woodcock
N2	27-10	H	Harrogate	W 32-14		Stephens	Voortman	Healey	Rose/t	Woodcock/t
N2	10-11	A	Esher	W 25-22		Dodds	Balmer	Rose	Voortman/t	Woodcock
N2	17-11	H	Orrell*	L 18-41		Healey	Balmer	Rose	Voortman	Woodcock
N2	24-11	A	Stourbridge	W 26-23	300	Healey	Balmer	Rose	Voortman	Woodcock
N2	01-12	H	Fylde	W 27-18		Healey	Spiby/t	Rose	Voortman	Woodcock
N2	08-12	A	Newbury	L 22-23		Healey	Balmer/t	Rose	Voortman	Woodcock
N2	15-12	H	Waterloo*	W 37-17		Dodds/t	Balmer	Rose	Healey	Woodcock
N2	22-12	A	Preston Grasshoppers	W 46-17	680	Dodds	Balmer/t	Healey/t	Malherbe/t	Woodcock/t
N2	12-01	A	Orrell	L 9-29		Dodds	Balmer	Malherbe	Voortman	Woodcock
N2	19-01	H	Esher	L 12-14		Dodds	Balmer	Malherbe	Voortman	Woodcock
N2	26-01	A	Harrogate	L 12-25	493	Stephens	Balmer/2t	Malherbe	Voortman	Woodcock
N2	02-02	H	Nottingham	L 30-32		Healey	Balmer	Malherbe	Voortman/3t	Woodcock
N2	09-02	H	Plymouth Albion	L 0-7		Healey	Balmer	Malherbe	Voortman	Woodcock
N2	16-02	H	Stourbridge	W 31-13		Healey	Spiby	Malherbe/2t	Voortman/t	Woodcock
N2	23-02	A	Rosslyn Park	L 3-26		Healey	Spiby	Malherbe	Voortman	Woodcock
N2	09-03	H	Sedgley Park	L 12-23	350	Healey	Dodds	Malherbe/t	Voortman	Woodcock
N2	16-03	A	Wharfedale	L 21-22		Healey/t	Balmer	Malherbe	Voortman	Woodcock
N2	30-03	H	Preston Grasshoppers	W 48-8		Dodds/t	Balmer/t	Voortman/2t	Rose	Malherbe
N2	06-04	A	Waterloo	L 22-27		Stephens	Balmer/t	Malherbe/t	Voortman	Dodds
N2	13-04	H	Newbury	L 22-35		Dodds	Balmer/3t	Malherbe	Voortman	Myers
PGC	29-09	H	Doncaster	W 30-17		Stephens	Balmer	Healey	Rose/t	Woodcock
PGC	13-10	H	Manchester	L 6-16		Stephens	Spiby	Healey	Voortman	Woodcock

** after opponents name indicates a penalty try. Brackets after a player's name indicates he was replaced. eg (a) means he was replaced by replacement code "a" and so on. / after a player or replacement name is followed by any scores he made - eg /t, /c, /p, /dg or any combination of these*

EVER PRESENT Mike Scott

Most Appearances:
26: Mike Scott.
25: Adrian Bateson.
24: Ian Voortman.
23: Matthew Woodcock.

PLAYERS USED

31 plus four as a replacement

MOST POINTS

Pts	Player	T	C	P	DG
271	M Scott	2	36	57	6
50	I Voortman	10	-	-	-
50	J Balmer	10	-	-	-
25	C Malherbe	5	-	-	-
25	R Harryman	5	-	-	-

MATCH FACTS

10	9	1	2	3	4	5	6	7	8
Scott/2pdg	Mee	Harryman	Gowing	Thompson	Robinson	Capstick	Bowman	Burnett	Bateson
Scott/c4p	Mee	Harryman	Gowing	Thompson	Capstick	Robinson	Bowman	Burnett	Bateson
Scott/4p	Mee	Lund	Gowing	Thompson	Robinson	Capstick	Wolstenholme	Bowman	Bateson
Scott/3c6p	Mee	Lund	Gowing	Thompson	Robinson	Hayton/t	Wolstenholme	Burnett	Bateson
Scott/4p	Mee	Harryman	Gowing	Thompson	Hayton	Capstick	Wolstenholme	Burnett	Bateson
Scott/2c2p	Mee	Coxon	Thompson	Harryman	Preston	Capstick	Wolstenholme	Burnett	Bateson/t
Scott/2cp	Mee/t	Coxon	Gowing/t	Thompson	Harryman/t	Capstick	Wolstenholme	Burnett	Bateson
Scott/c4p2dg	Mee	Coxon	Gowing	Harryman	Robinson	Preston	Wolstenholme	Burnett	Bateson
Scott/c2p	Mee	Coxon	Gowing	Harryman	Robinson	Capstick/t	Wolstenholme	Burnett	Bateson
Scott/2c4p	Mee	Coxon/t	Gowing	Harryman	Capstick/t	Robinson	Wolstenholme	Burnett	Bateson
Scott/t3c2p	Mee	Coxon	Gowing	Pearson	Robinson	Capstick	Wolstenholme/t	Burnett	Bateson
Scott/c5p	Mee	Coxon	Gowing	Harryman	Robinson	Capstick	Bowman	Burnett	Bateson
Scott/t3c2p	Mee	Coxon	Gowing	Harryman/2t	Robinson	Capstick	Bowman	Burnett	Bateson
Scott/3c	Airey(a/t)	Coxon	Gowing	Harryman	Robinson/t	Capstick	Wolstenholme/t	Bowman	Bateson/t
Scott/3p	Airey	Coxon	Gowing	Harryman	Robinson	Capstick	Wolstenholme	Burnett	Bateson
Scott/4p	Airey	Coxon	Gowing	Harryman	Robinson	Capstick	Wolstenholme	Bowman	Bateson
Scott/c	Airey	Coxon	Gowing	Harryman	Preston	Robinson	Bowman	Burnett	Bateson
Scott/2cpdg	Airey	Coxon	Learney	Harryman/t	Robinson	Preston	Wolstenholme	Bowman	Bateson
Scott	Airey	Coxon	Learney	Harryman	Robinson	Preston	Burnett	Bowman	Bateson
Scott/3c	Airey	Coxon/t	Thompson	Harryman	Preston	Capstick	Wolstenholme	Bowman	Bateson/t
Scott/p	Airey	Coxon	Thompson	Harryman	Preston	Capstick	Burnett	Bowman	Bateson
Scott/c	Sharpe	Coxon	Thompson	Harryman	Robinson	Capstick	Wolstenholme	Bowman/t	Bateson
Scott/2dg	Sharpe	Coxon	Gowing	Thompson	Harryman/t	Robinson	Wolstenholme/t	Bowman	Bateson
Scott/5cp	Airey	Coxon	Thompson	Pearson	Robinson/t	Capstick	Wolstenholme/t	Bowman/t	Bateson
Scott/4p	Morris	Coxon	Gowing	Pearson	Hayton	Quarry	Wolstenholme	Burnett	Robinson
Scott/2cp	Morris	Coxon	Gowing	Thompson	Robinson	Preston	Wolstenholme	Bowman	Bateson
Scott/c6p	Mee	Learney	Gowing	Thompson	Hayton	Capstick	Wolstenholme/t	Burnett	Bateson
Scott/2p	Mee	Harryman	Gowing	Thompson	Robinson	Capstick	Wolstenholme	Burnett	Bateson

REPLACEMENTS: a - Casey Mee.

WHERE	Total	Home	Away
The POINTS were scored	576	332	244
The POINTS were conceded	607	353	254
The TRIES were scored	63	41	22
The TRIES were conceded	70	44	26

HOW the TRIES were scored

Total	Backs	Forwards	F Back	Wing	Centre	H Back	F Row	Lock	B Row	Pen. Try
63	39	22	4	14	17	4	6	7	9	2

HOW the TRIES were conceded

Total	Backs	Forwards	F Back	Wing	Centre	H Back	F Row	Lock	B Row	Pen. Try
70	47	21	6	13	19	9	7	1	13	2

KENDAL

LEAGUE STATISTICS

compiled by Stephen McCormack

SEASON	Division	P	W	D	L	F	A	Pts Diff	Lge Pts	Lge Pos		Coach		Captain
92-93	D4N	12	6	0	6	182	189	-7	12	6				
93-94	D5N	12	4	1	7	142	171	-29	9	10				
94-95	D5N	12	9	1	2	226	162	64	19	2		P Kremer		J Nicholson
												Most Points		**Most Tries**
95-96	D5N	12	5	0	7	215	227	-12	10	9	36	Paul Dodds	6	Paul Dodds
96-97	D4N	26	11	1	14	541	451	90	23	9	163	Jason Hudson	7	Paul Dodds
97-98	N2N	26	18	2	6	614	357	257	38	3	135	Jon Nicholson	15	Jason Balmer
98-99	N2N	26	18	0	8	635	347	288	36	4	200	Casey Mee	12	Jason Balmer
99-00	N2N	26	24	0	2	817	305	512	48	1	273	Casey Mee	15	Jason Balmer
00-01	N2	26	16	1	9	622	467	155	33	4	235	Mike Scott	7	by Three players
01-02	N2	26	10	0	16	576	607	-31	20	10	271	Mike Scott	10	Jason Balmer & Ian Voortman

BIGGEST MARGINS

Home Win	92pts - 92-0 v W Hartlepool27.1.01
Away Win	51pts - 56-5 v Liverpool StH
Home Defeat	28pts - 6-34 v Harrogate 3.10.92
Away Defeat	45pts - 12-57 v Plymouth 6.10.01

MOST CONSECUTIVE

Appearances	
Matches scoring Tries	
Matches scoring points	
Victories	19
Defeats	5

MOST POINTS

Scored at Home	92 v W Hartlepool 27.01.01
Scored Away	56 v Liverpool StH
Conceded at Home	39 v Wharfedale 13.1.96
Conceded Away	62 v Rugby 14.4.01

MOST TRIES

Scored in a match	14 v Hereford 12.4.97
Conceded in a match	8 v Plymouth 6.10.01 (A)

MOST APPEARANCES

by a forward	
by a back	

	MOST IN A SEASON	MOST IN A CAREER	MOST IN A MATCH
Points	273 Casey Mee 1999-20	520 Casey Mee 1998-02	42 Mike Scott v W Hartlepool 27.1.01
Tries	15 Jason Balmer 1997-98 & 1999-00	59 Jason Balmer 1997-02	6 Jason Slater v Barker's Butts 14.1.95
Conversions	53 Casey Mee 1999-00	92 Casey Mee 1998-01	11 Mike Scott v W Hartlepool 27.1.01 (H)
Penalties	57 Mike Scott 2001-02	94 Mike Scott 2000-02	7 Jon Nicholson v Sandal 27.12.97 (A)
Drop Goals	6 Mike Scott 2001-02	8 Mike Scott 2000-02	2 Mike Scott v Esher 10.11.01 (A)

OVERALL PLAYING RECORD

	P	W	D	L	F	A	Pts Diff
Home	6	4	0	2	119	110	9
Away	17	10	0	7	303	329	-26
Neutral	-	-	-	-	-	-	-
Total	23	14	0	9	422	439	-17

SEASON BY SEASON

1971-72	DNQ
1972-73	DNQ
1973-74	DNQ
1974-75	DNQ
1975-76	DNQ
1976-77	DNQ
1977-78	DNQ
1978-79	DNQ
1979-80	DNQ
1980-81	DNQ
1981-82	DNQ
1982-83	DNQ
1983-84	DNQ
1984-85	DNQ
1985-86	DNQ
1986-87	DNQ
1987-88	DNQ
1988-89	DNQ
1989-90	DNQ
1990-91	DNQ
1991-92	DNQ
1992-93	DNQ
1993-94	1R
1994-95	1R
1995-96	1R
1996-97	5R
1997-98	3R
1998-99	4R
99-2000	3R
2000-01	2R
2001-02	3R

KENDAL
RFU SENIOR CUP
STATISTICS
compiled by Stephen McCormack

TEAM RECORDS

Highest Score
32 v Sandal 96/97
Biggest Winning Margin
27 (27-0) v Belgrave 99/00
Highest Score Against
79 v Coventry 96/97
Biggest Losing Margin
62 (79-17) v Coventry 96/97

INDIVIDUAL RECORDS

Most Points in a match

Most Tries in a match

Most Conversions in a match

Most Penalties in a match

Most Drop Goals in a match

PLAYERS

	Position	D.o.B.	Apps.	Pts.	T	C	P	DG
Stephen Healey	Centre	21.07.71	148(1)+	31+	155+	-	-	-
Jason Balmer	Winger	16.04.71	107(3)	295	59	-	-	-
Dan Stephens	Full back	20.09.77	77(4)	80	15	1	1	-
Mike Scott	Fly half		50	516	8	80	94	8
Paul Dodds	Winger	29.01.71	141(9)	175	31			
Mark Airey	Scrum half		40(11)	55	11	-	-	-
Aaron Myers	Winger		3(7)	-	-	-	-	-
Ian Voortman	Centre	13.04.74	103	192	38	1	-	-
Matthew Woodcock	Centre		23	10	2	-	-	-
Casey Mee	Scrum half	11.06.73	87(1)	520	21	92	76	1
Billy Coxon	Prop	27.07.75	156(1)+	55+	11+	-	-	-
Ian Gowing	Hooker	13.07.75	75(11)	50	10	-	-	-
Ian Thompson	Prop	31.10.69	87(13)	5	1	-	-	-
Nigel Pearson	Prop	17.06.67	76(48)+	20+	4+	-	-	-
Mike Capstick	Lock	29.04.74						
Richard Harryman	Prop/Lock	16.11.76	114(15)	195	39	-	-	-
Colin Wolstenholme	Back row	18.03.67	109(21)	185	37	-	-	-
Keith Robinson	Back row	09.03.70	109(12)+	85+	17+	-	-	-
Adrian Bateson	Back row	14.02.76	102	25	5	-	-	-
Phil Learney	Prop		2(4)	-	-	-	-	-
James Lund	Prop		2(3)	-	-	-	-	-

KENDAL

FACT FILE

Founded : 1905
Nickname : The Black & Ambers
Colours: Black and amber.
Change colours: Amber jerseys with black trim

GROUND

Address: Mint Bridge, Shap Road, Kendal. LA9 6DL.
Tel: 01539 734039
Capacity: 1900 Seated: 400 Standing: 1500

Directions: From the M6 junction 36 take A591. Then A6 (Kendal to Penrith). Keep left at the `Duke of Cumberland' and the ground is 400 metres onthe left.
Nearest Railway Station: Kendal (via Oxenholme)

Car Parking: Space for 120 cars on ground.

Admission: Matchdays - Adults members £4.00 non-members £6; Children/OAPs £2
Season Ticket: £35 (members only)

Clubhouse: Has two bars and has food available. Functions: Capacity up to 200.

Club Shop: Shop manager - David Robinson 01539 720355

Training Nights: Tuesday and Thursday

PROGRAMME Size: A5 Price: £1 Pages: 24 + cover
Editor: John Kremer 01539 734039
Advertising Rates Prices on application Contact MTP Publications Ltd. 01539 740937

Billy Coxon

LAUNCESTON RFC

President	John Fry	Thorne Farm, St. Giles on the Heath, Launceston PL15 9SA. 01566 784308
Hon. Secretary	Jim O'Hara	Maranatha, Highcliffe, Polzeath, Wadebridge PL27 6TN Tel: 01208 862725 email: jimolrfc@aol.com
Fixture Secretary	Mervyn Yeo	Whiterow Farm, Lewdown, Okehampton, Devon EX20 4QL 01566 783230
Treasurer	Dave Baker	Heightleigh, Tavistock Road, Launceston PL15 9HB 01566 773070
Match Secretary	Jim O'Hara	as Hon. Secretary

Launceston renewed their National Leagues campaign after finishing as runners-up to Plymouth Albion the previous season. Dean Shipton took over the mantle of player/coach but, as the campaign unfolded, he took a more managerial role, and directed operations from the touchline - not his usual berth at the back of the pack.

The season once again ended in drama.

Cornish rivals, the Pirates, pipped them for the league by just one point and the All Blacks settled for second spot with a home play-off against Dudley Kingswinford, which they won by twenty six points to nil, after a very entertaining game from both sides.

Launceston's big results were at North Walsham, recording their first league victory there; Barking away and Westcombe Park away. These three games in particular set the tone for the Blacks and helped somewhat offset the two defeats of the season to Penzance. A long-term injury to fly-half, Andy Birkett, picked up in the first ten minutes of the home game to his old team, Penzance, disrupted the game plan for ten weeks, and Jimmy Tucker reverted back to his old slot from the centre, until Birkett's return. South African, Barney Vorster, signed from 3 North club, Blaydon, made his debut in that first clash with the Pirates and moved to full-back from where he began to score many tries as well as take over the kicking duties from long time servant, Danny Sloman, who found himself in the seconds. He completed the season as top points scorer for the club with centre, Mark Fatialofa, bagging the most tries with twenty.

Wing forward, Steve Dyer was outstanding in all aspects of play and was rightly awarded the Player of the Season mantle. Glyn Hutchings, at lock, retired after the play-off, after completing thirteen years in the first team, having come through the club system from mini to senior, a credit to both himself and his club.

Launceston now look forward to making new friends in National Two as well as renewing some old acquaintances.

The players celebrate promotion to Division Two after beating Dudley Kikingswinford in the play-off.
Photo courtesy of ACME Photo Agency, Plymouth.

LAUNCESTON

Comp.	Date	H/A	Opponents	Result & Score	Att	15	14	13	12	11
N3 S	01-09	H	North Walsham	W 23-16		Sloman/6p	Trinder	Fatialofa	Tucker	Nancekivell
N3 S	08-09	A	Blackheath	W 9-5		Sloman/3p	Nancekivell	Tucker	Fatialofa	Rose
N3 S	22-09	H	Clifton	W 39-5	350	Fatialofa/t	Trinder/2t	Tucker	Nancekivell	Rose(b/2c)
N3 S	06-10	A	Barking	W 27-19		Birkett/tcp	Rose/c	Nancekivell	Fatialofa/t	Yates/t
N3 S	20-10	H	Tabard	W 40-15	250	Fatialofa/t	Sloman/2t3c3p	Tucker/t	Nancekivell/t	Trinder
N3 S	27-10	A	Old Patesians*	W 34-22		Sloman/2t3cp	Trinder	Yates	Tucker	Cudmore/t
N3 S	03-11	H	Penzance & Newlyn	L 17-30	2000	Sloman/4p	Vorster/t	Tucker	Nancekivell	Trinder
N3 S	10-11	H	Lydney	W 21-13		Vorster	Sloman/c3p	Yates	Fry	Trinder/t
N3 S	17-11	A	Old Colfeians*	W 23-18		Vorster	Sloman/2c3p	Yates	Tucker	Robertson
N3 S	24-11	H	Camberley	W 29-18		Vorster/2t	Sloman/3cp	Yates	Carter	Robertson
N3 S	01-12	A	North Walsham*	W 21-13	400	Vorster	Sloman/c3p	Fatialofa/t	Yates	Trinder
N3 S	08-12	H	Redruth*	W 33-29	1200	Vorster/t	Sloman/2c3p	Fatialofa/t	Yates	Trinder
N3 S	15-12	A	Westcombe Park	W 32-16	200	Vorster	Sloman/3c2p	Fatialofa/2t	Yates	Trinder
N3 S	22-12	H	Cinderford	W 39-23	450	Vorster/t	Sloman/3cp	Fatialofa/t	Nancekivell/t	Bushin/t
N3 S	12-01	H	Old Colfeians	W 57-12	420	Vorster/2t6c	Yates/t	Nancekivell/2t	Fatialofa/2t	Bushin
N3 S	19-01	A	Lydney	W 30-3	526	Vorster/t2cp	Sloman/tp	Nancekivell	Fatialofa	Bushin
N3 S	26-01	A	Penzance & Newlyn	L 8-32	3000	Vorster	Sloman/p	Nancekivell	Fatialofa	Bushin
N3 S	09-02	A	Tabard	W 24-9		Vorster/2c	Trinder/t	Fatialofa	Goldsmith	Gray
N3 S	16-02	A	Camberley	W 38-16	100	Vorster/t2c3p	Trinder	Nancekivell/t	Tucker/t	Cudmore
N3 S	23-02	H	Barking	W 74-7		Fatialofa/2c	Cudmore(d/t)	Nancekivell/3t	Tucker/t	Vorster/2t5c
N3 S	09-03	A	Clifton	W 24-10	150	Fatialofa	Yates	Nancekivell	Tucker/t	Vorster/t3c
N3 S	16-03	H	Blackheath	W 35-19	450	Fatialofa/3t	Vorster/2c2p	Nancekivell	Tucker/t	Trinder
N3 S	23-03	H	Old Patesians	W 54-3	400	Tucker	Trinder/t	Nancekivell	Fatialofa/4t	Vorster/t7c
N3 S	30-03	A	Cinderford	W 40-15	200	Tucker/2t	Trinder/t	Nancekivell	Fatialofa	Vorster/t5c
N3 S	06-04	H	Westcombe Park	W 43-14		Tucker/2t	Briskham/t	Yates	Fatialofa/t	Vorster/2t4c
N3 S	13-04	A	Redruth*	W 62-15	1200	Tucker(d/t)	Vorster/7cp	Yates	Fatialofa/2t	Briskham
PGC	15-09	N	Barnstaple	W 34-0		Sloman/2cp	Rose	Yates(f/t)	Tucker/t	Trinder
PGC	29-09	N	Esher	W 19-10	350	Sloman/p	Trinder	Nancekivell/t	Fatialofa	Rose
PGC	13-10	N	Exeter	L 26-40		Birkett/c2pdg	Rose	Nancekivell	Fatialofa/2t	Trinder/t
NL Po	27-04	H	Dudley Kingwinsford	W 26-0	2500	Tucker/t	Briskham	Nancekivell	Fatialofa/t	Vorster/c3p

** after opponents name indicates a penalty try. Brackets after a player's name indicates he was replaced. eg (a) means he was replaced by replacement code "a" and so on. / after a player or replacement name is followed by any scores he made - eg /t, /c, /p, /dg or any combination of these*

EVER PRESENT None

Most Appearances:
25: Jimmy Tucker.
24: Steve Dyer, Ian Lagridge (1).
23: Julian Wilce.

PLAYERS USED

35 plus three as a replacement only

MOST POINTS

Pts	Player	T	C	P	DG
191	B Vorster	16	45	7	-
176	D Sloman	5	23	35	-
104	M Fatialofa	20	2	-	-
50	J Tucker	10	-	-	-
48	A Birkett	7	2	2	1

MATCH FACTS

10	9	1	2	3	4	5	6	7	8
Birkett	Chudleigh	Risdon	Lucas	Langridge	Hutchings	Wilce	Uglow	Dyer	Durbin(a/t)
Birkett	Chudleigh	Risdon	Lucas	Bolt	Hutchings	Wilce	Uglow	Dyer	Shipton
Birkett/cp	Chudleigh	Risdon/t	Lucas	Langridge	Hutchings	Wilce	Uglow	Dyer/2t	Hammond
Tucker	Chudleigh	Risdon/t	Lucas	Langridge	Hutchings	Wilce	Uglow	Hammond	Shipton
Birkett	Chudleigh	Risdon	Lucas	Langridge	Hutchings	Wilce	Uglow	Dyer	Hammond
Birkett	Chudleigh	Risdon	Lucas	Langridge	Goldsmith	Wilce/t	Uglow	Dyer	Hutchings
Birkett	Thomas	Risdon	Lucas	Langridge	Hutchings	Wilce	Uglow	Dyer	Hammond
Tucker	Thomas/t	Langridge	Lucas	Rush	Goldsmith	Wilce	Uglow	Dyer	Hutchings
Rose	Thomas	Langridge	Risdon	Rush/t	Goldsmith	Wilce	Uglow	Dyer	Hutchings
Tucker	Thomas/t	Langridge	Lucas	Rush	Goldsmith	Wilce	Uglow/t	Dyer	Hutchings
Tucker	Thomas	Langridge	Lucas	Rush	Goldsmith	Wilce	Hammond	Dyer	Hutchings
Tucker	Thomas	Risdon	Lucas	Rush	Goldsmith	Wilce	Hammond	Dyer/t	Hutchings
Tucker	Thomas	Risdon	Lucas	Langridge	Goldsmith	Wilce	Hammond/t	Dyer	Burnett/t
Tucker	Thomas	Risdon	Lucas	Langridge	Goldsmith	Wilce	Uglow/t	Dyer/t	Burnett
Tucker/t	Thomas	Langridge	Risdon	Rush	Goldsmith	Wilce	Hammond	Dyer(c/t)	Burnett
Tucker	Thomas/t	Langridge	Risdon	Rush	Goldsmith	Wilce	Hammond/t	Dyer	Burnett
Tucker	Thomas	Langridge	Risdon	Rush	Goldsmith	Wilce	Hammond/t	Dyer	Burnett
Hutchings	Langridge	Lucas	O'Donnell	Uglow	Yates	Thomas	Hammond/t	Redwood	Burnett/2t
Birkett/t	Thomas	Langridge	Risdon	Rush	Goldsmith	Wilce	Hammond/t	Dyer	Burnett
Birkett/2t	Thomas/t	Risdon	Lucas	Langridge	Hutchings	Wilce	Hammond	Dyer/t	Burnett/t
Birkett/dg	Thomas	Risdon	Lucas	Langridge	Hutchings	Wilce	Hammond	Dyer/t	Burnett
Birkett	Thomas	Risdon	Lucas	Langridge	Hutchings	Wilce	Hammond/t	Dyer	Burnett
Birkett/t	Thomas/t	Langridge	Lucas	Rush	Hutchings	Wilce	Hammond	Dyer	Burnett
Birkett/t	Thomas	Langridge	Lucas	Rush	Hutchings	Wilce/t	Uglow	Dyer	Burnett
Birkett	Thomas	Langridge	Lucas	Rush	Hutchings	Goldsmith	Uglow	Dyer/t	Burnett
Birkett/t	Thomas	Langridge	Risdon	Rush	Hutchings	Goldsmith/t	Uglow/2t	Dyer	Hammond/t
Birkett/tc	Chudleigh/t	Risdon	Lucas	Rice	Goldsmith	Wilce	Uglow	Dyer	Boundy(e/t)
Tucker	Birkett/2p	Risdon	Lucas	Langridge	Hutchings	Wilce	Hammond	Uglow	Shipton/t
Tucker	Chudleigh	Risdon	Lucas	Langridge	Hutchings	Wilce	Hammond	Dyer	Shipton
Birkett	Thomas	Risdon	Lucas	Langridge	Hutchings	Wilce	Uglow(g/t)	Dyer	Hammond

REPLACEMENTS: a - Adam Boundy. b - Phil Sloman. c - Dave Uglow. d - Matt Trinder. e - Chris Hammond. f - Mark Fatialofa. g - Nick Burnett.

WHERE

	Total	Home	Away
The POINTS were scored	876	504	372
The POINTS were conceded	397	193	204
The TRIES were scored	119	70	49
The TRIES were conceded	45	19	26

HOW the TRIES were scored

Total	Backs	Forwards	F Back	Wing	Centre	H Back	F Row	Lock	B Row	Pen. Try
119	84	30	21	23	28	12	3	3	24	5

HOW the TRIES were conceded

Total	Backs	Forwards	F Back	Wing	Centre	H Back	F Row	Lock	B Row	Pen. Try
45	23	20	1	14	7	1	6	1	13	2

LAUNCESTON

LEAGUE STATISTICS

compiled by Stephen McCormack

SEASON	Division	P	W	D	L	F	A	Pts Diff	Lge Pts	Lge Pos	Coach/ Most Points	Captain/ Most Tries
92-93	SW-WC	12	11	0	1	317	75	242	22	2		
93-94	SW-WC	12	8	0	4	204	110	94	16	3		
94-95	SW-WC	12	12	0	0	438	90	348	24	1		
95-96	SW2	12	11	1	0	493	107	386	22	1		
96-97	SW1	22	18	0	4	752	324	328	36	2		
97-98	SW1	22	17	1	4	614	263	351	35	2		
98-99	SW1	22	20	0	2	1021	228	793	40	2		
99-00	SW1	21	19	0	2	693	266	427	38	1	Danny Sloman	
00-01	N3S	26	20	1	5	777	396	381	41	2	288 Danny Sloman	13 Mark Fatialofa
01-02	N3S	26	24	0	2	876	397	479	48	2p	191 Barend Vorster	20 Mark Fatialofa

BIGGEST MARGINS

Home Win	67pts	74-7 v Barking 23.2.02
Away Win	47pts	62-15 v Redruth 13.4.02
Home Defeat	13pts	17-30 v Penzance 3.11.01
Away Defeat	24pts	8-32 v Penzance 26.1.02

MOST POINTS

Scored at Home	74 v Barking 23.2.02
Scored Away	62 v Redruth 13.4.02
Conceded at Home	30 v Penzance 3.11.01
Conceded Away	43 v Penzance 17.2.02

MOST CONSECUTIVE

Appearances	52 Jimmy Tucker
Matches scoring Tries	5 Mark Fatialofa 1.12.01-12.10.02
Matches scoring points	
Victories	10
Defeats	2

MOST TRIES

Scored in a match	12 v Barking 23.2.02 (H)
Conceded in a match	7 v Penzance 17.2.02 (A)

MOST APPEARANCES

by a forward	51 Steve Dyer
by a back	52 Jimmy Tucker

	MOST IN A SEASON	MOST IN A CAREER	MOST IN A MATCH
Points	288 Danny Sloman 00-01	464 Danny Sloman 00-02	25 Danny Sloman v Tabard 20.10.01 (H)
Tries	20 Mark Fatialofa 01-02	33 Mark Fatialofa 00-02	4 Matt Bradshaw v Cheltenham 30.9.00 (H) Mark Fatialofa v Old Patesians 23.3.02 (H)
Conversions	59 Danny Sloman 00-01	82 Danny Sloman 00-02	7 Barend Vorster v Old Patesians 23.3.02 (H) Barend Vorster v Redruth 13.4.02 (A)
Penalties	45 Danny Sloman 00-01	80 Danny Sloman 00-01	6 Danny Sloman v N Walsham 1.9.01 (A)
Drop Goals	1 Andrew Birkett 00-01 & 01-02	2 Andrew Birkett 00-02	1 Andrew Birkett v Westcombe Park 9.9.00 (A) v Clifton 9.3.02 (A)

All records relate to National league rugby only.

OVERALL PLAYING RECORD

	P	W	D	L	F	A	Pts Diff
Home	10	6	0	4	281	190	91
Away	8	3	0	5	145	204	-59
Neutral	-	-	-	-	-	-	-
Total	18	9	-	9	426	394	32

SEASON BY SEASON

Season	Result
1971-72	DNQ
1972-73	DNQ
1973-74	DNQ
1974-75	DNQ
1975-76	DNQ
1976-77	DNQ
1977-78	DNQ
1978-79	DNQ
1979-80	DNQ
1980-81	DNQ
1981-82	DNQ
1982-83	DNQ
1983-84	1R
1984-85	DNQ
1985-86	DNQ
1986-87	DNQ
1987-88	DNQ
1988-89	DNQ
1989-90	DNQ
1990-91	DNQ
1991-92	DNQ
1992-93	DNQ
1993-94	DNQ
1994-95	3R
1995-96	1R
1996-97	1R
1997-98	3R
1998-99	2R
1999-2000	1R
2000-01	3R
2001-02	3R

LAUNCESTON
RFU SENIOR CUP
STATISTICS
compiled by Stephen McCormack

TEAM RECORDS

Highest Score
58 v Bicester 97/98

Biggest Winning Margin
52 (58-6) v Bicester 97/98

Highest Score Against
67 v Rotherham 97/98

Biggest Losing Margin
52 (67-15) v Rotherham 97/98

INDIVIDUAL RECORDS

Most Points in a match

Most Tries in a match

Most Conversions in a match

Most Penalties in a match

Most Drop Goals in a match

PLAYERS

	Position	D.o.B.	Apps.	Pts.	T	C	P	DG
Danny Sloman	Centre		40(2)	464	12	82	80	-
Jimmy Tucker	Fly half		52	110	22	-	-	-
Mark Fatialofa	Centre		37(2)	169	33	2	-	-
Mark Chudleigh	Scrum half		30(1)	25	5	-	-	-
Eddie Nancekivell	Centre		42	80	16	-	-	-
Barend Voster	Winger		20	191	16	45	7	-
Andy Yates	Centre		12(7)	15	3	-	-	-
Dan Briskam	Winger		11(8)	25	5	-	-	-
Lee Thomas	Scrum half		20	25	5	-	-	-
Andy Birkett	Fly half		15	48	7	2	2	1
Harry Bushin	Winger		4(5)	5	1	-	-	-
Andrew Cudmore	Winger		7(2)	15	3	-	-	-
Ian Langridge	Prop		32(10)	-	-	-	-	-
Dave Risdon	Prop		20(14)	5	1	-	-	-
Barry Lucas	Hooker		44(6)	-	-	-	-	-
Steve Rush	Prop		39(10)	20	4	-	-	-
Ian Goldsmith	Lock		14(8)	5	1	-	-	-
Julian Wilce	Lock		50	20	4	-	-	-
Glyn Hutchings	Lock		46(4)	5	1	-	-	-
Steve Dyer	Back row		51	65	13	-	-	-
Dave Uglow	Back row		14(11)	25	5	-	-	-
Chris Hammond	Back row		17(2)	35	7	-	-	-
Nick Burnett	Back row		13(3)	20	4	-	-	-

LAUNCESTON

FACT FILE

Founded: 1948
Nickname: Cornish All Blacks
Colours: All black
Change colours: Red/white/green shirts

Ground Address: Polson Bridge, Launceston, Cornwall PL15 9QU - (No post please)
Tel: 01566 773406 Fax & e-mail: to Secretary
Capacity: 2,500 **Covered seating:** 220

Directions M5 to Exeter, then A30 to Launceston.
After 45 minutes look for sign on left "Tavistock, Liftondown, Lifton" - turn left, down to T junction, left again, down hill to river Tamar, ground on the left.

Nearest Railway Station: Exeter 1hr, Plymouth 45 mins
Car Parking: Plenty at the ground

Admission: Matchday: Ground: Adults: £5.00 Children/OAP: £3 Stand: £4
Season tickets: Yes, price on application

Clubhouse: Open matchdays & training evenings.

Club Shop: Yes, selling replica kits, ties etc.
Training Nights: Tuesday & Thursday
Programme **Size**: A5 **Pages**: 25 **Price**: £1
Editor: Bill Gladwell
Advertising: Contact John Dunn 01822 870300

Launceston prop, Dave Risdon, getting to grips with Dudley Kingswinford in the play-off, with Steve Dyer, Ian Langbridge and Barry Lucas in support. Photo courtesy of ACME Photo Agency, Plymouth.

NEWBURY RFC

Newbury RFC, Monks Lane, Newbury. RG14 7RW
Tel: 01635 40103 Fax: 01635 40533 email: info@newburyrfc.co.uk

President	David G H Smith	c/o Newbury RFC	01264 342342 (B), 07801 666116 (M)
Club Secretary	Rosie Golby	c/o Newbury RFC	07775 915785 (M)
Rugby Co-ordinator	Ally Pankhurst	c/o Newbury RFC	07771 550494 (M)
Chairman of Rugby	Pete Simmons	c/o Newbury RFC	01635 863242
Commercial Manager	Morgan Davis	c/o Newbury RFC	01635 40103 (B) 07785 525816 (M)
Ist XV Manager	Simon Little	c/o Newbury RFC	07768 710577 (M)
Fixture Co-ordinator	John Mills	c/o Newbury RFC	01635 200743

Despite the disappointments of the previous season, Blues set out with high hopes and the optimism that new blood brings to a squad. The return of coach Keith Richardson and the influx of talent from the west country and NSW set the scene for a return to the top six position Newbury had enjoyed throughout the 1990's.

This target took a massive dent in the first two months of the season, as Blues plunged to rock bottom before a vital win away at struggling Waterloo, and a battling victory at the fortress in the Dales.

A remarkable comeback from the dead for an 'easy' extra time cup win at Blackheath (!) set up a great Senior Cup run, finally ended by the new look Orrell who went on to give Leeds a fright and many league sides a lesson. The squad was beginning to fit together well by December, and although the backs saw many changes and reshuffles, the pack enabled some tight victories and the great kicking stats of Ian Morgan clinched many vital league points. After Christmas the roller coaster continued, but the prolonged flirt with relegation was overcome with five wins from seven games at the turn of the year, including a priceless chance win at home against expensive Sedgley Park.

Three real away trouncings at the hands of Fylde's forwards, Plymouth's all round power and Orrell's expensive and expansive style were offset by wins against the doomed Waterloo, Preston Grasshoppers and the slumping Stourbridge – and the climax of the season saw Blues register two more wins after the narrowest of defeats against nearest neighbours Esher and the ill fated Rosslyn Park. Points difference left Newbury level with three other teams in mid-table obscurity-cum-security, repeating their ninth placing for the second year running, but allowing the prospect of building aspirations in a brief summer of squad strengthening.

The regret of losing three great names from the division is perhaps tempered by the return of two derby rivals in Henley and Bracknell, and the appetite is further whetted by the arrival of new northern power Doncaster and the formidable Cornish challengers. Another tough season beckons for Blues!

NEWBURY

Comp.	Date	H/A	Opponents	Result & Score	Att	15	14	13	12	11
N2	01-09	H	Harrogate	L 20-38		Southwell	Czerpak	Morgan/p	Wakfer	Westall
N2	08-09	A	Esher*	L 22-33		Southwell	Griffiths	Roberts	Morgan/2p	Czerpak
N2	15-09	H	Orrell	W 26-24		Southwell/t	Stoker/t	Roberts/t	Morgan/3c	Griffiths
N2	22-09	A	Stourbridge	L 14-37		Southwell	Wilson(a/t)	Roberts	Morgan	Griffiths
N2	06-10	H	Preston Grasshoppers	L 20-30		Southwell/t	McCormick	Roberts	Morgan/2c2p	Hart/t
N2	20-10	H	Plymouth Albion	L 12-40		Martin	Southwell	Evans	Morgan/c(b/t)	Wilson
N2	27-10	A	Waterloo	W 26-20		Southwell	McCormick	Martin	Evans	Williams
N2	10-11	H	Fylde	L 16-29		Martin/t	Southwell	Griffiths	Morgan	Stoker
N2	17-11	A	Wharfedale	W 24-23		Martin	Southwell/t	Roberts	Evans	Griffiths
N2	01-12	A	Harrogate*	L 19-29		Martin	Southwell	Griffiths	Evans	Robinson
N2	08-12	H	Kendal	W 23-22		Morgan/t2c3p	Southwell	Czerpak	Evans	McCormick
N2	15-12	A	Nottingham	L 15-23	322	Morgan/cp	Southwell	Czerpak	Martin	McCormick
N2	22-12	H	Rosslyn Park	W 25-15		Morgan/2cpdg	Southwell	Czerpak	Evans	McCormick
N2	29-12	H	Sedgley Park	W 9-7		Morgan/3p	McCormick	Wakfer	Evans	Williams
N2	12-01	H	Wharfedale	W 30-21		Morgan/3c3p	Robinson	Roberts/t	Evans/t	Southwell
N2	19-01	A	Fylde	L 3-39		Balzan	Wilson	Robinson	Southwell	Williams
N2	26-01	H	Waterloo	W 22-20		Morgan/2cp	Robinson/t	Thorpe/t	Evans	Southwell
N2	02-02	A	Plymouth Albion	L 10-57	1080	Morgan/cp	Reeves/t	Southwell	Evans	Green
N2	16-02	A	Sedgley Park	L 24-32	250	Morgan/3cp	Greenwood	Southwell	Evans	Evans
N2	23-02	H	Stourbridge	W 31-20		Martin	Morgan/2c4p	Southwell	Evans	Lavin/t
N2	02-03	A	Preston Grasshoppers	W 54-24		Southwell/t	Morgan/6c4p	Greenwood	Evans	Phillips/t
N2	09-03	A	Orrell	L 7-57	700	Martin	Morgan/c	Southwell	Evans	Phillips
N2	16-03	H	Esher	L 22-24		Morgan/t2cp	Greenwood/t	Roberts	Evans	Southwell
N2	30-03	A	Rosslyn Park	L 23-25		Martin	Lavin	Roberts/2c2p	Evans	Southwell
N2	06-04	H	Nottingham	W 16-12		Martin	Lavin	Southwell	Evans/t	Morgan/2p
N2	13-04	A	Kendal	W 35-22		Lavin	Reeves	Roberts/3c3p	Evans/t	Phillips
PGC	29-09	A	Blackheath	W 37-18		Czerpak	McCormick/t	Roberts	Morgan/2cp	Hart
PGC	03-11	H	Nuneaton	W 29-8		Martin	Southwell	Evans/t	Roberts	Williams
PGC	24-11	H	Orrell	L 25-30		Martin	Southwell	Roberts	Evans	Griffiths

** after opponents name indicates a penalty try. Brackets after a player's name indicates he was replaced. eg (a) means he was replaced by replacement code "a" and so on. / after a player or replacement name is followed by any scores he made - eg /t, /c, /p, /dg or any combination of these*

EVER PRESENT

None

Most Appearances:

24: Shaune Edwards (1), Brad Gill (1), Hugo Southwell, Bernie Williams (2).

23: Chris Hart.

PLAYERS USED

42 plus seven as a replacement

MOST POINTS

Pts	Player	T	C	P	DG
165	I Morgan	2	31	30	1
50	D Coen	1	6	11	-
40	C Davies	8	-	-	-
35	M Roberts	2	5	5	-
35	SGully	7	-	-	-

MATCH FACTS

10	9	1	2	3	4	5	6	7	8
Martin/c	Stoker/t	Binnie	Gill	Collins	Thorpe	Edwards	Nicholas	Porter	Hart/2t
Martin/c2pdg	Stoker	Binnie	Gill	Collins	Thorpe	Edwards	Hart	Nicholas	Davies
Martin	Wakfer	Binnie	Gill	Williams	Hunt	Edwards	Hart	Nicholas	Davies/t
Martin/2c	Stoker	Binnie	Gill	Williams	Hunt	Edwards	Hart	Nicholas/t	Davies
Coen	Wakfer	Binnie	Gill	Williams	Thorpe	Edwards	Nicholas	Pickthall	Davies
Coen	Wakfer	Williams	Gill	Collins	Hart	Edwards	Davies/t	Gully	Pickthall
Coen/2c4p	Green	Williams	Gill	Collins	Hart	Edwards/t	Davies	Gully/t	Pickthall
Coen/c3p	Green	Binnie	Gill	Williams	Hart	Edwards	Davies	Gully	Pickthall
Coen/c4p	Green	Collins/t	Gill	Williams	Hart	Edwards	Davies	Porter	Pickthall
Coen/t2c	Green	Williams	Gill	Collins	Hart/t	Edwards	Davies	Porter	Pickthall
Martin	Wakfer/t	Williams	Gill	Collins	Botha	Edwards	Hart	Porter	Pickthall
Coen	Wakfer	Williams	Gill	Collins	Hart/t	Edwards	Davies	Porter	Pickthall/t
Martin	Green	Williams	Gill	Collins	Hart	Thorpe/3t	Davies	Porter	Pickthall
Martin	Green	Williams	Lampty	Binnie	Hart	Edwards	Thorpe	Porter	Davies
Martin	Green	Williams	Gill	Binnie	Hart	Edwards	Thorpe	Porter	Davies/t
Martin/p	Green	Williams	Gill	Binnie	Hart	Cockram	Thorpe	Kingdon	Porter
Martin	Green	Williams	Gill	Collins	Hart/t	Edwards	Kingdon	Porter	Davies
Coen	Pinder	Williams	Gill	Collins	Hart	Edwards	Kingdon	Porter	Thorpe
Czerpak/t	Green	Williams	Lampty	Collins	Hart	Edwards	Thorpe	Kingdon	Davies/2t
Czerpak	Green	Williams	Gill	Collins	Thorpe/t	Edwards	Porter	Kingdon	Davies/t
Czerpak	Green/t	Williams	Gill	Collins	Thorpe	Edwards	Nicholas	Porter/t	Davies/2t
Czerpak/t	Wakfer	Williams	Gill	Collins	Thorpe	Edwards	Nicholas	Kingdon	Davies
Martin	Green	Williams	Gill	Binnie	Hart/t	Edwards	Thorpe	Kingdon	Davies
Czerpak/tdg	Green	Williams	Gill/t	Binnie	Hart	Edwards	Pickthall	Kingdon	Davies
Czerpak	Wakfer	Williams	Gill/t	Binnie	Hart	Edwards	Pickthall	Gully	Davies
Martin/t	Wakfer	Gough/t	Gill	Williams	Hart	Edwards	Byrne	Nicholas	Pickthall/t
Westall	Wakfer/2t(c/t)	Binnie	Gill	Collins	Thorpe/t	Edwards	Nicholas	Pickthall/t	Davies
Coen/2c5p	Wakfer	Williams	Gill	Collins	Hart/t	Edwards	Davies	Gully	Pickthall
Coen/c6p	Wakfer	Williams	Gill	Collins	Hart	Edwards	Davies/t	Gully	Pickthall

REPLACEMENTS: a - Jason Williams. b - Chris Thomas. c - Simon Stoker.

WHERE	**Total**	**Home**	**Away**
The POINTS were scored	548	272	276
The POINTS were conceded	723	421	302
The TRIES were scored	60	31	29
The TRIES were conceded	92	57	35

HOW the TRIES were scored

Total	Backs	Forwards	F Back	Wing	Centre	H Back	F Row	Lock	B Row	Pen. Try
60	30	28	6	9	7	8	4	9	15	2

HOW the TRIES were conceded

Total	Backs	Forwards	F Back	Wing	Centre	H Back	F Row	Lock	B Row	Pen. Try
92	62	27	8	28	16	10	4	8	15	3

NEWBURY

LEAGUE STATISTICS

compiled by Stephen McCormack

SEASON	Division	P	W	D	L	F	A	Pts Diff	Lge Pts	Lge Pos		Coach		Captain
92-93	SW1	12	8	1	3	251	158	93	17	3		T Burwell		W Phillips
93-94	SW1	12	8	1	3	173	165	8	17	3		T Burwell		J Booth
94-95	SW1	12	9	1	2	376	113	263	19	2		S Czerpak		J Brammer
95-96	SW1	12	11	0	1	364	169	195	22	1p		S Czerpak		J Brammer
												Most Points		**Most Tries**
96-97	D4S	25	25	0	0	1170	295	875	50	1p	398	Nick Grecian	27	Brian Johnson
97-98	JN1	26	12	2	12	639	545	94	26	6	172	Nick Grecian	16	Criag Davies
98-99	JN1	26	14	1	11	552	476	76	29	6	72	Justin Poihippi	10	Tyrone Howe
99-00	JN1	26	15	1	10	550	483	67	31	5	123	Dave Griffiths	10	Jeremy Griffiths
00-01	N2	*25	10	1	14	437	502	-65	21	9	85	Mal Roberts	8	Jeremy Griffiths
01-02	N2	26	12	0	14	548	723	-175	24	9	165	Ian Morgan	8	Craig Davies

BIGGEST MARGINS

Home Win	87pts - 87-0 v Met. Police 22.2.97
Away Win	69pts - 74-5 v Askeans 19.4.87
Home Defeat	50pts - 3-53 v Bracknell 7.4.01
Away Defeat	50pts - 7-57 v Orrell 9.3.02

MOST CONSECUTIVE

Appearances	30 Colin Hall
Matches scoring Tries	5 Brian Johnson
Matches scoring points	24 Nick Grecian
Victories	26
Defeats	4

MOST POINTS

Scored at Home	91 v Tabard 28.3.97
Scored Away	74 v Askeans 19.4.97
Conceded at Home	53 v Bracknell 7.4.01
Conceded Away	57 v Plymouth 2.2.02/Orrell 9.3.02

MOST TRIES

Scored in a match	15 v Tabard 28.3.97
Conceded in a match	9 v Plymouth 2.2.02/Orrell 9.3.02

MOST APPEARANCES

by a forward	120 (4) Craig Davies
by a back	87(1) Tom Holloway

	MOST IN A SEASON	MOST IN A CAREER	MOST IN A MATCH
Points	391 Nick Grecian 96-97	563 Nick Grecian 96-98	32 Nick Grecian v Charlton Park 25.1.97 (H) v Met. Police 22.2.97 (H)
Tries	27 Brian Johnson 96-97	63 Craig Davies 96-02	4 Brian Johnson v Askeans 19.4.97 (A) v Plymouth 26.4.97 (H)
Conversions	100 Nick Grecian 96-97	135 Nick Grecian 96-98	11 Nick Grecian v Charlton Park 25.1.97 (H)
Penalties	42 Nick Grecian 96-97	71 Nick Grecian 96-98	5 Nick Grecian v Liverpool St. Helens 21.2.98 (H)
Drop Goals	2 Morgan Davis 99-00 Ian Morgan 01-02	3 Morgan Davis 97-00 Ian Morgan 01-02	1 by five players

OVERALL PLAYING RECORD

	P	W	D	L	F	A	Pts Diff
Home	8	7	0	1	252	125	127
Away	14	8	0	6	342	302	40
Neutral	-	-	-	-	-	-	-
Total	22	15	0	7	594	327	167

SEASON BY SEASON

Season	Result
1971-72	DNQ
1972-73	DNQ
1973-74	DNQ
1974-75	DNQ
1975-76	DNQ
1976-77	DNQ
1977-78	DNQ
1978-79	DNQ
1979-80	DNQ
1980-81	DNQ
1981-82	DNQ
1982-83	DNQ
1983-84	DNQ
1984-85	DNQ
1985-86	DNQ
1986-87	DNQ
1987-88	DNQ
1988-89	DNQ
1989-90	DNQ
1990-91	DNQ
1991-92	DNQ
1992-93	1R
1993-94	DNQ
1994-95	DNQ
1995-96	DNQ
1996-97	5R
1997-98	5R
1998-99	4R
1999-2000	3R
2000-01	3R
2001-02	5R

NEWBURY
RFU SENIOR CUP
STATISTICS
compiled by Stephen McCormack

TEAM RECORDS

Highest Score
58 v Clifton 96/97

Biggest Winning Margin
46 (58-12) 96/97

Highest Score Against
46 v Richmond 98/99

Biggest Losing Margin
34 (46-12) v Richmond 98/99

INDIVIDUAL RECORDS

Most Points in a match

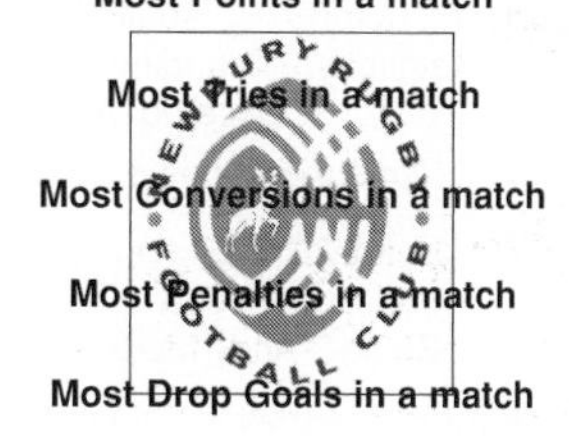

Most Tries in a match

Most Conversions in a match

Most Penalties in a match

Most Drop Goals in a match

PLAYERS

	Position	D.o.B.	Apps.	Pts.	T	C	P	DG
Ian Morgan	Fly half	05.05.75	25	190	2	33	36	2
Jeremy Griffiths	Winger	10.05.74	67	135	27	-	-	-
Brett Wakfer	Scrum half	15.04.73	38(20)	15	3	-	-	-
Mal Roberts	Centre	04.08.77	38	175	6			
SImon Stoker	Scrum half	27.12.77	24(2)	40	8	-	-	-
Hugo Southwell	Winger		24	20	4	-	-	-
Jon Martin	Fly half		22	30	2	4	3	1
Will Green	Scrum half		15(1)	5	1	-	-	-
Will Greenwood	Winger		3	5	1	-	-	-
Jamie Phillips	Winger		3(1)	5	1	-	-	-
Martin Reeves	Winger		2	5	1	-	-	-
Brad Gill	Hooker		24(1)	5	1	-	-	-
Andrew Binnie	Prop		27(9)	10	2	-	-	-
Bernie Williams	Prop		50(7)	-	-	-	-	-
Kevin Gough	Prop		1(1)	5	1	-	-	-
Shaune Edwards	Lock		24(1)	5	1	-	-	-
Chris Hart	Lock	20.12.74	71(7)	100	20	-	-	-
Simon Gully	Back row	12.08.75	49(7)	45	9	-	-	-
John Kingdon	Back row	24.06.67	86(15)	20	4	-	-	-
Craig Davies	Back row	25.11.69	120(4)	315	63	-	-	-
David Thorpe	Back row		14(5)	25	5	-	-	-

NEWBURY

FACT FILE

Founded: 1928
Nickname: The Blues
Web site: www.newburyrfc.co.uk

Colours: Navy, sky & white irregular hoops
Change colours: Red

GROUND

Address: Monks Lane, Newbury, Berkshire RG14 7RW
Tel : 01635 40103 Fax: 01635 40533 e-mail: info@newburyrfc.co.uk
Capacity: 7,850 Seated: 350 Standing: 7,500

Directions: From M4 take A34 to Newbury, at 4th r'about on Newbury ring road(A34) turn right. Keep left at mini-r'about, ground is half mile on left. From south turn left at1st r'about on A34 ring road.
Nearest Railway Station: Newbury (10 minutes walk from ground)

Car Parking: 300 on ground, 1000 nearby @ £1.

Admission: Season Adults Standing £90, Seated £150. No concessions
Matchday Standing: Adults £7, Children £4, OAPs £3
Seated: Adults £8,Children £5, OAPs £4.

Club Shop: Open weekends & training evenings

Clubhouse: Normal licensing hours - 3 bars. Snacks & bar food available.
Functions: 4 rooms avail. Corporate hospitality available.
Contact Andy McKelvie 01635 40103

Training Nights: Tuesday & Thursday

PROGRAMME
Size: A5 Pages: 40
Price: £1 Editor: Morgan Davis
ADVERTISING RATES
Colour Page £600
Half £400
Qtr. £250

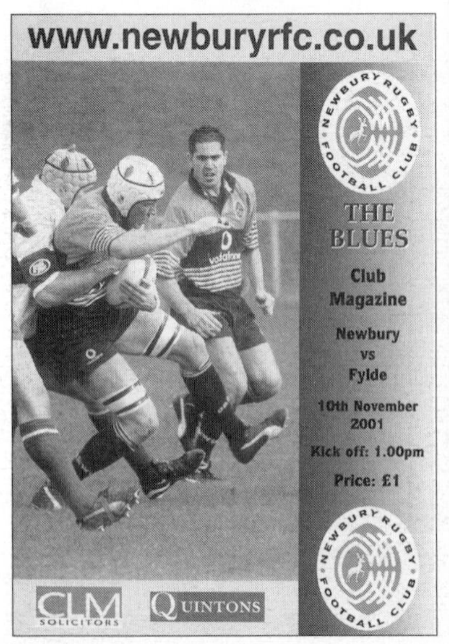

Ian Morgan - Player of the Season

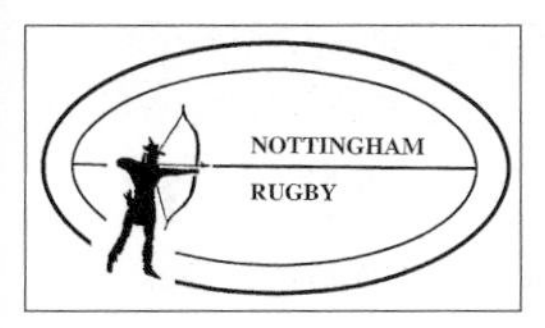

NOTTINGHAM RFC

Chairman	Bryan Ford,
Secretary	Keith Mitchell
Director of Coaching	Mike Pennistone
Treasurer	John Hughes
Administrator	Janet Allen
Advertising	Nigel Eatch

c/o Nottingham RFC
Ireland Avenue
Beeston
Nottingham
NG9 1JD.
Tel: 0115 925 4238
Fax: 0115 925 4255

Nottingham began last season with the usual wave of optimism. Coach Roger Whittaker had rejoined the club during the summer and all looked promising. An ambitious tour to Italy saw them give a good account of themselves against European qualifiers Viadana and Calvisano. Sadly they could not carry their impressive pre-season form into the league campaign. Defeats in their first four games were all the more disappointing given that two, at least, were avoidable. To then be knocked out of the cup at Dudley Kingswinford proved the final straw for Whittaker, and he announced his decision to retire from the game the following week.

The club faced a dilemma. Without the financial muscle to approach a big name coach they decided that the policy of home grown talent which has served them well on the playing side was just as applicable to the coaching side. Up stepped Simon Beatham, who had only taken over coaching the club,s second team a year earlier following his retirement through injury as a player.

Beatham is one of the youngest coaches in senior rugby, and his sheer enthusiasm and positive approach brought an immediate reversal of fortunes with six wins from the next eight matches.

The previous two seasons had both been long struggles to avoid relegation, so this was a welcome change indeed. Division Two survival never seemed in doubt, and they achieved that goal comfortably in the end with four games remaining. They eventually settled for eighth place, but only on points difference. One more win and they would have finished sixth. That is no small achievement, either for a club which has struggled to keep pace with the financial demands of the modern game, or for a young coach in his first season at the helm.

NOTTINGHAM

Comp.	Date	H/A	Opponents	Result & Score	Att	15	14	13	12	11
N2	01-09	A	Waterloo	L 14-25		Murphy	Elford	Robinson	Campbell	Clark
N2	08-09	H	Fylde	L 16-18	311	Murphy	Jackson/c3p	Robinson/t	Campbell	Clark
N2	15-09	A	Wharfedale	L 13-46		Murphy	Booth/p	Robinson	Rolt	Jackson
N2	22-09	H	Sedgley Park	L 8-48		Murphy	Booth/p	Robinson	Rolt	Williams
N2	06-10	A	Rosslyn Park	W 18-11		Clark	Booth/c2p	Rolt	Swetman	Williams
N2	20-10	H	Kendal	W 34-20		Clark	Booth/2c	Robinson/2t	Campbell	Williams(b/t)
N2	27-10	A	Plymouth Albion	L 12-46		Clark	Booth/c	Robinson	Campbell	Reynolds
N2	10-11	A	Harrogate	L 16-25		Murphy	Booth/2p	Robinson	Campbell	Reynolds
N2	17-11	H	Esher	W 25-6	284	Murphy	Booth	Robinson	Campbell	Southam/t2c2p
N2	01-12	H	Waterloo	W 35-5	288	Murphy	Booth	Robinson	Campbell/t	Southam/3c3p
N2	08-12	A	Preston Grasshoppers	W 27-25		Murphy	Booth	Robinson	Campbell/2t	Southam/3c2p
N2	15-12	H	Newbury	W 23-15	322	Murphy	Booth/2t	Robinson	Campbell	Southam/2c3p
N2	22-12	A	Stourbridge	L 22-32		Murphy	Booth	Robinson/t	Campbell	Southam/c5p
N2	29-12	A	Orrell	L 5-52		Murphy	Clark	Rolt	Campbell	Reynolds
N2	12-01	A	Esher	W 24-23		Murphy/t	Clark	Rolt	Campbell/t	Southam/3cp
N2	19-01	H	Harrogate	L 5-24		Murphy	Robinson	Campbell	Rolt	Southam
N2	26-01	H	Plymouth Albion	L 13-26	342	Murphy	Robinson	Rolt	Campbell	Southam/c2p
N2	02-02	A	Kendal	W 32-30		Rolt	Murphy	Robinson/t	Campbell	Southam/t3c2p
N2	09-02	H	Rosslyn Park	L 11-30		Rolt/t	Murphy	Robinson	Campbell	Southam/2p
N2	23-02	A	Sedgley Park	L 16-25	240	Rolt	Murphy/t	Robinson	Campbell	Southam/c3p
N2	09-03	H	Wharfedale	W 21-9	406	Rolt	Murphy	Robinson	Campbell	Southam/tc3p
N2	16-03	A	Fylde**	W 30-13	500	Murphy	Jackson	Robinson	Clark	Southam/3c3p
N2	30-03	H	Stourbridge	W 29-12	521	Murphy/t	Booth/t	Rolt	Campbell	Southam/3cp
N2	06-04	A	Newbury	L 12-16		Murphy	Booth	Robinson	Clark	Southam/c
N2	13-04	H	Preston Grasshoppers	W 63-10	346	Murphy/2t	Robinson	Rolt	Campbell	Southam/t6c2p
N2	20-04	H	Orrell	L 15-66	546	Murphy	Robinson	Rolt	Campbell	Southam/2tcp
PGC	29-09	N	Dudley Kingwinsford	L 3-36		Murphy	Booth/p	Robinson	Carroll	Williams

** after opponents name indicates a penalty try. Brackets after a player's name indicates he was replaced. eg (a) means he was replaced by replacement code "a" and so on. / after a player or replacement name is followed by any scores he made - eg /t, /c, /p, /dg or any combination of these*

EVER PRESENT Mark Bradley, Dan Moore.

Most Appearances:
26: Mark Bradley, Dan Moore.
25: Neil Fowkes.
23: Nick Adams (3), Ben Murphy.
22: David Jackson (3).

PLAYERS USED

35 plus three as a replacement

MOST POINTS

Pts	Player	T	C	P	DG
203	R Southam	6	34	35	-
41	N Booth	3	4	6	-
36	D Jackson	5	1	3	-
25	R Robinson	5	-	-	-
25	A Corcoran	5	-	-	-
25	B Murphy	5	-	-	-

MATCH FACTS

10	9	1	2	3	4	5	6	7	8
Rolt/2pdg	Royer/t	Adams	Bailey	Fowkes	Roberts	Moore	Elford	Lloyd	Bradley
Rolt	Royer	Fowkes	Bailey	Adams	Armstrong	Moore	Roberts	Schrafft	Bradley
Windle(a/t)	Carroll	Fowkes	Bailey	Adams	Armstrong	Moore	Roberts/t	Schrafft	Bradley
Jackson	Carroll	Fowkes	Harding	Adams/t	Armstrong	Moore	Roberts	Corcoran	Bradley
Jackson	Jackson	Fowkes	Bailey	Adams/t	Blackwell	Moore	Corcoran/t	Pearson	Bradley
Jackson/2t	Jackson	Fowkes	Bailey	Adams	Blackwell	Moore	Corcoran/t	Pearson	Bradley
Jackson	Jackson	Fowkes	Bailey	Adams/t	Blackwell	Moore/t	Corcoran	Pearson	Bradley
Jackson	Jackson	Fowkes	Harding	Adams	Hammond	Moore	Corcoran	Pearson/t	Bradley/t
Jackson	Jackson	Fowkes	Bailey	Adams	Hammond/t	Moore	Corcoran/t	Pearson	Bradley
Jackson	Jackson	Fowkes	Bailey/t	Adams/t	Hammond	Moore	Corcoran	Pearson/t	Bradley
Jackson	Jackson	Fallon	Bailey/t	Adams	Hammond	Moore	Corcoran	Pearson	Bradley
Jackson	Jackson	Fowkes	Bailey	Adams	Hammond	Moore	Corcoran	Pearson	Bradley
Jackson	Jackson	Fowkes	Bailey	Adams	Hammond	Moore	Corcoran	Pearson	Bradley
Jackson	Royer/t	Fowkes	Harding	Adams	Hammond	Moore	Corcoran	Lloyd	Bradley
Jackson	Royer	Fowkes	Harding	Adams	Hammond	Moore	Corcoran/t	Lloyd	Bradley
Jackson	Royer	Fowkes	Bailey/t	Adams	Hammond	Moore	Corcoran	Lloyd	Bradley
Jackson/t	Royer	Fowkes	Bailey	Adams	Hammond	Moore	Corcoran	Lloyd	Bradley
Jackson/t	Royer	Fowkes	Harding	Adams	Hammond	Moore	Corcoran	Pearson/t	Bradley
Jackson	Royer	Fowkes	Harding	Adams	Hammond	Moore	Corcoran	Pearson	Bradley
Jackson	Royer	Fowkes	Bailey	Adams	Hammond	Moore	Corcoran	Pearson	Bradley
Jack	Royer	Fowkes	Bailey	Fallon	Hammond	Moore	Thompson	Lloyd/t	Bradley
Jack	Royer	Fowkes	Bailey	Fallon	Hammond/t	Moore	Thompson	Lloyd	Bradley
Jack/2t	Royer	Fowkes	Bailey	Fallon	Hammond	Moore	Thompson	Pearson	Bradley
Jackson	Royer	Fowkes	Bailey/t	Adams	Hammond	Moore(c/t)	Thompson	Pearson	Bradley
Jackson/t	Royer/2t	Fowkes/t	Harding	Adams	Hammond/t	Moore	Thompson	Lloyd/t	Bradley
Jack	Royer	Fowkes	Bailey	Adams	Hammond	Moore	Thompson	Lloyd	Bradley
Jackson	Jackson	Fowkes	Harding	Fallon	Armstrong	Moore	Roberts	Corcoran	Bradley

REPLACEMENTS: a - Brendan Clarke. b - Tom Rolt. c - Adam Corcoran

WHERE

	Total	Home	Away
The POINTS were scored	539	298	241
The POINTS were conceded	658	369	289
The TRIES were scored	64	37	27
The TRIES were conceded	85	47	38

HOW the TRIES were scored

Total	Backs	Forwards	F Back	Wing	Centre	H Back	F Row	Lock	B Row	Pen. Try
64	37	25	5	12	9	11	9	5	11	2

HOW the TRIES were conceded

Total	Backs	Forwards	F Back	Wing	Centre	H Back	F Row	Lock	B Row	Pen. Try
85	49	35	6	19	16	8	10	7	18	1

NOTTINGHAM

LEAGUE STATISTICS

compiled by Stephen McCormack

SEASON	Division	P	W	D	L	F	A	Pts Diff	Lge Pts	Lge Pos	Most Points		Most Tries	
92-93	2	12	8	0	4	249	145	104	16	4	106	Guy Gregory	3	Richard Byrom
93-94	2	18	8	1	9	254	326	-62	17	6	171	Guy Gregory	5	Andy Smallwood
94-95	2	18	8	1	9	299	322	-23	17	7	97	Ian Stent	4	Andy Smallwood
95-96	2	18	5	1	12	333	433	-100	11	9	158	Simon Hodgkinson	7	Alan Royer
96-97	2	22	2	0	20	344	827	-483	4	12r	55	David Evans	5	Richard Bygrave
97-98	JN1	26	13	0	13	527	602	-75	26	7	262	Chris Atkinson	7	Alan Royer
98-99	JN1	26	16	0	10	590	467	123	32	4	272	Chris Atkinson	13	Alan Royer
99-00	JN1	26	8	1	17	460	574	-114	17	11	155	Tom Rolt	7	Tom Rolt
00-01	N2	26	10	0	16	544	584	-40	20	11	219	Russell Southam	16	Jamie Morley
01-02	N2	26	12	0	14	539	658	-119	24	8	203	Russell Southam	6	Russell Southam

BIGGEST MARGINS

Home Win	78pts - 78-0 v Morley 24.10.92
Away Win	55pts - 55-0 v Liverpool StH 28.11.98
Home Defeat	65pts - 5-70 v Richmond 16.11.96
Away Defeat	80pts - 22-102 v Coventry 5.10.96

MOST CONSECUTIVE

Appearances	41 Guy Gregory 23.11.91 - 30.4.94
Matches scoring Tries	4 Andy Smallwood
Matches scoring points	38 Chris Atkinson
Victories	5
Defeats	12

MOST POINTS

Scored at Home	78 v Morley 24.10.92
Scored Away	55 v Liverpool StH 28.11.98
Conceded at Home	74 v Newcastle 14.9.96
Conceded Away	102 v Coventry 5.10.96

MOST TRIES

Scored in a match	12 v Morley 24.10.92 (H)
Conceded in a match	14 v Coventry 5.10.96 (A)

MOST APPEARANCES

by a forward	197(6) Martin Freer
by a back	167 (3) Richard Byrom

	MOST IN A SEASON	MOST IN A CAREER	MOST IN A MATCH
Points	272 Chris Atkinson 98-99	597 Simon Hodgkinson 87-93 & 95-97	25 Guy Gregory v Otley 11.9.93 (H)
Tries	16 Jamie Morley 00-01	37 Alan Royer 94-00	4 Gary Hartley v Morley 24.10.92 (H) Alan Royer v Liverpool St H 28.11.98 (A)
Conversions	36 Russell Southam 00-01	70 Russell Southam 00-02	9 Guy Gregory v Morley 24.10.92 (H)
Penalties	64 Chris Atkinson 97-98 & 98-99	142 Simon Hodgkinson 87-93 & 95-97	6 Guy Gregory v Saracens 12.3.94 Chris Atkinson v Camberley 19.09.98 (A)
Drop Goals	9 Guy Gregory 92-93	19 Guy Gregory 91-94	2 Andy Sutton v Harlequins 31.3.90 (A) Guy Gregory v Rosslyn Park 4.4.92 (H) v Rosslyn Park 21.1.92 (A) v Fylde 9.1.93 (H) & v Bedford 13.2.93 (A) Simon Hodgkinson v L Irish 17.2.96 (A)

NOTTINGHAM
RFU SENIOR CUP
STATISTICS
compiled by Stephen McCormack

OVERALL PLAYING RECORD

	P	W	D	L	F	A	Pts Diff
Home	36	19	0	17	613	521	92
Away	24	12	0	12	358	433	-75
Neutral	-	-	-	-	-	-	-
Total	60	31	0	29	971	954	17

SEASON BY SEASON

1971-72	2R
1972-73	1R
1973-74	1R
1974-75	1R
1975-76	1R
1976-77	DNQ
1977-78	1R
1978-79	DNQ
1979-80	2R
1980-81	QF
1981-82	3R
1982-83	QF
1983-84	SF
1984-85	4R
1985-86	QF
1986-87	4R
1987-88	3R
1988-89	QF
1989-90	QF
1990-91	SF
1991-92	3R
1992-93	4R
1993-94	4R
1994-95	4R
1995-96	5R
1996-97	5R
1997-98	2R
1998-99	4R
1999-2000	4R
2000-01	2R
2001-02	2R

TEAM RECORDS

Highest Score
50 v Preston 98/99

Biggest Winning Margin
47 (50-3) v Preston 98/99

Highest Score Against
52 v Bath 91/92

Biggest Losing Margin
52 (52-0) v Bath 91/92

INDIVIDUAL RECORDS

Most Points in a match
20 Chris Atkinson v Preston 98/99

Most Tries in a match
3 Mark Bradley v Wharfedale 98/99

Most Conversions in a match
6 Chris Atkinson v Preston 98/99

Most Penalties in a match

Most Drop Goals in a match

PLAYERS

	Position	D.o.B.	Apps.	Pts.	T	C	P	DG
Ben Murphy	Full back	03.09.80	73(2)	115	23	-	-	-
Russell Southam	Fly half	28.04.74	41	422	15	70	68	1
Alan Royer	Scrum half	01.12.70	139(1)	210	42	-	-	-
Nick Booth	Winger	28.10.76	14(1)	50	3	4	9	-
Tom Rolt	Centre	05.08.79	51(17)	192	11	25	26	3
Sam Jack	Fly half		55	80	9	2	1	6
Mike Swetman	Centre	26.11.80	12(3)	53	5	-	-	-
Nick Carroll	Centre	09.01.70	36(4)	64	4	-	-	-
David Jackson	Scrum half		22(3)	36	5	1	3	-
Stuart Bailey	Hooker	23.03.79	46(8)	25	5	-	-	-
Neil Fowkes	Prop	05.11.80	37(10)	5	1	-	-	-
Duncan Holland	Prop	15.05.74	19(12)	-	-	-	-	-
Ben Blackwell	Lock	07.06.80	12(2)	-	-	-	-	-
Dan Moore	Lock		26	5	1	-	-	-
Craig Hammond	Lock		19(1)	15	3	-	-	-
Richard Lloyd	Back row	02.12.77	78	55	11	-	-	-
Mark Bradley	Back row	21.12.69	186(4)	85	17	-	-	-
Robbie Harding	Hooker		7(12)	-	-	-	-	-
Adam Corcoran	Back Row		20(6)	30	6	-	-	-
Nick Adams	Prop		29(3)	20	4	-	-	-

NOTTINGHAM

Founded: 1877
Nickname: 'Green & Whites'
Web Site: nottinghamrugby.co.uk

Colours: Green & white hoops
Change colours: Yellow

GROUND

Address: Ireland Avenue, Dovecote Lane, Beeston, Nottingham. NG9 1JD.
Tel: 0115 925 4238 Fax: 0115 925 4255 email: enquiries@nottinghamrugby.co.uk
Capacity: 4,950 Seated: 450 Standing: 4,500

Directions: Off Queens Road, Beeston. Main Nottingham to Long Eaton Road
Nearest Railway Station: Beeston (200 yards from the ground)

Car Parking: 175 on ground

Admission: Matchday
Adults £7
OAPs/Children £3

Club Shop: Open matchdays.
Club Marketing 0115 925 4238

Clubhouse: Open matchday & training nights,
snacks available.
Functions: Yes

Training Nights: Tuesdays & Thursdays (Sen.)

PROGRAMME

Size: A5
Pages: 36 + cover
Price: £1
Editor: George Holohan
0115 925 4238

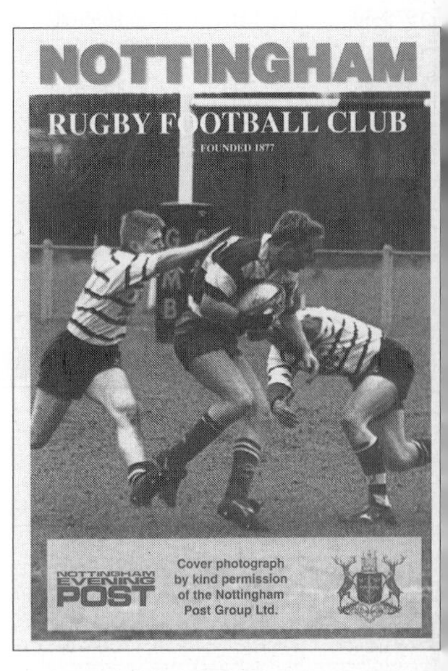

Advertising Rates

Colour	Full page £500
	Half page £250
Mono	Full page £300
	Half page £150

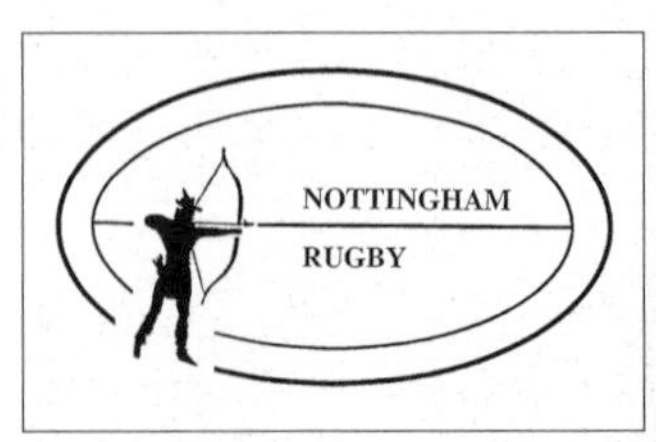

Russell Southam
Leading try scorer and leading points scorer for Nottingham last season

PENZANCE & NEWLYN RFC

President	Dicky Evans	
Chairman	Robin Turner	01736 367317
Club Administrator	Terry Drew	01736 351568
Chief Executive	Martin Scrase	01736 335315
Coaching Director	Kevin Moseley	01736 335311

c/o Penzance & Newlyn RFC,
Westholme, Alexandra Road, Penzance, Cornwall. TR18 4LY

The 2001/2002 saw The Pirates take top spot in National League 3 (South) and win automatic promotion to National Two. In a title race with close Cornish rivals Launceston, which continued to the last game of the season, to clinch promotion, The Pirates had to win at Westcombe Park on 13th April.

On a bone hard pitch, and in dry conditions, the team, after a titanic battle, eventually came out victors with a slightly flattering score line of 27-42. The Pirates started the promotion campaign on 1st September with a try scoring feast, rattling up 240 points in the first four league matches of the season. The leagues were then interrupted by the Senior Cup competition. In Round Two The Pirates were drawn away to league rivals, North Walsham, where we suffered out first defeat of the season, going down 20-10 in a very lack lustre performance.

It was then back to league business where normal service was resumed - that is until 1st December. We had to travel to what had become our bogey team, Blackheath, and again we were involved in a major battle before coming away with a flattering 17-17 draw. The one league point gained would become relevant as the season was to reach its climax. On 15th December, we were to suffer our only league defeat of the season, away to our old rivals, North Walsham, going down 18-7. The defeat led to some indifferent performances from The Pirates, before hitting top form against Tabard on 23rd February, where we recorded a 76-11 victory. The promotion campaign then began to gather momentum and in the last seven matches of the season The Pirates scored 416 points.

For the 2001/2002 season, The Pirates' pack was bolstered by the arrival of Ma'asi, Waqanivere and Haag, who combined well with the established members. Several youngsters were also very impressive, notably Seal, Hodge, Hilton and Morcom.

Behind the pack, the backs were led by team captain, Mark Roderick, The Pirates expansive style again reaping rewards for established try scorers Newton, Hawken, Saumi, Olonga and Richards while Nat Saumi again complimented his fine try scoring ability with some superb place kicking performances.

The Pirates would like to thank all the teams in National League 3 (South) for their hospitality and friendship and we wish them every success in the forthcoming season.

KEVIN MOSELEY

PENZANCE & NEWLYN

Comp.	Date	H/A	Opponents	Result & Score	Att	15	14	13	12	11
N3 S	01-09	H	Blackheath	W 58-15	900	Hawken	Richards/t	Evans	Saumi/2t6c2p	Newton/t
N3 S	08-09	A	Clifton	W 48-21	210	Hawken	Richards/2t	Evans/t	Saumi/6c2p	Newton/2t
N3 S	22-09	H	Barking	W 54-10	950	Hawken	Richards	Evans/t	Saumi/3t5c3p	Newton(b/t)
N3 S	06-10	A	Tabard	W 45-33	185	Redgrave	Richards/t	Evans/t	Saumi/t3c3p	Hawken
N3 S	20-10	H	Old Patesians	W 73-10	700	Hawken	Richards/t	Evans	Saumi/t9c	Newton/3t
N3 S	27-10	H	Lydney	W 34-14	900	Hawken	Richards	Evans/t	Saumi/2c4p	Newton/t
N3 S	03-11	A	Launceston	W 30-17	2000	Hawken	Richards	Evans	Saumi/2c2p	Newton/2t
N3 S	10-11	H	Old Colfeians	W 62-7		Redgrave	Richards/3t	Evans/6c	Gadsdon	Newton/4t
N3 S	17-11	A	Camberley	W 23-20	250	Redgrave(f/c2p)	Hawken	Evans/cp	Gadsdon	Newton
N3 S	24-11	H	Cinderford	W 27-10	600	Hawken	Redgrave	Evans/2c2p	Gadsdon(f/tc)	Newton
N3 S	01-12	A	Blackheath	D 17-17		Hawken	Richards	Evans/t	Saumi/t2cp	Newton
N3 S	08-12	H	Westcombe Park	W 32-7	900	Hawken	Richards	Evans	Saumi/3c2p	Newton/2t
N3 S	15-12	A	North Walsham	L 7-18	400	Hawken	Richards	Evans	Saumi/c	Newton
N3 S	22-12	H	Redruth	W 38-22	1600	Hawken/t	Richards	Olonga	Saumi/t4c	Newton
N3 S	12-01	H	Camberley	W 52-7	850	Olonga/t	Hawken/3t	Gadsdon/t	Saumi/c2p	Newton
N3 S	19-01	A	Old Colfeians	W 56-19	225	Olonga/t	Hawken/t	Bearman/t	Gadsdon	Newton
N3 S	26-01	H	Launceston	W 32-8	3000	Hawken	Olonga	Gadsdon	Saumi/c5p	Newton/2t
N3 S	09-02	A	Old Patesians	W 26-20		Hawken/t	Richards	Gadsdon	Saumi/c3p	Newton
N3 S	16-02	A	Cinderford	W 32-19	200	Olonga/t	Hawken/2t	Gadsdon/t	Saumi/2cp	Newton
N3 S	23-02	H	Tabard	W 76-11	800	Olonga/4t	Hawken	Richards/3t	Saumi/6c	Newton/2t
N3 S	02-03	A	Lydney	W 41-28	378	Olonga/t	Hawken	Richards/t	Saumi/4cp	Newton/t
N3 S	09-03	A	Barking	W 37-10		Olonga/t	Richards/3t	Gadsdon	Saumi/2cp	Newton/t
N3 S	16-03	H	Clifton	W 76-24		Olonga/t	Hawken/t	Saumi/2t9cp	Gadsdon	Newton/3t
N3 S	30-03	A	Redruth	W 76-22	2000	Olonga/2t	Hawken/t	Richards/2t	Saumi/t9cp	Newton/t
N3 S	06-04	H	North Walsham	W 64-7	1200	Olonga/2t	Bearman/t	Gadsdon	Saumi/2t7c	Newton/2t
N3 S	13-04	A	Westcombe Park	W 42-27	700	Olonga/3t	Bearman	Gadsdon	Saumi/4c3p	Newton/t
PGC	15-09	N	Cinderford	W 80-12	800	Hawken/2t	Richards/t	Evans/2t	Saumi/11cp	Newton/t
PGC	29-09	A	North Walsham	L 10-20	400	Redgrave	Richards	Evans	Saumi/cp	Hawken

** after opponents name indicates a penalty try. Brackets after a player's name indicates he was replaced. eg (a) means he was replaced by replacement code "a" and so on. / after a player or replacement name is followed by any scores he made - eg /t, /c, /p, /dg or any combination of these*

EVER PRESENT

One

Most Appearances:
26: Steve Evans.
25: Richard Newton.
24: Victor Olonga (1).
23: Martin Haag (1), James Hawken.

PLAYERS USED

29 plus two as repalcement only

MOST POINTS

Pts	Player	T	C	P	DG
374	N Saumi	15	91	39	-
140	R Newton	28	-	-	-
118	V Olonga	23	-	-	1
115	L Waqinevere	23	-	-	-
101	S Evans	9	19	6	-

MATCH FACTS

10	9	1	2	3	4	5	6	7	8
Olonga	Roderick	Davey	Andrews/2t	Seal	Haag	Carroll/t	Bearman	Penrose	Durant(a/t)
Olonga/t	Roderick	Morcom	Nicholas	Seal	Haag	Hilton	Bearman	Penrose	Durant
Olonga	Roderick	Morcom	Nicholas	Seal/t	Haag	Carroll	Bearman	Penrose	Waqanivere/t
Olonga	Kearey	Morcom	Clackworthy	Seal	Haag	Hodge/t	Carroll/t	Penrose	Waqanivere/t
Olonga/3t	Kearey	Meddick	Clackworthy	Seal	Haag	Hodge	Durant	Penrose/t	Waqanivere/2t
Olonga/dg	Kearey	Morcom	Clackworthy	Meddick	Haag	Hodge	Durant	Penrose	Waqanivere(c/t)
Olonga	Kearey	Morcom	Clackworthy	Meddick	Haag	Hodge	Durant(d/t)	Penrose	Waqanivere/t
Hawken	Roderick	Morcom/t	Andrews	Seal	Hilton/t	Carroll	Durant	Penrose/t	Bearman
Olonga/t	Roderick	Morcom	Clackworthy	Seal	Hilton(f/t)	Carroll	Durant	Penrose	Bearman
Olonga	Kearey	Seal	Turner	Meddick	Hilton	Carroll	Bearman/t	Penrose	Waqanivere/t
Olonga	Kearey	Morcom	Clackworthy	Meddick	Haag	Hodge	Durant	Penrose	Waqanivere
Olonga	Kearey	Morcom	Clackworthy	Meddick	Haag/t	Hodge	Carroll	Durant	Waqanivere/t
Olonga/t	Kearey	Morcom	Clackworthy	Meddick	Haag	Hodge	Durant	Carroll	Waqanivere
Evans/2t	Roderick	Seal	Ma'asi	Meddick	Haag	Hodge	Carroll	Durant/t	Waqanivere/t
Evans/t2c	Kearey	Morcom	Ma'asi	Seal	Haag/t	Carroll	Durant	Penrose	Waqanivere/t
Evans/6c3p	Roderick	Morcom	Clackworthy	Seal(g/t)	Haag	Carroll/t	Hilton(a/2t)	Penrose	Durant
Evans	Roderick	Seal	Ma'asi	Meddick	Haag	Carroll	Bearman/t	Penrose	Waqanivere
Evans	Roderick	Seal	Ma'asi/t	Morcom	Haag/t	Hilton	Bearman	Penrose	Waqanivere
Evans	Roderick	Seal	Ma'asi	Morcom	Haag	Hilton	Durant	Penrose	Waqanivere/t
Evans/2c	Kearey	Seal	Ma'asi/t	Higgins	Haag	Carroll	Hilton	Durant/t	Waqanivere/t
Evans	Roderick/t	Morcom	Ma'asi	Seal	Haag/t	Hilton	Carroll	Penrose	Waqanivere/t
Evans	Kearey	Seal	Ma'asi	Morcom	Haag	Hilton	Durant	Penrose	Waqanivere/t
Evans/t	Roderick	Morcom	Ma'asi	Higgins	Haag	Carroll	Durant/t	Penrose	Waqanivere/2t
Evans	Roderick	Morcom	Ma'asi	Seal	Haag	Hilton/t	Carroll	Penrose	Waqanivere/3t
Evans	Roderick	Seal	Ma'asi	Higgins	Haag	Hilton/t	Carroll	Penrose	Waqanivere/2t
Evans	Roderick	Seal	Ma'asi	Higgins	Haag	Hilton	Penrose/t	Carroll	Waqanivere
Olonga/2t	Roderick	Morcom	Williams	Seal	Haag/t	Hilton	Bearman	Penrose	Waqanivere/2t
Olonga	Roderick	Morcom	Clackworthy	Seal	Haag	Carroll	Durant	Penrose	Waqanivere/t

REPLACEMENTS: a - Laka Waqanivere. b - Ali Durant. c - Richard Carroll. d - Joe Bearman. e - Brian Andrew. f - Nat Saumi. g - Stuart Meddick

WHERE

	Total	Home	Away
The POINTS were scored	1158	678	480
The POINTS were conceded	683	392	291
The TRIES were scored	160	96	64
The TRIES were conceded	52	32	20

HOW the TRIES were scored

Total	Backs	Forwards	F Back	Wing	Centre	H Back	F Row	Lock	B Row	Pen. Try
160	108	52	19	49	29	11	7	11	34	-

HOW the TRIES were conceded

Total	Backs	Forwards	F Back	Wing	Centre	H Back	F Row	Lock	B Row	Pen. Try
52	29	23	1	12	7	9	9	3	11	-

PENZANCE & NEWLYN

LEAGUE STATISTICS

compiled by Stephen McCormack

SEASON	Division	P	W	D	L	F	A	Pts Diff	Lge Pts	Lge Pos	Coach	Captain
92-93	Western Cos.	38	25	0	13	975	510	465	50	4	P Greaves	A Bick
93-94	Western Cos.	37	26	0	11	686	428	258	52	4	P Greaves	A Bick
94-95	Western Cos.	33	24	0	9	787	400	387	48	4	P Greaves	A Bick
95-96	Western Cos.	38	22	1	15	923	685	238	45	3p	R Tonkin	A Ellery
96-97	SW 2	31	25	0	6	1074	441	633	50	1p	R Tonkin	M Murrish
97-98	SW 1	39	26	1	12	1102	716	386	53	4	M Ring/P Johnson	M Murrish
98-99	SW1	32	26	0	6	1336	464	872	52	1p	P Johnson	A Bick
											Most Points	**Most Tries**
99-00	N2S	26	20	1	5	1055	479	576	41	2	204 Nat Saumi	38 Richard Newton
00-01	N3S	26	18	2	6	823	492	331	38	3	336 Nat Saumi	20 Victor Olonga
01-02	N3S	26	24	1	1	1158	423	735	49	1p	374 Nat Saumi	28 Richard Newton

BIGGEST MARGINS

Home Win	136pts	136-0 v Met Police 15.4.00
Away Win	65pts	76-11 v Tabard 23.2.02
Home Defeat	23pts	13-36 v Plymouth 24.3.01
Away Defeat	26pts	5-31 v Launceston 27.1.01

MOST POINTS

Scored at Home	136 v Met Police 15.4.00
Scored Away	76 v Tabard 23.2.02
Conceded at Home	40 v Esher 6.11.99
Conceded Away	38 v Blackheath 3.2.01

MOST CONSECUTIVE

Appearances	56 Steve Evans 22.4.00 to date
Matches scoring Tries	10 Richard Newton
Matches scoring points	
Victories	13
Defeats	2

MOST TRIES

Scored in a match	22 v Met Police 15.4.00
Conceded in a match	5 on four occasions

MOST APPEARANCES

by a forward	60 Kevin Penrose, Richard Carroll
by a back	77 Steve Evans

	MOST IN A SEASON	MOST IN A CAREER	MOST IN A MATCH
Points	374 Nat Saumi 01-02	914 Nat Saumi 99-02	41 Nat Saumi v Met Police 15.4.00
Tries	38 Richard Newton 99-00	76 Richard Newton 99-02	7 Richard Newton v Met Police 15.4.00
Conversions	91 Nat Saumi 01-02	213 Nat Saumi 99-02	13 Nat Saumi v Met Police 15.4.00
Penalties	39 Nat Saumi 00-01 & 01/02	91 Nat Saumi 01-02	5 Bryan Easson v Plymouth 27.11.99 (A) Bryan Easson v Redruth 4.12.99 (H)
Drop Goals	1 by three plaers	2 Andrew Birkett 99-01	1 By three players

All records relate to National league rugby only.

OVERALL PLAYING RECORD

	P	W	D	L	F	A	Pts Diff
Home	5	3	0	2	199	80	119
Away	4	2	0	2	68	68	0
Neutral	-	-	-	-	-	-	-
Total	9	5	0	4	267	148	119

SEASON BY SEASON

Season	Result
1971-72	DNQ
1972-73	DNQ
1973-74	DNQ
1974-75	DNQ
1975-76	DNQ
1976-77	DNQ
1977-78	DNQ
1978-79	DNQ
1979-80	DNQ
1980-81	DNQ
1981-82	DNQ
1982-83	DNQ
1983-84	DNQ
1984-85	DNQ
1985-86	DNQ
1986-87	DNQ
1987-88	DNQ
1988-89	DNQ
1989-90	DNQ
1990-91	DNQ
1991-92	DNQ
1992-93	DNQ
1993-94	DNQ
1994-95	DNQ
1995-96	DNQ
1996-97	DNQ
1997-98	DNQ
1998-99	2R
1999-2000	3R
2000-01	3R
2001-02	2R

PENZANCE & NEWLYN RFU SENIOR CUP

STATISTICS

compiled by Stephen McCormack

TEAM RECORDS

Highest Score
80 v Cinderford 01/02

Biggest Winning Margin
68 (80-12) v Cinderford 01/02

Highest Score Against
27 v Moseley 99/00

Biggest Losing Margin
16 (5-21) v Reading 98/99

INDIVIDUAL RECORDS

Most Points in a match

Most Tries in a match

Most Conversions in a match

Most Penalties in a match

Most Drop Goals in a match

PLAYERS

	Position	D.o.B.	Apps.	Pts.	T	C	P	DG
Victor Olonga	Full back	30.06.74	66	338	67			1
Richard Newton	Winger	07.02.79	64	380	76	-	-	-
Paul Gadsdon	Centre	22.02.71	40(6)	40	8	-	-	-
Nat Saumi	Centre	03.09.70	61	914	43	213	91	-
Steve Evans	Fly half	25.03.78	77	266	26	41	17	1
Mark Roderick	Scrum half	17.09.71	36(3)	40	8	-	-	-
James Hawken	Winger	18.04.81	42(2)	90	18	-	-	-
Mark Richards	Winger	25.08.79	42(2)	150	30	-	-	-
Peter Redgrave	Centre	25.03.79	37	135	24	3	3	-
Blane Kearey	Scrum half	19.10.78	11(5)	-	-	-	-	-
Dan Seal	Prop	23.10.79	20(5)	5	1	-	-	-
Viliami Ma'asi	Hooker		12(3)	10	2	-	-	-
Regan Higgins	Prop		4(3)	-	-	-	-	-
Dan Clackworthy	Hooker	18.12.79	22(14)	-	-	-	-	-
Stuart Meddick	Prop	28.03.78	9(2)	5	1	-	-	-
Ashley Morcom	Prop	11.11.81	18(6)	5	1	-	-	-
Martin Hagg	Lock	28.07.66	23(1)	20	4	-	-	-
Ollie Hodge	Lock	24.03.80	8	5	1	-	-	-
Ben Hilton	Lock	12.12.81	13(9)	15	3	-	-	-
Laka Waqanivere	Back row	02.04.68	21(3)	115	23	-	-	-
Richard Carroll	Back row	09.07.75	60(8)	30	6	-	-	-
Joe Bearman	Back row	28.02.79	49(9)	60	12	-	-	-

PENZANCE & NEWLYN

FACT FILE

Founded: 1945

Colours: Black, white & red hoops
Change colours: Black with red & white trims

Web site: www.pirates-rfc.co.uk

GROUND

Address: Westholme, Alexandra Road, Penzance, Cornwall. TR18 4LY
Tel: 01736 351568 / 364227 Fax: 01736 335319 e-mail: terry.drew@btclic.com
Capacity: 5,000 Seated: 560 Standing - Covered: 750 Uncovered: 3,690

Directions: Follow the sea road (via the harbour), past the Jubilee bathing pool to end of the promenade until mini roundabout at Beachfield Hotel, then turn right and the ground is 400 yards up on the left.
Nearest Railway Station: Penzance, 250 yds from town centre

Car Parking: Limited at ground. Car Park on promenade for 300 cars. Off street parking available.

Admission: Season tickets - Adults £90 Sen. Citizens £50
Matchday - Standing: Adults £7, Sen. Cit./Students £4 Stand £2

Clubhouse: Open every eve. except Sun. & Mon. 7-11, Sun 12-3 & matchdays 12-11.
4 bars with snacks & bar meals available. Corporate hospitality & Functions available.

Club Shop: At club - open during the week incl. matchdays

Training Nights: Tuesday & Thursday

PROGRAMME

Size: A5 Price: £2
Pages: 52 Editor: Des Hosken
Advertising Rates (all + V.A.T.)
Page £400; 1/2 £220;
1/4 £110; 1/8 £60

Lakalaka Waqanivere is stopped close to the line by Cinderford's fly-half Jenitt.

SEDGLEY PARK RUFC

President	Geoff Roberts	Salesis Farm, Salesis Lane, Walmersley, Bury BL9 6TH 0161 764 6914 (H), 0161 925 9998 (B), 0161 833 2872 (Fax)
Chairman of Rugby	David Smith	95 Bury Old Road, Whitefield, Manchester. 0161 280 2921 (H), 0161 280 3509 (B).
Club Secretary	Mark Mold	32 Vicarage Avenue, Cheadle Hulme, Cheadle, Ches. SK8 7JW 0161 486 0496 (H) 0161 839 9000 (B)
Treasurer	Peter Ratcliffe	22 Hilltop Avenue, Wilmslow, Cheshire SK9 2JE 01625 535542 (H)
Press Officer	Colin Stephens	c/o club 0161 796 2626
Fixture Secretary	Stuart Tattersall	c/o club 0161 723 6539 (B)

This was 'arguably' the most successful season in the club's 70 year history.

Newly promoted to National League 2, Sedgley finished third behind Orrell and Plymouth and had the satisfaction of a win over their Lancashire rivals.

Other notable victories were against Rosslyn Park, Nottingham, Wharfedale, Harrogate and Fylde - merely to play such opposition was a dream come true - and the 'double' was achieved over them all by a team playing basic yet attractive rugby.

Equally important, for the first time, home supporters had a comfortable stand from which to watch their best-ever team.

Sedgley Park also won the Lancashire Cup for the first time, adding another defeat of Fylde in the process and with many young players getting their first taste of 1st XV action in this competition; the same players had performed gamely, and with some success, in the Northern 2nd XV Championship.

The National Cup run was curtailed by Coventry, who somehow managed to turn a 22-16 deficit into a 40-16 victory in the last ten minutes.

Many of Sedgley's junior players achieved representative honours, though it remains a cause for concern that a young man can play for his country only, it seems, if he allows himself to be 'head-hunted' by one of the elite schools. There were four such players last season, all proud to consider themselves of Sedgley but often frustratingly unable to combine club with school matches.

The Lancashire Cup winning team 2002. Photo: Peter Barton (0161 969 0508)

SEDGLEY PARK

Comp.	Date	H/A	Opponents	Result & Score	Att	15	14	13	12	11
N2	01-09	A	Plymouth Albion	L 13-34	1600	Moon	Wilcock/t	Hassan	Scales	Morris
N2	08-09	A	Rosslyn Park	W 39-13		Moon/c	Wilcock/3t	Hassan	Scales/t	Morris/t
N2	15-09	H	Kendal	W 31-12	800	Peacock	Wilcock	Scales	Hassan	Morris
N2	22-09	A	Nottingham	W 48-8		Peacock	Wilcock	Hassan/t	Scales/t	Morris(a/t)
N2	06-10	H	Harrogate	W 33-27	325	Moon/t	Wilcock/t	Hassan	Scales	Morris/t
N2	20-10	A	Esher	L 14-16		Wilcock	Bullough	Hassan	Scales	Morris
N2	27-10	H	Orrell	W 25-12		Moon	Wilcock	Hassan	Scales/t	Bullough
N2	10-11	A	Stourbridge	W 29-17	300	Wilcock	Bullough	O'Hare	Scales/t	Morris/2t
N2	17-11	H	Preston Grasshoppers	W 17-12	350	Peacock	Wilcock/t	Scales	O'Hare	Morris/t
N2	01-12	H	Plymouth Albion	L 13-32	500	Peacock	Wilcock	O'Hare	Scales/t	Morris
N2	08-12	A	Fylde	W 22-19	450	Moon	Wilcock	Hassan	Scales	Morris
N2	15-12	H	Wharfedale	W 50-24	450	Moon/2t	Wilcock/t	Hassan	Scales	Morris/t
N2	22-12	A	Waterloo	W 27-13		Moon	Wilcock	Hassan	Scales	Morris
N2	29-12	A	Newbury	L 7-9		Moon	Wilcock	Hassan	O'Hare	Morris
N2	12-01	A	Preston Grasshoppers	W 37-18	460	Moon/t	Wilcock	Hassan	Scales/t	Morris
N2	19-01	H	Stourbridge*	W 34-24	350	Moon/t	Wilcock	Hassan	O'Hare	Morris
N2	26-01	A	Orrell	L 16-43	1000	Moon/t	Wilcock	Hassan	Scales	O'Hare
N2	02-02	H	Esher	W 20-16		Moon/t	Wilcock	Hassan	Scales	O'Hare/t
N2	09-02	A	Harrogate	W 13-10	487	Wilcock	Bullough/2t	Hassan	Scales	O'Hare
N2	16-02	H	Newbury	W 32-24	250	Wilcock	Bullough/2t	Hassan	Scales/t	O'Hare
N2	23-02	H	Nottingham	W 25-16	240	Wilcock	Bullough/t	Hassan/t	Scales	O'Hare(c/t)
N2	09-03	A	Kendal	W 23-12	350	Wilcock/t	Bullough	Hassan/t	Scales	Morris
N2	16-03	H	Rosslyn Park	W 26-19	250	Wilcock/t	Bullough/t	Peacock	Scales	Morris
N2	30-03	H	Waterloo	D 20-20		Wilcock	Bullough/t	Hassan	Scales	Morris
N2	06-04	A	Wharfedale	W 33-3	650	Peacock	Bullough/3t	Hassan	Scales	Wilcock
N2	13-04	H	Fylde	W 37-15	550	Peacock/t	Wilcock/t	Hassan	Scales/t	Bullough/t
PGC	29-09	H	Stourbridge	W 33-13	375	Peacock	Bullough/t	Hassan	Scales	Morris/t
PGC	13-10	H	Coventry	L 22-40	550	Moon	Bullough/t	Hassan	Scales	Morris

** after opponents name indicates a penalty try. Brackets after a player's name indicates he was replaced. eg (a) means he was replaced by replacement code "a" and so on. / after a player or replacement name is followed by any scores he made - eg /t, /c, /p, /dg or any combination of these*

EVER PRESENT Three

Tim Fourie, Richard Senior, Mike Wilcock.Most Appearances:
26: Tim Fourie, Richard Senior, Mike Wilcock.
25: Paul Arnold.
24: Jon Scales.
23: Kern Yates.

PLAYERS USED **26** plus two as a replacement

MOST POINTS

Pts	Player	T	C	P	DG
244	C Stephens	4	37	46	4
110	R Moon	12	13	8	-
60	R Bullough	12	-	-	-
50	M Wilcock	10	-	-	-
40	J Scales	8	-	-	-

MATCH FACTS

10	9	1	2	3	4	5	6	7	8
Stephens/c2p	McCormack	Latham	Keys	Johnston	Rees	Radacanu	Senior	Yates	Fourie
Stephens/2cdg	McCormack/t	Alcock	Keys	Johnston	Arnold	Rees	Senior	Yates	Fourie
Moon/2t4cp	McCormack	Alcock	Keys	Johnston	Arnold	Rees	Senior	Yates/t	Fourie/t
Moon/t4c5p	McCormack	Alcock	Keys	Johnston	Arnold	Rees	Senior	Yates	Fourie/t
Stephens/c2p	McCormack	Latham	Keys	Johnston	Arnold/t	Rees(b/t)	Senior	Yates	Fourie
Stephens/2c	McCormack	Latham	Keys	Johnston	Arnold	Rees	Senior	Yates	Fourie/2t
Stephens/5p	McCormack	Latham	Keys	Johnston	Arnold/t	Rees	Senior	Yates	Fourie
Moon/t2c	McCormack/t	Latham	Keys	Alcock	Arnold	Grainey	Senior	Yates	Fourie
Moon/tc	McCormack	Alcock	Keys	Latham	Arnold	Grainey	Senior	Yates	Fourie
Moon/c2p	McCormack	Alcock	Keys	Latham	Arnold	Rees	Senior	Yates	Fourie
Stephens/tc3p2dg	Smith	Alcock	Tresco	Thomas	Arnold	Rees	Senior	Yates	Fourie
Stephens/2t4c3pdg	Smith	Alcock	Tresco	Thomas	Arnold	Rees	Senior	Yates	Fourie
Stephens/c5p	Smith	Alcock	Tresco	Thomas	Arnold	Rees	Senior	Yates/t	Fourie/t
Stephens/c	Smith	Alcock	Tresco	Thomas	Arnold	Rees	Senior/t	Yates	Fourie
Stephens/4c3p	McCormack	Alcock	Tresco/t	Thomas	Arnold	Rees	Senior	Yates/t	Fourie
Stephens/4c2p	McCormack/t	Alcock	Tresco	Thomas	Arnold/t	Rees	Senior	Yates	Fourie
Stephens/c3p	McCormack	Alcock	Tresco	Thomas	Arnold	Rees	Senior	Yates	Fourie
Stephens/2c2p	McCormack	Latham	Tresco	Thomas	Arnold	Rees	Senior	Yates	Fourie
Stephens/p	McCormack	Latham	Tresco	Thomas	Arnold	Rees	Senior	Yates	Fourie
Stephens/3c2p	McCormack	Latham	Tresco	Thomas	Arnold	Rees	Senior	Yates	Fourie/t
Stephens/2c2p	McCormack	Latham	Tresco	Thomas	Rees	Arnold	Senior	Yates	Fourie
Stephens/2c3p	McCormack	Latham	Tresco	Thomas	Arnold	Rees	Senior	Yates	Fourie
Stephens/3c	McCormack/2t	Latham	Tresco	Thomas	Arnold	Rees	Senior	Yates	Fourie
Stephens/5p	McCormack	Latham	Tresco	Thomas	Arnold	Rees	Senior	Grainey	Fourie
Stephens/tp	McCormack	Latham	Tresco	Thomas	Arnold	Stockdale	Senior/2t	Grainey	Fourie
Stephens/3c2p	McCormack	Roberts	Tresco	Thomas	Arnold/t	Stockdale	Senior	Grainey	Fourie
Moon/2c3p	McCormack	Latham	Keys	Johnston	Arnold	Rees	Senior/t	Yates/t	Fourie
Stephens/3pdg	McCormack	Latham	Keys	Johnston	Arnold/t	Rees	Senior	Yates	Fourie

REPLACEMENTS: a - Ross Bullough. b - Christian Radacanu. c - Paul Morris.

WHERE	Total	Home	Away
The POINTS were scored	684	363	321
The POINTS were conceded	468	215	253
The TRIES were scored	82	44	38
The TRIES were conceded	53	24	29

HOW the TRIES were scored

Total	Backs	Forwards	F Back	Wing	Centre	H Back	F Row	Lock	B Row	Pen. Try
82	63	18	10	28	11	14	1	5	12	1

HOW the TRIES were conceded

Total	Backs	Forwards	F Back	Wing	Centre	H Back	F Row	Lock	B Row	Pen. Try
53	38	13	5	13	6	14	3	1	9	2

SEDGLEY PARK

LEAGUE STATISTICS
compiled by Stephen McCormack

SEASON	Division	P	W	D	L	F	A	Pts Diff	Lge Pts	Lge Pos		Coach		Captain
92-93	NW 1	12	4	0	8	149	188	-36	6*	11		V Baker		P Renwick
93-94	NW 1	12	5	2	5	201	134	67	12	5		C Hebbut		R Hall
94-95	NW 1	12	12	0	0	421	60	361	24	1p		K Fletcher		P Egan
95-96	North 2	12	10	0	2	257	141	116	20	2p		K Fletcher		R Klmmins
96-97	North 1	22	17	1	4	650	398	252	35	1p		K Fletcher		R Kimmins
												Most Points		**Most Tries**
97-98	N2N	26	14	2	10	655	595	109	30	5	97	Darren Weatherall	10	Jon Duncan Mike Wilcox
98-99	N2N	26	12	1	13	710	553	157	25	8	150	Rob Moon	13	Jon Duncan
99-00	N2N	26	14	2	10	686	484	202	30	5	141	Rob Moon	12	Elijah Sobanjo
00-01	N3N	*25	21	0	4	887	327	560	42	2	235	Colin Stephens	18	Mike Wilcock
01-02	N2	26	20	1	5	684	468	216	41	3	244	Colin Stephens	12	Rob Moon

MOST POINTS

Scored at Home	70 v Winnington Park 05.12.98
Scored Away	66 v Sandal 17.03.01
Conceded at Home	43 v Stourbridge 27.03.99
Conceded Away	49 v Stourbridge 23.09.00

MOST CONSECUTIVE

Appearances	46	Mike Wilcock
Matches scoring Tries	6	Christian Raducanu 1999-00
Matches scoring points	19	Colin Stephens 2000-01
Victories	13	2000-01
Defeats	3	

BIGGEST MARGINS

Home Win	69pts	69-0 v Bedford Ath 10.02.01
Away Win	51pts	51-0 v Whitchurch 10.10.98
Home Defeat	10pts	24-43 v Stourbridge 27.03.99
Away Defeat	37pts	12-49 v Stourbridge 23.09.00

MOST TRIES

Scored in a match	11 v Sandal 17.03.01
Conceded in a match	8 v Stourbridge 23.09.00

MOST APPEARANCES

by a forward	93 Andy Kimmins
by a back	116 Mike Wilcock

	MOST IN A SEASON	MOST IN A CAREER	MOST IN A MATCH
Points	244 Colin Stephens 2001-02	540 Rob Moon 1998-02	34 Rob Moon v Bedford Ath 10.02.01 (H)
Tries	18 Mike Wilcock 2000-01	47 Mike Wilcock 1997-01	4 Ben Cohen v Winnington Park 27.12.98 (H) Mike Wilcock v Whitchurch 02.12.00 (H)
Conversions	50 Colin Stephens 2000-01	94 Rob Moon 1998-02	8 Rob Moon v Bedford Ath 10.02.01 (H)
Penalties	46 Colin Stephens 2001-02	77 Colin Stephens -00-02	8 Neil Lomax v Stourbridge 27.03.99 (H)
Drop Goals	4 Colin Stephens 00-01 & 01-02	8 Colin Stephens 2000-01	2 Colin Stephens v Fylde 8.12.01 (A)

SEDGLEY PARK RFU SENIOR CUP

STATISTICS

compiled by Stephen McCormack

OVERALL PLAYING RECORD

	P	W	D	L	F	A	Pts Diff
Home	7	3	0	4	124	177	-53
Away	5	3	0	2	100	102	-2
Neutral	-	-	-	-	-	-	-
Total	12	6	0	6	224	279	-55

SEASON BY SEASON

Season	Result
1971-72	DNQ
1972-73	DNQ
1973-74	DNQ
1974-75	DNQ
1975-76	DNQ
1976-77	DNQ
1977-78	DNQ
1978-79	DNQ
1979-80	DNQ
1980-81	DNQ
1981-82	DNQ
1982-83	DNQ
1983-84	DNQ
1984-85	DNQ
1985-86	DNQ
1986-87	DNQ
1987-88	DNQ
1988-89	DNQ
1989-90	DNQ
1990-91	DNQ
1991-92	DNQ
1992-93	1R
1993-94	DNQ
1994-95	DNQ
1995-96	DNQ
1996-97	DNQ
1997-98	1R
1998-99	4R
1999-2000	2R
2000-01	3R
2001-02	3R

TEAM RECORDS

Highest Score
34 v Bromsgrove 98/99

Biggest Winning Margin
24 (34-10) v Bromsgrove 98/99

Highest Score Against
53 v Wasps 98/99

Biggest Losing Margin
50 (53-3) v Wasps

INDIVIDUAL RECORDS

Most Points in a match

Most Tries in a match

Most Conversions in a match

Most Penalties in a match

Most Drop Goals in a match

PLAYERS

	Position	D.o.B.	Apps.	Pts.	T	C	P	DG
Ross Bullough	Winger	19.02.76	16(6)	90	18	-	-	-
Paul Morris	Winger	10.12.74	107(1)	235	47	-	-	-
Mike Wilcock	Winger	05.05.72	116	285	57	-	-	-
Dave McCormack	Scrum half	20.05.79	47(1)	50	10	-	-	-
Sion O'Hare	Centre	24.01.78	54	55	11	-	-	-
Rob Moon	Full back	27.03.76	77	540	44	94	44	-
Colin Stephens	Fly half	29.11.69	41(1)	479	10	87	76	8
Jon Scales	Winger	28.07.74	41	90	18	-	-	-
Alun Peacock	Centre	16.01.74	12	15	3	-	-	-
Carlos Hassan	Centre		22(1)	15	3	-	-	-
Gareth Roberts	Prop	30.04.81	11(9)	10	2	-	-	-
Leon Tresco	Hooker	27.09.78	28(8)	15	3	-	-	-
Rhodri Latham	Prop		15(9)	-	-	-	-	-
Paul Keys	Hooker		10(9)	-	-	-	-	-
Chris Johnston	Prop		7(2)	-	-	-	-	-
Huw Thomas	Prop		16	-	-	-	-	-
Paul Arnold	Lock	30.07.80	31	25	5	-	-	-
Paul Rees	Lock		22	-	-	-	-	-
Christian Raducanu	Lock	02.10.67	54(1)	125	25	-	-	-
Richard Senior	Back row	17.11.71	51	55	11	-	-	-
Tim Fourie	Back row	12.03.68	51	55	11	-	-	-
Kern Yates	Back row	12.02.74	66	75	15	-	-	-
Ian Grainey	Back row		5(10)	-	-	-	-	-

SEDGLEY PARK

FACT FILE

Founded: 1932
Nickname: Tigers
Colours: Black shirts with fine gold, white & claret hoops, black shorts & socks
Change: Gold shirts with fine black, claret & white hoops, black shorts & socks
Website: www.sprufc.com

GROUND

Address: Park Lane, Whitefield, Manchester M45 7DZ
Tel: 0161 766 5050 / 0161 796 2626 e-mail: admin@sprufc.com
Capacity: 2,500 Seated: 300 Standing: 2,200

Directions: From M60, junction 17 onto A56 for Bury. take the left filter at the 2nd set of traffic lights, left at the next lights (Park Lane),ground 1/2 mile on left
Nearest Railway Station: Whitefield (Manchester Metro), take taxi about £2

Car Parking: 150 on ground, 150 nearby free.

Admission: Season tickets - Adult standing £45
Matchdays - Adult £5 Children Free

Clubhouse: Normal licensing hours, snacks & bar meals available
Functions: Capacity 150 - 2 function rooms & lounge Contact John Grundy 07774 637064, 0161 280 5752

Club Shop: Yes, in club

Training Nights: Tuesday & Thursday (seniors)
Juniors -Wed.

PROGRAMME

Size: A5 Price: £1 Pages: 40
Editor: Simon Tushingham
Tel/Fax: 0161 796 7755 or 0161 796 2626
e-mail: admin@sprufc.com

Advertising Rates
Mono - Full page £170, half £90, Qtr £50

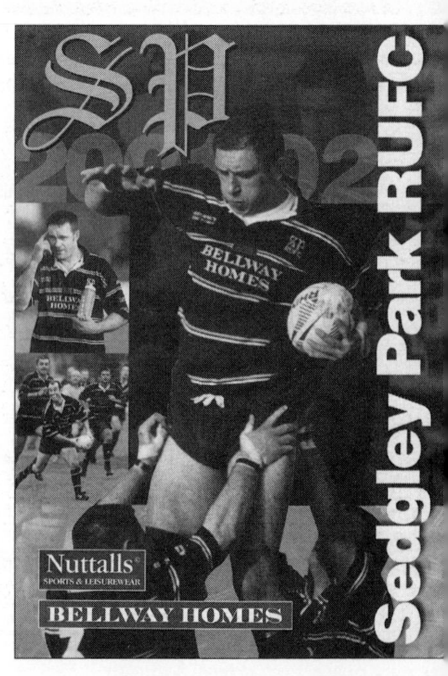

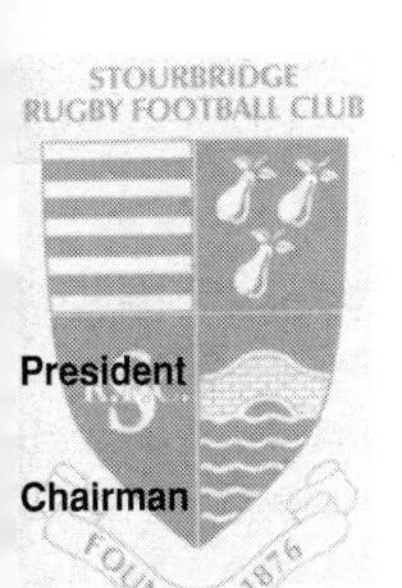

STOURBRIDGE RFC

President	Peter Millard	Tel: 01384 873636 (H) 01384 571181 (B) email: peter.millard@dudley-tool.co.uk
Chairman	Peter Trinham	Tel: 01384 393948 (H), 01384 254453 (O) email: dudley@wortonrock.co.uk
Secretary	Robert Browne	01562 882020 (H)
1st XV Manager	Richard Stanley	01384 370676 (H) 01384 441122 (O)
Director of Coaching	TBA	
Press Officer	Vernon Davies	36 Beckman Road, Pedmore, Stourbridge.

Tel: 01562 883640 (H) 01562 720534 (Fax) email: davies-email@breathemail.net

Stourbridge's first every season in National Division Two proved an intriguing and valuable experience as early success faded so that with two games left to play they faced the real prospect of relegation. It was a timely and convincing home win over Esher that guaranteed survival.

A pre season mini tour of South Wales set the squad up for a promising start in which four out of the first five league games were won, so that by mid October they were comfortably third in the table. Unfortunately, injury deprived the club for the whole season of two key props, Nathan Webber and captain Simon Baylie, and a succession of injuries throughout the campaign did test the strength and depth of the squad in the face of increased quality opposition. After remaining undefeated at Stourton in 2000-01 Stourbridge found less comfort in home advantage and only won six out of the thirteen games. They completed the double over relegated Waterloo and Preston. The best performances were both away from home, in November against Rosslyn Park, and in March in a narrow and unlucky defeat at Plymouth, but the most significant win was that late home success against Esher. The most bizarre score was a home loss by one point to Wharfedale, 41-42, after leading 36-10 at half time.

Stourbridge used a total of 45 players, nineteen of whom were making their debuts. These included Ben Harvey who scored in every game and who, with 298 league points, smashed Duncan Hughes' record established last year. Dominic Feaunati scored tries in his first four games, an unprecedented feat. There were only two ever presents, Nick Tisdale and Bob Merritt. Bob has now played in the last 74 games and, with 175 league appearances in total, is well ahead of all his rivals. Scrum half Bruce Fenley's season was curtailed by injury and after two inspirational seasons he has left the club for a coaching appointment.

Stourbridge lost to Sedgley Park in their only cup game. The pressure of the league and the danger to key players is such that clubs no longer take advantage of open dates to play friendly fixtures. Thus, this season the fixture list consisted of 27 completed games, the lowest number since 1916-17

STOURBRIDGE

Comp.	Date	H/A	Opponents	Result & Score	Att	15	14	13	12	11
N2	01-09	H	Orrell	W 21-18	700	Harvey/c3p	Beechy/t	McLaughlin	Wilson	Coates
N2	08-09	H	Plymouth Albion	L 10-34	650	Harvey/cp	Coates	McLaughlin/t	Eastwood	Beechy
N2	15-09	A	Preston Grasshoppers	W 16-13	280	Harvey/tc3p	Wilson	McLaughlin	Eastwood	Beechy
N2	22-09	H	Newbury	W 37-14		Wylde	Wilson	Eastwood	Hughes/3t	Beechy/t
N2	06-10	A	Waterloo	W 31-12		John	Eastwood/t	Hughes	McLaughlin	Trigg
N2	20-10	H	Fylde	L 12-35		Beauchamp	Myler	Hughes	Eastwood	Farani
N2	27-10	A	Wharfedale	D 29-29		Beauchamp	Trigg	Myler	Eastwood	Coates/t
N2	10-11	H	Sedgley Park	L 17-29	300	Harvey/4p	Coates/t	John	Eastwood	Beauchamp
N2	17-11	A	Rosslyn Park	W 42-10		Harvey/4c3p	Coates/t	John/t	Eastwood	Wilson
N2	24-11	H	Kendal	L 23-26	300	Wylde	Wilson	John	Eastwood	Coates/t
N2	01-12	A	Orrell	L 16-43	600	Wilson	Trigg	John/t	Feaun'ati/t	Coates
N2	08-12	H	Harrogate	L 21-39	200	Harvey/3c	Wilson	John	Feaun'ati/t	Coates/t
N2	15-12	A	Esher	L 17-45		Harvey/2cp	Trigg/t	John	Feaun'ati/t	Coates
N2	22-12	H	Nottingham	W 32-22		Harvey/c5p	Myler/t	John/t	Feaun'ati/t	Farani
N2	12-01	H	Rosslyn Park	L 20-25		Harvey/2c2p	Farani/t	John	Feaun'ati	Myler
N2	19-01	A	Sedgley Park	L 24-34	350	Hughes/t	Farani	Feaun'ati/t	Eastwood	Myler
N2	02-02	A	Fylde	L 20-33		Hughes	Farani	Eastwood	Feaun'ati	Myler/t
N2	09-02	H	Waterloo	W 18-14	250	Hughes/t	Farani	McLaughlin	Eastwood	Wilson
N2	16-02	A	Kendal	L 13-31		Hughes/t	Myler	Feaun'ati	McLaughlin	Farani
N2	23-02	A	Newbury	L 20-31		Hughes	Wilson/2t	Myler	McLaughlin	Eastwood
N2	02-03	H	Wharfedale	L 41-42	100	Hughes/t	Eastwood/2t	McLaughlin	Farani/t	Wilson
N2	09-03	H	Preston Grasshoppers	W 32-7	280	Eastwood	Feaun'ati	McLaughlin/t	John/t	Myler
N2	16-03	A	Plymouth Albion	L 16-23	1550	Eastwood	Hall	McLaughlin	Feaun'ati/t	Carpenter
N2	30-03	A	Nottingham	L 12-29	521	Eastwood	Hall	John	McLaughlin	Feaun'ati
N2	06-04	H	Esher	W 45-19	300	Eastwood	Myler/t	Feaun'ati(a/t)	McLaughlin	Hall
N2	13-04	A	Harrogate	L 15-45	329	Eastwood	Yiend/t	Feaun'ati	McLaughlin	Hall
PGC	29-09	A	Sedgley Park	L 13-33	375	Wylde	Trigg	Hughes	McLaughlin	Beechy

** after opponents name indicates a penalty try. Brackets after a player's name indicates he was replaced. eg (a) means he was replaced by replacement code "a" and so on. / after a player or replacement name is followed by any scores he made - eg /t, /c, /p, /dg or any combination of these*

EVER PRESENT Rob Merritt

Most Appearances:
26: Rob Merritt.
25: Virgil Hartland, Ben Harvey, Nick Tisdale(1).
24: Duncan Hughes.

PLAYERS USED

39 plus seven as a replacement

MOST POINTS

Pts	Player	T	C	P	DG
298	B Harvey	9	44	55	-
67	D Hughes	9	2	5	1
35	D Farini	7	-	-	-
30	D Feaunati	6	-	-	-
25	L Coates	5	-	-	-

MATCH FACTS

10	9	1	2	3	4	5	6	7	8
ghes	Fenley	Richardson	Merritt	Hartland	Tisdale	Taylor	Jones/t	Richardson	Hynes
ıghes	Fenley	Richardson	Merritt	Hartland	Tisdale	Taylor	Jones	Richardson	Scriven
ıghes	Fenley	Hartland	Merritt	Erven	Tisdale	Aston	Scriven	Richardson	Farani
arvey/4c3p	Fenley	Ferguson	Merritt	Hartland	Tisdale	Aston	Hynes	Dawes	Scriven
arvey/c3p	Fenley	Richardson	Merritt	Hartland	Tisdale	Aston	Scriven	Jones	Farani/2t
arvey/4p	Fenley	Hartland	Merritt	Ferguson	Tisdale	Aston	Scriven	Richardson	Hynes
ıghes/2c5p	Fenley	Hartland	Merritt	Ferguson	Taylor	Russell	Scriven	Richardson	Farani/t
ıghes	Fenley	Hartland	Merritt	Ferguson	Tisdale	Taylor	Russell	Dawes	Farani
ıghes	Fenley/t	Hartland	Merritt	Richardson/t	Tisdale	Russell	Hynes	Richardson/t	Farani
arvey/2c3p	Fenley	Hartland	Merritt	Richardson	Tisdale	Taylor	Hynes	Jones	Farani/t
arvey/2p	Fenley	Hartland	Merritt	Ferguson	Tisdale	Taylor	Jones	Richardson	Farani
ıghes/t	Fenley	Hartland	Merritt	Ferguson	Tisdale	Taylor	Jones	Bradley	Farani
ıghes	Fenley	Richardson	Merritt	Hartland	Tisdale	Taylor	Jones	Dawes	Farani
ıghes	Fenley	Fellows	Merritt	Hartland	Tisdale	Aston	Taylor	Dawes	Russell
ıghes/t	Fenley	Fellows	Merritt	Hartland	Tisdale	Aston	Taylor	Dawes	Russell
arvey/t3cp	Fenley	Hartland	Merritt	Sigley	Tisdale	Aston	Russell	Taylor	Scriven
arvey/2c2p	Fenley	Hartland/t	Merritt	Sigley	Tisdale	Aston	Russell	Taylor	Scriven
arvey/c2p	Fenley/t	Hartland	Merritt	Sigley	Tisdale	Aston	Russell	Hall	Scriven
arvey/c2p	Fenley	Fellows	Merritt	Sigley	Tisdale	Aston	Russell	Hall	Scriven
arvey/2c2p	Fenley	Hartland	Merritt	Sigley	Tisdale	Russell	Scriven	Hickey	Hynes
arvey/2t4cp	Fenley	Fellows	Merritt	Hartland	Tisdale	Taylor	Russell	Hickey	Hynes
ughes	Harvey/t2cp	Fellows	Merritt	Hartland/t	Tisdale	Taylor	Russell	Mellors/t	Hynes
ughes/dg	Harvey/c2p	Fellows	Merritt	Hartland	Tisdale	Taylor	Russell	Mellors	Hynes
ughes	Harvey/tc	Sigley	Merritt/t	Hartland	Tisdale	Taylor	Russell	Mellors	Hynes
ughes	Harvey/2t4c4p	Hartland	Merritt	Sigley	Tisdale	Taylor	Russell	Mellors/t	Hynes
ıghes	Harvey/tcp	Hartland	Merritt	Sigley	Tisdale	Taylor	Russell	Mellors	Scriven
arvey/c2p	Fenley	Hartland	Merritt	Ferguson	Tisdale	Aston/t	Hynes	Richardson	Scriven

EPLACEMENTS: a - Daniel Farini.

WHERE	Total	Home	Away
The POINTS were scored	600	329	271
The POINTS were conceded	702	378	324
The TRIES were scored	65	36	29
The TRIES were conceded	87	48	39

HOW the TRIES were scored

Total	Backs	Forwards	F Back	Wing	Centre	H Back	F Row	Lock	B Row	Pen. Try
65	53	12	5	18	18	12	4	-	8	-

HOW the TRIES were conceded

Total	Backs	Forwards	F Back	Wing	Centre	H Back	F Row	Lock	B Row	Pen. Try
87	54	31	8	19	16	11	7	8	16	2

STOURBRIDGE

LEAGUE STATISTICS
compiled by Stephen McCormac

SEASON	Division	P	W	D	L	F	A	Pts Diff	Lge Pts	Lge Pos		Most Points		Most Tries
92-93	D4N	12	5	1	6	161	144	17	11	9	108	Simon Pennington	2	Mark Wilson/Richard Trigg/Dale Smallman
93-94	D5N	12	6	0	6	162	188	-26	12	5	90	Chris Mann	5	Richard Trigg
94-95	D5N	12	6	0	6	166	174	-8	12	6	98	Chris Mann	4	Adrian James
95-96	D5N	12	6	0	6	200	177	23	12	7	100	Chris Mann	4	Richard Trigg
96-97	D4N	26	14	1	11	704	579	125	29	6	206	Chris Mann	15	Kevin Hickey
97-98	N2N	26	14	0	12	685	605	80	28	6	107	Chris Mann	14	Alan Dickens
98-99	N2N	26	22	0	4	895	413	482	44	2	105	Simon Baylie	13	Richard Trigg & Simon Baylie
99-00	N2N	26	21	1	4	730	411	319	43	2	116	Hamish Pearson	10	Jacob John & Spencer Bradley
00-01	N3N	*25	21	1	3	861	368	493	43	1p	224	Duncan Hughes	15	Duncan Hughes
01-02	N2	26	9	1	16	600	702	-102	19	11	298	Ben Harvey	9	Ben Harvey & Duncan Hughes

MOST POINTS

Scored at Home	72 v Morley 02.09.90
Scored Away	74 v Lichfield 17.04.99
Conceded at Home	45 v Aspatria 19.10.96
Conceded Away	62 v Manchester 31.01.98

MOST CONSECUTIVE

Appearances	48	Bob Merritt
Matches scoring Tries	6	Rob Myler 2000-01
Matches scoring points	24	Chris Mann 1993-96
Victories	12	1998-99
Defeats	6	1993

BIGGEST MARGINS

Home Win	58pts	65-7 v Whitchurch 14.10.00
Away Win	74pts	74-0 v Lichfield 17.04.99
Home Defeat	25pts	7-32 v Otley 02.03.91
Away Defeat	45pts	17-62 v Manchester 31.01.98

MOST TRIES

Scored in a match 12 v Morley 02.09.00
v Lichfield 17.04.99

Conceded in a match 8 v Nanchester 31.01.98

MOST APPEARANCES

by a forward 175 Bob Merritt

by a back 100 Jacob John

	MOST IN A SEASON	MOST IN A CAREER	MOST IN A MATCH
Points	298 Ben Harvey 2001-02	635 Chris Mann 1993-99	30 Ben Harvey v Esher 6.4.02 (H)
Tries	15 Kevin Hickey 1996-97 Duncan Hughes 2000-01	43 Richard Trigg 1987-00	3 by eight players - twice each by Simon Bayl and Richard Trigg
Conversions	47 Chris Mann 1996-97	105 Chris Mann 1993-99	7 Duncan Hughes v Whitchurch 14.10.00
Penalties	55 Ben Harvey 2001-02	116 Chris Mann 1993-99	8 Steve Baker v Hereford 26.01.91
Drop Goals	2 Andy Dickens 1987-88 Chris Mann 1995-96	4 Chris Mann 1993-99	2 Chris Mann v Birmingham & Sol 30.09.95

OVERALL PLAYING RECORD

	P	W	D	L	F	A	Pts Diff
Home	11	6	-	5	238	201	37
Away	17	7	-	10	282	432	-150
Neutral	-	-	-	-	-	-	-
Total	28	13	-	15	520	633	-113

SEASON BY SEASON

1971-72	DNQ
1972-73	DNQ
1973-74	DNQ
1974-75	DNQ
1975-76	DNQ
1976-77	DNQ
1977-78	DNQ
1978-79	DNQ
1979-80	DNQ
1980-81	DNQ
1981-82	2R
1982-83	DNQ
1983-84	3R
1984-85	2R
1985-86	1R
1986-87	1R
1987-88	DNQ
1988-89	DNQ
1989-90	DNQ
1990-91	DNQ
1991-92	1R
1992-93	DNQ
1993-94	4R
1994-95	2R
1995-96	3R
1996-97	1R
1997-98	3R
1998-99	3R
1999-2000	2R
2000-01	3R
2001-02	2R

STOURBRIDGE
RFU SENIOR CUP
STATISTICS
compiled by Stephen McCormack

TEAM RECORDS

Highest Score
69 v Taunton 97/98
Biggest Winning Margin
64 (69-5) v Taunton 97/98
Highest Score Against
78 v Coventry 95/96
Biggest Losing Margin
58 (20-78) v Coventry

INDIVIDUAL RECORDS

Most Points in a match

Most Tries in a match

Most Conversions in a match

Most Penalties in a match

Most Drop Goals in a match

PLAYERS STOURBRIDGE

	Position	D.o.B.	Apps.	Pts.	T	C	P	DG
Lee Coates	Winger	02.11.79	10(1)	25	5	-	-	-
Mark Eastwood	Centre	15.11.79	19	15	3	-	-	-
Dominic Feaunati	Winger	14.06.78	14(1)	30	6	-	-	-
Bruce Fenley	Scrum half	07.09.68	45	60	12	-	-	-
Jon Hall	Winger	20.04.78	62(12)	100	20	-	-	-
Ben Harvey	Fly half	26.06.74	25	298	9	44	55	-
Jacob John	Centre	02.12.75	113(13)	253	44	-	-	-
Ali McLaughlin	Centre	31.05.76	48	60	12	-	-	-
Rob Myler	Winger	04.03.70	30(3)	70	14	-	-	-
Matt Ashton	Lock	22.02.73	14(3)	-	-	-	-	-
Simon Daws	Back row	13.01.79	9(4)	-	-	-	-	-
Daniel Farini	Back row	14.06.78	21(4)	35	7	-	-	-
Matthew Ferguson	Prop	12.06.78	52(12)	10	2	-	-	-
Virgil Hartland	Prop	23.04.77	25	5	1	-	-	-
James Hynes	Back row	01.05.79	33(10	15	3	-	-	-
Bob Merritt	Hooker	05.02.72	175(2)	130	26	-	-	-
Matt Richardson	Prop	24.01.75	23(11)	15	3	-	-	-
Nigel Richardson	Back row	01.02.71	13(6)	5	1	-	-	-
Jon Russell	Back row	29.06.72	129(7)	50	10	-	-	-
Brett Scriven	Back row	05.12.78	29(7)	35	7	-	-	-
Gareth Taylor	Lock	01.03.76	86(15)	50	10	-	-	-
Nick Tisdale	Lock	26.08.70	98(2)	30	6	-	-	-

STOURBRIDGE

FACT FILE

Founded: 1876

Colours: Navy blue with narrow white bands
Change colours: Red & white hoops, trimmed navy blue

GROUND

Address: Bridgnorth Road, Stourton, Stourbridge, W. Midlands. DY7 6QZ
Tel: 01384 393889.
Capacity: 3500 Seated: 499 Standing: 3001

Directions: The ground is situated on the A458 (Bridgnorth road), two miles west of Stourbridge town centre. The ground is on the left hand side 1/2mile past the `Foresters Arms' public house.
Nearest Railway Station: Stourbridge Junction.

Car Parking: 200 spaces are available at the ground.

Admission: Matchday - Adults £7, including prog.,
U16 No charge

Clubhouse: Three bars and food is available.
Functions: Three rooms able to hold functions. Contact Steward

Club Shop: Open match days only

Training Nights: Tuesday and Thursday.

PROGRAMME

Size: A5
Price: With admission
Pages: 40 plus cover
Editor: Vernon Davies
01562 883640

Advertising Rates: Full page £100.

BELOW:
Nick Tisdale
winning good line out ball.

WHARFEDALE RUFC

resident	John Spencer	High Pasture, Threshfield, Nr Skipton, N Yorks BD23 5NS 01756 752456 (H), 01756 753015 (B), 01756 753020 (Fax)
lub Secretary	Antony Davies	21 Raikeswood Drive, Skipton, N. Yorks. BD23 1NA 01756 798435 (H), 01756 753015 (B), 01756 753020 (Fax)
irector of Rugby / Fixture Secretary	Michael Harrison	Old Hall Farm,Threshfield, Skipton, N. Yorks. BD23 5PL 01756 752777 (H & B & Fax)
hairman / Administration	Graham Currier	Fell View Cottage, Hartlington Raikes, Bursnall, N. Yorks. BD23 6BX 01756 720257 (Tel & Fax)
ress Officer	Chris Ellwood	28 Carleton Avenue, Skipton, N. Yorks. BD23 2TE 01756 798077 (Tel & Fax), email: ellwood@netcomuk.co.uk

Another erratic season. One in which the Greens regularly subjected their loyal fans to agonies of anxiety, leavened ith a few truly joyous interludes. The final 6th place in the table - equalling the second-best achievement in National Two - oks comfortable enough at first sight. Nevertheless, only points difference separated Wharfedale from 9th position, and it as not until well into February that the coaches eased up on motivational lectures on the subject of relegation.

The undisputed highlight was the honour of ending Plymouth Albion's magnificent run of 41 consecutive league vicries. The 28-20 win was no fluke, but the topsy-turvy nature of the Greens' season was typified by their next result - a 54-0 beating at the hands of Sedgley Park (albeit in a splendid match).

One thing became very clear as the campaign progressed: you could be unwise to leave early! In 12 league matchs (plus 2 Cup games) the sides were separated by less than a score. Noteworthy in itself, but that includes an amazing 6 ecided by a single point, or drawn! That 4 of these - the nail-biters against Kendal (lost 24-23 away, won 22-21 home) and tourbridge (29-29 home, won 42-41 away) - were against the surviving sides that finished closest to the relegated trio, nderlines just how tight National Two had become (below perhaps the top 3 or 4).

You have to search for other genuine highlights. We made our first-ever appearance in the Yorkshire Cup Final, but issed out on the bonus chance to get a win over Harrogate after a defeat and a draw in the league. There was a first win gainst Kendal, and some determined away performances - particularly at Rosslyn Park and Esher. Our biggest victory was 9-8 over Grasshoppers, but that against a side that, even in January, seemed resigned to relegation.

On an individual level, Jonathan Davies collected records. He now holds Highest League Points in a season at 278, est with the Boot at 253 and also equalled the club's Most League Points in One Match with 29 against Grasshoppers. John awn again captained the County team, leading them to the semi-finals of the County Championship. He was joined in the quad by Andy Hodgson, David Lister and Hedley Verity. John and Andy were included in the England Counties squad that toured Chile in June, John getting a try in the final 'test' match against Chile.

Finally - the most impressive records of them all:
lock David Lister (below right) now sits on a remarkable 109 consecutive league appearances (a National best by a street), and counting! Flanker Hedley Verity (pictured left) also has a National record in his sights: his 214 total league starts is just 5 short of the current highest for a single club.

Photos courtesy of the Craven Herald

WHARFEDALE

Comp.	Date	H/A	Opponents	Result & Score	Att	15	14	13	12	11
N2	01-09	H	Rosslyn Park	L 15-18		Davies/cp	Eccleston/t	Hodgson	Burnett	Smithson
N2	08-09	A	Kendal	L 23-24		Davies/2c3p	Eccleston/t	Hodgson/t	Whitfield	Burnett
N2	15-09	H	Nottingham	W 46-13		Hodgson/t	Burnett/3t	Heseltine	Whitfield	Davies/4cp
N2	22-09	A	Harrogate	L 36-51		Hodgson/t	Burnett/3t	Heseltine	Whitfield	Davies/2c
N2	06-10	H	Esher	W 16-13		Davies/c3p	Burnett	Hodgson	Whitfield	Smithson
N2	20-10	A	Orrell	L 16-44		Davies/c3p	Burnett/t	Heseltine	Whitfield	Smithson
N2	27-10	H	Stourbridge	D 29-29		Davies/2c5p	Burnett	Hodgson	Whitfield/t	Smithson
N2	10-11	A	Preston Grasshoppers	W 25-23	275	Davies/2c2p	Burnett	Hodgson/2t	Whitfield	Smithson
N2	17-11	H	Newbury	L 23-24		Davies/2c3p	Burnett	Hodgson/t	Whitfield	Smithson/t
N2	24-11	A	Waterloo	W 38-14		Davies/3c3pdg	Burnett	Hodgson/t	Whitfield	Smithson/2
N2	01-12	A	Rosslyn Park	W 23-8		Davies/2c3p	Burnett	Hodgson/2t	Whitfield	Smithson
N2	08-12	H	Plymouth Albion	W 28-20		Davies/tcp	Burnett	Hodgson/t	Whitfield	Smithson/t
N2	15-12	A	Sedgley Park	L 24-50	450	Davies/3cp	Burnett	Hodgson	Whitfield/t	Smithson/t
N2	22-12	A	Fylde	L 13-17		Davies/c2p	Burnett	Hodgson/t	Baggett	Smithson
N2	12-01	A	Newbury	L 21-30		Davies/2p	Burnett/2t	Hodgson	Whitfield	Eccleston
N2	19-01	H	Preston Grasshoppers	W 59-8		Davies/t6c4p	Burnett/t	Hodgson	Whitfield	Smithson
N2	02-02	H	Orrell	L 8-18		Davies/p	Burnett	Hodgson/t	Whitfield	Smithson
N2	09-02	A	Esher	W 17-13		Davies/2cp	Burnett	Hodgson	Whitfield	Johnson/t
N2	16-02	H	Waterloo	W 37-27		Davies/c5p	Burnett	Hodgson/t	Whitfield	Johnson
N2	23-02	H	Harrogate	D 6-6		Davies/2p	Smithson	Hodgson	Whitfield	Johnson
N2	02-03	A	Stourbridge	W 42-41	100	Davies/t4c3p	Smithson	Hodgson/t	Whitfield	Johnson
N2	09-03	A	Nottingham	L 9-21	406	Davies/3p	Smithson	Hodgson	Whitfield	Johnson
N2	16-03	H	Kendal	W 22-21		Davies/tc	Smithson/t	Hodgson/t	Whitfield	Johnson
N2	30-03	H	Fylde	L 21-27		Davies/t3c	Smithson	Hodgson	Johnson	Burnett
N2	06-04	H	Sedgley Park	L 3-33	650	Davies/p	Smithson	Hodgson	Johnson	Burnett
N2	13-04	A	Plymouth Albion	L 3-45	1800	Davies/p	Eccleston	Hodgson	Baggett	Johnson
PGC	29-09	A	Nuneaton	L 29-31		Hodgson/2t	Burnett/2c	Heseltine	Whitfield	Davies/cp

** after opponents name indicates a penalty try. Brackets after a player's name indicates he was replaced. eg (a) means he was replaced by replacement code "a" and so on. / after a player or replacement name is followed by any scores he made - eg /t, /c, /p, /dg or any combination of these*

EVER PRESENT

Anthony Capstick, Jonathan Davies, David Lister.

Most Appearances:
26: Anthony Capstick, Jonathan Davies, David Lister.
25: Hedley Verity, Andrew Hodgson, Paul Evans.
23: Philip Peel.

PLAYERS USED

27 plus five as replacement

MOST POINTS

Pts	Player	T	C	P	DG
278	J Davies	5	44	54	1
75	A Hodgson	15	-	-	-
50	C Burnett	10	-	-	-
30	D Lister	6	-	-	-
30	G Smithson	6	-	-	-

MATCH FACTS

10	9	1	2	3	4	5	6	7	8
Baggett	Smith	Peel/t	Lawn	Dickinson	Lister	Capstick	Gains	Verity	Evans
Baggett	Smith	Peel	Hindle	Ingram	Lister	Capstick	Gains	Verity	Evans
Baggett	Smith/t	Peel	Lawn	Ingram	Lister/t	Capstick	Gains	Verity/t	Evans
Baggett/c	Smith	Peel	Lawn	Dickinson	Lister/2t	Capstick	Gains	Verity	Evans
Baggett	Smith	Peel	Lawn	Ingram	Lister	Capstick	Kirkbride	Verity	Evans/t
Baggett	Smith	Peel	Lawn	Ingram	Lister	Capstick	Kirkbride	Verity	Evans
Baggett	Smith	Peel	Lawn	Ingram	Lister/t	Capstick	Allen	Verity	Evans
Baggett	Smith	Peel	Lawn	Ingram	Lister	Capstick	Kirkbride	Hargreaves	Evans/t
Baggett	Smith	Peel	Lawn	Ingram	Lister	Capstick	Kirkbride	Verity	Evans
Baggett	Smith/t	Peel	Lawn	Dickinson	Lister	Capstick	Evans	Verity	Buckroyd
Baggett	Smith	Peel	Hindle	Dickinson	Lister	Capstick	Evans	Verity	Buckroyd
Heseltine	Smith	Peel	Lawn	Dickinson/t	Lister	Capstick	Evans	Verity	Buckroyd/dg
Heseltine	Smith	Peel	Lawn	Dickinson	Lister/t	Capstick	Evans	Verity	Buckroyd
Heseltine	Whitfield	Peel	Hindle	Ingram	Lister	Capstick	Evans	Verity	Buckroyd
Heseltine	Smith	Peel	Lawn	Dickinson	Lister	Capstick	Kirkbride(a/t)	Verity	Evans
Heseltine	Harrison	Peel	Lawn	Dickinson/t	Lister/t	Capstick	Evans	Verity/2t	Allen/t
Heseltine	Harrison	Peel	Lawn	Dickinson	Lister	Capstick	Evans	Verity	Allen
Baggett	Harrison/t	Peel	Lawn	Ingram	Lister	Capstick	Evans	Verity	Allen
Baggett/t	Harrison	Peel	Hindle	Ingram	Lister	Capstick	Evans(b/t)	Verity	Allen/t
Baggett	Harrison	Peel	Lawn	Dickinson	Lister	Capstick	Evans	Verity	Allen
Baggett/2t	Harrison/t	Peel	Lawn	Ingram	Lister	Capstick	Buckroyd	Verity	Allen
Baggett	Harrison	Ingram	Lawn	Dickinson	Lister	Capstick	Evans	Verity	Buckroyd
Baggett	Harrison	Peel	Lawn	Ingram	Lister	Capstick/t	Evans	Verity	Buckroyd
Baggett/t	Harrison	Peel	Hindle	Ingram(c/t)	Lister	Capstick	Evans	Verity	Hargreaves
Baggett	Harrison	Ingram	Lawn	Dickinson	Lister	Capstick	Evans	Verity	Hargreaves
Slater	Harrison	Ingram	Lawn	Dickinson	Lister	Capstick	Evans	Verity	Hargreaves
Baggett	Smith/t	Peel	Lawn	Ingram	Lister	Capstick	Allen	Verity	Evans

REPLACEMENTS: a - Sam Allen. b - Russ Buckroyd. c - Neil Dickinson.

WHERE

	Total	Home	Away
The POINTS were scored	603	313	290
The POINTS were conceded	638	381	257
The TRIES were scored	69	37	32
The TRIES were conceded	81	50	31

HOW the TRIES were scored

Total	Backs	Forwards	F Back	Wing	Centre	H Back	F Row	Lock	B Row	Pen. Try
68	49	19	7	19	15	8	4	7	8	-

HOW the TRIES were conceded

Total	Backs	Forwards	F Back	Wing	Centre	H Back	F Row	Lock	B Row	Pen. Try
81	57	24	9	27	12	9	6	1	17	-

WHARFEDALE

LEAGUE STATISTICS

compiled by Stephen McCormack

SEASON	Division	P	W	D	L	F	A	Pts Diff	Lge Pts	Lge Pos	Most Points	Most Tries
92-93	North 1	12	7	0	5	216	207	9	14	3	45 Mark Toseland	5 Glen Harrison
93-94	North 1	12	12	0	0	327	77	250	24	1p	127 Alex Howarth	8 Alex Howarth & Simon Slater
94-95	5N	12	6	1	5	209	198	11	13	4	94 Alex Howarth	5 Daniel Harrison
95-96	5N	12	12	0	0	331	146	185	24	1p	143 Alex Howarth	10 Neil Heseltine
96-97	3	30	17	0	13	710	635	75	34	7	182 Adam Mounsey	21 Andrew Hodgson
97-98	JN1	26	8	3	15	476	684	-208	19	10	247 Adam Mounsey	8 Jonathon Davies
98-99	JN1	26	13	1	12	477	421	51	27	7	235 David Pears	8 Adam Mounsey
99-00	JN1	26	19	1	6	646	317	329	39	3	274 Adam Mounsey	19 Andrew Hodgson
00-01	N2	*25	14	0	11	594	475	119	28	6	171 Adam Mounsey	7 Adam Mounsey & Chris Armitage
01-02	N2	26	11	2	13	603	638	-35	24	6	278 Jonathan Davies	15 Andrew Hodgson

BIGGEST MARGINS

Home Win	62pts - 72-10 v Fylde 23.9.00
Away Win	34pts - 68-34 v Lichfield 30.3.96
Home Defeat	42pts - 8-50 v Walsall 25.3.95
Away Defeat	47pts - 24-71 v London Welsh 21.3.98

MOST CONSECUTIVE

Appearances	61 David Lister
Matches scoring Tries	6 Andrew Hodgson
Matches scoring points	50 Adam Mounsey
Victories	14 x 2
Defeats	8 (18.4.98 - 10.10.98)

MOST POINTS

Scored at Home	72 v Fylde 23.9.00
Scored Away	68 v Lichfield 30.3.96
Conceded at Home	53 v Worcester
Conceded Away	71 v London Welsh 21.3.98

MOST TRIES

Scored in a match	12 v Sandbach 29.2.92
Conceded in a match	11 v London Welsh 21.3.98 (A)

MOST APPEARANCES

by a forward	214 Hedley Verity
by a back	171 (4) Neil Heseltine

	MOST IN A SEASON	MOST IN A CAREER	MOST IN A MATCH
Points	278 Jonathan Davies 01-02	951 AdamMounsey 96-01	29 Adam Mounsey v Reading 15.01.00 Jonathan Davies v Preston 19.1.02 (H)
Tries	21 Andrew Hodgson 96-97	67 Andrew Hodgson 96-01	6 Les Ingham v Sandbach 29.2.92
Conversions	44 Jonathan Davies 01-02	123 Adam Mounsey 96-00	8 David Pears v Fylde 23.9.00
Penalties	55 Adam Mounsey 97-98 & 99-00	175 Adam Mounsey 96-00	6 Mark Toseland v Lymm 14.1.89 David Pears v Liverpool St H 7.11.98
Drop Goals	4 David Pears 98-99	9 Russ Buckroyd 87-97	1 on 22 occasions including 9 by Russ Buckroyd

OVERALL PLAYING RECORD

	P	W	D	L	F	A	Pts Diff
Home	6	5	-	1	150	88	62
Away	11	3	-	8	254	229	25
Neutral	-	-	-	-	-	-	-
Total	17	8	-	9	404	309	87

SEASON BY SEASON

1971-72	DNQ
1972-73	DNQ
1973-74	DNQ
1974-75	DNQ
1975-76	DNQ
1976-77	DNQ
1977-78	DNQ
1978-79	DNQ
1979-80	DNQ
1980-81	DNQ
1981-82	DNQ
1982-83	DNQ
1983-84	DNQ
1984-85	DNQ
1985-86	DNQ
1986-87	DNQ
1987-88	DNQ
1988-89	DNQ
1989-90	DNQ
1990-91	DNQ
1991-92	DNQ
1992-93	DNQ
1993-94	4R
1994-95	3R
1995-96	1R
1996-97	3R
1997-98	3R
1998-99	3R
1999-2000	2R
2000-01	3R
2001-02	2R

WHARFEDALE RFU SENIOR CUP

STATISTICS

compiled by Stephen McCormack

TEAM RECORDS

Highest Score
59 v Scunthorpe 93/94

Biggest Winning Margin
53 (59-6) Scunthorpe 93/94

Highest Score Against
34 v Otley 96/97

Biggest Losing Margin
21 (8-29) v Worcester

INDIVIDUAL RECORDS

Most Points in a match

Most Tries in a match

Most Conversions in a match

Most Penalties in a match

Most Drop Goals in a match

PLAYERS

	Position	D.o.B.	Apps.	Pts.	T	C	P	DG
Andrew Hodgson	Centre	09.02.76	120(1)	67	335	-	-	-
Neil Heseltine	fly half	16.07.68	171(4)	158	31	-	-	1
Craig Eccleston	Winger	19.04.78	17(6)	40	8	-	-	-
Andrew Baggett	fly half		21(4)	22	4	1	-	-
Carl Burnett	Winger		21(2)	50	10	-	-	-
Dan Harrison	Scrum half	26.10.71	103(4)	120	24	-	-	-
Jonathan Davies	Full back	28.03.72	130(2)	465	27	79	63	1
David Whitfield	Centre	08.08.72	78(12)	40	8	-	-	-
Graham Smith	Scrum half		65(1)	40	8			
George Smithson	Winger		23(1)	30	6	-	-	-
Richard Lancaster	Prop	12.03.73	54(13)	25	5	-	-	-
Neil Dickinson	Prop	30.07.69	111(19)	20	4	-	-	-
John Lawn	Hooker	07.08.70	189(2)	100	20	-	-	-
Craig Ingrams	Prop	04.07.74	40(27)	5	1	-	-	-
David Lister	Lock	19.10.73	154	90	18	-	-	-
Anthony Capstick	Lock	26.12.74	46(5)	10	2	-	-	-
Paul Evans	Lock	03.01.67	113(7)	75	15	-	-	-
Sam Allen	Back row	23.07.78	30(31)	20	4	-	-	-
Russ Buckroyd	Back row	31.01.67	137(14)	264	28	-	-	10
Hedley Verity	Back row	20.04.70	214	173	36	-	-	-
John Hartley	Back row	17.08.75	5(3)	5	1	-	-	-

WHARFEDALE

FACT FILE

Founded: 1923
Nickname: Green Machine
Colours: Emerald green
Change colours: Scarlet & white hoops

GROUND

Address: Wharfeside Avenue, Threshfield, Skipton, N Yorks BD23 5ND
Tel : 01756 752547 Fax: 01756 720257 e-mail: elephant@netcomuk.co.uk
web site: www.wharfedalerufc.co.uk
Capacity: 3,000 Seated: 120 Standing: Covered 180, Uncovered 2,700

Directions: Take B6256 from Skipton bypass, signed Grassington after 8 miles turn right after Old Hall Inn in Threshfield, left after 400 metres down 'The Avenue'
Nearest Station: Skipton, no bus service. Group transport can be arranged through club secretary

Car Parking: 120 adjacent, no charge

Admission: Matchday Adults (incl. prog.) £5, u16 No Charge

Club Shop: Open 1 hour before & after 1st XV matches. Manager Mary Watkinson 01756 790282

Clubhouse: Normal licensing hours matchdays. Snacks etc available.
Functions Capacity 120 Contact Frank House 01756 753546

Training Nights: Monday & Wednesday

PROGRAMME Size: A5 Pages: 36 + cover Price: Included with entry
Editor: Gordon Brown 01756 752410
Advertising Rates Colour: Negotiable Mono: Full page £300 Half page £150

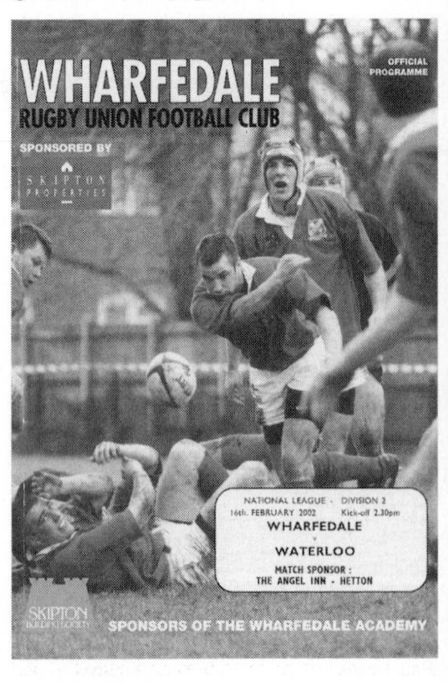

Jonathan Davies (pictured left) set a new club record with 278 league points.

Photo courtesy of the Craven Herald

RECORDS SECTION

DIVISION THREE
(CURRENTLY NATIONAL LEAGUE TWO)

THE LAST TEN YEARS DIVISION THREE

1992-93

Champions Otley
Runners-up Havant
Relegated Sheffield, Leeds. Clifton, Askeans, Liverpool St. Helens, Aspatria, Plymouth Alb., Broughton Park
Most
Points: 122 Andy Green (Exeter)
Tries: 8 Martin Kelly (Broughton Park)
Mark Sephton (Liverpool St. Helens)
Penalties: 14 Peter Rutledge (Otley)
Conversions: 31 Andy Green (Exeter)
D.Gs: 3 Andy Green (Exeter)
Simon Hogg (Clifton)

1993-94

Champions Coventry
Runners-up Fylde
Relegated Havant, Redruth
Most
Points: 172 Andy Finnie (Bedford)
Tries: 12 Brebdan Hanavan (Fylde)
Penalties: 45 Andy Finnie (Bedford)
Conversions: 23 Richard Angel (Coventry)
D.Gs: 3 Jamie Grayshon (Morley)

1994-95

Champions Bedford
Runners-up Blackheath
Relegated Clifton, Exeter
Most
Points: 228 Andy Finnie (Bedford)
Tries: 8 David Bishop (Rugby)
Penalties: 56 Andy Finnie (Bedford)
Conversions: 24 Andy Finnie (Bedford)
D.Gs: 5 Jamie Grayshon (Morley)

1995-96

Champions Coventry
Runners-up Richmond
Relegated No relegation
Most
Points: 215 Ralph Zoing (Harrogate)
Tries: 12 Colin Phillips (Reading)
Penalties: 53 Ralph Zoing (Harrogate)
Conversions: 28 John Gregory (Richmond)
D.Gs: 8 Jamie Grayshon (Morley)

1996-97

Champions Exeter
Runners-up Fylde
Relegated Walsall, Havant, Redruth, Clifton
Most
Points: 404 Steve Gough (Fylde)
Tries: 22 Mark Kirby (Otley)
Penalties: 82 Steve Gough (Fylde)
Conversions: 63 Ralph Zoing (Harrogate)
D.Gs: 7 Craig Raymond (London Welsh)

1997-98

Champions Worcester
Runners-up Leeds
Relegated No relegation
Most
Points: 322 Sateki Tuipolotu (Leeds)
Tries: 29 Nick Baxter (Worcester)
Penalties: 64 Chris Atkinson (Nottingham)
Conversions: 64 Craig Raymond (London Welsh)
D.Gs: 4 Colin Stephens (Leeds)

1998-99

Champions Henley
Runners-up Manchester
Relegated Morley, Liverpool St. Helens
Most
Points: 365 Steve Swindells (Manchester)
Tries: 15 Lafaele Filipo (Otley)
Adam Standeven (Morley)
Penalties: 70 Steve Swindells (Manchester)
Conversions: 60 Steve Swindells (Manchester)
D.Gs: 5 Phil Osman (Henley)
Sam Jack (Nottingham)

1999-00

Champions Otley
Runners-up Birmingham & Solihull
Relegated Reading, Blackheath
Most
Points: 274 Adam Mounsey (Wharfedale)
Tries: 22 Mark Kirby (Otley)
Penalties: 61 Lee Osborne (Lydney)
Conversions: 61 Dan Clappison (Otley)
D.Gs: 3 by 3 players

2000-01

Champions Bracknell
Runners-up Rugby Lions
Relegated Camberley, Lydney, West Hartlepool
Most
Points: 260 Jonathon Gregory (Lydney)
Tries: 17 Ed Smithies (Harrogate)
Penalties: 47 Jonathon Gregory (Lydney)
Conversions: 44 Mike Scott (Kendal)
D.Gs: 2 by 3 players

2001-02

Champions Orrell
Runners-up Plymouth Albion
Relegated Rosslyn Park, Waterloo, Preston Grasshoppers
Most
Points: 343 Phil Jones (Orrell)
Tries: 23 Dan Ward-Smith (Plymouth Albion)
Penalties: 76 Jonathan Gregory (Esher)
Conversions: 68 Lee Cholewa
D.Gs: 6 Mike Scott (Kendal)

ALL TIME RECORDS — TEAM RECORDS — DIVISION THREE

Highest score:	**103**	Otley 103 Blackheath 3. 04.12.99
Highest aggregate:	**106**	As above
Highest score by a losing side:	**42**	Walsall 42 Reading 44. 12.4.97
Highest scoring draw:	**34**	Reading v Rosslyn Park. 17.2.96
Most consecutive wins:	**14**	Exeter 1996-97
Most consecutive defeats:	**26**	26 West Hartlepool 2000-01
Most points for in a season:	**1209**	Leeds 1996-97
Least points for in a season:	**46**	Birmingham Solihull 1987-88
Most points against in a season:	**1347**	Clifton 1996-97
Least points against in a season:	**89**	Plymouth 1988-89
Most tries for in a season:	**158**	Leeds 1996-97
Most tries against in a season:	**184**	Clifton 1996-97
Least tries for in a season:	**3**	Birmingham Solihull 1987-88
Least tries against in a season:	**5**	Plymouth 1988-89
Most conversions for in a season:	**94**	Leeds 1996-97
Most conversions against in a season:	**125**	Clifton 1996-97
Most penalties for in a season:	**85**	Fylde 1996-97
Most penalties against in a season:	**74**	Otley 1996-97
Least penalties for in a season:	**8**	Morley 1987-88
Least penalties against in a season:	**10**	West Hartlepool 1990-91
Most drop goals for in a season:	**8**	Morley 1994-95, London Welsh 1996-97
Most drop goals against in a season:	**8**	Rotherham 1995-96, Havant 1996-97

ALL TIME RECORDS — INDIVIDUAL RECORDS — DIVISION THREE

Most points in a season:	**404**	Steve Gough (Fylde) 1996-97
Most tries in a season:	**29**	Nick Baxter (Worcester) 1997-98
Most conversions in a season:	**64**	Craig Raymond (London Welsh) 1997-98
Most penalties in a season:	**82**	Steve Gough (Fylde) 1996-97
Most drop goals in a season:	**8**	Jamie Grayson (Morley) 1995-96
Most points in a match:	**42**	Mike Scott *Kendal* v W Hartlepool 27.1.01
Most tries in a match:	**6**	Nick Baxter, *Worcester* v Otley 21.2.98
Most conversions in a match:	**12**	Paul Brett, *Liverpool St. Helens* v Clifton 15.2.97
Most penalties in a match:	**9**	Paul Morris, *Lydney* v Otley 14.9.96
		Rob Ashworth, *Havant* v Clifton 21.9.96
Most drop goals in a match:	**4**	Andy Rimmer, *Broughton Park* v Sheffield 17.11.90

ALL TIME RECORDS MOST POINTS IN A SEASON DIVISION THREE

Points	Player	Club	Season	Tries	Cons.	Pens.	D.G.
404	Steve Gough	Fylde	1996-97	7	57	82	3
365	Steve Swindells	Manchester	1998-99	7	60	70	0
343	Phil Jones	Orrell	2001-02	15	59	50	-
338	Richard Mills	Walsall	1996-97	1	42	81	2
322	Sateki Tuipulotu	Leeds	1997-98	11	60	49	
311	Jonathan Gregory	Esher	2001-02	5	29	76	-
307	Gerry Ainscough	Leeds	1996-97	14	45	49	
305	Ralph Zoing	Harrogate	1996-97	4	63	48	5
300	Andy Green	Exeter	1996-97	5	58	50	3
300	Craig Raymond	London Welsh	1996-97	6	39	57	7
298	Ben Harvey	Stourbridge	2001-02	9	44	55	-
289	Lee Cholewa	Harrogate	2001-02	9	68	35	1
287	Peter Rutledge	Otley	1996-97	8	56	45	
281	Jason Dance	Reading	1996-97	6	61	43	
278	Jonathan Davies	Wharfedale	2001-02	5	44	54	1
275	Paul Morris	Lydney	1996-97	3	31	66	
274	Adam Mounsey	Wharfedale	99-2000	7	37	55	
272	Chris Atkinson	Nottingham	1998-99	2	35	64	
271	Mike Scott	Kendal	2001-02	2	36	57	6
264	Craig Raymond	London Welsh	1997-98	8	64	29	3
262	Chris Atkinson	Nottingham	1997-98	6	30	64	
262	Dan Clappison	Otley	99-2000	1	61	42	3
260	Jonathan Gregory	Esher	2000-01	7	42	47	-
248	Lee Osborne	Lydney	99-2000	3	25	61	
247	Adam Mounsey	Wharfedale	1997-98	4	31	55	
246	Jason Dance	Reading	1997-98	4	35	52	
244	Colin Stephens	Sedgley Park	2001-02	4	37	46	4
235	David Pears	Wharfedale	1998-99	5	24	50	4
235	Mike Scott	Kendal	2000-01	6	44	37	2
228	Andy Finnie	Bedford	1994-95		24	56	4
221	Guy Gregory	Camberley	1998-99	2	29	50	1
219	Chris Glynn	Preston	2000-01	8	40	33	-
219	Russell Southam	Nottingham	2000-01	9	36	33	1
216	Richard Lebas	Worcester	1997-98	9	60	16	1
215	Ralph Zoing	Harrogate	1995-96	3	19	51	3
211	Tom Barlow	Plymouth	2001-02	10	40	23	4
210	Paul Brett	Liverpool St Helens	1996-97	14	40	20	
210	Chris Glynn	Preston	2001-02	6	21	45	1
206	Jamie Grayshon	Morley	1995-96	2	20	44	8
203	Russell Southam	Nottingham	2001-02	6	34	35	-
197	Sateki Tuipulotu	Leeds	1996-97	15	37	16	
196	John Gregory	Richmond	1995-96	4	28	40	
195	Jamie Grayshon	Morley	1996-97	2	40	31	4
194	Nick Booth	Fylde	99-2000	4	24	42	
193	Jason Dance	Reading	1998-99	1	28	49	
190	Matt Duncombe	Harrogate	99-2000	7	31	28	3
183	Jim Quantrill	Rugby	1995-96	3	21	42	
182	Adam Mounsey	Wharfdale	1996-97	10	39	18	
178	Andy Maddock	Rosslyn Park	1997-98	4	28	32	2
172	Andy Finnie	Bedford	1993-94		14	45	3
172	Nick Grecian	Newbury	1997-98	3	35	29	
171	Jim Quantrill	Rugby	1997-98	6	33	25	
171	Adam Mounsey	Wharfedale	2000-01	7	11	38	-
170	Matt Birch	Birmingham & S	1998-99	1	30	35	

ALL TIME RECORDS MOST POINTS IN A MATCH DIVISION THREE

Points	Player	Match	Date
42	Mike Scott	Kendal v W Hartlepool	27.01.01
39	Paul Brett	Liverpool St Helens v Clifton	15.02.97
30	Paul Brett	Liverpool St Helens v Redruth	01.02.97
	Nick Baxter	Worcester v Otley	21.02.98
	Ben Harvey	Stourbridge v Esher	06.04.02
	Colin Stephens	Sedgley Park v Wharfedale	15.12.01
29	Paul Morris	Lydney v Otley	14.09.96
	Rob Ashworth	Havant v Clifton	21.09.96
	Adam Mounsey	Wharfedale v Reading	15.01.00
	Jonathan Davies	Wharfedale v Preston G.	19.01.02
28	Steve Burnage	Fylde v Birmingham	07.11.87
	Craig Raymond	London Welsh v Clifton	28.12.96
	Jaques Steyn	Rugby v Camberley	02.12.00
	Rob Moon	Nottingham v Sedgley Park	22.09.01
	Jonathan Gregory	Esher v Preston G.	01.12.01
	Lee Cholewa	Harrogate v Preston G.	15.12.01

27

Player	Match	Date
Ralph Zoing	Harrogate v Fylde	14.10.95
Gerry Ainscough	Leeds v Rosslyn Park	14.09.96
Craig Raymond	London Welsh v Lydney	09.11.96
Gerry Ainscough	Leeds v Walsall	01.03.97
Nat Saumi	Redruth v Clifton	03.05.97
Adam Standeven	Morley v Newbury	25.04.98
David Pears	Wharfedale v Fylde	23.09.00

26

Player	Match	Date
Greg Way	Reading v Harrogate	16.09.95
Andy Green	Exeter v Wharfedale	07.09.96
Richard Mills	Walsall v Clifton	07.09.96
Sateki Tuipulotu	Leeds v Nottingham	18.10.97
Craig Raymond	London Welsh v Wharfedale	21.03.98
Jason Dance	Reading v Liverpool St H	25.04.98
Duncan Roke	Henley Hawks v Camberley	06.02.99
John Gregory	Esher v Newbury	17.02.01
Phil Jones	Orrell v Waterloo	22.09.01
Phil Jones	Orrell v Fylde	09.02.02
Richard Welding	Nottingham v Orrell	20.04.02

25

Player	Match	Date
Domonic Cundy	Plymouth v Met Police	26.11.89
Mark Rodgers	Sheffield v Askeans	13.03.93
Richard Angell	Coventry v Redruth	30.04.94
Steve Gough	Fylde v Rosslyn Park	26.10.96
Mark Kirkby	Otley v Redruth	08.02.97
Jason Dance	Reading v Clifton	01.03.97
Richard Mills	Walsall v Redruth	19.04.97
Simon Middleton	Leeds v Morley	14.02.98
Matt Hoskin	Manchester v Camberley	12.09.98
Steve Swindells	Manchester v Liverpool St H	28.12.98
Steve Swindells	Manchester v Wharfedale	17.04.99
Matt Duncombe	Harrogate v Blackheath	18.03.00
Jim Quantrill	Birmingham Solihull v Preston G	23.10.99

24

Player	Match	Date
Chris Howard	Rugby v Maidstone	26.11.88
Richard Mills	Walsall v Leeds	12.10.96
Jason Dance	Reading v Walsall	29.03.97
Ralph Zoing	Harrogate v Clifton	05.04.97
Steve Gough	Fylde v London Welsh	26.04.97
Ralph Zoing	Harrogate v Liverpool St H	17.05.97
Nick Booth	Fylde v Blackheath	15.01.00
Mike Scott	Kendal v Rosslyn Park	22.09.01
Ian Morgan	Preston G. v Newbury	02.03.02

23

Player	Match	Date
John Stabler	West Hartlepool v Broughton Park	09.03.91
Ralph Zoing	Harrogate v Reading	16.09.95
John Gregory	Richmond v Rotherham	30.09.95
Phil Belshaw	Reading v Morley	14.10.95
Peter Rutledge	Otley v Walsall	09.11.96
Craig Raymond	London Welsh v Rosslyn Park	18.02.97
Jamie Grayshon	Morley v London Welsh	12.04.97
Murray Withington	Morley v Lydney	22.11.97
Richard Le Bas	Worcester v Otley	07.02.98
Nick Grecian	Newbury v Liverpool St H	21.02.98
Morgan Davies	Newbury v Nottingham	11.04.98
Nick Paisley	Lydney v Reading	05.12.98
Guy Gregory	Camberley v Birmingham & S	19.12.98
Ben Stafford	Camberley v Nottingham	10.10.99
Dan Clappison	Otley v Blackheath	04.12.99
Chris Glynn	Preston v Camberley	25.03.00
Adam Mounsey	Wharfedale v Esher	23.12.00
Phil Jones	Orrell v Sedgley Park	26.01.02
Russell Southam	Nottingham v Preston G.	13.04.02

ALL TIME RECORDS MOST TRIES IN A MATCH DIVISION THREE

	6	
Nick Baxter	**Worcester v Otley**	**21.02.98**
	5	
Mark Kirkby	Otley v Redruth	08.02.97
Simon Middleton	Leeds v Morley	14.02.98
Matt Hoskin	Manchester v Camberley	12.09.98
	4	
Brendan Hanavan	Fylde v Exeter	03.10.87
Steve Walklin	Plymouth v Birmingham	17.10.87
Ian Russell	Plymouth v Fylde	31.10.87
Brendan Hanavan	Fylde v Birmingham	07.11.87
Dan Cottrell	Clifton v Askeans	04.01.92
Mark Sephton	Liverpool St H v Aspatria	13.03.93
Dean Crompton	Liverpool St H v Aspatria	13.03.93
Mark Farrar	Otley v Askeans	27.03.93
Brendan Hanavan	Fylde v Redruth	09.04.94
Richard Matthias	Leeds v Clifton	07.12.96
Simon Dovell	Exeter v Havant	21.12.96
Ben Wade	Morley v Clifton	18.01.97
Mark Sephton	Liverpool StH v Clifton	15.02.97
Colin Stephens	Leeds v Lydney	15.03.97
Toby Rakison	Rosslyn Park v Otley	29.03.97
Steve Bartliffe	Leeds v Havant	26.04.97
Nick Baxter	Worcester v L St Helens	21.03.98
Alan Royer	Nottingham v L St. Helens	28.11.98
Jeremy Griffiths	Newbury v Harrogate	02.01.99
Lafaele Filipo	Otley v Reading	03.04.99
Mark Kirby	Otley v Blackheath	04.12.99
Iain Bruce	Preston G. v Camberley	25.03.00
Mike Scott	Kendal v W Hartlepool	27.01.01
Mark Farrar	Preston G.v Harrogate	06.04.02

2001-02 THREE TRIES IN A MATCH DIVISION THREE

Andy Craig	Esher v Orrell	13.04.02
Jason Balmer	Kendal v Newbury	13.04.02
Ross Bullough	Wharfedale v Sedgley Park	06.04.02
Andy Craig	Preston Grasshoppers v Orrell	16.03.02
Neil Kerfoot	Preston Grasshoppers v Orrell	16.03.02
John Allen	Sedgley Park v Rosslyn Park	16.03.02
William James	Plymouth Albion v Preston G'hoppers	23.02.02
Graeme Sarjaent	Harrogate v Esher	16.02.02
T Matthewson	Rosslyn Park v Preston G'hoppers	16.02.02
Phil Jones	Orrell v Fylde	09.02.02
Wes Davies	Orrell v Fylde	09.02.02
Ian Voortman	Kendal v Nottingham	02.02.02
Dan Ward-Smith	Plymouth Albion Newbury	02.02.02
Ben Godfrey	Fylde Newbury	19.01.02
Gary Connelly	Rosslyn Park Orrel	19.01.02
David Thorpe	Newbury Rosslyn Park	22.12.01
Spencer Bromley	Esher Stourbridge	15.12.01
Neil Kerfoot	Orrell Esher	08.12.01
Glenn Bunny	Plymouth Albion Harrogate	17.11.01
Dan Ward-Smith	Plymouth Albion Harrogate	17.11.01
C Burnett	Harrogate Wharfedale	22.09.01
Duncan Hughes	Stourbridge Newbury	22.09.01
C Burnett	Wharfedale Nottingham	15.09.01
Mike Wilcock	Rosslyn Park Sedgley Park	08.09.01

TEN YEAR RECORDS DIVISION THREE

Club	92-93	93-94	94-95	95-96	96-97	97-98	98-99	99-00	00-01	01-02
	SEASONS									
Askeans	10	-	-	-	-	-	-	-	-	-
Aspatria	9	-	-	-	-	-	-	-	-	-
Birmingham & Solihull	-	-	-	-	-	-	11	2	-	-
Broughton Park	11	-	-	-	-	-	-	-	-	-
Bedford	-	3	1	-	-	-	-	-	-	-
Blackheath	-	4	2	-	-	-	-	14	-	-
Bracknell	-	-	-	-	-	-	-	7	1	-
Camberley	-	-	-	-	-	-	9	12	-	-
Clifton	8	-	9	-	16	-	-	-	12	-
Coventry	-	1	-	1	-	-	-	-	-	-
Esher	-	-	-	-	-	-	-	-	8	7
Exeter	3	6	10	-	1	-	-	-	-	-
Fylde	-	2	-	10	2	-	-	9	9	5
Harrogate	-	-	7	6	5	14	12	6	5	4
Havant	2	9	-	-	14	-	-	-	-	-
Headingley	-	-	-	-	-	-	-	-	-	-
Henley	-	-	-	-	-	-	1	-	-	-
Kendal	-	-	-	-	-	-	-	-	4	10
Leeds	6	-	-	-	3	2	-	-	-	-
Liverpool St Helens	7	-	-	-	12	11	14	-	-	-
London Welsh	-	-	-	-	11	3	-	-	-	-
Lydney	-	-	-	-	10	12	8	10	13	-
Manchester	-	-	-	-	-	-	2	-	-	-
Morley	-	8	5	5	4	13	13	-	-	-
Newbury	-	-	-	-	-	6	6	5	10	9
Nottingham	-	-	-	-	-	7	4	11	11	8
Nuneaton	-	-	-	-	-	-	-	-	-	-
Orrell	-	-	-	-	-	-	-	-	-	1
Otley	1	-	6	7	9	9	5	1	-	-
Plymouth Albion	12	-	-	-	-	-	-	-	-	2
Preston Grasshoppers	-	-	-	-	-	-	-	8	7	14
Reading	-	-	-	8	6	8	10	13	-	-
Redruth	4	10	-	-	15	-	-	-	-	-
Richmond	-	7	8	2	-	-	-	-	-	-
Rosslyn Park	-	5	4	9	8	5	3	4	3	12
Rotherham	-	-	-	4	-	-	-	-	-	-
Roundhay	-	-	-	-	-	-	-	-	-	-
Rugby	-	-	3	3	-	4	-	-	2	-
Sedgley Park	-	-	-	-	-	-	-	-	-	3
Sheffield	5	-	-	-	-	-	-	-	-	-
Stourbridge	-	-	-	-	-	-	-	-	-	11
Walsall	-	-	-	-	13	-	-	-	-	-
Waterloo	-	-	-	-	-	-	-	-	-	13
Wharfedale	-	-	-	-	7	10	7	3	6	6
West Hartlepool	-	-	-	-	-	-	-	-	14	-
Worcester	-	-	-	-	-	1	-	-	-	-

NATIONAL DIVISION
THREE NORTH

									HOME									AWAY								
														For		Against							For		Against	
	P	W	D	L	F	A	PD	Pts	W	D	L	F	A	Tries	Pens	Tries	Pens	W	D	L	F	A	Tries	Pens	Tries	Pens
Doncaster	26	25	0	1	1074	357	717	50	13	0	0	627	147	91	23	19	11	12	0	1	447	210	62	18	29	11
Dudley K'ford	26	20	3	3	837	417	420	43	11	2	0	398	171	54	19	23	12	9	1	3	439	246	57	27	27	23
Liverpool St Helens	26	18	0	8	742	584	158	36	10	0	3	373	203	48	24	24	19	8	0	5	369	381	47	25	53	16
New Brighton	26	16	2	8	748	526	222	34	9	1	3	444	250	60	24	34	11	7	1	5	304	276	39	23	34	25
Darlington MP	26	14	1	11	583	587	-4	29	8	0	5	326	258	46	12	34	14	6	1	6	257	329	38	11	39	24
Tynedale	26	14	0	12	530	528	2	28	10	0	3	294	211	33	27	25	20	4	0	9	236	317	29	16	37	28
Blaydon	26	13	0	13	625	494	131	26	9	0	4	392	245	51	25	26	27	4	0	9	233	249	28	21	23	34
Nuneaton	26	12	0	14	599	585	14	24	6	0	7	323	315	43	21	42	17	6	0	7	276	270	36	18	35	21
Scunthorpe	26	11	0	15	638	738	-100	22	5	0	8	338	404	45	19	51	31	6	0	7	300	334	38	17	44	22
Bedford Athletic	26	10	1	15	599	624	-25	21	9	0	4	392	274	51	27	38	11	1	1	11	207	350	27	18	48	17
Whitchurch	26	10	1	15	524	701	-183	21	6	0	7	291	306	41	14	38	24	4	1	8	233	395	33	12	58	17
Morley	26	8	1	17	541	600	-59	17	5	1	7	269	297	31	26	39	22	3	0	10	272	303	36	17	37	25
Sandal	26	3	1	22	316	1009	-693	7	1	1	11	183	434	26	9	61	15	2	0	11	133	575	14	15	90	11
West Hartlepool	26	3	0	23	412	1018	-606	6	2	0	11	181	422	20	21	61	18	1	0	12	231	596	31	14	86	17

REVIEW OF THE SEASON

Doncaster were convincing and deserved winners of National Three North. They ended the season seven points clear of second placed Dudley dropping just two points all season. The only match lost all season was the away match at second placed Dudley. They ended the season with the best scoring record and the best defensive record. Winger Chris Conway and back row man Derek Eves both finished on 24 tries for the season, second only to Dudley's Shaun Perry, and they also had two other players in the top 10 try scorers list. Full back John Liley racked up an impressive 359 points to finish as the clubs leading points scorer for the third consecutive season. In that time he has amassed 876 points. If he can score 124 points in the coming season he will become the first player to score 1000 points for two clubs in league rugby, having scored 1070 points for Leicester.

Dudley Kingswinford pushed Doncaster for most of the season but in the end were glad to hold of Liverpool St Helens to finish second and go into the Play off to get into National Two. They had to travel to Launceston and they were beaten 26-0 by the Cornish side and so stay in National Three North for another season. Scrum half Shaun Perry ended the season as the leading try scorer in the division with 25 tries whilst Steve Smart finished second in the points scorers list with 320, only the fifth man ever to pass 300 in the division and enough to move into third place on the all time list. They ended the season unbeaten at home with 11 wins and two draws from their 13 matches.

Liverpool St Helens showed a big improvement on their previous seasons in the division and ended up in third place. At one stage they seemed to be in a position to challenge Dudley for second place but a run of five defeats from six matches at the end of the season put paid to that. Prior to that they won 14 out of 16 league matches to put some pressure on Dudley. Centre Sean Casey finished leading try scorer for the second successive season but this time smashed the club record for tries in a league season with 22, eight better than the previous record and 13 better than his own previous best.

New Brighton went into the New Season in a positive frame of mind and with promotion on the agenda. Their season though fell apart in the opening weeks of the season with just two wins from their opening seven league fixtures. By mid December they started to find some form and put together a run after that which was impressive and saw them rise up the table to finish in fourth place just two points behind Liverpool St Helens. In that period they took 25 points out of a possible 30 with 12 wins and a draw from 15 matches. One of those losses was to the Champions Doncaster by just a single point. Paul Brett again led the scoring for the third consecutive season as he passed 1000 points in National League rugby.

Tynedale were glad to get back to playing rugby after the Foot and Mouth crisis on the previous season, which severely disrupted their first ever, campaign of National League rugby. They ended their second season of National League rugby in fifth place just ahead of their North East rivals Darlington MP and Blaydon. Whilst not the heaviest of scorers in the division they did have one of the better defences. After a bad start to the league season with just two wins from seven matches they turned their season round winning 12 of their remaining 19 matches. Phil Belgian made a big difference to the side when he joined in December and played in all but one of Tynedale's remaining matches to end the season as their leading points scorer with 120.

Darlington Mowden Park ended up fifth in their first season of National League rugby. They started the season superbly with eight wins in their first ten matches including winning their first four matches. After that initial run they managed just one win in their next eight matches before getting their season back on track again. They did not score enough points with the boot, which may well have cost them on a number of occasions. Park continued their good form in the Cup of the last couple of season reaching the fourth round before going out to National One side Manchester.

Blaydon did well in their first season at this level and ended up a very creditable seventh. They never managed to get a run going and never won or lost more than two games in a row. Outside half James Lofthouse made a big difference in his first season at the club and his consistent goal kicking saw him notch up 180 points with the boot and he also added 10 points from two tries. In the try scoring stakes scrum half Andrew Foreman easily led the way with 15 tries including four in one match against West Hartlepool. Where Blaydon did shine was defensively with the third best record in the division.

Nuneaton again flattered to deceive and ended the season in eighth place and over the last five seasons have finished between fifth or eighth each time. Of their 12 wins only one was against a side that finished above them in the league the other 13 matches against those sides they lost. Of the 12 matches against the teams below them they lost just one in 12 home and away. They did though have a good run in the PowerGen Cup with excellent wins over Tynedale, Wharfedale and New Brighton before losing at National Two side Newbury. Did well mid season with a run of eight wins from 12 matches before going on a run that saw them lose seven of their last 10 matches in the league.

Scunthorpe's first season of National League rugby saw them finish ninth and after their start to the campaign they would probably have settled for that. They lost five of their first six matches and seemed to be struggling, but they were probably adjusting and after that we saw a big improvement. They them went on to win six out of seven with the only defeat a 38-41 reverse at Bedford Athletic. In that run they had wins against New Brighton, Liverpool and Blaydon. After that they had a losing run of six matches before rallying to win three of their last five matches and retained their National League status. Tim Robinson led the points scoring with 198 points They had seven players who played in 23 matches or more and both Phil Sidebottom and Michael Coult were ever present.

Bedford Athletic made a dreadful start to the season with six successive defeats before beating Tynedale in early November. They found themselves at the wrong end of the table a facing certain relegation. But for somewhere they produced an amazing finish to the season with four straight wins which included impressive wins against both Liverpool St Helens and New Brighton before going to Scunthorpe on the final day of the season and getting another excellent win to keep their National Three status. Centre Olly Ryan was their scoring sensation in the second half of the season with 16 tries in the New Year to add to the two he scored before Christmas. In the home match against West Hartlepool he crossed the line five times as Bedford ran up their biggest score of the season.

Whitchurch finished eleventh but with Dudley losing to Launceston in the Play offs they find themselves relegated back into Midlands One. They started the season well with four wins in their opening seven matches including an excellent win at New Brighton. After that they lost eight out of nine had two points deducted for fielding an un registered player and slipped down the table. In their last four matches they took five out of eight points but with Bedford Athletic winning their last four matches they found themselves in that dangerous position of eleventh, which proved so costly in the end. Whitchurch have had four season of National League rugby and have finished 11th twice before but that was before the play-offs.

A disastrous season for Morley who seemed to be heading for mid table mediocrity before taking just three points from as possible 22 at the end of the season. They now find themselves out of National League rugby for the first time since league rugby started in 1987-88. Suffered seven defeats by seven points or less and did better defensively than the three sides immediately above them in the league and seven sides conceded more tries than them. Did not get a settled goal kicker whilst their leading try scorer was front row man Stewart Kneale with nine tries, the best by a front row player in the league.

After just surviving last season Sandal ended their seven year stay in the division as they were relegated back into North One. They managed just three wins all season with two of them being away from home. They did not score enough points scoring 96 fewer than bottom of the table West Hartlepool. Full back Mark Wolff was an ever present and ended as leading try scorer with seven tries whilst the leading points scorer was Matt Bacon with just 53 points. They had a worse record at home than on the road with 575 points and 90 tries conceded at home compared to 434 and 61 away from Milnthorpe Green.

West Hartlepool continued to drop down the leagues after being relegated for a fourth consecutive season after falling out of the Premiership in 1998/99. In that time they have managed just seven wins in 104 league matches. Last season they managed just three wins and finished bottom of the table one point adrift of Sandal. Refused to give up and near the end of the season put in some better performances to go down fighting with spirit. Jamie Connolly led by example being an ever present and finishing the season as the leading try scorer with eight and the second highest points scorer behind Michael Walton.

2001-2002 RECORD REVIEW
(Individual Records)

MOST POINTS - IN A SEASON

Doncaster's John Liley moved into second place on the all time list in the division with 359 points for Doncaster last season. Dudley's Steve Smart moved into fourth place as he became the fifth player to score 300 points in a season in National Three North.

EVOLUTION OF RECORD

118	Steve Kerry	Preston G'hoppers	1987-88
127	Paul Grayson	Preston G'hoppers	1991-92
131	Ralph Zoing	Harrogate	1992-93
164	Richard Mills	Walsall	1994-95
317	Steve Kerry	Preston G'hoppers	1996-97
398	Steve Swindells	Manchester	1997-98

ALL-TIME LIST

398	Steve Swindells	Manchester	1997-98
359	John Liley	Doncaster	2001-02
320	Steve Smart	Dudley K	2001-02
317	Steve Kerry	Preston G.	1996-97
302	Paul Brett	New Brighton	1999-00
296	Matt Birch	Birmingham & Sol.	1997-98
288	Paul Brett	New Brighton	2001-02
273	John Liley	Doncaster	1999-00
273	Casey Mee	Kendal	1999-00
271	Jonathon Smart	Birmingham & Sol.	1996-97
268	Ian Shuttleworth	Sandal	1997-98
258	Paul Brett	New Brighton	2000-01
251	Mike Scott	Aspatria	1996-97
251	Steve Swindells	Manchester	1996-97
248	Mark Hardcastle	Sandal	1996-97
244	John Liley	Doncaster	2000-01

MOST TRIES - IN A SEASON

The Dudley K scrum half Shaun Perry topped the try scorers last season with 25 which was the second best haul ever in the division. He was closely followed by the Doncaster pair of Chris Conway and Derek Eves who both ran in 24 tries. The fourth player to pass 20 tries last season was the LSH centre sean Casey who set a new club record for tries in a season.

EVOLUTION OF RECORD

7	Eddie Saunders	Rugby	1987-88
10	Jim Mallinder	Roundhay	1988-89
16	Jon Walker	Otley	1990-91
18	Nick Baxter	Worcester	1996-97
21	Matt Hoskin	Manchester	1997-98
27	Michael Lough	Preston	1998-99

ALL-TIME LIST

27	Michael Lough	Preston	1998-99
25	Iain Bruce	Preston	1998-99
25	Shaun Perry	Dudley K	2001-02
24	Chris Conway	Doncaster	2001-02
24	Derek Eves	Doncaster	2001-02
22	Chris Hall	Morley	1999-00
22	Sean Casey	Liverpool St H	2001-02
21	Matt Hoskin	Manchester	1997-98
20	Gary Marshall	Nuneaton	2000-01
19	Chris Conway	Doncaster	1999-00
19	Stephen Hanley	Aspatria	1997-98

MOST CONVERSIONS - IN A SEASON

Doncaster full back John Liley moved into second place on the all time list with 89 conversions in Doncaster's Championship season. He miss the record by just two and will not have a chance to beat it as he will be playing in National Two next season. Steve Smart Dudley moved into 4th place on the all time list with 59 conversions.

EVOLUTION OF RECORD

12	Steve Kerry	Preston G'hoppers	1987-8
	Chris Howard	Rugby	1987-8
13	Gary Walker	Roundhay	1988-8
17	Jon Howarth	Otley	1990-9
28	Ralph Zoing	Harrogate	1992-9
29	Richard Mills	Walsall	1994-9
61	Tim Smith	Worcester	1996-9
91	Steve Swindells	Manchester	1997-9

ALL-TIME LIST

91	Steve Swindells	Manchester	1997-9
89	John Liley	Doncaster	2001-0
61	Tim Smith	Worcester	1996-9
59	Steve Smart	Dudley K	2001-0
58	Matt Birch	Birmingham & Solihull	1997-9
53	Martin Emmett	Preston	1998-9
53	Casey Mee	Kendal	1999-0
51	Paul Brett	New Brighton	1999-0
50	Colin Stephens	Sedgley Park	2000-0
50	Chris Mann	Stourbridge	1996-9
50	Colin Stephens	Sedgley Park	2000-0

MOST PENALTIES - IN A SEASON

Last season sawNew Brighton's Paul Brett getting into the top 1 after kicking 47 penalties last season for his side.

EVOLUTION OF RECORD

21	Steve Kerry	Preston G'hoppers	1987-8
23	Jamie Grayshon	Morley	1988-8
28	Paul Grayson	Preston G'Hoppers	1990-9
31	Simon Pennington	Stourbridge	1992-9
31	Richard Mills	Walsall	1994-9
64	Steve Kerry	Preston G'hoppers	1996-9

ALL-TIME LIST

64	Steve Kerry	Preston G.	1996-9
62	Steve Swindells	Manchester	1997-9
55	Matt Birch	Birmingham & Sol.	1997-9
55	Ian Shuttleworth	Sandal	1997-9
53	Mark Hardcastle	Sandal	1996-9
48	Mike Scott	Aspatria	1996-9
48	Simon Worsley	Liverpool St H	2000-0
47	Paul Brett	New Brighton	2001-0
43	Jonathan Smart	Birmingham & Sol	1996-9
43	Rob Pound	Sheffield	1997-9
43	Alan Moses	Tynedale	2000-0
43	Paul Brett	New Brighton	2000-0

MOST DROP GOALS - IN A SEASON

Nobody challenged the drop goal record with the best haul for th season being four by Tim Robinson, Scunthorpe, and Phil Belgia Tynedale.

EVOLUTION OF RECORD

5	Steve Kerry	Preston G'hoppers	1987-8
6	Paul Grayson	Preston G'hoppers	1991-9
9	Steve Kerry	Preston G'hoppers	1996-9

ALL-TIME LIST

9	Steve Kerry	Preston G'hoppers	1996-9
6	Paul Grayson	Preston G'hoppers	1991-9
5	Steve Kerry	Preston G'hoppers	1987-8
5	Simon Worsley	Liverpool St Helens	2000-0
4	Richard Mills	Walsall	1990-9
4	Ian Shuttleworth	Sandal	1997-9
4	Rob Pound	Sheffield	1997-9
4	Colin Stephens	Sedgley Park	2000-0

2001-02

NATIONAL DIVISION THREE NORTH

MOST POINTS

POINTS			T	C	P	DG
359	John Liley	Doncaster	11	89	41	1
320	Steve Smart	Dudley K	17	59	39	-
288	Paul Brett	New Brighton	7	56	47	-
227	Simon Worsley	Liverpool St H	2	47	39	2
198	Tim Robinson	Scunthorpe	1	44	31	4
190	James Lofthouse	Blaydon	2	36	36	-
143	Alastair Sherlock	Morley	8	20	21	-
138	Shaun Perry	Dudley K	25	2	1	-
136	Jamie Elphick	Bedford Ath	6	20	22	-
120	Philip Belgian	Tynedale	1	17	23	4
120	Chris Conway	Doncaster	24	-	-	-
120	Derek Eves	Doncaster	24	-	-	-
119	Jody Peacock	Nuneaton	8	17	15	-
116	Kevin Oliphant	Darlington MP	4	27	12	2
115	Lee Cassell	Nuneaton	4	19	19	-
110	Sean Casey	Liverpool St H	22	-	-	-
97	Mark Bedworth	Darlington MP	6	17	11	-

MOST TRIES

25	Shaun Perry	Dudley K
24	Chris Conway	Doncaster
24	Derek Eves	Doncaster
22	Sean Casey	Liverpool St H
18	Olly Ryan	Bedford Ath
17	Steve Smart	Dudley K
17	Emrys Evans	New Brighton
17	Matt Brain	Doncaster
17	Matt Donkin	Doncaster
15	Andrew Foreman	Blaydon
14	Alastair Baron	Nuneaton
11	James Mortimore	Doncaster
11	John Liley	Doncaster
11	Jonathan Storey	Doncaster
11	James Moore	New Brighton

MOST CONVERSIONS

89	John Liley	Doncaster
59	Steve Smart	Dudley K
56	Paul Brett	New Brighton
47	Simon Worlsey	Liverpool St H
44	Tim Robinson	Scunthorpe
36	James Lofthouse	Blaydon
27	Kevin Oliphant	Darlington MP
20	Jamie Elphick	Bedford Ath
20	Alistair Sherlock	Morley
19	Lee Cassell	Nuneaton
18	Chris Hares	Whitchurch
17	Phil Belgian	Tynedale
17	Jody Peacock	Nuneaton
17	Mark Bedworth	Darlington MP

MOST PENALTIES

47	Paul Brett	New Brighton
41	John Liley	Doncaster
39	Steve Smart	Dudley K
39	Simon Worsley	Liverpool St H
36	James Lofthouse	Blaydon
31	Tim Robinson	Scunthorpe
23	Philip Belgian	Tynedale
22	Jamie Elphick	Bedford Ath
21	Alastair Sherlock	Morley
19	Lee Cassell	Nuneaton
15	Jody Peacock	Nuneaton
15	Mark Hardcastle	Sandal
13	Gareth Williams	Bedford Ath
13	Alan Moses	Tynedale
13	Mark Sales	Morley
13	Michael Walton	W Hartlepool

MOST DROP GOALS

4	Tim Robinson	Scunthorpe
4	Philip Belgian	Tynedale
3	Mark Sales	Morley
2	Kevin Oliphant	Darlington MP
2	Simon Worlsey	Liverpool St H
2	Gareth Davies	Dudley K
1	John Liley	Doncaster
1	Alan Moses	Tynedale

NATIONAL DIVISION 3 NORTH

FIXTURES 2002-2003

Away Teams

	HOME TEAMS	Bedford Athletic	Blaydon	Broadstreet	Darlington M. P.	Dudley Kingswinsford	Halifax	Hull Ionians	Liverpool St. Helens	New Brighton	Nuneaton	Preston Grasshoppers	Scunthorpe	Tynedale	Waterloo	
1	Bedford Athletic	XXX	18-01	12-04	15-03	12-10	07-12	14-09	14-12	09-11	22-02	26-10	04-01	23-11	01-02	1
2	Blaydon	01-03	XXX	25-01	08-02	31-08	11-01	29-03	19-10	07-12	12-10	14-09	02-11	21-12	23-11	2
3	Broadstreet	21-12	22-02	XXX	18-01	23-11	31-08	07-12	04-01	12-10	01-02	09-11	15-03	14-09	26-10	3
4	Darlington M. P.	11-01	26-10	01-03	XXX	07-12	29-03	21-12	01-02	14-09	09-11	23-11	25-01	31-08	12-10	4
5	Dudley Kingswinsford	16-11	14-12	28-09	07-09	XXX	19-10	08-02	22-02	18-01	12-04	15-03	30-11	02-11	04-01	5
6	Halifax	07-09	15-03	14-12	04-01	09-11	XXX	23-11	30-11	26-10	18-01	01-02	12-04	12-10	22-02	6
7	Hull Ionians	30-11	04-01	11-09	12-04	26-10	28-09	XXX	16-11	01-02	15-03	22-02	14-12	09-11	18-01	7
8	Liverpool St. Helens	31-08	09-11	29-03	02-11	25-01	14-09	12-10	XXX	11-01	23-11	21-12	01-03	08-02	07-12	8
9	New Brighton	19-10	07-09	16-11	30-11	01-03	08-02	02-11	15-03	XXX	14-12	04-01	28-09	25-01	12-04	9
10	Nuneaton	25-01	16-11	02-11	19-10	21-12	01-03	11-01	28-09	31-08	XXX	07-12	08-02	29-03	14-09	10
11	Preston Grasshoppers	08-02	30-11	19-10	28-09	11-01	02-11	25-01	12-04	29-03	07-09	XXX	16-11	01-03	14-12	11
12	Scunthorpe	29-03	01-02	11-01	22-02	14-09	21-12	31-08	18-01	23-11	26-10	12-10	XXX	07-12	09-11	12
13	Tynedale	28-09	12-04	30-11	14-12	01-02	16-11	19-10	26-10	22-02	04-01	18-01	07-09	XXX	15-03	13
14	Waterloo	02-11	28-09	08-02	16-11	29-03	25-01	01-03	07-09	21-12	30-11	31-08	19-10	11-01	XXX	14

BEDFORD ATHLETIC RUFC

Chairman	Paul McGuckian	c/o Bedford Athletic RUFC, Putnoe Wood, Wentworth Drive, Bedford MK41 8QA 01234 350874
Secretary	Jean Ross	63 Avon Drive, Brickhill, Bedford MK41 7UR 01234 305814 (H)
Director of Rugby	Mark Ward	Mill House, Mill Lane, Thurleigh, Bedford MK44 01234 771391 (H)
Fixture Secretary	John Ross	63 Avon Drive, Bedford MK41 7UR 01234 305814 (H) 01234 225116 (B)
Club Coach	Peter Cook	17 Church End, Catworth, Huntingdon PE8 0PB 01832 170064

With some cautious optimism the Ath began the campaign for their third year in the National leagues. The playing squad had seen significant changes with the loss of several key players to higher reaches of the game (with some success we are pleased to note), work commitments and retirements. This was particularly felt through the absence of long term regular fly half Ashley Tapper. Add to that a horrendous injury list, including inspirational skipper James Thorp, and it was obvious that the early part of the season could be difficult.

A dismal start to the season saw six straight league losses. During this period team spirit was not diminished, and thereafter things began to pick up. With the introduction of Olly Ryan at centre, the movement of Jamie Elphick to fly-half and the return of Giles Whitheat there came a harder finishing edge to the speedy back line.

We had to keep our eyes on the relegation issue right up to the end due to the likelihood of four and even five clubs being relegated due to geographical matters - (is this really justified in a league of only fourteen teams?). In the end our tenth place represented a very satisfactory recovery from our dire position in November. The season ended on a high note with four straight wins, including some of the league's high flyers. This period showed what the Ath are capable of with some outstanding displays led by a recovered James Thorp ably abetted by back row colleagues Phil Elphick, Ross Thompson and the experienced Ian Skingsley.

It is the aim of the Ath to improve the away record. Last season nine out of thirteen games were won at home (after the loss of the first three) but only one game was won away.

There is an air of confidence about the coming season as for the first time since entering the National leagues they will be starting with the basis of an established squad.

We are delighted to welcome on board new head coach Peter Cook and pleased that long serving Mark Ward is to assume the Director of Rugby role.

Finally, although very glad to have escaped the relegation scramble we are sorry at the loss of Midlands colleagues Whitchurch, but pleased to welcome back old adversaries Broad Street.

BEDFORD ATHLETIC

Comp.	Date	H/A	Opponents	Result & Score	Att	15	14	13	12	11
N3 N	01-09	H	Dudley Kingwinsford	L 16-63		Guguen	Philips	Elphick	Wells	Lloyd
N3 N	08-09	A	Whitchurch	L 15-31	350	Wells	Lloyd	Philips	Elphick	Taylor
N3 N	22-09	H	Blaydon	L 19-30	150	Elphick/p	Philips	Porteous	Wells	Peck
N3 N	06-10	A	West Hartlepool	L 16-18		Williams	Peck	Wells	Elphick/t	Philips
N3 N	20-10	H	Doncaster	L 12-20		Williams	Peck/t	Wells	Elphick/t	Philips
N3 N	27-10	A	Darlington MP	L 20-29		Williams/t	Wells	Elphick/t	Elphick	Philips
N3 N	03-11	H	Tynedale	W 26-10	200	Williams/tcp	Wells/t	Guguen	Ryan/t	Philips
N3 N	10-11	A	Sandal	D 13-13		Williams/tp	Philips	Wells	Guguen	Ryan
N3 N	17-11	H	Nuneaton	W 25-14		Williams/cp	Philips	Ryan/t	Elphick/t	Wells/t
N3 N	24-11	A	Morley	L 15-31		Williams/cp	Philips	Elphick	Ryan	Wells
N3 N	01-12	A	Dudley Kingwinsford	L 17-39	600	Williams/3p	Frost	Ryan	Elphick	Philips
N3 N	08-12	H	Scunthorpe	W 41-38		Williams/tc2p	Frost	Ryan/t	Guguen	Philips/t
N3 N	15-12	A	New Brighton	L 17-37		Williams	Lloyd	Ryan	Elphick	Frost
N3 N	12-01	A	Nuneaton	L 17-23		Williams	Wells/t(b/2t)	Ryan	Witheat	Elphick
N3 N	19-01	H	Sandal	W 53-0	150	Williams	Elphick/t	Ryan/2t	Witheat	Wells/t
N3 N	26-01	A	Tynedale	L 18-20	150	Porteous	Philips	Ryan	Guguen	Elphick/t
N3 N	02-02	H	Darlington MP	W 27-5	150	Williams/t	Philips	Ryan	Witheat	Lloyd
N3 N	09-02	A	Doncaster	L 10-23		Williams	Philips	Ryan/2t	Witheat	Wells
N3 N	16-02	A	Liverpool St Helens	L 10-34	200	Surridge	Philips	Ryan	Witheat	Wells/t
N3 N	23-02	H	West Hartlepool	W 62-20	150	Surridge/2c	Philips/t	Ryan/5t	Witheat/t	Lloyd
N3 N	09-03	A	Blaydon	L 9-35	250	Porteous	Coleburn	Ryan	Elphick	Taylor
N3 N	16-03	H	Whitchurch	L 18-30	125	Wells	Lloyd	Ryan/t	Elphick	Porteous
N3 N	23-03	H	Morley	W 23-17	150	Williams	Wells/t	Ryan	Witheat	Lloyd
N3 N	30-03	H	Liverpool St Helens	W 42-20		Elphick/4c3p	Wells/t	Ryan/2t	Witheat	Lloyd
N3 N	06-04	H	New Brighton	W 28-7	150	Elphick/tc2p	Wells	Ryan/t	Witheat	Lloyd
N3 N	13-04	A	Scunthorpe	W 30-17	400	Surridge	Williams/t	Ryan/2t	Witheat	Lloyd
PGC	15-09	N	Morpeth	W 32-17		Williams/3c2p	Taylor	Porteous	Wells/2t	Philips
PGC	29-09	H	Preston Grasshoppers	L 16-44		Wells	Peck	Elphick/c3p	Elphick	Philips

** after opponents name indicates a penalty try. Brackets after a player's name indicates he was replaced. eg (a) means he was replaced by replacement code "a" and so on. / after a player or replacement name is followed by any scores he made - eg /t, /c, /p, /dg or any combination of these*

EVER PRESENT None

Most Appearances:
24: P Elphick, C Mitcheson (1).
23: Gareth Williams (1).
22: James Smith. 21: Jamie Elphick(1)

PLAYERS USED

37 plus 4 as replecement only

MOST POINTS

Pts	Player	T	C	P	DG
136	J Elphick	6	20	22	-
90	O Ryan	18	-	-	-
86	G Williams	7	6	13	-
50	A Gallagher	10	-	-	-
45	J Thorp	9	-	-	-
45	P Elphick	9	-	-	-

MATCH FACTS

10	9	1	2	3	4	5	6	7	8
Williams/c3p	Stapleton/t	Porter	Simmonds	Otte	Curry	Hudson	Elphick	Thorp	Skingsley
Williams/cp	Gallagher/t	Otte	Simmonds	Mitcheson	Curry	Hudson	Thorp	Elphick/t	Skingsley
Davies/2p	Gallagher/t	Mitcheson	Ashworth	Otte	Curry	Hudson	Lio/t	Elphick	Williams
Davies/c3p	Gallagher	Mitcheson	Smith	Otte	Curry	Hudson	Williams	Lio	Skingsley
Tapper/c	Gallagher	Mitcheson	Smith	Otte	Curry	Hudson	Thorp	Thompson	Lio
Tapper/cp	Gallagher/t	Mitcheson	Smith	Otte	Curry	Hudson	Lio	Thompson	Skingsley
Davies/p(a/p)	Gallagher	Mitcheson	Smith	Otte	Curry	Hudson	Thompson	Thorp	Skingsley
Davies	Gallagher	Mitcheson	Smith	Otte	Thompson	Hudson	Lio	Thorp/t	Skingsley
Davies	Gallagher/t	Mitcheson	Smith	Otte	Curry	Hudson	Thompson	Thorp	Skingsley
Davies/t	Gallagher	Mitcheson	Smith	Otte	Curry	Hudson	Elphick	Thorp/t	Thompson
Elphick/p	Gallagher/t	Squires	Smith	Mitcheson	Curry	Hudson	Lio	Thorp	Thompson
Elphick/c2p	Gallagher	Squires	Smith	Mitcheson	Curry	Hudson	Lio	Elphick/2t	Thorp
Elphick/2cp	Gallagher/t	Squires	Smith	Mitcheson	Curry	Hudson	Lio/t	Thompson	Skingsley
Tapper/c	Gallagher	Squires	Smith	Otte	Curry	Thompson	Elphick	Lio	Thorp
Tapper/t5cp	Gallagher/2t	Otte	Squires	Mitcheson	Curry	Thompson	Elphick	Thorp/t	Skingsley
Tapper/p	Williams	Mitcheson	Smith	Otte	Curry	Thompson	Elphick	Thorp/2t	Skingsley
Elphick/3c2p	Gallagher/t	Squires	Smith	Mitcheson	Curry	Hudson	Elphick	Thorp/t	Thompson
Elphick	Gallagher	Squires	Smith	Mitcheson	Curry	Thompson	Elphick	Thorp	Skingsley
Elphick/cp	Williams	Squires	Smith	Mitcheson	Curry	Thompson	Elphick	Thorp	Skingsley
Elphick/t5cp	Williams/t	Squires	Smith	Mitcheson	Curry	Du Plessis	Thompson	Elphick	Skingsley
Elphick/3p	Williams	Squires	Smith	Mitcheson	Du Plessis	Thompson	Egan	Hawks	Skingsley
Elphick/tc2p	Williams	Squires	Smith	Mitcheson	Du Plessis	Thompson	Thorp	Hawks	Skingsley
Elphick/c2p	Eldridge	Squires	Smith	Mitcheson	Curry	Hudson	Elphick/t	Thorp/t	Du Plessis
Tapper	Gallagher	Squires	Smith	Mitcheson	Du Plessis	Hudson	Elphick/t	Egan	Thorp/t
Tapper	Gallagher/t	Squires	Smith	Mitcheson	Thompson	Hudson	Elphick	Egan	Thorp/t
Elphick/cp	Gallagher	Squires	Smith	Mitcheson	Thompson	Hudson	Elphick/t	Egan(c/t)	Thorp
Elphick	Gallagher	Porter	Patterson	Otte/t	Wright	Hudson	Elphick/t	Thorp	Curry
Davies	Gallagher	Mitcheson/t	Smith	Otte	Curry	Hudson	Lio	Williams	Skingsley

REPLACEMENTS: a - S Colebiurn b - C Philips c - I Skingsley
Most replacement nappearances in the league: 12: Tom Webb. 5: Mike Hudson, Simon Williams.
Most times replaced: 10: N Squires. 9: James Smith

WHERE	Total	Home	Away
The POINTS were scored	599	392	207
The POINTS were conceded	624	350	274
The TRIES were scored	78	51	27
The TRIES were conceded	86	48	38

HOW the TRIES were scored

Total	Backs	Forwards	F Back	Wing	Centre	H Back	F Row	Lock	B Row	Pen. Try
78	60	18	6	15	23	16	-	-	18	-

HOW the TRIES were conceded

Total	Backs	Forwards	F Back	Wing	Centre	H Back	F Row	Lock	B Row	Pen. Try
82	62	20	12	23	14	13	5	2	13	4

BEDFORD ATHLETIC

SEASON	Division	P	W	D	L	F	A	Pts Diff	Lge Pts	Lge Pos	Most Points		Most Tries	
95-96	Mid 2	12	3	2	7	150	163	-13	8	10				
96-97	Mid 2	17	11	1	5	362	206	156	23	7				
97-98	Mid 2	16	16	0	0	718	151	567	32	1				
98-99	Mid 1	16	15	0	1	569	163	406	30	1		Ashley Tapper		Mike Curry & Adam Lowles
99-00	N2N	26	11	0	15	563	729	-162	22	9	164	Ashley Tapper	10	Paul Alston
00-01	N3N	*24	8	0	16	386	613	-227	16	10	94	Ashley Tapper	7	Simon Lincoln
01-02	N3N	26	10	1	15	599	624	-25	21	10	136	Jamie Elphick	18	Olly Ryan

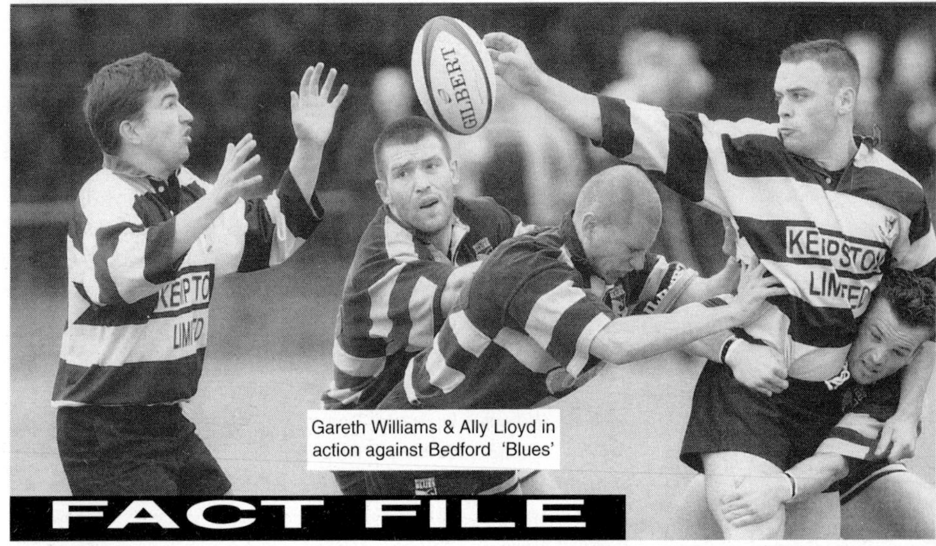

Gareth Williams & Ally Lloyd in action against Bedford 'Blues'

FACT FILE

Founded: 1908
Nickname: 'The Ath'

Colours: Black and white hoops/black/black
Change colours: Blue shirts, blue shorts

GROUND

Address: Putnoe Woods, Wentworth Drive, Bedford MK41 8QA
Tel: 01234 350874 Website: www.bedfordathrugby.com

Directions: From the A1 (1mile south of Wyboston or 3 miles north of Sandy) take A421/428 towards Bedford. At first r'about (approx. 7 miles) exit at right fork and at next r'about (MFI on corner) turn RIGHT into Norse Road. Foillow on to next r'about and go straight across into Wentworth Drive. Club is on RIGHT (0.6 miles) past Mark Rutherford School. For alternative routes via M1 and M6 contact J A Ross (Fixture Sec.)

Nearest Railway station: Bedford Midland Road

Capacity: 400 all uncovered standing

Car Parking: Spaces for approx. 50 cars at clubhouse.

Admission: £5 incl. programme Senior citizens £2.50 u16s Free

Clubhouse: Open matchdays & training evenings.

Club Shop: Open matchdays.

Training Nights Tuesday & Thursday

PROGRAMME Size: A5 Price: with admission Pages: 24 + cover
Advertising: Contact Sven Elkjaer 01234 364844

BLAYDON RFC

President	James Buchanan FRCS	c/o Blaydon RFC	0191 285 3232 (H)
Chairman	Jim Huxley	The Mount, 59 Sunniside Rd.,	Sunniside, Newcastle upon Tyne NE16 5NF 0191 488 7280 P/F 0788 4358060 email: jimhux@btopenworld.com
Director of Rugby	Andy Howells	c/o Blaydon RFC	07950 927745 (M)
Secretary	George March	c/o Blaydon RFC	01207 545397 (H)
Fixture Secretary	Hedley Redpath	13 Bridgewater Close, West Denton,	Newcastle upon Tyne NE15 8UT. 0191 267 3805 (H)

Blaydon RFC, Crow Trees, Hexham Rd., Swalwell, Newcastle upon Tyne NE16 3BM 0191 420 0505

Our first season in 3 North was a huge learning curve , struggling in the early stages, we eventually, after a narrow PowerGen Cup win at Walsall, got our league campaign off the mark at Bedford, followed by a good home victory over New Brighton and thereafter we always looked like retaining our position.

Possibly on reflection, a final 4th/5th placing, could have been ours, particularly if we had produced the level of rugby that we saw against Dudley Kingswinford, winning 50-26, or at Doncaster where we led until the final two minutes. However being the side we were, Doncaster still did the business and every credit must be given to them for their success and we wish them well at the higher level.

Our goal last campaign, was to stabilise, and at the beginning of the season, 7th place would have been acceptable, but we must now build from this position and our Director of Rugby, Andy Howells, has made several additions to the squad and Dave Guthrie, embarking on his 9th season as Captain, still full of enthusiasm, is confident that we will be challenging at the top, but whilst we are all equal in September, April will give the answer.

To help develop our squad, the club has been accepted as a member of the Northern Second Teams's League and matches against the sides in this competition, can only be of benefit to the overall strength of the club, offering a good standard of rugby to those players immediately below the 1st XV.

Apart from Dave Guthrie's continued leadership, several other players made their mark last season, scrum half Andy Foreman notching 18 tries, fly half James Lofthouse accumulating 199 points, lock forward Jason Oakes being selected for the County's tour of Chile, and Graham Spearman, in his 20th season of senior rugby, appearing until injuries (or age) took over, on the wing. His appearances this season however, may be extremely limited as he has joined our coaching panel.

Blaydon look forward to the coming season with anticipation and the new fixtures against Waterloo and the renewal of friendships with Preston Grasshoppers, Hull Ionians, and old rivals, Halifax.

JIM HUXLEY

BLAYDON

Comp.	Date	H/A	Opponents	Result & Score	Att	15	14	13	12	11
N3 N	01-09	A	Morley	L 23-24	400	Dixon/2t	Savory	Vorster/t	King	O'Malley
N3 N	08-09	H	Liverpool St Helens	L 22-42	280	King	Dixon/t	Vorster/t	Lofthouse (a/2t)	O'Malley
N3 N	22-09	A	Bedford Athletic	W 30-19	150	King/t	O'Malley/t	Bell	Lofthouse/3c3p	Spearman
N3 N	06-10	H	New Brighton	W 18-11		King	O'Malley	Bell	Lofthouse/6p	Spearman
N3 N	20-10	A	Dudley Kingwinsford	L 13-27		King	O'Malley	Bell	Michneiwcz	Savory/t
N3 N	27-10	H	Whitchurch	W 42-12		King/2t	O'Malley	Bell/2t	Michneiwcz	Savory
N3 N	03-11	A	Scunthorpe	L 16-21	250	King	O'Malley	Bell	Michneiwcz	Bennett
N3 N	10-11	H	West Hartlepool	W 44-27		King	O'Malley/t	Bennett/t	Michneiwcz	Alexander
N3 N	17-11	H	Doncaster	L 10-29	300	King	O'Malley	Bell/t	Michneiwcz	Alexander
N3 N	24-11	A	Darlington MP	L 12-18		King	O'Malley	Bell	Michneiwcz	Alexander/t
N3 N	01-12	H	Morley	W 26-15		King	O'Malley/t	Dixon	Michneiwcz	Alexander
N3 N	08-12	A	Sandal	W 27-10	180	Spearman	O'Malley/t	Dixon	Ganle	Alexander/t
N3 N	15-12	H	Nuneaton	L 3-10	150	King	O'Malley	Dixon	Gawdy	Alexander
N3 N	12-01	A	Doncaster	L 15-23		King	Dixon/t	Marais	Gawdy	Alexander/t
N3 N	19-01	A	West Hartlepool	W 29-9	150	King	Dixon/t2c	Gawdy	Marais	Alexander/t
N3 N	26-01	H	Scunthorpe	W 25-15		King	Dixon/2tcp	Green	Marais	O'Malley/t
N3 N	02-02	A	Whitchurch	L 16-18		King	O'Malley	Dixon/2p	Green	Alexander/t
N3 N	09-02	H	Dudley Kingwinsford	W 50-21		King	Dixon/t5c5p	Golightly	Green/2t	Alexander
N3 N	16-02	A	Tynedale	L 10-19	400	King	Dixon	Golightly	Green	Alexander
N3 N	23-02	A	New Brighton	L 21-23		King	Gawdy	Golightly/t	Green	Tyrrell
N3 N	02-03	H	Darlington MP	W 29-23		King/t	O'Malley/t	Gawdy	Green	Tyrrell/t
N3 N	09-03	H	Bedford Athletic	W 35-9	250	King/t	Gawdy	Golightly	Green	Tyrrell/2t
N3 N	16-03	A	Liverpool St Helens	L 3-23	250	King	Dixon	Golightly	Green	Tyrrell
N3 N	30-03	H	Tynedale	L 21-31		King	Tyrrell	Green	Gawdy	Dixon/t
N3 N	06-04	A	Nuneaton	W 18-15		King	Dixon	Golightly	Green	Tyrrell/t
N3 N	13-04	H	Sandal	W 67-0		King/2t	Dixon	Golightly/t	Green/2t	Tyrrell/t
PGC	15-09	A	Walsall	W 21-17	150	King	Vorster/t	Bell/t	Lofthouse/t3c	Spearman
PGC	29-09	H	Fylde	L 22-28						

** after opponents name indicates a penalty try. Brackets after a player's name indicates he was replaced. eg (a) means he was replaced by replacement code "a" and so on. / after a player or replacement name is followed by any scores he made - eg /t, /c, /p, /dg or any combination of these*

EVER PRESENT

None

Most Appearances:
25: Gareth King (1).
23 Philip Ritson (3).
21: James Lofthouse (1).

PLAYERS USED

43 plus five as replacement only

MOST POINTS

Pts	Player	T	C	P	DG
190	J Lofthouse	2	36	36	-
85	I Dixon	9	8	8	-
75	A Foreman	15	-	-	-
35	G King	7	-	-	-
25	P Alexander	5	-	-	-
25	James O'Malley	5	-	-	-
25	J Tyrrell	5	-	-	-

MATCH FACTS

10	9	1	2	3	4	5	6	7	8
Dalrymple/c2p	Foreman	Dixon	Ritson	Clarke	Houghton	Falconer	Guthrie	Wright	Goose
Howe/c	Foreman	Dixon	Ritson	Clarke	Davidson	Houghton	Guthrie	Wright	Goose
Dalrymple	Mason	Dixon	Ritson/t	Donoghue	Oakes	Falconer	Guthrie	Wright	Goose
Dalrymple	Wright	Dixon	Ritson	Donoghue	Houghton	Falconer	Guthrie	Guthrie	Roe
Lofthouse/c2p	Wright	Knowles	Ritson	Dixon	Falconer	Houghton	Guthrie	O'Malley	Elminger
Lofthouse/3c2p	Ganle	Dixon	Ritson	Donoghue/t	Houghton	Oakes	Elminger (b/t)	Wright	Roe
Lofthouse/c3p	Ganle (c/t)	Dixon	Ritson	Donoghue	Houghton	Oakes	Elminger	Wright	Roe
Lofthouse/4c2p	Foreman/4t	Dixon	Ritson	Donoghue	Houghton	Oakes	Elminger	Wright	Roe
Lofthouse/cp	Foreman	Dixon	Ritson	Donoghue	Falconer	Maeer	Elminger	O'Malley	Roe
Lofthouse/c	Foreman	Dixon	Ritson	Donoghue	Oakes	Maeer	O'Malley	Wright	Elminger/t
Lofthouse/c3p	Foreman/2t	Winter	Ritson	Donoghue	Guthrie	Oakes	Elminger	O'Malley	Kotze
Lofthouse/3c2p	Foreman/t	Winter	Ritson	Donoghue	Guthrie	Oakes	Kotze	O'Malley	Roe
Lofthouse/p	Foreman	Winter	Ritson	Donoghue	Guthrie	Oakes	Kotze	O'Malley	Roe
Lofthouse/cp	Foreman	Dixon	Ritson	Winter	Oakes	Houghton	Kotze	O'Malley	Roe
Lofthouse	Foreman/t	Winter	Ritson/t	Dixon	Oakes	Houghton	Kotze/t	O'Malley	Guthrie
Gawdy	Foreman	Winter	Ritson	Dixon	Oakes	Houghton/t	Roe	O'Malley	Guthrie
Gawdy	Foreman/t	Dixon	Ritson	Winter	Houghton	Maeer	Kotze	O'Malley	Roe
Gawdy	Foreman/t	Winter	Ritson	Donoghue	Oakes	Houghton	Kotze	Wright	Guthrie/t
Gawdy	Foreman/t	Winter	Ritson	Donoghue	Oakes	Houghton	Kotze	Wright/t	Guthrie
Lofthouse/c3p	Foreman	Winter	Tuhana	Donoghue/t	Houghton	Oakes	Dye	O'Malley	Guthrie
Lofthouse/t3cp	Foreman	Winter	Ritson	Donoghue	Houghton	Oakes	Roe	Wright	Guthrie
Lofthouse/3c3p	Foreman/t	Winter	Tuhana	Donoghue	Houghton	Oakes	Roe	Wright	Guthrie
Lofthouse/p	Foreman	Winter	Ritson	Donoghue	Houghton	Oakes	Roe	Wright	Guthrie
Lofthouse/3c	Foreman/t	Winter	Ritson	Donoghue	Houghton	Oakes	Dye	Wright	Guthrie/t
Lofthouse/c2p	Hannah	Clarke	Tuhana/t	Winter	Guthrie	Oakes	Reaney	Wright	Dye
Lofthouse/t6c	Foreman/t	Winter	Ritson	Clarke	Oakes	Guthrie/t	Roe(d/t)	Wright	Dye/t
Howe	Mason	Knowles	Ritson	Clarke	Houghton	Falconer	Guthrie	Wright	Dye

REPLACEMENTS: a- G Spearman. b- Jonathan O'Malley. c - Andrew Foreman. d - O Hopley
Most replacement appearances in the league: 8: Jonathan O'Malley. 6: Charles Roe. 5: Tasi Tuhana.
Most times replaced: 9: Derek Dixon. 6: Goerge Donoghue.5: Philip Ritson, Charles Roe.

WHERE	Total	Home	Away
The POINTS were scored	625	393	233
The POINTS were conceded	494	249	245
The TRIES were scored	79	51	28
The TRIES were conceded	49	23	26

HOW the TRIES were scored

Total	Backs	Forwards	F Back	Wing	Centre	H Back	F Row	Lock	B Row	Pen. Try
79	64	15	9	24	14	17	5	2	8	-

HOW the TRIES were conceded

Total	Backs	Forwards	F Back	Wing	Centre	H Back	F Row	Lock	B Row	Pen. Try
49	35	14	5	13	10	7	7	-	7	-

BLAYDON

LEAGUE STATISTICS

compiled by Stephen McCormack

SEASON	Division	P	W	D	L	F	A	Pts Diff	Lge Pts	Lge Pos		Most Pts	Most Tries
92-93	NE1	12	8	2	2	307	92	215	18	2			
93-94	NE1	12	6	1	5	171	106	65	13	4			
94-95	NE1	12	11	0	1	212	116	96	22	1c			
95-96	N2	12	9	1	2	247	80	167	19	3			
96-97	N2	22	14	0	8	479	382	97	28	3			
97-98	N2	22	19	1	2	568	251	317	37	2p			
98-99	N1	22	13	2	7	483	308	145	28	5			
99-00	N1	22	10	1	11	402	457	-55	21	6			
00-01	N1	21	19	0	2	588	306	282	40	2	189	Ryan Roberts	23 Gareth King
01-02	N3N	26	13	0	13	625	494	131	26	7	190	James Lofthouse	15 Andrew Foreman

FACT FILE

Founded: 1888
Colours: Red and white
Web Site: www.blaydonrfc.com

GROUND

Address: Crow Trees Ground, Hexham Road, Swalwell, Newcastle upon Tyne NE16 3BM
Tel: 0191 420 0505 (Reception) Tel/Fax: 0191 420 0506 (Office)
email: brfcdevelopment@hotmail.com
Capacity: unlimited Covered seating: 400

Directions Take A1 north past Gateshead Metro Centre, then take the next exit for Swalwell (B6316). Over mini roundabout, through the village to the lights and the ground is straight ahead.

Car Parking: 500 spaces

Nearest Railway station: Newcastle Central

Admission £4 incl. programme Season Tickets £35

Clubhouse Open daily 7am - 11.30pm.
Bar meals available. Public gymnasium.
Private functions & corporate hospitality.
Car boot sale, Mar. - Nov., every Sunday

Club Shop Yes open with clubhouse.

Programme

Size: A5 Pages: 16
Price: with admission
Editor: Jim Huxley

BROADSTREET RFC

President	D Branston	114 Earle Court, Bell Green, Coventry CV7 7GX	02476 663866
Chairman	G Watts	15 Coopers Walk, Bubbenhall, Coventry CV8 3JB 02476 301838 (H) 02476 633336 (B)	
Secretary	C J McGinty	14 Glendower Ave., Whoberley, Coventry CV5 8BE 02476 679261 (H) 00353 7323155 (H) 00353 7323349 (F) 07801 869730 (M)	
Coach	R Harcourt	69 Heather Road, Binley Woods, Coventry CV3 2DD 02476 542788 (T/F) 07887 884932 (M)	
Fixture Secretary	D Wilkinson	4 Court Leet, Binley Woods, Coventry CV3 2DD	02476 543548 (H)

Pre- season saw the arrival of Birmingham and Solihull ever-presents and former Coventry trio, Paul Lydster, Steve Chapman and Ben Shepherd, to boost the First Team Squad, but all picked up pre-league and NC match injuries, along with another nine squad members. A 30-3 loss to Bromsgrove in the National Cup qualifier sent shock waves through the club, with the first league match against Walsall, who had dropped from N3N under seemingly unfair circumstances, only a week away.

In the absence of injured Captain, John Warne, and under the Vice-Captaincy of No 8 Steve Wood the team excelled to record a 34-20, six try win to restore confidence in our ability to compete for top spot in the League.

With both Chapman (broken leg) and Lydster (knee injury) cruelly ruled out for the rest of the season and other injured players taking time to return, the squad showed strength in depth only losing one away match during the first round of matches. A three-week period in December could have put paid to League success, with losses to League favourites Leicester Lions away and the only home loss of the season to Luctonians.

County Cup exit to old rivals, Barkers' Butts, after five consecutive cup wins put expectations for an improved New Year performance on hold. Bowing out of the Warwickshire Cup competition proved advantageous as the team could concentrate on the League. With just one slip up, away at Longton, the rest of the League matches were won with improved scores on first encounters.

Second rower Dean Lewis pipped his scrummaging companion, Dave Cummins, to Player of the Season with Andrew Skene deservedly taking Most Improved Player Award. The Best Young Player of the Season honour went without surprise to `home-grown' eighteen year old, Jordan Simpson, who went on to represent Warwickshire and Midlands Under 20s at scrum-half.

Over the past fourteen years the club has climbed from Warwickshire One to National League status under the coaching of Bob Harcourt, assisted more recently by backs coach, Andy Parker. In this time there have been just three First XV captains, John Dodd, Paul Harridine and John Warne - all centres.

With just one season at our new premises, promotion adds to the business adjustment that moving presents. We look forward to the future with a degree of excitement and a healthy measure of apprehension. There is nothing like the unknown for sharpening attitudes and increasing resolve.

BROADSTREET

Comp.	Date	H/A	Opponents	Result & Score	15	14	13	12	11
M1	15-09	A	Walsall	W 34-20	M Wood	A Skene	Barden/t	Watts/2c	Vigor/t
M1	22-09	A	Banbury	W 20-8	M Wood(d)	A Skene	Barden	Watts/cp	Vigor/t
M1	29-09	H	Camphill	W 24-11	M Wood	A Skene	Barden	Watts/2c	Vigor
M1	06-10	A	Kenilworth	L 21-25	M Wood/p	A Skene	Watts/c2p	Warne	Barden
M1	20-10	H	Longton	W 32-24	Rogers/dg	A Skene/t	Chapman	Warne	Shepherd/t
M1	27-10	A	Malvern*	W 31-18	M Wood/3c	Vigor	Barden	Warne	Shephers/2
M1	10-11	H	Barkers' Butt	W 34-15	Rogers/tc3p	Vigor	A Skene	Warne	Shepherd/t
M1	17-11	A	Dunstabilians	W 16-14	Rogers/c3p	Vigor	A Skene	Warne	Shepherd
M1	01-12	H	Hereford	W 44-17	Tee/t	Vigor/t	Rogers/t3cp	Warne	Shepherd
M1	08-12	A	Leicester Lions	L 9-32	Tee/2p	Vigor	Barden	Warne	Shepherd
M1	22-12	H	Luctonians	L 19-26	Rogers/3p	Vigor	Gee	Warne	Shepherd
M1	12-01	H	Dunstabilians	W 29-20	M Wood/t3cp	S Skene	Gee	Warne	Shepherd/t
M1	26-01	A	Hereford	W 13-9	M Wood/cp	A Skene	Gee	Warne	Shephers
M1	02-02	H	Malvern	W 34-8	M Wood/2c	A Skene	Barden(p)	Warne/2t	Shepherd/t
M1	23-02	H	Kenilworth	W 25-18	Tee	Vigor	A Skene(w)	Warne	Shepherd/t
M1	02-03	A	Camphill*	W 33-11	M Wood/3c4p	Vigor(p)	A Skene	Warne	Shepherd/t
M1	09-03	H	Banbury	W 48-0	M Wood/4c	Vigor(/tj)	A Skene	Warne	Shepherd/2
M1	16-03	H	Walsall	W 25-0	M Wood/2cp(t)	Tee	A Skene	Warne/t	Shepherd/t
M1	23-03	A	Longton	L 3-21	M Wood/p(u)	Tee	A Skene	Warne	Vigor
M1	30-03	A	Barkers'Butt	W 28-13	M Wood/c2p	Vigor	A Skene	Warne	Shepherd
M1	06-04	A	Luctonians	W 21-15	Tee/t	Vigor	Watts/p	Warne	Shepherd/t
M1	13-04	H	Leicester Lions	W 30-15	Tee/t	Vigor	Watts/2c2p	Warne	Shepherd
PGC	00-00	N	Bromsgrove	L 3-38	Rogers/p	S Skene	Barden	Warne	Vigor

** after opponents name indicates a penalty try. Brackets after a player's name indicates he was replaced. eg (a) means he was replaced by replacement code "a" and so on. / after a player or replacement name is followed by any scores he made - eg /t, /c, /p, /dg or any combination of these*

EVER PRESENT Tim Harrison

Most Appearances:
22: Tim Harrison.
21: Dean Lewis, Eddy SImkiss.
19: Matt Dearden, Chris Gardner, John Warne.

PLAYERS USED

27 plus seven as replacements

MOST POINTS

Pts	Player	T	C	P	DG
82	M Wood	1	19	13	-
65	C Rogers	2	8	9	4
65	B Shepherd	13	-	-	-
45	E Blundell	9	-	-	-
37	A Watts	-	11	5	-

MATCH FACTS

10	9	1	2	3	4	5	6	7	8
Gee	Blundell/4t	Dearden(a)	Harrison	Sheasby	Simkiss	Cummins(c)	Lewis	Gardner	S Wood
Gee	Blundell/t	Dearden	Harrison	Sheasby	Simkiss	Cummins	Lewis	Gardner	S Wood/t
Gee	Blundell/t	Dearden	Harrison	Sheasby	Simkiss	Cummins/t	Lewis	Gardner/t	S Wood/t
Gee/dg(d)	Blundell	Dearden	Harrison	Sheasby	Simkiss	Cummins	Lewis/t	Gardner	S Wood
Watts/2c	Blundell/t	Dearden	Harrison(a)	Sheasby	Cummins	Lewis/t	Skurr/t	Gardner	Simkiss
Watts	Blundell	Dearden	Harrison	Garcia/t	Cummins	Lewis	Skurr(g/t)	Gardner	Simkiss
Gee	Blundell	Garcia(h)	Harrison	Dearden	Cummins(i)	Skurr/t	Gardner	Tauti/t	Simkiss
Gee	Blundell	Dearden	Harrison	Dearden	Cummins	Lewis	Gardner	Tauti	Simkiss/t
Gee	Blundell/2t	Dearden	Harrison	Sheasby	Lewis	Skurr/2t	Gardner	Tauti	Simkiss
Gee/dg	Blundell	Dearden	Harrison	Sheasby	Lewis	Skurr(k)	Gardner	Tauti	Simkiss
Watts	Tee/t	Garcia(h)	Harrison	Dearden	Cummins	Lewis	Skurr/t	Tauti	Simkiss
Rogers	Tee	Dearden	Harrison/t	Sheasby	Cummins	Lewis	Gardner/t	Tauti	Simkiss
Rogers/dg	Tee	Dearden	Harrison	Sheasby(o)	Lewis/t	Simkiss	Skurr	Tauti	S Wood(n)
Rogers	Simpson	Morgan(h)	Harrison	Dearden	Cummins(n)	Lewis/2t	Simkiss	Gardner/t	S Wood
Rogers/cp	Simpson	Morgan	Harrison	Sheasby(q)	Cummins/2t	Lewis/t	Simkiss	Shillinglaw(c)	S Wood
Rogers	Simpson	Morgan	Harrison	Dearden	Cummins	Lewis	Simkiss	Shillinglaw(s)	S Wood/t
Rogers	Simpson	Morgan(h)	Harrison	Dearden	Cummins	Lewis	Simkiss/2t	Gardner(s/t)	S Wood/2t
Rogers/dg	Simpson/t	Dearden	Harrison	Sheasby	Cummins	Lewis	Simkiss	Gardner(r)	S Wood
Rogers	Simpson	Morgan(h)	Harrison	Dearden	Lewis	Skurr	Shillinglaw(k)	Gardner	S Wood
Rogers	Simpson	Dearden	Harrison	Sheasby(a)	Cummins/2t	Lewis(c)	Simkiss/t	Gardner	S Wood/t
Rogers/dg	Simpson	Morgan	Harrison	Sheasby	Cummins	Lewis	Skurr/t	Gardner(v)	Simkiss
Rogers	Simpson(x)	Morgan	Harrison	Sheasby	Cummins(b/t)	Lewis	Skurr/2t	Gardner(q)	S Wood
Gee	Blundell	Campbell	Harrison	Dearden	Bonas	Donaldson	Lewiss	Simkiss	S Wood

REPLACEMENTS:

a - Garcia.	b - S Wood
c - Skurr.	d - Warne
e - Rogers.	f - M Wood.
g - Tauti.	h - Sheasby.
i - Lewis.	j - Tee.
k - Cummins.	l -Barden.
m - Gardner.	n - MacMillan.
o - Morgan.	p - A Watts.
q - Dearden.	r - Shillinglaw.
s - Masters.	t - Vigor.
u - Shepherd.	v - D Watts
w - S Skene.	x - A Skene.

Eddie Simkiss in action against Walsall last season.

Photo courtesy of Roy Kilcullin

BROADSTREET

LEAGUE STATISTICS *compiled by Stephen McCormack*

SEASON	Division	P	W	D	L	F	A	Pts Diff	Lge Pts	Lge Pos	Coach	Captain
92-93	MW1	11	5	1	5	169	127	42	11	7	Bob Harcourt	Paul Harridine
93-94	Mid 2	12	5	0	7	193	132	61	12	7	Bob Harcourt	Paul Harridine
94-95	Mid 2	12	10	0	2	291	129	162	20	2p	Bob Harcourt	John Warne
95-96	Mid 1	12	6	2	4	242	199	43	14	5	Bob Harcourt	John Warne
96-97	Mid 1	16	11	0	5	434	230	204	22	5	Bob Harcourt	John Warne
97-98	Mid 1	15	12	1	2	420	211	209	25	3	Bob Harcourt	John Warne
98-99	Mid 1	16	10	1	5	342	248	94	21	5	Bob Harcourt	John Warne
99-00	Mid 1	16	10	0	6	338	273	65	20	5	Bob Harcourt	John Warne
00-01	Mid 1	22	14	0	8	474	394	80	28	4	Bob Harcourt	John Warne
01-02	Mid 1	22	18	0	4	573	340	233	36	1p	Bob Harcourt	John Warne

FACT FILE

Founded: 1929
Nickname: 'The Street'

Colours: Red with green & white bands
Change colours: Green with red & white bands

GROUND

Address: Ivor Preece Field, Rugby Road, Binley Woods, Coventry CV3 2AY
Tel: 024 7654 1070 (Club) Fax: 024 7654 1069 Steward: 024 7654 1068
Website: www.broadstreet-rfc.co.uk

Capacity: Unlimited. Seated: 250

Directions: M6 J2. Follow signs for Warwick/Stratford/Banbury along the A46. Look for signs for Binley Woods. At the island junction with the A428 (Coventry/Rugby road) turn left towards Rugby. The ground is 100m on the left in the village of Binley Woods.

Car Parking: 150 spaces plus overspill. Coach Parking: First left off access road.

Admission: £5 incl. programme Concessions: Varied Season Tickets available.

Clubhouse: Open evenings except Monday & Sunday pius Saturday & Sunday lunchtimes.
Fully licensed & meals are available - varied menu.

Functions: Four corporate and private function rooms available for hire.
Brochure on request.

Club Shop: Open match-day, Sunday & training nights.

Training Nights Tuesday & Thursday 7pm.

PROGRAMME Size: A5 Price: with admission
Pages: 40

Editor: C. McGinty (Club Sec.)
Advertising Rates: Brochure available

DARLINGTON MOWDEN PARK RFC

President	Tony Hammond	49 Neville Road, Darlington, Co. Durham Tel: 01325 381390
Chairman	John Parkinson	c/o Darlington Mowden Park RFC Tel: 07764 177545 (M)
Treasurer	John Heslop	5 Netherby Drive, Darlington DL3 8SE Tel: 01325 488568 (H)
Secretary / Fixture Sec.	George Nevill	7 Millbank Crescent, Darlington, Co. Durham DL3 8LY Tel: 01325 469001(H/Fax) 07790 569289 (M)
Director of Rugby	John Parkinson	as Chairman

Our first season in National League Rugby concluded with a very satisfactory sixth position and an awareness of what is required to compete effectively at this level.

After a promising start and featuring as early to mid-season promotion candidates, we could not sustain our initial momentum. If we had been able to finish the season with the same side which had begun it, it may have been different story but injuries and other circumstances affecting the availability of experienced, key players ultimately had its inevitable effect.

Nonetheless, we took heart from the performance of a number of our promising youngsters who were thrown into the fray a little sooner than anticipated and acquitted themselves extremely well in a very competitive league.

As with all successful sides over a prolonged period, the time comes when the original core of the team moves on and, whilst a number of our more experienced players will still be with us in the season ahead, the summer months have been busy talking to potential new players and establishing a new coaching team.

As in previous seasons, we enjoyed our games in the National Knockout Cup, finally losing to Manchester in the 4th round.

DARLINGTON MOWDEN PARK

Comp.	Date	H/A	Opponents	Result & Score	Att	15	14	13	12	11
N3 N	01-Sep	A	Tynedale	W 15-3		McCallum	Jones	Bedworth	Elwine/t	Howland
N3 N	08-Sep	H	Sandal	W 41-0	300	McCallum	Jones	Bedworth/c	Elwine/t	Howland/2t
N3 N	22-Sep	A	Nuneaton*	W 32-12		McCallum/t	Howland/2t	Golightly	Elwine	Mattinson
N3 N	06-Oct	H	Morley*	W 19-12	400	McCallum	Jones	Bedworth	Elwine	Kent
N3 N	20-Oct	A	Liverpool St Helens	L 10-30		McCallum/t	Jones	Golightly	Stewart	Mattinson/t
N3 N	27-Oct	H	Bedford Athletic	W 29-20		McCallum/t	Mattinson/t	Golightly	Strong	Jones/2t
N3 N	10-Nov	H	Dudley Kingwinsford	L 31-43		Keelan	Jones	Golightly/t	Strong	Kent
N3 N	17-Nov	A	Whitchurch	W 33-6		Keelan	Mattinson	Bedworth/t2c3p	Wilkinson	Kent/2t
N3 N	24-Nov	H	Blaydon	W 18-12		McCallum	Mattinson/t	Bedworth	Wilkinson	Kent
N3 N	01-Dec	H	Tynedale	W 26-25		McCallum/t	Mattinson	Bedworth/2p	Strong	Jones
N3 N	08-Dec	H	Doncaster	L 7-21		McCallum/t	Mattinson	Golightly	Kent	Jones
N3 N	15-Dec	A	Scunthorpe	L 19-48	250	McCallum	Jones	Bedworth	Kent	Mattinson
N3 N	29-Dec	A	New Brighton	L 20-21		McCallum/t	Mattinson	Bedworth	Wilkinson	Jones/2t
N3 N	12-Jan	H	Whitchurch	W 58-5		McCallum/t	Mattinson/t	Bedworth/t5cp	Kent	Jones/t
N3 N	19-Jan	A	Dudley Kingwinsford	D 17-17	550	McCallum/t	Mattinson	Bedworth	Wilkinson	Jones
N3 N	26-Jan	H	New Brighton	L 19-39		Oliphant/t2c	Mattinson/t	Bedworth	Kent	Jones
N3 N	02-Feb	A	Bedford Athletic	L 5-27	150	McCallum	Mattinson	Bedworth	Strong	Jones
N3 N	09-Feb	H	Liverpool St Helens*	L 24-31		Keelan	Mattinson	Bedworth/t	Kent	Jones
N3 N	16-Feb	H	West Hartlepool	W 25-24		Keelan	Mattinson	Bedworth	Kent	Jones/t
N3 N	23-Feb	A	Morley	W 17-16		Bedworth	Mattinson	Wilkinson	Kent/t	Jones
N3 N	02-Mar	A	Blaydon	L 23-29		Bedworth/c2p	Mattinson/t	Wilkinson/t(d/t)	Kent	Jones
N3 N	09-Mar	H	Nuneaton	W 17-9		Bedworth/2cp	Mattinson	Phillips	Kent/t	Jones
N3 N	16-Mar	A	Sandal	W 36-19		Bedworth/2t3c	Mattinson	Wilkinson/t	Kent/2t	Jones
N3 N	30-Mar	A	West Hartlepool	W 27-15		Bedworth/2cp	Mattinson	Strong	Kent/t	Jones
N3 N	06-Apr	H	Scunthorpe	L 12-17		Bedworth/tc	Mattinson	Strong	Kent	Jones
N3 N	13-Apr	A	Doncaster	L 3-86		Bedworth/p	Mattinson	Thompson	Strong	Jones
PGC	15-Sep	N	Bromsgrove	W 48-0		McCallum/t	Mattinson/t	Golightly/t	Howland/2t	Jones
PGC	29-Sep	A	Waterloo	W 32-20		McCallum	Mattinson	Bedworth	Elwine	Howland
PGC	13-Oct	N	Dudley Kingwinsford	W 31-25		McCallum	Jones	Golightly	Elwine	Kent
PGC	03-Nov	N	Manchester*	L 27-39		McCallum	Jones	Strong/t	Golightly	Kent
PGC										

** after opponents name indicates a penalty try. Brackets after a player's name indicates he was replaced. eg (a) means he was replaced by replacement code "a" and so on. / after a player or replacement name is followed by any scores he made - eg /t, /c, /p, /dg or any combination of these*

EVER PRESENT None

Most Appearances:
25: Billy McKinnon. Kevin Oliphant (2).
23: J Marston (1), Stephen Jones (1).
22: Chris Mattinson (1)

PLAYERS USED

38 plus three as replacement only.

MOST POINTS

Pts	Player	T	C	P	DG
116	K Oliphant	4	27	12	2
97	M Bedworth	6	17	11	-
40	K McCallum	8	-	-	-
35	M Kent	7	-	-	-
35	J Golightly	7	-	-	-
30	C Mattinson	6	-	-	-

MATCH FACTS

10	9	1	2	3	4	5	6	7	8
Oliphant/cp	Woollam	Brown	Tuhana	Sinclair	Sanderson	James	Mitchell	McKinnon	Radaelli/t
Oliphant/2c(a/t)	Woollam/t	Brown	Tuhana/t	Sinclair	Sanderson	Sanderson	James	McKinnon/t	Radaelli
Oliphant/2cp	Woollam/t	Brown	Tuhana	Sinclair	Malcolm	Marston	Irwin	Hall	Radaelli
Oliphant/c4p	Woollam	Keeligan	Hall	Sinclair	Marston	Sanderson	James	McKinnon	Radaelli
Oliphant	Woollam	Keeligan	Hall	Sinclair	Sanderson	Marston	Wilks	Kerr	McKinnon
Oliphant/2c	Woollam	Brown	Hall/t	Sinclair	Sanderson	Marston	Russell	Boatman	McKinnon
Oliphant/4cp	Woollam	Brown/t(b/t)	Tuhana	Keeligan	Sanderson	Marston	Irwin/t	McKinnon	Russell
Golightly/t	Woollam	Brown	Tuhana	Keeligan	Sanderson	Marston	Irwin	Wilks	McKinnon
Oliphant/c2p	Woollam	Brown	Tuhana/t	Sinclair	Sanderson	Marston	Irwin	Long	McKinnon
Golightly(c/cdg)	Woollam	Brown/t	Tuhana/t	Sinclair	Sanderson	Marston	Irwin	Long	McKinnon
Oliphant/c	Woollam	Keeligan	Tuhana	Isaacson	Sanderson	Marston	Irwin	McKinnon	Dowson
Oliphant/2c	Golightly/2t	Isaacson/t	Tuhana	Keeligan	Marston	Malcolm	Irwin	Wilks	McKinnon
Oliphant/cp	Woollam	Brown	Wilks	Sinclair	Sanderson	Marston	Irwin	McKinnon	Dowson
Golightly/2t	Woollam/2t	Isaacson	Tuhana	Sinclair	Sanderson	Marston	Irwin/t	Wilks	McKinnon
Oliphant/tc	Golightly	Sinclair	Tuhana/t	Isaacson	James	Marston	Irwin	Wilks	McKinnon
Oliphant/t2c	Woollam/t	Keeligan	Tuhana	Brown	James	Marston	Irwin	Wilks	McKinnon
Oliphant	Woollam	Sinclair	Tuhana	Isaacson	Sanderson	Marston	Irwin	Wilks	McKinnon/t
Oliphant/2c	Woollam	Keeligan	Brown/t	Isaacson	Marston	Sanderson	Wilks/t	McKinnon	Long
Oliphant/2t2cpdg	Holborough	Sinclair	Brown	Isaacson	Marston	Sanderson	Wilks	McKinnon	Long
Oliphant/2cp	Holborough	Keeligan	Brown	Isaacson/t	Marston	Sanderson	Boatman	McKinnon	Wilks
Oliphant	Holborough	Keeligan	Brown	Sinclair	Sanderson	Marston	Boatman	McKinnon	Wilks
Oliphant	Holborough	Isaacson	Brown	Sinclair	Sanderson	Marston	Boatman	McKinnon	Wilks
Oliphant	Holborough	Isaacson	Brown/t	Sinclair	Marston	Mangles	Boatman	Wilks	McKinnon
Oliphant	Holborough	Keeligan/2t	Hall	Sinclair	Mangles	Marston	Boatman(e/t)	McKinnon	Wilks
Oliphant	Holborough	Keeligan	Brown	Isaacson/t	Sanderson	Marston	Boatman	Wilks	McKinnon
Oliphant	Holborough	Keeligan	Brown	Sinclair	Sanderson	Mangles	Boatman	McKinnon	Wilks
Oliphant/4c2p	Oliphant/4c2p	Keeligan	Tuhana	Sinclair	Marston	Sanderson	McKinnon/t	Irwin	Radaelli
Oliphant/3c2p	Woollam/t	Keeligan	Tuhana/t	Sinclair	Marston	James	Irwin/t	McKinnon/t	Radaelli
Oliphant/2c4p	Woollam/2t	Keeligan	Hall	Sinclair	Sanderson/t	Marston	James	McKinnon	Russell
Oliphant/t3c2p	Woollam	Keeligan	Tuhana	Brown	Sanderson	Marston	Irwin	Long	McKinnon

REPLACEMENTS:a - Jonny Golightly b - Dave Sinclair. c - Kevan Oliphant. d - Chris Strong. e - Del Russell.
Most replacement appearances in the league: 8: Danny Brown. 7: Ian Keeligan. 6: Matt Hall, Dave Sinclair.
Most times replaced: 11: Danny Brown. 8: Ian Keeligan. 6: Jonathan Boatman.

WHERE	Total	Home	Away
The POINTS were scored	583	326	257
The POINTS were conceded	587	329	258
The TRIES were scored	84	46	38
The TRIES were conceded	73	39	34

HOW the TRIES were scored

Total	Backs	Forwards	F Back	Wing	Centre	H Back	F Row	Lock	B Row	Pen. Try
81	59	22	12	18	14	15	15	-	7	3

HOW the TRIES were conceded

Total	Backs	Forwards	F Back	Wing	Centre	H Back	F Row	Lock	B Row	Pen. Try
73	53	20	11	18	17	7	4	4	12	-

DARLINGTON MOWDEN PARK

LEAGUE STATISTICS *compiled by Stephen McCormack*

SEASON	Division	P	W	D	L	F	A	Pts Diff	Lge Pts	Lge Pos	Most Pts		Most Tries	
92-93	D&N 1	12	7	0	5	185	130	55	14	5				
93-94	D&N 1	12	12	0	0	256	76	180	24	1p				
94-95	NE2	12	7	1	4	168	106	62	15	4				
95-96	NE2	12	9	0	3	272	139	133	18	3				
96-97	NE2	18	9	1	8	417	330	87	19	6				
97-98	NE2	18	17	0	1	617	147	470	36	1p	164	Kevin Oliphant	15	Mick Kent
98-99	NE1	18	18	0	0	729	223	506	36	1p	231	Kevin Oliphant	25	Mick Kent
99-00	North 2	22	21	0	1	893	277	616	42	1p	224	Kevin Oliphant	21	Mick Kent
00-01	North1	20	20	0	0	719	163	556	40	1p	171	Kevin Oliphant	17	Mark Bedworth
01-02	Nat 3N	26	14	1	11	583	587	-4	27*	6	116	Kevin Oliphant	8	Kevin McCallum

FACT FILE

Founded: 1946
Nickname:

Colours: Royal blue with white & red piping
Change colours: White, with royal blue top & red piping

GROUND

Address 22 Yiewslew Drive, Darlington, Co. Durham DL3 9XS
Tel: 01325 465932 Web site: dmprfc.co.uk
Capacity: 1,200 Seated: 300

Directions Travelling **South**
From A1(M) follow A68 into Darlington. Follow signs to Staindrop and turn left at Mowden pub into Barnes Rd. At 'T' junction turn right into Fulthorpe Ave. and first right into Yiewsley Dr.
Travelling **North**
From A1(M) follow A66(M). At the 2nd r'about take 1st exit and turn left at next r'about onto A67 Barnard Castle Rd. At the 40mph sign turn right into Edinburgh Dr. which merges with Fulthorpe Ave. Yiewsley Dr. is 1st left after shopping precinct car park.
Nearest Railway Station: Darlington (BR)

Car Parking Limited, but 100 close by.

Admission Matchday - £5 incl. prog.
Children £2
Season Ticket £50

Clubhouse Open Mon-Wed 7.30-11pm,
Thur. 6.30-11pm, Fri. 4-11pm
& Sat & Sun 12-11pm

Club Shop Yes, contact Colin Pearson
or Martin Sayers

Training Nights Monday & Thursday 6.45

PROGRAMME Size: A5
Pages: 16
Price: with admission
Editor: Glen Wilson
01325 288364

Action from last season's campaign.

DUDLEY KINGSWINFORD RFC

President	David Evans	156 Common Road, Wombourne, West Midlands WV5 0LT	01902 894463 (H)
Chairman	Roger Port	Church House, High St., Claverley, Shropshire WV5 7DU	01746 710793 (H)
Secretary	Ken Crane	Two Oaks, Penstone Lane, Lower Penn, Wolverhampton WV4 4XE 01902 332952 (H) 07970 855729 (M)	
Fixture Secretary	Bill Jones	54 Dingle View, Sedgley, West Midlands DY3 3LE 0121 606 7777 (B) 07721 716500 (M) email: bjones@atotech.co.uk	01902 678427 (H)
Match Confirmer & Referees Contact	Bill McLachlan	32 Lynwood Ave., Wallheath, Kingswinford, W. Mids. DY6 9AJ 01384 831279 (H) 07802 749909 (M) email: willmacdk@blueyonder.co.uk	
Playing Administrator	Gordon Bannatyne	47 Windermere Drive, Kingswinford, W. Mids DY6 8AN 01384 271863 (H) 07850 395544 (M)	
Director of Rugby	Mark Wilson	50 Gladston Drive, Solihull B91 3YE	0121 709 2183 (H) 07967 047157 (M)

D.K entered its second year as a National League club with some trepidation and much anticipation. Unable to expand their squad significantly, Director of Coaching Mark Wilson and his assistant, Dale Smallman directed their efforts to further improvements of this largely home based and amateur group of players.

It is a testament to their success that they reached Christmas, top of the league remaining the only unbeaten side in the National Leagues. During this time they inflicted a spectacular defeat on Nottingham 36-3 in the RFU senior cup and beat Doncaster 16-0, their only defeat as they powered their way through the league.

The much contested decision to play on a frost bound Nuneaton pitch was costly in terms of injuries, coupled with a five week lay off, were to prove too much for such a small but enthusiastic squad in the second half of the season. Three defeats and unusually three draws meant second place was only secured after a close fought victory at Liverpool St Helens.

This placed the club in the unenviable position of an expensive trip to Launceston in the play off. Doing no justice to the rugby they have played all year they were fairly defeated by a well prepared team playing in front of its own supporters.

Top points scorer was Steve Smart with 320 points placing him second behind John Liley. Shaun Perry was the league's leading try scorer with 25.

None of this would have been possible without the support of the Development side managed by Andrew Gallis and coached by Tony Lanaway and Chris Parsons together with the efforts by Brian Westwood and Graham Robbins in forging a highly effective Colts side.

Finally a word of thanks once again to our President David Evans, the committee, our loyal band of sponsors, our magnificent supporters, and all the unsung heroes who do so much at this club to make sure all sides remain competitive.

Gordon Bannatyne

L-R - Back Row: Tony Lanaway; Dale Smallman (asst coach); Matt Halstead; John Fallon; Stuart Homer; Layton Wilkinson; John Davies; Gavin Tipper; Ben Connett; Charlie Lowe; Richard Port; Mark Lockley; Wayne Millard; Mark Wilson (director of coaching)
Front Row: James Benedict (inset) Richard Smith; Chris Barker; Mark Lindsay; Shaun Perry; Gareth Davies; Ian Langford (Capt.); Warren Port; Steve Smart; Barrie Kirwan; Matt Wagstaff; Marc Millward; Robbie Jones; Mike Davies (inset)

DUDLEY KINGSWINFORD

Comp.	Date	H/A	Opponents	Result & Score	Att	15	14	13	12	11
N3 N	01-09	A	Bedford Athletic	W 63-16		Smart/2t6c2p	Millward/t	Kirwan	Davies/t	Benedict
N3 N	08-09	H	New Brighton	D 21-21	450	Smart/p	Millward/t	Kirwan	Davies/dg	Benedict
N3 N	22-09	A	Scunthorpe	W 43-23	250	Smart/3c4p	Benedict	Kirwan/t	Davies	Millward
N3 N	06-10	A	Whitchurch	W 53-24	300	Smart/2t3c4p	Benedict	Port/t	Davies	Millward/t
N3 N	20-10	H	Blaydon	W 27-13		Smart/t3c2p	Benedict	Kirwan/t	Port	Lindsay
N3 N	27-10	A	West Hartlepool	W 42-10		Smart/t3c2p	Lindsay/t	Kirwan/t	Port	Millward
N3 N	03-11	H	Doncaster	W 16-0	750	Leaupepe	Benedict/t	Kirwan	Davies	Millward
N3 N	10-11	A	Darlington MP	W 43-31		Smart/t5cp	Benedict/t	Kirwan	Davies/t	Millward
N3 N	17-11	H	Tynedale	W 38-15		Smart/3c4p	Benedict/t	Port	Davies	Millward/2t
N3 N	24-11	A	Sandal	W 71-0	100	Smart/3t8c	Benedict/t	Port	Davies/t	Midler-Price/t
N3 N	01-12	H	Bedford Athletic	W 39-17	600	Smart/2t4c2p	Benedict	Port/t	Davies	Midler-Price
N3 N	08-12	A	Morley	W 24-8		Smart/3p	Benedict	Port/2t	Davies	Millward
N3 N	15-12	H	Liverpool St Helens	W 46-7	600	Leaupepe/t	Benedict	Kirwan/t	Davies	Millward/2t
N3 N	19-01	H	Darlington MP	D 17-17	550	Port	Lindsay/t	Kirwan	Davies	Millward/t(c/cp
N3 N	26-01	A	Doncaster	L 8-20	2000	Smart/p	Millward	Kirwan	Davies	Lindsay
N3 N	02-02	H	West Hartlepool	W 46-5	350	Smart/4cp	Benedict	Port	Davies/t	Lindsay/t
N3 N	09-02	A	Blaydon	L 21-50		Smart/tc3p	Benedict	Port	Davies	Lindsay
N3 N	16-02	A	Nuneaton	W 24-13		Smart/3cp	Benedict	Port	Davies/t	Lindsay
N3 N	23-02	H	Whitchurch	W 22-19	475	Smart/c	Benedict	Port/2t	Davies	Lindsay
N3 N	02-03	H	Sandal	W 17-3	300	Smart/tc	Benedict/t	Kirwan	Davies	Millward
N3 N	09-03	H	Scunthorpe	W 43-5	420	Smart/2t5cp	Benedict	Kirwan	Davies/t	Millward
N3 N	16-03	A	New Brighton	D 22-22	450	Smart/2c	Benedict	Kirwan/t	Davies/2tdg	Millward
N3 N	23-03	A	Tynedale	L 13-19	200	Halstead	Benedict	Kirwan	Wagstaffe	Millward
N3 N	30-03	H	Nuneaton	W 34-19	550	Halstead	Benedict/t	Kirwan	Davies	Lindsay/t
N3 N	06-04	A	Liverpool St Helens	W 12-10		Smart/4p	Millward	Kirwan	Davies	Lindsay
N3 N	13-04	H	Morley	W 32-30	475	Smart/t3c2p	Millward	Kirwan	Wagstaffe	Lindsay/t
PGC	29-09	N	Nottingham	W 36-3		Smart/2t4cp	Midler-Price	Port	Kirwan	Millward/t
PGC	13-10	N	Darlington MP	L 25-31		Smart/2c2p	Benedict/t	Port	Kirwan	Millward
NL PO	27-04	A	Launceston	L 0-26	2500	Smart	Benedict	Kirwan	Davies	Millward

** after opponents name indicates a penalty try. Brackets after a player's name indicates he was replaced. eg (a) means he was replaced by replacement code "a" and so on. / after a player or replacement name is followed by any scores he made - eg /t, /c, /p, /dg or any combination of these*

EVER PRESENT None

Most Appearances:
25: Charlie Lowe.
24: Shaun Perry, Gareth Davies.
23: Stuart Homer (3).
22 Mickey Davies (3).

PLAYERS USED

29 plus three as replecement only

MOST POINTS

Pts	Player	T	C	P	DG
320	S Smart	17	59	39	-
138	S Perry	25	5	1	-
56	G Davies	10	-	-	2
40	M Millward	8	-	-	-
30	J Benedict	6	-	-	-
30	W Port	6	-	-	-

MATCH FACTS

10	9	1	2	3	4	5	6	7	8
Halstead/t	Perry/2t	Homer	Davies	Fallon	Lowe	Tipper	Wilkinson	Port/t	Langford
Halstead	Perry/cp	Homer	Davies	Lockley	Lowe	Tipper	Langford	Port	Wilkinson/t
Halstead/t	Perry/3t	Homer	Davies	Lockley	Lowe	Tipper	Langford	Port	Wilkinson
Halstead/t	Perry/2t	Homer	Davies	Fallon	Lowe	Tipper	Langford	Port	Wilkinson
Halstead	Davies/t	Homer	Davies	Lockley	Lowe	Davies	Langford	Asipito	Connett
Barker	Davies/t	Homer	Smith/t	Fallon	Davies	Lowe	Wilkinson/t	Port	Connett
Barker/2p	Perry	Homer	Davies	Fallon	Lowe	Davies	Wilkinson	Port	Connett/t
Barker/t	Perry/t	Homer	Davies	Fallon	Tipper	Lowe	Langford/t	Port	Connett
Barker	Perry	Millard	Smith	Lockley	Lowe	Tipper	Langford	Asipito(a/t)	Connett
Barker	Perry/4t	Millard(b/t)	Davies	Fallon	Tipper	Lowe	Port	Port	Langford
Halstead	Perry/t	Homer	Davies	Lockley	Lowe	Tipper	Shillingford	Langford/t	Connett
Barker	Perry	Homer	Davies	Fallon	Lowe	Davies	Langford	Port	Connett/t
Halstead	Perry/t3c	Homer	Davies	Lockley	Lowe	Davies	Wilkinson/t	Port/cp	Connett/t
Halstead	Perry/c	Homer	Davies	Fallon	Lowe	Davies	Langford	Port	Connett
Halstead	Perry	Homer	Davies	Fallon/t	Lowe	Davies	Wilkinson	Port	Connett
Halstead	Perry/2t	Homer	Davies	Lockley	Lowe/t	Tipper/t	Wilkinson	Langford	Connett/t
Halstead	Perry/t	Homer	Davies	Fallon	Lowe	Tipper	Wilkinson	Langford	Connett
Barker	Perry/t	Homer	Davies	Lockley	Lowe	Tipper	Langford/t	Port	Wilkinson
Barker	Perry/2t	Homer	Davies	Fallon	Lowe	Tipper	Langford	Port	Wilkinson
Halstead	Perry	Millard	Smith	Fallon	Lowe	Shillingford	Port	Asipito(d/t)	Langford
Halstead	Perry/t	Homer/t	Davies	Lockley	Lowe	Shillingford	Langford	Port	Wilkinson/t
Barker	Perry	Homer	Davies	Fallon	Lowe	Davies	Shillingford	Langford	Wilkinson
Barker/c2p	Perry	Homer	Davies	Fallon	Lowe	Davies/t	Wilkinson	Langford	Connett
Barker/3cp	Perry/2t	Homer	Davies	Fallon/t	Davies	Lowe	Langford	Port	Connett
Barker	Perry	Homer	Davies	Fallon	Lowe	Davies	Wilkinson	Port	Connett
Barker	Perry/2t	Homer	Smith	Lockley	Tipper	Davies	Wilkinson	Langford	Connett
Halstead	Perry/2t	Homer	Davies	Fallon	Tipper	Lowe	Langford	Asipito	Connett
Halstead	Davies	Millard	Davies	Fallon	Davies/t	Lowe	Langford	Connett	Wilkinson/t
Halstead	Perry	Homer	Davies	Fallon	Lowe	Davies	Wilkinson	Port	Connett

REPLACEMENTS: a - R Port. b - Stuart Homer. c- Steve Smart. d - Leyton Wilkinson.

Most replacement appearances in the league: 10: Mark Lockley. 6: Ben Connett,, John Fallon, Warren Port, Richard Smith.

Most times replaced: 8: John Fallon. 7: Mark Lockley. 6: Mickey Davies.

WHERE	Total	Home	Away
The POINTS were scored	837	398	439
The POINTS were conceded	417	246	171
The TRIES were scored	111	54	57
The TRIES were conceded	50	27	23

HOW the TRIES were scored

Total	Backs	Forwards	F Back	Wing	Centre	H Back	F Row	Lock	B Row	Pen. Try
111	88	23	18	20	19	31	5	2	9	-

HOW the TRIES were conceded

Total	Backs	Forwards	F Back	Wing	Centre	H Back	F Row	Lock	B Row	Pen. Try
49	26	23	3	7	7	9	11	2	10	1

DUDLEY KINGSWINFORD

LEAGUE STATISTICS *compiled by Stephen McCormack*

SEASON	Division	P	W	D	L	F	A	Pts Diff	Lge Pts	Lge Pos	Most Points	Most Tries
92-93	M W1	12	5	1	6	152	119	33	11	7		
93-94	M W1	12	7	1	4	167	160	7	15	4		
94-95	M W1	12	8	0	4	157	107	50	*14	5		
95-96	M W1	12	9	0	3	202	181	21	18	2p		
96-97	M 2	17	13	0	4	434	212	222	*24	6		
97-98	M 2	16	14	1	1	528	145	383	29	2p		
98-99	M 1	15	13	0	2	391	205	186	26	3		
99-00	M 1	16	14	1	1	412	194	218	29	1p	196 Steve Smart	10 Steve Smart
00-01	N3N	*24	11	1	12	485	519	-34	23	6	230 Steve Smark	12 Shaun Perry
01-02	N3N	26	20	3	3	837	417	420	43	2	320 Stev Smart	25 Shaun Perry

FACT FILE

Founded: 1927

Nickname: "D.K"

Web site: www.dkrfc.co.uk (under contruction)

Colours: Cambridge blue and navy hoops, navy shorts

Change colours: White/red/navy

GROUND

Address Heathbrook, Swindon Road, Wallheath, Kingswinford, W. Mids. DY6 0AW

Tel/Fax: 01384 287006 e-mail: gordon@lastdrop.fsnet.co.uk

Capacity: 2,700 Covered Seating: 250 Uncovered Standing: 2,500

Directions: Just off the A449 at Wallheath, midway between Kidderminster and Wolverhampton.
Nearest Railway Station: Stourbridge or Wolverhampton

Car Parking: Spaces for 300+ at the ground

Admission: Matchday: £5 non-members, £4 members.
Season tickets are available.

Clubhouse: Open 7 days per week, from 7pm , also lunch-times at weekend.

Club Shop: Open matchdays and Sunday lunch 12-2

Training Nights: Tuesday & Thursday 7.30pm

Programme: Size: A5 Pages: 20
Price: incl with admission
Editor: David Coyle 01384 830508

Advertising Contact Martin Chard 01384 274560 (H)

Lock forward Charlie Lowe securing another line out ball against Bedford Athletic - another product of our mini junior section.

HALIFAX RUFC

President	David Brook MBE, MA	Hall Park House, Hall Park Rd., Walton, Wetherby Tel/Fax: 01937 8444734
Chairman	Peter Smith	'Torrington', 446 Burnley Road, Halifax HX2 7LW Tel/Fax: 01422 360143 07887 520383 (M)
Secretary	Mike Smith	The Lowe, Wainstalls, Halifax, W. Yorks. HX2 7TR Tel/Fax: 01422 882879 (H) 07850 233019 (M) Email: thelowe@aol.com
Treasurer	Chris Mellor	37 Harewood Ave., Highroad Well, Halifax HX2 0LU Tel: 01422 362619
Fixture Secretary	Glyn Kenyon	18 Watkinson Road, Illingworth, Halifax, HX2 9DB Tel/Fax: 01422 245193 07733 226745 (M) Email: glyn@gkenyon.freeserve.co.uk

2001-2002 saw Halifax not only secure promotion for the third successive season, but also win the RFU Powergen Intermediate Cup, by defeating Gosport & Fareham (43-19) at Twickenham - squad photograph below. This unique League and Cup double, crowned a year in which the pre-season aim was simply `to consolidate in North 1".

The success achieved has truly been a team effort, both `on and off the field'. Led by president David Brook, who is the club's major sponsor, and well supported by chairman Peter Smith and other officials, the coaching team of Kevin McCallion (director of rugby), Tony Price and Andy Smith worked hard to produce a side whose quality of rugby was acknowledged by many to be of a high standard. Much credit goes to the players. Led by skipper Carl Mortimer, the side lost only two league games, away at Sheffield and Aspatria, but clinched the North 1 title by a margin of three points over runners up Hull Ionians with two games left unplayed.

With North 1 arguably the strongest Level 5 league in England, the success of the club in also winning the Powergen Intermediate Cup, by achieving nine consecutive wins, was remarkable, especially with having to travel away to play leading Midlands 1 side Luctonians, and London 2 North Champions Hertford. Fortunately, the club was lucky to draw a strong Richmond side at home in the Quarter Final, which brought a 20-19 win after a thrilling match.

Kiwi full back Glen Strang was the club's leading points scorer with 327 points, which included a record 130 successful kicks at goal, of which twelve of these were achieved in the home game against Wigton. Leading try scorer was winger Oliver Marns with nineteen, followed by centre Jeff Morley with fifteen. Lock Martin Smith was the only ever present in a season which saw 37 players being selected for 1st XV duty. Six players - Smith, Morley, Marns, Strang, centre Richard Thompson and flanker Bob Davis - were selected for the Yorkshire Squad.

The long standing plan of Halifax to vacate their 80 year old Ovenden Park ground, and relocate to another site in Halifax, at last seems as if it will be achieved within the next eighteen months.

Numerous problems have been encountered in completing arrangements, but the long overdue move will be soon completed, and thus enable the club to provide first class modern facilities for members, players and supporters, whose loyalty over many seasons deserves to be rewarded.

HALIFAX

Comp.	Date	H/A	Opponents	Result & Score	15	14	13	12	11
N1	08-09	A	Sheffield	L 18-22	Canning	Rowe	R Thompson/t(c)	Morley/tc2p	Kersey-Brown
N1	22-09	H	Hull Ionians	W 26-21	O'Connor	Canning/t	R Thompson	Morley	Kersey-Brown(e)
N1	29-09	A	Middlesbrough	W 32-8	O'Connor	Canning/2t(g)	Marsden	Morley/t	Marns
N1	06-10	A	Darlington	W 28-17	O'Connor	Kersey-Brown(h/t)	Marns	Morley	Greenwood/t
N1	20-10	H	Macclesfield	W 16-5	O'Connor	Greenwood	Morley	Marns	Rowe/t
N1	27-10	A	Bradford & Bingley	W 17-10	O'Connor	Canning	Morley	Marsden	Marns
N1	10-11	H	Chester	W 26-6	R Thompson	Canning	Marsden	Morley	Marns
N1	17-11	A	Wigton	W 47-0	O'Connor	Canning(j/t)	Marsden/t	R Thompson	Marns/t
N1	01-12	H	West Park St H	W 13-8	R Thompson(k)	Canning/t	Marsden	Morley	Marns/t
N1	08-12	A	Aspatria	L 11-13	O'Connor	Canning/t	R Thompson	Morley	Marns
N1	26-01	A	Chester	W 26-13	Strang/3c(m)	Canning	Morley/2t	Marsden/t	Marns
N1	02-02	H	Bradford & Bingley	W 15-10	Strang/5p	Canning	R Thompson(o)	Marsden	Marn
N1	16-02	H	Wigton	W 94-0	R Thompson/t	Canning/t(j/t)	Morley/3t	Marsden/2t	Marns/3t
N1	23-02	H	Darlington	W 19-10	R Thompson	Canning	Morley	Marsden/t	Marns
N1	02-03	H	Middlesbrough	W 39-12	R Thompson(p)	Canning/4c2p	Morley/3t	Marsden	Marns/t
N1	16-03	H	Sheffield	W 30-14	Strang/2c2p	Canning(j)	Morley	Marsden	Marns/t
N1	23-03	H	Driffield	W 36-3	Strang/2c3p	Canning/t(j)	Thompson	Marsden/t	Marns/t
N1	06-04	A	Driffield	W 36-22	Strang/3c5p	Rowe	Thompson/t	Marsden/t	Marns(r)
N1	13-04	H	Aspatria	W 71-14	Strang/2t9cp	Canning(r)	Thompson	Marsden/t	Marns/2t
N1	27-04	A	Hull Ionians	W 55-5	Strang/6cp	Canning/2t	Morley	Marsden(m/t)	Marns/t
IC1	15-09	A	Old Crossleyans	W 51-3	Canning	Rowe(s)	Marsden	Morley/2t6c3p	Kersey-Brown/t
IC2	13-10	A	Dinnington	W 21-12	O'Connor	Gleeson	R Thompson	Morley	Marns
IC3	03-11	H	Broughton Park	W 87-3	Canning/3c(p)	Greenwood/c	Marsden	Morley/3t	Marns/4t
IC4	24-11	H	Stockport	W 20-10	O'Connor	Canning(u)	Marsden/t	Thompson	Marns/t(j)
IC5	15-12	A	Bradford & Bingley	W 26-5	Strang/2c4p	Canning(j)	Marsden(m)	Morley/t	Marns/t
IC6	11-01	A	Luctonians	W 16-0	Strang/t2p	Canning	Marsden	Morley(m)	Marns
ICQF	09-02	H	Richmond	W 20-19	Strang/cp	Canning	Marsden	Morley	Marns
ICSF	09-03	A	Hertford	W 27-17	Strang/3c2p	Canning/t(j)	Marsden/t(m)	Morley	Marns
ICFin	20-04	N	Gosport & Fareham	W 43-19	Strang/t3c4p	Canning/t(j)	Marsden	Thompson(o)	Marns/2t

** after opponents name indicates a penalty try. Brackets after a player's name indicates he was replaced. eg (a) means he was replaced by replacement code "a" and so on. / after a player or replacement name is followed by any scores he made - eg /t, /c, /p, /dg or any combination of these*

EVER PRESENT Martin Smith.

Most Appearances:
20: Martin Smith.
19: Carl Mortimer, Joe Bartlett.

PLAYERS USED 37

MOST POINTS

Pts	Player	T	C	P	DG
240	G Strang	2	52	42	-
64	A Canning	5	4	2	-
58	J Morley	5	1	2	-
55	O Marns	11	-	-	-
40	J Marsden	8	-	-	-

MATCH FACTS

10	9	1	2	3	4	5	6	7	8
O'Connor	Bartlett	R Thomas	Mortimer	Richardson(b)	Hagerty(a)	Smith	Lewis	M Thomas	Davis
Strsng/7p	Bartlett	Binns(d)	Mortimer	R Thomas	Hagerty	Smith	Davis	Lewis	Walker
Strang/3c2p	Bartlett	Binns	Mortimer	Richardson(b)	Hagerty/t(a)	Smith	Davis	M Thomas	Horton
Strang/2c3p	Bartlett	Binns	Mortimer	R Thomas	Hagerty	Smith/t	Davis	Lewis	Walker(d)
Strang/2p	Bartlett	Binns/t	Mortimer	Richardson(f)	Hagerty(a)	Smith	Davis(g)	M Thomas	Horton
Strang/4p	Bartlett	Binns	Mortimer	R Thomas(d)	Hill(l)	Smith	Davis	M Thomas(h)	Horton/t
Strang/2c4p	Bartlett/2t	Binns(f)	Mortimer	Richardson	Hill	Smith	Davis(h)	Lewis	Horton
Strang/6c	Bartlett/2t	Binns	Mortimer	Richardson/t(f/t)	Hagerty(a)	Smith	Lewis	M Thomas	Davis
Strang/p	Bartlett	Binns	Mortimer	Richardson	Hill	Smith	Ledger(f)	M Thomas	Davis
Strang/2p	Bartlett	Binns	Mortimer	Richardson(f)	Hagerty	Smith(a)	Ledger	M Thomas	Davis
O'Connor	Bartlett	Binns	Mortimer	Richardson(f)	Hill	Smith	Ledger	M Thomas(l)	Davis/t
O'Connor	Bartlett	Binns	Mortimer	R Thomas(d)	Hill	Smith	Ledger	Lewis	Horton(n)
Strang/12c	Emmerson/t	Binns(d/t)	R Thomas	Szabo	Hill/t	Smith	Davis(g)	Ledger	Horton
Strang/2c(k)	Bartlett	Binns	Mortimer	Szabo(f/t)	Hill	Smith	Lewis	Ledger	Davis(l)
O'Connor	Bartlett/t	Richardson(f)	Mortimer	Szabo	Hill	Smith	Ledger(q)	Lewis	Horton
O'Connor	Bartlett	Binns(d)	Mortimer	R Thomas	Hill	Smith	Ledger(q)	Lewis	Davis
O'Connor/dg	Bartlett	Binns	Mortimer	Szabo(f)	Hill(d)	Smith	Davis	Lewis	Lord/t
O'Connor	Bartlett	Richardson	Mortimer(f)	Szabo(b)	Hill	Smith/t	Davs	Lewis	Lord
O'Connor/2t	Bartlett/t	Binns	Mortimer	Szabo(f/t)	Hill(d)	Smith	Davis	Ledger/t	Lord
O'Connor/t	Bartlett	Binns(d)	Mortimer/t	Szabo	Hill	Smith(g)	Davis/t	Ledger	Lord/t
O'Connor/t	Bartlett/t	R Thomas	Mortimer	Richardson(b)	Hagerty(a/t)	Smith	Davis/t	M Thomas(g)	Walker
Strang/tc3p	Bartlett/t(t)	Binns	Mortimer	R Thomas(d)	Hill	Smith	Davis	Lewis	Lord(l)
Strang4c2p(k)	Bartlett/2t	Richardson(b)	Mortimer	R Thomas/t	Hagerty/t	Smith	Davis	Lewis/t(h)	Horton/t
Strang/2c2p	Bartlett	Richardson(b)	Mortimer	R Thomas	Hagerty	Smith	Davis	Lewis	Davis
O'Connor	Bartlett	Binns	Mortimer	R Thomas	Hill(i)	Smith	M Thomas	Lewis	Kitchen
O'Connor	Bartlett	Binns	Mortimer	Richardson(f/t)	Hagerty(v)	Hill	Ledger	Lewis(w)	Horton
O'Connor(m)	Bartlett	Binns	Mortimer/t	Richardson(f)	Hill	Smith	Davis/t	Lewis/t	Horton
O'Connor	Bartlett	Binns	Mortimer	Richardson(f)	Stewart	Smith	Davis(w)	Ledger(g)	Horton
O'Connor	Bartlett	Binns	Mortimer	Szabo	Hill	Smith	Davis	Lewis(w)	Horton(q)

REPLACEMENTS:

a - Hill. b - Binns. c -Walker. d -Richardson. e - Marns.
f - R Thomas. g - Lewis. h - M Thomas. i - Hagerty. j - Rowe.
k - N O'Connor. l - Horton. m - Thompson. n - Davis. O - Morley.
P Strang. p - Fraine. q - Lord. r - Fraine. s - S Connor.
t - Gardiner. u - Gleeson. v - Smith. w - Ledger

League & Cup double

Third successive promotion

Consecutive home league wins now totals 32.

Club's overall success record was 90%

Glen Strang won the North One leading goalkicker award, and also scored 107 points in the Intermediate Cup

Oliver Marns was the leading try scorer in the Intermediate Cup with 8.

HALIFAX

LEAGUE STATISTICS *compiled by Stephen McCormack*

SEASON	Division	P	W	D	L	F	A	Pts Diff	Lge Pts	Lge Pos	Most Points		Most Tries	
92-93	N2	12	2	0	10	153	265	-112	4	12	26	Darren Dinsmore	3	Philip Horton
93-94	N2	12	4	0	8	153	241	-88	8	10	33	Adam Mounsey	4	Jeffrey Morley
94-95	N2	12	4	0	8	146	229	-83	4*	11	70	Adam Mounsey	7	Adam Mounsey
95-96	N2	12	6	0	6	175	209	-34	12	8	89	Aaron Canning	7	Jeffrey Morley
96-97	N2	22	6	0	16	366	509	-143	12	10	125	Aaron Canning	7	Aaron Canning
97-98	N2	22	4	0	18	521	903	-382	8	12	102	Aaron Canning	9	Aaron Canning
98-99	NE1	18	14	1	3	825	660	165	29	2	146	Simon Tidey	10	Simon Tidey
99-00	NE1	18	17	0	1	711	190	521	34	1	263	Aaron Canning	19	Aaron Canning
00-01	N2E	21	20	1	0	883	146	737	41	1	266	Aaron Canning	14	Nicholas O'Connor
01-02	N1	20	18	0	2	655	213	442	36	1	240	Glen Strang	11	Oliver Marns

FACT FILE

Founded: 1923
Nickname: 'Fax'

Colours: Dark blue, light blue & white hooped shirts, dark blue shorts
Change colours: Red shirts, dark blue shorts

GROUND

Address: Standeven Memorial Ground, Ovenden Park, Halifax HX2 8AR
Tel: 01422 365926

Capacity: 5,000 Covered Seating: 200 Standing: 300 covered, 4,500 uncovered.

Directions: From Halifax town centre, take the main A629 road signposted Keighley. HRUFC is approx 2.5 miles from the town centre on the right behind Moorside Junior School. Entry road (un-named) is on the right immediately past the School, and between the School and Moorside Garage.

Car Parking: Spaces for 500 in the ground.

Admission: £5 incl. programme & Car Park
Senior Citizens: £2.50
Schoolchildren: Free

Clubhouse: Open match-days and training evenings.

Club Shop: Open match-days and training evenings.

Training Nights Tuesday & Thursday

PROGRAMME Size: A5 Price: with admission
Pages: 64 + cover
Editor: Mike Smith (Secretary)
Advertising: Contact the Chairman.

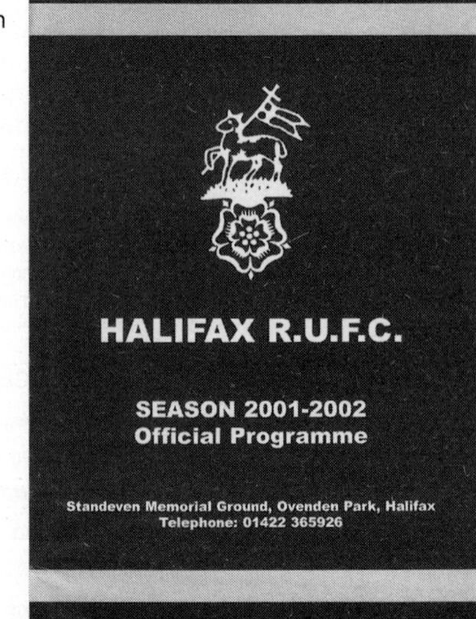

HULL IONIANS RUFC

President	B Appleyard	c/o the club
Chairman	R Gosling	c/o the club
Secretary	Peter G Hewitt	24 Melton Road, North Ferriby, E. Yorks. HU14 3ET Tel: 01482 633626 e-mail: peterghewitt@hotmail.com
Director of Rugby	Saun Carty	c/o the club

Having finished eighth in the previous season, Hull Ionians recruited heavily as they aimed to become the first side from East Yorkshire ever to reach the national leagues.

In came Guy Hope (Otley), Glenn Boyd (Pontefract), Rob Danby (local rugby league), Neil Lyon (Goole), Darren McIntyre (Rotherham), Chris Cain (Hull University) and Matt Rhodes from the under-18 squad. These players quickly gelled and Ionians won six of their opening seven North One matches and progressed to the second round of the Powergen Cup.

A tight defence and the ability to win narrow matches soon became a pattern in those early games. Ionians then received the boost that strengthened the squad and helped them in their quest for promotion. Three foreign players joined the club in quick succession, with New Zealand-born hooker Brad McDonnell, and Tongan internationals Viliami Vaki and Tevita Fifita signing up, although the club quickly lost the services of Viliami Vaki to Parma of Italy.

Despite only being able to play two of these at any given time, Ionians continued to challenge Halifax at the top, despite a controversial defeat at Aspatria in January. With the season coming nicely to a dramatic close, Ionians went to Darlington and secured a nail-biting draw and then showed their mettle in successive away wins at Bradford & Bingley and Sheffield.

With their nearest rivals Darlington and West Park St Helens starting to drop points as the pressure increased, Ionians clinched at least a promotion play-off in their 48-19 victory against local rivals Driffield.

Halifax's excellent form saw them crowned champions, with runners-up Ionians taking on Walsall in the play-off at Brantingham Park. Tries by Fifita, Hope, Danby (2), Simon Smith and new recruit Andy Metcalfe, saw Ionians home and looking forward to the challenge of next season, where they will meet some old and new friends.

HULL IONIANS

Comp.	Date	H/A	Opponents	Result & Score	15	14	13	12	11
N1	08-09	A	Middlesbrough	W 28-24	Boyd	Swift	Bone/t	Hope	Windas/t
N1	22-09	A	Halifax	L 21-26	Burrell/t	Swift	Danby/t	Hope	Windas
N1	06-10	A	Macclesfield	W 29-20	Boyd/2c5p	Bone	Danby	Hope	Cain
N1	13-10	H	Darlington	W 18-11	Boyd/tc2p	Bone	Danby/t	Hope	Cain
N1	20-10	H	Bradford & Bingley	W 16-11	Boyd/tp	Bone	Danby	Hope/t	Cain
N1	27-10	A	Chester	W 20-19	Boyd/2pc	Windas/t	Danby	Bone	Cain
N1	10-11	H	Wigton	W 53-11	Boyd/2t2c	Windas/t	Danby	Bone	Cain/2t
N1	17-11	A	West Park St H	L 15-33	Boyd	Windas	Danby/t	Bone	Cain
N1	01-12	H	Aspatria	W 27-13	Boyd	Windas/t	Danby	Bone	Cain
N1	08-12	A	Driffield	L 15-23	Boyd	Windas	Danby	Hope	Cain
N1	29-12	H	Sheffield	W 28-20	Hope	D Smith	Danby/t	Bone	Cain
N1	05-01	A	Aspatria	L 25-31	Hope	Swift	Danby/t	Bone	Cain/t
N1	12-01	H	West Park St H	W 18-11	Hope	Swift	Danby/t	Bone	Cain/t
N1	26-01	A	Wigton	W 31-0	Hope/2t	Swift	Danby	Bone	Windas
N1	02-02	H	Chester	W 34-15	Hope	Swift/t	Danby	Bone	Windas
N1	23-02	H	Macclesfield	W 29-0	Hope	Swift	Danby/t	Bone/t	Windas
N1	02-03	A	Darlington	D 22-22	Hope/t	Swift	Danby	Bone	Windas
N1	16-03	H	Middlesbrough	W 51-10	Hope/t	Metcalfe	Danby/t	Bone	Windas/3t
N1	30-03	A	Bradford & Bingley	W 37-24	Hope/t	Metcalfe	Danby	Bone	Windas
N1	06-04	A	Sheffield	W 29-6	Hope	Boothroyd	Boyd/2c5p	Bone	Windas
N1	13-04	H	Driffield	W 48-19	Hope/t	Windas	Danby	Bone	Metcalfe
N1	27-04	A	Halifax	L 5-55	Burrell	Stockton	Swift	Cowling	Fifita
P off	11-05	H	Walsall	W 35-22	Hope/t	Rhodes	Danby/2t	Bone	Metcalfe/t
PGC	01-09	A	Middlesbrough	W 22-14	Boyd/t	Swift	Bone	Hope/t	Windas
PGC	15-09	H	Westoe	W 13-12	Boyd	Windas	Bone/t	Hope	Danby
PGC	29-09	A	Liverpool St H	L 15-37	Boyd/cp	Boothroyd	Bone	Hope	Cain

** after opponents name indicates a penalty try. Brackets after a player's name indicates he was replaced. eg (a) means he was replaced by replacement code "a" and so on. / after a player or replacement name is followed by any scores he made - eg /t, /c, /p, /dg or any combination of these*

EVER PRESENT None.

Most Appearances:
20: Dykes.
19: Binks, Bone, Danby.

PLAYERS USED

42

MOST POINTS

Pts	Player	T	C	P	DG
222	G Boyd				
70	Paterson	4	7	10	2
65	Guy Hope	13	-	-	-
60	Rob Danby	12	-	-	-

MATCH FACTS

10	9	1	2	3	4	5	6	7	8
Paterson/t2c2pdg	Rhodes	Lyon	Middleton	Russell	Binks	S Bates	Smith	K Bates	Dykes
Paterson	Rhodes/c3p	Lyon	Middleton	Russell	Binks	S Bates	Smith	K Bates	Dykes
McIntyre	Rhodes	Farnsworth	Middleton	Lyon	Binks	Zibeck(a/t)	Smith	K Bates	Dykes
McIntyre	Rhodes	Farnsworth	Middleton	Russell	Binks	S Bates	Smith	K Bates	Dykes
Paterson/p	Rhodes	Lyon	Middleton	Russell	Binks	S Bates	Smith	K Bates	Dykes
Paterson/p	Rhodes	Skinner	Middleton	Russell	Binks/t	S Bates	Smith	K Bates	Dykes
Paterson/3t2c	Penna	Lyon	McDonnell/t	Skinner	Bennett	S Bates	Emmerson	K Bates	Binks
Paterson/cp	Rhodes	Lyon	McDonnell/t	Russell	Binks	S Bates	Smith	K Bates	Dykes
Paterson/2cp	Rhodes	Farnsworth	McDonnell/t	Russell	Binks	Vaki	Smith/2t	K Bates	Dykes
Paterson/4pdg	Rhodes	Farnsworth	Middleton	Russell	Binks	Vaki	Smith	Fifita	Dykes
Boyd/2c3p	Rhodes	Farnsworth	McDonnell/t	Lyon	S Bates	Vaki/t	Smith	K Bates	Dykes
Boyd/2c2p	Rhodes	Farnsworth	McDonnell	Lyon	Binks	S Bates	Smith	Vaki/t	Dykes
Boyd/p	McIntyre	Farnsworth	McDonnell	Lyon	Binks	Jones	Smith	Vaki/t	Dykes
McIntyre	Rhodes/2p	Farnsworth	McDonnell	Russell/t	S Bates	Jones/t	Fifita	K Bates	Dykes
McIntyre/c	Rhodes/t2cp	Farnsworth	McDonnell/t	Russell	Binks	Smith/t	K Bates	Vaki/t	Dykes
Boyd/3cp	Penna	Farnsworth	McDonnell	Russell	Binks/t	S Bates	Fifita	K Bates	Dykes/t
Boyd/c5p	Rhodes	Lyon	McDonnell	Russell	Binks	S Bates	Fifita	K Bates	Dykes
Boyd/5c2p	Rhodes	Lyon	McDonnell/t	Russell	Binks	S Bates	Fifita	K Bates/t	Dykes
Boyd/4c3p	Rhodes/t(b/t)	Lyon	McDonnell	Russell/t	Binks	S Bates	Smith	Fifita	Dykes
McIntyre	Rhodes	Farnsworth	McDonnell	Russell	Binks/t	Smith	Fifita/t	K Bates	Dykes
Boyd/t3c3pdg	McIntyre/t	Lyon	McDonnell	Russell	Binks	Smith	Fifita/t	K Bates	Dykes
Wade-Jones	Cook	Farnsworth	Oliver/t	Russell	Wilson	Bennett	Moore	Moses	Zibeck
Boyd/cp	McIntyre	Lyon	McDonnell	Russell	Binks	S Bates	Fifita/t	K Bates	Smith/t
Paterson/2cdg	Rhodes	Lyon	Middleton	Russell	Binks	Dickenson	Zgoda	K Bates	Smith
Paterson/p	Rhodes(b/t)	Lyon	Middleton	Russell	Binks	S Bates	Smith	Marshall	Dykes
McIntyre	Rhodes	Farnsworth	Middleton	Skinner	Binks	S Bates	Smith	K Bates/t	Dykes

REPLACEMENTS: a - M Emmerson. b - D McIntyre

2001-02 Highlights

New signing Glenn Boyd finished the season as top points scorer with 222 points.

Hull Ionians get promotion for the first time ever to the National Leagues, culminating in play-off victory against Walsall, having finished 8th the previous season.

Were unbeaten at home in the league winning all 10 matches

HULL IONIANS

LEAGUE STATISTICS *compiled by Stephen McCormack*

SEASON	Division	P	W	D	L	F	A	Pts Diff	Lge Pts	Lge Pos	Coach/ Most Points	Captain/ Most Tries
92-93												
93-94												
94-95	N1	12	5	1	6	198	196	2	11	5		
95-96	N1	12	10	0	2	294	133	161	20	3		
96-97	N1	22	7	2	13	359	456	-97	16	9		
97-98	N1	21	5	3	13	397	524	-127	13	10		
98-99	N1	22	10	0	12	422	492	-70	20	6		
99-00	N1	22	17	0	5	663	327	336	34	2		
00-01	N1	22	8	0	14	399	516	-117	16	8		
01-02	N1	22	16	1	5	599	411	188	33	2P		

FACT FILE

Founded: 1989
Nickname: 'I's

Colours: White shirts with red & green trim
Change colours: Blue shirts

GROUND
Address: Brantingham Park, Brantingham Road, Elloughton, Brough, E. Yorks. HU15 1HX

Tel: 01482 667342 Fax: 01482 666695

Capacity: 2,500 . Covered Seating: 225

Directions: Take M62 East. Becomes A63. Take first exit. Follow signs to Brough. After 1 mile take left turn to Brantingham (2nd of two left turns). At T junction turn right. Club 1/2 mile on RHS.

Car Parking: Spaces for 120 cars (plus overflow if reqd.)
Nearest Railway Station: Brough

Admission: Matchday £3 incl. programme

Clubhouse: Open 7 days. 2 bars, 3 sponsors' rooms, gym, sports hall & solarium. Functions catered up to 200

Club Shop: Open match-day & training nights.

Training Nights Tuesday & Thursday

PROGRAMME Size: A5 Price: with admission Pages: 30
Editor: Karl Hornsey
Advertising: Contact Craig Bone

LIVERPOOL St. HELENS RFC

President	Ray French	
Chairman	Alan Walker	
Club Secretary	Terry Ryan	Trenance, Ben Lane, Bickerstaffe, West Lancs. L39 0HL 01695 722986 (H) email: tryan123@compuserve.com
Fixtures Secretary	Ron Hall	21 Childwall Abbey Road, Liverpool. L16 0JL. 0151 722 3588 (H & Fax)
Director of Rugby	Eric Hughes	
Press Officer	John Williams	18 Old Lane, Rainford, St. Helens 01744 886270 (H) 0161 796 7222 (B) email: johnw@juniorcricket.fsnet
Treasurer	Not yet appaonted	

Eric Hughes began the season with the aim of improving on the previous year's position (seventh) and ended it having taken LSH to the verge of a promotion place. This was a hugely enjoyable and successful season that promised a lot by early spring but fell away in the month of April.

As the alliance with Sporting Club St. Helens moved into a second year LSH enjoyed one of their best starts ever by winning eight out of the first nine league games, including away wins at Blaydon and Tynedale. This on-the-road form was continued in the New Year with a crushing win at Morley and a tremendous victory at Darlington Mowden Park. Locked in a battle with Dudley Kingswinford for the best part of the season Moss Lane was not a place for the faint hearted. The elation of the last gasp win against neighbours New Brighton was matched by the agony of the final kick miss against Dudley Kingswinford. The defeats at Scunthorpe and Bedford were ultimately decisive before the final loss to worthy winners Doncaster brought an excellent season to a close. Eric Hughes and his young team had met their objective of progression, finishing in a satisfactory and deserved third place.

Player of the Season Sean Casey, alternating between centre and full back, set a new club record with 23 league tries. Alan Marsh and Martin Gaskell jointly won the most improved player award and together with the experienced Jon Hitchen and Davd Lupton were instrumental in LSH's improved fortunes. Young South African props Stefan Ferreira and Petrus DuPlessis also impressed and following a summer with Saints RL academy will return this season.

Club President Ray French, at the annual dinner, congratulated skipper Steve Cook and everyone at the club on a tremendous season and echoed the thoughts of everyone hoping to go one better next year.

JOHN WILLIAMS

LIVERPOOL ST. HELENS

Comp.	Date	H/A	Opponents	Result & Score	Att	15	14	13	12	11
N3 N	01-09	H	Whitchurch	W 23-12		Jones	Cross	Casey/t	Hitchen	Jones
N3 N	08-09	A	Blaydon	W 42-22	280	Jones	Cross/2t	Hitchen	Casey/t	Jones/t(b/t)
N3 N	22-09	H	West Hartlepool	W 45-17	150	Hull(c/t)	Jones/t	Cross	Hitchen/t	Walker/t
N3 N	06-10	A	Doncaster	L 22-49		Casey/2t	Jones	Hitchen	Cross	Doolan
N3 N	20-10	H	Darlington MP	W 30-10		Casey	Jones	Hitchen	Cross/t	Doolan
N3 N	27-10	A	Tynedale	W 22-18		Hull	Doolan/t	Hitchen	Casey/2t(d/t)	Jones
N3 N	03-11	H	Sandal	W 55-0		Casey/2t	Jones	Hitchen/t	Cross	Doolan/t
N3 N	10-11	A	Nuneaton	W 37-34		Casey	Jones/t	Hitchen	Cross/t	Doolan/t
N3 N	17-11	H	Morley	W 26-23		Casey	Jones	Hitchen	Cross/t	Doolan
N3 N	24-11	H	Scunthorpe	L 28-34	200	Casey/t	Jones	Hitchen/t	Cross	Doolan
N3 N	01-12	A	Whitchurch	W 43-29		Casey/t	Hull	Hitchen	Cross/t	Doolan
N3 N	08-12	H	New Brighton	W 18-16		Casey	Hull/t	Hitchen	Cross	Doolan
N3 N	15-12	A	Dudley Kingwinsford	L 7-46	600	Worsley/c	Hull	Casey	Cross	Doolan
N3 N	12-01	A	Morley	W 55-15		Jones/t	Jones/2t	Casey/t	Cross	Doolan/2t
N3 N	19-01	H	Nuneaton	W 29-26		Jones	Jones/t	Casey/2t	Cross	Doolan
N3 N	02-02	H	Tynedale	W 35-7		Casey/t	Jones	Hitchen	Cross	Jones/t
N3 N	09-02	A	Darlington MP	W 31-24		Casey/t	Doolan/t	Cross/t	Hitchen	Jones
N3 N	16-02	H	Bedford Athletic	W 34-10	200	Casey	Doolan	Cross	Hitchen	Jones/t2c
N3 N	02-03	A	West Hartlepool	W 32-11		Casey	Jones/t	Hitchen	Cross	Jones
N3 N	16-03	H	Blaydon	W 23-3	250	Jones	Jones	Hitchen	Cross	Doolan
N3 N	23-03	A	Scunthorpe	L 16-30		Casey	Jones	Hitchen	Cross	Roach/t
N3 N	30-03	A	Bedford Athletic	L 20-42		Jones	Roach	Cross/t	Casey/2t	Jones
N3 N	06-04	H	Dudley Kingwinsford	L 10-12		Jones	Jones	Casey/t	Cross	Roach
N3 N	13-04	A	New Brighton	L 8-54		Jones	Jones	Cross/t	Hitchen	Doolan
N3 N	20-04	A	Sandal	W 34-7	150	Jones	Hull	Hitchen(g/t)	Casey/2t	Doolan
N3 N	27-04	H	Doncaster	L 17-33		Jones/t	Jones/2t	Hitchen	Cross	Collins(h/c)
PGC	15-09	N	Morley	W 28-23		Hull/t	Jones	Walker(i/t)	Cross	Orford
PGC	29-09	H	Hull Ionians	W 37-0		Casey/t	Jones	Cross	Hitchen/t	Doolan/t
PGC	13-10	A	Henley Hawks	L 14-54		Casey	Jones/t	Cross	Hitchen	Doolan

** after opponents name indicates a penalty try. Brackets after a player's name indicates he was replaced. eg (a) means he was replaced by replacement code "a" and so on. / after a player or replacement name is followed by any scores he made - eg /t, /c, /p, /dg or any combination of these*

EVER PRESENT None

Most Appearances:
25: Alan Cook.
24: Alan Cross(1), Martin Gaskell (1), Alan Marsh (1), Sean Casey (1).

PLAYERS USED

31 plus four as replecement only

MOST POINTS

Pts	Player	T	C	P	DG
227	S Worsley	2	47	39	2
110	S Casey	22	-	-	-
51	G Close	1	8	10	-
50	D Jones	10	-	-	-
45	A Cross	9	-	-	-
40	D Lupton	8	-	-	-

MATCH FACTS

10	9	1	2	3	4	5	6	7	8
Worsley/2c3p	Cook	Hewitt	Keenaghan	Jackson	Nugent	Marsh	Gaskell	Evans	Lupton(a/t)
Worsley/4c2pdg	Cook	De Jagger	Jackson	Hewitt	Marsh	Bailey	Gaskell	Evans	Tchakoute
Worsley/3c3p	Cook	Jackson	Ferreira	Hewitt	Marsh	Bailey	Gaskell	Evans	Lupton/2t
Worsley/2cp	Cook	Hewitt	Ferreira	Jackson	Nugent	Marsh	Tchakoute	Evans/t	Lupton
Worsley/3c3p	Cook	Hewitt	Hitchen	Ferreira	Nugent	Tchakoute	Gaskell	Evans/t	Lupton/t
Worsley/2cp	Cook	Hewitt	Hitchen	Ferreira	Nugent	Marsh	Gaskell	Evans	Lupton
Worsley/5c	Cook	Ferreira	Hitchen	Jackson/t	Nugent	Marsh/t	Gaskell/t	Evans	Lupton/t
Worsley/4c3p	Cook	Ferreira	Hitchen	Jackson	Nugent	Marsh	Gaskell/t	Evans	Tchakoute
Worsley/tc2pdg	Cook	Jackson	Hitchen	Ferreira	Marsh	Tchakoute	Gaskell	Nugent/t	Lupton
Worsley/2c3p	Cook	Hewitt/t	Hitchen	Ferreira	Marsh	Nugent	Tchakoute	Evans	Lupton
Close/t4c5p	Cook	Hewitt/t	Ferreira	Jackson	Marsh	Tchakoute	Gaskell	Nugent	Lupton
Close/c2p	Cook	Hewitt	Ferreira	Jackson	Marsh	Tchakoute	Gaskell	Nugent	Lupton/t
Close	Cook	Hewitt	Hitchen	Ferreira	Nugent	Marsh	Gaskell/t	Nugent	Tchakoute
Worsley/3c2p	Cook	Hewitt	Hitchen	Du Plessis/t	Marsh	Nugent	Gaskell	Nugent/t	Tchakoute
Close/3cp	Cook	Hewitt	Hitchen	Du Plessis	Nugent/t	Marsh	Gaskell	Nugent	Lupton
Worsley/3c3p	Cook/t	Ferreira	Hitchen/t	Du Plessis	Nugent	Tchakoute	Gaskell	Nugent	Lupton
Worsley/2c3p(e/p)	Cook	Ferreira	Hitchen	Du Plessis	Marsh	Tchakoute	Gaskell	Nugent	Lupton
Close(k/t)	Cook/2t	Hewitt	Hitchen	Du Plessis	Marsh	Nugent	Gaskell	Tchakoute	Lupton/2t
Worsley/t2cp	Cook	Ferreira(f/t)	Hitchen	Du Plessis	Marsh	Nugent	Tchakoute/t	Gaskell	Lupton/t
Casey/t	Worsley/2c3p	Hewitt	Hitchen	Du Plessis	Marsh	Nugent	Gaskell/t	Nugent	Lupton
Worsley/2p	Cook	Ferreira	Hitchen/t	Du Plessis	Marsh	Tchakoute	Gaskell	Nugent	Lupton
Worsley/cp	Cook	Ferreira	Hitchen	Du Plessis	Marsh	Nugent	Gaskell	Nugent	Cashman
Worsley/cp	Cook	Ferreira	Hitchen	Du Plessis	Nugent	Marsh	Gaskell	Nugent	Lupton
Worsley/p	Cook	Ferreira	Hitchen	Du Plessis	Nugent	Marsh	Gaskell	Nugent	Lupton
Worsley/3cp	Cook/2t	Ferreira	Hitchen	Du Plessis	Marsh	Nugent	Gaskell	Keulemans	Cashman
Casey	Cook	Ferreira	Hitchen	Du Plessis	Nugent	Marsh	Gaskell	Keulemans	Cashman
Worsley/2c3p	Cook	Hewitt/t	Ferreira	Jackson	Nugent	Marsh	Gaskell	Evans	Bailey
Worsley/3c2p	Cook/2t	Hewitt	Ferreira	Jackson	Nugent	Bailey	Tchakoute	Gaskell	Lupton
Worsley/2c	Worsley/2c	Ferreira	Hitchen	Hewitt	Nugent(j/t)	Marsh	Gaskell	Evans	Lupton

REPLACEMENTS: a - David Bailey. b - Chris Walker. c - Sean Casey. d - Neil Hull. e - Graham Close. f - Phil Hewitt. g - Dan Collins. h - Simon Worlsey. i - Michael Hitchen. j - Njike Tchakoute. k - Danny Jones.

Most replacement appearances in the league: 8: James Cashman. 6: Phil Hewitt. Most times replaced: 8: Stefsan Ferreira. 7: Matt Nugent.

WHERE	**Total**	**Home**	**Away**
The POINTS were scored	742	373	369
The POINTS were conceded	584	381	203
The TRIES were scored	95	48	47
The TRIES were conceded	71	53	24

HOW the TRIES were scored

Total	Backs	Forwards	F Back	Wing	Centre	H Back	F Row	Lock	B Row	Pen. Try
95	68	27	13	22	23	10	7	2	18	-

HOW the TRIES were conceded

Total	Backs	Forwards	F Back	Wing	Centre	H Back	F Row	Lock	B Row	Pen. Try
71	48	23	4	19	20	5	7	4	12	6

LIVERPOOL St. HELENS

LEAGUE STATISTICS *compiled by Stephen McCormack*

SEASON	Division	P	W	D	L	F	A	Pts Diff	Lge Pts	Lge Pos	Most Points		Most Tries	
92-93	3	11	5	0	6	203	130	73	10		98	Andy Higgin	8	Mark Sephton
93-94	4	18	11	1	6	396	275	121	23		140	Simon Mason	9	Mark Sephton
94-95	4	18	10	3	5	374	243	134	23		155	Andy Higgin	7	Mark Sephton
95-96	4	18	11	1	6	471	343	128	23		120	Mark Wellens	14	Simon Humphreys
96-97	3	30	8	0	22	665	827	162	16		210	Paul Brett	14	Paul Brett
97-98	JN1	26	8	1	17	430	767	-337	17		85	Paul Brett	8	Mark Sephton
98-99	JN1	26	4	0	22	335	859	-524	8	14r	55	Chris Glynn	9	Mark Sephton
99-00	N2N	26	5	0	21	335	848	-513	10	13	88	Paul Cumming	7	Mark Sephton
00-01	N3N	*25	10	0	15	511	666	-155	20	9	228	Simon Worsley	9	Sean Casey
01-02	N3N	26	18	0	8	742	584	158	36	3	227	Simon Worlsey	22	Sean Casey

FACT FILE

Founded: 1857 (Merged 1986)
Nickname: LSH

Colours: Red with blue sleeves & white banding
Change colours: Blue with red sleeves & white banding

GROUND

Address: Moss Lane (off Rainford Rd.) Windle, St. Helens. WA11 7PL.
Tel : 01744 25708
Capacity: 2300 Seated: 300 Standing: 2000

Directions: M6, leave at A580 (Haydock) towards Liverpool. After approx 4 miles, take A570 (right), immediate left, left again and follow lane straight ahead - the clubhouse will come into view on the left after 1/2 mile.
Nearest Railway Station: St Helens, 5mins by taxi

Car Parking: 200

Admission: Season tickets £60
Matchdays Adults £5 (incl prog)
Children/OAPs £1.

Club Shop: Yes.

Clubhouse: 3 bars & has food available.
Functions: Up to 100 seated can be catered for.
Contact Chairman or Secretary for bookings.

Training Nights: Monday, Wednesday & Friday

PROGRAMME
Size: A5 Pages: 20 + cover Price: £1
Editor: Correspondence c/o Club.

Advertising Rates
Full page £300

NEW BRIGHTON FC

President	Dennis Morgan	c/o New Brighton FC Reeds Lane, Moreton, Wirral CH46 3RH. 0151 677 2442
Chairman	Harry K Leyland	c/o New Brighton FC.
Hon. Secretary	Peter Hartley	2 Tynron Grove, Noctorum, Wirral CH43 9WL 0151 653 8889 (H) email: PHartley@ic24.net
Hon. Treasurer	Paul Horner	1 Farndon Ave., Wallasey, Wirral CH45 3JX 0151 639 8606 (H)
Fixtures Secretary	B M Murphy	43 Brookfield Gardens, West Kirby, Wirral L48 4EL 0151 625 8835 (H), 0151 708 7904 (B)
Press Officer	Geoff Stone	0151 625 6188 (H)
Director of Coaching	L Connor	c/o New Brighton FC.
Director of Rugby	A Saverimutto	c/o New Brighton FC.

"For the first time in 10 seasons New Brighton took a backward step when finishing fourth, this after three consecutive 3rd places since reaching the National League. Suffering from what should have been totally avoidable internal politics during the close season, hanging on for a fortunate win in the opener against Scunthorpe and one over lowly West Hartlepool were the only victories in the first 7 league matches. Losses included a humiliating drubbing [51-10] at the hands of Doncaster and an embarrassing home defeat by Whitchurch who had been already beaten the previous week in the Cup. With all thought of promotion soon forgotten the talk in the clubhouse veered towards which clubs below us could save us from relegation.

Everything changed however in December when Steve Dorrington rejoined the club as forwards' coach and installed into the squad a team spirit that was immediately obvious both on and off the field.

Our record of no one ever having done the double over us in a season and which looked at one stage as if it would be taken by any number of clubs was finally only relinquished to Doncaster and then only with a speculative drop kick some10 minutes into injury time. Highlights were a fine win at Darlington [19-39] when they were confident of redressing an earlier two point loss at Reeds Lane and an end of season romp at the expense of LSH [54-8] Also noteworthy were our two draws against Dudley [21-21 & 22-22] and although we commiserate with their play off loss it will be exciting to do battle again next season.

Congratulations must go to Doncaster for their terrific season and we wish them good luck in Div.2 whilst we also have to say goodbye to Whitchurch, West Hartlepool, Sandal and Morley who are headed in the other direction. Replacing them will be a newcomer to us in Broadstreet and four old adversaries in Hull, Preston, Halifax and Waterloo.

We are certainly looking forward to meeting them all and do so with great optimism having recently strengthened our playing squad aided in no little manner by our new major sponsors, Wirral solicitors Becket Bemrose and Hagan. In recognition of their support the 1st XV will be known as B B H New Brighton during the forthcoming season."

NEW BRIGHTON

Comp.	Date	H/A	Opponents	Result & Score	Att	15	14	13	12	11
N3 N	01-09	A	Scunthorpe	W 36-32		Brett/3c5p	Johnson/t	Coast	Fredericks	Evans/t
N3 N	08-09	A	Dudley Kingwinsford	D 21-21	450	Brett/c3p	Johnson	Fredericks/t	Coast	Wakelam
N3 N	22-09	H	Whitchurch	L 28-35		Brett/t2c3p	Wakelam	Coast	Fredericks/t	Williams
N3 N	06-10	A	Blaydon	L 11-18		Brett/2p	Wakelam/t	Coast	Evans	Murray
N3 N	20-10	H	West Hartlepool	W 69-5		Brett/2t8cp	Moore/t	Coast/t	Fredericks/2t	Tupoa
N3 N	27-10	A	Doncaster	L 10-51		Brett	Moore	Coast	Fredericks	Tupoa/2t
N3 N	10-11	A	Tynedale	L 6-18		Brett/2p	Tupoa	Coast	Fredericks	Moore
N3 N	17-11	H	Sandal	W 55-10		Brett/t6cp	Moore	Coast	Fredericks(a/t)	Tupoa
N3 N	24-11	A	Nuneaton	W 23-3	150	Brett/2c3p	Moore/t	Evans/t	Fredericks	Murray
N3 N	01-12	H	Scunthorpe	L 21-49		Brett/c3p	Murray	Coast	Evans	Wakelam/t
N3 N	08-12	A	Liverpool St Helens	L 16-18		Brett/t2p	Moore	Coast	Fredericks	Murray
N3 N	15-12	H	Bedford Athletic	W 37-17		Brett/3c2p	Moore/2t	Coast	Fredericks/t	Murray/t
N3 N	29-12	H	Darlington MP	W 21-20		Brett/c3p	Moore	Evans	Fredericks	Wakelam
N3 N	12-01	A	Sandal	W 40-11	150	Brett/2c2p	Moore/t(b/t)	Coast/t	Fredericks	Murray
N3 N	19-01	H	Tynedale	W 35-5		Brett/2c2p	Moore/t	Coast	O'Connor	Murray
N3 N	26-01	A	Darlington MP	W 39-19		Brett/3cp	Moore/t	Evans/3t	O'Connor	Birley
N3 N	02-02	H	Doncaster	L 19-20		Brett/t3p	Coast/t	Evans	O'Connor	Moore
N3 N	09-02	A	West Hartlepool	W 41-19		Brett/3c	Moore/t	Evans/t	O'Connor/2t	Birley/2t
N3 N	16-02	A	Morley	W 27-16		Brett/2cp	Moore/2t	O'Connor	Evans	Coast
N3 N	23-02	H	Blaydon	W 23-21		Brett/c2p	Moore/t	Evans	O'Connor	Coast
N3 N	09-03	A	Whitchurch	W 27-22		Brett/3c2p	Moore	Coast	Evans	Birley
N3 N	16-03	H	Dudley Kingwinsford	D 22-22	450	Brett/t2cp	Birley	Coast	Evans	Moore
N3 N	23-03	H	Nuneaton	W 20-19		White/t	Murray/2t	Ashcroft	Brett/cp	Moore
N3 N	30-03	H	Morley*	W 40-19		Brett/2c2p	Birley/2t	Coast	O'Connor	Moore
N3 N	06-04	A	Bedford Athletic*	L 7-28	150	Brett/c	Murray	O'Connor	Ashcroft	Birley
N3 N	13-04	H	Liverpool St Helens	W 54-8		Brett/7c	Birley/t	Evans/2t	Coast/2t	Moore
PGC	15-09	N	Whitchurch*	W 32-21		Brett/3c2p	Wakelam/t	Coast/t	Fredericks	Williams
PGC	13-10	A	Nuneaton	L 7-31		Brett/c	Johnson/t	Coast	Fredericks	Wakelam

** after opponents name indicates a penalty try. Brackets after a player's name indicates he was replaced. eg (a) means he was replaced by replacement code "a" and so on. / after a player or replacement name is followed by any scores he made - eg /t, /c, /p, /dg or any combination of these*

EVER PRESENT Paul Brett

Most Appearances:
26 Paul Brett.
24: Jez Lamb (2).
23: Riaz Fredericks.
21: Paul Campbell (2), James Moore, Christian Saverimutto (2)

PLAYERS USED

38 plus three as replacement only

MOST POINTS

Pts	Player	T	C	P	DG
288	P Brett	7	56	47	-
85	Emrys Evans	17	-	-	-
55	J Moore	11	-	-	-
45	A Birley	9	-	-	-
35	R Fredericks	7	-	-	-
35	L Tupoa	7	-	-	-

MATCH FACTS

10	9	1	2	3	4	5	6	7	8
O'Connor	Saverimutto/t	Dorrington	Saffy	Gazzola	Atkinson	Campbell	Keulemans	Jones	Lamb
O'Connor	Saverimutto	Dorrington	Davies	Gazzola	Atkinson	Campbell	Kettle	Lamb/t	Irwin
Birley	Cottrell	Dorrington	Saffy	Moore	Campbell	Atkinson	Kettle	Evans/t	Lamb
O'Connor	Saverimutto	Dorrington	Saffy	Evans	Campbell	Atkinson	Kettle	Sewell	Tupoa
Birley/t	Saverimutto	Dorrington	Davies	Evans	Campbell/t	Lamb/t	Kettle	Evans	Sewell/t
Birley	Saverimutto	Dorrington	Buckley	Evans	Lamb	Campbell	Kettle	Evans	Sewell
Birley	Cottrell	Morton	Davies	Evans	Campbell	Lamb	Kettle	Evans	Sewell
Birley/2t	Saverimutto	Dorrington	Davies	Evans	Campbell	Turley	Lamb	Evans/3t	Sewell/t
Birley	Saverimutto	Dorrington	Davies	Evans	Turley	Atkinson	Tupoa	Lamb	Sewell
Birley	Moore	Dorrington	Davies	Evans	Atkinson	Turley	Kettle	Lamb	Sewell/t
Birley	Saverimutto	Dorrington	Davies	Evans	Turley	Atkinson	Lamb	Tupoa/t	Sewell
Birley	Saverimutto	Dorrington	Davies	Davies	Campbell	Turley	Tupoa	Evans/t	Lamb
Birley	Saverimutto	Dorrington	Davies	Evans	Campbell/2t	Turley	Tupoa	Lamb	Sewell
Birley/t	Saverimutto	Dorrington	Davies	Evans	Campbell	Lamb	Tupoa	Evans/2t	Sewell
Fredericks	Saverimutto	Dorrington/t	Davies	Evans	Campbell	Lamb/(c/t)	Tupoa	Evans/2t	Sewell
Fredericks/t	Saverimutto	Dorrington	Davies	Evans	Campbell/t	Turley	Tupoa	Lamb	Sewell
Fredericks	Saverimutto	Dorrington	Davies	Evans	Campbell	Turley	Tupoa	Lamb	Sewell
Fredericks	Saverimutto	Dorrington	Davies	Evans	Campbell	Turley/t	Tupoa	Lamb	Sewell
Fredericks	Saverimutto	Dorrington	Davies	Evans	Stirrett	Turley	Tupoa/t	Lamb	Sewell/t
Fredericks	Saverimutto	Dorrington	Davies	Evans	Campbell	Turley	Kettle/t	Lamb	Sewell/t
Fredericks	Saverimutto	Dorrington	Davies/t	Evans	Campbell	Turley	Tupoa/t	Lamb/t	Sewell
Fredericks	Saverimutto	Davies	Davies	Dorrington	Campbell	Turley	Tupoa/t	Lamb/t	Sewell
Birley	Saverimutto	Morton	Buckley	Evans	Stirrett	Aird	Naylor	Lamb	Jones
Fredericks/t	Cottrell/t	Morton	Davies	Evans	Campbell	Turley	Kettle/t	Evans	Lamb
Fredericks	Cottrell	Morton	Buckley	Evans	Campbell	Turley	Tupoa	Kettle	Sewell
Fredericks	Saverimutto/t	Morton	Buckley	Evans	Campbell	Turley	Tupoa/t	Lamb	Sewell/t
Birley/t	Saverimutto	Dorrington	Davies	Gazzola	Campbell	Atkinson	Kettle	Jones	Lamb
O'Connor	Saverimutto	Morton	Saffy	Evans	Campbell	Stirrett	Kettle	Evans	Atkinson

REPLACEMENTS: a - Leon Burns. b - Steve O'Connor. c - Carl Turley.
Most replacement appearances in the league: 14: Adam Kettle. 6: Tim Morton. 5: Carl Turley, Steve O'Connor.
Most times replaced: 9: Carl Turley. 6: Jez Lamb, Loa Tupoa. 5: Mark Dorrington

WHERE	Total	Home	Away
The POINTS were scored	748	444	304
The POINTS were conceded	526	276	250
The TRIES were scored	99	60	39
The TRIES were conceded	69	34	34

HOW the TRIES were scored

Total	Backs	Forwards	F Back	Wing	Centre	H Back	F Row	Lock	B Row	Pen. Try
97	63	34	8	27	19	9	2	7	25	2

HOW the TRIES were conceded

Total	Backs	Forwards	F Back	Wing	Centre	H Back	F Row	Lock	B Row	Pen. Try
69	48	21	7	20	9	12	7	-	14	-

NEW BRIGHTON

LEAGUE STATISTICS *compiled by Stephen McCormack*

SEASON	Division	P	W	D	L	F	A	Pts Diff	Lge Pts	Lge Pos	Most Points	Most Tries
92-93	NW 1	12	9	1	2	243	103	140	19	2		
93-94	NW 1	12	10	1	1	310	87	223	21	1p		
94-95	North 2	12	9	0	3	376	140	236	18	3		
95-96	North 2	12	10	1	1	232	105	127	21	1p		
96-97	North 1	21	14	1	6	484	381	103	29	3		
97-98	North 1	22	17	2	3	599	293	306	36	1p	243 Alex Guest	15 Ian Kennedy
98-99	N2N	26	20	0	6	703	329	374	40	3	159 Murray King	17 Ian Kennedy
99-00	N2N	26	21	0	5	784	283	501	42	3	302 Paul Brett	17 Geoff Jones
00-01	N3N	*24	19	0	5	668	336	332	38	3	258 Paul Brett	16 Steve Bellis
01-02	N3N	26	16	2	8	748	526	222	34	4	288 Paul Brett	17 Emrys Evans

FACT FILE

Founded: 1875

Colours: Light blue, navy blue & white quarters/black/black
Change colours: White

Web site: www.newbrightonrugby.co.uk

GROUND

Address: Reeds Lane, Moreton, Wirral CH46 3RH
Tel: 0151 677 1873/2442 Fax: 0151 606 9745 e-mail: office@newbrightonrugby.co.uk
Capacity: 5,400 Seated: 400 Standing: 5,000

Directions: M53 Junc 1 direction for New Brighton, 1st turning left (sign posted NBFC, Moreton).
After approx 1 mile turn left into Reeds Lane, ground entrance approx. 200 yards on left
Nearest Railway Station: Leasowe (Wirral Line)

Car Parking: 400 at ground

Admission: **Season** tickets - Adult £50. **Matchday** - Adults £5. Children/OAPs £2.50

Clubhouse: Open 7 days a week
Functions: Capacity 300. Contact C Cattrall c/o Club

Club Shop: Yes

Training Nights: Tuesday & Thursday. Women: Wednesday

PROGRAMME Size: A5 Price: £1 Pages: 32
Editor:
Advertising rates:
Colour - Full page £300
Mono - Full page £200, Half £120, Qtr £70

NUNEATON RFC

President	Keith Howells	Tel: 012476 348286
Secretary	Maggie Mander	Homeland, Weddington Rd., Caldecote, Nuneaton CV10 0TS Tel: 02476 381803 (H) 07808 734054 (Mob) e-mail: maggie@mander.softnet.co.uk
Treasurer	Mrs Susan Ryan	Tel: 02476 384482 (H) 02476 642226 (B)
Director of Rugby	Chris Tarbuck	Tel: 07971 434813
1st XV Manager	Paul Vowles	Tel: 02476 641406 (H) 07775 626679 (M)
Fixture Secretary	Steve Lucas	02476 392858 (H)

After finishing in 5th position in 2000-01, we began last season with very high hopes of improving on that position but unfortunately our ambitions were not fulfilled and we ended in 8th place. Our Director of Rugby, Chris Tarbuck, is currently busy strengthening our squad for the new season.

We began with serious injury problems to Steven Marshall and Stuart Pearman putting them out for the whole season. We were then hit by further injuries to several other players including our top try scorer Alistair Baron breaking his ankle in the third from last game of the season. We are hopeful of all these players being fit to resume training on 1 July. On the brighter side, the serious injury sustained by Gary Marshall at the end of 2000-01 did not prevent him from resuming training at the beginning of the season and holding his first team position.

Our Colts had a very successful season and reached the quarter final of the National Cup Competition. We welcome Kevin Venus as their coach for the new season.

Several of our players were selected for County duty and these included: Stuart Gibson, Andy Goodall, Dave Lockey, Gary Marshall, Richard Moore, Jody Peacock, and Alan Roberts. We were delighted when Warwickshire beat Berkshire in the final at Twickenham when all the above players (with the exception of Lockey due to work commitments) were in the team. Alan Roberts was also voted player of the Tournament.

To end the season on a high we were extremely proud of Rich Moore who was selected to tour Chile with the National County Squad. Rich was also voted Forward of the Year at our Annual Dinner in May along with Jody Peacock Player of the Year, Neil Saunders Most Improved Player, Jonty Carter Extras Player, Al Jones and John Cowley shared Saracen of the Year and finally Eddie Atchinson Clubman of the Year.

MAM

Left to Right - **Standing**: Gail Cadden (Ass Physio), Karen Steward (Physio), Andy Savage (Ass Coach), Alistair Baron, Chris Tarbuck (Director of Rugby), Chris O'Reilly, Hayden Sergeant, Paul Rees, Jody Peacock, Al Roberts, Andy Goodall, Stuart Pearman, Damien Evans, Dave Docherty, Chris Warden (Kit Manager), David Cadden (fixtures Secretary), David Warden (Publicity Manager), Maggie Mander (Secretary), Keith Howells (President). **Sitting**: Steve Marshall, Craig Quick, Dan Bailey, Aidi Nightingale, Martin Smith, Craig Court, Chris Atchinson, Adam Jones, Sam Viggers, James Hadfield. **Front Row:** Mark Elvidge (Ass Coach), Gary Marshall, Jonty Carter, Dave Lockey, Paul Vowels (1st XV Manager)

NUNEATON

Comp.	Date	H/A	Opponents	Result & Score	Att	15	14	13	12	11
N3 N	01-09	H	West Hartlepool*	W 36-17		Peacock/4cp	Baron/t	Marshall/t	Dutton/t	Smith
N3 N	08-09	A	Doncaster	L 13-49		Peacock/c2p	Baron	Marshall	Dutton/t	Smith
N3 N	22-09	H	Darlington MP	L 12-32		Peacock/3p	Baron	Marshall	Dutton	Shaw
N3 N	06-10	A	Tynedale	L 20-26	200	Peacock/2c2p	Baron/t	Sargeant	Dutton	Smith
N3 N	20-10	H	Sandal	W 51-27		Smith	Baron/4t	Quick(b/t)	Dutton	Marshall
N3 N	27-10	H	Scunthorpe	W 26-23		Peacock/c3p	Baron	Marshall/t	Dutton/t	Smith
N3 N	10-11	H	Liverpool St Helens	L 34-37		Peacock/3cp	Baron/t	Blackmore	Dutton/t	Marshall
N3 N	17-11	A	Bedford Athletic*	L 14-25		Peacock/2c	Baron	Blackmore	Dutton	Carter
N3 N	24-11	H	New Brighton	L 3-23	150	Peacock/p	Carter	Blackmore	Dutton	Smith
N3 N	01-12	A	West Hartlepool	W 37-12		Peacock/t2cp	Smith	Blackmore/t	Dutton	Marshal(b/
N3 N	08-12	H	Whitchurch	W 37-12		Peacock/2tc	Carter/2t	Blackmore/t	Dutton/t	Marshall
N3 N	15-12	A	Blaydon	W 10-3	150	Peacock/t	Carter	Blackmore	Dutton	Smith
N3 N	12-01	H	Bedford Athletic	W 23-17		Peacock/t	Carter(c/t)	Quick	Dutton	Marshall
N3 N	19-01	A	Liverpool St Helens	L 26-29		Peacock/t	Baron	Blackmore	Dutton	Smith/t
N3 N	02-02	A	Scunthorpe	W 35-5	250	Peacock	Baron/t	Blackmore	Dutton	Smith/t
N3 N	09-02	A	Sandal	W 25-18	150	Peacock	Baron/t	Blackmore	Dutton	Carter
N3 N	16-02	H	Dudley Kingwinsford	L 13-24		Peacock	Baron	Blackmore	Dutton	Smith
N3 N	02-03	A	Morley	W 19-9		Peacock/t	Shaw	Blackmore	Dutton	Marshall
N3 N	09-03	A	Darlington MP	L 9-17		Peacock	Baron	Blackmore	Dutton	Marshall
N3 N	16-03	H	Doncaster	L 32-51		Blackmore	Baron/3t	Shaw	Dutton	Marshall
N3 N	23-03	A	New Brighton	L 19-20		Cassell/2c	Baron/t	Blackmore	Benson	Smith
N3 N	30-03	A	Dudley Kingwinsford	L 19-34	550	Peacock	Baron	Benson	Dutton	Smith
N3 N	06-04	H	Blaydon	L 15-18		Peacock/tcp	Baron	Benson	Dutton	Marshall
N3 N	13-04	A	Whitchurch	W 30-23		Peacock	Smith	Benson/t	Dutton	Marshall/t
N3 N	20-04	H	Morley	W 28-19		Jones/t	Baron	Benson	Dutton	Marshall/t
N3 N	27-04	H	Tynedale	L 13-15	120	Quick	Jones	Benson/t	Dutton	Carter
PGC	15-09	N	Tynedale	W 17-9		Peacock/2cp	Baron/t	Sargeant	Marshall	Smith
PGC	29-09	H	Wharfedale	W 31-29		Peacock/t4cp	Baron	Sargeant	Dutton/t	Smith
PGC	13-10	H	New Brighton	W 31-7		Peacock/c	Baron/2t	Quick	Dutton/t	Marshall/t
PGC	03-11	A	Newbury	L 8-29		Peacock/p	Baron	Marshall	Dutton	Marshall

** after opponents name indicates a penalty try. Brackets after a player's name indicates he was replaced. eg (a) means he was replaced by replacement code "a" and so on. / after a player or replacement name is followed by any scores he made - eg /t, /c, /p, /dg or any combination of these*

EVER PRESENT None

Most Appearances:
25: Craig Dutton.
23: Alan ROberts (1).
21: Jody Peacock.

PLAYERS USED

38 plus one as replacement only.

MOST POINTS

Pts	Player	T	C	P	DG
119	J Peacock	8	17	15	-
115	L Cassell	4	19	19	-
70	A Baron	14	-	-	-
40	C Tarbuck	8	-	-	-
30	D Bailey	6	-	-	-
27	W Masser	-	6	5	-

MATCH FACTS

10	9	1	2	3	4	5	6	7	8
Mitchell	Viggers	Pearman	Atchenson	Hadfield	Goodall	Roberts	Chaplin(a/t)	Docherty	Evans
Jones	Viggers	Pearman	Atchenson	Court	Goodall	Roberts	Chaplin	Nightingale	Docherty
Quick/dg	Viggers	Pearman	Atchenson	Hadfield	Goodall	Roberts	Nightingale	Docherty	Evans
Mitchell	Bailey	Pearman	Atchenson	Hadfield	Goodall	Roberts	Nightingale	Docherty(a/t)	Evans
Cassell/5c2p	Viggers	Moore	Gibson	Hadfield	Chaplin	Roberts	Tarbuck/t	Docherty/t	Evans
Cassell	Bailey/t	Moore	Gibson	Hadfield	Chaplin	Roberts	Rees	Nightingale	Evans
Cassell/t	Viggers/t	Moore	Gibson	Court/t	Goodall	Roberts	Tarbuck	Chaplin	Evans
Jones	Bailey/t	Moore	Gibson	Hadfield	Goodall	Roberts	Rees	Nightingale	Evans
Cassell	Bailey	Moore	Atchenson	Hadfield	Goodall	Roberts	Rees	Saunders	Tarbuck
Jones	Bailey	Pearman/t	Gibson	Court	Goodall	Roberts/t	Tarbuck/t	Saunders	Evans
Cassell/cp	Viggers	Pearman	Gibson	Moore	Goodall	Roberts	Tarbuck	Saunders	Evans
Mitchell	Bailey/t	Moore	Gibson	Pearman	Lockley	Roberts	Mitchell	Docherty	Evans
Masser/c2p	Mitchell	Moore	Gibson	Pearman	Goodall	Roberts	Tarbuck/t	Saunders	Evans
Masser/3c	Bailey	Moore	Gibson	Pearman/t	Goodall	Roberts	Mitchell	Evans	Tarbuck/t
Masser/cp	Viggers	Pearman	Gibson/t	Court	Goodall	Roberts	Mitchell	Evans/2t	Tarbuck/t
Cassell/2cp(d/p)	Bailey/t	Pearman	Gibson	Moore	Goodall	Roberts	Mitchell/t	Chaplin	Evans
Masser/p	Mitchell	Pearman	Gibson/t	Moore	Goodall	Roberts	Mitchell	Rees/t	Evans
Cassell/c4p	Bailey	Pearman	Gibson	Moore	Lockley	Roberts	Mitchell	Rees	Tarbuck
Cassell/3p	Bailey	Moore	Gibson	Court	Lockley	Roberts	Mitchell	Rees	Tarbuck
Cassell/tcp(d/c)	Viggers	Moore	Gibson/t	Court	Lockley	Roberts	Mitchell	Docherty	Tarbuck
Masser	Bailey/t	Moore	Burnside	Court/t	Tarbuck	Roberts	Mitchell	Rees	Evans
Cassell/t2c	Viggers(e/t)	Moore	Burnside	Court	Lockley/t	Pape	Tarbuck	Rees	Evans
Masser	Bailey	Moore	Burnside/t	Allen	Goodall	Lockley	Mitchell	Rees	Tarbuck
Cassell/3c3p	Viggers	Moore	Burnside	Allen	Goodall	Roberts	Mitchell/t	Rees	Tarbuck
Cassell/t2c3p	Bailey	Moore	Burnside	Allen	Roberts	Goodall	Mitchell	Rees	Tarbuck
Cassell/p	Mitchell	Allen	Burnside	Court	Lockley	Atchenson	Mitchell	Rees	Tarbuck/t
Jones	Viggers	Pearman	Atchenson	Court	Goodall	Roberts	Nightingale	Docherty/t	Evans
Bailey	Bailey	Pearman	Atchenson	Court	Goodall	Roberts	Nightingale/t	Docherty	Tarbuck/t
Cassell/2c	Bailey	Moore	Gibson	Court	Goodall	Roberts	Tarbuck	Nightingale	Evans/t
Cassell	Bailey	Moore	Gibson	Hadfield	Chaplin	Roberts	Tarbuck	Docherty(f/t)	Evans

REPLACEMENTS: a - Chris Tarbuck. b - John Carter. c - Alastair Baron. d - Warwick Masser. e - Dan Bailey. f - Adrian Nightingale.

Most repalcement appearances in the league: 8: Sam Viggers. 7: Chris Tarbuck. 6: Gary Marshall, Paul Rees.

Most times replaced: 7: Dan Bailey. 5: Damian Evans, Sam Viggers.

WHERE	Total	Home	Away
The POINTS were scored	599	323	276
The POINTS were conceded	585	270	315
The TRIES were scored	79	43	36
The TRIES were conceded	77	35	42

HOW the TRIES were scored

Total	Backs	Forwards	F Back	Wing	Centre	H Back	F Row	Lock	B Row	Pen. Try
77	53	24	9	21	12	11	8	2	14	2

HOW the TRIES were conceded

Total	Backs	Forwards	F Back	Wing	Centre	H Back	F Row	Lock	B Row	Pen. Try
75	55	20	6	26	13	10	5	4	11	1

NUNEATON

LEAGUE STATISTICS *compiled by Stephen McCormack*

SEASON	Division	P	W	D	L	F	A	Pts Diff	Lge Pts	Lge Pos		Most Points		Most Tries
92-93	D4N	12	2	0	10	138	269	-131	4	12				
93-94	D5N	12	4	1	7	122	200	-78	9	11				
94-95	D5N	12	4	0	8	129	161	-32	8	11				
95-96	D5N	12	4	1	7	176	329	-151	9	10	92	Warwick Masser	2	Darren Barry & Andy Brown, Paul Jones
96-97	D4N	26	8	1	7	457	667	-210	17	12	68	Marc Thomas & Gavin Henderson	9	Clive Bent
97-98	N2N	26	13	0	13	453	570	-117	26	7	141	Marc Thomas	7	Craig Court
98-99	N2N	26	14	2	10	596	533	66	30	5	135	Jez Harris	13	Steve Carter
99-00	N2N	26	11	1	14	610	665	-55	23	8	145	Marc Thomas	11	Steve Carter
00-01	N3N	26	15	1	10	597	605	-8	31	5	139	Warwick Masser	20	Gary Marshall
01-02	N3N	26	12	0	14	599	585	14	24	8	119	Jody Peacock	14	Alistair Baron

FACT FILE

Founded: 1879
Nickname: Nuns

Colours: Red with white & black
Change colours: Green, white, black

GROUND

Address: Liberty Way, Attleborough Fields, Nuneaton, Warks. CV11 6RR.
Tel: 02476 383206 Fax: 02476 383925
Capacity (all standing) No limit

Directions: **From M6**
Follow A444 to Nuneaton, follow ring road towards M69/A5 (Leicester/Hinckley). Ring road enters Eastborough Way, club is signposted off mini roundabout opposite Crematorium

From M69/A5 (south)
Follow A5 north to A47 Nuneaton town centre left turning (The Longshoot), Continue down this road to the next r'about and go left into Eastborough Way - then as above.

From A5 (north) - Continue south to Nuneaton town centre A47 turning as above.

Nearest Railway Station: Nuneaton, 5 mins by taxi

Car Parking: Ample parking within the ground

Admission: Matchday - Adults £5, OAPs £2, Children £1

Clubhouse: Normal licensing hours
Functions: Capacity up to 100 (seated).
Bookings thro' Club Secretary

Club Shop: Open Matchdays & Sunday mornings.

Training Nights: Tuesday and Thursday.

PROGRAMME Size: A5 Price: £1 Pages: 28 + cover
Editor: Maggie Mander, Club Sec.

ADVERTISING Contact Maggie Mander

PRESTON GRASSHOPPERS RFC

President	Lawrie Holland	
Chairman	John Heritage	
Club Secretary	Peter Ashcroft	01772744066 (H).
Admin Officer/ Commercial	Ken Moore	01772 720878 (H) .
Fixtures Secretary	John Powell	121 Bare Lane, Bare, Morecambe, Lancs. LA4 4RD. 01524 424514 (H), 01772 861605 (Fax)
Director of Rugby	Alex Keay	

c/o Preston Grasshoppers RFC,
Lightfoot Green,Fulwood,
Preston, Lancs PR4 0AP
Tel: 01772 863546
Fax: 01772 861605

Hoppers season was one of two distinct parts. The period up to the end of November produced a record of four wins and six defeats. With two of the wins and four of the defeats having a winning or losing margin of five points or less, Hoppers looked set for another mid table finish.

The first of December, however, started the alarm bells ringing. A 43 point defeat at Esher was a preview of what would follow. A run of sixteen defeats saw Hoppers drop to the foot of the table and for some the end of the season could not come quickly enough. Defeats were, for the most part, heavy with only two exceptions. The home game against Fylde produced a level of passion as befits a local derby with the lowest scoring game of the season the result. The following week an early lead at Waterloo was wasted when a sending off turned the game.

The lack of strength in depth in the pack proved Hoppers undoing but Charlie Du Pre's tireless efforts at scrum half in difficult circumstances won him both player of the year awards. The loss of lock Martin Boyd and hooker Jason Brittin before the season started was a major blow. Career moves took flanker Glyn Dewhurst to London and lock Chris Hufferdine to America during the season. Injury ended John Fowler's playing career and limited Michael Bailey's appearances and the last straw was when a rather imposing Fijian forward turned into a non starter. Allegedly his previous club in Wales had suggested to him that his 26 week ban did not apply in England.

The appointment of Alex Keay from Manchester as Director of Rugby signals the club's determination to bounce back. The continued success of the club's mini-rugby section and the club's recently announced link up with Myerscough College will hopefully continue to produce quality players. A much changed line up is likely to take the field in the new season.

PRESTON GRASSHOPPERS

Comp.	Date	H/A	Opponents	Result & Score	Att	15	14	13	12	11
N2	01-09	H	Esher	W 22-21	260	Glynn/c5p	Flynn	Monaghan	Barrow	Bailey
N2	08-09	A	Orrell	L 16-28	800	Glynn/c3p	Lough	Monaghan	Barrow/t	Bailey
N2	15-09	H	Stourbridge	L 13-16	280	Glynn/c2p	Lough/t	Monaghan	Barrow	Bailey
N2	22-09	H	Plymouth Albion	L 22-36	330	Glynn/tc5p	Lough	Monaghan	Barrow	Bailey
N2	06-10	A	Newbury	W 30-20		Glynn/3c3p	Lough	Chesworth	Barrow	Bailey/2t
N2	20-10	H	Waterloo	L 18-21		Glynn/c2p	Lough	Bailey	Chesworth	Monaghan
N2	27-10	A	Fylde	W 21-10		Glynn/c3p	Lough/t	Chesworth	Bailey	Monaghan/t
N2	10-11	H	Wharfedale	L 23-25	275	Glynn/2p	Lough/t	Bailey/c	Chesworth(a/t)	Monaghan
N2	17-11	A	Sedgley Park	L 12-17	350	McKenna	Lough	Chesworth	Bailey/c	Monaghan
N2	24-11	H	Rosslyn Park	W 16-14	175	Glynn/c2pdg	Lough	Bailey	Barrow/t	Monaghan
N2	01-12	A	Esher	L 0-43		Glynn	Lough	Bailey	Chesworth	Monaghan
N2	08-12	H	Nottingham	L 25-27		Glynn/t2c2p	Lough/t	Bailey	Barrow	Flynn/t
N2	15-12	A	Harrogate	L 3-53	402	Glynn/p	Lough	Bailey	Chesworth	Flynn
N2	22-12	H	Kendal	L 17-46	680	Glynn/t2cp	Lough	Barrow	Chesworth	Flynn
N2	12-01	H	Sedgley Park	L 18-37	460	Glynn/2tp	Lough	Monaghan	Chesworth	Flynn
N2	19-01	A	Wharfedale	L 8-59		Glynn/tp	Lough	Monaghan	Barrow	Flynn
N2	26-01	H	Fylde	L 5-17	495	Glynn	Lough	Monaghan	Chesworth	Flynn/t
N2	02-02	A	Waterloo	L 22-34		Glynn/c5p	Monaghan	Barrow	Chesworth	Flynn
N2	16-02	A	Rosslyn Park	L 17-43	175	Glynn/2cp	Lough	Bailey	Chesworth	Flynn
N2	23-02	A	Plymouth Albion	L 12-66	1200	Glynn/c	Lough	Bailey	Chesworth	Flynn
N2	02-03	H	Newbury	L 24-54		Glynn/c4p	Lough	Bailey	Barrow	Flynn
N2	09-03	A	Stourbridge	L 7-32	280	Glynn	Lough	Bailey	Barrow	Flynn
N2	16-03	H	Orrell	L 8-67		Glynn/p	Lough	Bailey	Barrow	Flynn/t
N2	30-03	A	Kendal	L 8-48		Glynn/p	Lough	Monaghan	Barrow	Flynn
N2	06-04	H	Harrogate	L 24-62	95	Glynn/2c	Lough	Chesworth	Monaghan/t	Flynn
N2	13-04	A	Nottingham	L 10-63	346	Glynn	Lough/t	Monaghan/t	Barrow	Flynn
PGC	29-09	A	Bedford Athletic	W 44-16		Glynn/5c3p	Lough	Monaghan/2t	Chesworth	Bailey
PGC	13-10	H	Birmingham & Solihull	L 15-59	210	Glynn/cp	Lough	Chesworth	Bailey	Monaghan/t

** after opponents name indicates a penalty try. Brackets after a player's name indicates he was replaced. eg (a) means he was replaced by replacement code "a" and so on. / after a player or replacement name is followed by any scores he made - eg /t, /c, /p, /dg or any combination of these*

EVER PRESENT Charlie Du Pre.

Most Appearances:
26: Charlie Du Pre.
25: Chris Glynn, Rob Parkinson.
24: Paul Bailey, Michael Lough, Tim Lough.

PLAYERS USED

31 plus one as a replacement

MOST POINTS

Pts	Player	T	C	P	DG
210	C Glynn	6	21	45	1
25	T Lough	5	-	-	-
25	M Lough	5	-	-	-
19	P Bailey	3	2	-	-

MATCH FACTS

10	9	1	2	3	4	5	6	7	8
ough	Dupre	Fenton	Porteous/t	Wilkinson	Williams	Bailey	Parkinson	Dewhurst	Ashton
ough	Dupre	Fenton	Porteous	Wilkinson	Parkinson	Bailey	Dewhurst	Welsh	Ashton
ough	Dupre	Fenton	Porteous	Wilkinson	Williams	Bailey	Parkinson	Dewhurst	Ashton
ough	Dupre	Fenton	Carter	Shepherd	Williams	Bailey	Parkinson	Dewhurst	Ashton
ough/t	Dupre	Fenton	Carter	Shepherd	Fowler	Williams	Parkinson	Dewhurst	Bailey
ough	Dupre	Fenton	Carter	Wilkinson	Williams	Jebb	Parkinson	Ashton/2t	Bailey
ough	Dupre	Fenton	Carter	Wilkinson	Williams	Bailey	Parkinson	Ashton	Ashton
ough	Dupre	Fenton	Carter	Wilkinson	Williams	Jebb	Parkinson/t	Ashton	Bailey
ough/2t	Dupre	Fenton	Porteous	Shepherd	Williams	Jebb	Parkinson	Ashton	Bailey
ough	Dupre	Fenton	Porteous	Wilkinson	Williams	Jebb	Parkinson	Ashton	Bailey
ough	Dupre	Fenton	Porteous	Wilkinson	Williams	Jebb	Parkinson	Welsh	Ashton
ough	Dupre	Chadwick	Carter	Wilkinson	Williams	Jebb	Parkinson	Welsh	Ashton
ough	Dupre	Fenton	Carter	Chadwick	Bailey	Jebb	Parkinson	Welsh	Ashton
Bailey	Dupre	Fenton(b/t)	Carter	Chadwick	Steel	Jebb	Parkinson	Welsh	Ashton
Bailey/t	Dupre	Shepherd	Carter	Chadwick	Jebb	Steel	Welsh	Lough	Parkinson
Bailey	Dupre	Fenton	Porteous	Shepherd	Williams	Jebb	Welsh	Lough	Parkinson
Bailey	Dupre	Shepherd	Horton	Fenton	Williams	Hufferdine	Welsh	Lough	Parkinson
Bailey	Dupre	Fenton	Horton	Shepherd	Williams	Hufferdine	Welsh/t	Lough	Parkinson
Lough/t	Dupre	Fenton	Porteous	Shepherd	Williams	Hufferdine	Parkinson/t	Welsh	Ashton
Lough/t	Dupre	Shepherd	Porteous	Fenton	Williams/t	Hufferdine	Parkinson	Welsh	Ashton
Lough	Dupre	Fenton	Porteous/t	Shepherd	Williams/t	Hufferdine	Parkinson	Welsh	Ashton
Gough/c	Dupre	Fenton	Horton	Wildig	Williams	Hufferdine	Jebb(c/t)	Lough	Ashton
Gough	Dupre	Fenton	Horton	Wildig	Williams	Hufferdine	Parkinson	Lough	Ashton
Bailey	Dupre/t	Fenton	Porteous	Wildig	Williams	Jebb	Parkinson	Lough	Ashton
Quigley	Dupre	Fenton	Porteous/t	Wildig	Williams	Jebb	Parkinson/t	Welsh	Ashton/t
Quigley	Dupre	Chadwick	Porteous	Shepherd	Williams	Jebb	Welsh	Lough	Parkinson
Lough	Dupre/2t	Fenton	Carter/t	Shepherd	Fowler	Williams	Bailey	Dewhurst	Ashton
Lough	Dupre	Fenton	Carter	Shepherd(b/t)	Williams	Bailey	Parkinson	Welsh	Dewhurst

REPLACEMENTS: a - Paul Barrow. b - Nick Wilkinson. c - Ged Welsh.

WHERE	Total	Home	Away
The POINTS were scored	401	235	166
The POINTS were conceded	959	516	443
The TRIES were scored	43	25	18
The TRIES were conceded	127	69	58

HOW the TRIES were scored

Total	Backs	Forwards	F Back	Wing	Centre	H Back	F Row	Lock	B Row	Pen. Try
43	29	14	6	11	5	7	4	2	8	-

HOW the TRIES were conceded

Total	Backs	Forwards	F Back	Wing	Centre	H Back	F Row	Lock	B Row	Pen. Try
127	75	50	12	24	21	18	12	12	26	2

PRESTON GRASSHOPPERS

LEAGUE STATISTICS
compiled by Stephen McCormack

SEASON	Division	P	W	D	L	F	A	Pts Diff	Lge Pts	Lge Pos	Most Points		Most Tries	
92-93	D4N	12	8	0	4	144	140	4	16	3	27	Andy Taylorson	3	John Bleasdale
93-94	D5N	12	10	0	2	191	128	63	20	2	62	Mark Kirby	3	Joe Hindle
94-95	D5N	12	8	1	3	187	137	50	17	3	94	Willie Mould	2	Three players
95-96	D5N	12	5	1	6	167	209	-42	11	8	45	Nick Bell	3	Three players
96-97	D4N	26	17	2	7	568	394	174	36	3	317	Steve Kerry	7	Glyn Dewhurst
97-98	J2N	26	14	2	10	549	469	80	30	4	91	Rob Smith	15	Iain Bruce
98-99	J2N	26	23	0	3	822	341	481	46	1p	216	Martin Emmett	27	Michael Lough
99-00	JN1	26	12	0	14	608	580	28	24	8	110	Chris Glynn	15	Iain Bruce
00-01	N2	26	12	2	12	569	517	52	26	7	219	Chris Glynn	10	Josh Williams
01-02	N2	26	4	0	22	401	959	-558	8	14r	210	Chris Glynn	6	Chris Glynn

FACT FILE

Founded: 1869
Nickname: Hoppers

Colours: White with navy blue hoops/navy blue/navy blue & white
Change colours: Emerald green, red collar & cuffs.

GROUND

Address: Lightfoot Green, Fulwood, Preston, Lancs. PR4 0AP.
Web site: www.pgrfc.co.uk e-mail: info@pgrfc.co.uk
Tel: 01772 863546 Fax: 01772 861605 Press Line: 01772 861605
Capacity: 3,700 Seated: 250 Standing: 3,450

Directions: Leave the M6 at Junct. 32 and head towards A6 Garstang. Turnleft at the end of the slip road towards Preston. Take first left and followsigns for Ingol.
The ground is 1/2 mile on the right.
Nearest Railway Station: Preston (BR)

Car Parking: 400 spaces available adjacent to the ground.

Admission: Match days - Adults - Members £4, Others £6
OAPs £3 Under 14s Free

Clubhouse: Open Mon-Thurs 4.30-11.00, Fri 12-12
Sat 12-11, Sun 12-10.30,
snacks, bar meals & restaurant available
Functions: Capacity 250,
Contact K Moore 01772 863546

Club Shop: Open daily Contact K Moore 01772 863546

PROGRAMME Size: A5 Pages: 32 + cover
Price: With admission
Advertising Rates
Colour: Full page £300, half £175
Mono: Full page £250, half £140, qtr £85

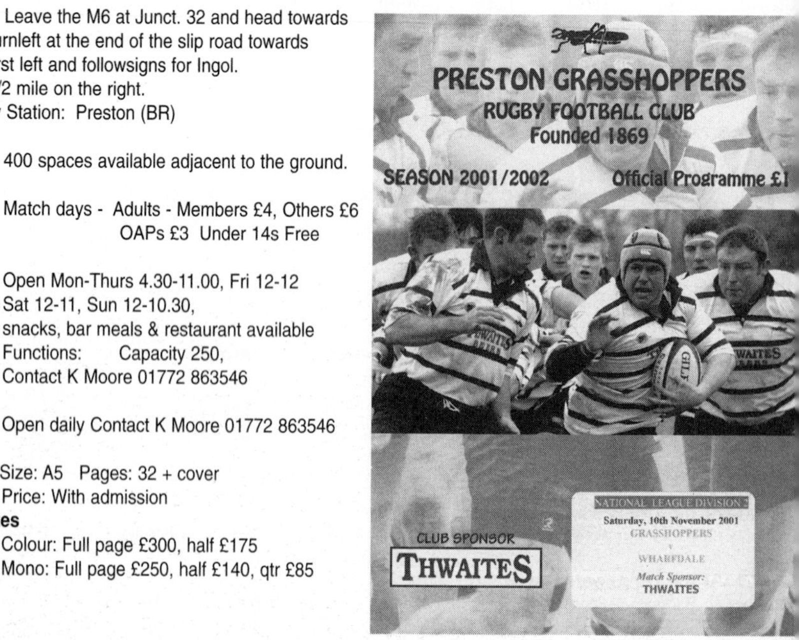

SCUNTHORPE R.U.F.C.

President	Allan Bell		
Chairman	Lew Clayton	2 Langley Drive, Bottesfor, N. Lincs.	
Secretary	Mick Hill	15 Peveril Ave., Scunthorpe DN17 1BQ 01724 403014 (B) 01724 359432 (H) 07730 803050 (M) email: michael.hill@capara-merchant-bar.co.uk	
Fixture Secretary	Ray Wilson	70 Wiltshire Ave., Burton-on-Stather, N. Lincs.	01724 720915
Treasurer	Jim Lynch	3 Neath Road, Scunthorpe	01724 343678

Director of rugby Doug Chapman paid tribute to each of the Greens' first team squad for their efforts in what was a satisfying first season in the National League.

The fact that the Greens retained their status in National Three North was not made certain until the penultimate game which saw a hard fought 17-12 victory at Darlington Mowden Park. The season was certainly a roller coaster affair.

Chapman, himself a new face in the role of director of rugby, said " that the season had been a huge success for the club and he was delighted that despite some trepidation and doubt the objective had been achieved, namely to retain our position in the National League. There were times when we gave the impression of being akin to Jeckyll and Hyde, but considering our limited playing resource we have made significant progress".

After a poor start to the campaign in which they lost all three of their opening matches, the Greens finally managed to get some points on the board with a 27-8 victory at Sandal. Defeats then followed against Whitchurch and Nuneaton and at the start of November Scunthorpe were struggling in the lower reaches of the table.

A reverse in fortunes then followed; Kevin Westgarth was asked to come and do some coaching sessions, and play the odd game. The team responded, and to their credit they came back strongly and played undoubtedly some their best rugby of the season in a five match winning run which saw them reach the dizzy heights of fifth in the league. A superb second half comeback saw them beat Liverpool St Helens 34-18 away and then two memorable wins, the first away to New Brighton, which saw a tremendous result of 49-21 and then, a superb performance at home to Darlington Mowden Park resulting in a 48 –19 victory. In good heart the Greens went to Castle Park, and gave runaway league leaders Doncaster a fright in the pre Xmas derby encounter, the home side just edging home 20 –13.

Following the Xmas break and a postponement due to bad weather the Greens looked rusty when they returned to action and were unimpressive despite winning 35-22 at West Hartlepool. The roller coaster syndrome continued with the Greens then suffering a losing run of six matches. Relegation then became a possibility but full credit must be given to the whole playing squad who dug deep and again found their form when it was most needed. Home victories then followed against Tynedale and Liverpool SH to move the Greens to within one win of securing their National League status.

After being beaten convincingly by local rivals Doncaster at home the Greens went to Darlington Mowden Park on April 6th and the 17-12 victory in the north east guaranteed Scunthorpe their place in National Three North, thus fulfilling the objective of retaining National League status for season 2002/2003.

Photo courtesy of Scunthorpe Evening Telegraph

SCUNTHORPE

Comp.	Date	H/A	Opponents	Result & Score	Att	15	14	13	12	11
N3 N	01-09	H	New Brighton	L 32-36		Forster	Sherwood	Watterson	Coult/t	Saini/2t
N3 N	08-09	A	Tynedale	L 16-43		Robinson/cp	Astbury/2p	Coult	Saini	Sherwood
N3 N	22-09	H	Dudley Kingwinsford	L 23-43	250	Forster	Sherwood	Coult	Hadfield	Saini
N3 N	06-10	A	Sandal	W 27-8	150	Conroy	Boughton	Coult	Watterson/t	Saini
N3 N	20-10	H	Whitchurch	L 19-35	250	Conroy	Astbury/2c	Coult	Watterson	Saini/t
N3 N	27-10	A	Nuneaton	L 23-26		Robinson	Astbury/c2p	Watterson	Coult	Saini/t
N3 N	03-11	H	Blaydon	W 21-16	250	Sherwood	Hadfield	Coult	Watterson	Saini
N3 N	10-11	A	Morley	W 16-11		Sherwood	Boughton	Coult	Watterson	Saini/t
N3 N	17-11	H	West Hartlepool	W 45-28		Sherwood	Boughton/t	Coult/t	Watterson	Saini
N3 N	24-11	A	Liverpool St Helens	W 34-28	200	Sherwood	Boughton	Coult/t	Watterson/t	Astbury
N3 N	01-12	A	New Brighton	W 49-21		Sherwood/t(c/t)	Astbury	Watterson	Coult/t	Saini/t
N3 N	08-12	A	Bedford Athletic*	L 38-41		Sherwood	Astbury	Coult	Watterson/t	Saini/t
N3 N	15-12	H	Darlington MP	W 48-19	250	Conroy/2tdg	Astbury/t	Coult	Watterson	Boughton/t
N3 N	22-12	A	Doncaster	L 13-20	1000	Conroy	Astbury	Watterson	Coult	Saini
N3 N	12-01	A	West Hartlepool	W 35-22		Conroy/t	Boughton	Coult	Saini	Forster
N3 N	19-01	H	Morley	L 26-36	450	Conroy	Saini/t	Coult/t	Watterson	Forster/t
N3 N	26-01	A	Blaydon	L 15-25		Robinson	Astbury/tcp	Coult	Conroy	Saini
N3 N	02-02	H	Nuneaton	L 5-35	250	Conroy	Astbury	Coult	Watterson	Saini
N3 N	09-02	A	Whitchurch	L 12-34		Robinson/tc	Forster/t	Coult	Dix	Sherwood
N3 N	23-02	H	Sandal	L 20-22		Sherwood/t	Forster	Coult	Dix	Saini
N3 N	09-03	A	Dudley Kingwinsford	L 5-43	420	Sherwood	Coult	Watterson	Dix	Forster/t
N3 N	16-03	H	Tynedale	W 19-16	300	Robinson/3p	Sherwood	Coult/t	Watterson	Forster
N3 N	23-03	H	Liverpool St Helens*	W 30-16		Robinson/2c2p	Coult	Watterson	Dix	Forster/3t
N3 N	30-03	H	Doncaster	L 33-72		Robinson/4c	Coult	Watterson	Dix(e/t)	Forster/t
N3 N	06-04	A	Darlington MP	W 17-12		Robinson/2cp	Astbury	Coult	Saini/t	Forster
N3 N	13-04	H	Bedford Athletic	L 17-30	400	Robinson/c	Astbury	Coult	Watterson	Forster/t
PGC	15-09	H	Winnington Park	W 20-19	450	Forster	Vavaitamana	Coult	Watterson/t	Saini
PGC	29-09	A	Orrell	L 8-83	500	Forster	Boughton	Coult	Hadfield	Saini

** after opponents name indicates a penalty try. Brackets after a player's name indicates he was replaced. eg (a) means he was replaced by replacement code "a" and so on. / after a player or replacement name is followed by any scores he made - eg /t, /c, /p, /dg or any combination of these*

EVER PRESENT Phil Sidebottom, Michael Coult

Most Appearances:
26: Phil Sidebottom, Michael Coult.
25: Scott Taylor.
24: Tim Robinson (1).
23: Richard Southee (1), Mark Hyde (1), Rob Page (1).

PLAYERS USED

36 plus three as a replecement only.

MOST POINTS

Pts	Player	T	C	P	DG
198	T Robinson	1	44	31	4
45	A Saini	9	-	-	-
45	M Kelly	9	-	-	-
45	T Forster	9	-	-	-
38	J Astbury	3	4	5	-
35	S Taylor	7	-	-	-

MATCH FACTS

10	9	1	2	3	4	5	6	7	8
Robinson/2cp	Locke	Page	McSherry/t	Taylor	Stevens	Dunk	Sidebottom	Clayton/t	Southee
Sherwood	Locke	Page	Hyde	Taylor	Stevens	Dunk	Sidebottom(a/t)	Clayton	Southee
Robinson/2c3p	Locke(b/2t)	Page	Hyde	Clark	Sidebottom	Dunk	Southee	Clayton	Kelly
Robinson/3c2p	Slade-Jones/t	Page	Hyde	Taylor/t	Stevens	Scargill	Sidebottom	Proctor	Kelly
Sherwood/t	Slade-Jones	Page	Hyde	Taylor	Scargill	Dunk/t	Sidebottom	Proctor	Kelly
Sherwood	Slade-Jones	Wilson	Hyde	Taylor/t	Dunk	Sidebottom	Southee	McSherry	Kelly/t
Robinson/6pdg	Brinck	Page	Hyde	Taylor	Sidebottom	Dunk	Southee	McSherry	Kelly
Robinson/2p	Brinck	Page/t	Hyde	Taylor	Scargill	Dunk	Sidebottom	McSherry	Southee
Robinson/3c3p	Slade-Jones/2t	Page	Hyde	Taylor	Sidebottom	Dunk	Southee/t	Clayton	Kelly/t
Robinson/4c2p	Slade-Jones	Page	Hyde	Taylor/t	Scargill	Dunk	Southee	Sidebottom	Kelly/t
Robinson/5c2pdg	Brinck	Page	Hyde	Taylor/t	Scargill	Stevens	Sidebottom	Southee	Kelly/t
Robinson/5cdg	Brinck	Page/t	Hyde	Taylor/t	Scargill	Stevens	Southee	Sidebottom	Kelly
Robinson/5c	Brinck	Buttrick/t	Hyde	Taylor	Scargill(f/t)	Stevens	Southee	Sidebottom	Kelly/t
Robinson/dg	Brinck	Page	Hyde	Taylor	Dunk	Stevens	Sidebottom	Southee	Kelly/2t
Robinson/2c2p	Brinck(b/t)	Page	Hyde	Taylor/t	Stevens	Dunk	Sidebottom	Clayton/t(a/t)	Southee
Robinson/c(d/t2c)	Slade-Jones	Page	Hyde	Taylor	Stevens	Scargill	Southee	Sidebottom	Kelly
Sherwood	Brinck	Page/t	Hyde	Taylor	Stevens	Scargill	Sidebottom	Clayton	Kelly
Sherwood	Brinck	Page	Hyde/t	Taylor	Stevens	Dunk	Sidebottom	Clayton	Southee
Sherwood	Slade-Jones	Clarke	Hyde	Taylor	Westgarth	Sidebottom	Henning	Clayton	Southee
Robinson/cp	Brinck	Page/t	Johal/t	Taylor	Sidebottom	Dunk	Southee	Clayton	Kelly
Robinson	Brinck	Page	Johal	Taylor	Sidebottom	Dunk	Southee	Clayton	Kelly
Conroy	Parratt/t	Page	Hyde	Taylor	Westgarth	Dunk	Southee	Sidebottom	Kelly
Conroy	Parratt	Page	Hyde	Taylor	Sidebottom	Dunk	Southee	Clayton	Kelly
Conroy/t	Parratt	Page	Hyde	Taylor/t	Sidebottom	Dunk	Southee/t	Clayton	Kelly
Conroy	Sherwood	Page/t	Hyde	Taylor	Westgarth	Dunk	Sidebottom	Clayton	Southee
Conroy/t	Sherwood	Page	Hyde	Taylor	Westgarth	Dunk/t	Sidebottom	Clayton	Southee
Robinson/cp	Locke	Page	Hyde/t	Buttrick	Sidebottom	Dunk	Southee/t	Clayton	Kelly
Robinson/p	Slade-Jones	Page	Hyde	Clarke	Sidebottom	Scargill/t	Proctor	Clayton	Kelly

REPLACEMENTS: **a - Mark Kelly** **b - Gareth Slade-Jones.** **c - Tom Forster.** **d - Ben Sherwood.** **e - John Astbury.** **f - Tim Dunk**

Most replacement appearances in the league: 6: Kevin Westgarth, Richard Proctor, Tom Forster, Wayne Clayton, Chris Conroy.

Most times replaced: 10: Dean Stevens. 5: Wayne Clayton, Rob Page.

WHERE	**Total**	**Home**	**Away**
The POINTS were scored	638	338	300
The POINTS were conceded	738	334	404
The TRIES were scored	83	45	38
The TRIES were conceded	95	44	51

HOW the TRIES were scored

Total	Backs	Forwards	F Back	Wing	Centre	H Back	F Row	Lock	B Row	Pen. Try
81	49	32	7	20	11	11	16	3	13	2

HOW the TRIES were conceded

Total	Backs	Forwards	F Back	Wing	Centre	H Back	F Row	Lock	B Row	Pen. Try
93	58	35	7	21	16	14	11	4	20	2

SCUNTHORPE

LEAGUE STATISTICS
compiled by Stephen McCormack

SEASON	Division	P	W	D	L	F	A	Pts Diff	Lge Pts	Lge Pos		Most Pts/ Coach		Most Tries/ Captain
92-93	ME1	12	6	2	4	234	155	79	14	5				
93-94	ME1	12	9	0	3	172	109	63	20	2				
94-95	ME1	12	11	0	1	366	86	280	22	1p				
95-96	M2	12	10	0	2	306	118	188	20	1p				
96-97	M1	16	12	0	4	435	253	182	24	4				
97-98	M1	16	10	0	6	415	279	136	20	4				
98-99	M1	16	15	0	1	590	187	403	30	2				
99-00	M1	16	11	0	5	364	206	158	22	2				
00-01	M1	22	19	2	1	762	258	504	40	1p	343	John Astbury	21	John Astbury
01-02	N3N	26	11	0	15	638	738	-100	22	9	198	Tim Robinson	9	By three players

FACT FILE

Founded: 1929
Nickname: The Greens
Colours: Green shirts with 2 narrow black bands bordered by 2 narrow white bands/black shorts/green & black hooped socks
Change colours: Red shirts with bands as above

Ground: Heslam Park, The Queensway, Scunthorpe (entrance from Ashby Rd.) Tel: 01724 843013

Capacity: 1000
Covered seating for 200 due this season.

Directions: End of M181 - A18 (Kingsway) to 'Beefeater' Roundabout, Turn right A159 - 300 metres on left sign post for 'Heslam Park'

Nearest Railway Station: Scunthorpe

Car Parking Spaces for 100 cars at ground

Admission Matchday: £4

Clubhouse Open evey day 12-2.30pm & 5-11pm

Club Shop Open Saturday lunchtime & Sunday morning

Training Nights Monday & Thursday
Colts: Wed Women: Thur.

Programme Size: A4 Price: 50p
Editor: Mal Yates

TYNEDALE RFC

President	Tony Smith	West Fell, Ladycutter Lane, Corbridge NE45 5RZ 01434 632044
Chief Executive	Douglas Hamilton	Woodvale, Main Road, Wylam NE41 8ED 01661 852017 (Tel/Fax)
Hon. Secretary	Bill Stewart	2 Beech Hill, Hexham NE46 3AG 01434 603970 (Tel/Fax)
Hon. Treasurer	Andy Briggs	01434 673689 (tel) 0789 491917 (M)
Fixture Secretary	Craig Johnston	01434 607696 (Tel/Fax) 07759 020052 (M) email: jcjohnston@supanet.com
Chairman Senior Rugby	John Shotton	01434 320598 (Tel) 01434 321650 (Fax) 07968 839043 (M) jbs@agma.co.uk
1st XV Coach	Dr. Steve Oliver	01670 788575 (Tel) 0191 227 4713 (Fax) 07931 477633 (M)
1st XV Manager	Peter Simpson	01661 834498 (Tel) 07810 180880 (M)

Tynedale's first season (2000/1) in the National Leagues was seriously curtailed due to the foot and mouth epidemic, which meant the club virtually closed from the 26th February and meant the last nine matches were not played.

The club, in their 125th Anniversary season, was really hopefully looking forward to playing their first full season in the National Leagues, under a new coach in South African Steve Olivier.

The club has a playing strength amounting to five senior sides, a Colts XV and a growing mini/Midi junior section, and well over half the first XV squad has come through the Tynedale system.

Unfortunately the early part of the season up to Xmas and into January, was badly disrupted due to a large number of injuries in the first XV squad and the team was going into games with between five and six first choice players not available.

Around the turn of the year a number of matches were postponed due to the weather, which gave us a little bit of breathing space, and in the run up to the end of the season results started to pick up.

The club was more than happy to finish a creditable fifth in the league, in their first full season in the National Leagues, and one hopes that it all bodes well for next season, as the average age for the squad is still under twenty-five.

TYNEDALE

Comp.	Date	H/A	Opponents	Result & Score	Att	15	14	13	12	11
N3 N	01-09	H	Darlington MP	L 3-15		Forth/p	Shotton	Fitzgerald	Fleming	Roberts
N3 N	08-09	H	Scunthorpe	W 43-16		Shotton	Holmes/t	Fleming	Moses/5cp	Roberts
N3 N	22-09	A	Sandal	L 10-17		Shotton	Roberts	Fletcher/t	Boston	Holmes
N3 N	06-10	H	Nuneaton	W 26-20	200	Moses/c3p	Holmes/t	Fleming	Boston	Roberts/t
N3 N	20-10	A	Morley	L 23-25		Moses/c2p	Holmes/t	Fleming	Boston	Shotton
N3 N	27-10	H	Liverpool St Helens*	L 18-22		Moses/c2p	Holmes	Fleming	Boston	Shotton/t
N3 N	03-11	A	Bedford Athletic	L 10-26	200	Moses/cp	Shotton	Fleming	Kriger	Holmes
N3 N	10-11	H	New Brighton	W 18-6		Moses/c2p	Johnston	Fleming	Fletcher	Shotton
N3 N	17-11	A	Dudley Kingwinsford	L 15-38		Moses/cp	Shotton	Fleming	Walton	Johnston
N3 N	24-11	H	Whitchurch	W 18-6		Moses/p	Holmes	Boston	Walton	Johnston/t
N3 N	01-12	A	Darlington MP	L 25-26		Moses/t	Johnston	Walton/t	Boston	Kriger
N3 N	08-12	H	West Hartlepool*	W 42-27		Moses	Johnston	Boston/t	Walton/t	Fitzgerald
N3 N	15-12	A	Doncaster	L 13-40		Moses	Kriger	Boston	Walton	Johnston
N3 N	19-01	A	New Brighton	L 5-35		Moses	Johnston	Boston	Hopps	Fitzgerald
N3 N	26-01	H	Bedford Athletic*	W 20-18	150	Moses	Roberts	Fleming	Hopps	Johnston
N3 N	02-02	A	Liverpool St Helens	L 7-35		Moses	Johnston	Hopps	Fleming	Roberts
N3 N	09-02	H	Morley	W 16-11		Moses	Holmes	Fleming	Murray	Roberts
N3 N	16-02	H	Blaydon	W 19-10	400	Moses	Holmes	Fleming	Murray	Roberts
N3 N	02-03	A	Whitchurch	W 36-13		Holmes	Roberts/t	Fleming	Murray	Johnston
N3 N	09-03	H	Sandal	W 37-14		Holmes	Roberts	Fleming	Moses	Johnston
N3 N	16-03	A	Scunthorpe	L 16-19	300	Moses	Roberts	Boston/t	Fleming	Holmes
N3 N	23-03	H	Dudley Kingwinsford	W 19-13	200	Moses	Lytollis	Fleming	Boston	Roberts
N3 N	30-03	A	Blaydon	W 31-21		Moses	Roberts/t	Fleming	Boston	Lytollis/t
N3 N	06-04	H	Doncaster	L 15-33	350	Moses/t	Lytollis	Fleming	Walton	Roberts/t
N3 N	13-04	A	West Hartlepool	W 30-9		Moses	Lytollis	Boston	Fleming	Roberts
N3 N	27-04	A	Nuneaton	W 15-13	120	Moses	Lytollis	Walton	Boston	Roberts
PGC	15-09	A	Nuneaton	L 9-17		Shotton	Holmes	Fleming	Boston	Roberts

** after opponents name indicates a penalty try. Brackets after a player's name indicates he was replaced. eg (a) means he was replaced by replacement code "a" and so on. / after a player or replacement name is followed by any scores he made - eg /t, /c, /p, /dg or any combination of these*

EVER PRESENT One

Most Appearances:
26: Keith Johnson.
25: Alan Moses (1) .Edward Holmes, Andrew Robson, Steven Turnbull.

PLAYERS USED

40 plus two as replacement only.

MOST POINTS

Pts	Player	T	C	P	DG
120	P Belgian	1	17	23	4
76	A Mosses	2	12	13	1
76	A Murray	8	9	6	-
40	E Holmes	8	-	-	-

MATCH FACTS

10	9	1	2	3	4	5	6	7	8
Allen	Dungait	Parker	Charlton	Winter	Johnson	Turnbull	Robson	Rastall	Murray
Allen	Dungait	Johnson/t	Charlton	Winter	Johnson/t	Turnbull	Robson/2t	Rastall	Murray/t
Moses/cdg	Dungait	Parker	Charlton	Winter	Johnson	Turnbull	Robson	Ponton	Murray
Fletcher	Dungait/t	Parker	Charlton	Southern	Turnbull	Johnson	Robson	Ponton	Murray
Fletcher	Dungait/t	Parker	Charlton	Southern	Johnson	Turnbull	Robson	Ponton	Murray/t
Allen	Dungait	Parker	Charlton	Southern	Johnson	Turnbull	Robson	Murray	Murray
Allen	Dungait	Johnson	Charlton	Southern	Johnson	Turnbull	Robson	Murray/t	Murray
Dungait	Holmes/t	Johnson	Charlton	Southern	Turnbull	Johnson	Robson	Murray	Murray/t
Allen	Hollies	Parker	Parker	Johnson	Turnbull	Johnson	Robson	Murray/2t	Murray
Fletcher	Dungait/t	Parker	Charlton	Johnson	Johnson	Turnbull	Robson	Brown	Murray/t
Dungait/t	Holmes	Parker	Charlton	Johnson	Johnson	Turnbull	Robson	Brown	Murray/2c2p
Fletcher/t	Holmes	Parker	Charlton	Johnson	Johnson	Turnbull	Robson	Murray	Murray/t4c3p
Belgian/cp	Holmes/t	Southern	Charlton	Johnson	Johnson	Turnbull	Robson	Murray/p	Murray
Belgian	Donton	Parker	Parker	Johnson	Johnson	Steadman	Auld/t	Rastall	Murray
Belgian/2cpdg	Holmes/t	Parker	Charlton	Johnson	Johnson	Turnbull	Murray	Rastall	Murray
Belgian/c	Holmes	Parker	Charlton	Southern	Johnson/t	Robson	Murray	Ponton	Murray
Belgian/c3p	Donton	Parker	Parker	Southern	Johnson/t	Turnbull	Robson	Rastall	Murray
Belgian/c3pdg	Donton(a/t)	Parker	Parker	Southern	Johnson	Turnbull	Robson	Rastall	Murray
Moses(b/t)	Donton/t	Parker	Parker	Southern	Johnson	Turnbull	Robson	Rastall/2t	Murray/t3c
Belgian/3c2p	Donton/t	Parker	Parker	Southern	Turnbull/2t	Johnson	Robson	Rastall/t	Murray/t
Belgian/c3p	Douglas	Parker	Parker	Southern	Johnson	Turnbull	Robson	Rastall	Murray
Belgian/c4p	Holmes	Parker	Parker	Batey	Johnson	Turnbull	Robson/t	Rastall	Murray
Belgian/2c3pdg	Holmes	Parker	Parker	Southern	Johnson	Turnbull	Robson	Rastall/t	Murray
Belgian/cp	Holmes	Parker	Parker	Southern	Johnson	Turnbull	Robson	Rastall	Murray
Belgian/t2cpdg	Holmes/2t	Batey	Parker/t	Southern	Irving	Johnson	Jewitt	Rastall	Murray
Belgian/cp	Allen	Millburn	Charlton	Batey	Johnson/t	Irving	Auld/t	Rastall	Jewitt
Allen/3p	Dungait	Johnson	Charlton	Winter	Johnson	Smith	Robson	Rastall	Murray

REPLACEMENTS: a - Craig Johnston. b - S Allen.
Most replacement appearances in the league: 10: Aaron Charlton. 9: Edward Parker. 5: S Allen.
Most times replaced: 10: Edward Parker, Aaron Charlton. 6: Craig Johnston. 5: G Rastall, Andrew Robson.

WHERE	**Total**	**Home**	**Away**
The POINTS were scored	530	294	236
The POINTS were conceded	528	317	211
The TRIES were scored	62	33	29
The TRIES were conceded	62	37	25

HOW the TRIES were scored

Total	Backs	Forwards	F Back	Wing	Centre	H Back	F Row	Lock	B Row	Pen. Try
59	32	27	2	11	5	14	2	6	19	3

HOW the TRIES were conceded

Total	Backs	Forwards	F Back	Wing	Centre	H Back	F Row	Lock	B Row	Pen. Try
61	40	21	5	16	9	10	5	2	14	1

TYNEDALE

LEAGUE STATISTICS *compiled by Stephen McCormack*

SEASON	Division	P	W	D	L	F	A	Pts Diff	Lge Pts	Lge Pos	Most Points		Most Tries	
92-93	North1	12	9	0	3	323	111	212	18	2				
93-94	North1	12	7	0	5	255	168	87	14	5				
94-95	North1	12	4	1	7	184	154	30	9	11				
95-96	North1	12	7	1	4	212	163	49	15	5				
96-97	North1	22	14	1	7			225	29	3				
97-98	North1	22	13	2	7	510	332	178	28	5				
98-99	North1	22	15	0	7	573	298	275	30	3				
99-00	North1	22	22	0	0	710	221	489	44	1	246	Alan Moses	13	Simon Clayton-Hibbott & Epi Taione
00-01	N3N	*18	6	1	11	282	311	-29	13	8	159	Alan Mose	7	Simon Clayton-Hibbott
01-02	N3N	26	14	0	12	530	528	2	28	5	120	Phil Belgian	8	Edward Holmes & A Murray

FACT FILE

Founded: 1876
Colours: Royal blue & white hoops/white/royal blue
Change colours: Navy blue, narrow yellow & white hoops/white/navy
Web site: www.tynedalerfc.co.uk

GROUND

Address: Tynedale Park, Station Rd., Corbridge, Northumberland NE45 5AY
Tel: 01434 632997 Office: Tel/Fax: 01434 632996
e-mail: tynedalerfc@hotmail.com
Capacity: Unlimited Covered Seats: 350

Directions: From A69 westbound: 2nd exit at Styford roundabout (signed Corbridge) follow signs for Hexham. Cross single lane bridge to roundabout. First exit signed Gateshead. 250 yds to left fork into Station Road - 150 yards to entrance.

Nearest Railway Station: Corbridge, next to ground entrance

Car Parking: plentiful, within ground

Admission Matchday: £4 adult. Season: £50

Clubhouse: Open Mon & Thur 6.30-11, matchdays & Sun lunch. Private functions & special events.

Club Shop: Open on matchdays.
Contact Andy Deacon 01434 609750

Training Nights: Tuesday & Thursday, 7pm.

Programme Size: A5 Pages: 8
Price: With admission
Editor: Keith Laidler
Advertising Rates: Contact Andy Deacon (Chief Executive)

WATERLOO FC

The Pavillion, St Anthony's Rd., Blundellsands, Liverpool. L23 8TW
Tel: 0151 924 4552 Fax: 0151 924 0900 email: WaterlooRugby@btinternet.com

President	Tony Pugh	c/o Waterloo FC
Chairman & Company Director of Finance	Colin Brennand	6 St Antonys Road, Blundellsands, Liverpool L23 0151 924 1599
Club Secretary	Keith Alderson	66 St Michaels Road, Blundellsands, Liverpool.L23 7UW 0151 924 1168 (H)
Fixtures Secretary	John Rimmer	01772 814277 (H) 01772 885000 (B)
Chairman of Rugby	Malcolm Baucher	c/o Waterloo FC
Club Coach	Ian Aitchison	c/o Waterloo FC

The 2001/02 season started well when Waterloo won their first match, but their joy was to be short lived. The only other win before Christmas was to be at Preston in October, when after a nail biting victory coach Tony Cross announced his resignation as with his wife being pregnant he decided to return to Australia. David Blyth, Steve Christopherson and Tony Handley kept things going until the appointment of Ian Aichtinson as Head Coach early in the new year.

Improvement started and games got closer and Waterloo were unlucky to lose a few matches by the odd point or two, so their fate was sealed. However, through all this apparent disaster the team spirit in the squad stayed at a very high level, the entire squad has decided to stay with the club and improvements shown at the end of the season should stand them in good stead as they rise Phoenix like from the ashes to start the Waterloo revival. New players are expected and the squad will be suitably strengthened to push for promotion.

Hopefully the sale of the back pitch will be sorted before the start of the new season putting the club back on an even keel with the accountants scrabbling to find their long lost black pens! New training facilities should be in place at Maguire Avenue which will make winter nights a lot more comfortable as there are extensive indoor facilities available as well as at least one pitch floodlit for our use. It may seem strange and hard to believe but despite recent results Waterloo are looking forward to the new season with more hope and anticipation than for a long time. The excitement is mounting as kick off draws nearer, let's hope it translates to performances on the pitch where it really counts!

RICH BAXENDALE

Last season's leading point scorer, Tony Handley in action against Rosslyn Park. Photo: Courtesy of the Crosby Herald

WATERLOO

Comp.	Date	H/A	Opponents	Result & Score	Att	15	14	13	12	11
N2	01-09	H	Nottingham	W 25-14		Jessermino	Lunt	Payne	Telford	Tattersall
N2	08-09	A	Harrogate	L 32-48	487	Jessermino	Lunt	Payne	Telford/t	Tattersall
N2	15-09	H	Esher	L 15-50		Jessermino	Lunt/t	Payne/t	Telford/c	Cairns
N2	22-09	A	Orrell	L 18-51		Jessermino	Edwards	Payne/t	Tattersall	Lunt(a/t)
N2	06-10	H	Stourbridge	L 12-31		Hitchmough/t	Cairns	Tattersall	Payne/t	Lunt
N2	20-10	A	Preston Grasshoppers	W 21-18		Hitchmough/t	Jessermino	Tattersall	Payne	Walton
N2	27-10	H	Newbury	L 20-26		Hitchmough	Jessermino	Tattersall	Payne/t	Walton
N2	10-11	H	Plymouth Albion	L 0-37		Hitchmough	Tattersall	Payne	Van Deventer	Walton
N2	17-11	A	Fylde	L 15-32		Hitchmough	Walton/t	Van Deventer	Payne	Tattersall/t
N2	24-11	H	Wharfedale	L 14-38		Hitchmough	Tattersall/t	Payne/t	Van Deventer	Walton
N2	01-12	A	Nottingham	L 5-35	288	Hitchmough	Van Deventer	Payne/t	Tattersall	Walton
N2	08-12	H	Rosslyn Park	D 25-25		Hitchmough	Jessermino/t	Tattersall	Payne	Van Deventer
N2	15-12	A	Kendal	L 17-37		Hitchmough	Van Deventer	Tattersall	Payne/2t	Jessermino
N2	22-12	H	Sedgley Park*	L 13-27		Hitchmough	Jessermino	Tattersall	Payne	Van Deventer
N2	12-01	H	Fylde	L 10-20		Van Deventer	Jessermino	Tattersall	Payne	Payne
N2	19-01	A	Plymouth Albion	L 15-43	1205	Van Deventer(b/t)	Jessermino	Tattersall/t	Payne	Cameron
N2	26-01	A	Newbury	L 20-22		Van Deventer	Cameron	Tattersall	Payne/2t	Walton
N2	02-02	H	Preston Grasshoppers	W 34-22		Hitchmough	Cameron	Tattersall/t	Payne	Van Deventer
N2	09-02	A	Stourbridge	L 14-18	250	Hitchmough/t	Van Deventer	Payne/t	Tattersall	Cameron
N2	16-02	A	Wharfedale	L 27-37		Hitchmough	Van Deventer/t	Payne/t	Tattersall	Cameron/t
N2	23-02	H	Orrell	L 16-27		Hitchmough	Van Deventer	Tattersall/t	Payne	Walton
N2	09-03	A	Esher	L 26-33		Jessermino	Corlett	Van Deventer/3c	Payne/2t	Walton
N2	16-03	H	Harrogate	L 21-26		Van Deventer/c3p	Lunt	Payne/t	Tattersall/t	Walton
N2	30-03	A	Sedgley Park	D 20-20		Van Deventer/t2c2p	Corlett	Payne	Tattersall	Lunt
N2	06-04	H	Kendal	W 27-22		Hitchmough	Corlett/t	Payne/t	Tattersall/t	Van Deventer
N2	13-04	A	Rosslyn Park	L 14-33		Hitchmough/t	Barry	Payne	Van Deventer	Corlett
PGC	29-09	H	Darlington MP	L 20-32		Hitchmough	Cairns	Tattersall	Payne/t	Edwards

** after opponents name indicates a penalty try. Brackets after a player's name indicates he was replaced. eg (a) means he was replaced by replacement code "a" and so on. / after a player or replacement name is followed by any scores he made - eg /t, /c, /p, /dg or any combination of these*

EVER PRESENT Freeman Payne, Dan Smith

Most Appearances:
26: Freeman Payne, Dan Smith.
23: Mark Tattersall.
22: Tony Handley, Craig Aikman

PLAYERS USED

35 plus five as a replacement

MOST POINTS

Pts	Player	T	C	P	DG
160	T Handley	2	27	32	-
80	F Payne	16	-	-	-
35	M Tattersall	7	-	-	-
35	C Aikman	7	-	-	-

MATCH FACTS

10	9	1	2	3	4	5	6	7	8
Handley/t2c2p	Aikman/t	Reay	Tyms	Dennehy	Newsham/t	Blyth	Mercer	Wands	Smith
Handley/c5p	Aikman/t	Reay	Tyms	Dennehy	Temmen/t	Coyne	Mercer	Palmer	Smith
Handley/p	Aikman	Reay	Tyms	Davies	Temmen	Fisher	Mercer	Wands	Smith
Handley/c2p	Aikman	Dennehy	Tyms	Reay	Temmen	Newsham	Mercer	Wands	Smith
Handley/c	Jessermino	Reay	Guise	Dennehy	Temmen	Blyth	Mercer	Wands	Smith
Handley/2p	Aikman/t	Dennehy	Tyms/t	Reay	Blyth	Temmen	Mercer	Wands	Smith
Handley/2c2p	Aikman/t	Reay	Tyms	Dennehy	Blyth	Temmen	Mercer	Wands	Smith
Handley	Aikman	Davies	Tyms	Dennehy	Wolfenden	Fisher	Mercer	Smith	Blyth
Handley/cp	Aikman	Reay	Tyms	Dennehy	Fisher	Temmen	Blyth	Wands	Smith
Handley/2c	Jessermino	Reay	Tyms	Dennehy	Fisher	Temmen	Blyth	Wands	Smith
Handley	Jessermino	Reay	Tyms	Dennehy	Wolfenden	Temmen	Blyth	Wands	Smith
Handley/2c2p	Aikman	Davies	Tyms	Reay	Fisher	Temmen	Wolfenden	Wands	Smith/2t
Handley/2cp	Aikman	Davies	Edwards	Reay	Wolfenden	Temmen	Blyth	Corlett	Smith
Handley/c2p	Aikman	Davies	Edwards	Reay	Wolfenden	Temmen	Blyth	Corlett	Smith
Handley/cp	Aikman/t	Edwards	Tyms	Dennehy	Wolfenden	Temmen	Blyth	Corlett	Smith
Handley/cp	Aikman	Reay	Edwards	Dennehy	Wolfenden	Blyth	McCarrick	Wands	Smith
Handley/2c2p	Aikman	O'Keefe	Edwards	Reay	Blyth	Temmen	McCarrick	Wands	Smith
Handley/t3cp	Aikman/t	O'Keefe	Edwards	Dennehy	Blyth/t	Temmen(c/t)	McCarrick	Wands	Smith
Handley/2c	Aikman	Edwards	Tyms	Dennehy	McGowan	Clarke	McCarrick	Wands	Smith
Handley/4p	Aikman	Edwards	Tyms	Dennehy	McGowan	Blyth	McCarrick	Wands	Smith
Handley/c3p	Aikman	Edwards	Tyms	Dennehy	Blyth	McGowan	McCarrick	Wands	Smith
Hitchmough	Aikman/t	O'Keefe/t	Tyms	Dennehy	Blyth	Mercer	McCarrick	Wands	Smith
Hitchmough	Aikman	O'Keefe	Tyms	Dennehy	Blyth	Wolfenden	McCarrick	Corlett	Smith
Hitchmough/t	Aikman	O'Keefe	Tyms	Dennehy	Blyth	Wolfenden	Mercer	Wands	Smith
Hunter/2cp	Barry	O'Keefe	Tyms	Dennehy	Blyth	Wolfenden	McCarrick	Wands/t	Smith
Handley/2c	Aikman	O'Keefe	Edwards	Dennehy	Blyth/t	Wolfenden	McCarrick	Wands	Smith
Handley/2c2p	Aikman/t	Reay	Guise	Dennehy	Temmen	Wolfenden	Mercer	Shepherd	Smith

REPLACEMENTS: a - Dave Cairns. b - Alex Walton. c - Ian Clarke.

WHERE	**Total**	**Home**	**Away**
The POINTS were scored	476	232	244
The POINTS were conceded	638	381	257
The TRIES were scored	58	28	30
The TRIES were conceded	95	55	40

HOW the TRIES were scored

Total	Backs	Forwards	F Back	Wing	Centre	H Back	F Row	Lock	B Row	Pen. Try
58	47	10	6	9	22	10	2	5	3	1

HOW the TRIES were conceded

Total	Backs	Forwards	F Back	Wing	Centre	H Back	F Row	Lock	B Row	Pen. Try
95	45	47	5	13	14	13	7	10	30	3

WATERLOO

LEAGUE STATISTICS

compiled by Stephen McCormack

SEASON	Division	P	W	D	L	F	A	Pts Diff	Lge Pts	Lge Pos	Most Points		Most Tries	
92-93	2	12	10	0	2	228	138	90	20		126	Paul Grayson	3	Austin Healey
93-94	2	18	6	2	10	231	346	-115	14		137	Steve Swindells	2	Gary Meredith, Steve Swindells & John Ashcroft
94-95	2	18	8	0	10	287	331	-44	16		160	Steve Swindells	4	Neil Ryan & Steve Wright
95-96	2	18	7	2	9	309	482	-173	16		134	Martin Emmett	4	Peter McCaugheran
96-97	2	22	7	0	15	506	661	-155	14		99	Lyndon Griffiths	7	David Blyth
97-98	P2	22	11	0	11	510	525	-15	22		261	Lyndon Griffiths	7	Marcus Coates & Shaun Woof
98-99	P2	26	12	0	14	419	634	-215	24		198	Lyndon Griffiths	5	Shaun Woof
99-00	P2	26	6	2	18	441	830	-389	14	12	201	Lyndon Griffiths	5	Gareth Davies & Karelle Dixon
00-01	N1	26	6	1	19	450	676	-226	35	14r	190	Phil Belgian	6	Matt Holt
01-02	N2	26	4	2	20	476	792	-316	10	13r	160	Tony Handley	16	Freeman Payne

FACT FILE

Founded: 1882

Colours: Myrtle, scarlet & white hoops/ myrtle shorts

Change colours: White with myrtle,scarlet & white thin striped `V'

GROUND

Address: The Pavillion, St Anthony's Rd., Blundellsands, Liverpool. L23 8TW

Tel: 0151 924 4552 Fax: 0151 924 0900 email: WaterlooRugby@btinternet.com

Capacity: 6,000 Standing:6,000

Directions: From the end of the M57/58 follow signs for Crosby. Waterloo FC is then sign-posted to the ground. Nearest Railway Station: Crosby & Blundellsands, 1/2 mile down St Anthony's Road.

Car Parking: 100 spaces, Saturday only.

Admission Matchdays
Adults £8, OAPs & Children u16 Free

Club Shop: Open only on matchdays. Contact the club on other days.

Clubhouse: Open during normal licensing hours on matchdays. Three bars, with snacks and meals available. Functions: Capacity 150. contact Paul Coyne 0151 924 4552.

Training Nights: Monday, Tuesday and Thursday.

PROGRAMME Size: A5 Pages: 34 Price: £1.50
Editor: Geoff Lightfoot

Advertising Rates
Colour: Page £500 Half £275

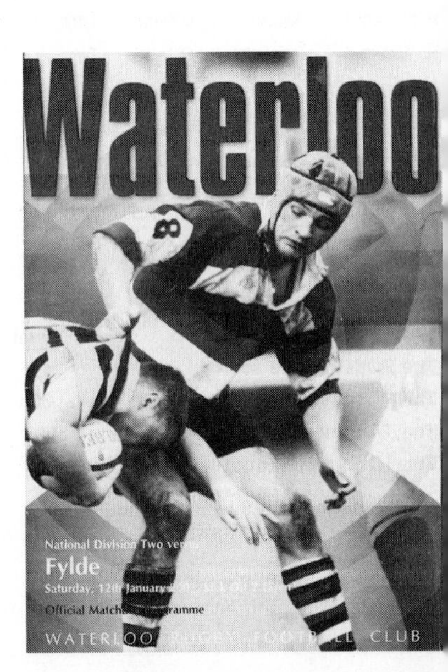

RECORDS SECTION

DIVISION FOUR NORTH

(CURRENTLY NATIONAL DIVISION THREE NORTH)

Previously also Area League North & Division Five North

LEAGUE RECORDS

Relegated clubs' Match Facts for season 2001-02

WHITCHURCH

Comp.	Date	H/A	Opponents	Result & Score	Att	15	14	13	12	11
N3 N	01-09	A	Liverpool St Helens	L 12-23		Canney/4p	McGillivary	Slater	Milward	Lewis
N3 N	08-09	H	Bedford Athletic	W 31-15	350	McGillivary/t	Dunn/t	Lewis/t	Lutton	Edwards/t
N3 N	22-09	A	New Brighton	W 35-28		McGillivary	Dunn/t	Lewis	Lutton/t	Wynn
N3 N	06-10	H	Dudley Kingwinsford	L 24-53	300	McGillivary/t	Dunn	Lewis	Lutton/t	Wynn
N3 N	20-10	A	Scunthorpe	W 35-19	250	Wynn	Ravenhill	Lewis	Lutton	Paton/t
N3 N	27-10	A	Blaydon	L 12-42		Wynn	Edwards	Lewis	Lutton/t	Paton
N3 N	03-11	H	West Hartlepool	W 22-5	350	Wynn	Edwards	Lewis	Lutton	Paton/2t
N3 N	10-11	A	Doncaster	L 7-74		Mason	Edwards	Lewis	Lutton	Paton
N3 N	17-11	H	Darlington MP	L 6-33		Mason	Wynn	Lewis	Lutton	Paton
N3 N	24-11	A	Tynedale	L 6-18		Mason	Dunn	Lewis	Lutton	Paton
N3 N	01-12	H	Liverpool St Helens*	L 29-43		Canney/3cp	Dunn	Lewis	Lutton/t	Paton
N3 N	08-12	A	Nuneaton	L 12-37		Canney(c/t)	Mason	Lewis	Lutton	Paton
N3 N	15-12	H	Morley	W 13-7	375	Dunn	Burgess	Wynn	Lutton/t	Hares
N3 N	12-01	A	Darlington MP	L 5-58		Burgess	Dunn	Lewis/t	Lutton	Edwards
N3 N	19-01	H	Doncaster	L 0-13		Burgess	Dodd	Lewis	Lutton	Hares
N3 N	26-01	A	West Hartlepool	L 12-14		McGillivary	Burgess	Lewis	Lutton	Hares/c
N3 N	02-02	H	Blaydon	W 18-16		McGillivary	Lewis	Slater	Lutton	Hares/c2p
N3 N	09-02	H	Scunthorpe**	W 34-12		McGillivary	Lewis	Slater	Lutton	Hares/t4c2p
N3 N	16-02	A	Sandal	W 29-23	100	McGillivary	Lewis	Slater/t	Lutton	Hares/t2c
N3 N	23-02	A	Dudley Kingwinsford*	L 19-22	475	McGillivary	Lewis	Slater	Lutton	Hares/t2c
N3 N	02-03	H	Tynedale	L 13-36		McGillivary/t	Paton	Lewis	Lutton	Hares/c2p
N3 N	09-03	H	New Brighton	L 22-27		McGillivary	Lewis	Wynn/c	Lutton	Hares/2t
N3 N	16-03	A	Bedford Athletic	W 30-18	125	McGillivary/t	Lewis	Wynn/t	Lutton	Hares/2c2p
N3 N	30-03	H	Sandal	W 56-16	275	McGillivary/t	Lewis/c	Wynn	Lutton/t	Hares/t2c(e/2
N3 N	06-04	A	Morley	D 19-19		McGillivary	Lewis	Wynn	Lutton	Hares/2c
N3 N	13-04	H	Nuneaton	L 23-30		McGillivary/t	Lewis	Wynn	Lutton/t	Hares/c2p
PGC	15-09	A	New Brighton	L 21-32		McGillivary	Dunn	Lewis	Lutton	Edwards

** after opponents name indicates a penalty try. Brackets after a player's name indicates he was replaced. eg (a) means he was replaced by replacement code "a" and so on. / after a player or replacement name is followed by any scores he made - eg /t, /c, /p, /dg or any combination of these*

EVER PRESENT None

Most Appearances:
25: Dean Lutton, Simon Lewis (1).
24: Russell Lear.
23: Richard Wynn.
22: Tom Hares.

PLAYERS USED

38 plus five as a replacement only.

MOST POINTS

Pts	Player	T	C	P	DG
96	C Hares	6	18	10	-
73	J Canney	1	16	12	-
45	P Appleby	9	-	-	-
35	D Lutton	7	-	-	-
30	P Mullock	6	-	-	-
30	R McGillivary	6	-	-	-

MATCH FACTS

10	9	1	2	3	4	5	6	7	8
Wynn	Mullock	Willis	Barber	Lear	Douglas	Pemberton	Emmerson	Appleby	Hares
Canney/3c	Mullock	Willis	Barber	Lear	Douglas	Pemberton	Hollins	Appleby/t	Hares
Canney/t2c2p	Mullock/t	Anderson	Barber	Lear/t	Douglas	Pemberton	Hares	Appleby	Pemberton
Canney/3cp	Mullock	Anderson	Barber	Lear	Douglas(a/t)	Pemberton	Hares	Appleby	Pemberton
Canney/2c2p	Slater(b/t)	Anderson	Wynn	Lear	Hollins	Charmley	Hares	Appleby/2t	Pemberton/t
Canney/c	Hares	Anderson	Wynn	Lear/t	Hollins	Charmley	Hares	Appleby	Pemberton
Canney/c	Hares	Anderson	Wynn/t	Lear	Douglas	Charmley	Hares	Appleby/t	Pemberton
Canney/c	Hares	Anderson/t	Wynn	Lear	Douglas	Charmley	Hares	Appleby	Pemberton
Canney/2p	Hares	Willis	Barber	Anderson	Douglas	Leonard	Charmley	Appleby	Pemberton
Wynn/2p	Hares	Willis	Barber	Anderson	Charmley	Leonard	Winson	Appleby	Pemberton
Wynn	Mullock/t	Anderson	Barber/t	Lear	Charmley	Pemberton	Owen	Appleby	Pemberton
Wynn/c	Mullock/t	Anderson	Barber	Lear	Douglas	Pemberton	Owen	Appleby	Pemberton
Suckley/c2p	Mullock	Willis	Wynn	Lear	Hollins	Pemberton	Owen	Hares	Pemberton
Mullock	Hares	Willis	Turnbull	Lear	Douglas	Pemberton	Hares	Appleby	Pemberton
Wynn	Mullock	Willis	Barber	Lear	Charmley	Pemberton	Hares	Appleby	Pemberton
Wynn	Mullock	Hazelton	Barber	Lear	Charmley	Pemberton	Hares	Appleby/2t	Pemberton
Wynn	Mullock	Hazelton	Barber/t	Lear/t	Charmley	Pemberton	Hares	Appleby	Pemberton
Wynn	Mullock	Hazelton	Barber	Lear	Charmley	Pemberton/t	Owen	Hares	Pemberton
Wynn	Mullock/t	Hazelton	Barber	Lear	Charmley	Pemberton/t	Owen	Hares	Pemberton/t
Wynn	Mullock	Hazelton	Barber(d/t)	Lear	Charmley	Pemberton	Charmley	Hares	Pemberton
Wynn	Mullock	Hazelton	Barber	Lear	Charmley	Pemberton	Charmley	Hares	Pemberton
Suckley/t	Mullock	Hazelton	Turnbull	Lear	Charmley	Pemberton	Hares	Appleby	Pemberton/t
Suckley	Mullock	Hazelton	Wynn	Lear	Charmley	Pemberton/t	Hares	Appleby/t	Hares
Suckley/t	Mullock/t	Hazelton	Wynn	Lear	Charmley	Pemberton/t	Hares	Appleby/t	Owen/t
Suckley/t	Mullock	Hazelton	Wynn	Lear	Charmley	Pemberton	Hares	Appleby/t	Owen/t
Suckley	Mullock	Hughes	Wynn	Lear	Charmley	Pemberton	Hares	Hares/t	Owen
Canney/2p	Mullock/t	Willis	Wynn/t	Anderson/t	Douglas	Pemberton	Hares	Appleby	Pemberton

REPLACEMENTS: a - Tim Charmley. b - Phil Mullock. c - Jamie Dunn. d - Mike Turnbull. e - Elliot Roe.

Most replacement appearances in the league: 6: Simon Wynn. 5: Giles Hazelton.

Most times replaced: 6: Simon Wynn, Jebba Anderson. 5: Kevin Barber.

WHERE	Total	Home	Away
The POINTS were scored	524	291	233
The POINTS were conceded	701	395	306
The TRIES were scored	74	41	33
The TRIES were conceded	96	58	38

HOW the TRIES were scored

Total	Backs	Forwards	F Back	Wing	Centre	H Back	F Row	Lock	B Row	Pen. Try
70	42	28	7	14	11	10	8	5	15	4

HOW the TRIES were conceded

Total	Backs	Forwards	F Back	Wing	Centre	H Back	F Row	Lock	B Row	Pen. Try
96	75	21	12	18	25	20	4	2	15	-

MORLEY

Comp.	Date	H/A	Opponents	Result & Score	Att	15	14	13	12	11
N3 N	01-09	H	Blaydon	W 24-23	400	Evans	Hutchinson	Murray/t	Sherlock(a/t)	Johnson
N3 N	08-09	A	West Hartlepool	W 50-15		Evans	Hutchinson/t	Murray	Sherlock/2t4c3p	Johnson
N3 N	22-09	H	Doncaster	L 15-41		Evans	Hutchinson	Murray	Fieldhouse/t	O'Callaghan
N3 N	06-10	A	Darlington MP	L 12-19	400	Evans	Sherlock/c	Murray	Fieldhouse/t	Johnson
N3 N	20-10	H	Tynedale	W 25-23		Evans	Sherlock/t2cp	Murray	Fieldhouse(a/t)	Johnson
N3 N	27-10	A	Sandal	W 20-12	200	Evans	Luxton	Murray/t	Fieldhouse	Johnson
N3 N	10-11	H	Scunthorpe	L 11-16		Evans	Luxton	Murray	Sherlock/t2p	Johnson
N3 N	17-11	A	Liverpool St Helens*	L 23-26		Evans	Hutchinson	Murray	Sherlock	Johnson/t
N3 N	24-11	H	Bedford Athletic	W 31-15		Evans	Hutchinson/2c3p	Murray/t	Maynard/t	Johnson/t
N3 N	01-12	A	Blaydon	L 15-26		Evans	Hutchinson/5p	Murray	Maynard	Johnson
N3 N	08-12	H	Dudley Kingwinsford	L 8-24		Evans	Hutchinson/p	Murray	Maynard	Johnson
N3 N	15-12	A	Whitchurch	L 7-13	375	Evans	Hutchinson	O'Callaghan	Maynard(b/t)	Johnson
N3 N	12-01	H	Liverpool St Helens	L 15-55		Evans	Sherlock/cp	O'Callaghan	Murray/t	Johnson
N3 N	19-01	A	Scunthorpe	W 36-26	450	Evans	Sherlock/2t3c	Murray	Maynard/t	Johnson
N3 N	02-02	H	Sandal	W 32-6		Evans	Luxton/2t	Murray	Maynard	Johnson
N3 N	09-02	A	Tynedale	L 11-16		Evans	Luxton	Murray	Maynard	Johnson
N3 N	16-02	H	New Brighton	L 16-27		Evans	Sherlock/2p	Murray	Maynard	Johnson
N3 N	23-02	H	Darlington MP	L 16-17		Evans	Sherlock/c3p	Murray	Maynard	Johnson/t
N3 N	02-03	H	Nuneaton	L 9-19		Evans	Sherlock/3p	Murray	Maynard	Johnson
N3 N	09-03	A	Doncaster	L 13-27		Stokes	Evans	Murray/t	Sherlock/p	Johnson
N3 N	16-03	H	West Hartlepool	W 48-12		Evans	Hutchinson	Murray	Sherlock/t5cp	Johnson/t
N3 N	23-03	A	Bedford Athletic	L 17-23	150	Evans	Hutchinson/c	O'Callaghan	Sherlock/t	Johnson/t
N3 N	30-03	A	New Brighton	L 19-40		Evans/c	Hutchinson/c	O'Callaghan	Murray	Johnson/t
N3 N	06-04	H	Whitchurch	D 19-19		Evans	Hutchinson	Sherlock/3p	Murray	Johnson
N3 N	13-04	A	Dudley Kingwinsford	L 30-32	475	Evans	Hutchinson/t	Sherlock/cp	Murray	Johnson
N3 N	20-04	A	Nuneaton	L 19-28		Evans	Stokes	Murray	Sherlock/2c	Johnson/t
PGC	15-09	N	Liverpool St Helens	L 23-28		Evans/t	Hutchinson	Murray/t	Sherlock/c2p	Johnson/t

** after opponents name indicates a penalty try. Brackets after a player's name indicates he was replaced. eg (a) means he was replaced by replacement code "a" and so on. / after a player or replacement name is followed by any scores he made - eg /t, /c, /p, /dg or any combination of these*

EVER PRESENT Scott Evans.

Most Appearances:
26: Scott Evans.
25: Chris Johnson, Simon Chippendale.
24: Alan Pierre, Neil Murray (1), Paul Gabriel.

PLAYERS USED

34 plus six as replacement only.

MOST POINTS

Pts	Player	T	C	P	DG
143	A Sherlock	8	20	21	-
76	M Sales	8	20	21	-
45	S Kneale	9	-	-	-
45	E Hutchinson	2	4	9	-
35	C Johnson	7	-	-	-
35J Tiffen	7	-	-	-	

MATCH FACTS

10	9	1	2	3	4	5	6	7	8
Sales/c4p	Tiffen	Gabriel	Kneale	Sykes	Pierre	Chippendale	Hare	Hopton	Shaw
Sales/p	Evans	Gabriel	Kneale/2t	Sykes	Chippendale	Pierre	Kite	Hare	Shaw/t
Sales/cp	Tiffen	Gabriel	Brain	Sykes	Pierre	Chippendale	Hare	Wheelwright	Shaw
Sales	Tiffen	Gabriel	Kneale	Sykes	Pierre	Chippendale	Kite	Wheelwright/t	Shaw
Sales/dg	Tiffen/t	Gabriel	Kneale	Sykes	Kite	Chippendale	Anderson	Wheelwright	Shaw
Sales/t2cpdg	Tiffen	Gabriel	Kneale	Sykes	Pierre	Chippendale	Kite	Wheelwright	Shaw
Sales	Tiffen	Gabriel	Farmery	Sykes	Pierre	Chippendale	Osbourne	Wheelwright	Shaw
Sales/2c3p	Tiffen	Gabriel	Kneale	Sykes	Pierre	Chippendale	Wheelwright	Osbourne	Shaw
Sales/dg	Tiffen	Gabriel	Kneale	Benn	Pierre	Chippendale	Wheelwright	Osbourne	Kite
Sales	Tiffen	Gabriel	Kneale	Benn	Pierre	Chippendale	Wheelwright	Osbourne	Kite
Sales	Murray	Gabriel	Kneale/t	Sykes	Pierre	Chippendale	Kite	Osbourne	Shaw
Sales/c	Murray	Gabriel	Farmery	Sykes	Chippendale	Scott	Kite	Osbourne	Shaw
Sales	Tiffen	Benn	Kneale/t	Sykes	Pierre	Chippendale	Hopton	Osbourne	Shaw
Sales	Tiffen/t	Gabriel/t	Kneale	Sykes/t	Pierre	Chippendale	Kite	Wheelwright	Shaw
Sales/t2cp	Tiffen	Gabriel	Kneale	Sykes	Pierre	Chippendale	Kite	Osbourne	Shaw/t(c/t)
Sales/2p	Tiffen	Gabriel	Kneale/t	Sykes	Chippendale	Pierre	Kite	Osbourne	Shaw
Walmsley	Tiffen	Gabriel	Kneale	Sykes	Pierre	Chippendale	Kite/t	Osbourne/t	Shaw
Hutchinson	Tiffen	Benn	Kneale	Sykes	Pierre	Chippendale	Kite	Osbourne	Ball
Hutchinson	Tiffen	Benn	Farmery	Gabriel	Pierre	Chippendale	Kite	Osbourne	Ball
Hutchinson	Tiffen/t	Gabriel	Kneale	Sykes	Chippendale	Pierre	Kite	Ball	Shaw
Sales	Tiffen/2t	Gabriel	Kneale/2t	Sykes	Pierre	Chippendale	Kite	Ball	Shaw/t
Sales	Tiffen	Gabriel	Kneale/t	Sykes	Pierre	Chippendale	Kite	Ball	Shaw
Sales/t	Stokes	Gabriel	Kneale	Benn	Kite	Pierre	Wheelwright	Ball	Shaw(d/t)
Sales	Tiffen/t	Gabriel/t	Kneale	Sykes	Pierre	Chippendale	Kite	Wheelwright	Shaw
Sales	Tiffen/t	Gabriel/t	Kneale/t	Sykes/t	Pierre	Chippendale	Ball	Field	Shaw
Sales	Tiffen	Gabriel	Kneale	Sykes	Chippendale	Pierre	Ball(e/t)	Osbourne	Shaw/t
Sales	Tiffen	Benn	Kneale	Sykes	Chippendale	Pierre	Kite	Wheelwright	Hare

REPLACEMENTS: a - Andy Sales. b - Neil Murray. c - James Ball. d - Craig Field. e - Jon Kite.

Most replacement appearances in the league: 11: Alan Benn. 7: Andy Sales. 5: Craig Field, Jon Kite.

Most times replaced: 7: Paul Gabriel, Jon Kite. 5: Neil Murray, Peter Osbourne, Neil Shaw, Alastair Sherlock.

WHERE	Total	Home	Away
The POINTS were scored	541	269	272
The POINTS were conceded	600	303	297
The TRIES were scored	67	31	36
The TRIES were conceded	76	37	39

HOW the TRIES were scored

Total	Backs	Forwards	F Back	Wing	Centre	H Back	F Row	Lock	B Row	Pen. Try
66	42	24	-	15	17	10	14	-	10	1

HOW the TRIES were conceded

Total	Backs	Forwards	F Back	Wing	Centre	H Back	F Row	Lock	B Row	Pen. Try
74	53	21	6	20	13	14	4	2	15	2

SANDAL

Comp.	Date	H/A	Opponents	Result & Score	Att	15	14	13	12	11
N3 N	01-09	H	Doncaster	L 28-71		Wolff/2t	Howarth	Barker/t	Brindley	Ell
N3 N	08-09	A	Darlington MP	L 0-41	300	Wolff	Howarth	Barker	Brindley	Ell
N3 N	22-09	H	Tynedale	W 17-10		Wolff/t	Mitchell	Lockwood	Brindley	Greenhalgh
N3 N	06-10	H	Scunthorpe	L 8-27	150	Wolff	Howarth	Barker	Lockwood	Greenhalgh
N3 N	20-10	A	Nuneaton	L 27-51		Wolff	Greenhalgh	Brindley	Wolff	Ell/t
N3 N	27-10	H	Morley	L 12-20	200	Wolff	Mitchell	Brindley	Wolff	Greenhalgh
N3 N	03-11	A	Liverpool St Helens	L 0-55		Wolff	Greenhalgh	Lockwood	Brindley	Mitchell
N3 N	10-11	H	Bedford Athletic	D 13-13		Wolff/t	Greenhalgh	Brindley	Lockwood	Mitchell/t
N3 N	17-11	A	New Brighton	L 10-55		Wolff	Greenhalgh	Brindley	Frazer	Plummer
N3 N	24-11	H	Dudley Kingwinsford	L 0-71	100	Wolff	Mitchell	Frazer	Brindley	Plummer
N3 N	01-12	A	Doncaster	L 7-70		Wolff/t	Greenhalgh	Frazer	Brindley	Plummer
N3 N	08-12	H	Blaydon	L 10-27	180	Wolff	Greenhalgh	Brindley	Frazer	Wolfenden
N3 N	15-12	A	West Hartlepool	W 28-21		Wolff/t	Greenhalgh	Brindley	Wolff/t	Howarth/t
N3 N	12-01	H	New Brighton	L 11-40	150	Wolff	Greenhalgh	Brindley	Frazer	Howarth/t
N3 N	19-01	A	Bedford Athletic	L 0-53	150	Wolff	Greenhalgh	Frazer	Howarth	Ell
N3 N	02-02	A	Morley	L 6-32		Wolff	Greenhalgh	Brindley	Frazer	Howarth
N3 N	09-02	H	Nuneaton	L 18-25	150	Wolff	Greenhalgh/t	Brindley	Frazer	Ell
N3 N	16-02	H	Whitchurch	L 23-29	100	Wolff	Howarth	Brindley	Frazer/t	Greenhalgh
N3 N	23-02	A	Scunthorpe	W 22-20		Wolff	Greenhalgh	Brindley	Frazer/t	Howarth
N3 N	02-03	A	Dudley Kingwinsford	L 3-17	300	Wolff	Greenhalgh	Frazer	Brindley	Howarth
N3 N	09-03	A	Tynedale*	L 14-37		Wolff	Greenhalgh/t	Brindley	Frazer	Howarth
N3 N	16-03	H	Darlington MP	L 19-36		Wolff	Marshall	Brindley	Bacon	Ell/t
N3 N	30-03	A	Whitchurch	L 16-56	275	Wolff/t	Wolfenden/t	Frazer	Brindley	Marshall
N3 N	06-04	H	West Hartlepool	L 17-31		Wolff	Ell	Frazer	Brindley	Greenhalgh
N3 N	13-04	A	Blaydon	L 0-67		Wolff	Plummer	Ell	Barrett	Marshall
N3 N	20-04	H	Liverpool St Helens*	L 7-34	150	Wolff	Ell	Brindley	Mitchell	Marshall
PGC	15-09	N	Doncaster	L 8-41		Wolff	Mitchell	Barker	Brindley	Greenhalgh

** after opponents name indicates a penalty try. Brackets after a player's name indicates he was replaced. eg (a) means he was replaced by replacement code "a" and so on. / after a player or replacement name is followed by any scores he made - eg /t, /c, /p, /dg or any combination of these*

EVER PRESENT M Wolff

Most Appearances:
26: M Wolff.
25: Rob Dawson (1).
24: Ben Brindley (1).
23: G Swift.

PLAYERS USED

43 plus three as a replacement

MOST POINTS

Pts	Player	T	C	P	DG
57	M Bacon	3	12	6	-
53	M Hardcastle	-	4	15	-
35	M Wolff	7	-	-	-
25	P Greenhalgh	5	-	-	-
16	P Ure	-	5	2	-
15	V Proctor	3	-	-	-

MATCH FACTS

10	9	1	2	3	4	5	6	7	8
3rindley/t	Bacon/4c	Goodwin	Swift	Waterhouse	Harrison	Hargrave	McIntosh	Key	Lockwood
Brindley	Bacon	Goodwin	Swift	Wilson	Harrison	Dawson	Lockwood	Ledger	Livermore
Brindley/t	Bacon/2cp	Wilson	Swift	Goodwin	Harrison	Dawson	Key	Phillips	Hargrave
Brindley	Bacon/p	Wilson	Key	Wareham	Harrison	Dawson/t	Phillips	Livermore	Hargrave
Brindley	Bacon/t2cp	Goodwin	Swift	Wareham	McIntosh	Dawson	Livermore	Ledger/t	Hargrave/t
Froggatt	Bacon/c	Waterhouse	Swift	McSwiney/t	McIntosh	Dawson	Livermore	Ledger	Hargrave
Froggatt	Bacon	Wilson	Swift	McSwiney	Dawson	Hargrave	Brindley	Ledger	Livermore
Froggatt/p	Bacon	Wilson	Swift	McSwiney	Dawson	Hargrave	Key	Ledger	Ledger
Wolff	Bacon/tcp	Wilson	Swift	McSwiney	Dawson	McIntosh	Key	Ledger	Livermore
Froggatt	Wolfenden	Wilson	Lig	McSwiney	Dawson	Hargrave	Livermore	Key	Walker
Wolff	Bacon/c	McSwiney	Swift	Allchurch	Dawson	Hargrave	Key	Knapp	Walter
Wolff	Bacon/cp	Wilson	Swift/t	Wareham	Dawson	Hargrave	Key	Livermore	Walter
Hardcastle/2c3p	Bacon	McSwiney	Swift	Wilson	Dawson	Hargrave	Key	Knapp	McIntosh
Hardcastle/2p	Bacon	Wilson	Swift	McSwiney	Dawson	Hargrave	Key	Marshall	McIntosh
Hardcastle	Bacon	McSwiney	Swift	Wilson	Dawson	Hargrave	McIntosh	Knapp	Proctor
Hardcastle/2p	Bacon	McSwiney	Swift	Wilson	Dawson	Proctor	Norris	Knapp	Hargrave
Hardcastle/c2p	Bacon	McSwiney	Swift/t	Wilson	Dawson	Proctor	Livermore	Knapp	Norris
Hardcastle/p	Bacon/t	McSwiney	Swift	Wilson	Dawson	Hargrave/t	Livermore	Knapp	Norris
Hardcastle/c5p	Bacon	Wareham	Swift	Wilson	Dawson	Proctor	Norris	Knapp	Hargrave
3acon/p	Wolfenden	McSwiney	Key	Wilson	Dawson	Proctor	Norris	Knapp	McIntosh
Jre/2c	Bacon	McSwiney	Swift	Wareham	Dawson	Proctor	Key	Knapp	Norris
Jre/2c	Wolfenden	McSwiney	Swift	Wilson	Dawson	Hargrave	Norris	Knapp	Proctor/2t
Jre/2p	Bacon	Raison	Swift	McSwiney	Dawson	Hargrave	Norris	Phillips	Proctor
Jre/c	Wolfenden	Raison	Swift	McSwiney	Dawson	Hargrave	Phillips/t	Key	Proctor/t
3rindley	Wolfenden	Wilson	Swift	McSwiney	Dawson	Proctor	Key	Hughes	McIntosh
3rindley/c	Wolfenden	Wareham	Swift	McSwiney	Dawson	Norris	Key	Phillips	Proctor
3rindley	Bacon/p	Waterhouse	Swift	Wilson	Harrison	Dawson/t	Lockwood	Livermore	Hargrave

REPLACEMENTS:

Most replacement appearances in the league: 7: Richard Wareham. 6: Paul McIntosh.

Most times replaced: 9: Nick Hargrave. 6: Lee Norris, Darrel Mcswiney. 5: Andy Wilson.

WHERE	Total	Home	Away
The POINTS were scored	316	183	133
The POINTS were conceded	1009	575	434
The TRIES were scored	40	26	14
The TRIES were conceded	151	90	61

HOW the TRIES were scored

Total	Backs	Forwards	F Back	Wing	Centre	H Back	F Row	Lock	B Row	Pen. Try
38	27	11	7	11	4	5	3	2	6	2

HOW the TRIES were conceded

Total	Backs	Forwards	F Back	Wing	Centre	H Back	F Row	Lock	B Row	Pen. Try
151	102	49	17	28	29	28	8	7	34	-

WEST HARTLEPOOL

Comp.	Date	H/A	Opponents	Result & Score	Att	15	14	13	12	11
N3 N	01-09	A	Nuneaton	L 17-36		Lilley	Grand/t	Milne	Connolly/t	Thompson
N3 N	08-09	H	Morley	L 15-50		Lilley	Grand	Milne	Connolly/2t	Kerr
N3 N	22-09	A	Liverpool St Helens	L 17-45	150	Walton	Kerr	Connolly	Milne	Lilley
N3 N	06-10	H	Bedford Athletic	W 18-16		Laycock/t	Lilley	Thompson	Connolly	Kerr/t
N3 N	20-10	A	New Brighton	L 5-69		Walton	Thomas	Kerr	Connolly	Lilley/t
N3 N	27-10	H	Dudley Kingwinsford	L 10-42		Walton	Lilley/t	Kerr	Connolly	Thomas
N3 N	03-11	A	Whitchurch	L 5-22	350	Walton	Thomas/t	Kerr	Thompson	Lilley
N3 N	10-11	A	Blaydon	L 27-44		Walton/2cp	Thomas	Kerr	Thompson/2t	Lilley/t
N3 N	17-11	A	Scunthorpe	L 28-45		Walton/2c3p	Lilley	Laycock	Thompson/t	Kerr/t
N3 N	24-11	A	Doncaster	L 13-95		Hodgson	Kerr	Lilley	Walton/c2p	Thomas
N3 N	01-12	H	Nuneaton	L 12-37		Walton/c	Kerr	Milne	Thompson	Thomas
N3 N	08-12	A	Tynedale	L 27-42		Walton/2cp	Thomas	Milne	Connolly	Kerr
N3 N	15-12	H	Sandal	L 21-28		Walton/c3p	Thomas	Cuff	Thompson	Kerr
N3 N	12-01	H	Scunthorpe	L 22-35		Thomas	Whitehead/t	Kerr	Thompson	Hodgson
N3 N	19-01	H	Blaydon	L 9-29	150	Thomas	Masshedar/3p	Kerr	Thompson	Hodgson
N3 N	26-01	H	Whitchurch	W 14-12		Thomas	Masshedar/2c	Kerr	Thompson	Hodgson
N3 N	02-02	A	Dudley Kingwinsford	L 5-46	350	Thomas	Masshedar	Kerr	Thompson	Hodgson
N3 N	09-02	H	New Brighton	L 19-41		Walton/t2c	Thomas/t	Kerr	Thompson	Hodgson
N3 N	16-02	A	Darlington MP	L 24-25		Laycock/t	Thomas/t	Kerr	Thompson/t	Hodgson
N3 N	23-02	A	Bedford Athletic	L 20-62	150	Rudd	Thomas	Kerr/t	Thompson	Hodgson
N3 N	02-03	H	Liverpool St Helens	L 11-32		Thomas	Barff	Kerr	Thompson	Hodgson
N3 N	16-03	A	Morley	L 12-48		Walton/c	Kerr	Cuff/t	Milne/t	Thomas
N3 N	23-03	H	Doncaster	L 6-43		Cuff	Barff	Kerr	Milne	Tones
N3 N	30-03	H	Darlington MP	L 15-27		Cuff	Lassey	Kerr	Connolly	Barff
N3 N	06-04	A	Sandal	W 31-17		Cuff	Lassey	Kerr/t	Connolly	Barff
N3 N	13-04	H	Tynedale	L 9-30		Cuff	Lassey	Kerr	Connolly	Barff
PGC	15-09	A	Dudley Kingswinford	L 0-00						

** after opponents name indicates a penalty try. Brackets after a player's name indicates he was replaced. eg (a) means he was replaced by replacement code "a" and so on. / after a player or replacement name is followed by any scores he made - eg /t, /c, /p, /dg or any combination of these*

EVER PRESENT Jamie Connolly

Most Appearances:
26: Jamie Connolly.
25: Gareth Kerr, Brett Cullinane.
23: Chris Webb.

PLAYERS USED 35

MOST POINTS

Pts	Player	T	C	P	DG
74	M Walton	1	15	13	-
68	J Connolly	8	5	6	-
47	J Stabler	-	4	13	-
35	D Tighe	7	-	-	-

MATCH FACTS

10	9	1	2	3	4	5	6	7	8
Walton/2cp	Tighe	Cholmondeley	McNeish	Cook	Webb	Davies	Cullinane	Tones	Wright
Walton/cp	Tighe	Cholmondeley	McNeish	Cook	Webb	Davies	Rudd	Wright	Cullinane
Stabler/c	Tighe	Geritz	McNeish	Robinson/t	Webb/t	Davies/t	Rudd	Tones	Cullinane
Walton/p(a/cp)	Tighe	Cholmondeley	McNeish	Cook	Webb	Davies	Cullinane	Rudd	Wright
Stabler	Tighe	Cholmondeley	Robinson	Cook	Webb	Davies	Cullinane	Rudd	Wright
Stabler	Tighe	Cholmondeley	McNeish/t	Cook	Baggs	Davies	Cullinane	Rudd	Wright
Connolly	Tighe	Cholmondeley	McNeish	Cook	Baggs	Davies	Webb	Hodgson	Cullinane
Connolly	Tighe/t	Geritz	McNeish	Cook	Webb	Davies	Baggs	Rudd	Cullinane
Connolly/t	Tighe	Geritz	McNeish	Cook	Webb	Davies	Rudd	Hodgson	Cullinane
Connolly	Tighe/t	Geritz	Robinson	Cook	Webb	Rudd	Cook	Tones	Baggs
Connolly/2t	Tighe	Geritz	Robinson	Cook	Webb	Davies	Sawyer	Hodgson	Cullinane
Stabler	Tighe/3t	Geritz	Robinson	Cook	Webb	Davies	Sawyer/t	Tones	Cullinane
Connolly/t	Tighe	Painter	Cullinane	Geritz	Webb	Davies	Sawyer/t	Hodgson	Baggs
Connolly/c	Tighe	Cholmondeley	Cullinane/t	Geritz	Webb	Baggs	Rudd	Tones/2t	Sawyer
Connolly	Tighe	Cullinane	Robinson	Cook	Webb	Baggs	Rudd	Tones	Sawyer
Connolly	Tighe/t	Cholmondeley	Cullinane	Cook	Webb	Davies	Rudd	Tones	Sawyer/t
Connolly	Tighe	Bennett	Cullinane/t	Cook	Webb	Davies	Rudd	Tones	Sawyer
Connolly	Tighe	Cholmondeley	Cullinane	Cook	Webb	Davies	Baggs	Bennett	Sawyer/t
Connolly/3cp	Tighe	Cholmondeley	Cullinane	Cook	Webb	Rudd	Wright	Sawyer	Bennett
Connolly/tcp	Tighe/t	Cholmondeley	Cullinane	Cook	Webb	Wright	Tones	Sawyer	Bennett
Connolly/2p	Tighe	Cholmondeley	Cullinane	Cook	Webb	Davies/t	Wright	Sawyer	Bennett
Connolly	Tighe	Bennett	Cullinane	Cook	Webb	Davies	Sawyer	Tones	Wright
Connolly/2p	Thomas	Cholmondeley	Robinson	Cullinane	Wright	Davies	Rudd	Sawyer	Bennett
Stabler/5p	Thomas	Geritz	Cullinane	Cook	Baggs	Davies	Wright	Sawyer	Bennett
Stabler/2c4p	Thomas	Geritz	Cullinane/t	Cook	Webb	Davies	Sawyer	Tones/t	Wright
Stabler/3p	Thomas	Geritz	Cullinane	Cook	Webb	Davies	Rudd	Tones	Wright

REPLACEMENTS: a - John Stabler

WHERE	Total	Home	Away
The POINTS were scored	412	181	231
The POINTS were conceded	1018	596	422
The TRIES were scored	51	20	31
The TRIES were conceded	147	86	61

HOW the TRIES were scored

Total	Backs	Forwards	F Back	Wing	Centre	H Back	F Row	Lock	B Row	Pen. Try
51	36	15	3	10	11	12	5	3	7	-

HOW the TRIES were conceded

Total	Backs	Forwards	F Back	Wing	Centre	H Back	F Row	Lock	B Row	Pen. Try
147	94	51	8	32	30	24	13	9	29	2

THE LAST TEN YEARS DIVISION 4 NORTH

1992-93

Champions	Runners-up	Relegated
Harrogate	Rotherham	Towcestrians

Most
Points: 131 Ralph Zoing (Harrogate) *Tries:* 9 Guy Easterby (Harrogate), Steve Baker (Harrogate)
Penalties: 31 Simon Pennington (Stourbridge) *Conversions:* 28 Ralph Zoing (Harrogate) *D.Gs:* N.A.

1993-94

Champions	Runners-up	Relegated
Rotherham	Preston Grasshoppers	Bradford & Bingley, Durham City

Most
Points: 118 Kevin Plant (Rotherham) *Tries:* 8 John Dudley (Rotherham)
Penalties: 23 Richard Mills (Walsall) *Conversions:* 22 Kevin Plant (Rotherham) *D.Gs:* N.A.

1994-95

Champions	Runners-up	Relegated
Walsall	Kendal	Hereford, Barkers' Butts

Most
Points: 164 Richard MIlls (Walsall) *Tries:* 11 Jon Rowe (Walsall)
Penalties: 31 Richard Mills (Walsall) *Conversions:* 29 Richard Mills (Walsall) *D.Gs:* N.A.

1995-96

Champions	Runners-up	Relegated
Wharfedale	Worcester	Broughton Park

Most
Points: 143 Alex Howarth (Wharfedale) *Tries:* 10 Neil Hezeltine (Wharfedale), Spencer Bradley (Worcester)
Penalties: 29 Alex Howarth (Wharfedale) *Conversions:* 23 Alex Howarth (Wharfedale) *D.Gs:* 3 Warwick Masser (Nuneaton)

1996-97

Champions	Runners-up	Relegated
Worcester	Birmingham Solihull	Hereford, Stoke on Trent

Most
Points: 317 Steve Kerry (Preston G) *Tries:* 18 Nick Baxter (Worcester)
Penalties: 64 Steve Kerry (Preston G) *Conversions:* 61 Tim Smith (Worcester) *D.Gs:* 9 Steve Kerry (Preston G)

1997-98

Champions	Runners-up	Relegated
Birmingham Solihull	Manchester	-

Most
Points: 398 Steve Swindells (Manchester) *Tries:* 21 Matt Hoskin (Manchester)
Penalties: 62 Steve Swindells (Manchester) *Conversions:* 91 Steve Swindells (Manchester) *D.Gs:* 4 Ian Shuttleworth (Sandal), Rob Pound (Sheffield)

1998-99

Champions	Runners-up	Relegated
Preston Grasshoppers	Stourbridge	Hinckley, Lichfield, Winnington Park

Most
Points: 246 Ian Shuttleworth (Sandal) *Tries:* 27 Michael Lough (Preston G.)
Penalties: Martin Emmett (Preston G.) *Conversions:* Martin Emmett (Preston G.) *D.Gs:* 3 Ian Shuttleworth (Sandal)

99-2000

Champions	Runners-up	Relegated
Kendal	Stourbridge	Sheffield

Most
Points: 302 Paul Brett (New Brighton) *Tries:* 22 Chris Hall (Morley)
Penalties: 55 Paul Brett (New Brighton) *Conversions:* 53 Casey Mee (Kendal) *D.Gs:* 2 Jamie Grayshon (Morley)

2000-01

Champions	Runners-up	Relegated
Stourbridge	Sedgley Park	Walsall, Aspatria

Most
Points: 258 Paul Brett (New Brighton) *Tries*: 20 Garry Marshall (Nuneaton)
Penalties: Simon Worsley (Liverpool St Helens) *Conversions:* 50 Colin Stephens (Sedgley Park) *D.Gs:* 5 Simon Worlsey (Liverpool St H.)

2001-02

Champions	Runners-up	Relegated
Doncaster	Dudley Kingswinford	Whitchurch, Morley, Sandal, West Hartlepool.

Most
Points: 359 John Liley (Doncaster) *Tries:* 25 Shaun Perry (Dudley Kingsw.)
Penalties: 47 Paul Brett (New Brighton) *Conversions:* 89 John Liley (Doncaster) *D.Gs:* 4 Tim Robinson (Scunthorpe)

ALL TIME RECORDS — TEAM RECORDS — DIVISION 4 NORTH

Highest score:	**101**	Manchester 101 Nuneaton 12, 25.4.98
Highest aggregate:	**113**	as above
Highest score by a losing side:	**38**	Nuneaton 40 Aspatria 38, 9.11.96
Highest scoring draw:	**33**	Nuneaton v Kendal, 25.1.98
Most consecutive wins:	**19**	Kendal 1999-2000
Most consecutive defeats:	**18**	Stoke-on-Trent 1996-97
Most points for in a season:	**1029**	Manchester 1997-98
Least points for in a season:	**29**	Birmingham Solihull 1988-89
Most points against in a season:	**972**	Hereford 1996-97
Least points against in a season:	**67**	Roundhay 1987-88
Most tries for in a season:	**135**	Stourbridge 1998-99
Most tries against in a season:	**131**	Hereford 1996-97
Least tries for in a season:		
Least tries against in a season:		
Most conversions for in a season:	**98**	Manchester 1997-98
Most conversions against in a season:	**82**	Hereford 1996-97
Most penalties for in a season:	**73**	Sheffield 1996-97
Most penalties against in a season:	**60**	Winnington Park 1996-97
Least penalties for in a season:		
Least penalties against in a season:		
Most drop goals for in a season:	**10**	Preston Grasshoppers 1996-97
Most drop goals against in a season:	**8**	Aspatria 1996-97

ALL TIME RECORDS — INDIVIDUAL RECORDS — DIVISION 4 NORTH

Most points in a season:	**398**	Steve Swindells (Manchester) 1997-98
Most tries in a season:	**22**	Chris Hall (Morley) 1999-2000
Most conversions in a season:	**91**	Steve Swindells (Manchester) 1997-98
Most penalties in a season:	**64**	Steve Kerry (Preston Grasshoppers) 1996-97
Most drop goals in a season:	**9**	Steve Kerry (Preston Grasshoppers) 1996-97
Most points in a match:	**44**	Jamie Morley, *Sheffield* v Lichfield 7.9.97
Most tries in a match:	**6**	Jason Slater, *Kendal* v Barkers Butts 14.1.95
Most conversions in a match:	**10**	Steve Swindells, *Manchester* v Nuneaton 25.4.98
		Kevin Plant, *Rotherham* v Durham 19.2.94
Most penalties in a match:	**8**	Steve Baker, *Stourbridge* v Hereford 26.1.91
Most drop goals in a match:	**4**	Steve Kerry, *Preston G.* v Aspatria 7.9.96

TEN YEAR RECORDS DIVISION 4 NORTH

Club	92-93	93-94	94-95	95-96	96-97	97-98	98-99	99-00	00-01	01-02
	SEASONS									
Aspatria	-	-	-	-	10	9	10	12	14r	-
Barkers Butts	-	-	12	-	-	-	-	-	-	-
Bedford Athletic	-	-	-	-	-	-	-	9	10	10
Birmingham Solihull	-	9	10	3	2	1p	-	-	-	-
Blaydon	-	-	-	-	-	-	-	-		7
Bradford & Bingley	-	13	-	-	-	-	-	-	-	-
Broughton Park	-	-	-	13	-	-	-	-	-	-
Darlington Mowden Park	-	-	-	-	-	-	-	-	-	6
Doncaster	-	-	-	-	-	-	-	6	4	1P
Dudley Kingswinford	-	-	-	-	-	-	-	-	6	2
Durham City	8	12	-	-	-	-	-	-	-	-
Harrogate	1	-	-	-	-	-	-	-	-	-
Hereford	11	8	13	-	13	-	-	-	-	-
Hinckley	-	-	-	-	-	12	12r	-	-	-
Kendal	6	10	2	9	9	3	4	1p	-	-
Lichfield	5	7	5	12	11	13	13r	-	-	-
Liverpool St. Helens	-	-	-	-	-	-	-	13	9	3
Manchester	-	-	-	-	4	2p	-	-	-	-
Morley	-	-	-	-	-	-	-	7	11	12r
New Brighton	-	-	-	-	-	-	3	3	3	4
Northern	-	-	-	-	-	-	-	-	-	-
Nuneaton	12	11	11	10	12	7	5	8	5	8
Preston Grasshoppers	3	2	3	8	3	4	1p	-	-	-
Rotherham	2	1	-	-	-	-	-	-	-	-
Sandal	-	-	-	6	5	8	7	10	12	13r
Sedgley Park	-	-	-	-	-	5	8	5	2p	-
Scunthorpe	-	-	-	-	-	-	-	-	-	9
Sheffield	-	-	9	5	8	10	6	14r	-	-
Stoke on Trent	4	6	7	11	14	-	-	-	-	-
Stourbridge	9	5	6	7	6	6	2	2	1p	-
Towcestrians	13	-	-	-	-	-	-	-	-	-
Tynedale	-	-	-	-	-	-	-	-	8	5
Vale of Lune	-	-	-	-	-	-	-	-	-	-
Walsall	7	3	1	-	-	11	9	4	13r	-
West Hartlepool	-	-	-	-	-	-	-	-	-	14r
Winnington Park	10	4	8	4	7	14	14r	-	-	-
Wharfedale	-	4	1	-	-	-	-	-	-	-
Whitchurch	-	-	-	-	-	-	11	11	7	11r
Worcester	-	-	-	2	1	-	-	-	-	-

NATIONAL DIVISION THREE NORTH

RFU SENIOR CUP

STATISTICS

compiled by Stephen McCormack

PAST WINNERS

1971-72	Gloucester	**1986-87**	Bath
1972-73	Coventry	**1987-88**	Harlequins
1973-74	Coventry	**1988-89**	Bath
1974-75	Bedford	**1989-90**	Bath
1975-76	Gosforth	**1990-91**	Harlequins
1976-77	Gosforth	**1991-92**	Bath
1977-78	Gloucester	**1992-93**	Leicester
1978-79	Leicester	**1993-94**	Bath
1979-80	Leicester	**1994-95**	Bath
1980-81	Leicester	**1995-96**	Bath
1981-82	Gloucester	**1996-97**	Leicester
1982-83	Bristol	**1997-98**	Saracens
1983-84	Bath	**1998-99**	Wasps
1984-85	Bath	**1999-00**	Wasps
1985-86	Bath	**2000-01**	Newcastle

BEDFORD ATHLETIC

THIS SEASON (2001-02) 2nd Round

OVERALL PLAYING RECORD

	P	W	D	L	F	A	Pts Diff
Home	3	1	0	2	90	94	-4
Away	6	3	0	3	152	148	4
Neutral	-	-	-	-	-	-	-
Total	9	4	0	5	242	242	0

TEAM RECORDS

Highest Score
60 v Fylde 99/00

Biggest Winning Margin
39 Pts - 60-21 v Fylde 99/00

Highest Score Against
49 v Preston G'hoppers 00/01

Biggest Losing Margin
30 Pts - 19-49 v Preston G'hoppers 00/01

SEASON BY SEASON

1971-72	DNQ	**1986-87**	DNQ
1972-73	DNQ	**1987-88**	DNQ
1973-74	DNQ	**1988-89**	DNQ
1974-75	DNQ	**1989-90**	DNQ
1975-76	DNQ	**1990-91**	DNQ
1976-77	DNQ	**1991-92**	DNQ
1977-78	DNQ	**1992-93**	DNQ
1978-79	DNQ	**1993-94**	DNQ
1979-80	DNQ	**1994-95**	DNQ
1980-81	DNQ	**1995-96**	DNQ
1981-82	DNQ	**1996-97**	DNQ
1982-83	DNQ	**1997-98**	DNQ
1983-84	1R	**1998-99**	2R
1984-85	DNQ	**1999-00**	3R
1985-86	DNQ	**2000-01**	2R

BLAYDON

THIS SEASON (2001-02) 2nd Round

OVERALL PLAYING RECORD

	P	W	D	L	F	A	Pts Diff
Home	3	1	0	2	56	62	-6
Away	3	2	0	1	41	44	-3
Neutral	-	-	-	-	-	-	-
Total	6	3	0	3	97	106	-9

TEAM RECORDS

Highest Score
22 v Fylde 01/02

Biggest Winning Margin
4 pts - 21-17 v Walsall 01/02

Highest Score Against
28 v Fylde 01/02

Biggest Losing Margin
8 Pts - 15-7 v Bridlington 96/97

SEASON BY SEASON

1971-72	DNQ	**1986-87**	DNQ
1972-73	DNQ	**1987-88**	DNQ
1973-74	DNQ	**1988-89**	DNQ
1974-75	DNQ	**1989-90**	DNQ
1975-76	DNQ	**1990-91**	DNQ
1976-77	DNQ	**1991-92**	DNQ
1977-78	DNQ	**1992-93**	DNQ
1978-79	DNQ	**1993-94**	DNQ
1979-80	DNQ	**1994-95**	DNQ
1980-81	DNQ	**1995-96**	DNQ
1981-82	DNQ	**1996-97**	2R
1982-83	DNQ	**1997-98**	DNQ
1983-84	DNQ	**1998-99**	DNQ
1984-85	DNQ	**1999-00**	2R
1985-86	DNQ	**2000-01**	DNQ

BROADSTREET

THIS SEASON (2001-02) **DNQ**

OVERALL PLAYING RECORD

	P	W	D	L	F	A	Pts Diff
Home	6	3	-	3	137	124	13
Away	1	0	-	1	17	49	-32
Neutral	-	-	-	-	-	-	-
Total	7	3	-	4	154	173	-19

TEAM RECORDS

Highest Score
41 v Huddersfield 97/98
Biggest Winning Margin
38 (41-3) v Huddersfield 97/98
Highest Score Against
49 v Rugby 95/96
Biggest Losing Margin
32 (17-49) v Rugby 95/96

SEASON BY SEASON

Season	Result	Season	Result
1971-72	DNQ	1986-87	DNQ
1972-73	DNQ	1987-88	DNQ
1973-74	DNQ	1988-89	DNQ
1974-75	DNQ	1989-90	DNQ
1975-76	DNQ	1990-91	DNQ
1976-77	DNQ	1991-92	DNQ
1977-78	DNQ	1992-93	DNQ
1978-79	DNQ	1993-94	1R
1979-80	DNQ	1994-95	DNQ
1980-81	DNQ	1995-96	2R
1981-82	DNQ	1996-97	DNQ
1982-83	DNQ	1997-98	3R
1983-84	DNQ	1998-99	DNQ
1984-85	DNQ	1999-00	1R
1985-86	DNQ	2000-01	DNQ

DARLINGTON MOWDEN PARK

THIS SEASON (2001-02) **4th Round**

OVERALL PLAYING RECORD

	P	W	D	L	F	A	Pts Diff
Home	7	6	0	1	203	126	77
Away	6	4	0	2	171	11	60
Neutral	-	-	-	-	-	-	-
Total	13	10	0	3	374	137	137

TEAM RECORDS

Highest Score
48 v Guildford & God 99/00, Bromsgrove 01/02
Biggest Winning Margin
42 v Bromsgrove 01/02
Highest Score Against
39 v Manchester 01/02
Biggest Losing Margin
21 pts - 29-8 v Harlequins 99/00

SEASON BY SEASON

Season	Result	Season	Result
1971-72	DNQ	1986-87	DNQ
1972-73	DNQ	1987-88	DNQ
1973-74	DNQ	1988-89	DNQ
1974-75	DNQ	1989-90	DNQ
1975-76	DNQ	1990-91	DNQ
1976-77	DNQ	1991-92	DNQ
1977-78	DNQ	1992-93	DNQ
1978-79	DNQ	1993-94	DNQ
1979-80	DNQ	1994-95	DNQ
1980-81	DNQ	1995-96	DNQ
1981-82	DNQ	1996-97	DNQ
1982-83	DNQ	1997-98	DNQ
1983-84	DNQ	1998-99	DNQ
1984-85	DNQ	1999-00	5R
1985-86	DNQ	2000-01	4R

DUDLEY KINGSWINFORD

THIS SEASON (2001-02) **3rd Round**

OVERALL PLAYING RECORD

	P	W	D	L	F	A	Pts Diff
Home	4	3	0	1	117	44	73
Away	6	2	0	4	125	183	-58
Neutral	-	-	-	-	-	-	-
Total	10	5	0	5	242	227	15

TEAM RECORDS

Highest Score
59 v West Hartlepool 01/02
Biggest Winning Margin
56 Pts - 59-3 v West Hartlepool 01/02
Highest Score Against
57 v Waterloo 00/01
Biggest Losing Margin
30 Pts - 27-57 v Waterloo 00/01

SEASON BY SEASON

Season	Result	Season	Result
1971-72	DNQ	1986-87	DNQ
1972-73	DNQ	1987-88	DNQ
1973-74	DNQ	1988-89	DNQ
1974-75	DNQ	1989-90	2R
1975-76	DNQ	1990-91	DNQ
1976-77	DNQ	1991-92	DNQ
1977-78	DNQ	1992-93	DNQ
1978-79	DNQ	1993-94	DNQ
1979-80	DNQ	1994-95	DNQ
1980-81	DNQ	1995-96	DNQ
1981-82	1R	1996-97	DNQ
1982-83	DNQ	1997-98	DNQ
1983-84	1R	1998-99	DNQ
1984-85	DNQ	1999-00	DNQ
1985-86	DNQ	2000-01	3R

HALIFAX

THIS SEASON (2001-02) **DNQ**

OVERALL PLAYING RECORD

	P	W	D	L	F	A	Pts Diff
Home	4	3	-	1	56	36	20
Away	2	0	-	2	3	52	-49
Neutral	-	-	-	-	-	-	-
Total	6	3	-	3	59	88	-29

TEAM RECORDS

Highest Score
18 v Tynedale 00/01
Biggest Winning Margin
9 (17-8) v Stourbridge 91/92
Highest Score Against
30 v Wigton 91/92
Biggest Losing Margin
27 (3-30) v Wigton 91/92

SEASON BY SEASON

Season	Result	Season	Result
1971-72	QF	1986-87	DNQ
1972-73	DNQ	1987-88	DNQ
1973-74	DNQ	1988-89	DNQ
1974-75	DNQ	1989-90	DNQ
1975-76	DNQ	1990-91	DNQ
1976-77	DNQ	1991-92	2R
1977-78	DNQ	1992-93	DNQ
1978-79	DNQ	1993-94	DNQ
1979-80	DNQ	1994-95	DNQ
1980-81	DNQ	1995-96	DNQ
1981-82	DNQ	1996-97	DNQ
1982-83	DNQ	1997-98	DNQ
1983-84	DNQ	1998-99	DNQ
1984-85	DNQ	1999-00	DNQ
1985-86	DNQ	2000-01	1R

HULL IONIANS

THIS SEASON (2001-02) **2nd round**

OVERALL PLAYING RECORD

	P	W	D	L	F	A	Pts Diff
Home	5	4	0	1	144	54	90
Away	2	0	0	2	23	52	-29
Neutral	-	-	-	-	-	-	-
Total	7	4	0	3	167	106	61

TEAM RECORDS

Highest Score
59 v Egremont 98/99
Biggest Winning Margin
59 (59-0) v Egremont 98/99
Highest Score Against
37 v Liverpool St H 01/02
Biggest Losing Margin
24 (7-31) v Newbury 98/99

SEASON BY SEASON

Season	Result	Season	Result
1971-72	DNQ	1986-87	DNQ
1972-73	DNQ	1987-88	DNQ
1973-74	DNQ	1988-89	DNQ
1974-75	DNQ	1989-90	DNQ
1975-76	DNQ	1990-91	DNQ
1976-77	DNQ	1991-92	DNQ
1977-78	DNQ	1992-93	DNQ
1978-79	DNQ	1993-94	DNQ
1979-80	DNQ	1994-95	DNQ
1980-81	DNQ	1995-96	2R
1981-82	DNQ	1996-97	DNQ
1982-83	DNQ	1997-98	DNQ
1983-84	DNQ	1998-99	3R
1984-85	DNQ	1999-00	DNQ
1985-86	DNQ	2000-01	DNQ

LIVERPOOL ST. HELENS

THIS SEASON (2001-02) **3rd Round**

OVERALL PLAYING RECORD

	P	W	D	L	F	A	Pts Diff
Home	21	12	-	9	345	354	-9
Away	26	9	-	17	310	517	-207
Neutral	-	-	-	-	-	-	-
Total	47	21	-	26	655	871	-216

TEAM RECORDS

Highest Score
37 v Hull Ionians 01/02
Biggest Winning Margin
22 Pts - 37-15 v Hull Ionians 01/02
Highest Score Against
79 v Morley 97/98
Biggest Losing Margin
69 Pts - 79-10 v Morley 97/98

SEASON BY SEASON

Season	Result	Season	Result
1971-72	1R	1986-87	4R
1972-73	DNQ	1987-88	3R
1973-74	DNQ	1988-89	3R
1974-75	2R	1989-90	3R
1975-76	2R	1990-91	3R
1976-77	DNQ	1991-92	2R
1977-78	QF	1992-93	1R
1978-79	1R	1993-94	2R
1979-80	2R	1994-95	2R
1980-81	DNQ	1995-96	3R
1981-82	QF	1996-97	4R
1982-83	3R	1997-98	3R
1983-84	3R	1998-99	2R
1984-85	4R	1999-00	1R
1985-86	DNQ	2000-01	3R

NEW BRIGHTON

THIS SEASON (2001-02) **3rd Round**

OVERALL PLAYING RECORD

	P	W	D	L	F	A	Pts Diff
Home	13	10	0	3	273	183	90
Away	6	2	0	4	171	130	41
Neutral	-	-	-	-	-	-	-
Total	19	12	0	7	444	313	131

TEAM RECORDS

Highest Score
93 v Selly Oak 99/00

Biggest Winning Margin
83 Pts - 83 Selly Oak 99/00

Highest Score Against
34 v Waterloo 98/99

Biggest Losing Margin
24 Pts - 31-7 Nuneaton 01/02

SEASON BY SEASON

Season	Result	Season	Result
1971-72	DNQ	1986-87	DNQ
1972-73	DNQ	1987-88	DNQ
1973-74	DNQ	1988-89	DNQ
1974-75	DNQ	1989-90	DNQ
1975-76	DNQ	1990-91	DNQ
1976-77	DNQ	1991-92	DNQ
1977-78	DNQ	1992-93	DNQ
1978-79	DNQ	1993-94	3R
1979-80	DNQ	1994-95	1R
1980-81	DNQ	1995-96	DNQ
1981-82	DNQ	1996-97	2R
1982-83	DNQ	1997-98	DNQ
1983-84	DNQ	1998-99	3R
1984-85	DNQ	1999-00	4R
1985-86	DNQ	2000-01	4R

NUNEATON

THIS SEASON (2001-02) **4th Round**

OVERALL PLAYING RECORD

	P	W	D	L	F	A	Pts Diff
Home	18	10	0	8	327	295	32
Away	16	6	0	10	205	403	-198
Neutral	-	-	-	-	-	-	-
Total	34	16	0	18	532	698	-166

TEAM RECORDS

Highest Score
33 v Fylde 83/84

Biggest Winning Margin
27 v Stockwood Park 89/90

Highest Score Against
118 v Northampton 99/00

Biggest Losing Margin
115 Pts - 118-3 v Northampton 99/00

SEASON BY SEASON

Season	Result	Season	Result
1971-72	DNQ	1986-87	DNQ
1972-73	DNQ	1987-88	1R
1973-74	DNQ	1988-89	2R
1974-75	DNQ	1989-90	3R
1975-76	DNQ	1990-91	1R
1976-77	DNQ	1991-92	1R
1977-78	DNQ	1992-93	DNQ
1978-79	DNQ	1993-94	1R
1979-80	DNQ	1994-95	1R
1980-81	DNQ	1995-96	1R
1981-82	3R	1996-97	1R
1982-83	DNQ	1997-98	2R
1983-84	3R	1998-99	2R
1984-85	2R	1999-00	4R
1985-86	1R	2000-01	2R

SCUNTHORPE

THIS SEASON (2001-02) **2nd Round**

OVERALL PLAYING RECORD

	P	W	D	L	F	A	Pts Diff
Home	7	3	0	4	94	215	-121
Away	7	2	0	5	95	208	-113
Neutral	-	-	-	-	-	-	-
Total	14	5	0	9	189	423	-234

TEAM RECORDS

Highest Score
27 v Kendal 94/95

Biggest Winning Margin
7 Pts - 22-15 Manchester 96/97

Highest Score Against
83 v Orrell 01/02

Biggest Losing Margin
75 Pts - 83-8 v Orrell 01/02

SEASON BY SEASON

Season	Result	Season	Result
1971-72	DNQ	1986-87	DNQ
1972-73	DNQ	1987-88	DNQ
1973-74	DNQ	1988-89	DNQ
1974-75	DNQ	1989-90	DNQ
1975-76	DNQ	1990-91	DNQ
1976-77	DNQ	1991-92	DNQ
1977-78	DNQ	1992-93	DNQ
1978-79	DNQ	1993-94	1R
1979-80	DNQ	1994-95	3R
1980-81	DNQ	1995-96	2R
1981-82	DNQ	1996-97	1R
1982-83	DNQ	1997-98	1R
1983-84	DNQ	1998-99	2R
1984-85	DNQ	1999-00	1R
1985-86	DNQ	2000-01	1R

PRESTON GRASSHOPPERS

THIS SEASON (2001-02) 3R

OVERALL PLAYING RECORD

	P	W	D	L	F	A	Pts Diff
Home	12	6	-	6	264	196	68
Away	13	7	-	6	242	240	2
Neutral	-	-	-	-	-	-	-
Total	25	13	-	12	506	436	70

TEAM RECORDS

Highest Score
49 v Bedford Athletic 00/01

Biggest Winning Margin
39 (39-0) v Stoke 93/94

Highest Score Against
50 v Nottingham 98/99

Biggest Losing Margin
47 (3-50) v Nottingham 98/99

SEASON BY SEASON

Season		Season	
1971-72	DNQ	1986-87	1R
1972-73	DNQ	1987-88	DNQ
1973-74	DNQ	1988-89	DNQ
1974-75	DNQ	1989-90	DNQ
1975-76	DNQ	1990-91	2R
1976-77	DNQ	1991-92	DNQ
1977-78	DNQ	1992-93	DNQ
1978-79	DNQ	1993-94	3R
1979-80	DNQ	1994-95	2R
1980-81	DNQ	1995-96	1R
1981-82	DNQ	1996-97	5R
1982-83	DNQ	1997-98	2R
1983-84	DNQ	1998-99	2R
1984-85	1R	1999-00	3R
1985-86	DNP	2000-01	3R

TYNEDALE

THIS SEASON (2001-02) 1st Round

OVERALL PLAYING RECORD

	P	W	D	L	F	A	Pts Diff
Home	12	10	0	2	281	209	72
Away	16	6	0	10	198	252	-54
Neutral	-	-	-	-	-	-	-
Total	28	16	0	12	468	437	18

TEAM RECORDS

Highest Score
47 v Winnington Park 98/99

Biggest Winning Margin
37 Pts - 47-10 v Winnington Park 98/99

Highest Score Against
76 v Worcester 00/01

Biggest Losing Margin
64 Pts - 76-12 v Worcester 00/01

SEASON BY SEASON

Season		Season	
1971-72	DNQ	1986-87	1R
1972-73	DNQ	1987-88	3R
1973-74	DNQ	1988-89	3R
1974-75	DNQ	1989-90	DNQ
1975-76	DNQ	1990-91	DNQ
1976-77	DNQ	1991-92	3R
1977-78	DNQ	1992-93	3R
1978-79	DNQ	1993-94	1R
1979-80	DNQ	1994-95	DNQ
1980-81	DNQ	1995-96	DNQ
1981-82	DNQ	1996-97	2R
1982-83	DNQ	1997-98	3R
1983-84	DNQ	1998-99	2R
1984-85	DNQ	1999-00	DNQ
1985-86	2R	2000-01	4R

WATERLOO

THIS SEASON (2001-02) 2nd Round

OVERALL PLAYING RECORD

	P	W	D	L	F	A	Pts Diff
Home	23	16	0	7	396	364	32
Away	27	10	0	17	373	506	-133
Neutral	1	0	0	1	11	27	-16
Total	51	26	0	25	780	897	-117

TEAM RECORDS

Highest Score
57 v Dudley K 00/01

Biggest Winning Margin
31 Pts - 39-8 v Lichfield 92/93

Highest Score Against
59 v Sale 00/01

Biggest Losing Margin
47 Pts - 59-12 v Sale 00/01

SEASON BY SEASON

Season		Season	
1971-72	DNQ	1986-87	3R
1972-73	DNQ	1987-88	QF
1973-74	DNQ	1988-89	4R
1974-75	1R	1989-90	2R
1975-76	DNQ	1990-91	3R
1976-77	Runners-up	1991-92	4R
1977-78	2R	1992-93	QF
1978-79	DNQ	1993-94	4R
1979-80	1R	1994-95	5R
1980-81	4R	1995-96	4R
1981-82	4R	1996-97	5R
1982-83	DNQ	1997-98	3R
1983-84	QF	1998-99	5R
1984-85	QF	1999-00	3R
1985-86	3R	2000-01	QF

NATIONAL DIVISION
THREE SOUTH

LEAGUE TABLE

									HOME									AWAY								
														For		Against							For		Against	
	P	W	D	L	F	A	PD	Pts	W	D	L	F	A	Tries	Pens	Tries	Pens	W	D	L	F	A	Tries	Pens	Tries	Pens
Penzance & New	26	24	1	1	1158	423	735	49	13	0	0	678	152	96	21	20	6	11	1	1	480	271	64	24	32	27
Launceston	26	24	0	2	876	397	479	48	12	0	1	504	204	70	24	26	14	12	0	1	372	193	49	20	19	25
North Walsham	26	18	1	7	631	396	235	37	12	0	1	391	103	54	23	11	12	6	1	6	240	293	22	36	36	25
Westcombe Park	26	15	0	11	631	544	87	30	10	0	3	391	240	43	36	30	31	5	0	8	240	273	24	28	32	24
Old Patesians	26	15	0	11	596	683	-87	30	10	0	3	406	291	56	22	36	22	5	0	8	190	392	25	15	53	18
Lydney	26	13	0	13	513	520	-7	26	9	0	4	314	217	40	23	24	22	4	0	9	199	303	23	17	34	29
Blackheath	26	11	3	12	538	476	62	25	8	2	3	321	185	44	18	17	24	3	1	9	217	291	28	14	33	28
Redruth	26	12	0	14	629	736	-107	24	8	0	5	348	281	47	21	45	15	4	0	9	281	406	36	19	49	31
Tabard	26	10	1	15	511	710	-199	21	7	1	5	292	263	33	28	28	29	2	0	11	219	447	30	13	59	28
Barking	26	8	1	17	407	623	-216	17	6	1	6	266	290	29	29	39	18	2	0	11	141	333	16	15	42	23
Old Colfeians	26	8	1	17	554	841	-287	17	5	0	8	248	298	22	35	36	24	3	1	9	306	543	34	27	77	20
Camberley	26	8	0	18	422	629	-207	16	6	0	7	238	256	23	33	31	23	2	0	11	184	373	19	21	50	25
Clifton	26	6	0	20	469	698	-229	12	5	0	8	273	313	32	25	37	24	1	0	12	196	385	24	14	49	28
Cinderford	26	6	0	20	390	649	-259	12	5	0	8	243	239	31	15	31	16	1	0	12	147	410	17	17	55	22

Penzance & Newlyn - After just three seasons in the division The Pirates make it to National Two for the first time in their history. They dropped just three points all season but were chased all the way by Launceston. It was the backs who ran the show running in 160 tries from all parts of the pitch with 108 of those tries. Nat Saumi again proved prolific in the points scoring stakes with 374 including 91 conversions, the second highest total ever in the division. In the try-scoring department they had three players top the 20 mark for the season - a record for any side in National League rugby. Richard Newton led the way with 28 and in the process passed the 100 mark for tries in league rugby.

In most other seasons **Launceston** would have found themselves Champions but not this time as they finished a point behind Penzance & Newlyn. They did though get promotion via the play-offs where they beat Three North runners-up Dudley Kingswinford 26-0 at home. In fairness they were both times by The Pirates but those were their only losses. They had a better defensive record than the Champions but scored 300 points fewer than Champions Penzance. Centre Mark Fatialofa led the try scoring with an impressive 20 tries.

North Walsham kept up their good recent record in the division with third place, seven points clear of the chasing pack. They again showed superb form at home with 12 wins and just one defeat in their 13 matches. The only side to leave with the points were Launceston with the Champions Penzance losing their only match of the season at North Walsham. After an indifferent start to the season they got into top gear just after Christmas and won 10 out of the last 11 league matches to finish third for the third time in four seasons.

Westcombe Park had their best ever season in the division with an impressive fourth place. Derek Coates again led the way notching up a superb 326 points, second only to Penzance's Nat Saumi. He was also the club's only ever present in their league campaign. Most of the good work was done at home where they beat all the teams in the division apart from the three who finished above them in the table.

Old Patesians had an excellent fifth place in their first ever season in the division. They finished level on points with Westcombe Park but had a negative points difference. Like Westcombe Park they won 10 of their 13 home matches whilst winning five times on the road. Apart from the top two the only other side to leave with both points were Lydney early in the season with a narrow 21-15 win.

Lydney had a stabilising season after their relegation from the previous campaign and finished sixth which they would have settled for at the start of the season. They were not the heaviest of scorers and had to rely on a reasonable good defence as they won eight matches by fewer than five points. Julian Hill topped the points scorers with 117 points, the only Lydney player to top the 100 point mark for the season.

Blackheath had a more settled season finishing seventh in their second season in this division, a two place improvement on the previous season. Did well against the top two at home, they drew 17 all with Champions Penzance and lost narrowly 9-5 to runners-up Launceston. Two players topped the 100 point mark for the season, Jonathan Griffin who did the kicking early season and Chris Trace who took over the kicking mid season.

Redruth after finishing fifth the two previous seasons dropped to eighth in a disappointing season. They scored plenty of points but were found wanting defensively as the let in 736 points. Steve Larkins dominated both the try and points scoring and finished top in both with 11 tries and 217 points. Larkins topped the points scorers for a third consecutive season with his best total to date.

Tabard got inside the top 10 as they done in each of their nine seasons in the division finishing four points clear of tenth placed Barking. With no Nick Churchman and Justin Azzopardi back at Barking Micky Skinner took over the goal kicking responsibilities and ended the season with 203 points, the fifth best total in the division. Skinner along with Barney Lockwood were the sides only ever presents.

Barking had not finished outside the top six in the division in their seven-year stay until last season when they finished a very disappointing 10th. They started the season with four wins from six matches before the rot started after that they managed just four more wins all season. They ended the season with seven straight defeats and were just a point ahead of third bottom Camberley. Justin Azzopardi returned to the club and ended the season as the leading points scorer with 105 whilst Droston McDonald topped the try scoring with 11.

Old Colfeians survived their first season of National League rugby thanks to a three-match winning run in their final matches of the season. They looked in a dangerous position but away wins at Camberley and Cinderford and a home win against Redruth was enough to survive for another season. Matthew Townsend make a huge contribution to their season with 248 points, the third highest total in the division.

Camberley survived for another season after Launceston beat Dudley Kingswinford in the play-off for the right to go into National Two. That meant that only two sides were relegated from National Three South and Whitchurch suffered as a consequence with an extra side going down in Three North. Camberley have now finished in 12th place in their last three seasons of League rugby.

Clifton, drop back into South West One after a five-season stay in the division since dropping to this level back in 1996-97. With three straight wins against Tabard, Lydney and North Walsham at the turn of the year they seemed to have found some form but after that they went on a dreadful run. They lost 10 consecutive matches before beating Barking on the final day of the season but by then they were seven points away from safety. Winger Chris Randall did have a good season running in 13 tries whilst John Barnes topped the scoring with 126 points.

Cinderford could not survive their first season of National League rugby and ended the season four points off safety. They were the lowest scorers in the division with just 390 points but did not do to badly defensively. They conceded 649 points a figure which was exceeded by five teams above them. They were always looking like being relegated. They managed just one away win all season when they were 15-0 winners at Barking in January.

2001-2002 RECORD REVIEW
(Individual Records)

MOST POINTS - IN A SEASON

Fijian Nat Saumi moved into second placce on the Divisions all time list after scoring 374 points for Penzance & Newlyn as they took the National Three South title. Also moving into the top five is the Westcombe Park full back Derek Coates who became the fourth player to reach 300 points in a season in the division.

EVOLUTION OF RECORD

69	John Field	Askeans	1987-88
83	Simon Harvey	Clifton	1989-90
122	Melvin Badger	Weston-s-Mare	1990-91
129	Pete Russell	Havant	1991-92
133	Phil Belshaw	Reading	1993-94
176	Richard Perkins	Henley	1995-96
391	Nick Grecian	Newbury	1996-97

ALL-TIME RECORDS

391	Nick Grecian	Newbury	1996-97
374	Nat Saumi	Penzance & New	2001-02
351	Jon Gregory	Esher	1999-00
336	Nat Saumi	Penzance & New	2000-01
326	Derek Coates	Westcombe Park	2001-02
313	Jonathan Gregory	Esher	1998-99
288	Danny Sloman	Launceston	2000-01
264	Nick Churchman	Tabard	1996-97
260	Chris Atkinson	Plymouth	1999-00
256	Rob Thirlby	Redruth	1997-98
255	Tom Barlow	Plymouth	2000-01
253	James Shanahan	N Walsham	1997-98
248	Nick Thomson	Barking	1996-97
248	Matthew Townsend	Old Colfeians	2001-02

MOST TRIES - IN A SEASON

Penzance & Newlyn utility back Victor Olonga topped the 20 mark for the third successive season - the first man to achieve this in the history of National League rugby. He did though have to settle for secon spot in the try scorers list behind his team mate Richard Newton whfo holds the top two marks for the division. In all the Pirates had three players score 20 tries in a season - which was also a National League record.

EVOLUTION OF RECORD

7	John Willis	Redruth	1988-89
8	Melvin Badger	Weston-s-Mare	1990-91
9	Will Knight	Havant	1991-92
12	Steve Titcombe	Sudbury	1992-93
27	Brian Johnson	Newbury	1996-97
38	Richard Newton	Penzance & New	1999-00

ALL-TIME RECORDS

38	Richard Newton	Penzance & New	1999-00
28	Richard Newton	Penzance & New	2001-02
27	Brian Johnson	Newbury	1996-97
25	Craig Davies	Newbury	1996-97
24	Victor Olonga	Penzance & New	1999-00
23	Victor Olonga	Penzance & New	2001-02
23	Laka Waqanivere	Penzance & New	2001-02
21	James Shanahan	North Walsham	1999-00
20	Victor Olonga	Penzance & New	2000-01
20	Dan Ward-Smith	Plymouth	2000-01
20	Mark Fatialofa	Launceston	2001-02
19	Tom Holloway	Newbury	1996-97
17	Robert Thirlby	Redruth	1997-98
17	Nat Saumi	Penzance & Newlyn	2000-01
17	Peter Redgrave	Penzance & Newlyn	2000-01
17	Mark Richards	Penzance & New	2001-02

MOST PENALTIES - IN A SEASON

Westcombe Park full back Derek Coates set a new record for penaltioes in a season with 64 which helped Park to their best ever finish in National League rugby. Also breaking the old record was the Old Colfeians back Matthew Townsend with 60 which helped his side avoid going straight back down to London One.

EVOLUTION OF RECORD

13	John Field	Askeans	1987-8
15	Simon Harvey	Clifton	1989-9
27	Rob Ashworth	Havant	1990-9
34	Phil Belshaw	Reading	1993-9
53	Nick Churchman	Tabard	1996-9
58	Jon Gregory	Esher	1998-9
59	Chris Atkinson	Plymouth	1999-0
64	Derek Coates	Westcombe Park	2001-0

ALL-TIME RECORDS

64	Derek Coates	Westcombe Park	2001-0
60	Matthew Townsend	Old Colfeians	2001-0
59	Chris Atkinson	Plymouth	1999-0
58	Jon Gregory	Esher	1998-9
53	Nick Churchman	Tabard	1996-9
53	Neil Coleman	Weston	1999-0
51	James Shanahan	N Walsham	1997-9
50	Nick Edmonds	Bridgwater & A	1997-9
50	Jon Gregory	Esher	1999-0
49	Derek Coates	Westcombe Park	1999-0
46	Derek Coates	Westcombe Park	2000-0

MOST CONVERSIONS - IN A SEASON

Nat Saumi now holds the second and fourth best returns for a National Three South season. He was within sight of Nick Grecians all time record but fell nine short in the end.

EVOLUTION OF RECORD

9	John Field	Askeans	1987-88
10	Simon Harvey	Clifton	1989-90
16	Simon Blake	Redruth	1990-91
23	Pete Russelll	Havant	1991-92
28	Mike Hamlin	London Welsh	1992-93
100	Nick Grecian	Newbury	1996-97

ALL-TIME RECORDS

100	Nick Grecian	Newbury	1996-97
91	Nat Saumi	Penzance & Newlyn	2001-02
78	Jon Gregory	Esher	1999-00
67	Nat Saumi	Penzance & Newlyn	2000-01
59	Danny Sloman	Launceston	2000-01
55	Nat Saumi	Penzance & New	1999-00
52	Jon Gregory	Esher	1998-99
52	Derek Coates	Westcombe Park	2001-02
48	Robert Thirlby	Redruth	1997-98
46	Steve Larkins	Redruth	2000-01
45	Barend Vorster	Launceston	2001-02
42	Tom Barlow	Plymouth Albion	2000-01
39	Carson Russell	Bracknell	1998-99
38	Nick Thomson	Barking	1996-97

MOST DROP GOALS - IN A SEASON

No movement here with the best for the season was four by the Lydeny outside half Neil Merrett.

EVOLUTION OF RECORD

2	Andy Perry	Havant	1987-88
	Andy Perry	Havant	1988-89
6	Simon Harvey	Clifton	1989-90
10	Simon Cattermole	Weston-s-Mare	1996-97
11	Nick Edmonds	Bridgwater & Alb.	1997-98

ALL-TIME RECORDS

11	Nick Edmonds	Bridgwater & Alb.	1997-98
10	Simon Cattermole	Weston-s-Mare	1996-97
7	Bede Brown	Redruth	2000-01
6	Simon Harvey	Clifton	1989-90
6	James Shanahan	N Walsham	1997-98
6	Stewart Whitworth	Redruth	1999-00

2001-02

NATIONAL THREE SOUTH

MOST POINTS

POINTS			T	C	P	DG
374	Nat Saumi	Penzance & New	15	91	39	-
326	Derek Coates	Westcombe Park	6	52	64	-
248	Matthew Townsend	Old Colfeians	-	34	60	-
217	Steve Larkins	Redruth	11	33	32	-
203	Micky Skinner	Tabard	2	35	41	-
191	Barend Vorster	Launceston	16	45	7	-
176	Danny Sloman	Launceston	5	23	35	-
140	Richard Newton	Penzance & New	28	-	-	-
126	John Barnes	Clifton	-	21	26	2
125	Len Wilmott	N Walsham	3	19	24	-
125	Mark Roberts	Cinderford	-	16	29	2
121	Chris Trace	Blackheath	12	17	9	-
118	Victor Olonga	Penzance & New	23	-	-	1
117	Julian Hill	Lydney	7	17	16	-
115	Laka Waqanivere	Penzance & New	23	-	-	-
111	Jomathan Griffin	Blackheath	3	18	18	2
107	Russell Nunn	Old Patesians	3	16	20	-
105	Justin Azzopardi	Camberley	1	8	26	2

MOST TRIES

28	Richard Newton	Penzance & New
23	Victor Olonga	Penzance & New
23	Laka Waqanivere	Penzance & New
17	Marc Richards	Penzance & New
16	Berend Vorster	Launceston
16	Andy Thorpe	N Walsham
15	Nat Saumi	Penzance & New
13	Chris Randall	Clifton
13	Will Morgan	
12	Chris Trace	Blackheath
12	Charles Abban	Blackheath
11	Droston McDonald	Barking
11	Steve Larkins	Redruth
11	Ben Thomas	Old Patesians

MOST CONVERSIONS

91	Nat Saumi	Penzance & New
52	Derek Coates	Westcombe Park
45	Berend Vorster	Launceston
35	Micky Skinner	Tabard
34	Matthew Townsend	Old Colfeians
33	Steve Larkins	Redruth
23	Danny Sloman	Launceston
22	Scott Pollock	Old Patesians
21	John Barnes	Clifton
19	Steve Evans	Penzance & New
19	Len Wilmott	N Walsham
18	Jonathan Griffin	Blackheath
17	Chris Trace	Blackheath
17	Julian Hill	Lydney

MOST PENALTIES

64	Derek Coates	Westcombe Park
60	Matthew Townsend	Old Colfeians
41	Micky Skinner	Tabard
39	Nat Saumi	Penzance & New
35	Danny Sloman	Launceston
32	Steve Larkins	Redruth
29	Mark Roberts	Cinderford
28	Rob Smart	Camberley
26	John Barnes	Clifton
26	Justin Azzopardi	Barking
24	Len Wilmott	N Walsham
20	Russell Nunn	Old Patesians
18	Jonathan Griffin	Blackheath
18	Phil Friel	N Walsham
17	John Dwight	N Walsham

MOST DROP GOALS

4	Neil Merrett	Lydney
2	John Barnes	Clifton
2	Mark Roberts	Cinderford
2	Jonathan Griffin	Blackheath
2	Justin Azzopardi	Barking
1	Victor Olonga	Penzance & New
1	Andy Birkett	Launceston

NATIONAL DIVISION 3 SOUTH

FIXTURES 2002-2003

Away Teams

	HOME TEAMS	Barking	Basingstoke	Blackheath	Camberley	Havant	Lydney	North Walsham	Old Colfeians	Old Patesians	Redruth	Rosslyn Park	Tabard	Westcombe Park	Weston super Mare	
1	Barking	XXX	19-10	07-09	04-01	16-11	28-09	12-04	25-01	08-02	01-03	30-11	15-03	02-11	14-12	1
	Basingstoke	09-11	XXX	18-01	26-10	12-04	04-01	01-02	23-11	07-12	12-10	15-03	14-12	14-09	22-02	2
3	Blackheath	07-12	01-03	XXX	14-09	25-01	02-11	23-11	21-12	11-01	14-12	08-02	19-10	29-03	12-10	3
	Camberley	29-03	08-02	30-11	XXX	19-10	16-11	14-12	01-03	02-11	11-01	28-09	12-04	25-01	07-09	4
5	Havant	12-10	21-12	22-02	09-11	XXX	15-03	26-10	14-09	31-08	23-11	18-01	04-01	07-12	01-02	5
	Lydney	23-11	29-03	01-02	12-10	11-01	XXX	09-11	07-09	21-12	14-09	22-02	18-01	31-08	26-10	6
7	North Walsham	21-12	02-11	28-09	31-08	08-02	19-10	XXX	11-01	25-01	29-03	16-11	07-09	01-03	30-11	7
	Old Colfeians	22-02	28-09	12-04	18-01	30-11	07-12	15-03	XXX	16-11	01-02	14-12	26-10	19-10	04-01	8
9	Old Patesians	26-10	07-09	15-03	01-02	14-12	12-04	22-02	12-10	XXX	09-11	29-03	30-11	23-11	18-01	9
	Redruth	18-01	16-11	14-12	15-03	28-09	30-11	04-01	02-11	19-10	XXX	07-09	22-02	08-02	08-02	10
11	Rosslyn Park	14-09	11-01	31-08	23-11	01-03	25-01	12-10	31-08	04-01	07-12	XXX	01-02	21-12	09-11	11
	Tabard	11-01	31-08	09-11	21-12	29-03	01-03	07-12	08-02	14-09	25-01	02-11	XXX	12-10	23-11	12
13	Westcombe Park	01-02	30-11	04-01	22-02	07-09	14-12	18-01	09-11	28-09	26-10	12-04	16-11	XXX	15-03	13
	Weston super Mare	31-08	25-01	16-11	07-12	02-11	08-02	14-09	29-03	01-03	21-12	19-10	28-09	11-01	XXX	14

BARKING RUFC

President	Gerald Mansfield	Bob Guy 45 Wallers Close, Dagenham, Essex 020 8984 9162
Club Secretary	Jim Marner	Meadow View, Kirkham Road, Horndon-on-the-hill, Essex SS17 8QE 01708 858136 (B) 01268 490550 (H) 07957 328363 (M) 01708 858660 (F)
Treasurer	Debbie Weekes	Meadow View, Kirkham Road, Horndon-on-the-hill, Essex SS17 8QE 0207 650 2301 (B) 01268 490550 (H) 07957 328363 (M)
Press Officer	Martin Dutt	70 Netherfield Gardens, Barking, Essex IG11 9TN 020 8507 7308 (H&Fax) 07703 486375 (M) email: scoop@dutt.co.uk
1st XV Manager	Mark Diable	Highview, 21 Hillside Rd., Billericay, Essex CM11 2DA 01277 657069 (H) 07764 182226 (M) email: mark.diable@ubsw.com
Director of Rugby	Dean Cutting	0208 502 6398 (H) 07939 155380 (M)
Coaching Staff	Mike Lovett, Eric Williams, Lee Stannard, Gary Cutting, Fred Lewis	

The 2001/2002 season was an annus horribilis for Barking from the points of view of injuries and it ended with their lowest ever finish in this league in tenth place – and at times there were relegation fears being freely expressed around the club.

The loss of vital players such as skipper Fred Lewis, vice-captain Paul Everitt, scrum half Andy Eaton, hooker Justin Murphy and second row James Bailey for most or all of the season, coupled with less serious injuries to other players at various stages of the campaign meant that the club were in the end grateful for the good start they made, as that provided the necessary cushion against the bad times later in the season.
Even the coaching staff were not exempt as Mike Lovett spent several weeks in hospital during the course of the season.

To make up for the poor league season though the club did manage a first ever triumph in the Basildon Bond Eastern Counties Cup, beating league rivals North Walsham 20-16 in a thrilling final at Barking – and this after losing both league games against the Norfolk side.
The injury jinx though even raised its head at the final, with Fred Lewis, having returned after suffering a detached retina, being stretchered off with a neck injury.

Fortunately he returned from hospital that same evening, but then announced his retirement from the game and will now become the club's fitness coach.

Of the individual successes last season, wingers Drostan McDonald and Scott Gregory scored 30 tries between them in all games, hooker turned flanker Francis Ambrose raced in for seven tries and second row/back row Macer Twydell collected the Player of the Year Award.

Now, with most of the long-term injury problems resolved, Barking are looking forward with relish to the new season.

BARKING

Comp.	Date	H/A	Opponents	Result & Score	Att	15	14	13	12	11
N3 S	01-09	A	Tabard	W 21-14		Green/t	McDonald	Stannard	Wyatt	Osunsami
N3 S	08-09	H	Old Patesians	W 30-11		Green	McDonald	Wyatt	Mahoney/t	Gregory/t
N3 S	22-09	A	Penzance & Newlyn	L 10-54	950	Williams	Gregory	Wyatt	Mahoney	McDonald/t
N3 S	06-10	H	Launceston	L 19-27		Green	Gregory	Wyatt	Mahoney	McDonald/t
N3 S	20-10	A	Old Colfeians	W 32-12		Green	McDonald	Stannard	Mahoney	Hill/t
N3 S	27-10	H	Camberley	W 28-27		Green	McDonald	Stannard/t	Mahoney/t	Hill
N3 S	03-11	A	Cinderford	L 0-8		Green	Martin	Stannard	Mahoney	Hill
N3 S	10-11	H	Redruth	W 35-31		Green/t	Gregory/t	Wyatt/t	Mahoney	Osunsami
N3 S	17-11	A	Westcombe Park	L 5-28	250	Green	Gregory/t	Stannard	Mahoney	Osunsami
N3 S	24-11	H	North Walsham	L 12-20		Leverington/t	Gregory	Wyatt/t	Mahoney	Osunsami
N3 S	01-12	H	Tabard	L 13-16		Leverington	Gregory/2t	Wyatt	Mahoney	McDonald
N3 S	08-12	H	Clifton	W 35-30		Leverington	Gregory/t	Wyatt/t	Mahoney	McDonald/t
N3 S	15-12	A	Lydney	L 3-15	326	Green	Hill	Wyatt	Green	Osunsami
N3 S	22-12	H	Blackheath	D 19-19	300	Green	McDonald	Leverington	Mahoney	Hill
N3 S	12-01	H	Westcombe Park	W 23-21		Green	McDonald/t	Wyatt	Mahoney	Gregory
N3 S	19-01	A	Redruth	L 3-27	700	Green	McDonald	Wyatt	Mahoney	Hill
N3 S	26-01	H	Cinderford	L 0-15		Green	Gregory	Wyatt	Mahoney	McDonald
N3 S	02-02	A	Camberley	L 15-23	150	Green/t	Gregory	Lewis	Wyatt	McDonald/t
N3 S	09-02	H	Old Colfeians	W 29-19	300	Green	Gregory	Wyatt	Green(c/t)	McDonald/3t
N3 S	16-02	A	North Walsham	L 6-17		Lewis	Green	Wyatt	Green	McDonald
N3 S	23-02	A	Launceston	L 7-74		Green	Gregory	Wyatt	Green	Riches
N3 S	09-03	H	Penzance & Newlyn	L 10-37		Green	Gregory	Mahoney/tcp	Bradley	Riches
N3 S	16-03	A	Old Patesians	L 12-28	300	Lewis	Gregory	Mahoney/c	Bradley/t	McDonald/t
N3 S	30-03	A	Blackheath*	L 16-19	350	Azzopardi/c3p	Gregory	Lewis	Mahoney	McDonald
N3 S	06-04	H	Lydney	L 13-17		Azzopardi/c2p	Hill	Stannard	Mahoney	McDonald/t
N3 S	13-04	A	Clifton	L 11-14		Lewis	Gregory	Stannard	Mahoney	McDonald/t
PGC	15-09	N	Old Patesians	W 26-11		Green	Gregory/2t	Gilmore	Mahoney	Martin
PGC	29-09	H	Old Colfeians	W 27-18		Williams	Gregory	Wyatt	Mahoney	McDonald/2t

** after opponents name indicates a penalty try. Brackets after a player's name indicates he was replaced. eg (a) means he was replaced by replacement code "a" and so on. / after a player or replacement name is followed by any scores he made - eg /t, /c, /p, /dg or any combination of these*

EVER PRESENT None

Most Appearances:
25: Macer Twydell.
24: Pete Mahoney (1), Bradley Stone.
23: Lee Stannard.

PLAYERS USED

43 plus four as replacement only.

MOST POINTS

Pts	Player	T	C	P	DG
105	J Azzopardi	1	8	26	2
55	D Gilmore	-	8	13	-
55	D McDonald	11	-	-	-
37	P Mahoney	3	5	4	-
30	S Gregory	6	-	-	-

MATCH FACTS

10	9	1	2	3	4	5	6	7	8
Azzopardi/c3p	Eaton	Walker	Ambrose/t	Ward	Stone	Twydell	Everitt	Clay	Stannard
Azzopardi	Eaton/cp	Walker	Ambrose/2t	Ward	Twydell/t	Tucker	Martin	Clay	Stannard
Azzopardi/cp	Eaton	Walker	Ambrose	Ward	Twydell	Stone	Martin	Jenkins	Stannard
Azzopardi/2pdg	Eaton	Walker	Ambrose	Rate	Tucker	Twydell	Martin	Clay	Stannard(a/t
Gilmore/3c2p	Eaton/t	Walker	Murphy(b/t)	Ward	Twydell/t	Stone	Martin	Jenkins	Clay
Gilmore/2c3p	Eaton	Usher/t	Ambrose	Walker	Twydell	Stone	Martin	Jenkins	Stannard
Gilmore	Cutting	Walker	Ambrose	Ward	Tucker	Stone	Martin	Jenkins	Stannard
Gilmore/c6p	Cutting	Usher	Bowyer	Walker	Tucker	Stone	Twydell	Jenkins	Stannard
Gilmore	Cutting	Walker	Bowyer	Ward	Twydell	Stone	Martin	Jenkins	Stannard
Gilmore/c	Cutting	Walker	Ambrose	Ward	Tucker	Stone	Twydell	Leonard	Stannard
Gilmore/p	Cutting	Usher	Griffiths	Walker	Tucker	Stone	Twydell	Leonard	Martin
Azzopardi/3c3p	Riches/t	Walker	Bowyer	Ward	Tucker	Stone	Twydell	Leonard	Stannard
Azzopardi/p	Riches	Usher	Ambrose	Walker	Twydell	Stone	Knowles	Leonard	Stannard
Azzopardi/tc3pdg	Riches	Usher	Ambrose	Walker	Twydell	Stone	Batho	Leonard	Stannard
Azzopardi/6p	Riches	Usher	Ambrose	Walker	Tucker	Stone	Twydell	Leonard	Stannard
Azzopardi	Gilmore/p	Usher	Ambrose	Walker	Tucker	Stone	Twydell	Knowles	Stannard
Gilmore	Riches	Halsey	Bowles	Rate	Tucker	Stone	Twydell	Leonard	Stannard
Mahoney	Gilmore	Ambrose/t	Ambrose	Ward	Twydell	Stone	Batho	Leonard	Stannard
Mahoney/3cp	Gilmore	Ambrose	Ambrose	Ward	Twydell	Stone	Jenkins	Leonard	Stannard
Mahoney/2p	Gilmore	Walker	Smith	Ward	Twydell	Stone	Batho	Ambrose	Stannard
Gilmore/c	Mahoney	Ambrose	Ambrose	Ward	Twydell	Stone	Batho	Leonard	Stannard/t
Diable	Cutting	Ambrose	Bowles	Ward	Twydell	Stone	Batho	Ambrose	Stannard
Diable	Cutting	Usher	Bowles	Ambrose	Twydell	Tucker	Batho	Ambrose	Stone
Diable	Cutting	Usher	Bowles	Ambrose	Twydell	Stone	Batho	Ambrose	Stannard
Diable	Cutting	Usher	Bowyer	Ambrose	Twydell	Stone	Batho	Ambrose	Stannard
Azzopardi/2p	Riches	Usher	Bowyer	Rate	Twydell	Tucker	Stone	Batho	Stannard
Azzopardi/tc3p	Eaton	Usher	Murphy	Walker	Twydell	Stone	Bury	Martin	Stannard
Azzopardi/cp(d/c)	Eaton	Usher	Murphy/t	Ward/t	Tucker	Stone	Martin	Clay	Stannard

REPLACEMENTS: a - Banrey Bury. b - Francis Ambrose. c - Glen Stannard. d - Dave Gilmore.

WHERE	Total	Home	Away
The POINTS were scored	407	266	141
The POINTS were conceded	623	333	290
The TRIES were scored	45	29	16
The TRIES were conceded	81	42	39

HOW the TRIES were scored

Total	Backs	Forwards	F Back	Wing	Centre	H Back	F Row	Lock	B Row	Pen. Try
45	34	10	4	18	9	3	6	2	2	1

HOW the TRIES were conceded

Total	Backs	Forwards	F Back	Wing	Centre	H Back	F Row	Lock	B Row	Pen. Try
81	58	23	7	19	19	13	7	1	15	-

BARKING

LEAGUE STATISTICS *compiled by Stephen McCormack*

SEASON	Division	P	W	D	L	F	A	Pts Diff	Lge Pts	Lge Pos		Coach		Captain
92-93	Lon 1	12	6	1	5	183	171	12	13	7				
93-94	Lon 1	12	10	1	1	290	149	141	21	1p				
94-95	D5S	12	7	0	5	223	190	33	14	5		M Lovett		D Cutting
												Most Points		**Most Tries**
95-96	D5S	12	8	0	4	243	187	56	16	4	51	Lee Evans	6	P Green, C Tate, D Cutting
96-97	D4S	26	16	1	9	740	496	244	33	3	248	Nick Thompson	14	Chris Tate, N Thomson
97-98	N2S	26	19	0	7	762	450	312	38	3	69	Andy Tunningley	12	J Murphy, P Goodey
98-99	N2S	26	19	1	6	644	327	317	39	4	217	Justin Azzopardi	11	Scott Gregory
99-00	N2S	26	15	0	11	628	523	105	23	6	88	Justin Azzopardi	13	Scott Gregory
00-01	N3S	26	15	1	10	611	481	130	31	4	192	Billy Murphy	15	Fred Lewis
01-02	N3S	26	8	1	17	407	623	-216	17	10	105	Justin Azzopardi	11	Droston McDonald

FACT FILE

Founded: 1930 **Colours:** Cardinal and grey **Change colours:** Blue

GROUND

Address: Goresbrook, Gale St., Dagenham, Essex RM9 4TY

Tel: 0208 595 7324 **Website:** www.barkingrugby.com

Capacity: 2,000 - all uncovered standing

Directions: From Dartford Tunnel, follow A13 (London bound). Past the Ford works, continue for 2 miles to 2nd r'about (beneath a flyover). 4th exit and return back on A13 in opposite direction. The ground is half a mile on the left hand side.

From M11 - At end of M11 take A406 EAST bound towards the A13. Onto A13, signposted Dartford Tunnel, and ground is 4 miles on the left.

Nearest Railway Station:
Becontree (District Line - Upminster direction).
Turn right on leaving the station into Gale Street.
The ground is 1 mile on the left.

Car Parking: 200 spaces available at ground

Admission: Season Tickets (members only) £30.
Matchday (incl. programme):
Members £3 Non-members: £5.00

Clubhouse: Normal Licensing hours, snacks available.
Functions: Capacity 120.

Training Nights: Tuesdays & Thursday (seniors).
Juniors: Monday & Wednesday

PROGRAMME Size: A5 Price: With admission
Pages: 22 plus cover
Editor: Martin Dutt - Press Officer
Advertising Rates - Colour only
Full Page £250
Half Page £150

BASINGSTOKE RFC

President:	John Evans, CBE, TD.	Meadow View, Green Lane, Ellisfield, RG25 2QP 01256 381470 (H)
Chairman:	Dr Stephen Tristram	5 Paddock View, Old Basing, Basingstoke RG24 0DB 01256 328327 (H) 07770 227312
Secretary:	David Crabbe	126 Pack Lane, Kempshott, Basingstoke RG22 5HP, 01256 465085
Treasurer:	Peter Allen	155 Pack Lane, Kempshott, Basingstoke, RG22 5HP 01256 811466 (H)
Fixture Sec:	Arthur Hardy	12 Meon Road, Oakley, Basingstoke RG23 7AL 01256 782058 (H) 07711 971299 (M)
Chairman of Playing:	John Byett	42 Byfleet Avenue, Old Basing, Basingstoke RG24 7HR 01256 323313 (H) 07747 018706 (M)
Director of Rugby	Ian Calder	c/o Basingstoke RFC 07903 685233 (M)

Community Development Officer: Jon Cant, c/o Basingstoke RFC 07811 338122 (M)

After relegation from the National League 3 South, the season in London 1 was looked on with nervous ambition.

A new Director of Rugby, Ian Calder, a New Zealander with experience in South Africa and Ireland, was taken on from Worcester and with the addition of overseas players, Chris Norton and Ash Riley, it was hoped that Basingstoke could challenge to go back up.

The first round exit from the Senior Cup at Marlow did nothing to calm the nerves. An awful draw away to newly promoted Cheshunt added to this growing gloom, but the side was getting to know each other and this started to show with wins at home over Cambridge and Harlow.

The first real test of the season was away to Havant, one of the pre-season favourites for promotion. A defeat (16-17) was masked by a last minute conversion hitting the post which would have brought victory.

The next five league games, two won, two lost and a draw, did not help the confidence. But after the last loss at home to Sutton & Epsom (12-20), it was the start of a remarkable run of 18 matches, with only one defeat, culminating in a victory over Ding's Crusaders from South West 1 (29-13) to secure the second promotion place back into the Nationals. We also retained the Hampshire Caffrey's Cup for a third successive season with defeat of arch rivals Havant.

The team under the captaincy of Richard Baker and direction of Ian Calder at outside half played adventurous rugby which resulted in 22 tries for Chris Norton and Ian Calder with 335 points was the top points scorer in London 1. The Youth section of the Club goes from strength to strength and has also enjoyed a very successful season. There was another milestone for Basingstoke RFC last season, the women's team was founded. 'The Sirens' played a number of friendly matches with some good results and will be playing league rugby in the coming season.

BASINGSTOKE

Comp.	Date	H/A	Opponents	Result & Score	15	14	13	12	11
L1	08-09	A	Cheshunt	D 16-16	Dangerfield	Joseph	G Jones	N Taylor	Norton
L1	15-09	H	Cambridge	W 69-14	Norton	G Jones/2t	J Rees	N Taylor/t	Dangerfield/4
L1	22-09	H	Harlow	W 33-12	Norton/t	Joseph/t	G Jones	N Taylor	Dangerfield
L1	29-09	A	Havant	L 16-17	Norton/2t	G Jones	J Rees	N Taylor	Dangerfield
L1	06-10	H	Haywards Heath	W 33-24	Norton/t	G Jones/2t	J Rees	N Taylor/t	Dangerfield
L1	20-10	A	London Nigerians	L 22-30	G Jones/t	Palmer	J Rees	N Taylor	Holmes
L1	27-10	H	Norwich	W 39-25	Norton	G Jones	J Rees/2t	N Taylor/t	Holmes
L1	10-11	A	Staines	D 13-13	G Jones	Joseph	J Rees/t	N Taylor	Holmes
L1	24-11	H	Sutton	L 12-22	Calder/c	G Jones	J Rees/2t	N Taylor	Holmes
L1	01-12	A	Thanet Wanderers	W 45-33	Norton/2t	G Jones/2t	J Rees	N Taylor	Holmes/t
L1	08-12	H	Winchester	W 22-7	Norton	G Jones/t	J Rees/t	N Taylor	Holmes
L1	22-12	A	Sutton	W 28-12	Norton	G Jones	J Rees	N Taylor	Holmes
L1	05-01	H	Staines	W 41-8	Norton/2t	G Jones/t	J Rees	N Taylor/t	Joseph
L1	12-01	A	Norwich	W 13-7	Norton	G Jones/t	J Rees	N Taylor	Joseph/t
L1	26-01	H	London Nigerians	W 21-8	Norton	Joseph	J Rees/t	G Jones	Holmes/t
L1	02-02	A	Haywards Heath	W 27-19	Norton/t	Joseph	J Rees	N Taylor	G Jones
L1	09-02	H	Havant	W 25-8	Norton	Joseph	J Rees	N Taylor	G Jones/2tdg
L1	23-02	A	Harlow	W 26-24	Norton/2t	Holmes	J Rees	N Taylor/t	G Jones
L1	09-03	H	Cheshunt	W 60-9	Norton	Joseph	J Rees/2t	N Taylor/t	G Jones
L1	16-03	A	Cambridge	L 6-13	D Jones	Joseph	J Rees	G Jones	Holmes
L1	06-04	A	Winchester	W 47-3	D Jones	Joseph/t	J Rees/2t	N Taylor/3t	G Jones
L1	13-04	H	Thanet Wanderers	W 39-20	Norton/3t	Joseph	J Rees	N Taylor/t	G Jones/t
P off	27-04	H	Ding's Crusaders	W 29-14	Norton	Holmes	J Rees/t	N Taylor	G Jones

** after opponents name indicates a penalty try. Brackets after a player's name indicates he was replaced. eg (a) means he was replaced by replacement code "a" and so on. / after a player or replacement name is followed by any scores he made - eg /t, /c, /p, /dg or any combination of these*

EVER PRESENT Richard Baker, Gary Jones.

Most Appearances:
22: Richard Baker, Gary Jones.
21: Neil Young, Ian Calder.
20: Neal Taylor J Rees.

MOST POINTS

Pts	Player	T	C	P	DG
252	I Calder	7	59	33	-
65	Norton	13	-	-	-
63	G Jones	12	-	-	1
55	J Rees	11	-	-	-

MATCH FACTS

10	9	1	2	3	4	5	6	7	8
Calder/c3p	S Taylor/t	Young	Bushnell	Wanoa	Hopkins	Hooker	Baker	Lovegrove	Della-Savina
Calder/t8cp	S Taylor	Young	Lovegrove	Wanoa	Hopkins	Drawbridge/t	Baker/t	Appleby	Della-Savina
Calder/2c3p	S Taylor	Young	Riley	Buttle	Hooker	Drawbridge	Baker	Appleby/2t	Hopkins
Calder/2p	S Taylor	White	Riley	Young	Hooker	Drawbridge	Baker	Appleby	Hopkins
Calder/2c3p	S Taylor	Young	Riley	Buttle	Hopkins	Wilson	Baker	Appleby	Reeve
Calder/2cp	S Taylor	Young	Riley	Buttle	Hopkins	Drawbridge	Baker/t	Appleby/t	Lovegrove
Calder/2t4c2p	S Taylor	Young	Riley	Buttle	Hopkins	Drawbridge	Baker	Reeve	Hopkins
Calder/c2p	S Taylor	Young	Riley	Buttle	Wilson	Drawbridge	Baker	Reeve	Hopkins
Paynter	S Taylor	Young	Riley	Buttle	Wilson	Drawbridge	Baker	Reeve	Hopkins
Calder/4c4p	Dean	Young	Riley	Collins	Hooker	Drawbridge	Baker	Wilson	Hopkins
Calder/2cp	Dean/t	Young	Riley	Collins	Hooker	Drawbridge	Baker	Wilson	Reeve
Calder/t4c	S Taylor/t	Young	Evans	Collins	Hooker	Drawbridge	Baker/t	D-Savina	Reeve/t
Calder/4cp	Dean	Young	Riley	Collins	Hooker	Wilson	Baker/t	D-Savina/t	Reeve
D Jones/p	Dean	Young	Riley	Collins	Hooker	Drawbridge	Baker	D-Savina	Wilson
Calder/3c	Dean	Young	Riley	Collins	Hooker	Drawbridge/t	Baker	D-Savina	Wilson
Calder/2cp	Dean	Young	Riley(a/t)	Collins	Hooker	Drawbridge/t	Baker	Reeve	Wilson/t
Calder/t2cp	Dean	Young	Riley	Collins	Hooker	Drawbridge	Baker	D-Savina	Reeve
Calder/3c	Dean	Young	Evans	Collins	Hooker	Drawbridge	Baker/t	Reeve	Wilson
Calder/2t5c5p	S Taylor	Young	Evans	Collins	Wilson	Drawbridge	Baker	D-Savina/t	Appleby/t
Calder/2p	Baker	Young	Riley	Collins	Wilson	Drawbridge	Reeve	D-Savina	Appleby
Calder/6c	Dean	Young	Evans	Colins	Hooker	Drawbridge	Reeve/t	D-Savina	Baker
Calder/3cp	Dean/t	Young	Evans	Collins	Hooker	Drawbridge	Reeve	D-Savina	Baker
Calder/2t3cp	Dean	Young	Riley	Collins	Hooker	Chapman	Reeve	D-Savina	Baker

REPLACEMENTS: a - Evans.

2001-02 Highlights

Won the Hasmpshire Cup

Won promotion back to National Three South at the first attempt

Ian Calder topped the points scoring list win an impressive 252 points.
In the home win against Cheshunt he scored 35 points, his best return of the season.

Only team to win at Bassingstoke was Sutton.

BASINGSTOKE

LEAGUE STATISTICS *compiled by Stephen McCormack*

SEASON	Division	P	W	D	L	F	A	Pts Diff	Lge Pts	Lge Pos	Most Points		Most Tries	
92-93	D4S	12	7	0	5	194	145	47	14	5	208	Richard Rowledge	15	B Mercer
93-94	D5S	12	5	0	7	191	210	-19	10	11	220	Richard Rowledge	10	Simon Denning
94-95	D5S	12	2	0	10	122	181	-59	4	13r				
95-96	Lon 1	12	3	1	8	179	210	-31	7	11				
96-97	Lon 1	13	7	1	5	237	246	-9	15	5				
97-98	Lon 1	16	11	2	3	413	271	142	24	3				
98-99	Lon 1	16	8	0	8	423	280	143	16	8				
99-00	Lon 1	16	14	0	2	660	147	513	28	1	342	Matt Hart	7	Denville Elliston
00-01	N3S	26	7	1	18	333	686	-353	15	13	66	Matt Hart	4	Phil Della-Savina
01-02	L1	22	16	2	4	648	342	306	34	2	335	Ian Calder	22	Chris Norton

FACT FILE

Founded: 1948

Colours: Blue / amber (white) shirts, blue shorts
Change colours: White with blue & yellow hoops

Web site: www.basingstokerfc.com

GROUND:

Address: Down Grange, Pack Lane, Kempshott, Basingstoke RG22 5HH
Tel: 01256 323308 Fax: 01256 814390 e-mail: basingstokerfc@btinternet.com
Capacity: 2,000 approx 150 Covered Seats

Directions: M3 J7 Head towards town, turn left at 2nd r'bout (1st Sainsburys 2nd Kempshott) into Heather Way, right at junction (Kempshott Lane) and right at lights into Pack Lane. 250 yards on right turn into Coniston Rd. clubhouse on left.
Nearest railway station, Basingstoke – 3 miles.
Directions and maps from both sides of town available on the club's website.

Car Parking: Spaces at ground + 2 nearby overflow car parks

Admission: Matchday - £3 members £5 non-members

Clubhouse: Open during normal licensing hours.
Meals available Seats 150.
Contact David Crabbe – Club House Manager

Club Shop: Open during clubhouse hours.

Training Nights: Monday and Thursday

Programme Size: A5 Pages: 20
Price: with admission
Editor: Colin Hibberd,
Microset Graphics 01256 844340

Advertising: Contact Sue Byett 01256 323308 or club e-mail

BLACKHEATH FC

President	Sir Hal Miller	Moorcroft Farm, Sinton Green, Worcester WR2 6NW 01905 640309
Chairman	Mike Newson	24 Herons Way, Pembury, Kent TN2 4DN
Club Secretary	Barry Shaw	86 Crown Woods Way, Eltham, London. SE9 2NN. 0208 850 7976 (H), 0208 850 7421 (Fax)
Fixtures Secretary	Jim Collett	8 Vanbrugh Fields, Blackheath, London. SE3 7TZ. 0208 858 7571 (H), 0208 539 3348 (B)
Rugby Manager	Pat McCarthy	7 Beech Hill Road, London SE9 e-mail: plmccarthy@hotmail.com
General Manager	Albert Patrick	c/o Blackheath FC. 0208 304 5161 (H) 07957 110528 (M)
Operations Manager	Fran Cotton	c/o Blackheath FC
Press Liaison	Jack Kay	c/o Blackheath FC. 0208 858 8284 (H) 07971 580889 (M)
Head Coach	Chris Kibble	c/o Blackheath FC. 0208 657 6212 (H) 07801 107562 (M)

A frustrating season for players and fans alike at the Rectory Field last term, especially when one considers the statistics the expression "if only" recurs time and time again. Club won twelve, drew three and lost twelve matches...ten of them by NINE points or under.

The opening match of the season saw the Club sustain what was to be their heaviest defeat losing 58-15 away to Penzance, the fact that the visitors fielded a weakened side and lost scrum half Rhys Powell with a cracked ankle after only four minutes probably played a part in the outcome.

The next game saw us lose 9-5 at home to Launceston "if only" Club had kicked the points. Maximum points came from the next games against Old Colfeians, Camberley and Cinderford before a disappointing 20-15 loss at home to Redruth, the visitors getting the important points in the tenth minute of injury time ..."if only".

Thrilling draws were the next order of the day, Alan Knuckey getting his debut try in the dying seconds against North Walsham to level at 23-23.

Penzance did the same in the next game, managing to equalise with the games last move 17-17 and this was followed by a fortunate 19-19 away to Barking. Skipper Toby Booth marked his last game as captain with a star performance against Old Patesians winning 46-14. Club's run in to the end of the season saw losses to Redruth(by four points) Camberley (four points) and Old Patesians (two points)......."if only!"

Scrum half Mark Percival will captain the side this season with Canadian International prop Dave Penney as vice captain. Club have lost two players during the close season, Harvey Biljon returning to Wasps and Ross O'Connor back to Ireland. Head coach Chris Kibble and all the boys are looking forward to the new season and with the talents of players like Alex Natera, Charlie Abban, Chris Trace, Robin Morrow, Ian Collins the strength of locks Lee Evans and Mark Colgate and the evergreen Dave Fitzgerald and Dominic Walton who's to say we won't be saying "if only" next season.

Jack Kay

BLACKHEATH

Comp.	Date	H/A	Opponents	Result & Score	Att	15	14	13	12	11
N3 S	01-09	A	Penzance & Newlyn	L 15-58	900	Hadley	Trace	Hoare	Mullen	Abban/t
N3 S	08-09	H	Launceston	L 5-9		Morrow	Trace/t	Hoare	Fitzgerald	Abban
N3 S	22-09	A	Old Colfeians	W 28-17		Morrow	Trace	Fitzgerald/t	Hoare/2c3p	Abban/t
N3 S	06-10	H	Camberley	W 22-10	200	Morrow/t	Trace	Evans	Fitzgerald	Abban
N3 S	20-10	A	Cinderford	W 25-14		Morrow/t	Trace	Evans	Fitzgerald/t	Abban
N3 S	27-10	H	Redruth	L 15-20		Morrow	Trace/t	Evans	Fitzgerald	Abban/t
N3 S	03-11	A	Westcombe Park	L 10-25	1000	Morrow	Trace/tcp	Evans	Fitzgerald	Abban
N3 S	10-11	H	North Walsham	D 23-23		Morrow/t	Dutton	Evans(b/t)	Fitzgerald	Powell
N3 S	17-11	A	Lydney	L 13-22		Morrow	Morrow	Fitzgerald	Dutton	Evans
N3 S	24-11	A	Clifton	W 19-10		Morrow	O'Connor	Fitzgerald/t	Dutton/t	Abban
N3 S	01-12	H	Penzance & Newlyn	D 17-17		Morrow	O'Connor	Dutton	Fitzgerald	Abban
N3 S	08-12	A	Tabard	L 13-16	200	Morrow	Biljon	Fitzgerald	Dutton	Abban/t
N3 S	15-12	H	Old Patesians	W 46-14	300	Morrow	Trace/t	Biljon	Fitzgerald	Abban/2t
N3 S	22-12	A	Barking	D 19-19	300	Morrow/t	Trace	Biljon	Fitzgerald	Abban
N3 S	12-01	H	Lydney	W 21-13		Morrow/t	Trace	Biljon	Fitzgerald	Abban/t
N3 S	19-01	A	North Walsham	L 5-14	300	Morrow	Trace/t	Biljon	Fitzgerald	Wharton
N3 S	26-01	H	Westcombe Park	L 18-22	250	Morrow	Trace	Biljon	Fitzgerald	Wharton
N3 S	02-02	A	Redruth	L 20-24	500	Morrow	Trace/tcp	Fitzgerald	Dutton	Abban
N3 S	09-02	H	Cinderford	W 37-10		Morrow	Trace/2t3c2p	Fitzgerald	Dutton/t	Abban/t
N3 S	16-02	H	Clifton	W 21-10		Morrow	Stubbs	Mitchell	Biljon/p	Abban/2t
N3 S	23-02	A	Camberley	L 10-14		Hadley	Wharton/t	Fitzgerald	Griffiths	Abban
N3 S	09-03	H	Old Colfeians	W 36-14	450	Hadley	Trace/t4cp	Fitzgerald/t	Dutton	Abban/t
N3 S	16-03	A	Launceston	L 19-35	450	Boyle	Trace/2c	Fitzgerald/t	Dutton	Abban
N3 S	30-03	H	Barking	W 19-16	350	Hadley	Trace/tc	Wharton	Fitzgerald/t	Abban
N3 S	06-04	A	Old Patesians	L 21-23	400	Morrow	Trace/c3p	Wharton	Fitzgerald/2t	Abban
N3 S	13-04	H	Tabard	W 41-7		Griffin	Trace/2t4cp	Biljon/t	Fitzgerald	Abban/t
PGC	29-09	H	Newbury	L 18-37		Morrow/t	Trace	Hoare/c2p	Fitzgerald	Abban

** after opponents name indicates a penalty try. Brackets after a player's name indicates he was replaced. eg (a) means he was replaced by replacement code "a" and so on. / after a player or replacement name is followed by any scores he made - eg /t, /c, /p, /dg or any combination of these*

EVER PRESENT None

Most Appearances:
24: Dave Fitzgerald, Matt Colgate.
23: Alex Natera (2).
22: Charles Abban, Robin Morrow.

PLAYERS USED

44 plus two as replacement only

MOST POINTS

Pts	Player	T	C	P	DG
121	C Trace	12	17	9	-
111	J Griffin	3	18	18	2
60	C Abban	12	-	-	-
40	D Fitzgerald	8	-	-	-
25	R Morrow	5	-	-	-
25	A Natera	5	-	-	-

MATCH FACTS

10	9	1	2	3	4	5	6	7	8
Griffin/cdg	Powell(a/t)	Hathaway	Natera	Penney	Colgate	Roques	Smith	Cassidy	Walton
Scott	Knuckey	Hathaway	Natera	Penney	Colgate	Milnes	Smith	Booth	Jarvis
Griffin	McKenzie	Hathaway/t	Natera	Penney	Milnes	Randall	Colgate	Booth	Jarvis
Griffin/2cp	Biljon	Hathaway/t	Natera	Penney	Colgate/t	Rendall	Booth	Longman	Temperley
Griffin/2c2p	Biljon	Hathaway	Natera/t	Penney	Colgate	Rendall	Booth	Longman	Temperley
Griffin/cp	Percival	Hathaway	Natera	Penney	Rendall	Colgate	Booth	Longman	Gleninning
Biljon	Percival	Hathaway	Natera	Penney	Rendall	Longman	Walton	Booth	Gleninning
Griffin/c2p	Percival	Penney	Bonner/t	Emery	Milnes	Colgate	Walton	Booth	Gleninning
Griffin/c2p	Percival	Emery	Bonner	Penney	Colgate/t	Milnes	Booth	Longman	Gleninning
Griffin/2c	Percival	Hathaway	Natera	Roques	Colgate	Rendall	Walton	Booth/t	Longman
Griffin/3pdg	Percival	Hathaway	Natera	Roques	Rendall	Colgate/t	Walton	Booth	Longman
Griffin/c2p	Percival	Hathaway	Natera	Roques	Colgate	Rendall	Walton	Booth	Longman
Griffin/2t3c	Percival	Hathaway	Natera/t	Penney	Longman/t	Colgate/t	Walton	Booth	Gleninning
Griffin/t2c	Percival/t	Penney	Natera	Emery	Colgate	Longman	Temperley	Collins	Gleninning
Griffin/c3p	Percival	Hathaway	Natera	Penney	Longman	Colgate	Walton	Collins	Gleninning
Griffin	Percival	Hathaway	Natera	Penney	Colgate	Milnes	Walton	Collins	Gleninning
Griffin/c2p	Percival	Hathaway/2t	Natera	Penney	Evans	Colgate	Walton	Collins	Gleninning
Biljon	Percival	Hathaway	Natera	Penney	Colgate	Evans	Dack/2t	Collins	Gleninning
Biljon	Percival	Hathaway	Natera	Penney	Evans	Colgate	Walton	Collins/t	Gleninning
Scott/p	Percival	Hathaway	Natera/t	Roques	Evans	Colgate	Dack	Collins	Gleninning
Biljon	Percival	Hathaway	Natera	Roques	Colgate	Evans	Walton	Collins/t	Dack
Biljon/t	Percival	Hathaway	Natera	Penney	Evans	Colgate	Walton/t	Collins	Gleninning
Biljon	Percival	Emery/t	Natera/t	Penney	Colgate	Evans	Walton	Longman	Gleninning
Biljon/c	Percival/t	Essenhigh	Booth	Emery	Colgate	Evans	Longman	Collins	Gleninning
Biljon	Percival	Penney	Natera	Emery	Colgate	Evans	Walton	Collins	Longman
Morrow	Percival/t	Emery	Natera/t	Penney	Milnes	Evans	Walton	Collins	Longman
Griffin	Biljon	Hathaway	Natera	Roques	Longman/t	Rendall	Booth	Temperley	Jarvis

REPLACEMENTS: a - Nick Evans. b - Alan Knuckley.

WHERE	Total	Home	Away
The POINTS were scored	538	321	217
The POINTS were conceded	476	291	285
The TRIES were scored	72	44	28
The TRIES were conceded	50	33	17

HOW the TRIES were scored

Total	Backs	Forwards	F Back	Wing	Centre	H Back	F Row	Lock	B Row	Pen. Try
72	50	22	5	25	13	7	11	5	6	-

HOW the TRIES were conceded

Total	Backs	Forwards	F Back	Wing	Centre	H Back	F Row	Lock	B Row	Pen. Try
50	27	19	3	9	10	5	6	5	8	4

BLACKHEATH

LEAGUE STATISTICS *compiled by Stephen McCormack*

SEASON	Division	P	W	D	L	F	A	Pts Diff	Lge Pts	Lge Pos	Most Points		Most Tries	
92-93	2	12	4	2	6	142	231	-89	10	10r	97	Grant Eagle	5	Joe McIntyre
93-94	3	18	11	0	7	305	222	83	22	4	78	Stuart Burns	9	Mike Friday
94-95	3	18	12	2	4	299	190	109	26	2p	147	Sam Howard	5	Matt Griffiths
95-96	2	18	6	1	11	341	469	-128	13	7	153	Sam Howard	5	Mike Hanslip
96-97	2	22	7	0	15	412	641	-229	14	10	137	Chris Braithwaite	8	Mike Hanslip
97-98	P2	22	8	0	14	474	621	-147	16	9	84	Chris Braithwaite	13	John Clarke
98-99	P2	26	5	0	21	419	842	-423	10	13r	102	Campbell Aitken	12	John Clarke
99-00	N1	26	2	1	23	316	1037	-721	5	14r	48	Mitch Hoare	5	Nick Daniel
00-01	N3S	26	10	0	16	562	641	-79	20	9	130	Jon Griffin	13	Charles Abban
01-02	N3S	26	11	3	12	538	476	62	25	7	121	Chris Trace	12	Charles Abban

FACT FILE

Founded: 1858
Nickname: The Club
Colours: Red & black hoops, blue trim/black.
Change colours: Blue with red & black hoops/black.

GROUND

Address: The Rectory Field, Charlton Road, Blackheath. SE3 8SR.
Tel: 0208 293 0853 (office) 0208 858 1578 (clubhouse) Fax: 0181 293 0854
Web site: www.blackheathrugby.co.uk e-mail: blackheathrugby@LineOne.net
Capacity: 6,000 Seated: 572 Standing: 5,428

Directions: The entrance to the Rectory Field is approx 800 yards from the start of Charlton Road B210 at its junction with Stratheden Road/Westcombe Hill which is a turning off Shooters Hill Road A2.
Nearest Railway Station: Blackheath (BR) or Westcombe Park (BR)

Car Parking: 250 spaces available on ground £3.
Off-street parking - 2 hours only, free

Admission:
Season Adults £75 U17 Free Matchday £5

Club Shop: Yes. Manageress Mandy Allen 0208 293 5980

Clubhouse: Normal Licensing hours, light refreshments, food from burger bar..
Available for private function hire 300 max. small bar 100

Training Nights: Tuesday & Thursday 7.30-9

PROGRAMME

Size: A5 Pages: 36 + cover Price: £1
Editor Peter Brown, Mandy Allen & Debbie Ubee

ADVERTISING RATES (+VAT)
Colour Full page £350
Half page £175
Quarter page £90

CAMBERLEY RFC

ʾresident	Gwynne Evans OBE	Woodcroft, 4 Paddock Close, Camberley Surrey GU15 2BN 01276 62024 (H)
Chairman	Roger Chamberlain	Harington, Kettlewell Hill, Horsell Woking Surrey GU21 4JJ 01483 723832 (H)
Secretary	Alan Forfar	15 Old Rectory Gardens, Farnborough, Hampshire GU14 7BS 01252 653715 (H) e-mail-alan.forfar@ntlworld.com
Director of Finance	Neil Doody	The Forge, The Village, Finchampstead, Berkshire RG40 4JN 0118 973 0910 (H)
Fixture Secretary	Bill Fletcher	01344 777701 (H)
Head Coach	Ricky Scott	07876 611245 (M)

Following relegation last season, the Club found itself in National Division Three South, renewing contact with a number of old friends.

Pre-season training under the guidance of coach, Ian Pickup went very well and the season started with consecutive victories against Redruth and at Westcombe Park. Crucially, however, new Club skipper, Martin Jennings was injured in the latter game, an injury that was to keep him out of the side for the whole season. We were brought down to earth with a bump the following week when we were outplayed by Stroud in the National Cup.

There then followed a period where the Club took the field with no recognised hooker or place kicker and this took its toll in the form of a number of close defeats and the club was to win only two games out of the next ten. During this period, the side put up its best display for some time in loosing by just three points to all conquering Penzance & Newlyn. Defeat at Tabard in late January left us rock bottom at the foot of the table but the team rallied briefly to record wins against Barking and Blackheath at home and, crucially, Clifton away and we had dragged ourselves up to fourth bottom with an easy run in to the end of the season – on paper that is!!!

However Old Colfeians staged a remarkable recovery, beating us at home in the process, and at the end of the season we were left in the third bottom position awaiting the outcome of the Launceston/Dudley Kingswinford play-off to find out whether we would be relegated for the second season running. Fortunately, Launceston won and we remain in the National Leagues for another year at least.

Inconsistency, injuries and non-availability of crucial players at crucial times were the main reasons for the Club's failure to establish a mid table position which is probably what we should have achieved. Sadly Ian Pickup has accepted a coaching appointment with the Harlequins academy and leaves the Club after two years and Ricky Scott who has experience coaching in Germany, Ireland and The Army will replace Ian as Head Coach.

Away from the first XV, the Club had a great season with the Second XV finishing as runners up to Rosslyn Park in the London Senior Clubs Amateur Merit Table. A youth academy has been formed, our girls youth section is amongst the best in the south of England and two of our juniors –Rodhri McAtee and Emma Buwick have gained Under 18 International Caps for England.

Action from Camberley v Redruth. Photo: Lee Crabbe

CAMBERLEY

Comp.	Date	H/A	Opponents	Result & Score	Att	15	14	13	12	11
N3 S	01-09	H	Redruth	W 12-9	250	Kane	Allen	McRoberts	Love	Sutton
N3 S	08-09	A	Westcombe Park	W 13-11	200	Kane	Allen	McRoberts	Love	Sutton
N3 S	22-09	H	North Walsham	L 11-21		Wood/2p	Allen	Graham	Kane	Sutton/t
N3 S	06-10	A	Blackheath	L 10-22	200	Kane	Allen	Graham	Love	Palladino
N3 S	20-10	H	Clifton	L 13-22		Kane	Allen/t2p	Love	Chivers(b/c)	Palladino
N3 S	27-10	A	Barking	L 27-28		Webb/3c2p	Allen/t	Kane	Love/t	Palladino
N3 S	03-11	H	Tabard	W 32-27	200	Webb/2c6p	Allen	Kane	Love(c/t)	Dolby-Wels
N3 S	10-11	A	Old Patesians	L 25-28	100	Allen	Dolby-Welsh	Kane/t5p	McRoberts	Palladino/t
N3 S	17-11	H	Penzance & Newlyn	L 20-23	250	Kane/p(b/c)	Palladino/t	Harbour/t	Allen	Dolby-Wels
N3 S	24-11	A	Launceston	L 18-29		Kane/tc2p	Palladino	Harbour	Allen	Dolby-Wels
N3 S	01-12	A	Redruth	L 13-23	600	Kane	Palladino	Harbour	Allen/p	Dolby-Wels
N3 S	08-12	H	Lydney	W 29-14		Kane	Palladino/t	Allen/t	Love	Dolby-Wels
N3 S	15-12	A	Cinderford	L 15-35		Kane/cp	Palladino	Allen/t	Love	Dolby-Wels
N3 S	22-12	A	Old Colfeians	L 21-23		Webb/3c	Allen/t	Kane	Love	Palladino
N3 S	12-01	A	Penzance & Newlyn	L 7-52	850	Kane	Saunders	Allen	Love	Dolby-Wels
N3 S	19-01	H	Old Patesians	L 13-15	150	Webb/cp	Palladino	Kane/t	Allen	Saunders
N3 S	26-01	A	Tabard	L 9-19	150	Kane	Palladino	McRoberts	Allen	Harbour
N3 S	02-02	H	Barking	W 23-15	150	Kane	Harbour	McRoberts	Chivers/t	Allen
N3 S	09-02	A	Clifton	W 19-11	100	Webb	Harbour	Kane	Chivers	Allen/t
N3 S	16-02	H	Launceston	L 16-38	100	Webb	Harbour	Kane	Allen	Dolby-Wels
N3 S	23-02	H	Blackheath	W 14-10		Kane	Harbour	Dolby-Welsh	Allen	Palladino
N3 S	09-03	A	North Walsham	L 0-48	300	Kane	Harbour	Allen	Dolby-Welsh	Palladino
N3 S	16-03	H	Westcombe Park	L 15-19	150	Kane	Harbour	Chivers	Allen/t	Dolby-Wels
N3 S	30-03	H	Old Colfeians	L 26-30		Kane	Harbour/t	Graham/t	Allen	Dolby-Wels
N3 S	06-04	H	Cinderford	W 14-13	200	Kane	Harbour	Allen/t	Chivers	Dolby-Wels
N3 S	13-04	A	Lydney	L 7-44	304	Allen	Davies	Davies	Graham	Dolby-Wels

PGC This is to go in for the last match of the season against Lydney

Kane/c, Harbour,McRoberts, Allen/t, Chivers, Peel, Hughes, Waters, Silvester, Orr, Morgan, Vanner, Fielding, Scott, Milne

** after opponents name indicates a penalty try. Brackets after a player's name indicates he was replaced. eg (a) means he was replaced by replacement code "a" and so on. / after a player or replacement name is followed by any scores he made - eg /t, /c, /p, /dg or any combination of these*

EVER PRESENT Two

Most Appearances:
26: Ali Allen, Brad Kane.
22: Alistair Vanner.

PLAYERS USED 53

MOST POINTS

Pts	Player	T	C	P	DG
105	R Smart	1	8	28	-
49	S Webb	-	11	9	-
49	A Allen	8	-	3	-
46	B Kane	3	2	9	-
20	E Pallardino	4	-	-	-

MATCH FACTS

10	9	1	2	3	4	5	6	7	8
Graham	Smart/4p	Orr	Jennings	McDonald	Jennings	Blackburn	Fielding	Templeman	Milne
Wood/c2p	Walsh	WIlmot	Jennings	McDonald	Vanner	Blackburn	Milne	Templeman/t	Du Rand
Peel	Hughes	WIlmot	McDonald	Sharp	Vanner	Blackburn	Milne	King	Du Rand
Wood/cp	Hughes(a/t)	WIlmot	Orr	Waters	Vanner	Blackburn	Crilley	King	Smith
Walsh	Hughes	Orr	McFarlane	Waters	Norman	Blackburn	Milne	Brace	Vanner
Walsh	Hughes	Waters	Szewczyk/t	Joyner	Fielding	Vanner	Milne	Brace	Du Rand
Walsh	Hughes/t	WIlmot	Szewczyk	Waters	Vanner	Butler	Milne	Brace	Du Rand
Walsh	Hughes	WIlmot	Szewczyk	Waters	Vanner	Butler	Fielding	Brace	Milne(d/t)
Walsh	Hughes	WIlmot	Szewczyk/t	Thomas	Fielding	Vanner	Milne	Scott	Du Rand
Walsh	Losardo	WIlmot	Szewczyk	Thomas	Fielding	Vanner	Milne	Brace	Du Rand
Walsh	Losardo	WIlmot	Delaney	Waters	Milne	Vanner	Vanner	Szewczyk	Glossop
Peel	Losardo	WIlmot	Szewczyk/2t	Waters	Vanner	Hayman/t	Fielding	Scott	Glossop/2c
Peel	Losardo	WIlmot	Szewczyk	Waters	Vanner	Hayman	Fleming	Scott	Glossop
Peel	Losardo	Rise	Szewczyk	Delaney	Pickup	Hayman	Fielding	Scott/2t	Milne
McRoberts	Smart/c	WIlmot	Szewczyk	Thomas	Pickup	Vanner	Fielding	Du Rand/t	Milne
Smart/p	Hughes	WIlmot	Szewczyk	Rise	Morgan	Hayman	Fielding	Scott	Pickup
Smart/3p	Hughes	WIlmot	Szewczyk	Delaney	Pickup	Hayman	Fielding	Templeman	Glossop
Smart/c2p	Hughes/t	Waters	Szewczyk/t	Thomas	Morgan	Pickup	Fielding	Vanner	Milne
Smart/c4p	Hughes	WIlmot	Szewczyk	Waters	Morgan	Hayman	Fielding	Vanner	Glossop
Smart/c3p	Hughes	WIlmot	Szewczyk	Waters	Pickup	Morgan	Fielding/t	Vanner	Milne
Smart/3p	Hughes	Waters	Szewczyk	Thomas	Morgan	Hayman	Fielding	Milne/t	Vanner
Smart	Hughes	WIlmot	Silvester	Waters	Pickup	Hayman	Fielding	Fleming	Vanner
Graham	Smart/tcp	Rise	Szewczyk	Silvester	Pickup	Smith	Fielding	Milne	Vanner
Smart/2c4p	Hughes	WIlmot	Szewczyk	Silvester	Pickup	Morgan	Fielding	Milne	Vanner
Peel	Smart/3p	Waters	Silvester	Orr	Hayman	Vanner	Milne	Scott	Pickup
Smart/c	Davies	Fielding	Fleming	Glossop	Gaynor	Gotting	Harbour	Jennings	Kane

REPLACEMENTS: a - Tom Bailey. b - Stephen Webb. c - E Palladino. d - Ben Glossop.

WHERE	Total	Home	Away
The POINTS were scored	422	238	184
The POINTS were conceded	629	272	256
The TRIES were scored	42	23	19
The TRIES were conceded	81	50	31

HOW the TRIES were scored

Total	Backs	Forwards	F Back	Wing	Centre	H Back	F Row	Lock	B Row	Pen. Try
42	28	14	1	12	11	4	5	2	7	-

HOW the TRIES were conceded

Total	Backs	Forwards	F Back	Wing	Centre	H Back	F Row	Lock	B Row	Pen. Try
81	48	31	8	17	15	8	12	4	15	2

CAMBERLEY

LEAGUE STATISTICS *compiled by Stephen McCormack*

SEASON	Division	P	W	D	L	F	A	Pts Diff	Lge Pts	Lge Pos		Coach		
92-93	Lon2S	12	10	2	0	241	94	147	72	1p		P Moyle		
93-94	Lon1	12	9	0	3	242	137	105	18	3		P Moyle		
94-95	Lon1	12	12	0	0	375	122	253	24	1p		P Moyle		
												Most Points		**Most Tries**
95-96	D5S	12	5	1	6	151	212	-61	11	7	41	Dave Whitfield	3	D Adamson
96-97	D4S	26	15	2	9	688	515	173	32	4	138	Jason Hoad	13	Craig Grevelle
97-98	N2S	26	23	1	2	803	372	431	47	1p	144	Guy Gregory	14	Craig Grevelle
98-99	JN1	26	10	1	15	529	661	-132	21	9	206	Guy Gregory	7	Bruno Green
99-00	JN1	26	7	0	19	398	882	-484	14	12	121	Ben Stafford	10	Brad Kane
00-01	N2	26	8	0	18	426	738	-312	16	12	64	Howard Graham	7	Ali Allen
01-02	N3S	26	8	0	18	422	629	-207	16	12	105	Rob Smart	8	Ali Allen

Founded: 1931

Colours: Black with amber collar.
Change colours: Yellow with black collar.

GROUND

Address: Watchetts Recreation Ground, Park Rd, Camberley, Surrey GU15 2SR
Tel: 01276 25395 Fax: 01276 25211
Capacity: 1,000 Seated: None Standing: 1000 (uncovered)

Directions: M3 Jnc 4, follow signs for Frimley/Guildford. At 1st roundabout turn left, signed Camberley, 1 1/2 miles to mini r'about, turn right into Park Rd.
Nearest Railway Station: Camberley

Car Parking: 500 nearby

Admission: Matchday £5 with programme

Club Shop: Open matchdays 12 noon - 5pm.
Contact Alex Boyden 01276 26200

Clubhouse: Mon - Fri 6-11, Sat. 11-11, Sun. 11-7.
Snacks available.
Functions up to 90. Contact Lydia Rise 01276 25395.

Training Nights: Tuesday & Thursday

PROGRAMME Size: A5 Pages: 24 + cover
Price: Included with admission
Editor: Alan Forfar 01252 653715

ADVERTISING RATES	Colour
Page	£500
1/2 Page	£300
1/4 Page	£150

HAVANT RFC

President:	Ray Quinn	5 Holt Gardens, Rowlands Castle, Hants. PO9 6BH Tel: 02392 - 413931 (H), 241122 (B) email: ray.quinn@fischerconnectors.co.uk
Chairman:	Richard Pearcey,	c/o Southern Cooperative Ltd.,, 17 The Square, Petersfield, Hants. GU32 3HP Tel: 01730 236236 (B)
Secretary:	Mick Chalk	16 Highclere Ave, Havant, Hants PO9 4RB. Tel: 02392 - 472239 (H) 723749 (B)
Chairman,Finance:	Steve Lawrence	Tel: 02392 365492 (H), 02392 834699 (B)
Chairman,Rugby:	Adam King	Tel: 07930 442749 (M)
Fixture Secretary/1st XV Manager:		Mick Chalk - see Secretary
Match Sec./ Commercial Manager:		Julian Davies c/o Havant RFC. Tel: 02392 477843 / 492311
Head Coach	Dave Cook	02392 470359 (H) 07976 587178 (M)
Other coaches		Simon Morgan, Derek Morris, Al Holl
Press Officer	Bill Sugden	37 Horndean Rd., Emsworth, Hants. PO10 7PU Tel: 01243 372323 (H) 01243 371103 (F)

After the heartache of losing out in the play-offs the previous year Havant continued their renaissance and returned to the National League after a three season absence in London League One and becoming League champions last year.

Their success was built on the hard work of a home grown coaching team of Dave Cook, Simon Morgan, Derek Morris and Al Holl, and a tremendous team spirit of a developing squad, with some shrewdly recruited additions by Chairman of Rugby, Adam King.

However, an inauspicious early season exit in the RFU Senior Cup at the hands of London Nigerian did not augur well for the Hooks Lane faithful, and gave no hint of the triumphs to come.

A dramatic 17-16 victory against local rivals Basingstoke in late September set Havant on a tremendous unbeaten home run, which was to last all season. However, they were only to lose once before a February reverse away at Basingstoke and this kept the championship alive.

The title should have been clinched at a rain sodden Sutton as early as March, but eventually the home fans were rewarded when `Hav' completed a double over Norwich at Hooks Lane with an emphatic 65-3 win, which saw them back in the big time.

Skipper Joe Duffett led by example, whilst South African Anton Petzer headed the try scoring charts, and fly half Steve Claffey's boot was a key ingredient in the success, but most important of all was the squad spirit which led to the meanest defence in the League by some distance.

The club knows of the massive challenges ahead, but, if the squad and ever flourishing Academy continue to develop, they know that National League rugby can be established once more at Havant.

Havant players, coaches (and ball boys) celebrate after beating Norwich and so winning the London 1 title.

HAVANT

Comp.	Date	H/A	Opponents	Result & Score	15	14	13	12	11
L1	08-09	A	Winchester	W 21-3	Stapleton	Jewitt	Davies	Ross	Andrew/t
L1	15-09	H	Sutton & Epsom	W 48-3	Stapleton/t	Andrew	Barnes	Petzer/t	Jewitt/2t
L1	22-09	H	Cheshunt	W 25-11	Stapleton	Andrew/t	Barnes	Petzer/t	Jewitt
L1	29-09	H	Basingstoke*	W 17-16	Stapleton/t	Elleston	Barnes	Petzer	Russell
L1	06-10	A	London Nigerians	L 13-18	Jewitt	Elleston	Barnes	Petzer/tp	Russell
L1	20-10	H	Staines	W 18-7	Stapleton	Jewitt	Barnes	Petzer	Elleston/t
L1	27-10	A	Thanet Wanderers	W 16-9	Dudley	Andrew	Davies/t	Petzer	Barnes
L1	10-11	H	Cambridge	W 50-3	Dudley(b/c)	Jewitt/t	Davies	Petzer/2t	Barnes/t
L1	17-11	A	Harlow	W 24-12	Dudley	Jewitt	Barnes/t	Petzer	Stapleton/3c
L1	01-12	H	Haywards Heath	W 14-7	Dudley/c	Barnes	Davies	Petzer	Jewitt
L1	08-12	A	Norwich	W 35-17	Stapleton/t	Elleston	Claffey/c6p	Petzer/t	Barnes
L1	22-12	H	Harlow	W 52-5	Stapleton/t	Davenport	Jewitt	Petzer	Elleston/2t
L1	12-01	H	Thanet Wanderers	W 41-0	Stapleton/t	Davenport/t	Jewitt	Petzer	Elleston/2t
L1	19-01	A	Cambridge	W 18-7	Jewitt	Barnes/t	Davies/2t	Petzer	Davenport
L1	26-01	A	Staines	W 6-3	Stapleton	Jewitt	Davies	Petzer	Elleston
L1	02-02	H	London Nigerians	W 16-7	Stapleton(c/t)	Jewitt	Davies	Petzer	Elleston
L1	09-02	A	Basingstoke	L 8-25	Jewitt	Barnes(d/t)	Davies	Petzer	Elleston
L1	23-02	A	Cheshunt	W 25-15	Dudley	Davenport	Jones	Petzer/t	Jewitt
L1	09-03	H	Winchester	W 32-16	Dudley	Elleston	Jones/t	Petzer/t	Jewitt/2t
L1	16-03	A	Sutton & Epsom	L 0-16	Dudley	Barnes	Jones	Petzer	Jewitt
L1	06-04	H	Norwich	W 65-3	Petzer/t	Jewitt/2t	Jones	Davies/t	Barnes/t
L1	13-04	A	Haywards Heath	L 26-36	Dudley	Barnes	Jewitt	O Jones	McGovern/t

** after opponents name indicates a penalty try. Brackets after a player's name indicates he was replaced. eg (a) means he was replaced by replacement code "a" and so on. / after a player or replacement name is followed by any scores he made - eg /t, /c, /p, /dg or any combination of these*

REPLACEMENTS: a - Grant Morris. b - Steve Stapleton. c -Alan Barnes. d -Liam Davenport.

EVER PRESENT S Jack, J Duffett.

Most Appearances:
22: S Jack, J Duffett.
21: D Raubenheimer.
20: A Petzer.

PLAYERS USED

33 plus two as replacements

MOST POINTS

Pts	Player	T	C	P	DG
164	S Claffey	3	31	29	-
64	D Jones	7	4	7	-
48	A Petzer	9	-	1	-
35	A Jewitt	7	-	-	-
31	S Stapleton	4	4	1	-

MATCH FACTS

10	9	1	2	3	4	5	6	7	8
Claffey/tc3p	Morris	Jack	Cruddas	McErlean	Duffett	Matthews	Fiers	Mitchell	Raubenheim
Claffey/5cp	Jones(a/t)	Jack	Cruddas	A Mitchell/t	Duffett	Matthews	Short	O Mitchell/t	Raubenheim
Claffey/2c2p	Jones	Jack	Powell	A Mitchell	Duffett	Matthews	Short	O Mitchell	Raubenheimer/t
Jones/2cp	Morris	Jack	Powell	A Mitchell	Duffett	Aung	Short	O Mitchell	Raubenheimer
Dudley	Morris/t	Jack	Tart	A Mitchell	Duffett	Aung	Short	O Mitchell	Raubenheimer
Jones/c2p	Davenport/t	Jack	Tart	A Mitchell	Duffett	Aung	Short	Barfoot	Raubenheimer
Jones/2p	Davenport/t	Jack	Tart	Conlon	Duffett	Aung	Archer	Barfoot	Raubenheimer
Jones/2tp	Davenport	Jack/t	Tart	Conlon	Duffett	Aung	Archer/t	Barfoot	Raubenheimer/t
Jones/t	Davenport	Jack	Powell	Conlon	Duffett/t	Aung	Archer	Barfoot	Raubenheimer
Jones/tc	Davenport	Jack	Cruddas	Conlon	Duffett	Whittle/t	Archer	Barfoot	Raubenheimer
Jones	Davenport	Jack	Powell	Conlon	Duffett/t	Whittle	Archer	Barfoot	Raubenheimer
Claffey/t7cp	Jones/t	Jack	Powell	Conlon	Duffett	Whittle	Archer/t	Barfoot	Raubenheimer/2
Claffey/4cp	Jones	Jack	Powell/t	Conlon	Duffett	Whittle	Archer	Barfoot/t	Raubenheimer
Jones/p	Morris	Jack	Powell	Conlon	Duffett	Whittle	Archer	Barfoot	Raubenheimer
Claffey/2p	Davenport	Jack	Powell	Conlon	Duffett	Whittle	Archer	Barfoot	Raubenheimer
Claffey/2p	Jones	Jack	Tart	Conlon/t	Duffett	Archer	Short	Barfoot	Raubenheimer
Claffey/p	Jones	Jack	Tart	Conlon	Duffett	Whittle	Archer	Barfoot	Raubenheimer
Claffey/2c2p	Jones	Conlon	Jack	A Mitchell/t	Duffett	Whittle/t	Archer	Barfoot	Raubenheimer
Claffey/3c2p	Jones	Conlon	Jack	A Mitchell	Duffett	Whittle	Short	Barfoot	Raubenheimer
Claffey/3p	Jones	Jack	Cruddas	Conlon	Duffett	Whittle	Archer	Short	Raubenheimer
Claffey/t5c	Jones/2t	Jack	Tart	Conlon	Duffett/t	Whittle	Short	Barfoot/2t	Raubenheimer
Claffey/c3p	Jones	Jack	Tart	Conlon/t	Duffett	Matthews	Short/t	Fiers	Whittle

Havant win good line out ball against Norwich, in the match that clinched the title.

HAVANT

LEAGUE STATISTICS *compiled by Stephen McCormack*

SEASON	Division	P	W	D	L	F	A	Pts Diff	Lge Pts	Lge Pos	Most Points	Most Tries
91-92	D4S	12	11	0	1	301	91	210	22	1	129 Pete Russell	9 Will Knight
92-93	3	11	8	1	2	185	93	92	17	2	54 Rob Ashworth	3 by 3 players
93-94	3	18	3	0	15	203	432	-229	6	9	32 Pete Russell	4 Nick Roach
94-95	4	18	10	2	6	390	330	60	22	4	85 Pete Russell	10 Nick Roach
95-96	4	18	7	1	10	287	368	-81	15	8	80 Pete Russell	4 Nick Roach
96-97	3	30	8	0	22	589	954	-365	16	14	123 Pete Russell	7 Brit Pearce & Andy Jewitt
97-98	N2S	26	8	1	17	388	643	-255	17	12	79 Hamish Ruskin	6 Andy Jewitt
98-99	N2S	26	7	0	19	361	675	-314	14	14	60 Syd Claffey	8 Denville Elleston
99-00	L1	16	9	1	6	407	321	86	19	8		
00-01	L1	20	16	0	4	550	294	256	32	2		
01-02	L1	22	18	0	4	579	239	340	36	1	168 Nick French	8 Steve Boydell & Adam Jowett

FACT FILE

Founded: 1951
Nickname: Hav
Web site: www.havant-rfc.co.uk

Colours: Irregular hoops of blue, white & red
Change colours: Red

GROUND

Address: Hooks Lane, Fraser Rd, Bedhampton, Havant, Hants. PO9 3EJ
Tel: 023 9249 2311 (Office) 023 9247 7843 (Club)
Fax: 023 9247 0451 email: havantrfc@aol.com
Capacity: 2,700 **Seated**: 200 **Standing**: 2,500

Directions: From A3 and A3(M): At Jct.5 of A3(M) take slip road to B2177 and take first exit off r'about passing Rusty Cutter pub on your left. By B2177, then over mini-r'about and forward to traffic lights. Straight on and then bear left at level crossing. Take 2nd left into James Road (sign post for Havant RFC) and then left at T-Junction into Fraser Road. Clubhouse is 200 yards on right just beyond Hooks Lane.

From M27 and A27: M27 changes to A27 at Hilsea, Portsmouth and in 1 mile (after crossing intersection leading to A2030), keep to nearside lane. Take A3(M) for London, staying in nearside lane. After 150 yards take slip road to Bedhampton. Take 3rd exit off r'about on to B2177, passing the Rusty Cutter pub on your left. then proceed as for directions above from A3 and A3(M).

Nearest railway station: Havant. From north exit turn left, over r'about and 3rd right into James Road, then left into Fraser Road.

Car Parking: 200 at ground

Admission: Season tickets - Standing Adults £60
Matchdays - Adult £tba. Extra for seat £tba.

Clubhouse: Normal licensing hours, snacks available

Functions: Up to 100, contact Julian Davies 0023 9247 7843

Club Shop: Open matchdays & Sun am
Manager: Julian Davies 023 9247 7843

Training Nights: Tuesday & Thusday.

PROGRAMME Size: A5 Price: With entry Pages: 36
Editor: Roger Boydell. Tel: 01243 373677
email: roger.boydell@btopenworld.com

ADVERTISING RATES
Full page: £400 Half page £200 Quarter page: £120

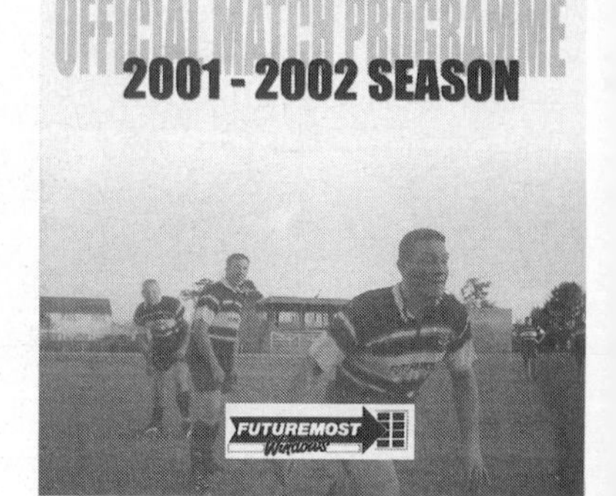

LYDNEY RFC

President	T C Bailey	Montrose, Highfield, Lydney, Glos. 01594 842287 (H)
Chairman	P J Price	Red Gables, 41a Park Road, Berry Hill, Coleford, Glos. 01594 834591 (H)
Secretary	A J Jones	5 Kimberley Close, Lydney, Glos. GL15 5AE 01594 842709 (H) Tel & Fax: (Club Office) 01594 843064
Treasurer	R A Jones	Sweetwater Cottage, Neds Top, Oldcroft, Glos. GL15 4NK 01594 845073 (B)
Fixture Secretary	R B Powell	Skalni-Mesto, Parkhill, Whitecroft, Lydney, Glos. GL15 4PL 01594 562820 07810 157101 (M)

After several seasons in National Division Two, Lydney faced the return to Three South with some trepidation. The season started with the coaching duties in the (unpaid) hands of three very experienced old stagers in the shape of Nick Nelmes, Julian Davis and Adrian Knox. It took some time for the shape of the team to emerge from a mixture of mature and young players but by Christmas our position in the division looked secure. Pat Kiely joined the coaching set-up towards the end of the season and the position for next year is still under review. As always we look forward to the continuing progress of the younger players with perhaps a sprinkling of more experienced campaigners from outside the town filling some key positions on the pitch.

In the New Year we were able to concentrate some fire on the County Cup and after an epic semi-final victory over Old Patesians we ran into a good patch of form with a flurry of wins securing a final position of sixth in the league.

Lydney went on to lift the Senior County Cup at Kingsholm for the tenth time in the 32 year history of the competition with a comfortable win over Bristol club Dings Crusaders.

The promotion and relegation issues mean that we will renew rivalry with old friends from Rosslyn Park, Basingstoke and Weston next season, but the travelling commitments will still be a burden on the club with several visits to the east of London.

Finally it is with great sadness that we record the untimely death of our popular past chairman, Dr. Peter Catlin. We shall sorely miss his considerable presence in all areas of the club's activities.

DAVE DOLAN

Pictured before the game against Cinderford. Photo: Steve Cassidy

LYDNEY

Comp.	Date	H/A	Opponents	Result & Score	Att	15	14	13	12	11
N3 S	01-09	H	Cinderford	W 20-12		Edwards	Vines/2t	Hill/2c2p	Bragg	Dunlop
N3 S	08-09	A	Tabard	L 22-24	150	Johnson	Betty	Edwards	Hill/cp	Saville/2t
N3 S	22-09	H	Redruth	W 33-17	521	Saville	Dunlop	Bragg	Edwards/t	Vines
N3 S	06-10	A	Old Patesians	W 21-15	300	Bendall	Dunlop/t	Johnson	Edwards	Vines
N3 S	20-10	H	Westcombe Park	W 23-18	397	Saville	Dunlop	Bragg	Edwards/2tp	Vines/t
N3 S	27-10	A	Penzance & Newlyn	L 14-34	900	Saville	Dunlop	Bragg	Edwards/2c	Vines
N3 S	03-11	H	North Walsham	W 15-14	407	Saville	Dunlop	Bragg	Edwards/5p	Hill
N3 S	10-11	A	Launceston	L 13-21		Saville	Dunlop	Bragg	Edwards/cp	Hill/p
N3 S	17-11	H	Blackheath	W 22-13		Saville	Dunlop	Bragg	Edwards/3p	Hill/t
N3 S	24-11	A	Old Colfeians	L 9-26	100	Edwards	Bendall	Johnson	Hill	Dunlop
N3 S	01-12	A	Cinderford	W 16-13		Saville	Dunlop	Bragg	Edwards	Vines/t
N3 S	08-12	A	Camberley*	L 14-29		Vines	Hill	Bragg	Edwards	Johnson
N3 S	15-12	H	Barking	W 15-3	326	Edwards	Dunlop	Bragg	Hill	Vine
N3 S	22-12	A	Clifton	L 20-28	180	Johnson/t	Dunlop	Edwards	Hill	Betty/t
N3 S	12-01	A	Blackheath	L 13-21		Betty	Dunlop	Bragg	Edwards/c	Vines/t
N3 S	19-01	H	Launceston	L 3-30	526	Johnson	Dunlop	Bragg	Edwards	Vines
N3 S	26-01	A	North Walsham	L 0-18	250	Johnson	Dunlop	Edwards	Johnson	Vines
N3 S	09-02	A	Westcombe Park	L 16-39	300	Johnson	Dunlop/t	Johnson	Edwards	Vines/t
N3 S	16-02	H	Old Colfeians	W 56-9	227	Johnson	Dunlop/t	Bragg	Johnson/t	Vines/t
N3 S	23-02	H	Old Patesians	L 11-15	365	Bendall	Dunlop/t	Johnson	Bragg	Vines
N3 S	02-03	H	Penzance & Newlyn	L 28-41	378	Bendall	Dunlop	Johnson	Bragg	Vine
N3 S	09-03	A	Redruth	W 24-22	800	Edwards	Dunlop	Johnson/t	Bragg	Vines/t
N3 S	16-03	H	Tabard	L 19-30	467	Edwards	Dunlop/t	Johnson	Bragg	Vines
N3 S	30-03	H	Clifton	W 25-8	301	Edwards/t	Dunlop	Johnson	Bragg	Vines/t
N3 S	06-04	A	Barking	W 17-13		Edwards	Vines	Johnson/t	Bragg	Dunlop
N3 S	13-04	H	Camberley	W 44-7	304	Edwards	Dunlop	Johnson	Bragg/3t	Vines/t
PGC	15-09	N	Kettering*	W 29-0		Edwards	Saville/t	Bragg	Hill	Vines
PGC	29-09	H	Reading	W 16-0		Saville	Betty	Bragg	Edwards	Vines/t
PGC	13-10	H	Worcester	L 0-45	987	Saville	Dunlop	Bragg	Edwards	Vines

** after opponents name indicates a penalty try. Brackets after a player's name indicates he was replaced. eg (a) means he was replaced by replacement code "a" and so on. / after a player or replacement name is followed by any scores he made - eg /t, /c, /p, /dg or any combination of these*

EVER PRESENT None

Most Appearances:
25: Paul Price, Paul Kiely.
24: Julian Dunlop, Julian Davis, James Roberts (2).

PLAYERS USED

30 plus four as a replacement

MOST POINTS

Pts	Player	T	C	P	DG
117	J Hill	7	17	16	-
78	N Merrett	-	12	14	4
58	G Edwards	4	4	10	-
50	C Vine	10	-	-	-
30	P Price	6	-	-	-

MATCH FACTS

10	9	1	2	3	4	5	6	7	8
Davis	Turner	Price	Nelmes	James	Roberts	Kiely	Kiely	Torua	Torua
Merrett/c	Davis	Price	Nelmes	Hunt	Roberts	Kiely	Groves	Wakeham	Knox/t
Merrett/3c2p2dg	Davis	Price	Nelmes	James/t	Roberts	Hale	Groves	Knox	Kiely/t
Merrett/c2pdg	Davis	Price/t	Nelmes	James	Roberts	Hale	Groves	Wakeham	Knox
Merrett/cp	Davis	Price	Beddis	James	Roberts	Kiely	Groves	Wakeham	Knox
Johnson/t	Davis	Price	Nelmes	James/t	Roberts	Kiely	Groves	Wakeham	Knox
Johnson	Davis	Price	Nelmes	James	Roberts	Kiely	Groves	Wakeham	Torua
Johnson	Davis	Price	Nelmes	James/t	Roberts	Kiely	Groves	Wakeham	Torua
Johnson(a/dg)	Davis	Price	Nelmes	Isaacs	Roberts/t	Newton	Groves	Wakeham	Torua
Merrett/3p	Turner	James	Nelmes	Isaacs	Roberts	Kiely	Groves	Wakeham	Torua
Merrett/c3p	Turner	Price	Nelmes	Isaacs	Roberts	Kiely	Groves	Jenkins	Torua
Merrett/2c	Davis	Price	Nelmes	Isaacs	Roberts	Kiely	Groves	Jenkins(b/t)	Torua
Merrett/cp	Davis	Price	Nelmes	Isaacs/t	Roberts	Kiely	Knox	Jenkins	Torua/t
Merrett/2c2p	Davis	Price	Nelmes	Isaacs	Roberts	Kiely	Knox	Jenkins	Torua
Hill/2p	Davis	Price	Nelmes	Isaacs	Roberts	Hale	Kiely	Jenkins	Torua
Hill/p	Davis	Price	Nelmes	Isaacs	Roberts	Hale	Kiely	Jenkins	Torua
Hill	Davis	Price	Nelmes	Isaacs	Roberts	Kiely	Groves	Jenkins	Torua
Hill/2p	Davis	Price	Nelmes	Isaacs	Hale	Kiely	Knox	Jenkins	Torua
Hill/t3c	Davis/t	Price	Nelmes	James	Hale	Kiely	Knox/t	Jenkins/2t	Torua/2t
Hill/2p	Davis	Price	Nelmes	Isaacs	Roberts	Kiely	Groves	Knox	Torua
Hill/tc2p	Davis/t	Price/2t	Nelmes	James	Roberts	Kiely	Groves	Jenkins	Torua
Hill/t2c	Davis	Price/t	Probert	Isaacs	Roberts	Kiely	Groves	Wakeham	Torua
Hill/2c	Davis/t	Price	Probert	Isaacs	Roberts	Kiely	Groves	Knox/t	Torua
Hill/2tcp	Davis	Price	Nelmes	James	Roberts	Kiely	Groves	Jenkins	Knox
Hill/tc	Davis	Price/t	Nelmes	Isaacs	Roberts	Kiely	Groves	Jenkins	Knox
Hill/4c2p	Davis	Price/t	Nelmes	James	Roberts	Kiely	Groves/t	Jenkins	Knox
Merrett/c3pdg	Bendall	Price	Nelmes	James	Roberts	Hale	Newton	Wakeham	Kiely/t
Merrett/c3p	Davis	Price	Nelmes	James	Roberts	Hale	Groves	Knox	Kiely
Merrett	Turner	Price	Nelmes	James	Roberts	Hale	Groves	Knox	Kiely

REPLACEMENTS: a - Neil Merritt. b - Adrian Knox.

WHERE	Total	Home	Awayf
The POINTS were scored	513	314	199
The POINTS were conceded	520	303	217
The TRIES were scored	63	40	23
The TRIES were conceded	58	34	24

HOW the TRIES were scored

Total	Backs	Forwards	F Back	Wing	Centre	H Back	F Row	Lock	B Row	Pen. Try
63	40	22	2	19	9	10	10	1	11	1

HOW the TRIES were conceded

Total	Backs	Forwards	F Back	Wing	Centre	H Back	F Row	Lock	B Row	Pen. Try
58	36	22	10	15	4	7	4	5	13	-

LYDNEY

LEAGUE STATISTICS

compiled by Stephen McCormack

SEASON	Division	P	W	D	L	F	A	Pts Diff	Lge Pts	Lge Pos	Most Points	Most Tries
92-93	D4S	12	8	0	4	187	170	17	16	3	102 Andy Halford	6 John Edwards
93-94	D5S	12	7	2	3	181	111	70	16	2	54 Andy Halford	5 Mike Stubbs & John Edwards
94-95	D5S	12	10	1	1	263	131	132	21	2	70 Andy Halford	7 Mike Stubbs
95-96	D5S	12	11	1	0	320	132	188	23	1	107 Robert Mills	6 Nick Nelmes & Julian Davis
96-97	D3	30	13	0	17	668	766	-98	26	10	275 Paul Morris	8 Mike Stubbs & Adrian Knox
97-98	JN1	26	5	0	21	361	575	-214	10	12	82 James Reid	7 Julian Davis
98-99	JN1	26	11	2	13	438	482	-44	24	8	104 Nick Paisley	7 L Smith/D Edwards
99-00	JN1	26	9	2	15	496	632	-136	20	10	248 Lee Osborne	6 Paul Price/ Charles Vine/Ross Armstrong
00-01	N2	*22	6	0	16	308	565	-257	12	13	70 Stephen Ward	4 by four players
01-02	N3S	26	13	0	13	513	520	-7	26	6	117 Julian Hill	10 Charles Vine

FACT FILE

Founded: 1887
Nickname: Seversiders
Website: romandelta.com/LydneyRFC

Colours: Black and white hoops
Change colours: Red

GROUND

Address: Regentsholm, Regent Street, Lydney, Glos GL15 5RN
Tel: 01594 842479 (Clubhouse) Tel/Fax: 01594 843064 (Office) email: best@romandelta.com
Capacity: 3,000 + Seated: 490 Standing: 2,500 +

Directions: Turn off by-pass at either end and follow signs to Lydney. Turn into Swan Road (next to Swan Hotel) off the A48 in the centre of town. Straight on to the entrance to the recreation grounds, turn left inside ground.
Nearest Railway Station: Lydney BR (Approx. 1 mile)

Car Parking: Restricted on ground, spaces nearby

Admission: Season Adults £60 Children/OAPs £ 30
Matchday Adults £6 Children/OAPs £3

Club Shop: None

Clubhouse: Open during normal licensing hours, with a range of snacks available on match days.
Functions: Contact Mrs Diane Emery 01594 841008 (H).

Training Nights: Tuesdays & Thursdays

PROGRAMME Size: A5 Pages: 32 Price: £1
Editor: Alan Keenan Tel: 01594 842228
Advertising Rates (Mono)
Contact Gary McKelvey, Sponsorship Secretary 01594 844623
or Ann Sargent 01594 843064

NORTH WALSHAM RFC

President	T.B.A.	
Chairman	George Bradford Tel: 01263 768159	2 Bell Yard, Gunton Hall, Hanworth, Norwich NR11 7HJ email: bradford3.freeserve.co.uk
Club Secretary	Joe Hodges Tel: 01692 598318 (H)	Church View, Town Street, Hickling, Norwich. NR12 0BQ email: joehodges@churchview-hickling.freeserve.co.uk
Press & Media	Tony Marcantonio 01493 751837 (H) 07944 690042 (M)	The White House, Southwood Road, Beighton,Norwich. NR13 3AB. email: tony.marcantonio@ukgateway.net
Fixtures Secretary	Richard Foulds Tel: 01603 736584 (H) 07941 296560 (M)	Flat 2, Church Farm Cottage, Hautbois, Norwich NR12 7JW email: richardfoulds@talk21.com

Successful but frustrating probably sums up North Walsham's season. Third behind Penzance/Newlyn and Launceston, albeit few points adrift, was an improvement on last season's sixth place and, although once the leaders pulled away there was little ›pe that they could be caught, Walsham stuck to their task with coach Jon Curry bringing in young players with an eye to the ture. There had been a few new faces at Scottow at the start of the season with three recruits from the University of East Anglia John Dwight, Peter Taggart and John Pritchard. They along with Andy Thorpe, Tim Groom (Diss) and Jason Child (Holt) all fig-ed strongly, with the exception of Groom who suffered a back injury early on. All worked hard to meet the demands of a higher ade of rugby and Child slotted seamlessly into the back row and outside half Dwight formed an excellent partnership with the ore experienced Phil Friel missing just two games all season.

The season started with a trip to Launceston resulting in defeat, but a good home win against Old Colfeians restored confi-ence, which was mightily enhanced by a National Cup win against Penzance/Newlyn with a performance rated by many as the est ever by a Walsham side. Impetus was lost with a single point defeat at Lydney and with a draw at Blackheath the run up to hristmas was mixed with the only home defeat of the season at the hands of Launceston, but a second defeat of Penzance.

The final game of 2001 at Tabard resulted in a single point defeat and the loss, for the remainder of the season, of influential entre and goal kicker Len Wilmot with a damaged cartilage.

The new year started badly with a defeat at Clifton, but the remainder of the season was all wins until the penultimate game, visit to Penzance, where the Pirates took revenge for the two early season defeats.

Highlights of the season were, of course, the two defeats of champions Penzance and the fact that the side suffered just one everse at home. The support from the Scottow faithful was, as ever, fantastic and much appreciated by the players. Walsham is a ub that thrives and succeeds on a `family spirit' and new players were welcomed and absorbed into the `family' and once the lead-rs established a gap Jon Curry blooded yet more young players, including James Cook and Joe Long from local side Crusaders. a club without `stars' still worthy of mention are Gideon Rossouw, who captained the side from hooker, and Jeff van Poortvliet, hose commitment sets the standard,. John Morfoot who continued to lay his body on the line despite approaching the big Four)h, Nick Greenhall who was always ready to step in when asked and the less established members of the squad whose appear-nces were restricted, but nonetheless gave 100 percent when called on, and finally team manager John Baines and the physios ho helped it all to happen.

TONY MARCANTONIO

NORTH WALSHAM

Comp.	Date	H/A	Opponents	Result & Score	Att	15	14	13	12	11
N3 S	01-09	A	Launceston	L 16-23		Wyatt	Cooke/t	Anthony	Wilmot/c3p	Brand
N3 S	08-09	H	Old Colfeians	W 57-10		Grennhall	Thorpe/2t	Aloe(a/3t)	Wilmot/6c	Cooke/t
N3 S	22-09	A	Camberley	W 21-11		Borrett	Thorpe	Kingsmill	Wilmot/c3p	Cooke
N3 S	06-10	H	Cinderford	W 85-5	200	Grennhall/2t	Thorpe/4t	Jenkins/t	Wilmot/2t6cp	Kingsmill
N3 S	20-10	A	Redruth	W 26-19		Wyatt	Kingsmill/t	Wilmot/2c4p	Greenhall	Bishop
N3 S	27-10	H	Westcombe Park	W 14-11		Grennhall	Kingsmill	Jenkins	Wilmot/3p	Thorpe/t
N3 S	03-11	A	Lydney	L 14-15	407	Grennhall	Thorpe/t	Jenkins	Wilmot/3p	Taggart
N3 S	10-11	A	Blackheath	D 23-23		Grennhall	Kingsmill/t	Jenkins	Greenhall	Cooke
N3 S	17-11	H	Clifton	W 23-7	250	Bishop	Thorpe/t	Jenkins	Greenhall	Kingsmill
N3 S	24-11	A	Barking	W 20-12		Bishop	Thorpe	Grennhall/t	Greenhall	Kingsmill/
N3 S	01-12	H	Launceston	L 13-21	400	Bishop	Thorpe	Grennhall/t	Wilmot/c2p	Taggart
N3 S	08-12	A	Old Patesians	L 12-38		Grennhall	Cooke	Cooke	Wilmot/c	Taggart
N3 S	15-12	H	Penzance & Newlyn	W 18-7	400	Grennhall	Brand/t	Cook	Wilmot/c2p	Cooke
N3 S	22-12	A	Tabard	L 21-22	200	Grennhall	Brand/t	Cook	Wilmot/t3p	Cooke
N3 S	12-01	A	Clifton	L 21-36		Bishop	Brand	Cook	Greenhall/t	Taggart
N3 S	19-01	H	Blackheath	W 14-5	300	Pritchard	Thorpe	Cook	Greenhall/t	Taggart
N3 S	26-01	H	Lydney	W 18-0	250	Pritchard	Thorpe/t	Cook	Long	Cooke
N3 S	02-02	A	Westcombe Park	W 32-13	250	Grennhall/t	Taggart/t	Cook	Long/t	Cooke
N3 S	09-02	H	Redruth	W 23-3	300	Pritchard	Thorpe/t	Cook	Long	Taggart
N3 S	16-02	H	Barking	W 17-6		Pritchard	Thorpe	Cook	Greenhall	Taggart
N3 S	23-02	A	Cinderford	W 8-7		Pritchard	Thorpe/t	Cook	Long	Taggart
N3 S	09-03	H	Camberley	W 48-0	300	Grennhall	Thorpe/2t	Cook	Long	Cooke/t
N3 S	16-03	A	Old Colfeians	W 19-10	175	Pritchard	Cooke/t	Cook	Long	Taggart
N3 S	30-03	H	Tabard	W 34-7	250	Borrett/t	Thorpe/2t	Cook	Long	Grennhall
N3 S	06-04	A	Penzance & Newlyn	L 7-64	1200	Pritchard	Brand	Cook	Long	Taggart/t
N3 S	13-04	H	Old Patesians	W 27-21	250	Borrett	Thorpe	Cook/t	Greenhall	Cooke/t
PGC	15-09	N	Staines	W 28-0		Borrett	Brand	Grennhall	Wilmot/t2c3p	Cooke/t
PGC	29-09	H	Penzance & Newlyn	W 20-10	400	Borrett	Thorpe	Jenkins/t	Wilmot/2c2p	Kingsmill
PGC	13-10	N	Moseley	L 17-25	350	Grennhall/t	Kingsmill	Jenkins	Wilmot/2cp	Thorpe/t

** after opponents name indicates a penalty try. Brackets after a player's name indicates he was replaced. eg (a) means he was replaced by replacement code "a" and so on. / after a player or replacement name is followed by any scores he made - eg /t, /c, /p, /dg or any combination of these*

EVER PRESENT None

Most Appearances:
24: Gideon Rossouw.
22: John Dwight, Stuart Loose, John Morfoot.

PLAYERS USED

37 plus two as replacement only

MOST POINTS

Pts	Player	T	C	P	DG
125	L Wilmott	3	19	24	-
88	P Friel	2	12	18	-
80	A Thorpe	16	-	-	-
68	J Dwight	1	6	17	-
40	K Dodds	8	-	-	-

MATCH FACTS

10	9	1	2	3	4	5	6	7	8
Brand	Friel	Loose	Rosseau	Scott	Morfoot	Walters	Rout	Childs	Baker
Dwight/t	Friel	Loose	Rosseau	Groom	Marlee	Walters	Childs	van Poortvliet/t	Baker/t
Dwight	Friel	Loose	Rosseau/t	Groom	Morfoot	Walters	Childs	van Poortvliet	Dodds/t
Dwight	Friel/t	Loose	Rosseau	Groom	Morfoot	Marlee	Childs/2t	van Poortvliet	Malone/t
Dwight	Jenkins	Loose	Rosseau	Groom	Morfoot	Marlee	Dodds/t	Childs	Baker
Dwight	Friel	Loose	Rosseau	Groom	Morfoot	Marlee	Childs	van Poortvliet	Hood
Dwight	Friel	Loose	Rosseau	Leonard	Morfoot	Hood	Dodds	Childs	Baker
Dwight/6p	Friel	Loose	Rosseau	Leonard	Morfoot	Hood	Malone	van Poortvliet	Dodds
Dwight/c2p	Friel	Loose	Rosseau/t	Groom	Morfoot	Hood	Childs	van Poortvliet	Dodds/t
Dwight/cp	Jenkins	Leonard	Rosseau	Scott	Morfoot	Hood	Childs	van Poortvliet	Dodds/t
Dwight	Jenkins	Loose	Rosseau	Leonard	Morfoot	Hood	Childs	van Poortvliet	Baker
Dwight	Jenkins	Jenkins	Rosseau/t	Leonard	Marlee	Hood	Baker	van Poortvliet/t	Dodds
Dwight	Jenkins	Loose	Rosseau	Leonard	Morfoot	Hood	Childs	van Poortvliet/t	Dodds
Dwight/c	Jenkins	Loose	Rosseau	Leonard	Morfoot	Hood	Baker	van Poortvliet	Dodds
Dwight/c3p	Friel	Loose	Hambling	Leonard	Morfoot	Hood	Childs	van Poortvliet	Malone/t
Dwight/3p	Wyatt	Loose	Hambling	Leonard	Morfoot	Malone	Childs	van Poortvliet	Dodds
Greenhall	Friel/c2p	Loose	Rosseau/t	Leonard	Morfoot	Malone	Childs	van Poortvliet	Dodds
Greenhall	Friel/c5p	Loose	Rosseau	Leonard	Morfoot	Malone	Baker	van Poortvliet	Dodds
Greenhall	Friel/c2p	Loose	Rosseau	Leonard	Morfoot	Malone	Baker/t	van Poortvliet	Dodds/t
Dwight	Friel/4p	Leonard	Rosseau	Scott	Morfoot	Marlee	Baker/t	van Poortvliet	Dodds
Dwight	Friel/p	Loose	Rosseau	Leonard	Morfoot	Tyler	Baker	Childs	Dodds
Dwight	Friel/t4c	Loose	Rosseau/2t	Leonard	Morfoot	Tyler	Baker	van Poortvliet	Dodds/2t
Dwight	Friel/c4p	Loose	Rosseau	Leonard	Morfoot	Tyler	Baker	Childs	Dodds
Dwight/p	Friel/3c	Loose	Rosseau	Leonard	Tyler	Marlee	Childs	van Poortvliet	Dodds/t
Dwight	Friel/c	Williams	Rosseau	Leonard	Tyler	Malone	Marlee	Dodds	Hood
Dwight/2cp	Scott	Loose	Rosseau	Leonard	Tyler	Morfoot	Childs/2t	van Poortvliet	Malone
Dwight	Friel	Loose	Rosseau	Groom	Marlee	Mutimer	Rout	Childs/t	Baker
Dwight	Friel	Loose	Rosseau	Groom	Morfoot	Marlee	Childs/t	van Poortvliet	Baker
Dwight	Friel	Loose	Rosseau	Groom	Morfoot	Marlee	Childs	van Poortvliet	Baker

REPLACEMENTS: a - Chris Borrett.

WHERE	Total	Home	Away
The POINTS were scored	631	391	240
The POINTS were conceded	396	293	103
The TRIES were scored	76	54	22
The TRIES were conceded	47	36	11

HOW the TRIES were scored

Total	Backs	Forwards	F Back	Wing	Centre	H Back	F Row	Lock	B Row	Pen. Try
76	50	26	4	30	13	3	6	-	20	-

HOW the TRIES were conceded

Total	Backs	Forwards	F Back	Wing	Centre	H Back	F Row	Lock	B Row	Pen. Try
47	28	17	7	9	9	3	5	5	7	2

NORTH WALSHAM

LEAGUE STATISTICS *compiled by Stephen McCormack*

SEASON	Division	P	W	D	L	F	A	Pts Diff	Lge Pts	Lge Pos		Coach		Captain
92-93	D4S	12	4	0	8	125	209	-84	8	11				
93-94	D5S	12	5	2	5	120	173	-53	12	8				
94-95	D5S	12	7	1	4	233	190	43	15	4		R Flatters		N Greenall
												Most Points		**Most Tries**
95-96	D5S	12	3	1	8	149	212	-63	7	11	51	Tony Kingsmill	3	Smith
96-97	D4S	26	10	1	15	426	605	-179	21	10	70	James Shanahan	10	Tom Rains
97-98	N2S	26	12	1	13	431	373	58	25	7	253	James Shanahan	8	James Shanahan Adain Brand
98-99	N2S	26	22	0	4	627	306	321	44	3	158	Phil Friel	16	James Shanahan
99-00	N2S	26	19	0	7	792	358	434	38	3	167	Tony Kingsmill	21	James Shanahan
00-01	N3S	26	12	1	13	550	461	89	25	6	149	Phil Friel	9	Kenny Dodds
01-02	N3S	26	18	1	7	631	396	235	37	3	125	Len Wilmot	16	Andy Thorpe

FACT FILE

Founded: 1962 **Colours**: Green with 1 wide black & 2 narrow white bands/black/green.
Nickname: Walsh **Change colours:** All white **Away colours:** Red, white and blue
Web site: www.vikingrugby.com

GROUND

Address: Norwich Road, Scottow, Norwich, NR10 5BU
Tel: 01692 538808 (Office & Fax) 01692 538461 (Clubhouse)
e-mail: vikingrugby@lineout.net
Capacity: 1,000 Seated: 160 Standing: 1,000

Directions: From Norwich take B1150 to North Walsham, go through Coltishall towards N Walsham.
Ground is on left just past "Three Horseshoes" Pub
Nearest Railway Station: North Walsham

Car Parking: Ample at ground

Admission: Adults £5 inc programme
Kick Off All home kick offs 3.00pm

Clubhouse: Open matchdays & training nights.
Snacks & barmeals available
Functions Capacity 80, contact David Robinson 01692 538808

Club Shop: Yes, contact Pat Narracott 01692 538808

Training Nights: Tuesday & Thursday 7.30pm

PROGRAMME

Size: A5 Price: With Entry
Pages: 44 + cover
Editor: Tony Marcantonio 01493 751837

ADVERTISING RATES

Contact David Robinson 01692 538808

OLD COLFEIANS RFC

President	Moby Wale	Foxdon Cottage, Foxdon Hill, Wadeford, Chard, Somerset TA20 3AN 01460 65190 (H) 07776 235304 (M) email: martnam@tinyworld.co.uk
Chairman	Dick Hussey	5 The Avenue, Bickley, Bromley, Kent BR1 2BS 020 8290 5548 (H) 020 7240 3444 (B)
Secretary	Dai Andrew	18 Bereta Road, New Eltham, London SE9 3TZ 020 8859 6698 (H) 020 8852 1250 (B) 07775 825728 (M) email: diaandrew@aol.com
Treasurer	Clive Corlett	1 Lasseter Place, Vanburgh Hill, Blackheath, London SE3 7UX 020 8305 1261 (H)
Match Secretary	John Nunn	The Mount, 27 Westmount Rd., Eltham Park, London SE9 1JB 020 8850 1853 (H&F) 020 8265 7447 (H) 07989 449469 (M)
Sponsorship Sec.	Clive Reffell	3 Prior St., Greenwich, London SE10 8SF 020 8853 1004 (H) 07788 444396 (M)
Press Secretary	Ray Phillips	39 Holme Lacey Rd., Lee, London SE12 0HD 020 8857 4049 (H) 020 8333 1941 (F)
1st XV Manager	Paul Wainman	22 Ryecroft Rd., Offord, Kent TN14 5LX 01959 524351 (H)

After the euphoria of the previous season in London One when Old Colfeians remained unbeaten, thus achieving National League status, the task ahead was expected to be difficult and so it proved. After eight weeks inactivity the Old Boys set off for a tour to Australia to follow the Lions Test Matches and to play some rugby against the host clubs. The tour was most successful with victory in every game, but this took its toll on the players with many injuries to key players and one player staying down under until almost Christmas. The situation was further compounded by a lack of the fitness required for National League rugby which led to still more injuries.

The combination of all of these factors meant that victories were hard to come by and at the turn of the year after fourteen games played we had only nine points to show for our efforts.

We scored fairly well but holes appeared in the defence and we conceded far too many points especially in the last ten to fifteen minutes of each game. We managed to complete the double over Clifton during February but as Easter approached we still only had eleven points and all was left to be done in the last four games. The return of Ben Hyde an inspirational scrum half for the game against North Walsham brought a much improved all round performance from the team, but not quite enough for victory.

Three games remained and if the improvement could continue then all might not be lost and so it proved; we won all three games completing the double over Camberley and Cinderford and claiming a notable victory over Redruth. We had reached seventeen points with double victories over the three sides below us and the victory over Lydney added to that over Redruth plus the one point gained against Tabard with a penalty off the crossbar being the last action of the game.

So we live to fight again as the only Old Boys club in the National Leagues. We hope to perform more consistently during our second season in National 3 South when the rugby club celebrates its 75th season.

In spite of the poor season on the field the support for the team has increased and a new 1st XV pitch has been prepared funded by donations from past players and supporters. Plans are now in hand to provide a stand for 110 people to sit and watch the game protected from the elements.

Despite the nail biting nature of the season the players, manager, coaches, physios, officials and supporters have enjoyed the hospitality of our new opponents, the new friendships made and the comradeship that rugby football still offers.

We look forward to the new season when the battle to maintain our national status will recommence The officials are all continuing in their respective offices, but the club has a new captain in Tim Tunnicliff.

OLD COLFEIANS

Comp.	Date	H/A	Opponents	Result & Score	Att	15	14	13	12	11
N3 S	01-09	A	Westcombe Park	L 22-26	450	Townsend/c5p	Lewis	Rutter	Powell	Hurley
N3 S	08-09	A	North Walsham	L 10-57		Townsend/cp(a/t)	Lewis	Keelan	Hurley	Jarrett
N3 S	22-09	H	Blackheath	L 17-28		Townsend/4p	Lewis(b/t)	Rutter	Powell	Leveringto
N3 S	06-10	A	Clifton	W 39-27	200	Townsend	Lewis/t	Rutter/2t	Powell/4cp	Leveringto
N3 S	20-10	H	Barking	L 12-32		Townsend/4p	Lewis	Rutter	Powell	Leveringto
N3 S	27-10	A	Tabard	D 26-26	200	Townsend/2c4p	Lewis	Rutter	Chapman	Jarrett/2t
N3 S	03-11	H	Old Patesians	L 15-23	150	Townsend/5p	Leverington	Rutter	Powell	Jarrett
N3 S	10-11	A	Penzance & Newlyn	L 7-62		Lewis	Wicks	Chapman	Davey	Jarrett/t
N3 S	17-11	H	Launceston	L 18-23		Hurley	Wicks/t	Chapman	Davey	Jarrett
N3 S	24-11	H	Lydney	W 26-9	100	Hurley/t	Wicks	Rutter	Chapman	Jarrett/t
N3 S	01-12	A	Westcombe Park	L 21-28		Townsend/2p	Jarrett/t	Rutter	Davey	Hurley/t
N3 S	08-12	H	Cinderford	W 37-18		Hurley	Rutter	Powell	Davey	Jarrett/2t
N3 S	15-12	A	Redruth	L 34-48	720	Chapman	Potts	Lock/t	Davey	Tilson/2t
N3 S	22-12	H	Camberley*	W 23-21		Chapman	Jarrett/t	Lock	Davey	Hurley
N3 S	12-01	A	Launceston	L 12-57	420	Powell	Tilson	Lock	Chapman	Jarrett
N3 S	19-01	H	Penzance & Newlyn	L 19-56	225	Townsend/c3p	Jarrett	Lock	Powell	Hurley
N3 S	02-02	H	Tabard	L 6-29	125	Hurley	Rutter	Powell	Davey	Jarrett
N3 S	09-02	A	Barking	L 19-29	300	Townsend/c4p	Rutter	Lock	Powell	Hurley
N3 S	16-02	A	Lydney	L 9-56	227	Townsend/3p	Lock	Powell	Davey	Jarrett
N3 S	23-02	H	Clifton	W 21-18	225	Townsend/c3p	Rutter	Lock	Powell	Hurley/t
N3 S	02-03	A	Old Patesians*	L 31-51	200	Lewis/t	Tilson	Davey	Birkett	Lewis/t
N3 S	09-03	A	Blackheath	L 14-36	450	Townsend	Lewis/t	Rutter	Davey	Hurley
N3 S	16-03	H	North Walsham	L 10-19	175	Powell/cp	Lewis	Rutter	Lock	Hurley
N3 S	30-03	A	Camberley	W 30-26		Townsend/3c3p	Jarrett	Rutter/2t	Lock/t	Hurley
N3 S	06-04	H	Redruth*	W 44-22	150	Townsend/3cp	Jarrett/t	Rutter	Lock/t	Hurley
N3 S	13-04	A	Cinderford	W 32-14	125	Townsend/2cp	Jarrett	Rutter/2t	Lock/t	Hurley
PGC	15-09	N	Swanagae	W 34-0		Townsend/t3cp	Lewis	Rutter/t	Powell	Leverington/
PGC	29-09	A	Barking	L 18-27		Townsend/6p	Lewis	Rutter	Powell	Leverington

** after opponents name indicates a penalty try. Brackets after a player's name indicates he was replaced. eg (a) means he was replaced by replacement code "a" and so on. / after a player or replacement name is followed by any scores he made - eg /t, /c, /p, /dg or any combination of these*

EVER PRESENT One

Most Appearances:
26: Stephen Corlett.
25: Matthew Townsend.
24: Tim Tunnicliffe.

PLAYERS USED

35 plus four as a replacement only

MOST POINTS

Pts	Player	T	C	P	DG
248	M Townsend	-	34	60	-
45	M Jarrett	9	-	-	-
35	R Berry	7	-	-	-
30	J Rutter	6	-	-	-

MATCH FACTS

10	9	1	2	3	4	5	6	7	8
Chapman	Hyde	Quilter	Corlett	Tunnicliffe	Sargent	Hodgkiss	Evans/t	Johnston	Blackwell
Chapman	Hyde	Quilter	Corlett	Tunnicliffe	Garland	Hodgkiss	Evans	Johnston	Blackwell
Chapman	Tilson	Quilter	Corlett	Tunnicliffe	Sargent	Hodgkiss	Evans	Berry	Baker
Chapman/dg	Vickers/t	Quilter	Corlett	Tunnicliffe	Sargent	Hodgkiss	Evans	Berry/t	Baker
Chapman	Vickers	Quilter	Corlett	Tunnicliffe	Sargent	Hodgkiss	Evans	Johnston	Williams
Kennedy	Vickers	Hughes	Corlett	Tunnicliffe	Sargent	Blackwell	Evans	Johnston	Williams
Chapman	Vickers	Quilter	Corlett	Tunnicliffe	Sargent	Blackwell	Johnston	Berry	Williams
Townsend/c	Vickers	Quilter	Corlett	Tunnicliffe	Walden	Hodgkiss	Johnston	Berry	Evans
Townsend/c2p	Vickers	Hughes	Corlett	Tunnicliffe	Walden	Hodgkiss	Johnston	Berry/t	Evans
Townsend/2c4p	Vickers	Quilter	Corlett	Tunnicliffe	Sargent	Walden	Johnston	Berry	Baker
Chapman	Tilson	Quilter	Corlett	Tunnicliffe	Walden	Walden	Evans	Berry/t	Baker
Townsend/4c3p	Vickers	Quilter	Corlett	Tunnicliffe	Sargent/t	Griffiths	Baker/t	Berry	Walden
Townsend/4c2p	Vickers	Quilter	Corlett	Tunnicliffe	Sargent	Griffiths	Baker	Berry/t	Walden
Townsend/2c3p	Vickers	Hughes	Corlett	Tunnicliffe	Walden	Griffiths	Evans	Berry	Baker
Townsend/c	Vickers	Hughes	Corlett	Tunnicliffe	Walden	Griffiths	Johnston/t	Berry/t	Evans
Chapman/dg	Vickers	Quilter	Corlett	Tunnicliffe	Walden	Griffiths	Evans	Berry/t	Baker
Townsend/2p	Vickers	Quilter	Corlett	Tunnicliffe	Hodgkiss	Griffiths	Baker	Berry	Walden
Kennedy	Holden	Quilter	Corlett	Tunnicliffe	Hodgkiss	Sargent	Griffiths/t	Baker	Walden
Kennedy	Holden	Quilter	Corlett	Tunnicliffe	Sargent	Griffiths	Evans	Baker	Walden
Kennedy	Holden	Quilter	Corlett	Tunnicliffe	Sargent	Hodgkiss	Baker	Berry	Walden/t
Townsend/4cp	Vickers	Hughes	Corlett	Tunnicliffe	Hodgkiss	Griffiths	Evans	Baker/t	Sargent
Kennedy/2c	Holden	Quilter	Corlett	Hughes	Sargent(c/t)	Griffiths	Evans	Baker	Walden
Kennedy	Hyde	Quilter	Corlett	Hughes	Garland	Hodgkiss/t	Evans	Berry	Walden
Kennedy	Hyde	Quilter	Corlett	Tunnicliffe	Garland	Hodgkiss	Baker	Berry	Walden
Kennedy	Hyde	Quilter	Corlett	Tunnicliffe	Garland/t	Hodgkiss	Evans/t	Baker/t	Walden/t
Kennedy	Hyde/t	Quilter	Corlett	Tunnicliffe	Garland	Hodgkiss	Evans	Baker	Walden/t
Chapman	Tilson	Quilter	Corlett	Tunnicliffe	Sargent	Hodgkiss	Garland	Johnston	Baker
Chapman	Tilson	Quilter	Corlett	Tunnicliffe	Sargent	Hodgkiss	Evans	Berry	Williams

REPLACEMENTS: a - Robert Berry. b - Gavin Hurley. c - Adam Hodgkiss.

WHERE	Total	Home	Away
The POINTS were scored	554	248	306
The POINTS were conceded	841	543	298
The TRIES were scored	56	22	34
The TRIES were conceded	113	77	36

HOW the TRIES were scored

Total	Backs	Forwards	F Back	Wing	Centre	H Back	F Row	Lock	B Row	Pen. Try
56	33	20	3	18	10	2	-	4	16	3

HOW the TRIES were conceded

Total	Backs	Forwards	F Back	Wing	Centre	H Back	F Row	Lock	B Row	Pen. Try
113	74	38	9	34	21	10	10	7	21	1

OLD COLFEIANS

LEAGUE STATISTICS *compiled by Stephen McCormack*

SEASON	Division	P	W	D	L	F	A	Pts Diff	Lge Pts	Lge Pos	Most Points	Most Tries
92-93	L1	12	5	2	5	198	203	-5	12	12		
93-94	L1	12	5	0	7	166	221	-55	10	12		
94-95	L1	12	4	0	8	202	256	-54	8	12		
95-96	L1	12	4	0	8	138	241	-103	8	12		
96-97	L1	12	7	0	5	258	347	-89	12*	12		
97-98	L1	16	5	0	11	336	504	-168	10	13		
98-99	L1	16	9	1	6	310	316	-6	19	7		
99-00	L1	16	12	1	3	512	310	202	25	3		
00-01	L1	20	18	0	2	742	212	530	38	1p	332 Matthew Townsend	18 David Lewis
01-02	N3S	26	8	1	17	554	841	-287	17	11	248 Matthew Townsend	9 Mark Jarrett

FACT FILE

Founded: 1928
Nickname:

Colours: Navy blue, burgundy, old gold & black bands/navy/navy
Change colours: Old gold with single narrow navy, burgundy & black bands

GROUND

Address Horn Park, Eltham Road, Lee, London SE12
Tel: 0208 852 1181

Directions Ground is in Eltham Road opposite Weigal Road, on the A20, 600 metres in the direction of Lee, Lewisham and London from the intersection of the A20 / A205 / South Circular Road.
Nearest Railway Station: Lee 10-15 min. walk or Lewisham (then taxi).

Capacity 1000 - all uncovered standing

Car Parking 200 at club

Admission £4 including programme & parking..
Season tickets: Not available.

Clubhouse Open during normal licensing hours, 7 days.
2 bars.

Club Shop Open during home League and Cup games.
Contact Josie Troke.

Training Nights Tuesday & Thursday

PROGRAMME
Size: A5
Pages: 24-28
Price: with admission
Editor: George Troke
Advertising: Page: £350 1/2 page £200

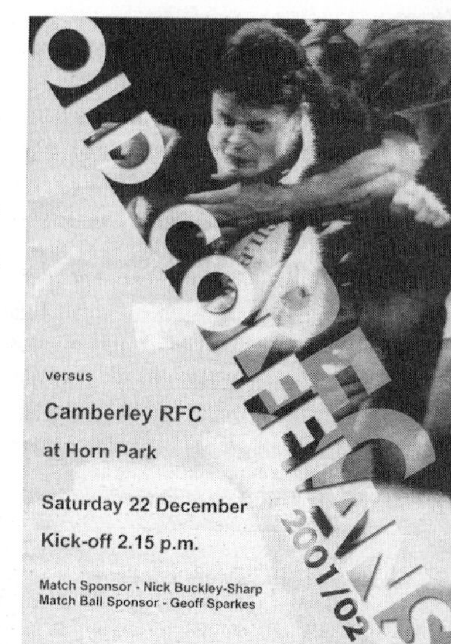

OLD PATESIANS RFC

President	David Powell	Rigi, Western Rd., Cheltenham	01242 514980 (H)
Chairman	Ray Kingscott	94 Leckhampton RD., Cheltenham GL53 0BZ	01242 519569 (H) 07957 594032 (M)
Secretary	Steve Webley	56 Mead Rd., Cheltenham GL53 7DT	01242 244865 (H)
Treasurer	James Luxton	6 Littledown Rd., Cheltenham GL53 9LP	01242 260715 (H)
Fixture Secretary	Mark Knight	14b Canterbury Walk, Cheltenham GL51 5HG	01242 698756(H) 01242 271583 (B) 07719 857761 (M)

The Old Patesians first season in National League Three (South) resulted in a creditable fifth position. Indeed no other clubs in Gloucestershire, other than Gloucester themselves, finished above us in the league structure. Considering where we started in league rugby all concerned with the Pats feel this is a remarkable achievement, though we will not be resting on our laurels, and fully intend to mount a serous challenge in the league and cup competitions.
Several new players were added to the squad at the begging of the season and a transitional period ensued. The players efforts both in training and on the field of play, were eventually rewarded. Consistent home form underpinned our rise up the league. By the end of the season every club other than the top two had been at least once, and five away wins ensured our healthy final placing.
Our second XV were runaway winners of the South West Merit Table and look forward to defending it vigorously next season. With 43 different players used in our national league campaign it demonstrated both a strength in depth and the ability of „unrecognized‰ players to step into the breach at times of need and perform well.
The county cup remained elusive, but with success in local competitions our high league position the season was far from unsatisfactory. For the first time having players chosen to represent the senior Gloucester squad, head coach Chris Raymond, Player of the year Scott Pollock and Matt Dawson were all in the squad for the County Championship against Cheshire.
For the coming season our ambition is evident with the addition of Bruce Fenley to our coaching team. Bruce like Chris Raymond is a product of the Pats juniors, has played senior rugby at Moseley, Gloucester, Worcester and Stourbridge and is currently three quarters coach for the county. The very strong coaching team that the Pats posses will aim to make the Pats competitive every Saturday.
The club continues to run four senior sides every Saturday and juniors over the weekend and welcomes all who want to either play or watch, and look forward to renewing old friendships and making new ones in the coming season.

Old Patesians - Cheltenahm Combination Senior Cup Winners 2002

L-R standing - Paul Morris (coach), Pat Poulton (manager), Pat Burford, Ben Matthews, Mark Bartlett, James Strickland, Chris Long, Scott Pollok, Russell Nunn, Ben Parker, Chris Penhale, Pete Mitchell, Andy MacDonald, Chris Raymond (head coach). L-R Kneeling: Jason Hyde, Ben Wilsdon, Mark Peacey, Joel Keen, Marcus Twinning, Matt Dawson, Ross Bisset, Dave Parry, Jon Steckbeck (captain), Ralph Tucker, James Saunders.

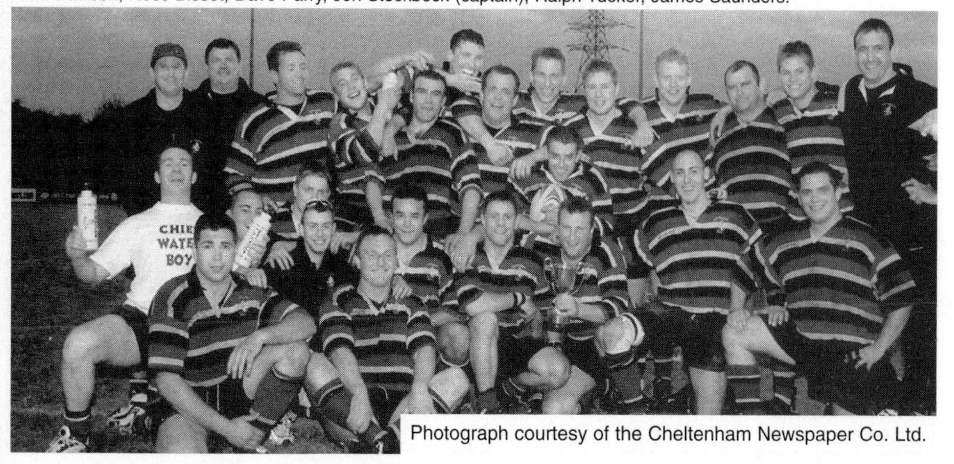

Photograph courtesy of the Cheltenham Newspaper Co. Ltd.

OLD PATESIANS

Comp.	Date	H/A	Opponents	Result & Score	Att	15	14	13	12	11
N3 S	01-09	H	Clifton	W 19-15		Robinson/t3p	Davies/t	Taylor	Bright	Matthews
N3 S	08-09	A	Barking	L 11-30		Davies	Nunn/2p	Parker	Taylor	Matthews
N3 S	22-09	H	Tabard	W 38-24	200	Pollock/t	Matthews/2t	Tucker	Taylor/t	Nunn/2c3p
N3 S	06-10	H	Lydney	L 15-21	300	Pollock/t	Davies	Tucker	Taylor	Nunn/cp
N3 S	20-10	A	Penzance & Newlyn	L 10-73	700	Pollock	Nunn	Tucker/t	Elliott-Square	Davies
N3 S	27-10	H	Launceston*	L 22-34		Pollock	Davies	Tucker/t	Taylor	Nunn/2cp
N3 S	03-11	A	Old Colfeians	W 23-15	150	Pollock/t	Matthews/t	Tucker	Taylor	Lockwood
N3 S	10-11	H	Camberley	W 28-25	100	Pollock	Matthews	Matthews	Taylor	Fraine
N3 S	17-11	A	Cinderford	L 3-13	400	Pollock	Matthews	Burley	Taylor	Nunn/p
N3 S	24-11	H	Redruth	W 59-35	300	Pollock/8cp	Matthews	Burley/3t	Taylor/t	Davies
N3 S	01-12	A	Clifton	W 18-15		Pollock/p	Matthews	Burley	Taylor	Davies
N3 S	08-12	H	North Walsham	W 38-12		Pollock/tc2p	Matthews/t	Burley	Taylor	Nunn/tcp
N3 S	15-12	A	Blackheath*	L 14-46	300	Pollock	Matthews	Burley	Taylor	Nunn/2c
N3 S	22-12	H	Westcombe Park*	W 31-30		Pollock/4cp	Matthews	Parker/t	Tucker/t	Burley
N3 S	05-01	A	Redruth	W 29-28	650	Pollock/t3cp	Matthews	Parker/t	Taylor	Tucker/t
N3 S	12-01	H	Cinderford	W 34-5		Pollock/c	Benjamin/t	Tucker	Taylor	Nunn/c
N3 S	19-01	A	Camberley	W 15-13	150	Pollock	Matthews/t	Parker/t	Tucker	Nunn/t
N3 S	09-02	H	Penzance & Newlyn	L 20-26		Pollock/c	Matthews	Taylor	Tucker	Nunn/p
N3 S	23-02	A	Lydney	W 15-11	365	Pollock/t	Matthews	Tucker	Taylor	Nunn/cp
N3 S	02-03	H	Old Colfeians	W 51-31	200	Pollock	Nunn/t4cp	Parker/t	Taylor/t	Davies
N3 S	09-03	A	Tabard*	L 13-22	200	Pollock	Nunn/c2p	Tucker	Bartlett	Davies
N3 S	16-03	H	Barking	W 28-12	300	Pollock/2c2p	Matthews	Parker	Taylor	Lockwood
N3 S	23-03	A	Launceston	L 3-54	400	Pollock/p	Matthews	Tucker	Taylor	Nunn
N3 S	30-03	A	Westcombe Park	L 15-45	250	Davies	Matthews/t	Parker	Taylor	Nunn/p
N3 S	06-04	H	Blackheath*	W 23-21	400	Pollock	Matthews	Parker	Bartlett	Nunn/c2p
N3 S	13-04	A	North Walsham	L 21-27	250	Pollock/c	Nunn/3p	Taylor	Parker	Matthews
PGC	15-09	N	Barking	L 11-26		Pollock	Nunn/2p	Tucker	Taylor	Matthews

** after opponents name indicates a penalty try. Brackets after a player's name indicates he was replaced. eg (a) means he was replaced by replacement code "a" and so on. / after a player or replacement name is followed by any scores he made - eg /t, /c, /p, /dg or any combination of these*

EVER PRESENT None

Most Appearances:
24: Scott Pollock.
23: Ross Bissett (2), Will Morgan (1).

PLAYERS USED

37 plus six as replacement only

MOST POINTS

Pts	Player	T	C	P	DG
107	R Nunn	3	16	20	-
101	S Pollock	6	22	9	-
65	W Morgan	13	-	-	-
30	B Matthews	6	-	-	-
28	J Steckbeck	5	-	-	1

MATCH FACTS

10	9	1	2	3	4	5	6	7	8
Steckbeck	Morgan	Harvey	Bisset	Mitchell	Wilsden	Raymond	Burford	Parry	Bunn
Armstrong	Morgan/t	Harvey	Bisset	Mitchell	Penhale	Raymond	Burford	Parry	Bunn
Steckbeck	Morgan	Harvey	Bisset	Mitchell	Stickland	Penhale(a/t)	Burford	Parry	Raymond
Steckbeck	Morgan/t	Harvey	Bisset	Long	Stickland	Wilsden	Burford	Parry	Raymond
Steckbeck/t	Morgan	Saunders	Bisset	Mitchell	Stickland	Wilsden	Burford	Parry	Jones
Armstrong	Morgan	Long	Bisset	Mitchell	Stickland	Wilsden	Jones	Parry	Dawson/t
Armstrong(b/p)	Morgan	Saunders	Bisset	Long	Penhale	Wilsden	Burford/cp	Parry	Dawson/t
Steckbeck/t	Morgan/t	Saunders	Bisset	Mitchell/2t	Penhale	Burford/c2p	Jones	Parry	Dawson
Steckbeck	Morgan	Long	Bisset	Mitchell	Stickland	Burford	Jones	Parry	Penhale
Steckbeck/t	Morgan/2t	Saunders	Bisset	Mitchell/t	Stickland	Wilsden	Jones	Parry	Dawson
Steckbeck	Morgan/2t	Saunders/t	Bisset	Long	Penhale	Wilsden	Burford	Jones	Dawson
Steckbeck/t	Elliott-Square	Saunders/t	Bisset	Mitchell	Stickland	Wilsden	Burford	Jones	Dawson
Armstrong/t	Morgan	Saunders	Bisset	Long	Stickland	Wilsden	Burford	Parry	Miller
Steckbeck	Morgan	Saunders/t	Bisset	Mitchell	Stickland	Wilsden	Burford	Parry	Dawson
Steckbeck	Morgan	Harvey	Bisset/t	Long	Penhale	Wilsden	Raymond	Parry	Dawson
Steckbeck/t	Morgan/2t	Saunders	Bisset	Mitchell	Stickland	Raymond	Burford	Parry/t	Dawson(c/t)
Steckbeck	Morgan	Saunders	Bisset	Mitchell	Wilsden	Penhale	Miller	Parry	Raymond
Steckbeck	Morgan/2t	Saunders	Bisset	Long	Raymond/t	Wilsden	Miller	Burford	Dawson
Steckbeck	Morgan	Saunders	Venner	Mitchell	Penhale/t	Wilsden	Dawson	Burford	Raymond
Steckbeck	Morgan	Saunders/t	Bisset	Venner(d/t)	Stickland/t	Wilsden/t	Dawson/t	Miller	Raymond
Steckbeck	Elliott-Square	Long	Bisset	Mitchell	Stickland	Wilsden	Miller	Raymond	Parry
Steckbeck	Morris/p(e/2t)	Saunders	Lutey	Long	Penhale	Raymond	Burford	Parry/t	Dawson
Steckbeck	Morgan	Harvey	Bisset	Mitchell	Wilsden	Raymond	Penhale	Parry	Dawson
Pollock/c	Morgan	Saunders	Lutey	Mitchell	Wilsden	Culafic	Penhale	Parry/t	Raymond
Steckbeck	Morgan	Saunders/t	Bisset	Mitchell/t	Raymond	Wilsden	Burford	Parry	Dawson
Steckbeck	Morgan	Saunders	Bisset	Long	Wilsden	Raymond/t	Dawson	Parry/t	Penhale
Steckbeck	Morgan	Long	Hyde	Mitchell	Stickland	Wilsden/t	Bunn	Parry	Raymond

REPLACEMENTS: a - Steve Bunn. b - Jon Steckbeck. c - Chris Penhale d - Chris Long. e - Gill Morgan

WHERE	Total	Home	Away
The POINTS were scored	596	406	190
The POINTS were conceded	683	392	191
The TRIES were scored	81	56	25
The TRIES were conceded	89	53	36

HOW the TRIES were scored

Total	Backs	Forwards	F Back	Wing	Centre	H Back	F Row	Lock	B Row	Pen. Try
81	51	25	7	12	13	19	11	6	8	5

HOW the TRIES were conceded

Total	Backs	Forwards	F Back	Wing	Centre	H Back	F Row	Lock	B Row	Pen. Try
89	60	25	7	26	15	12	6	10	9	4

OLD PATESIANS

LEAGUE STATISTICS *compiled by Stephen McCormack*

SEASON	Division	P	W	D	L	F	A	Pts Diff	Lge Pts	Lge Pos				
92-93	G&S1	12	11	0	1	307	94	213	22	1p				
93-94	WC	12	10	1	1	215	99	116	21	1p				
94-95	SW2	12	7	0	5	288	167	121	12*	5				
95-96	SW2	12	4	0	8	167	231	-64	8	10				
96-97	SW2w	22	13	0	9	447	341	106	26	3				
97-98	SW2w	22	19	0	3	485	257	228	38	1p				
98-99	SW1	22	6	1	15	320	506	-186	13	9				
99-00	SW1	22	8	1	13	386	583	-197	17	8				
00-01	SW1	22	21	0	1	593	209	384	42	1p	197	Tony Robinson	20	Will Morgan
01-02	N3S	26	15	0	11	596	683	-87	30	5	107	Russell Nunn	13	Will Morgan

FACT FILE

Founded: 1913
Nickname: The Pats

Colours: magenta, navy & white hoops
Change colours: Navy with white band

GROUND

Address Clubhouse, Everest Rd., Leckhampton, Cheltenham. GL53 9LG
Tel: 01242 524633 Web site: www.old-pats.freeuk.com

Capacity 500 all uncovered standing

Directions

From M5, J11a (Cirencester) towards Cirencester. Take exit A46 (Cheltenham/Stroud) towards Cheltenham. After approx. 1.5 miles turn right opposite Bell Inn signed Leckhampton. At mini r'about turn right then take 1st left (at Suzuki garage). Follow to end over crossroads and ground is thro' stone pillars at end.

From M4, J15 & follow signs for Cheltenham past Swindon then Cirencester. At end of dual carriageway follow to r'about with Air Balloon PH. Turn right and immediate left signed Leckhampton/Cheltenham. Follow down steep hill & turn right just after 30mph sign into Old Bath Road. Follow for approx 400 yds to Wheatsheaf pub. Turn right & ground at the end thro' stone pillars.

Nearest Railway Station: Cheltenham, 3 miles
Car Parking 100 spaces at the ground

Admission Matchday: £4.00 incl. programme.
Season tickets: Not available.

Clubhouse Open every evening &
Sat. & Sun. lunchtime. Food available.
Available for hire, contact club 01242 524633

Club Shop No

Training Nights Tuesday & Thursday

PROGRAMME **Size**: A5 **Pages**: 28
Price: With admission
Editor: Contact club

Advertising: Page £100; 1/2 page: £60; 1/4 page: £50

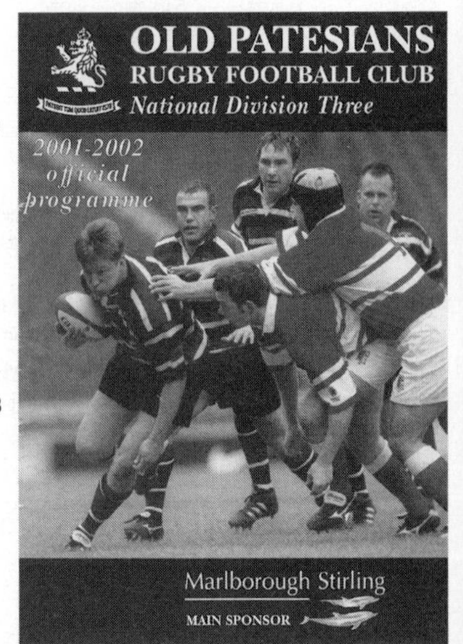

REDRUTH RFC

President	W J `Bill' Bishop OBE	Lafrowda, Tregolls Road, Truro TR1 1LE
Secretary	Roger Watson	Trelawny House, 30 Fore St., Tregony, Truro TR2 5RN Tel & Fax: 01872 530687 (H); Tel 01872 530675 (B); 07790 365250 (M) e-mail: watson_roger@hotmail.com
Fixtures Secretary	Denzil Williams	13 Boskennal Drive, Hayle, TR27 4DX 01736 752795 (H)
Assistant Fixtures Sec.	Mr Peter Flack	18 Sparnon Terrace, Redruth, TR15 2RG Tel: (H) 01209 213654; (B) 01209 213171
Treasurer	Cyril Harding	Chy-an-Brea, Silver Hill, Perrannell Station, Truro TR3 7LP 01872 863650
First XV Team Manager	David Penberthy	38 Merritts Way, Treloweth Gardens, Pool, Redruth TR15 3TY Tel: 01209 217488

Last season was always going to be difficult for "The Reds" as the closed season had seen the departure of a number of more experienced players and the emphasis was placed on developing the younger members of the squad. Although results did not always go in our favour the young side competed extremely well and will form the basis of the team for this season's campaign. With a season's league experience behind them, augmented by our talented older players there is a mood of quiet confidence in the camp and a determination to improve on our away form of recent seasons. We will, as always, be keen to give our visitors a warm welcome at Redruth where our loyal supporters will do their best to ensure that our guests have a day to remember off the pitch although we hope they will not have too much to celebrate on it!

This spring and summer has seen a number of changes on the coaching side and a new team management is in place so we are looking forward to improving on last term's mid table finish.

At the lower levels our colts continued to dominate, winning the county cup for a record fifth time in succession. They also had another great run in the national colts competition. The mini/junior section has a tremendously successful season showing that the future of Redruth RFC is in safe hands.

County finals day at Twickenham saw the Cornwall seven finish as runners up in their competition – a squad made up almost entirely of Redruth players. Another reason for pride and optimism at the Recreation Ground.

This summer's final boost came with the announcement that Phil Vickery, an ex Redruth player, was to captain England on their tour of Argentina. Congratulations Phil, both on the honour and on the results achieved by the young, talented England side.

Action from Camberley v Redruth. Photo: Lee Crabbe

REDRUTH

Comp.	Date	H/A	Opponents	Result & Score	Att	15	14	13	12	11
N3 S	01-09	A	Camberley	L 9-12	250	Larkins/3p	Hymans	Sweeney	Kirman	Bushin
N3 S	08-09	H	Cinderford	W 28-6	800	Sincock	Larkins/2c3p	Sweeney	Kirman/t	Whitcombe
N3 S	22-09	A	Lydney	L 17-33	521	Sincock	Veale	Sweeney	Kirman	Larkins/t2cp
N3 S	06-10	A	Westcombe Park	L 18-42	100	Larkins/c2p	Veale	Waterford	Bonds	Sweeney
N3 S	20-10	H	North Walsham	L 19-26		Sincock	Bushin	Waterford	Sweeney	Larkins/t3p
N3 S	27-10	A	Blackheath	W 20-15		Sincock	Whitcombe	Sweeney	Waterford	Larkins/2c2p
N3 S	03-11	H	Clifton	W 24-17	600	Chapple/t	Sincock	Sweeney	Waterford	Larkins/tc4p
N3 S	10-11	A	Barking	L 31-35		Chapple/t	Edyvean	Sincock	Kirman	Larkins/2t3c
N3 S	17-11	H	Tabard	W 49-10		Chapple	Edyvean/2t	Sincock/t	Kirman	Larkins/t3cp
N3 S	24-11	A	Old Patesians*	L 35-59	300	Chapple/3c2p	Sincock/2t	Waterford	Kirman	Larkins/p
N3 S	01-12	H	Camberley	W 23-13	600	Sincock/t	Pengilly	Bonds/t	Kirman	Edyvean
N3 S	08-12	A	Launceston*	L 29-33	1200	Pedley	Veale/t	Bonds	Kirman/t	Edyvean
N3 S	15-12	H	Old Colfeians	W 48-34	720	Pedley/2t	Veale/t	Bonds/t	Waterford	Edyvean/t
N3 S	22-12	A	Penzance & Newlyn	L 22-38	1600	Pedley	Sincock	Bonds	Waterford	Whitcombe/t
N3 S	05-01	H	Old Patesians	L 28-29	650	Larkins/t2c3p	Veale	Bonds/t	Waterford	Whitcombe/t
N3 S	12-01	A	Tabard	W 20-19		Larkins/2c2p	Veale	Whitcombe	Waterford/2t	Hymans
N3 S	19-01	H	Barking	W 27-3	700	Larkins/3c2p	Hymans	Bonds/3t	Waterford	Whitcombe
N3 S	02-02	H	Blackheath	W 24-20	500	Larkins/3cp	Hymans	Bonds	Waterford/t	Whitcombe
N3 S	09-02	A	North Walsham	L 3-23	300	Bonds	Hymans	Waterford	Kirman	Whitcombe
N3 S	23-02	H	Westcombe Park	W 19-10	600	Larkins/2c	Hymans	Bonds/t	Kirman/t	Whitcombe
N3 S	02-03	A	Clifton	W 34-33	100	Larkins/t3cp	Whitcombe	Bonds	Kirman/t	Hymans
N3 S	09-03	H	Lydney	L 22-24	800	Larkins/2tc	Whitcombe/t	Bonds	Waterford	Hymans
N3 S	16-03	A	Cinderford	W 21-20	300	Larkins/t2p	Whitcombe/t	Bonds	Waterford	Hymans/t
N3 S	30-03	H	Penzance & Newlyn	L 22-76	2000	Sincock	Whitcombe/t	Bonds/t	Kirman	Larkins/c
N3 S	06-04	A	Old Colfeians	L 22-44	150	Larkins/c	Hymans	Bonds	Kirman/t	Thirby/2t
N3 S	13-04	H	Launceston	L 15-62	1200	Larkins/cp	Hymans/t	Bonds	Kirman/t	Corcoran
PGC	15-09	N	Norwich	W 13-0		Sincock/t	Veale	Sweeney	Kirman	Larkins/c2p

** after opponents name indicates a penalty try. Brackets after a player's name indicates he was replaced. eg (a) means he was replaced by replacement code "a" and so on. / after a player or replacement name is followed by any scores he made - eg /t, /c, /p, /dg or any combination of these*

EVER PRESENT Two

Most Appearances:
26: Andy Hawken, Tom Sincock.
25Nick Croker.
22: Craig Bons, Liam Chapple(3), Neil Douch (2).

PLAYERS USED

35 plus five as replacement only

MOST POINTS

Pts	Player	T	C	P	DG
217	S Larkins	11	33	32	-
67	L Chapple	3	14	8	-
40	C Bonds	8	-	-	-
35	J Lancaster	7	-	-	-
30	S Kirman	6	-	-	-

MATCH FACTS

10	9	1	2	3	4	5	6	7	8
Sincock	Chapple	Douch	Croker	Filde	Robbins	Gray	Ellis	Boase	Hawken
Waterford	Chapple	Douch/t	May/t	Croker	O'Sullivan	Gray	Ellis	Boase	Hawken
Waterford	Turnbull	Douch	Harrison	Croker	O'Sullivan	Gray	Ellis	May/t	Hawken
Sincock	Turnbull	Douch/t	May	Croker	Hawken	Gray	Corin	Boase/t	Arnold
Bonds	Turnbull	Douch	Harrison	Croker	Hawken	Gray/t	Ellis	Boase	Arnold
Bonds(a/t)	Turnbull	Filde	Harrison	Croker	Hawken	Collins	Lancaster/t	Boase	Arnold
Bonds	Turnbull	Filde	Harrison	Croker	Hawken	Collins	Lancaster	Boase	Arnold
Bonds	Turnbull/t	Douch	Harrison	Croker	Hawken	Collins	Lancaster/t	Boase	Arnold
Bonds	Turnbull/t	Douch	Harrison	Croker(b/2t)	Hawken	Collins	Lancaster/t	Boase	Arnold
Bonds	Turnbull	Douch	Harrison	Croker	Collins/t	Gray	Instance	Boase	Hawken
Chapple/c2p	Turnbull	Douch	Harrison	Croker	Hawken	Collins	Lancaster	Boase/t	Arnold
Chapple/3cp	Sincock	Douch	Harrison	Croker	Hawken	Gray	Lancaster	Boase/t	Arnold
Chapple/t5cp	Sincock/t	Douch	Harrison	Croker	Hawken	Gray	Lancaster	Boase	Arnold
Chapple/2cp	Turnbull	Douch/t	Harrison	Croker	Hawken	Gray	Lancaster	Boase/t	Arnold
Chapple	Sincock	Douch	Bush	Croker	Hawken	Collins	May	Lancaster	Lancaster
Chapple	Sincock	Douch	Bush	Croker	Hawken	Collins	May	Lancaster	Arnold
Chapple	Sincock	Douch	Harrison	Croker	Hawken	Collins	Navin	Lancaster	Arnold
Chapple	Sincock	Filde	Harrison	Croker/t	O'Sullivan	Collins	Lancaster/t	Boase	Hawken
Chapple/p	Sincock	Filde	Harrison	Croker	Collins	Instance	Navin	Boase	Hawken
Chapple	Sincock	Douch	Harrison	Croker	Hawken	Instance	Lancaster/t	Boase	Arnold
Chapple	Sincock	Douch	Harrison	Croker	Hawken	Instance/t	Lancaster/2t	Boase	Arnold
Chapple	Sincock	Douch	Harrison	Croker	Hawken	Collins	Lancaster	Boase	Arnold/t
Chapple	Sincock	Douch	Harrison	Croker	Instance	Collins	Lancaster	Boase	Hawken
Chapple	Turnbull	Douch/t	Harrison	Croker	Hawken	Collins	Lancaster(c/t)	Boase	Arnold
Chapple	Sincock	Filde	Harrison	Douch	Hawken/t	Instance	Navin	Lancaster	Arnold
Chapple	Sincock	Douch	Harrison	Croker	O'Sullivan	Collins	Arnold	Lancaster	Hawken
Waterford	Chapple	Douch	May	Croker	O'Sullivan	Gray	Ellis	Boase	Hawken

REPLACEMENTS: a - Steve Instance. b - Jon Court. c - John Navin

WHERE	Total	Home	Away
The POINTS were scored	629	348	281
The POINTS were conceded	736	406	330
The TRIES were scored	83	47	36
The TRIES were conceded	94	49	45

HOW the TRIES were scored

Total	Backs	Forwards	F Back	Wing	Centre	H Back	F Row	Lock	B Row	Pen. Try
83	55	26	10	22	18	5	8	4	14	2

HOW the TRIES were conceded

Total	Backs	Forwards	F Back	Wing	Centre	H Back	F Row	Lock	B Row	Pen. Try
94	55	36	8	17	21	9	8	6	22	3

REDRUTH

LEAGUE STATISTICS *compiled by Stephen McCormack*

SEASON	Division	P	W	D	L	F	A	Pts Diff	Lge Pts	Lge Pos	Most Points	Most Tries
92-93	D3	11	7	2	2	175	125	50	16	4	89 Kevin Thomas	6 Andy Knowles
93-94	D3	18	2	0	16	178	488	-310	4	10	71 Simon Blake	2 Mark Rose & Chris Whitworth
94-95	D4	18	6	2	10	309	387	-78	14	7	179 Simon Blake	4 Simon Blake
95-96	D4	18	7	2	9	358	392	-34	16	7	126 Stu Whitworth	8 Peter Congo
96-97	D3	30	7	0	23	565	1116	-551	14	15	120 Ian Morgan	10 Peter Congo
97-98	N2S	26	10	0	16	720	580	140	20	9	256 Rob Thirlby	17 Rob Thirlby
98-99	N2S	26	8	1	17	503	652	-151	17	11	175 Chris Sidwell	8 Steve Lakins
99-00	N2S	26	16	0	10	597	523	74	32	5	195 Steve Larkins	10 Jamie Knight
00-01	D3S	26	14	1	11	691	600	91	29	5	207 Steve Larkins	12 Luke Waquanivere
01-02	N3S	26	12	0	14	629	736	-107	24	8	217 Steve Larkins	11 Steve Larkins

FACT FILE

Founded: 1875
Nickname: The Reds

Colours: Red with a green/yellow band
Change colours: Green with a red/yellow band

GROUND

Address: The Recreation Ground, Redruth, Cornwall TR15 1SY
Tel: 01209 215520 Fax: 01209 314438 web: redruth-rfc.cornwall.eu.org
Capacity: 15,000 Seated: 670 Standing: 14,330

Directions: A30 West through Cornwall, leave at Redruth exit over roundabout, down through council estate, 1/4 mile to crossroads, then left.
Nearest Railway Station: Redruth, walk thro Town Centre, down Green Lane grd at end, 10 mins

Car Parking: 50 on ground, 500 on Industrial Estate - free.

Admission: Season ticket -
Adults £75, OAP/children £45
Matchday -
Adults standing £6, seated £7, u16 Free

Clubhouse: Evenings 7-11, matchdays 12-11, Sun 12-2, 7-11.
Three bars, with snacks & bar meals available.
Functions catered for contact Social Committee

Club Shop: Open home matchdays.
Manageress Christina Thomas 01209 215520

Training Nights: Mondays & Wednesdays

PROGRAMME
Size: A5 Price: £1 Pages: 44
Editor: Nick Serpell 01579 348853
Advertising Rates
Full page £250, Half page £130, Qtr page £70

ROSSLYN PARK FC

President	Tony Tanner	c/o Rosslyn Park FC. 01732 740136 (H&B)
Chairman	Peter Warrener	c/o Warrener Stewart & Co., Harwood House, Harwood Rd., London SW6 4QP 0207 731 6163 (B)
Club Secretary	Bernard Wiggins	01403 711299 (H), 01273 323434 (B), 01273 202627(Fax)
Press Officer	Bernard Wiggins	01403 711299 (H), 01273 323434 (B), 01273 202627(Fax)
Fixtures Secretary	David Booth	7 Catherine Road, Surbiton, Surre. KT6 4HA 0208 399 0955 (H) 0208 339 9300 (Fax)

I seem to remember a line from Rudyard Kipling's "If", that goes something like " If you can meet with triumph and disaster, and treat those two impostors just the same" It rather sums up the last two seasons. Last year we were so nearly promoted, this season we suffered for the loss of key players through injury that started off a slide that was arrested late on in the season but by which time the damage had been done.

A very lucky opening day victory at Wharfedale when Neil Hallett eventually won the match with his third penalty attempt inside 8 minutes of injury time, was the only bright moment in September,. Even beating Plymouth Albion in the Cup avenging an injury time defeat at Beacon Park two weeks earlier did not reverse Park's fortunes. It wasn't till Oct 20th that another win was chalked up, away at Harrogate, an immense team performance with a pushover try in injury time.

More losses followed, the worst of which was away at Preston Grasshoppers. Park could be rightly indignant at the Referee's insistence on playing 7 minutes of injury time in a virtually injury free second half, Chris Glynn's miracle drop goal from the halfway line with the last kick of the match robbing Park of the points that they deserved.
At Waterloo, Park threw away a winning margin to end up with a draw, and incredibly Park had only 5 points at the end of 2001.

A heartening victory at Stourbridge in January and the best performance of the whole season winning at Nottingham 30-11 boosted the points count but worryingly there were 3 defeats in between. New blood in the side had enhanced Parks chances of avoiding the drop, but despite winning 3 on the trot (Nottingham [A], Preston Grasshoppers [H] and Kendal [H]) we were still looking down the wrong end of a loaded shotgun.

A narrow defeat away at Sedgley Park was followed by a miracle "victory from the jaws of defeat", 25-23 at home to Newbury, John Allen scoring with the last move of the match and Stuart Hibbert's conversion turning one point into two still had Park hanging on by a thread.

The rest as they say is history, defeat at Fylde (26-22) left Park facing life in Div 3 South for the first time in their history.

ROSSLYN PARK

Comp.	Date	H/A	Opponents	Result & Score	Att	15	14	13	12	11
N2	01-09	A	Wharfedale	W 18-15		Justice	Matthewson	Wyatt	Marval/2t	Jackson
N2	08-09	H	Sedgley Park	L 13-39		Justice	Matthewson(a/t)	Maddock	Ray	Jackson/p
N2	15-09	A	Plymouth Albion	L 15-19		Jackson	Henderson/2t	Maddock	Ray	Marval
N2	22-09	A	Kendal	L 9-39		Jackson	Henderson	Dowse	Maddock	Thompson
N2	06-10	H	Nottingham	L 11-18		Justice	Howell	Maddock	Jackson	Henderson
N2	20-10	A	Harrogate	W 36-29		Justice/t	Henderson	Maddock	Jackson	Matthewson/
N2	27-10	H	Esher*	L 10-17		Justice	Matthewson	Jackson	Maddock	Henderson
N2	10-11	A	Orrell	L 8-25		Justice/t	Casado	Maddock	Jackson	Anderson
N2	17-11	H	Stourbridge	L 10-42		Justice	Casado	Matthewson	Jackson	Henderson/t
N2	24-11	A	Preston Grasshoppers*	L 14-16	175	Casado	Matthewson	Maddock/2c	Jackson	Henderson
N2	01-12	H	Wharfedale	L 8-23		Casado	Matthewson	Jackson	Maddock/p	Henderson
N2	08-12	A	Waterloo	D 25-25		Justice/t	Anderson	Dowse/tcp	Jackson/t	Henderson
N2	15-12	H	Fylde	L 18-24		Casado	Matthewson	Singer	Jackson	Henderson
N2	22-12	A	Newbury	L 15-25		Casado/t	Morgan	Singer	Dowse	Henderson
N2	12-01	A	Stourbridge	W 25-20		Casado/t	Henderson	Singer	Maddock	Matthewson/
N2	19-01	H	Orrell	L 11-31		Casado(a/dg)	Henderson	Singer	Marval/t	Matthewson
N2	26-01	A	Esher	L 16-17		Jackson	Allen	Singer	Marval	Matthewson
N2	02-02	H	Harrogate*	L 17-20		Justice	Singer	Allen	Marval/t	Matthewson
N2	09-02	A	Nottingham	W 30-11		Justice/t	Allen/t	Marval	Singer	Matthewson
N2	16-02	H	Preston Grasshoppers	W 43-17	175	Justice/t	Allen	Singer	Maddock	Matthewson/
N2	23-02	H	Kendal	W 26-3		Justice	Allen	Maddock	Marval/t	Matthewson/
N2	09-03	H	Plymouth Albion	L 13-41		Justice	Allen	Brady	Marval	Matthewson
N2	16-03	A	Sedgley Park	L 19-26	250	Maddock	Allen/3t	Brady	Marval	Matthewson
N2	30-03	H	Newbury	W 25-23		Justice	Allen/t	Maddock	Marval	Anderson
PGC	06-04	A	Fylde	L 22-26	300	Justice	Allen/2t	Maddock	Singer	Anderson
PGC	13-04	H	Waterloo	W 33-14		Hendy/t	Allen/tc	Singer	Maddock	Lambo
PGC										
	29-09	H	Plymouth Albion	W 15-6		Justice	Henderson	Maddock	Jackson	Matthewson
	13-10	H	Orrell	L 32-40		Justice	Henderson	Maddock/2p	Jackson	Matthewson

** after opponents name indicates a penalty try. Brackets after a player's name indicates he was replaced. eg (a) means he was replaced by replacement code "a" and so on. / after a player or replacement name is followed by any scores he made - eg /t, /c, /p, /dg or any combination of these*

EVER PRESENT None

Most Appearances:
20: Lysander Strong.
19: Lee Gibson, Andy Maddock.

PLAYERS USED

51 plus three as a replacement

MOST POINTS

Pts	Player	T	C	P	DG
74	J Hendy	6	7	8	2
42	S Hibbert	1	8	7	-
42	J Allen	8	1	-	-
35	M Dowse	1	6	6	-
30	T Matthewson	6	-	-	-

MATCH FACTS

10	9	1	2	3	4	5	6	7	8
lallett/c2p	Colburn	Fennell	Kearns	Cano	Hayes	Gibson	Boardman	Clarke	Walker
lallett	Colburn	Fennell	Kearns/t	Allen	Joint	Gibson	Strong	Boardman	Easter
lallett/cp	Willis	Fennell	Kearns	Cano	Hayes	Gibson	Easter	Boardman	Walker
lallett/3p	O'Callaghan	Fennell	Kearns	Cano	Hayes	Gibson	Boardman	Clarke	Easter
)owse/2p	Campbell	Fennell	Hewlett	Cano	Hayes/t	Gibson	Easter	McBride	Walker
)owse/3c	Young	Fennell	Kearns/2t	Cano	Hayes	Benson	Strong	Nunan/2t	Ryan
)owse/cp	Young	Fennell	Hewlett	Cano	Hayes	Benson	Strong	Nunan	Ryan
)owse/p	Young	Cano	Kearns	Cooke	Hayes	Joint	Hankey	Clarke	McDonald
)owse/cp	Young	Cano	Kearns	Cooke	Hayes	Joint	Strong	Nunan	McBride
'oung	Willis	Fennell	Hewlett	Cooke	Hayes	Sedman	Strong	Nunan	Thirlwell/t
'oung	Willis/t	Fennell	Kearns	Cano	Hayes	Joint	Strong	McBride	Thirlwell
'oung	Willis	Fennell	Hewlett	Cure	Hayes	Joint	Boardman	McBride	Thirlwell/t
lendy/tc2p	Colburn	Fennell	Hewlett	Cure/t	Joint	Gibson	Strong	Boardman	Thirlwell
lendy/cp	Colburn	Fennell	Kearns	Cure	Joint	Gibson/t	Strong	McBride	Thirlwell
lendy/2cpdg	Willis	Cano	Hewlett/t	Cure	Hayes	Gibson	Strong	Boardman	Thirlwell
Maddock/p	Young	Cano	Hewlett	Cure	Hayes	Gibson	Strong	Boardman	Thirlwell
Maddock/2p	Young	Cooke	Keenan/t	Cure	Hayes	Gibson	Strong/t	Boardman	Thirlwell
Maddock	Hendy/tc	Cooke	Keenan	Cano	Hayes	Gibson	Strong	Boardman	Thirlwell
libbert	Hendy/2c2p	Cooke	Keenan	Cure	Sedman	Gibson	Strong	Boardman	Walker/2t
libbert/c	Hendy/2p	Cano/t	Keenan	Cure	Sedman	Gibson	Strong/t	Boardman/t	Walker
libbert/c3p	Hendy/t	Cano	Keenan	Cure	Sedman	Gibson	Strong	Nunan	Thirlwell
libbert/p	Hendy	Cooke	Keenan/t	Cure	Hayes	Gibson	Strong	Boardman	Thirlwell/t
libbert/2c	Hendy	Cooke	Keenan	Cano	Hayes	Gibson	Strong	Boardman	Thirlwell
libbert/t2c2p	Hendy/t	Cano	Keenan	Cure	Sedman	Gibson	Strong	Boardman	Walker
libbert/2cp	Hendy	Cano	Keenan	Cooke	Sedman	Gibson	Strong	Boardman	Walker/t
lowland/3c	Campbell	Cooke	Kearns/t	Cure	Sedman/t	Gibson/t	Strong	Boardman	Walker
Dowse/5p	Campbell	Buchannan	Hewlett	Cano	Benson	Gibson	McBride	Clarke	Walker
Dowse/c3p	Young/t	Fennell	Hewlett	Cooke	Hayes/t	Benson	McBride	Nunan	Easter/t

REPLACEMENTS: a - James Hendy

WHERE	Total	Home	Away
The POINTS were scored	490	238	252
The POINTS were conceded	605	293	312
The TRIES were scored	66	32	34
The TRIES were conceded	68	34	34

HOW the TRIES were scored

Total	Backs	Forwards	F Back	Wing	Centre	H Back	F Row	Lock	B Row	Pen. Try
66	39	24	8	18	7	6	9	4	11	3

HOW the TRIES were conceded

Total	Backs	Forwards	F Back	Wing	Centre	H Back	F Row	Lock	B Row	Pen. Try
68	44	24	6	16	12	10	6	7	11	-

ROSSLYN PARK

LEAGUE STATISTICS

compiled by Stephen McCormack

SEASON	Division	P	W	D	L	F	A	Pts Diff	Lge Pts	Lge Pos		Most Points		Most Tries
92-93	2	12	5	0	7	209	199	10	10	8r	61	John Graves & Gary Abraham	3	Paul Essenhigh
93-94	3	18	10	1	7	372	240	132	21	5	59	Paul Robin	9	Shane Roiser
94-95	3	18	10	0	8	313	280	33	20	4	54	Mike Griffin	5	Tim Smither & Adam Vander
95-96	3	18	3	2	13	290	426	-136	8	9	45	John Rowlands	5	Mike Griffin
96-97	3	30	17	0	13	630	620	10	34	8	121	Andy Holder	9	Toby Rakison
97-98	JN1	26	13	1	12	486	537	-51	27	5	178	Andy Maddock	11	Liam McCormick
98-99	JN1	26	17	1	8	588	371	217	35	3	93	Andy Maddock	7	Nick Marval
99-00	JN1	26	17	2	7	694	371	323	36	4	145	Stuart Hibbert	12	Crawford Henderson
00-01	N2	*25	19	2	4	752	439	313	40	3	157	Paul Roblin	18	James Justice
01-02	N2	26	8	1	17	490	605	-115	17	12r	74	James Hendy	8	John Allen

FACT FILE

Founded: 1879
Nickname: The Park

Colours: Red and white hoops.
Change colours: Dark blue

GROUND

Address: Priory Lane, Roehampton, London SW15 5JH
Tel: 0208 876 1879 (Clubhouse) 0208 876 6044 (Admin) Fax: 0208 878 7527
e-mail: rugby@rosslynparkfc.freeserve.co.uk
Capacity: 4,630 Seated: 630 Standing: 4,000

Directions: Ground situated at the junction of Upper Richmond Rd (Sth Circular) and Roehampton Lane
Nearest Railway Station: Barnes BR Southern from Waterloo.
Leave station on downside, cross strip of common to Upper Richmond Rd traffic lights.
Turn right entrance on Upper Richmond Rd.

Car Parking: 200 in the ground @ £1

Admission Season: Adult £85
Matchday: Adults £8
Concessions forChildren/OAPs

Club Shop: Yes, open Tues/Thurs/Sat/Sun
Contact Sarah Hughes 0208 876 6044

Clubhouse: Open every day, except Wednesday.
Snacks, barmeals & restaurant available.
Functions: Capacity 300, contact Sarah Hughes 020 8876 6044

Training Nights: Tuesday & Thursday

PROGRAMME

Size: A5 Price: £1 Pages: 32 + cover
Editor: Sarah Hughes 0208 876 6044

Advertising Rates	Colour	Page £600	Half £400
	Mono	Page £400	Half £250

TABARD RFC

Chairman	Ross Hopcroft	100 Manor Road, Barton-le-Clay, Bedfordshire MK45 4WR
Honorary Secretary:	Peter Cook	32 Pinewood Close, Boreham Wood, Herts, WD6 5NW 020 8207 5564 (H). peterccook@btopenworld.com
Fixture Secretary:	Nigel Gough	5 Winstre Road, Boreham Wood, Herts, WD6 5DR 020 8953 2910
Director of Rugby	Ivor Jones	
Publicity Officer:	Peter Cook	as above

Tabards first half of the season was barren indeed, although an early close win over Lydney and a game against Penzance and Newlyn that could have gone either way, showed the ability was there but the results were lacking. However, a draw against Colfeians and a win against Cinderford kept them in the hunt and then an away victory over Barking and good home wins against Blackheath and North Walsham, set them up for the new year. The second half of the season brought the victories they deserved, with six wins out of 12 starts. The win against Old Patesians ensuring National league rugby for another season and, perhaps the best win of the season, victory away at Lydney. A win that was notable because only the top sides won away at Lydney and also because the team coach broke down at the Severn Bridge and the warm up was done at a motorway service station!

Tabards success was in part due to the consistent kicking of scrum half Michael Skinner, who notched up 197 league points and his persistent enthusiasm throughout the season kept Tabard going. Top try scorer was flanker Dallas Adams with eight, although hooker Mark Sharp and number 8, Ron Matthews, were a close second with six tries each.

An under par performance in the Knockout Cup saw defeat in the first round against London Nigerians but Tabard entered the county cup competition and were rewarded with a victory against Letchworth to take this trophy for the tenth time.

Tim Andrews, Tabards senior coach for the last three seasons hung his notebook up after the final game and next season the coaching team of Ivor Jones and Tony Jorden will be in control at Tabard.

L-R - Back row: Tony Jorden (Backs Coach), Brendon Higgins ,Louis Botha, Peter Luders, Mike Finnie, James Drew, Rob Sussum, Ron Matthews, Richard Van Der Groot, Peter Webb, Ivor Jones (Forward Coach), Barry Lockwood, Andy Alford (fitness) Geoff Bird (Manager) **Front:** Tim Andrews (Coach), Dawn Irwin (Physio), Oscar Telling, Jag Johal, James Colette, Mark Sharp, Michael Skinner (Captain), Richard Woodard, Carl Lavin, Richard Bromham, Ben James.

TABARD

Comp.	Date	H/A	Opponents	Result & Score	Att	15	14	13	12	11
N3 S	01-09	H	Barking	L 14-21		Dudley	Webb	Langford	Williams	Choppin
N3 S	08-09	H	Lydney	W 24-22	150	Dudley/t	Higgins	Langford	Williams	Webb
N3 S	22-09	A	Old Patesians*	L 24-38	200	Webb	Higgins	Langford	Williams	Choppin
N3 S	06-10	H	Penzance & Newlyn	L 33-45	185	Telling	Higgins	Luders	Williams	Choppin
N3 S	20-10	A	Launceston	L 15-40	250	Dudley	Telling	Williams	Higgins	Higgins
N3 S	27-10	H	Old Colfeians	D 26-26	200	Dudley	Telling	Coetzee	Luders	Higgins
N3 S	03-11	A	Camberley	L 27-32	200	Telling	Smith(a/t)	Dudley	Webb/t	Higgins
N3 S	10-11	H	Cinderford	W 48-8		Dudley	Telling/2t	Williams	Webb/t	Higgins/t
N3 S	17-11	A	Redruth	L 10-49		Drew/t	Webb	Williams	Coetzee	Higgins
N3 S	24-11	H	Westcombe Park	L 18-35	120	Drew	James	Williams	Webb	Higgins
N3 S	01-12	A	Barking	W 16-13		Dudley	James	Williams	Mitchell	Higgins
N3 S	08-12	H	Blackheath	W 16-13	200	Dudley	James	Williams	Coetzee	Telling
N3 S	15-12	A	Clifton	L 23-31		Drew/t	James	Williams	Coetzee	Telling
N3 S	22-12	H	North Walsham	W 22-21	200	Telling	James	Williams	Mitchell	Higgins
N3 S	12-01	H	Redruth	L 19-20		Telling	James/t	Williams	Webb	Higgins
N3 S	19-01	A	Cinderford	L 7-30		Telling	Mitchell	Williams	Coetzee	Webb
N3 S	26-01	H	Camberley	W 19-9	150	Drew	James	Williams	Mitchell	Higgins/2t
N3 S	02-02	A	Old Colfeians	W 29-6	125	Drew/t	James	Williams	Botha	Higgins
N3 S	09-02	H	Launceston	L 9-24		Drew	James	Williams	Botha	Higgins
N3 S	16-02	A	Westcombe Park	L 13-38	150	Telling	James/t	Williams	Botha	Higgins/t
N3 S	23-02	A	Penzance & Newlyn	L 11-76	800	Drew	Telling	Williams	Mitchell	Collerre
N3 S	09-03	H	Old Patesians	W 22-13	200	Drew	James/t	Williams	Botha/t	Higgins
N3 S	16-03	A	Lydney	W 30-19	467	Drew	James	Williams/t	Botha	Higgins
N3 S	30-03	A	North Walsham*	L 7-34	250	Telling	Higgins	Williams	Webb	James
N3 S	06-04	H	Clifton	W 22-6	225	Drew	Telling	Higgins	Botha	James
N3 S	13-04	A	Blackheath	L 7-41		Drew	Higgins	Luders	Botha	James
PGC	15-09	N	London Nigerians	W 23-0		Crowne	Higgins	Williams	Webb	Choppin

** after opponents name indicates a penalty try. Brackets after a player's name indicates he was replaced. eg (a) means he was replaced by replacement code "a" and so on. / after a player or replacement name is followed by any scores he made - eg /t, /c, /p, /dg or any combination of these*

EVER PRESENT

Most Appearances:
26: Barney Lockwood, Micky Skinner.
25: Rob Sussum.
24: Richard Bromham.

PLAYERS USED

36 plus five as replacement only

MOST POINTS

Pts	Player	T	C	P	DG
203	M Skinner	2	35	41	-
40	D Adams	8	-	-	-
30	R Matthews	6	-	-	-
30	M Sharp	6	-	-	-

MATCH FACTS

10	9	1	2	3	4	5	6	7	8
Mansfield	Skinner/2c	Webb	Evenly	Lockwood	Sussum(a/t)	Evans	Johal	James	Adams/t
Chalmers	Skinner/c4p	Bromham	Evenly	Lockwood	Sussum/t	Lane	Johal	Adams	Matthews
Chalmers	Skinner/3cp	Lockwood	Webb	Sullivan	Finnie/t	Lane/t	Johal	Adams	Irons
Dudley(b/2t)	Skinner/2c3p	Bromham/t	Webb	Lockwood	Sussum	Finnie/t	Johal	Adams	Irons
Woodard	Skinner/cp	Bromham/t	Webb	Lockwood	Sussum	Finnie	Johal/t	Adams	Irons
Woodard	Skinner/t2c4p	Bromham	Webb	Lockwood	Sussum	Finnie/t	Johal	Adams	Irons
Woodard	Skinner/2cp	Bromham	Sharp/t	Lockwood	Sussum	Finnie	Johal	Adams/t	James
Woodard/dg	Skinner/5c	Bromham/2t	Sharp	Lockwood	Sussum	Finnie	Irons	Adams/t	Matthews
Woodard	Skinner	Bromham	Sharp/t	Lockwood	Sussum	Finnie	James	Adams	Matthews
Woodard	Skinner/c2p	Bromham	Sharp	Lockwood	Sussum	Finnie	Irons/t	Adams/t	Matthews
Woodard	Skinner/2p	Bromham	Sharp	Lockwood	Sussum	Finnie	Irons/t	Adams	Matthews/t
Woodard	Skinner/2p	Bromham	Sharp	Lockwood	Sussum	Finnie	Johal	Adams/2t	Matthews
Woodard	Skinner/c2p	Bromham	Sharp/2t	Lockwood	Sussum	Finnie	Irons	Adams	Matthews
Coetzee	Skinner/2cp	Bromham	Sharp/t	Lockwood	Sussum	Finnie	Johal	Adams/t	Matthews/t
Woodard	Skinner/c4p	Bromham	Sharp	Lockwood	Sussum	Finnie	Johal	Adams	Matthews
Woodard	Skinner/c	Van der Groot	Sharp/t	Lockwood	Sussum	Finnie	Bromham	James	Matthews
Woodard	Skinner/3p	Bromham	Sharp	Lockwood	Sussum	Finnie	Johal	Adams	Matthews
Woodard	Skinner/3cp	Bromham	Sharp	Lockwood	Sussum	Finnie	Johal	Adams/t	Matthews(c/t
Woodard	Skinner/3p	Bromham	Sharp	Lockwood	Sussum	Finnie	Webb	Adams	Irons
Woodard	Skinner/p	Bromham	Sharp	Lockwood	Sussum	Simpson	Johal	Adams	Irons
Woodard	Skinner/2p	Van der Groot	Evenly/t	Lockwood	Sussum	Simpson	Sharp	Adams	Bromham
Woodard/t	Skinner/2cp	Bromham	Sharp	Lockwood	Sussum	Finnie	Johal	Irons	Matthews
Woodard	Skinner/t2c2p	Bromham	Sharp	Lockwood	Sussum	Finnie	Irons(d/t)	Lavin	Matthews/t
Drew	Skinner/c	Van der Groot	Sharp	Lockwood	Sussum	Finnie	Johal	Lavin	Bromham
Woodard	Skinner/2cp	Bromham	Sharp	Lockwood	Sussum	Finnie	Johal/2t	Lavin	Matthews/t
Woodard	Skinner/c	Bromham	Evenly/t	Lockwood	Sussum	Finnie	Johal	Webb	Matthews
Chalmers	Skinner/t2c3p	Lockwood	Beadle	Collerre	Sussum	Finnie	Johal/t	Adams	Matthews

REPLACEMENTS: a - Ron Matthews. b - Richard Woodard. c - Jon Irons. d - Pat Leahy.

WHERE	Total	Home	Away
The POINTS were scored	511	292	219
The POINTS were conceded	710	447	263
The TRIES were scored	63	33	30
The TRIES were conceded	87	59	28

HOW the TRIES were scored

Total	Backs	Forwards	F Back	Wing	Centre	H Back	F Row	Lock	B Row	Pen. Try
63	23	38	4	10	4	5	12	6	20	2

HOW the TRIES were conceded

Total	Backs	Forwards	F Back	Wing	Centre	H Back	F Row	Lock	B Row	Pen. Try
87	64	22	8	31	16	9	5	2	15	1

TABARD

LEAGUE STATISTICS *compiled by Stephen McCormack*

SEASON	Division	P	W	D	L	F	A	Pts Diff	Lge Pts	Lge Pos		Coach		Captain
92-93	Lon 1	12	10	1	1	230	127	103	21	1p				
93-94	D5S	12	6	2	4	183	136	47	14	3				
94-95	D5S	12	7	0	5	207	208	-1	14	6		I Jones		R Malone
												Most Points		**Most Tries**
95-96	D5S	12	4	1	7	195	244	-49	9	9	112	Nick Churchman	3	Giles Hewson Nick Churchman
96-97	D4S	26	10	3	13	511	557	-46	23	8	264	Nick Churchman	8	Nick Churchman
97-98	N2S	26	14	0	12	556	532	-24	28	6	239	Nick Churchman	11	Nick Churchman
98-99	N2S	26	9	1	16	461	501	-40	19	8	148	Nick Churchman	6	Andy Pinnock
99-00	N2S	26	11	1	14	550	627	-77	23	8	141	Nick Churchman	16	Jag Johal
00-01	N3S	26	9	2	15	415	721	-306	20	10	152	Justin Azzopardi	6	Cameron Langford
01-02	N3S	26	10	1	15	511	710	-199	21	9	203	Micky Skinner	8	Dallas Adams

FACT FILE

Founded: 1951
Nickname: Tabs

Colours: Navy with broad yellow band edged with red.
Change colours: Dark green and white.

GROUND

Address: Cobden Hill, Radlett, Hertfordshire, WD7 7LN
Tel. Nos. 01923 855561
Capacity: 1,000 Seated: None Standing: 1,000

Directions: On A5183 Watling Street, from Elstree turn right after entryinto Radlett, blind entrance by high brick wall nearly opposite "Cat & Fiddle"Pub.
Nearest Railway Station: Radlett

Car Parking: 250 spaces adjacent to ground

Admission: Adult standing £5, Children/OAPs Free
Season Ticket £40

Clubhouse: Matchdays & training eves only.
Bar meals available.
Functions: Contact Nick Gray 0831 668204

Club Shop: Open Saturdays only

Training Nights: Tuesday & Thursday

PROGRAMME Size: A5 Price: with entry
Pages: 16 + cover
Editor: Ross Hopcroft

ADVERTISING RATES (Colour)
Full page £400,
Half page £200, Qtr page £100

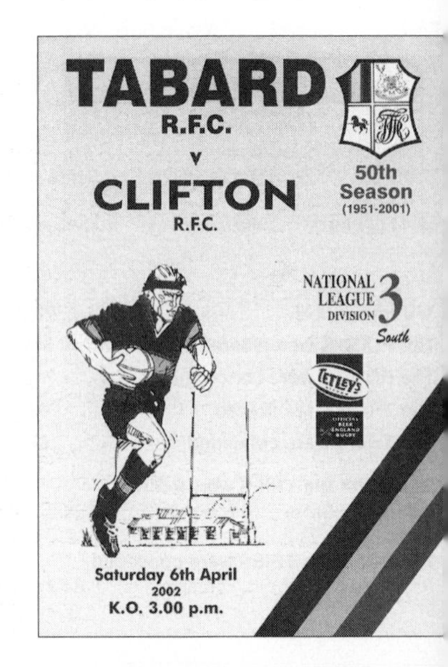

WESTCOMBE PARK RFC

President	Robin Taylor	24 Pinchbeck Road, Green Street Green,Orpington, Kent BR6 6DR 01689 855052(H) 020 8319 7768 (B) 077 74 212 029(M) e-mail: robintaylor@cwctv.net(H) rit@peterwilliams.uk.com (B)
Chairman	John Yeates	Coppers, Farthing Street,Downe, Kent BR6 7JB 01689 857495(H) e-mail: yeates@waitrose.com
Secretary	Keith Smith	14 Linslade Road, Green Street Green, Orpington, Kent BR6 6EA 01689 600939(H) e-mail: Keithsmith@westcombeparkrugby.co.uk
Chairman of Rugby **Playing/Fixtures Sec.**	John Bellinger	32A Courtyard,Eltham, London SE9 5QE 020 8850 7280(H) 020 7377 3060(B) e-mail: Be11inger@aol.com
Chairman of Marketing / **Programme Editor**	Paul Cavalli	30 Warren Road, Orpington, Kent BR6 6HY. 01689 854618 (H) 01732 455456 (B) 07836 570578 (M) 01732 741545 (F) e-mail: paulcavalli@westcombeparkrugby.co.uk
1stXV Team Manager	John Ward Turner	Westerham Lodge, Westerham Road, Keston Kent BR2 6DA 01689 854868(H) 01689 860 (F) e-mail: pr@wardturner.co.uk

Head Coach: Fraser Thomson 01689 607052 **1stXV Coach:** Peter Danckert 01474 331984

Westcombe Park have enjoyed yet another year in National Three South league and we were pleased to improve yet again on our position in the league finishing fourth. Credit must go to our Coaching staff Fraser Thomson and Peter Dankert and to the players some who travel great distances three times a week in order to play at a higher level than perhaps their own clubs can offer.

As icing on the cake 'Combe regained the Kent Cup last season with a fine game played at Blackheath against our old friends Thanet Wanderers. It was also pleasing that we were able to supply the Kent County side with seven players.

We have made new and renewed old friends in our third season and we will miss travelling to Penzance and Launceston where we have received some wonderful hospitality, as have our large travelling band of supporters. We shall enjoy renewing our meetings with Western-Super-Mare and Basingstoke.

For those who do not know us we were founded in 1904 and maintain the name of our original location on the fringes of Blackheath. We settled in Orpington in 1937 and moved to our present location in 1990. We are now very much part of the Orpington/Bromley scene and continue our objectives of fostering local sport at all levels and the strengthening of bonds between the club and the community.

We are very conscious of the importance of Mini and Junior rugby, not only in promoting a great sport, but in building the future of 'Combe. We are fortunate indeed to have so many good and enthusiastic coaches at all youth levels and also senior players willing to give up Sundays to aid their efforts. Westcombe Park Colts continue to flourish and retained the County Colts Cup by beating Thanet Wanderers in the final. It is pleasing to see that a number of our colts from the previous season represented the 1stXV last season.

WESTCOMBE PARK RFC 1stXV SEASON 2001/02 - KENT COUNTY CHAMPIONS

S. ANDERSON, J. WARD TURNER, N. OLDHAM, J. JONES, S. HARRISS, C. HINKINS, P. RICHARDSON, R. CAMPBELL, Q. WISEMAN
P. DANCKERT, S. JERVIS, D. TATE, N.BELCHER, B. THOMAS, B. MARTYR, P. BELCHER, D. SOLE, F.THOMSON
M. JONES, H. O'NEILL, C. AMBROSE, D. COATES, I.LEWIS, N. CLARKE, B. SMITH.

WESTCOMBE PARK

Comp.	Date	H/A	Opponents	Result & Score	Att	15	14	13	12	11
N3 S	01-09	H	Old Colfeians	W 26-22	450	Coates/t2c4p	Smith	Curnow/t	Sykes	Belcher
N3 S	08-09	H	Camberley	L 11-13	200	Coates/2p	Smith	Sykes	Curnow	Belcher
N3 S	22-09	A	Cinderford	W 30-21	300	Coates/3c3p	Smith	Sykes	Thomas/t	Daniel/t
N3 S	06-10	H	Redruth	W 42-18	100	Coates/4c3p	Smith	Sykes/2t	Jervis	Daniel
N3 S	20-10	A	Lydney	L 18-23	397	Smith	Palmer-Barnes	Sykes	Jervis	Daniel
N3 S	27-10	A	North Walsham	L 11-14		Coates/t2p	Daniel	Belcher	Lewis	Smith
N3 S	03-11	H	Blackheath	W 25-10	1000	Coates/2c2p	Daniel	Sykes/2t	Jervis	Smith
N3 S	10-11	A	Clifton	W 23-16		Coates/2c3p	Daniel	Lewis	Jervis	Smith
N3 S	17-11	H	Barking	W 28-5	250	Coates/t2c3p	Daniel	Sykes	Jervis	Smith/t
N3 S	24-11	A	Tabard	W 35-18	120	Coates/3c3p	Lewis	Sykes	Jervis	Smith/t
N3 S	01-12	H	Old Colfeians	W 28-21		Coates/2c3p	Lewis/t	Sykes	Jervis	Smith
N3 S	08-12	A	Penzance & Newlyn	L 7-32	900	Coates/c	Lewis	Sykes	Jervis/t	Smith
N3 S	15-12	H	Launceston	L 16-32	200	Coates/c3p	Sykes	Lewis	Belcher	Smith/t
N3 S	22-12	A	Old Patesians	L 30-31		Coates/2c2p	Finley/t	Sykes(c/t)	Jervis	Smith/t
N3 S	12-01	A	Barking	L 21-23		Smith/t	Lewis	Sykes	Belcher	Finley
N3 S	19-01	H	Clifton	W 33-24		Coates/3c4p	Lewis	Sykes/t	Belcher	Smith
N3 S	26-01	A	Blackheath	W 22-18	250	Smith	Tate	Belcher	Sykes	Lewis
N3 S	02-02	H	North Walsham	L 13-32	250	Smith	Tate	Sykes/t	Lewis	Belcher
N3 S	09-02	H	Lydney	W 39-16	300	Smith	Tate	Sykes	Lewis	Belcher
N3 S	16-02	H	Tabard	W 38-13	150	Coates/3c4p	Smith/t	Sykes	Lewis	Belcher
N3 S	23-02	A	Redruth	L 10-19	600	Coates/cp	Smith	Sykes	Lewis	Belcher
N3 S	09-03	H	Cinderford	W 20-8	150	Coates/2c2p	Smith	Belcher/t	Lewis	Tate
N3 S	16-03	A	Camberley	W 19-15	150	Coates/c4p	Smith	Belcher	Belcher	Tate
N3 S	30-03	H	Old Patesians	W 45-15	250	Coates/6cp	Smith/t	Jervis	Belcher	Lewis
N3 S	06-04	A	Launceston	L 14-43		Coates/2c	Tate	Jervis/t	Belcher	Lewis
N3 S	13-04	H	Penzance & Newlyn	L 27-42	700	Coates/t3c2p	Rowe	Jervis	Lewis	Belcher
PGC	15-09	N	Reading	W 16-0		Coates/c3p	Smith/t	Thomas	Belcher	Middleton

** after opponents name indicates a penalty try. Brackets after a player's name indicates he was replaced. eg (a) means he was replaced by replacement code "a" and so on. / after a player or replacement name is followed by any scores he made - eg /t, /c, /p, /dg or any combination of these*

EVER PRESENT One

Most Appearances:
26 Derek Coates.
24: Chris Hinkins (1), Qin Wiseman (1), Ben Smith.

PLAYERS USED

35 plus five as replacement only

MOST POINTS

Pts	Player	T	C	P	DG
326	D Coates	6	52	64	-
55	B Thomas	11	-	-	-
35	B Smith	7	-	-	-
30	P Sykes	6	-	-	-
25	Q Wiseman	5	-	-	-
25	Nick Oldham	5	-	-	-

MATCH FACTS

10	9	1	2	3	4	5	6	7	8
Jervis	Campling	Ambrose	Clarke	Anderson	Hinkins	Harriss	Spry	Sole	Wiseman
Pretorius	Campbell	Anderson	Clarke	Archer	Richardson	Harriss	Spry	Hinkins	Wiseman/t
Pretorius	Lawrence	Anderson	Clarke	Ambrose	Fotheringham	Hinkins	O'Neil	Spry	Wiseman/t
Pretorius	Thomas/t	Anderson	Clarke	Ambrose	Richardson/t	Hinkins	Sole	Wiseman/t	O'Neil
Coates/tc2p	Welch	Anderson	Clarke	Ambrose	Richardson	Hinkins	Sole(a/t)	Wiseman	O'Neil
Thomas	Jones	Anderson	Clarke	Ambrose	Richardson	Harriss	Hinkins	Wiseman	O'Neil
Thomas	Jones	Anderson	Clarke	Ambrose	Richardson(b/t)	Harriss	O'Neil	Hinkins	Wiseman
Thomas/t	Jones	Campbell/t	Clarke	Ambrose	Hinkins	Harriss	Sole	O'Neil	Wiseman
Thomas	Jones	Anderson	Clarke	Ambrose	Hinkins	Harriss	Sole	O'Neil/t	Wiseman
Thomas/t	Jones	Campbell	Clarke	Ambrose	Hinkins	Harriss	Sole/t	O'Neil	Wiseman/t
Thomas/t	Jones	Anderson	Clarke	Campbell	Hinkins	Harriss	Sole	O'Neil/t	Wiseman
Thomas	Jones	Anderson	Clarke	Campbell	Hinkins	Harriss	O'Neil	Sole	Wiseman
Jervis	Jones	Anderson	Clarke	Campbell	Hinkins	Harriss	O'Neil	Sole	Oldham
Thomas/t	Jones	Anderson	Martyr	Ambrose	Hinkins	Harriss	Oldham	O'Neil	Wiseman
Coates/c3p	Jones/t	Anderson	Martyr	Ambrose	Hinkins	Harriss	O'Neil	Oldham	Wiseman
Jervis/t	Jones	Anderson	Martyr	Ambrose	Hinkins	Harriss	Sole	Oldham	O'Neil/t
Coates/tc5p	Jones	Anderson	Martyr	Ambrose	Hinkins	Harriss	Wiseman	Oldham	O'Neil
Coates/p	Jones	Anderson	Martyr	Ambrose	Hinkins	Harriss	Sole	Oldham	Wiseman/t
Coates/4c2p	Jones/t	Anderson	Martyr	Ambrose/t	Hinkins	Harriss	Sole	Oldham/3t	Wiseman
Thomas/2t	Jones	Anderson	Martyr	Ambrose	Hinkins	Harriss	Sole/t	Oldham	Wiseman
Thomas	Jones	Anderson	Martyr	Ambrose	Hinkins	Harriss/t	Oldham	O'Neil	Wiseman
Thomas/t	Jones	Anderson	Martyr	Ambrose	Hinkins	Harriss	Oldham	O'Neil	Wiseman
Thomas	Welch/t	Anderson	Martyr	Ambrose	Hinkins	Harriss	Oldham	O'Neil	Wiseman
Thomas/t	Welch/2t	Campbell	Martyr	Ambrose	Hardcastle	Harriss	Sole/t	Wiseman	O'Neil/t
Thomas/t	Jones	Anderson	Martyr	Ambrose	Hardcastle	Harriss	Oldham	Wiseman	O'Neil
Thomas	Jones/t	Anderson	Martyr	Ambrose	Hinkins	Harriss	Oldham/t	Wiseman	O'Neil
Pretorius	Welch	Archer	Clarke	Ambrose	Richardson	Hinkins	Fotheringham	Spry	Wiseman

REPLACEMENTS: a - Fotheringham. b - Nick Oldham. c - Neil Belcher.

WHERE	Total	Home	Away
The POINTS were scored	631	391	240
The POINTS were conceded	544	273	271
The TRIES were scored	67	43	24
The TRIES were conceded	62	32	30

HOW the TRIES were scored

Total	Backs	Forwards	F Back	Wing	Centre	H Back	F Row	Lock	B Row	Pen. Try
67	45	22	5	9	12	19	2	3	17	-

HOW the TRIES were conceded

Total	Backs	Forwards	F Back	Wing	Centre	H Back	F Row	Lock	B Row	Pen. Try
61	42	19	8	22	11	1	5	1	13	1

WESTCOMBE PARK

LEAGUE STATISTICS *compiled by Stephen McCormack*

SEASON	Division	P	W	D	L	F	A	Pts Diff	Lge Pts	Lge Pos	Coach	Captain
92-93	Lon 2S	12	9	1	2	279	135	144	19	2	C Chapman	F Thomson
93-94	Lon 2S	12	10	1	1	259	130	129	21	2	F Thomson	P Harris
94-95	Lon 2S	12	7	1	4	228	177	51	15	4	F Thomson	G Mayor
95-96	Lon 2S	12	7	0	5	317	196	121	14	5	F Thomson	G Mayor
96-97	Lon 2S	12	7	0	5	414	228	186	14	4	F Thomson	J Hayday
97-98	Lon 2S	15	15	0	0	703	138	565	30	1p	F Thomson/D Vaughan	N Hayler
98-99	Lon 1	16	15	0	1	706	201	505	30	1p	F Thomson/P Danckert	R Chitty
											Most Points	**Most Tries**
99-00	N2S	26	11	0	15	550	706	-156	22	9	243 Derek Coates	9 Clark Goodwin
00-01	N3S	26	12	0	14	552	664	-112	24	7	215 Derek Coates	11 Pat Sykes
01-02	N3S	26	15	0	11	631	544	87	30	4	326 Derek Coates	11 Ben Thomas

FACT FILE

Founded: 1904
Nickname: "Combe"

Colours: Navy blue, with white hoops, navy shorts
Change colours: White, with navy hoops, blue shorts

ADDRESS: Goddington Dene, Goddington Lane, Orpington, Kent BR6 9SX
Tel: 01689 834902 **Fax:** 01689 822116 **Web site:** www.westcombeparkrugby.co.uk
Capacity: 2000 standing

Directions: From M25 - exit at J4. At next round-about exit A244 (Orpington), at 40 MPH sign (2.8 miles from M25) turn right into Goddington Lane, opposite the Highway.
From A20 - Leave A20 at Crittall's Corner (Orpington A224). Take A224 to Orpington, Sevenoaks Way, Continue into Court Road, following sign, M25-Sevenoaks. After six sets of lights turn LEFT into Goddington Lane (opposite Volvo show room)
From Croydon - follow A232 into Orpington, over War Memorial roundabout, up Spur Road to A224. Turn Right into Court Road at lights, 1/4 mile turn Left into Goddington Lane.

Nearest Station: Orpington (Taxis/Buses), Chelsfield (10mins. walk)

Car Parking: 200, Special events: 2500

Admission: By programme

Club Shop: Open Saturdays & Sundays
Manager Jane Hadaway. 01959 532067

Clubhouse: Normal licensing hours, snacks and bar meals.
Functions Rooms available for up to 200
Contact House Manager: 01689 834902

Trianing Nights: Tuesdays and Thursdays.

PROGRAMME **Size:** A5 **Price:** £4.00 **Pages:** 20
Editor: Contact: Paul Cavalli
01689 854618 (H) 01732 455456 (B)

Advertising Rates
Full Page: £150.00,
1/2 page: £100.00 1/4 Page: £65.00 plus VAT

WESTON super MARE RFC

President	John Brentnall	c/o Messers J W Ward, 37 The Boulevard, Weston super Mare 0117 922 0208 (H), 01934 413545 (B)
Chairman	Bill Poole	19 Worlebury Park Road, Worlebury, W-s-M. 01934 626870 (H)
Club Secretary	Andrew Simmons	c/o Weston-super-Mare RFC 01934 625643, 01934 814709 (H)
Treasurer	Graham Buller	15 Chalfont Rd., Weston-s-Mare BS22 3PZ 01934 429396
Fixture Secretary	John Fry	01934 415341(H)
Chairman of Rugby	Colin Reeves	20 Walsh Close, Hutton, , Weston-s-Mare. 01934 814714 (H)

Pre-season training started earlier than usual with former players making a much-appreciated contribution. We knew that we had a good squad and that our New Zealand coach Brett McCormack would provide great motivation and direction. We were determined to gain promotion!

Captain Paul Redman was in the best form of his career, and was an awesome example to everyone, as was the mercurial Yugoslav international Goran Vucicevic. Most of the previous season's team returned to take up the challenge of gaining promotion.

Game after game our opponents wondered why they had lost, and we had won! The answer was meted out each week throughout the season - organization, staunch defence, and consistent points scoring, when it mattered. Brett McCormack and Neil Coleman kicked the extra points that so often other teams failed to harvest!

We ran away with the Championship of our league winning nineteen straight games - losing only four matches the whole season! We won the Somerset Knockout Cup for the first time in 21 years, and only exited from the Intermediate Cup through an administrative error!

We are sad to say good-bye to our friends in (South West 1) most notably Cheltenham, who beat us at home and away! Old rivals Bridgwater, Dings, Chinnor, Dorchester, who we know are much better than their results suggest, Keynsham, who came close to beating us on two occasions, and all our other worthy opponents will be missed.

We now look forward to the challenges that we know the new season will bring, and meeting old adversaries. We know our new captain David Bird will lead the club forward by example.

BILL POOLE

WESTON S MARE

Comp.	Date	H/A	Opponents	Result & Score	15	14	13	12	11
SW1	08-09	H	Cheltenham	L 26-29	Morris	Steele	McHale	McCormack	Wiseman
SW1	22-09	A	Dings Crusaders	W 16-8	Sharp	Morris	Rainey	McCormack	Wiseman
SW1	29-09	H	Keynsham	W 12-11	Sharp	Morris	Rainey	McCormack	Steele
SW1	06-10	A	Reading	W 17-14	Vucicevic	Morris	Rainey	McCormack	Wiseman
SW1	20-10	H	Swanage & Ware	W 25-6	Vucicevic	Hember	Rainey	McCormack	Steele
SW1	27-10	A	Bridgwater	W 33-3	Vucicevic	Morris	Rainey	McCormack	Steele
SW1	10-11	H	Chinnor	W 38-9	Vucicevic	Wiseman	Rainey	McCormack	Steele
SW1	17-11	A	Dorchester	W 21-14	Vucicevic	Wiseman	Rainey	McCormack	McHale
SW1	01/12	H	Maidenhead	W 41-7	Vucicevic	Morris	Bennett	Rainey	Steele
SW1	08-12	A	Stroud	W 27-14	Vucicevic	Wiseman	Bennett	Rainey	Steele
SW1	22-12	H	Barnstaple	W 22-5	Vucicevic	Bennett	Rainey	McCormack	Steele
SW1	12-01	H	Dorchester	W 27-3	Vucicevic	Bennett	Rainey	McCormack	Steele
SW1	17-01	A	Maidenhead	W 31-16	Vucicevic	Bennett	Rainey	Taylor	Steele
SW1	26-01	A	Chinnor	W 19-9	Reid	Bennett	Rainey	Taylor	Steele
SW1	02-02	H	Bridgwater	W 21-7	Vucicevic	Bennett	Rainey	Taylor	Steele
SW1	09-02	A	Swanage & Ware	W 19-7	Vucicevic	Wiseman	Reid	Rainey	McHale
SW1	23-02	H	Reading	W 25-22	Vucicevic	Bennett	Rainey	Taylor	Reid
SW1	02-03	A	Keynsham	W 15-12	Vucicevic	Reid	Rainey	Bennett	Steele
SW1	09-03	H	Dings Crusaders	W 12-3	Reid	Bennett	Rainey	Taylor	Steele
SW1	16-03	A	Cheltenham	L 11-28	Reid	McHale	Rainey	Taylor	Steele
SW1	06-04	A	Barnstaple	W 24-15	Vucicevic	Wiseman	Reid	McCormack	Steele
SW1	13-04	H	Stroud	W 27-16	Vucicevic	Reid	Taylor	McCormack	Steele

REPLACEMENTS:a - Evans.

** after opponents name indicates a penalty try.*

Brackets after a player's name indicates he was replaced. eg (a) means he was replaced by replacement code "a" and so on.

/ after a player or replacement name is followed by any scores he made - eg /t, /c, /p, /dg or any combination of these

MATCH FACTS

10	9	1	2	3	4	5	6	7	8
Williams	Coleman	Steele	Burge	Down	Pitt	Perry	Fear	Simpson	Redman
Williams	Coleman	Steele	Burge	Down	Pitt	Curry	Perry	Kerslake	Redman
Williams	Coleman	Steele	Burge	Down	Pitt	Curry	Perry	Bird	Redman
Williams	Coleman	Steele	Bird	Down	Pitt	Curry	Perry	Doughty	Redman
Williams	Coleman	Webster	Bird	Down	Pitt	Curry	Glen	Doughty	Redman
Williams	Coleman	Webster	Bird	Down	Pitt	Curry	Glen	Simpson	Redman
Williams	Coleman	Steele	Bird	Down	Glen	Curry	Doughty	Simpson	Redman
Williams	Coleman	Steele	Bird	Down	Perry	Curry	Glen	Simpson	Redman
McCormack	Coleman	Webster	Bird	Down	Pitt	Curry	Glen	Simpson	Redman
McCormack	Coleman	Mathias	Bird	Down	Pitt	Curry	Glen	Simpson	Redman
Williams	Coleman	Mathias	Bird	Down	Pitt	Perry	Glen	Simpson	Smith
Williams	Coleman	Mathias	Bird	Down	Pitt	Perry	Glen	Simpson	Redman
McCormack	Coleman	Webster	Bird	Down	Pitt	Glen	Smith	Simpson	Redman
McCormack	Coleman	Mathias	Bird	Down	Pitt	Glen	Smith	Simpson	Redman
McCormack	Coleman	Webster	Bird	Down	Pitt	Glen	Smith	Simpson	Redman
Williams	McCormack	Webster	Bird	Down	Pitt	Perry	Glen	Simpson	Redman
McCormack	Coleman	Webster	Bird	Down	Pitt	Perry	Glen	Smith	Redman
McCormack	Coleman	Steele	Bird	Down	Pitt	Glen	Smith	Simpson	Redman
McCormack	Coleman	Webster	Bird	Down	Pitt	Perry	Glen	Simpson	Redman
Williams	Coleman	Webster	Bird	Down	Pitt	Perry	Glen	Simpson	Redman
Williams	Coleman	Steele	Bird	Down	Pitt	Glen	Smith	Simpson	Redman
Williams	Coleman	Webster	Bird	Down	Pitt	Glen	Smith	Simpson	Redman

WESTON super MARE

LEAGUE STATISTICS *compiled by Stephen McCormack*

SEASON	Division	P	W	D	L	F	A	Pts Diff	Lge Pts	Lge Pos	Most Points		Most Tries	
90-91	D4S	12	6	0	6	192	182	10	12	5	122	Melvin Badger	8	Melvin Badger
91-92	D4S	12	4	0	8	175	215	-40	8	9	39	Jarad Collard	5	Paul Whatley & Charlie Larkin
92-93	D4S	12	4	1	7	154	226	-72	9	10	81	Paul Thatcher	3	Barry Sparks
93-94	D5S	12	7	0	5	163	180	-17	14	5	91	Paul Thatcher	2	Neil Coleman & Robert Chamberlain
94-95	D5S	12	8	0	4	194	160	34	16	3	119	Paul Thatcher	2	Mark Venner & Alan Baskerville
95-96	D5S	12	10	0	2	207	123	84	20	2	105	Paul Thatcher	5	Mark Venner
96-97	D4S	26	11	0	15	482	515	-33	22	9	164	Paul Thatcher	8	Graham Biller
97-98	N2S	26	10	0	16	468	651	-183	20	10	76	Mark Armstrong	5	Matthew Hiles
98-99	N2S	26	9	1	16	415	588	-173	19	9	115	Mark Armstrong	14	David Bird
99-00	N2S	26	11	0	15	512	598	-86	20	11	230	Neil Coleman	11	David Bird
00-01	N2S	26	7	1	18	370	691	-321	15	12	99	Neil Coleman	4	by three players
01-02	SW1	22	19	0	3	479	259	220	38	1				

FACT FILE

Founded: 1875
Nickname: Seasiders
Web site: weston-warriors.co.uk

Colours: Royal blue with red and white flashings, blue shorts
Change colours: Red shirts, blue shorts

GROUND

Address: Recreation Ground, Drove Road, Weston Super Mare, North Somerset BS23 3PA
Tel: 01934 625643 (office) 01934 623118 (clubhouse)
Fax: 01934 625643 email: westonrfc@lineone.com
Capacity: 6,499 Seated: 499 Standing - Covered: 300 Uncovered: 5,700

Directions: M5 Jnc 21, follow dual carriageway into Weston, (following signs for town centre). At the 5th roundabout the ground is just over on the left.
Nearest Railway Station: Weston Super Mare, 100 yards from ground

Car Parking: 200 at ground, 50+ nearby

Admission: Season tickets £72 - £96, OAPs £20, Junior £15.
Matchday (incl. prog) £5, OAPs £2.50

Club Shop: Open Sat & Sun matchdays.

Clubhouse: Every evening (except Sunday) 7.00-11.00, matchdays 12.00-11.00, Sundays 12.00-3.00.
Snacks & bar meals available.

Functions: Contact Club Manager

Training Nights: Tuesday & Thursday

PROGRAMME

Size: A5 Price: with entry Pages: 16 + cover
Editor: Jon Cornish (Waterside Printers)
01275 340090, 343916 (Fax)
ADVERTISING RATES
Colour Full page £300
Mono - Full page £200, half £100

RECORDS SECTION

DIVISION FOUR SOUTH

(CURRENTLY NATIONAL DIVISION THREE SOUTH)

Previously also Area League South & Division Five South

LEAGUE RECORDS

Relegated clubs' Match Facts for season 2001-02

CINDERFORD

Comp.	Date	H/A	Opponents	Result & Score	Att	15	14	13	12	11
N3 S	01-09	A	Lydney	L 12-20		Hart	Verry	Edwards	Chant	Brookes
N3 S	08-09	A	Redruth	L 6-28	800	Hart	Verry	Edwards	Chant	Brookes
N3 S	22-09	H	Westcombe Park	L 21-30	300	Hart	Verry/t	Edwards	Chant	Brookes
N3 S	06-10	A	North Walsham	L 5-85	200	Hart	Verry	Edwards	Rich	Brookes
N3 S	20-10	H	Blackheath	L 14-25		Hart(b/2c)	Verry	Edwards	Chant/t	Brookes
N3 S	27-10	A	Clifton	L 14-21		Hart	Lamb	Jewitt	Chant	Brookes/t
N3 S	03-11	H	Barking	W 8-0		Hart/t	Verry	Edwards	Brookes	Lamb
N3 S	10-11	A	Tabard	L 8-48		Hart	Verry	Jewitt	Brookes	Lamb/t
N3 S	17-11	H	Old Patesians	W 13-3	400	Lamb/t	Verry	Edwards	Chant	Brookes
N3 S	24-11	A	Penzance & Newlyn	L 10-27	600	Roberts/c	Lamb	Edwards	Chant	Brookes
N3 S	01-12	H	Lydney	L 13-16		Hart/tcp	Brookes	Edwards	Chant	Lamb
N3 S	08-12	A	Old Colfeians	L 18-37		Hart	Lamb/t	Edwards/t	Chant	Brookes
N3 S	15-12	H	Camberley	W 35-15		Hart/t	Lamb	Edwards/t	Chant	Brookes/t
N3 S	22-12	A	Launceston	L 23-39	450	Hart	Lamb	Edwards	Jewitt	Brookes/t
N3 S	12-01	A	Old Patesians	L 5-34		Hart	Roberts	Goatley	Chant	Brookes
N3 S	19-01	H	Tabard	W 30-7		Hart	Verry	Brookes/t	Chant	Lamb/t
N3 S	26-01	A	Barking	W 15-0		Hart	Lamb/t	Chant	Brookes	Verry/t
N3 S	09-02	A	Blackheath*	L 10-37		Hart	Verry	Brookes	Chant	Carr
N3 S	16-02	H	Penzance & Newlyn	L 19-32	200	Hart	Verry/t	Evans	Chant	Brookes
N3 S	23-02	H	North Walsham	L 7-8		Hart	Verry	Evans	Brookes	Lamb
N3 S	09-03	A	Westcombe Park	L 8-20	150	Lamb/t	Verry	Evans	Hart	Brookes
N3 S	16-03	H	Redruth	L 20-21	300	Lamb	Verry	Hart	Evans/t	Brookes
N3 S	23-03	H	Clifton	W 34-10		Hart	Verry/t(d/t)	Evans/2t	Chant	Brookes
N3 S	30-03	H	Launceston	L 15-40	200	Hart	Verry/t	Evans	Chant	Brookes
N3 S	06-04	A	Camberley	L 13-14	200	Hart	Lamb	Evans	Chant	Brookes
N3 S	13-04	H	Old Colfeians	L 14-32	125	Hart	Verry	Chant	Roberts/2t	Bazeley
PGC	15-09	N	Penzance & Newlyn	L 12-80	800	Hart	Wood	Jewitt/t	Rich	Brookes

** after opponents name indicates a penalty try. Brackets after a player's name indicates he was replaced. eg (a) means he was replaced by replacement code "a" and so on. / after a player or replacement name is followed by any scores he made - eg /t, /c, /p, /dg or any combination of these*

EVER PRESENT None

Most Appearances:
25: Lex Brookes (1).
24: Michael Hart, Kerry Bourne.
22: Mark Nicholls.

PLAYERS USED

38 plus one as a replacement only

MOST POINTS

Pts	Player	T	C	P	DG
125	M Roberts	-	16	29	2
35	O Lamb	7	-	-	-
25	P Verry	5	-	-	-
25	K Bourne	5	-	-	-

MATCH FACTS

10	9	1	2	3	4	5	6	7	8
Roberts/4p	Arnott	Broady	Gunther	Price	Williams	Cowles	Duberley	Bourne	Hudson
Roberts/2p	Arnott	Martin	Gunther	Broady	Cowles	Williams	Hudson	Bourne	Nicholls
Roberts/c2pdg	Arnott	Phillips(a/t)	Rawlings	Broady	Cowles	Williams	Hudson	Bourne	Nicholls
Lamb	Arnott	Martin	Rawlings	Broady	Cowles/t	Gittens-Jones	Duberley	Wood	Nicholls
Lamb	Arnott	Broady	Rawlings	Price	Cowles	Gittens-Jones	Hudson/t	Bourne	Nicholls
Roberts/3p	Arnott	Martin	Rawlings	Price	Cowles	Gittens-Jones	Hudson	Bourne	Nicholls
Roberts/p	Arnott	Broady	Kantorowicz	Price	Cowles	Miles	Bourne	Best	Nicholls
Roberts/p	Arnott	Broady	Rawlings	Price	Cowles	Gittens-Jones	Bourne	Best	Nicholls
Roberts/cpdg	O'Neill	Martin	Rawlings	Broady	Miles	Gittens-Jones	Hudson	Bourne	Nicholls
Jewitt/dg	O'Neill	Martin	Rawlings	Price	Cowles	Gittens-Jones	Hudson	Best	Nicholls/t
Jewitt/dg	O'Neill	Martin	Rawlings	Phillips	Cowles	Miles	Hudson	Bourne	Nicholls
Roberts/p	O'Neill	Martin	Rawlings	Phillips	Cowles	Williams	Bourne/t	Best	Nicholls
Roberts/2c2p	Arnott	Martin	Poultney	Phillips	Hudson	Williams	Best	Bourne/2t	Nicholls
Roberts/c2p	Arnott	Martin/t	Poultney	Broady	Hudson/t	Williams	Best	Bourne	Nicholls
Roberts	O'Neill	Martin	Poultney	Phillips	Southern/t	Williams	Hudson	Bourne	Nicholls
Goatley/t2c2p	O'Neill	Martin	Poultney	Broady	Cowles	Miles	Hudson	Bourne/t	Southern
Roberts	O'Neill	Price	Poultney	Broady(a/t)	Cowles	Miles	Best	Bourne	Hudson
Roberts/cp	Lamb	Price	Poultney	Kennedy	Cowles	Miles	Hudson	Bourne	Nicholls
Roberts/3p	O'Neill	Broady	Poultney	Price	Cowles	Williams	Hudson	Bourne	Nicholls(c/t)
Roberts/c	O'Neill	Price	Martin	Kennedy/t	Miles	Gittens-Jones	Best	Bourne	Nicholls
Roberts/p	O'Neill	Martin	McGregor	Phillips	Cowles	Miles	Hudson	Bourne	Nicholls
Roberts/cp	O'Neill	Price	Martin	Phillips/t	Cowles	Gittens-Jones	Hudson/t	Bourne	Nicholls
Roberts/3cp	O'Neill	Price	Martin	Kennedy	Miles	Gittens-Jones	Southern	Bourne/t	Nicholls
Roberts/cp	O'Neill	Phillips	Poultney/t	Kennedy	Cowles	Gittens-Jones	Best	Bourne	Nicholls
Roberts/c2p	O'Neill	Martin	Poultney	Phillips	Williams	Gittens-Jones	Best	Bourne	Nicholls/t
Goatley/2c	O'Neill	Price	Wallis	Broady	Cowles	Miles	Hudson	Bourne	Southern
Roberts/c	Arnott	Price	Wallis	Phillips	Cowles	Williams	Hudson/t	Bourne	Nicholls

REPLACEMENTS: a - Andrew Martin. b - Mark ROberts. c - Chris SOuthern. d - Oliver Lamb.

WHERE

	Total	Home	Away
The POINTS were scored	390	243	147
The POINTS were conceded	649	410	239
The TRIES were scored	48	31	17
The TRIES were conceded	86	49	37

HOW the TRIES were scored

Total	Backs	Forwards	F Back	Wing	Centre	H Back	F Row	Lock	B Row	Pen. Try
48	28	19	5	13	9	1	6	3	10	1

HOW the TRIES were conceded

Total	Backs	Forwards	F Back	Wing	Centre	H Back	F Row	Lock	B Row	Pen. Try
86	60	26	8	27	18	7	7	3	16	-

CLIFTON

Comp.	Date	H/A	Opponents	Result & Score	Att.	15	14	13	12	11
N3 S	01-09	A	Old Patesians	L 15-19		Robertson	Randall/t	Fairweather	Kent	Beckerleg
N3 S	08-09	H	Penzance & Newlyn	L 21-48	210	Farndon/p	Robertson	Fairweather(a/t)	Kent	Randall
N3 S	22-09	A	Launceston	L 5-39	350	Stack	Robertson	Fairweather	Kent/t	Randall
N3 S	06-10	H	Old Colfeians	L 27-39	200	Stack/2cp	Randell	Jeffrey	Kent	Randall/t
N3 S	20-10	A	Camberley	W 22-13		Gill/2c	Robertson	Jeffrey	Kent	Randall
N3 S	27-10	H	Cinderford	W 21-14		Gill/c3p	Beckerleg	Jeffrey	Robertson	Randall/t
N3 S	03-11	A	Redruth	L 17-24	600	Randall	Robertson	Taylor	Kent/c	Beckerleg/t
N3 S	10-11	H	Westcombe Park	L 16-23		Randall/t	Randell/3p	Robertson	Kent/c	Beckerleg
N3 S	17-11	A	North Walsham	L 7-23	250	Gill/c	Randall	Fairweather	Kent/t	Beckerleg
N3 S	24-11	H	Blackheath	L 10-19		Gill	Randall	Fairweather	Kent	Robertson
N3 S	01-12	H	Old Patesians	L 15-18		Gill/t	Randall/t	Fairweather	Kent	Robertson
N3 S	08-12	A	Barking	L 30-35		Gill/2c	Randall/t	Fairweather	Kent/t	Robertson
N3 S	15-12	H	Tabard	W 31-23		Gill	Beckerleg	Taylor	Kent/t	Robertson/t
N3 S	22-12	H	Lydney	W 28-20	180	Gill	Randall/2t	Taylor	Kent	Robertson
N3 S	12-01	H	North Walsham	W 36-21		Lawrence	Randall/t	Taylor/t	Kent/t	Robertson
N3 S	19-01	A	Westcombe Park	L 24-33		Gill	Randall/t	Taylor	Jeffrey	Robertson/t
N3 S	09-02	H	Camberley	L 11-19	100	Gill/p	Randall	Kent	Taylor	Robertson/t
N3 S	16-02	A	Blackheath	L 10-21		Gill	Randall	Taylor	Kent	Robertson/2t
N3 S	23-02	A	Old Colfeians	L 18-21	225	Gill(c/t)	Edwards	Taylor	Kent	Randall/t
N3 S	02-03	H	Redruth	L 33-34	100	Gill	Randall	Taylor	Kent/t	Robertson
N3 S	09-03	H	Launceston	L 10-24	150	Gill	Randall/t	Taylor	Kent	Robertson
N3 S	16-03	A	Penzance & Newlyn	L 24-76		Randall	Robertson/t	Taylor	Kent	Edwards/t
N3 S	23-03	A	Cinderford	L 10-34		Randall	Beckerleg	Jeffrey	Kent	Robertson
N3 S	30-03	A	Lydney	L 8-25	301	Harraway	Beckerleg	Jeffrey	Kent	Robertson
N3 S	06-04	A	Tabard	L 6-22	225	Robertson	Randall	Jeffrey	Kent	Beckerleg
N3 S	13-04	H	Barking	W 14-11		Robertson	Randall/t	Jeffrey	Kent/t	Beckerleg

** after opponents name indicates a penalty try. Brackets after a player's name indicates he was replaced. eg (a) means he was replaced by replacement code "a" and so on. / after a player or replacement name is followed by any scores he made - eg /t, /c, /p, /dg or any combination of these*

EVER PRESENT None

Most Appearances:
25: Carl Butcher.
24: Barnaby Kent, Chris Randall (1).
23: Graham Robertson, Brendan Tracey.

PLAYERS USED

45 plus four as a replacement only

MOST POINTS

Pts	Player	T	C	P	DG
126	J Barnes	-	21	26	2
65	C Randall	13	-	-	-
39	B Kent	7	2	-	-
30	G Robertson	6	-	-	-
29	A Gill	1	6	4	-

MATCH FACTS

10	9	1	2	3	4	5	6	7	8
Lawrence/p	Harraway	Hussey	Stephens	Wymer/c	Roberts/t	Butcher	Harvey	McCarthy	Tracey
Lawrence	Burrows	Wymer/tp	Stephens	Alvis	Roberts	Butcher	O'Reilly	Harvey/t	Tracey
Lawrence	Harraway	Wymer	Stephens	Alvis	Roberts	Butcher	Smith	Burton	Tracey
Lawrence	Harraway	Hussey	Stephens	Alvis/2t(b/t)	Ford	Butcher	McInnally	Harvey	Smith
Lawrence/p	Harraway	Hussey/2t	Stephens	Alvis	Smith/t	Butcher	Schultz	Harvey	Burton
Lawrence	Harraway	Wymer	Stephens	Alvis	Smith	Butcher	Schultz/t	Harvey	Burton
Lawrence/t	Harraway	Hussey	Stephens	Alvis/t	Shortman	Butcher	Schultz	Harvey	Tracey
Lawrence	Taylor	Hussey	Stephens	Alvis	Smith	Butcher	Schultz	Harvey	Tracey
Lawrence	Taylor	White	Stephens	Wymer	Shortman	Amphlett	Tracey	O'Reilly	Smith
Lawrence	Harraway	Hussey	Stephens	Wymer/cp	Smith/t	Butcher	Tracey	O'Reilly	Spry
Barnes/cp	Taylor	Hussey	Shortman	Bird	Tracey	Butcher	Spry	Williams	Smith
Barnes/c2pdg	Harraway	Hussey	Shortman	Wymer	Tracey	Butcher	Spry	Williams/t	Smith
Barnes/2c4p	Lovell/t	Hussey	Shortman	Bird	Amphlett	Butcher	Tracey	Williams	Smith
Barnes/2c3p	Lovell	Hussey	Allen	Bird	Amphlett	Butcher	Tracey	Williams	Smith/t
Barnes/4cp	Harraway/t	Hussey	Stephens	Bird/t	Amphlett	Butcher	Tracey	Williams	Smith
Barnes/c4p	Harraway	Hussey	Stephens	Shortman	Armstrong	Butcher	Tracey	Williams	Spry
Barnes/p	Harraway	Hussey	Stephens	Bird	Armstrong	Butcher	Tracey	Williams	Smith
Harraway	Lovell	White	Stephens	Bird	Richards	Butcher	Tracey	Williams	Smith
Barnes/c2p	Harraway	White	Stephens	Bird	Richards	Butcher	Tracey	Williams	Smith
Barnes/2c3p	Harraway	Hussey	Shortman/t	Bird	Armstrong/t	Butcher	Tracey	Williams	Smith/t
Barnes/cp	Harraway	Shortman	Stephens	Bird	Armstrong	Butcher	Tracey	Ashley	Smith
Barnes/3cp	Harraway	Shortman	Stephens	Bird	Armstrong	Butcher	Tracey/t	Hardy	Smith
Barnes/cp	Harraway	Edwards	Stephens	Bird/t	Tracey	Butcher	Harvey	Hardy	Burton
Barnes/dg	Taylor	Edwards	Stephens	Bird	Purcell	Butcher	Tracey	Hardy	Burton/t
Barnes/2p	Taylor	Edwards	Stephens	Bird	Purcell	Butcher	Tracey	Hardy	Smith
Barnes/2c	Harraway	Edwards	Stephens	Bird	Purcell	Butcher	Tracey	Hardy	Smith

REPLACEMENTS: a - Mark Harraway. b - Craig Wymer. c - Sam Beckerleg.

WHERE	Total	Home	Away
The POINTS were scored	469	273	196
The POINTS were conceded	698	385	313
The TRIES were scored	56	32	24
The TRIES were conceded	86	49	37

HOW the TRIES were scored

Total	Backs	Forwards	F Back	Wing	Centre	H Back	F Row	Lock	B Row	Pen. Try
56	35	21	3	20	9	3	10	4	7	-

HOW the TRIES were conceded

Total	Backs	Forwards	F Back	Wing	Centre	H Back	F Row	Lock	B Row	Pen. Try
86	60	26	8	28	14	10	7	1	18	-

THE LAST TEN YEARS DIVISION 4 SOUTH

1992-93

Champions	*Runners-up*	*Relegated*
Sudbury	London Welsh	Thurrock

Most

Points: 123 Steve Dybler (Sudbury) *Tries:*12 Steve Titcombe (Sudbury)
Penalties: 31 Simon Pennington (Stourbridge) *Conversions:* 28 Ralph Zoing (Harrogate) *D.Gs:* N.A.

1993-94

Champions	*Runners-up*	*Relegated*
Reading	Lydney	Southend, Maidstone

Most

Points: 133 Phil Belshaw (Reading) *Tries:* N.A.
Penalties: 34 Phil Belshaw (Reading) *Conversions:* N.A. *D.Gs:* 5 Paul Tincknell (Weston-s-Mare)

1994-95

Champions	*Runners-up*	*Relegated*
London Welsh	Lydney	Sudbury, Basingstoke

Most

Points: 119 Paul Thatcher (Weston-s-Mare) *Tries:* N.A.
Penalties: 31 Paul Thatcher (Weston-s-Mare) *Conversions:* N.A. *D.Gs:* N.A.

1995-96

Champions	*Runners-up*	*Relegated*
Lydney	Weston-s-Mare	Camborne

Most

Points: 176 Richard Perkins (Henley) *Tries:* 10 Richard Perkins (Henley), Tommy Adams (Camborne)
Penalties: 28 Paul Thatcher (Weston-s-Mare), Richard Larkin (Askeans) *Conversions:* 27 Richard Perkins (Henley) *D.Gs:* 4 Simon Cattermole (Weston-s-Mare)

1996-97

Champions	*Runners-up*	*Relegated*
Newbury	Henley	Berry Hill, Askeans, High Wycombe, Charlton Park

Most

Points: 391 Nick Grecian (Newbury) *Tries:* 27 Brian Johnson (Newbury)
Penalties: 53 Nick Churchman (Tabard) *Conversions:* 100 Nick Grecian (Newbury) *D.Gs:* 10 Simon Cattermole (Weston-s-Mare

1997-98

Champions	*Runners-up*	*Relegated*
Camberley	Henley	-

Most

Points: 256 Rob Thirlby (Redruth) *Tries:* 17 Rob Thirlby (Redruth)
Penalties: 51 James Shanahan (N. Walsham) *Conversions:* 48 Rob Thirlby (Redruth) *D.Gs:* 11 Nick Edmonds (Bridgwater)

1998-99

Champions	*Runners-up*	*Relegated*
Bracknell	Esher	Havant

Most

Points: 313 Jonathon Gregory (Esher) *Tries:* 16 Nana Dontah (Esher), Andy Carter (Met Police), & James Shanahan (N. Walsham)
Penalties: 58 Jon Gregory (Esher) *Conversions:* 52 Jon Gregory (Esher) *D.Gs:* 3 by five players

99-2000

Champions	*Runners-up*	*Relegated*
Esher	Penzance & Newlyn	Bridgwater, Norwich & Met. Police

Most

Points: 351 John Gregory (Esher) *Tries:* 38 Richard Newton (Penzance & Newlyn)
Penalties: 59 Chris Atkinson (Plymouth A.) *Conversions:* 78 John Gregory (Esher) *D.Gs:* 6 Stewart Whitworth (Redruth)

2000-01

Champions	*Runners-up*	*Relegated*
Plymouth Albion	Launceston	Basingstoke, Cheltenham, Reading & Weston-s-M

Most

Points: 336 Nat Saumi (Penzance & Newlyn) *Tries*: 20 Dan Ward-Smith (Plymouth A.) & Victor Olonga (Penzance & N.)
Penalties: 46 Derek Coates (Westcombe P.) *Conversions:* 67 Nat Saumi (Penzance & N.) *D.Gs:* .7 Bede Brown (Redruth)

2001-02

Champions	*Runners-up*	*Relegated*
Penzance & Newlyn	Launceston	Clifton, Cinderford.

Most

Points: 374 Nat Saumi (Penzance & N.) *Tries:* 28 Richard Newton (Penzance & N)
Penalties: 64 Derek Coates (Westcombe P.) *Conversions:* 91 Nat Saumi (Penzance & N.) *D.Gs:* 4 Neil Merrett (Lydney)

ALL TIME RECORDS — TEAM RECORDS — DIVISION 4 SOUTH

Highest score:	**136**	Penzance & Newlyn 136 Met Police 6, 15.04.00
Highest aggregate:	**142**	as above
Highest score by a losing side:	**34**	Redruth 34 Otley 41, 21.9.96
Highest scoring draw:	**25**	Henley v Metropolitan Police, 5.4.97
Most consecutive wins:	**26**	Plymouth Albion 2000-01
Most consecutive defeats:	**28**	Metropolitan Police 1998-99/1999-2000
Most points for in a season:	**1170**	Newbury 1996-97
Least points for in a season:	**64**	Maidstone 1989-90
Most points against in a season:	**1308**	Met Police 1999-2000
Least points against in a season:	**61**	Reading 1993-94
Most tries for in a season:	**167**	Newbury 1996-97
Most tries against in a season:	**188**	Met Police 1999-2000
Least tries for in a season:		
Least tries against in a season:		
Most conversions for in a season:	**103**	Newbury 1996-97
Most conversions against in a season:	**95**	Charlton Park 1996-97
Most penalties for in a season:	**66**	Camberley 1997-98
Most penalties against in a season:	**65**	Plymouth Albion 1997-98
Least penalties for in a season:		
Least penalties against in a season:		
Most drop goals for in a season:	**14**	Bridgwater 1997-98
Most drop goals against in a season:	**8**	Metropolitan Police 1997-98

ALL TIME RECORDS — INDIVIDUAL RECORDS — DIVISION 4 SOUTH

Most points in a season:	**385**	Nick Grecian (Newbury) 1996-97
Most tries in a season:	**38**	Richard Newton (Penzance & Newlyn) 1999-00
Most conversions in a season:	**96**	Nick Grecian (Newbury) 1996-97
Most penalties in a season:	**59**	Chris Atkinson (Plymouth) 1999-2000
Most drop goals in a season:	**11**	Nick Edmonds (Bridgwater) 1997-98
Most points in a match:	**41**	Nat Saumi, *Penzance* v Met Police 15.4.00
Most tries in a match:	**7**	Richard Newton, *Penzance* v Met Police 15.4.00
Most conversions in a match:	**13**	Nat Saumi, *Penzance* v Met Police 15.4.00
Most penalties in a match:	**7**	Carson Russell, *Bracknell* v N Walsham 27.3.99
		Jon Gregory, *Esher* v Tabard 18.03.00
Most drop goals in a match:	**4**	Simon Cattermole, *Weston-s-M.* v Berry Hill 16.11.96

TEN YEAR RECORDS DIVISION 4 SOUTH

Club	SEASONS 92-93	93-94	94-95	95-96	96-97	97-98	98-99	99-00	00-01	01-02
Askeans	-	-	-	8	14	-	-	-	-	-
Barking	-	-	5	4	3	3	4	6	4	10
Basingstoke	5	11	13	-	-	-	-	-	13r	-
Berry Hill	7	7	11	5	11	-	-	-	-	-
Blackheath	-	-	-	-	-	-	-	-	9	7
Bracknell	-	-	-	-	-	-	1p	-	-	-
Bridgwater & Albion	-	-	-	-	-	8	10	12r	-	
Camberley	-	-	-	7	4	1p	-	-	-	12
Camborne	4	4	8	13	-	-	-	-	-	
Charlton Park	-	-	-	-	13	-	-	-	-	-
Cheltenham	-	-	-	6	5	5	13	11	14r	-
Cinderford	-	-	-	-	-	-	-	-	-	14r
Clifton	-	-	-	-	-	11	7	7	8	13r
Esher	-	-	-	-	-	4	2	1	-	-
Havant	-	-	-	-	-	12	14r	-	-	-
Henley	-	-	9	3	2	2p	-	-	-	-
High Wycombe	8	9	10	10	12	-	-	-	-	-
Launceston	-	-	-	-	-	-	-	-	2	2p
London Welsh	2	6	1	-	-	-	-	-	-	-
Lydney	3	2	2	1	-	-	-	-	-	6
Maidstone	12	13	-	-	-	-	-	-	-	-
Metropolitan Police	9	10	7	12	7	14	5	14r	-	-
Newbury	-	-	-	-	1	-	-	-	-	-
North Walsham	11	8	4	11	10	7	3	3	6	3
Norwich	-	-	-	-	-	-	6	13r	-	-
Old Colfeians	-	-	-	-	-	-	-	-	-	11
Old Patesians	-	-	-	-	-	-	-	-	-	5
Penzance & Newlyn	-	-	-	-	-	-	-	2	3	1
Plymouth Albion	-	-	-	-	6	13	12	4	1	-
Reading	-	1	-	-	-	-	-	-	11r	-
Redruth	-	-	-	-	-	9	11	5	5	8
Southend	6	12	-	-	-	-	-	-	-	-
Sudbury	1	-	12	-	-	-	-	-	-	-
Tabard	-	3	6	9	8	6	8	8	10	9
Thurrock	13	-	-	-	-	-	-	-	-	-
Westcombe Park	-	-	-	-	-	-	-	10	7	4
Weston-super-Mare	10	5	3	2	9	10	9	9	12r	-

NATIONAL DIVISION THREE SOUTH

RFU SENIOR CUP

STATISTICS

compiled by Stephen McCormack

PAST WINNERS

1971-72	Gloucester	1986-87	Bath
1972-73	Coventry	1987-88	Harlequins
1973-74	Coventry	1988-89	Bath
1974-75	Bedford	1989-90	Bath
1975-76	Gosforth	1990-91	Harlequins
1976-77	Gosforth	1991-92	Bath
1977-78	Gloucester	1992-93	Leicester
1978-79	Leicester	1993-94	Bath
1979-80	Leicester	1994-95	Bath
1980-81	Leicester	1995-96	Bath
1981-82	Gloucester	1996-97	Leicester
1982-83	Bristol	1997-98	Saracens
1983-84	Bath	1998-99	Wasps
1984-85	Bath	1999-00	Wasps
1985-86	Bath	2000-01	Newcastle

BARKING

THIS SEASON (2001-02) 3rd round

OVERALL PLAYING RECORD

	P	W	D	L	F	A	Pts Diff
Home	10	6	-	4	182	194	-12
Away	12	5	-	7	274	263	11
Neutral	-	-	-	-	-	-	-
Total	22	11	-	11	456	457	-1

TEAM RECORDS

Highest Score
53 v St Ives 97/98

Biggest Winning Margin
47 (53-6) v St Ives 97/98

Highest Score Against
65 v Leicester 98/99

Biggest Losing Margin
60 (65-5) v Leicester 98/99

SEASON BY SEASON

1971-72	DNQ	1986-87	DNQ
1972-73	DNQ	1987-88	DNQ
1973-74	DNQ	1988-89	2R
1974-75	DNQ	1989-90	2R
1975-76	DNQ	1990-91	DNQ
1976-77	DNQ	1991-92	DNQ
1977-78	DNQ	1992-93	DNQ
1978-79	DNQ	1993-94	1R
1979-80	DNQ	1994-95	2R
1980-81	DNQ	1995-96	1R
1981-82	DNQ	1996-97	1R
1982-83	DNQ	1997-98	3R
1983-84	DNQ	1998-99	4R
1984-85	DNQ	1999-00	1R
1985-86	DNQ	2000-01	3R

BASINGSTOKE

THIS SEASON (2001-02)

OVERALL PLAYING RECORD

	P	W	D	L	F	A	Pts Diff
Home	7	3	-	4	100	158	-58
Away	7	4	-	3	85	129	-44
Neutral	-	-	-	-	-	-	-
Total	14	7	-	7	185	287	-102

TEAM RECORDS

Highest Score
29 v Clifton 94/95

Biggest Winning Margin
19 twice v Ealing (26-7) & Sudbury (25-6)

Highest Score Against
52 v Harlequins 93/94

Biggest Losing Margin
49 (3-52) v Harlequins 93/94

SEASON BY SEASON

1971-72	DNQ	1986-87	DNQ
1972-73	DNQ	1987-88	DNQ
1973-74	DNQ	1988-89	DNQ
1974-75	DNQ	1989-90	DNQ
1975-76	DNQ	1990-91	DNQ
1976-77	DNQ	1991-92	1R
1977-78	DNQ	1992-93	1R
1978-79	DNQ	1993-94	4R
1979-80	DNQ	1994-95	3R
1980-81	DNQ	1995-96	2R
1981-82	DNQ	1996-97	DNQ
1982-83	DNQ	1997-98	1R
1983-84	DNQ	1998-99	DNQ
1984-85	DNQ	1999-00	DNQ
1985-86	DNQ	2000-01	1R

BLACKHEATH

THIS SEASON (2001-02) **2nd round**

OVERALL PLAYING RECORD

	P	W	D	L	F	A	Pts Diff
Home	23	11	0	12	382	345	37
Away	25	12	0	13	355	523	-168
Neutral	-	-	-	-	-	-	-
Total	48	23	-0	25	737	868	-131

TEAM RECORDS

Highest Score
40 v Sutton & Epsom 84/85 & Sevenoaks 99/00
Biggest Winning Margin
34 (40-6) v Sutton & Epsom 99/00
Highest Score Against
72 v Harlequins 92/93
Biggest Losing Margin
69 (3-72) v Harlequins 92/93

SEASON BY SEASON

Season	Round	Season	Round
1971-72	2R	1986-87	2R
1972-73	1R	1987-88	3R
1973-74	DNQ	1988-89	3R
1974-75	2R	1989-90	3R
1975-76	DNQ	1990-91	3R
1976-77	DNQ	1991-92	2R
1977-78	1R	1992-93	3R
1978-79	1R	1993-94	4R
1979-80	DNQ	1994-95	4R
1980-81	2R	1995-96	4R
1981-82	3R	1996-97	5R
1982-83	4R	1997-98	4R
1983-84	4R	1998-99	3R
1984-85	4R	1999-00	2R
1985-86	4R	2000-01	2R

CAMBERLEY

THIS SEASON (2001-02) **1st round**

OVERALL PLAYING RECORD

	P	W	D	L	F	A	Pts Diff
Home	7	4	-	3	158	139	19
Away	8	4	-	4	206	177	29
Neutral	-	-	-	-	-	-	-
Total	15	8	-	7	364	316	48

TEAM RECORDS

Highest Score
40 v Lewes 95/96
Biggest Winning Margin
30 (40-10) v Lewes 95/96
Highest Score Against
44 v Lydney 98/99
Biggest Losing Margin
20 (12-32) v Stroud 01-02

SEASON BY SEASON

Season	Round	Season	Round
1971-72	DNQ	1986-87	DNQ
1972-73	DNQ	1987-88	DNQ
1973-74	DNQ	1988-89	DNQ
1974-75	DNQ	1989-90	DNQ
1975-76	DNQ	1990-91	DNQ
1976-77	DNQ	1991-92	DNQ
1977-78	DNQ	1992-93	DNQ
1978-79	DNQ	1993-94	DNQ
1979-80	DNQ	1994-95	DNQ
1980-81	DNQ	1995-96	4R
1981-82	DNQ	1996-97	1R
1982-83	DNQ	1997-98	4R
1983-84	DNQ	1998-99	2R
1984-85	DNQ	1999-00	3R
1985-86	DNQ	2000-01	2R

HAVANT

THIS SEASON (2001-02)

OVERALL PLAYING RECORD

	P	W	D	L	F	A	Pts Diff
Home	17	9	-	8	242	267	-25
Away	18	7	-	11	292	428	-136
Neutral	-	-	-	-	-	-	-
Total	35	16	-	19	534	695	-161

TEAM RECORDS

Highest Score
72 v Hornets 97/98
Biggest Winning Margin
44 (72-28) v Hornets 97/98
Highest Score Against
100 v Henley 98/99
Biggest Losing Margin
81 (19-100) v Henley 98/99

SEASON BY SEASON

Season	Round	Season	Round
1971-72	DNQ	1986-87	1R
1972-73	DNQ	1987-88	1R
1973-74	DNQ	1988-89	4R
1974-75	DNQ	1989-90	2R
1975-76	2R	1990-91	DNQ
1976-77	DNQ	1991-92	1R
1977-78	DNQ	1992-93	1R
1978-79	1R	1993-94	4R
1979-80	DNQ	1994-95	3R
1980-81	2R	1995-96	1R
1981-82	DNQ	1996-97	3R
1982-83	DNQ	1997-98	3R
1983-84	DNQ	1998-99	2R
1984-85	2R	1999-00	1R
1985-86	3R	2000-01	2R

LYDNEY

THIS SEASON (2001-02) **3rd round**

OVERALL PLAYING RECORD

	P	W	D	L	F	A	Pts Diff
Home	24	12	-	12	452	409	43
Away	24	15	-	9	400	386	14
Neutral	-	-	-	-	-	-	-
Total	48	27	-	21	852	795	57

TEAM RECORDS

Highest Score
67 v Amersham & Chiltern 97/98

Biggest Winning Margin
67 (67-0) v Amersham & Chiltern 97/98

Highest Score Against
45 v Lon Scot 97/98 & Worcester 01/02

Biggest Losing Margin
45 (0-45) v Worcester 01/02

SEASON BY SEASON

Season	Round	Season	Round
1971-72	1R	1986-87	3R
1972-73	1R	1987-88	DNQ
1973-74	DNQ	1988-89	1R
1974-75	DNQ	1989-90	1R
1975-76	DNQ	1990-91	2R
1976-77	DNQ	1991-92	1R
1977-78	1R	1992-93	2R
1978-79	DNQ	1993-94	2R
1979-80	DNQ	1994-95	5R
1980-81	DNQ	1995-96	4R
1981-82	3R	1996-97	4R
1982-83	3R	1997-98	3R
1983-84	3R	1998-99	5R
1984-85	4R	1999-00	2R
1985-86	DNQ	2000-01	2R

NORTH WALSHAM

THIS SEASON (2001-02) **3rd round**

OVERALL PLAYING RECORD

	P	W	D	L	F	A	Pts Diff
Home	14	9	-	5	272	197	75
Away	13	4	-	9	198	233	-35
Neutral	-	-	-	-	-	-	-
Total	27	13	-	14	470	430	40

TEAM RECORDS

Highest Score
46 v Launceston 99/00

Biggest Winning Margin
46 (46-0) v Launceston 99/00

Highest Score Against
32 v Exeter 94/95 & Launceston 98/99

Biggest Losing Margin
28 (3-31) v Saracens 88/89

SEASON BY SEASON

Season	Round	Season	Round
1971-72	DNQ	1986-87	DNQ
1972-73	DNQ	1987-88	DNQ
1973-74	DNQ	1988-89	2R
1974-75	DNQ	1989-90	3R
1975-76	DNQ	1990-91	2R
1976-77	DNQ	1991-92	DNQ
1977-78	DNQ	1992-93	1R
1978-79	DNQ	1993-94	1R
1979-80	DNQ	1994-95	2R
1980-81	DNQ	1995-96	2R
1981-82	DNQ	1996-97	1R
1982-83	DNQ	1997-98	3R
1983-84	DNQ	1998-99	1R
1984-85	2R	1999-00	2R
1985-86	1R	2000-01	3R

OLD COLFEIANS

THIS SEASON (2001-02) **2nd round**

OVERALL PLAYING RECORD

	P	W	D	L	F	A	Pts Diff
Home	3	1	-	2	79	56	23
Away	6	2	-	4	135	117	18
Neutral	-	-	-	-	-	-	-
Total	9	3	0	6	214	173	41

TEAM RECORDS

Highest Score
43 v Ruislip 98/99

Biggest Winning Margin
36 (39-3) v Basingstoke 00/01

Highest Score Against
32 v Swanage 98/99

Biggest Losing Margin
14 (15-29) v Lydney 91/92

SEASON BY SEASON

Season	Round	Season	Round
1971-72	DNQ	1986-87	DNQ
1972-73	DNQ	1987-88	DNQ
1973-74	DNQ	1988-89	DNQ
1974-75	DNQ	1989-90	1R
1975-76	DNQ	1990-91	DNQ
1976-77	DNQ	1991-92	1R
1977-78	DNQ	1992-93	DNQ
1978-79	DNQ	1993-94	DNQ
1979-80	DNQ	1994-95	1R
1980-81	DNQ	1995-96	DNQ
1981-82	DNQ	1996-97	DNQ
1982-83	DNQ	1997-98	DNQ
1983-84	DNQ	1998-99	2R
1984-85	DNQ	1999-00	DNQ
1985-86	DNQ	2000-01	2R

OLD PATESIANS

THIS SEASON (2001-02) **1st round**

OVERALL PLAYING RECORD

	P	W	D	L	F	A	Pts Diff
Home	1	0	0	1	10	27	-17
Away	1	0	0	1	16	26	-10
Neutral	-	-	-	-	-	-	-
Total	2	0	-	2	26	53	-27

TEAM RECORDS

Highest Score
16 v Barking 01/02

Biggest Winning Margin
none

Highest Score Against
27 v Westcombe Park 99/00

Biggest Losing Margin
17 (10-27) v Westcombe Park 99/00

SEASON BY SEASON

Season	Result	Season	Result
1971-72	DNQ	1986-87	DNQ
1972-73	DNQ	1987-88	DNQ
1973-74	DNQ	1988-89	DNQ
1974-75	DNQ	1989-90	DNQ
1975-76	DNQ	1990-91	DNQ
1976-77	DNQ	1991-92	DNQ
1977-78	DNQ	1992-93	DNQ
1978-79	DNQ	1993-94	DNQ
1979-80	DNQ	1994-95	DNQ
1980-81	DNQ	1995-96	DNQ
1981-82	DNQ	1996-97	DNQ
1982-83	DNQ	1997-98	DNQ
1983-84	DNQ	1998-99	DNQ
1984-85	DNQ	1999-00	1R
1985-86	DNQ	2000-01	DNQ

REDRUTH

THIS SEASON (2001-02) **1st round**

OVERALL PLAYING RECORD

	P	W	D	L	F	A	Pts Diff
Home	15	8	-	7	214	215	-1
Away	15	6	0	9	205	334	-129
Neutral	-	-	-	-	-	-	-
Total	30	14	-	16	419	549	-130

TEAM RECORDS

Highest Score
27 v Barnstaple 99/00

Biggest Winning Margin
17 (26-9) v Old Culverhayians 97/88

Highest Score Against
96 v Leeds 96/97

Biggest Losing Margin
90 (96-6) v Leeds 96/97

SEASON BY SEASON

Season	Result	Season	Result
1971-72	DNQ	1986-87	DNQ
1972-73	DNQ	1987-88	2R
1973-74	DNQ	1988-89	2R
1974-75	DNQ	1989-90	2R
1975-76	DNQ	1990-91	DNQ
1976-77	DNQ	1991-92	1R
1977-78	DNQ	1992-93	4R
1978-79	DNQ	1993-94	2R
1979-80	DNQ	1994-95	3R
1980-81	3R	1995-96	3R
1981-82	DNQ	1996-97	3R
1982-83	DNQ	1997-98	1R
1983-84	DNQ	1998-99	1R
1984-85	3R	1999-00	3R
1985-86	DNQ	2000-01	2R

ROSSLYN PARK

THIS SEASON (2001-02) **3rd round**

OVERALL PLAYING RECORD

	P	W	D	L	F	A	Pts Diff
Home	39	23	0	16	890	527	363
Away	30	18	0	12	485	430	55
Neutral	2	0	0	2	26	51	-25
Total	71	41	0	30	1401	1008	393

TEAM RECORDS

Highest Score
58 v High Wycombe 77/78

Biggest Winning Margin
58 (58-0) v High Wycombe 77/78

Highest Score Against
41 v Rotherham 96/97

Biggest Losing Margin
22 (12-34) v Harlequins 91/92

SEASON BY SEASON

Season	Result	Season	Result
1971-72	DNQ	1986-87	3R
1972-73	2R	1987-88	3R
1973-74	SF	1988-89	4R
1974-75	Runners-up	1989-90	3R
1975-76	Runners-up	1990-91	QF
1976-77	2R	1991-92	QF
1977-78	2R	1992-93	3R
1978-79	QF	1993-94	5R
1979-80	SF	1994-95	2R
1980-81	4R	1995-96	2R
1981-82	4R	1996-97	5R
1982-83	3R	1997-98	4R
1983-84	3R	1998-99	3R
1984-85	3R	1999-00	4R
1985-86	3R	2000-01	4R

TABARD

THIS SEASON (2001-02) **1st round**

OVERALL PLAYING RECORD

	P	W	D	L	F	A	Pts Diff
Home	12	5	-	7	194	268	-74
Away	11	5	-	6	169	213	-44
Neutral	-	-	-	-	-	-	-
Total	23	10	-	13	363	481	-118

TEAM RECORDS

Highest Score
36 v High Wycombe 94/95
Biggest Winning Margin
25(30-5) v Ruislip 93/94
Highest Score Against
50 v Northampton 92/93
Biggest Losing Margin
38 (3-41) v Esher 98/99

SEASON BY SEASON

Season	Result	Season	Result
1971-72	DNQ	1986-87	DNQ
1972-73	DNQ	1987-88	DNQ
1973-74	DNQ	1988-89	1R
1974-75	DNQ	1989-90	DNQ
1975-76	DNQ	1990-91	1R
1976-77	DNQ	1991-92	DNQ
1977-78	DNQ	1992-93	3R
1978-79	DNQ	1993-94	2R
1979-80	DNQ	1994-95	4R
1980-81	DNQ	1995-96	3R
1981-82	DNQ	1996-97	1R
1982-83	DNQ	1997-98	2R
1983-84	1R	1998-99	2R
1984-85	DNQ	1999-00	1R
1985-86	DNQ	2000-01	2R

WESTCOMBE PARK

THIS SEASON (2001-02) **1st round**

OVERALL PLAYING RECORD

	P	W	D	L	F	A	Pts Diff
Home	6	1	-	5	72	126	-54
Away	6	3	-	3	96	178	-82
Neutral	-	-	-	-	-	-	-
Total	12	4	-	8	168	304	-136

TEAM RECORDS

Highest Score
27 v Old Patesians 99/00
Biggest Winning Margin
23 (23-0) v Olney 95/96
Highest Score Against
56 v Plymouth 00/01
Biggest Losing Margin
50 (6-56) v Plymouth 00/01

SEASON BY SEASON

Season	Result	Season	Result
1971-72	DNQ	1986-87	DNQ
1972-73	DNQ	1987-88	DNQ
1973-74	DNQ	1988-89	DNQ
1974-75	DNQ	1989-90	DNQ
1975-76	DNQ	1990-91	DNQ
1976-77	DNQ	1991-92	DNQ
1977-78	DNQ	1992-93	1R
1978-79	DNQ	1993-94	2R
1979-80	DNQ	1994-95	DNQ
1980-81	DNQ	1995-96	2R
1981-82	DNQ	1996-97	1R
1982-83	DNQ	1997-98	DNQ
1983-84	DNQ	1998-99	1R
1984-85	DNQ	1999-00	2R
1985-86	DNQ	2000-01	2R

WESTON SUPER MARE

THIS SEASON (2001-02) **DNQ**

OVERALL PLAYING RECORD

	P	W	D	L	F	A	Pts Diff
Home	15	6	-	9	228	334	-106
Away	6	4	-	2	112	83	29
Neutral	-	-	-	-	-	-	-
Total	21	10	-	11	340	417	-77

TEAM RECORDS

Highest Score
39 v Basingstoke 97/98
Biggest Winning Margin
29 (39-10) v Basingstoke 97/98
Highest Score Against
46 v Barnstaple 00/01
Biggest Losing Margin
31 (15-46) v Barnstaple 00/01

SEASON BY SEASON

Season	Result	Season	Result
1971-72	DNQ	1986-87	DNQ
1972-73	DNQ	1987-88	DNQ
1973-74	DNQ	1988-89	DNQ
1974-75	DNQ	1989-90	DNQ
1975-76	DNQ	1990-91	DNQ
1976-77	1R	1991-92	DNQ
1977-78	DNQ	1992-93	DNQ
1978-79	DNQ	1993-94	1R
1979-80	1R	1994-95	2R
1980-81	DNQ	1995-96	4R
1981-82	1R	1996-97	4R
1982-83	DNQ	1997-98	2R
1983-84	DNQ	1998-99	2R
1984-85	DNQ	1999-00	2R
1985-86	DNQ	2000-01	1R

Two of the RFU Senior Cup's greats - Stuart Barnes and Jeremy Guscott (with ball), who between them have no less than 12 winners medals, happily six each.

NORTHERN REGION

A complete club index appears at the back of the book.
This shows which Division and league each club is in for the 2002-03 season

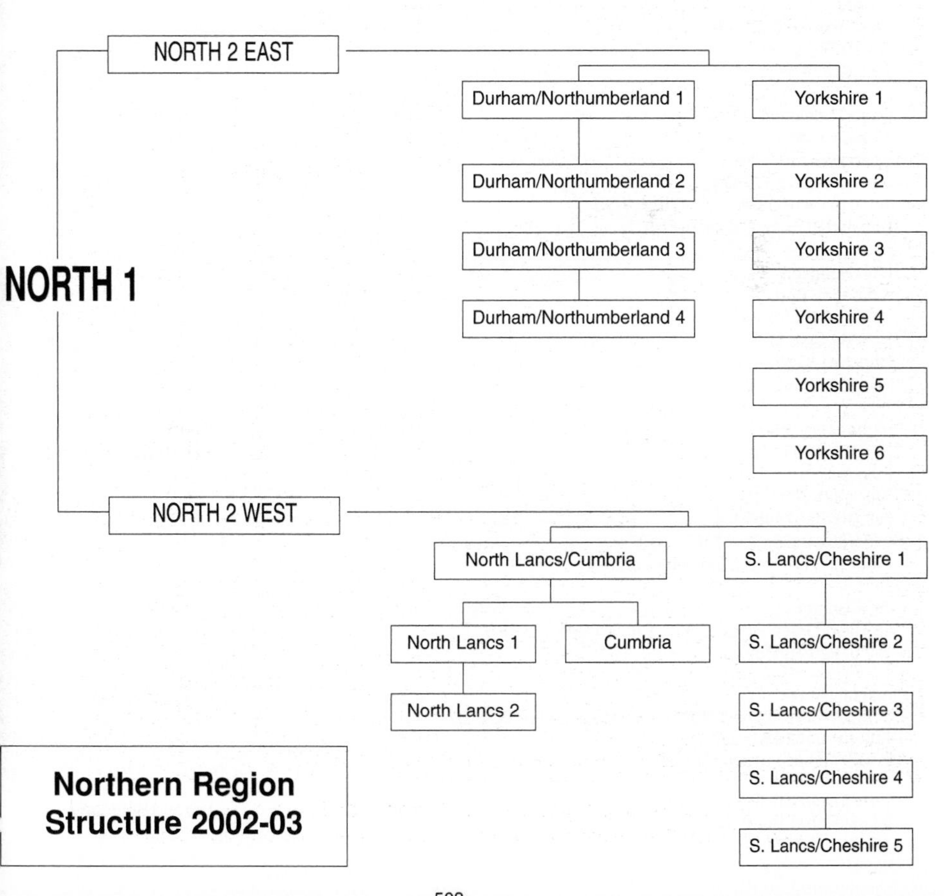

Northern Region Structure 2002-03

NORTHERN REGION OFFICIALS 2001-2002

Name / Address	Division	Position
Mike Lord 68 Hoole Street, Chester. CH2 3NL Tel: 01244 312702 07801 283506 Fax: 01244 347988 Email: mail@email321.freeserve.co.uk	North	Chairman
Mike Smith The Lowe, Wainstalls, Halifax, West Yorkshire HX2 7TR Tel: 01422 882879 07850 233019 Fax: 01422 882879 Email: TheLowe@aol.com	North	Hon Secretary
Dudley Gibbs 'Sandyford', Healey, Northumberland. NE44 6BA Tel: 01434 682496 Fax: 01434 682019 Email: dudleyg@compuserve.com	North	Northumberland rep RFU Competitions Committee rep
Les Bentley 32 Moorhead Terrace, Shipley, West Yorkshire. BD18 4LB Tel: 01274 585460 Fax: 01274 591245	North	Yorkshire rep
Dave Thompson 12 Aldsworth Close, Springwell, Gateshead NE9 7PG Tel: 0191 416 9839 07778 809125 Email: dat_rugby@hotmail.com	North	Hon Treasurer Durham rep
Ivon Hodgson Kimberley End, 22 Capesthorn Close, Holmes Chapel, Cheshire. CW4 7EW Tel: 01477 533406	North North 2 West	Lancashire rep League Secretary
Richard Haslehurst 217 Dickens Lane Poynton Stockport SK12 1SS Tel: 01625 874485 (H) 0161 869 0420 (B) 07887 751274 Email: Rhaslehurst@labmedics.co.uk	North	Cheshire rep Asst Treasurer - Fines
Jack Hamer 55 Rush Green Road, Lymm, Cheshire. WA13 9PS Tel: 01925 755584	North	Cumbria rep Asst Treasurer - offshore
Alan Johnson 6 Rugby Drive, Tytherington, Macclesfield, Ches. SK10 2DJ Tel/Fax: 01625 614697 Email: ajohnco@macc61.freeserve.co.uk	North 1	League Secretary
Terry Owen-Smith 3 Lindisfarne Road, Alnwick, Northumberland NE66 1AU Tel: 01665 602160	North 2 East	League Secretary

Colin Barton 4 Oulderhill Drive, Rochdale, Lancashire OL11 5LB Tel: 01706 350312	North Lancs 1	League Secretary
Bill Hopkinson Far Hey Head Farm, Littleborough, Rochdale OL15 9NS Tel: 01706 379879	North Lancs 2	League Secretary
Ian Scott Brown 7 Pendle View, Grindleton, Nr Clitheroe, Lancs. BB7 4QU Tel: 01200 440102	North Lancs Cumbria	League Secretary
Frank Sheppard 74 Meadowfield, Gosforth, Cumbria CA20 1HX Tel: 01946 725327	Cumbria	League Secretary
Mike Massey Fieldside, Grange Road, Bowden, Cheshire WA14 3EE Tel: 0161 9282997	South Lancs Cheshire 1	League Secretary
Brian Minor 45 Gorton St., Peel Green, Eccles, Manchester M30 8LX Tel: 0161 2885324	South Lancs Cheshire 2	League Secretary
Vic Thomas 5 Portree Close, Winton, Eccles, Manchester M30 8LX Tel: 0161 788 7540	South Lancs Cheshire 3	League Secretary
Peter Riley 27 Grappenhall Road, Stockton Heath, Warrington, Cheshire WA4 2AH Tel: 01925 6044896	South Lancs Cheshire 4	League Secretary
Gordon Gravil 6 Grampian Way, Thorne, South Yorkshire DN8 5YL Tel: 01405 813642	Durham Northumberland 1	League Secretary
Tony Brown 22 Mill Crescent, Hebburn, Tyne & Wear NE31 1UQ Tel: 0191 4693716	Durham Northumberland 2	League Secretary
Joyce Baty 5 Brooklands, Ponteland, Northumberland NE20 9LZ Tel: 01661 823527	Durham Northumberland 3	League Secretary
John Ker 4 Anlaby Close, Billingham, Cleveland TS23 3RA Tel: 01642 560536	Durham Northumberland 4	League Secretary
Trevor Graveson Attermire House, Castle Hill, Settle BD24 9EU Tel: 01729 823559	Yorkshire 1	League Secretary
Bill Cooper Moorcroft, Lucy Hall Drive, Baildon, W. Yorks. BD17 5BG Tel: 01274 584355	Yorkshire 2	League Secretary
Ron Lewis 17 Harewood Drive, Wrenthorpe, Wakefield. WF2 0DS Tel: 01924 299874	Yorkshire 3	League Secretary
Kathleen McNally 28 Cherry Tree Road, Armthorpe, Doncaster. DN3 2HP Tel: 01302 834252	Yorkshire 4	League Secretary
Graham Mapplebeck 46 Cranmore Crescent, Belle Isle, Leeds LS10 4AN Tel: 0113 270 4935	Yorkshire 5	League Secretary
Anthony McNally 28 Cherry Tree Rd, Armthorpe, Doncaster. DN3 2HP Tel: 01302 834252	Yorkshire 6	League Secretary

NORTH ONE

2001-02 LEAGUE TABLE

	P	W	D	L	PF	PA	PD	Pts
Halifax	20	18	0	2	655	213	442	36
Hull Ionians	22	16	1	5	599	411	188	33
West Park St Helens	21	14	0	7	574	300	274	28
Darlington	20	12	2	6	650	309	341	26
Chester	22	12	0	10	494	484	10	24
Macclesfield	20	11	1	8	400	391	9	23
Driffield	21	10	0	11	503	529	-26	20
Aspatria	21	10	0	11	495	576	-81	20
Sheffield	22	8	2	12	345	513	-168	18
Bradford & Bingley	22	8	1	13	474	438	36	17
Middlesbrough	22	4	1	17	393	619	-226	9
Wigton (-8)	21	0	0	21	119	918	-799	-8

2002-03 FIXTURE GRID

	Aspatria	Birkenhead	Chester	Cleckheaton	Darlington	Driffield	Huddersfield	Macclesfield	Morley	Sandal	West Hartlepool	West Park (St. H.)
Aspatria		07/09	23/11	01/03	21/12	07/12	28/09	12/04	01/02	12/10	11/01	02/11
Birkenhead Park	15/03		12/10	02/11	12/04	11/01	01/03	07/12	21/12	28/09	23/11	01/02
Chester	14/12	18/01		07/12	08/02	12/04	26/10	05/10	15/03	04/01	14/09	16/11
Cleckheaton	14/09	04/01	29/03		18/01	07/09	16/11	26/10	08/02	14/12	05/10	30/11
Darlington	16/11	30/11	28/09	12/10		01/02	29/03	14/12	11/01	07/09	02/11	01/03
Driffield	29/03	26/10	30/11	15/03	05/10		04/01	18/01	14/09	16/11	08/02	14/12
Huddersfield	08/02	14/09	11/01	21/12	07/12	02/11		15/03	23/11	01/02	12/04	12/10
Macclesfield	30/11	29/03	01/02	11/01	23/11	12/10	07/09		02/11	01/03	21/12	28/09
Morley	05/10	16/11	07/09	28/09	26/10	01/03	14/12	04/01		30/11	18/01	29/03
Sandal	18/01	08/02	02/11	23/11	15/03	21/12	05/10	14/09	12/04		07/12	11/01
West Hartlepool	26/10	14/12	01/03	01/02	04/01	28/09	30/11	16/11	12/10	29/03		07/09
West Park St Helens	04/01	05/10	21/12	12/04	14/09	23/11	18/01	08/02	07/12	26/10	15/03	

ASPATRIA RUFC

Founded: 1875

Secretary: Avril Quinn, 1 Beacon Close, Aspatria, CA5 3HU
016973 21610 (H) 016973 31234 (B) 016973 32749 (Fax) E-mail: avrilq@excite.com
Director of Rugby: Melvyn Hanley, 7 King Street, Aspatria, Cumbria, CA5 3AD.
016973 20328 (H), 01946 815111 (B), 01946 815082 (Fax)
President: Norman Lazonby, Croft House, Dubwath, Bass Lake, Cumbria 01768 776363
Chairman: John Heyworth **Treasurer:** Barney Clegg 016973 20285 **County Representative:** David Wilson
Fixture Secretary: P Gray 016973 21760 **Team Secretary**: M Ray 016973 21313
Ground Address: Bower Park, Station Road, Aspatria, Cumbria Tel: 016973 20420 Website: www.aspatriarufc.com
Capacity: 2,250 Seated: 250 Standing: 2,000
Directions: M6 Junc 41, B5305 to Wigton. Left in Wigton Town Centre - 2 miles left onto by-pass. 7 miles to Aspatria - left in town centre towards station Nearest Railway Station: Aspatria, right out of station, club 100yds on right
Car Parking: 200 at ground, 200 nearby **Admission:** tba
Clubhouse: Normal licensing hours. Snacks & bar meals available match days only
Club Shop: Open 2-5 matchdays Contact Mary Hanley 016973 20328
Colours: Black & red hoops/black **Change colours:** Black shirts/white
Training Nights: Tuesday & Thursday **Nickname**: Black/reds
Programme Size: A5 Price: 50p Pages: 56 Editor: Avril Quinn
Advertising Rates Mono only Full page £100, Half page £50, Qtr £25

BIRKENHEAD PARK

Founded:

Secretary: Peter Greville, 2 Howbeck Close, Oxton, Prenton, Wirral CH43 6TH
Tel: 0151 653 6070 (W)

Fixture Secretary: Bob Hardman, 32 Shamrock Road, Claughton, Birkenhead.
Tel: (H) 0151 652 5204

League Contact: As Secretary

Ground Address: The Upper Park, Park Road North, Birkenhead CH41 8AA
Tel: 0151 652 4646

Directions: M53 J1, follow signs for Bidston and Birkenhead centre.
Straight on at roundabout with church in centre. Take 1st right after Aldi Supermarket into Park Road North. Ground is on left.

Colours: Red, white and blue

CHESTER R.U.F.C.

Founded: 1925

President	C Cawthorn	21 Oaklands Avenue, Tattenhall, Chester CH3 9QU	Tel: 01829 770498
Chairman	W Evans	12 Orchard Croft, Guilden Sutton, Chester CH3 7SL	Tel: 01244 300515
Treasurer	D Gray	Applegarth, Little Heath Rd., Chester CH3 7AH	
Hon. Secretary	P Rhodes	The Hollies, off Carriage Drive, Frodsham, Cheshire WA6 6EF Tel: 01928 731485	
Fixture Sec.	C Cawthorn	21 Oaklands Avenue, Tattenhall, Chester CH3 9QU	Tel: 01829 770498
Director of Rugby	J Booth	The Old School House, Acres Rd., Bebington, Cheshire	

GROUND **Address:** Hare Lane, Littleton, Chester CH3 7DB Tel: 01244 336017
Website: www.chester-rufc.com
Capacity: 1,000 Covered Seating: 500
Directions: From the A55 - the Chester outer ring road - take the A51and then the first left into Hare Lane.
Car Parking: Included with admission **Nearest Railway Station:** Chester
Admission: Matchday £3 Season tickets: Not available
Clubhouse: Open Tues., Wed. & Thur. Sat. & Sun. & for private functions.
Club Shop: Open matchdays & Sundays.
Programme: **Size**: A5 **Price**: Incl. with admission Advertising: Contact A Rees 01244 675352
Training Nights: Tuesday & Thursday
Colours: Red shirts, black shorts **Change colours:** Blue shirts, black shorts

NORTHERN

CLECKHEATON RFC

Founded: 1924

Chairman Mike Smith, 42a Moortop, Drighlington, BD11 1BX, Tel. 0113 2852294
Treasurer Mike Tozer, 32 Latham Lane, Gomersal, Cleckheaton, BD19 4AL, Tel. 01274 861101
Hon. Secretary Chris Wharton, 8 Ingfield, Oakenshaw, BD12 7EF, Tel. 01274 674870 (email chris@frumple.com)
Fixture Sec. Peter Lawton, 5 York Place, Cleckheaton, BD19 3PA
Tel. 01274 864155 email peterlawton@designservices39.fsnet.co.uk)
League Contact Alan Bentley, 15 Sycamore Drive, Cleckheaton, BD19 6AP, Tel 01274 869364, 01274 861101 (work)
Director of Rugby John Bentley
Ground Address The Pavilion, Moorend,Cleckheaton, BD19 3UD
Tel. 01274 873410 email - enquiries@tozer-insurance.co.uk
Directions Off Junction 26 M62, take road to Dewsbury and in 200 yrds turn left into Cleckheaton Sports Club.
Ground Capacity 1500 inc 250 covered seating Car Parking 150 at ground
Nearest Railway station - Dewsbury
Admission prices Match day £4 season tickets N/a
Club house Monday - Friday 7pm - 11pm Saturday 12 noon - 11pm, Sunday 12 noon - 4pm **Club Shop** - N/a
Programme - size A5, price included with admission **Advertising** - contact treasurer
Editor - Martin Hall 01274 872589 **Training nights:** Monday's &Thursday's 7pm
Colours: Cherry Red & white hoops, black shorts, red socks with 2 white hoops **Change colours:** light/dark blue quarters.

DARLINGTON RFC

Founded: 1863

President	Eric Rogers	45 Barratt Rd., Darlington DL3 8LA	01325 468560
Chairman	Andrew Foster	45 Hartford Rd., Darlington DL3 8HF	01325 466501
Club Secretary	Peter Sanderson	School House, Chapel St., Middleton One Row, Darlington DL2 1DA	01325 332986
Fixtures Secretary	David Gardner,	'Shieldaig', Boldron Lane, Startford, Barnard Castle, Co.Durham. DL12 9AP email: davidandsusangardener@tesco.net	01833 630742
Treasurer	Frank Nelson	1 Mayfield, Barnard Castle, Co. Durham DL12 9AR	01833 638307
League Contact:	Tommy Miller	51 First Ave., Colburn, Catterick Garrison DL9 4RL	01748 832700

GroundAddress: Blackwell Meadows, Grange Road, Darlington. DL1 5NR Tel: 01325 363777 Fax: 01325 363888
Capacity: 2,150 Seated: 150 Uncovered Standing: 2000 Web site: www.darlingtonrfc.co.uk
Directions: From south take A66, DRFC directly off Blands Corner roundabout.
From north take A68 to Darlington and continue to A66 junction at Blands Corner r'about at Blackwell
Car Parking: Spaces for 200 cars & 4 coaches at ground. Nearest Railway Station: Darlington Bank Top
Clubhouse: Open Mon-Sat 11-11pm and Sunday 12-10.30pm **Club Shop:** Open weekends **Admission:** N/A
Training Nights: Monday & Thursday (seniors)
Programme: Size: A4 Price: With admission Pages: 10
Colours: Scarlet with black & white Hoop **Change colours:** Black & white quarters

DRIFFIELD F.C.

Founded: 1926

President	Mike Sellers	Low Kaythorpe, Rudston, Driffield YO25 0JD	Tel: 01262 420237
Chairman	John Harrison	9 Parsonage Close, Nafferton, Driffield YO25 0LH	Tel: 01377 253032
Hon. Secretary	Colin Seabrook	'Lilleygarth', Main Street, Skerne, Driffield YO25 9HS	Tel: 01377 253690
Fixture Sec.	John Leason	15 Albion Street, Driffield. YO25 6PZ	Tel: 01377 254036
Director of Rugby	Stuart Cooper	1 Orchard Drive, Middleton, Driffield YO25 9UW	

Ground Address Kelleythorpe, Driffield, E. Yorks. YO25 9DW Tel: 01377 256598
Capacity: Unlimited - all uncovered standing

Directions: From M62 follow A614 to the strat of the Driffield by-pass. Ground opposite.
From York take A166 to Driffield by-pass then right along by-pass for half mile. Ground on left.
Nearest Station: Driffield, 1 mile from ground.
Car Parking: Unlimited car parking at ground.

Admission: Matchday £3.00 including programme. No season tickets available.
Clubhouse: Open Tues & Thurs evs., matchdays & Sun morning. **Club Shop:** Open Sunday morning.
Colours: Blue/black/white **Change colours:** All red **Training Nights:** Tuesday & Thursday
Programme: **Size:** A5 **Pages:** 20 **Price:** With admission **Editor:** John Harrison (Chairman)
Advertising: Contact editor

HUDDERSFIELD RUFC

Founded: 1870

President: Stephen Thornton, 8 Manor Road Farnley Road Huddersfield HD4 6UL 01484 667372
Chairman Alan Ibberson, 3 Broadgate Cresent, Almonbury Huddersfield HD5 8HT Co club 01484 469 801
Secretary Ian Cleave, 2 Clough Way, Fenay Bridge Huddersfield HD8 OLJ 01484 306045
Head Coach Russell Lawrance, 33 Richmond Grove, Gomersal W.Yorks. BD19 4AG 01274 876030 (H) 07976 419964(M)
Fixture Secretary Brian Swift 01484 469801, 07713 607906 (M)
Director of Rugby Mark Birch 36 Gosport Close Outlane Huddersfield HD3 3FP 01484 469 801
Development Officer Hamish Pratt c/o club 01484 469 801
Ground Lockwood Park, Brewery Drive, Huddersfield HD4 6EN Web site: www.huddersfieldrugby.com
01484 469801(B) 01484 469880 (Fax) E-Mail: rugby.hrufc@virgin.net
Directions From M62 follow Huddersfield sign, from town centre take A616 Holmfirth, through lights signed Meltham B6108, club 300 yards on left. Nearest railway station – Lockwood (Penistone line)
Capacity - 3000- Covered seating 500 –Floodlights **Car parking**- 500 at ground
Admission- £3 including programme
Clubhouse Open evenings and all day Sat & Sun Functions catered up to 120, Conference facilities.
Out-door: All weather pitch's (floodlit). Multi sports. Training nights: Senior Mon & Thurs.
Club Shop: In Club opening hours. **Colours:** White, Claret and Gold. Change colours Claret
Programme: Size A5 (with Admission) Editor (Phone Club)

Huddersfield RU v Vale of Lune at Lockwood Park. Photo: Paul Welch

MACCLESFIELD R.U.F.C.

Founded: 187

President A. Simpson 01625 429100
Chairman Alan Johnson 01625 614697 Tel/Fax
6 Rugby Drive, Tytherington, Macclesfield SK10 2JD
e-mail: ajohnco@macc61.freeserve.co.uk
Secretary Alan Johnson as above
Hon. Treasurer D. A. J. Taylor 01625 431163
Chairman of Marketing; Publicity; Communications D. J. Roberts 01625 501803

Ground Priory Park, Priory Lane, Prestbury, Macclesfield, Cheshire SK10 4AF
Tel: 01625 827899 Fax: 01625 827899
Capacity: 5,500 Covered Seating: 200
Directions About 1 mile west of Town Centre on the B5087 - Macclesfield to Alderley Edge road, adjacent to Leisure Centre.
Nearest Railway Station: Macclesfield (in town centre) **Car Parking**: Spaces for 250 cars at ground
Admission: £3.50 including programme
Clubhouse: Open Saturdays & Sundays & every night except Wed. & Sunday
Club Shop: Open Saturady & Sunday & Tues & Thursday evenings.
Programme: Size: A5 Pages: 32 Price: £1 Editor: G A Allen
Advertising: O/S Back Cover £350 I/S Back Cover £160 Full page: £100 1/2 Page £
Colours: Blue and white hoops **Change colours:** Red/black/white vertical stripes
Nickmame: The Silkmen **Training Nights:** Tuesday & Thursday

MORLEY RFC

Founded: 1878

President Bob Lloyd c/o Morley RFC Tel:01924 494612 (H) 07885 741396 (M)
Club Chairman Trevor Richmond c/o Morley RFC 01274 480741 (B) 07831 131100 (M)
Club Secretary Dennis R Elam 26 The Roundway, Morley, W. Yorks. LS27 0JS
0113 252 4348 (H) 07751 443059 (M) e-mail: dennis.elam@ukgateway.net
Head of Rugby Ken Higgins c/o Morley RFC Tel: 01924 823135 (B) 01977 658582 (H)
Fixtures Secretary Peter Kneale c/o Morley RFC e-mail: peter@kneale7.freeserve.co.uk
Tel: 0113 282 4373 (H) 0771 3862413 (M)

Ground Address: Scatcherd Lane, Morley, West Yorkshire, LS27 0JJ Tel. 0113 253 3487 Fax: 0113 253 4144
Capacity: 2,899 Seated: 499 Standing: 2,400 Website: www.morleyrfc.co.uk
Directions: **From West:** Leave M62 Jnc 27 Follow A650 towards Wakefield for 1.2miles turn left St. Andrews Ave. Ground 0.3 miles on left. **From East**: Leave M62 Jnc 28 follow A650 towards Bradford for 1.7 miles, turn right into St Andrews Ave.
Nearest Railway Station: Morley Low BR **Car Parking:** 110 in & around ground
Admission: Season - Standing Adult £50, Family £100 Matchday - Standing Adults £5, Children/OAPs £2
Clubhouse: Weekdays 6-11, Sat 12-11, Sun 12-4 & 8-11 Three bars with snacks & bar meals available
Functions: Capacity 200 Contact Sheila Tonge 0113 253 3487 **Club Shop:** Manager Mr. Laurie Newsome 0113 253 3487
Colours: Maroon & white quarters, maroon shorts **Change colours:** All Blue. **Training Nights:** Tuesday & Thursday
Programme Size: A5 Pages: 16 Price: £1 **Editor:** Peter Aveyard Tel: 0113 253 8193 (H) e-mail: bruntcliffepete@cs.com
Advertising Rates - Mono Page £300 1/2 page £175 1/4 page £100

SANDAL RUFC

Founded: 1927

President Henry Everett 31 Mount Crescent, Thornes, Wakefield WF2 8QG 01924 378987 (H)
Chairman C R Hoyland 1 Moorhouse Lane, Haigh, nr Barnsley S74 4DD 01924 830572 (H)
Director of Rugby Steve Ackroyd c/o Sandal RUFC Home Tel: 01924 256004
Dir. of Youth Rugby Steve Hodges 14 Carr Lane, Sandal, Wakefield WF2 6HJ 01924 255009 (H)
Hon. Secretary Philip Harrison 46 Brandhill Drive, Crofton, Wakefield WF4 1PF 01924 863457 (H)
Press Officer Philip Harrison as Secretary
Fixtures Secretary Colin Critchett 48 Sinclair Garth, Sandal, Wakefield WF2 6RE 01924 254329
Ground Address Milnthorpe Green, Standbridge Lane, Sandal, Wakefield, W. Yorks. WF27JD. Tel: 01924 250661
Capacity: 1625 Seated: 75 Standing: 1500
Directions: From the M1, junction 39, take the A636 to Wakefield. After3/4 mile turn right at the roundabout into Ansdale Road, and after one mile the club will be found on the left.
Nearest Railway Station: Westgate, Wakefield. **Car Parking:** 200 spaces are available within the ground.
Admission: Matchdays - Adults: £5 (incl. car park & programme) Children/OAPs: £2.50.
Clubhouse: Open during normal licensing hours, two bars, bar meals available. Fitness centre.
Functions: Up to 120 can be catered for. **Club Shop:** Open matchdays & Sundays.
Training Nights: Tuesday and Thursday. **Nickname**: The Milnthorpers
Colours: Maroon, gold & white hoops **Change colours:** Gold with maroon & white hoops.
Programme Size: A5 Price: With admission Pages: 24 + cover Advertising Rates: Page £200, 1/2 £100, 1/4 £50

WEST HARTLEPOOL RFC

Founded: 1881

President Reg Turner
Chairman Ron Greig
Vice Chairman Stuart Murray
Coach John Stabler
Club Secretary Steve Smith Tel: 01423 536530 Fax: 01423 520125 Mob.: 07703 504730
All correspondence to: c/o West Hartlepool RFC, PO Box 132, Hartlepool TS25 5YW

Ground Address: Brinkburn, Blakelock Road, Hartlepool TS25 5PF
Capacity: 2,200 Seated: 700 Standing - uncovered: 1,500
Directions: A1/A19 proceeding north to A689 to Hartlepool. Turn left at the traffic lights as you enter the built-up area. Right at first junction (catcote Rd.) and continue for approx. 1.5 miles past schools on the left. Turn right at the traffic lights on shopping precinct, left at round about - Brinkburn (6th form College is 600 yds on left).
Nearest Railway Station: Hartlepool. **Car Parking:** Yes at ground.
Admission : (No concessions) Matchday: £5 Season tickets: £50
Clubhouse: Restricted opening, matchdays from 12.30 onwards.
Colours: Green, red and white shirts, navy shorts, green socks
Change colours: Dark green - shirts, shorts and socks
Nickname: West **Programme:** Not applicable

WEST PARK (St. HELENS) R.F.C.

Founded: 1947

President	Frank Cheetham	c/o West Park RFC	01744 617372
Chief Executive	John Bradbury	104 Mossbank rd., St. Helens WA11 7DG	01744 733578
Deputy Executive	R T J Briers	48 Avery Road, Seneley Green, Haydock	01744 634602
Director of Finance	Norman England	'Caleb View', 71 Dingle Rd., Upholland WN8 0EW	01695 622665
Director of Administration	John B Fletcher	'Cellduminn', 7 Kings Rd., Taylor Park, St. Helens WA10 3HT 01744 755895 (H) 01744 617372 (B & Fax) email: jean-fletcher@talk21.com	

Ground Address West Park RFC,
Redrocks, Prescot Road, St. Helens WA10 3AG
Tel: 01744 26138 **Fax:** 01744 617372 **website:** west-parkrfc.co.uk
email: jean-fletcher@talk21.com

Capacity: 1000 Covered Seating: 20
Standing: Covered - 250 Uncovered - 730

Directions: M62 off at J6 & take M57 towards Liverpool docks & Southport. Turn off at Prescot sign (Knowsley Safari Park sign) and follow signs to St. Helens. After passing the "Grapes' PH, West Park is approx. 1/2 mile on left.
Car Parking: 150 spaces at ground, a further 150 next door in Carmel College
Nearest Railway Station: Thatto Heath

Admission: Matchday £3
Clubhouse: Open every evening except Sunday
Club Shop: thro' Dir. of Admin..
Colours: Green & gold hooped shirts, green shorts
Change colours: All red
Training Nights: Tuesday & Thursday
Programme: **Size**: A5 **Pages**: 20
Price: £3 incl. parking & admission **Editor**: J B Fletcher
Advertising: 1/4 page £50 1/2 page: £100 Page: £200 - all + VAT - contact J B Fletcher

West Park captain, Sean Fletcher, in the lineout during the Lancashire Cup game against Fylde RFC.

NORTHERN REGION FINAL LEAGUE TABLES 2001-02

North 2 East	P	W	D	L	PF	PA	PD	Pts	-
Cleckheaton	22	18	2	2	698	293	405	38	
Huddersfield	22	18	2	2	565	301	264	38	
Morpeth	22	15	0	7	498	384	114	30	
Westoe	22	12	2	8	452	371	81	26	
Redcar	22	12	1	9	396	318	78	25	
Alnwick	22	9	2	11	373	371	2	20	
Stockton	22	10	0	12	346	423	-77	20	
Goole	22	10	0	12	352	501	-149	20	
Wheatley Hills	22	7	2	13	376	460	-84	16	
Northern	22	6	1	15	360	484	-124	13	
Old Crossleyans	22	5	2	15	359	503	-144	12	
Bridlington	22	3	0	19	184	550	-366	6	

North 2 West	P	W	D	L	PF	PA	PD	Pts	-
Birkenhead Park	22	19	0	3	690	290	400	38	
Vale of Lune	22	17	1	4	556	270	286	35	
Stockport	22	14	0	8	485	375	110	28	
Lymm	22	11	1	10	384	459	-75	23	
Aldwinians	22	11	0	11	376	465	-89	22	
Winnington Park	22	10	1	11	578	477	101	21	
Blackburn	22	10	0	12	376	438	-62	20	
Broughton Park	22	9	1	12	447	498	-51	19	
Altrincham Kersal	22	8	1	13	401	524	-123	17	
Warrington	22	8	1	13	287	450	-163	17	
Workington	22	8	0	14	380	407	-27	16	
Caldy	22	4	0	18	266	573	-307	8	

N. Lancs/Cumbria	P	W	D	L	PF	PA	PD	Pts	-
Rochdale	19	17	1	1	493	201	292	35	
Oldham	21	17	0	4	402	255	147	34	
Penrith	22	15	1	6	616	212	404	31	
Carlisle	21	13	3	5	384	181	203	29	
Rossendale	21	12	0	9	419	301	118	24	
De La Salle	18	10	0	8	254	185	69	20	
Kirkby Lonsdale	21	8	1	12	387	349	38	17	
*Tyldesley	22	8	1	13	313	503	-190	15	2
Blackpool	21	6	0	15	237	471	-234	12	
*St Benedict's	21	7	1	13	178	388	-210	11	4
*Netherhall	21	5	0	16	171	484	-313	8	2
*Cockermouth	18	1	0	17	67	391	-324	-2	4

North Lancs 1	P	W	D	L	PF	PA	PD	Pts	-
Fleetwood	22	22	0	0	862	155	707	44	
Bury	22	18	0	4	376	190	186	36	
Trafford MV	22	15	0	7	473	218	255	30	
Heaton Moor	22	14	2	6	403	296	107	30	
Eccles	22	11	1	10	386	349	37	23	
Didsbury Toc H	22	11	0	11	371	362	9	22	
Burnage	22	10	0	12	318	310	8	20	
Lytham	22	9	0	13	271	450	-179	18	
Bolton	22	8	0	14	249	320	-71	16	
Thornton Cleveleys	22	7	0	15	245	570	-325	14	
Old Bedians	22	5	1	16	197	501	-304	11	
Calder Vale	22	0	0	22	166	596	-430	0	

North Lancs 2	P	W	D	L	PF	PA	PD	Pts	-
Ashton-under-Lyne	19	17	1	1	802	108	694	35	
Littleborough	20	16	0	4	743	158	585	32	
Chorley	20	15	0	5	641	205	436	30	
Broughton	19	13	1	5	567	218	349	27	
Colne & Nelson	20	12	0	8	436	339	97	24	
*West Park Warriors	19	12	0	7	393	245	148	22	2
Carnforth	19	6	0	13	302	498	-196	12	
Clitheroe	19	6	0	13	243	663	-420	12	
North Manchester	18	4	0	14	170	457	-287	8	
Garstang	19	3	0	16	254	642	-388	6	
Lonsdale Wanderers	18	0	0	18	60	1078	-1018	0	

Lostock have withdrawn from the league

Cumbria	P	W	D	L	PF	PA	PD	Pts	-
Vickers Sports	24	21	1	2	739	183	556	43	
Windermere	24	19	1	4	690	264	426	39	
Upper Eden	24	18	1	5	586	305	281	37	
Millom	24	17	0	7	641	234	407	34	
Keswick	24	15	1	8	435	358	77	31	
Egremont	23	15	0	8	438	332	106	30	
*Moresby	21	10	0	11	261	271	-10	18	2
Greengarth	24	9	0	15	466	523	-57	18	
*Furness	22	7	0	15	247	414	-167	10	4
Whitehaven	24	5	0	19	277	586	-309	10	
*Creighton	23	4	0	19	194	796	-602	4	4
*Ambleside	20	5	1	14	208	512	-304	1	1
*Silloth	23	2	1	20	137	541	-404	1	4

South Lancs/Cheshire 1	P	W	D	L	PF	PA	PD	Pts	-
Wilmslow	21	17	1	3	548	332	216	35	
Aspull	21	15	1	5	505	272	233	31	
Widnes	22	12	2	8	420	303	117	26	
Wigan	21	12	2	7	389	277	112	26	
Birchfield (Lancs)	22	12	1	9	397	351	46	25	
Northwich	22	11	0	11	369	363	6	22	
Vagabonds (I.O.M.)	21	10	2	9	419	438	-19	22	
Ormskirk	22	9	2	11	427	342	85	20	
Oldershaw	22	9	2	11	395	399	-4	20	
Leigh	22	10	0	12	352	451	-99	20	
*Dukinfield	22	5	1	16	279	485	-206	9	2
St Edward's O.B.	22	1	0	21	219	706	-487	2	

S. Lancs/Cheshire 2	P	W	D	L	PF	PA	PD	Pts	-
Wirral	22	21	0	1	768	258	510	42	
Southport	22	18	0	4	779	224	555	36	
Ellesmere Port	22	13	2	7	472	301	171	28	
Anselmians	22	13	1	8	485	344	141	27	
Trentham	22	12	1	9	322	335	-13	25	
Sandbach	22	12	0	10	478	355	123	24	
Ashton on Mersey	22	10	0	12	331	508	-177	20	
Runcorn	21	7	1	13	320	414	-94	15	
Crewe and Nantwich	22	7	0	15	338	492	-154	14	
Moore	22	7	0	15	299	508	-209	14	
Wallasey	21	4	0	17	248	702	-454	8	
*St Mary's O.B. (Lancs)	22	4	1	17	228	627	-399	7	2

S. Lancs/Cheshire 3	P	W	D	L	PF	PA	PD	Pts	-
Hoylake	17	14	1	2	537	163	374	29	
Bowdon	18	14	0	4	448	210	238	28	
Sefton	17	11	1	5	306	192	114	23	
Orrell Anvils	18	11	0	7	360	252	108	22	
Ruskin Park	18	9	0	9	323	302	21	18	
Marple	18	8	0	10	294	302	-8	16	
Newton-le-Willows	17	8	0	9	350	363	-13	16	
Douglas (I.O.M.)	17	8	0	9	301	354	-53	16	
Eagle	18	3	1	14	152	457	-305	7	
Congleton	18	0	1	17	138	614	-476	1	

S. Lancs/Cheshire 4	P	W	D	L	PF	PA	PD	Pts	-
Prenton	17	15	0	2	549	128	421	30	
Liverpool Coll. O.B.	17	14	0	3	449	160	289	28	
Halton	18	11	1	6	409	286	123	23	
Manchester W'derers	16	11	0	5	457	208	249	22	
*Oswestry	18	10	1	7	373	342	31	19	2
Port Sunlight	18	7	0	11	278	460	-182	14	
Helsby	17	6	0	11	263	430	-167	12	
*Capenhurst	17	4	1	12	156	340	-184	7	2
Parkonians	17	3	0	14	128	413	-285	6	
*Vulcan	13	1	1	11	101	396	-295	1	2

NORTHERN

South Lancs/Cheshire 5

	P	W	D	L	PF	PA	PD	Pts	-
Holmes Chapel	6	6	0	0	92	24	68	12	
Mossley Hill A.C.	6	4	0	2	178	59	119	8	
Prescot	6	1	0	5	45	135	-90	2	
Burtonwood	6	1	0	5	17	114	-97	2	

Waterloo Vikings & Lucas have both withdrawn from the league

Durham/N'thm'land 1

	P	W	D	L	PF	PA	PD	Pts	-
Horden	22	19	1	2	748	290	458	39	
Ashington	22	19	0	3	573	362	211	38	
Durham City	22	14	2	6	553	356	197	30	
Percy Park	22	14	0	8	734	441	293	28	
Billingham	22	12	1	9	511	507	4	25	
Hartlepool Rovers	22	10	0	12	401	388	13	20	
W. Hartlepool TDSOB	22	9	1	12	314	435	-121	19	
Gosforth	22	9	0	13	363	509	-146	18	
Gateshead	22	7	1	14	358	577	-219	15	
Ryton	22	7	0	15	370	435	-65	14	
Consett	22	7	0	15	358	512	-154	14	
Winlaton Vulcans	22	2	0	20	234	705	-471	4	

Durham/N'thm'land 2

	P	W	D	L	PF	PA	PD	Pts	-
Acklam	21	20	1	0	869	179	690	41	
Hartlepool	20	18	0	2	798	313	485	36	
*Houghton	21	16	1	4	624	268	356	31	2
North Shields	21	13	1	7	465	426	39	27	
Wallsend	21	12	1	8	419	328	91	25	
Guisborough	22	10	0	12	422	465	-43	20	
Sunderland	22	8	0	14	369	615	-246	16	
Barnard Castle	22	7	0	15	295	728	-433	14	
*Whitby	22	8	0	14	324	372	-48	12	4
Blyth	22	6	0	16	332	708	-376	12	
Whitley Bay Rockcliff	22	5	0	17	286	510	-224	10	
Medicals	22	4	0	18	369	660	-291	8	

Durham/N'thm'land 3

	P	W	D	L	PF	PA	PD	Pts	-
Seaton Carew	21	19	0	2	843	170	673	38	
Novocastrians	20	19	0	1	542	208	334	38	
Yarm	21	17	0	4	420	211	209	34	
Ponteland	22	16	0	6	414	214	200	32	
Bishop Auckland	22	11	1	10	475	398	77	23	
Chester le Street	21	11	1	9	373	337	36	23	
*Seghill	21	9	1	11	385	320	65	17	2
Wearside	22	7	0	15	225	460	-235	14	
West Hartlepool Am.	22	6	0	16	206	545	-339	12	
Jarrovians	22	5	0	17	143	555	-412	10	
Wensleydale	22	3	2	17	201	455	-254	8	
*Newton Aycliffe	20	2	1	17	181	535	-354	1	4

Durham/N'thm'land 4

	P	W	D	L	PF	PA	PD	Pts	-
South Tyneside Coll.	12	11	0	1	534	92	442	22	
Richmondshire	12	10	0	2	303	117	186	20	
Hartlepool B.B.O.B.	12	6	0	6	228	134	94	12	
Seaham	12	5	0	7	124	216	-92	10	
Hartlepool Athletic	12	5	0	7	147	264	-117	10	
Shildon Town	11	2	0	9	105	274	-169	4	
Durham Constabulary	11	2	0	9	62	406	-344	4	

* denotes points deducted, shown in right hand column

Yorkshire 1

	P	W	D	L	PF	PA	PD	Pts	-
Hull	22	19	1	2	526	237	289	39	
Scarborough	22	14	2	6	424	305	119	30	
Old Brodleians	22	14	1	7	528	347	181	29	
Yarnbury	21	12	3	6	428	291	137	27	
Selby	22	12	1	9	478	328	150	25	
Pontefract	22	12	1	9	381	312	69	25	
York	22	9	2	11	414	340	74	20	
Sheffield Tigers	22	9	2	11	356	435	-79	20	
North Ribblesdale	22	8	2	12	328	388	-60	18	
Beverley	22	9	0	13	316	426	-110	18	
West Park Bramhope	22	3	1	18	193	519	-326	7	
Pocklington	21	2	0	19	210	654	-444	4	

Yorkshire 2

	P	W	D	L	PF	PA	PD	Pts	-
Huddersfield Y.M.C.A.	22	20	0	2	661	280	381	40	
Dinnington	22	15	1	6	688	363	325	31	
Skipton	22	11	2	9	463	441	22	24	
Keighley	22	11	1	10	458	370	88	23	
Leodiensians	22	11	1	10	489	494	-5	23	
Northallerton	22	10	3	9	314	369	-55	23	
Ripon	22	10	2	10	447	387	60	22	
Ilkley	22	10	1	11	394	373	21	21	
West Leeds	22	8	3	11	405	536	-131	19	
York Railway Institute	22	8	1	13	318	478	-160	17	
Castleford	22	6	1	15	308	386	-78	13	
Hemsworth	22	4	0	18	286	754	-468	8	

Yorkshire 3

	P	W	D	L	PF	PA	PD	Pts	-
Heath	22	19	0	3	676	135	541	38	
Malton and Norton	22	17	1	4	777	265	512	35	
Stocksbridge	22	15	2	5	371	244	127	32	
Leeds Corinthians	22	15	1	6	455	271	184	31	
Old Otliensians	22	12	1	9	334	211	123	25	
Bradford Salem	22	12	0	10	369	367	2	24	
Halifax Vandals	22	9	0	13	260	529	-269	18	
Bramley Phoenix Park	22	8	0	14	398	459	-61	16	
Wath on Dearne	22	8	0	14	253	594	-341	16	
*Barnsley	22	7	1	14	275	462	-187	13	2
Roundhegians	22	4	2	16	329	585	-256	10	
Hessle	22	2	0	20	222	597	-375	4	

Yorkshire 4

	P	W	D	L	PF	PA	PD	Pts	-
Knottingley	21	17	1	3	594	198	396	35	
Moortown	22	16	2	4	634	284	350	34	
Wakefield Cougars	22	17	0	5	470	283	187	34	
Wetherby	22	17	0	5	372	298	74	34	
*Danum Phoenix	22	11	2	9	420	362	58	22	2
Sheffield Oaks	22	10	1	11	343	346	-3	21	
Hullensians	22	8	1	13	259	460	-201	17	
Old Modernians	22	8	0	14	281	408	-127	16	
Baildon	22	7	2	13	289	447	-158	16	
Old Rishworthians	22	5	2	15	338	435	-97	12	
Stanley Rodillians	22	6	0	16	287	479	-192	12	
*Mosborough	21	3	1	17	248	535	-287	5	2

Yorkshire 5

	P	W	D	L	PF	PA	PD	Pts	-
Sheffield Medicals	18	16	0	2	463	234	229	32	
Thornensians	18	14	0	4	533	170	363	28	
Hornsea	18	12	1	5	584	206	378	25	
*Aireborough	18	9	0	9	310	280	30	16	2
Ossett	17	8	0	9	228	251	-23	16	
*Adwick le Street	18	8	1	9	377	431	-54	15	2
Wharfedale Rams	17	6	2	9	298	289	9	14	
*Marist	18	8	0	10	274	313	-39	10	6
*Rawmarsh	17	5	0	12	269	417	-148	8	2
*Rotherham Clifton	17	0	0	17	39	784	-745	-4	4

Edlington Granby have withdrawn from the league

Yorkshire 6

	P	W	D	L	PF	PA	PD	Pts	-
Knaresborough	16	15	0	1	611	127	484	30	
Wibsey	16	12	1	3	274	193	81	25	
Pontefract Pythons	16	10	1	5	233	196	37	21	
Garforth	16	7	1	8	278	261	17	15	
Burley	16	6	1	9	269	241	28	13	
Withernsea	16	6	1	9	208	337	-129	13	
Thirsk	16	6	0	10	174	228	-54	12	
Wickersley Exel	16	5	0	11	223	429	-206	10	
Walkington Rovers	16	2	1	13	173	431	-258	5	

NORTHERN REGION FIXTURE GRIDS 2001-2002

North 2 East

	Alnwick	Bradford & Bingley	Goole	Horden	Hull	Middlesbrough	Morpeth	Redcar	Scarborough	Stockton	Stockton	Westoe
Alnwick		01/03	02/11	29/03	11/01	21/12	28/09	01/02	07/09	30/11	12/10	23/11
Bradford & Bingley	14/09		12/04	08/02	23/11	07/12	11/01	02/11	05/10	18/01	21/12	15/03
Goole	04/01	30/11		16/11	28/09	18/01	29/03	07/09	14/12	05/10	01/03	26/10
Horden	07/12	28/09	21/12		02/11	23/11	01/02	12/10	01/03	15/03	11/01	12/04
Hull	26/10	14/12	08/02	04/01		05/10	30/11	29/03	16/11	14/09	07/09	18/01
Middlesbrough	16/11	29/03	12/10	14/12	01/02		07/09	01/03	30/11	26/10	28/09	04/01
Morpeth	08/02	26/10	07/12	05/10	12/04	15/03		21/12	18/01	04/01	23/11	14/09
Redcar	05/10	04/01	15/03	18/01	07/12	14/09	16/11		26/10	14/12	12/04	08/02
Scarborough	15/03	01/02	23/11	14/09	21/12	12/04	12/10	11/01		08/02	02/11	07/12
Sheffield	12/04	12/10	01/02	07/09	01/03	11/01	02/11	23/11	28/09		07/12	21/12
Stockton	18/01	16/11	14/09	26/10	15/03	08/02	14/12	30/11	04/01	29/03		05/10
Westoe	14/12	07/09	11/01	30/11	12/10	02/11	01/03	28/09	29/03	16/11	01/02	

North 2 West

	Aldwinians	Altrincham Kersal	Aspull	Blackburn	Broughton Park	Lymm	Rochdale	Stockport	Vale of Lune	Wigton	Wilmslow	Winnington Park
Aldwinians		18/01	26/10	12/04	14/12	08/02	15/03	16/11	14/09	04/01	07/12	05/10
Altrincham Kersal	12/10		01/03	11/01	15/03	12/04	21/12	01/02	23/11	28/09	02/11	07/12
Aspull	11/01	14/09		02/11	08/02	07/12	23/11	12/10	12/04	01/02	21/12	15/03
Blackburn	30/11	26/10	04/01		29/03	05/10	14/09	14/12	08/02	16/11	15/03	18/01
Broughton Park	23/11	07/09	28/09	07/12		21/12	01/02	02/11	11/01	12/10	01/03	12/04
Lymm	28/09	30/11	29/03	01/02	16/11		11/01	01/03	02/11	07/09	12/10	14/12
Rochdale	07/09	16/11	14/12	01/03	05/10	26/10		29/03	18/01	30/11	28/09	04/01
Stockport	21/12	05/10	18/01	23/11	04/01	14/09	07/12		15/03	26/10	12/04	08/02
Vale of Lune	01/03	14/12	30/11	28/09	26/10	04/01	12/10	07/09		29/03	01/02	16/11
Wigton	02/11	08/02	05/10	21/12	18/01	15/03	12/04	11/01	07/12		23/11	14/09
Wilmslow	29/03	04/01	16/11	07/09	14/09	18/01	08/02	30/11	05/10	14/12		26/10
Winnington Park	01/02	29/03	07/09	12/10	30/11	23/11	02/11	28/09	21/12	01/03	11/01	

North Lancs/ Cumbria

	BAe Barrow	Blackpool	Bury	Carlisle	De La Salle	Fleetwood	Kirkby Lonsdale	Oldham	Penrith	Rossendale	Tyldesley	Workington
BAe Barrow		14/09	23/11	07/12	15/03	21/12	02/11	12/04	12/10	11/01	08/02	01/02
Blackpool	01/03		21/12	12/04	07/12	02/11	11/01	23/11	01/02	12/10	15/03	28/09
Bury	14/12	16/11		26/10	04/01	28/09	01/03	18/01	29/03	07/09	05/10	30/11
Carlisle	29/03	30/11	11/01		14/12	12/10	01/02	02/11	01/03	28/09	16/11	07/09
De La Salle	07/09	29/03	02/11	23/11		11/01	12/10	21/12	28/09	01/02	30/11	01/03
Fleetwood	16/11	04/01	08/02	18/01	26/10		07/09	05/10	30/11	29/03	14/09	14/12
Kirkby Lonsdale	04/01	26/10	14/09	05/10	18/01	15/03		08/02	14/12	30/11	29/03	16/11
Oldham	30/11	14/12	12/10	04/01	16/11	01/02	28/09		07/09	01/03	26/10	29/03
Penrith	18/01	05/10	07/12	14/09	08/02	12/04	23/11	15/03		21/12	04/01	26/10
Rossendale	26/10	18/01	15/03	08/02	05/10	07/12	12/04	14/09	16/11		14/12	04/01
Tyldesley	28/09	07/09	01/02	21/12	12/04	01/03	07/12	11/01	02/11	23/11		12/10
Workington	05/10	08/02	12/04	15/03	14/09	23/11	21/12	07/12	11/01	02/11	18/01	

North Lancs 1

	Ashton-under-Lyne	Bolton	Burnage	Calder Vale	Didsbury Toc H	Eccles	Heaton Moor	Littleborough	Lytham	Old Bedians	Thornton Cleveleys	Trafford MV
Ashton-under-Lyne		02/11	11/01	21/12	07/12	12/10	12/04	23/11	15/03	14/09	08/02	01/02
Bolton	04/01		30/11	15/03	05/10	14/12	08/02	14/09	18/01	26/10	29/03	16/11
Burnage	26/10	12/04		07/12	08/02	16/11	14/09	15/03	05/10	18/01	14/12	04/01
Calder Vale	16/11	07/09	29/03		18/01	30/11	05/10	08/02	26/10	04/01	14/09	14/12
Didsbury Toc H	29/03	01/02	28/09	12/10		01/03	02/11	11/01	14/12	30/11	16/11	07/09
Eccles	18/01	23/11	21/12	12/04	14/09		15/03	07/12	08/02	05/10	04/01	26/10
Heaton Moor	30/11	28/09	01/03	01/02	04/01	07/09		12/10	16/11	14/12	26/10	29/03
Littleborough	14/12	01/03	07/09	28/09	26/10	29/03	18/01		04/01	16/11	05/10	30/11
Lytham	07/09	12/10	01/02	11/01	23/11	28/09	21/12	02/11		29/03	30/11	01/03
Old Bedians	01/03	11/01	12/10	02/11	12/04	01/02	23/11	21/12	07/12		15/03	28/09
Thornton Cleveleys	28/09	07/12	23/11	01/03	21/12	02/11	11/01	01/02	12/04	07/09		12/10
Trafford MV	05/10	21/12	02/11	23/11	15/03	11/01	07/12	12/04	14/09	08/02	18/01	

North Lancs 2

	Broughton	Carnforth	Chorley	Clitheroe	Colne & Nelson	Garstang	Lonsdale Wanderers	North Manchester	West Park Warriors
Broughton		18/01	07/12	08/02	15/03	12/10	28/09	12/04	04/01
Carnforth	26/10		01/02	14/09	04/01	05/10	12/04	01/03	16/11
Chorley	29/03	12/10		14/12	18/01	30/11	02/11	05/10	14/09
Clitheroe	05/10	15/03	16/11		12/04	01/03	07/12	04/01	01/02
Colne & Nelson	14/09	02/11	26/10	30/11		29/03	14/12	01/02	01/03
Garstang	01/02	08/02	12/04	28/09	07/12		15/03	16/11	26/10
Lonsdale Wanderers	01/03	30/11	04/01	29/03	16/11	14/09		26/10	05/10
North Manchester	30/11	28/09	08/02	02/11	12/10	14/12	18/01		29/03
West Park Warriors	02/11	14/12	15/03	12/10	28/09	18/01	08/02	07/12	

Cumbria

	Ambleside	Cockermouth	Creighton	Egremont	Furness	Greengarth	Keswick	Millom	Moresby	Netherhall	Silloth	St Benedict's	Upper Eden	Whitehaven	Windermere
Ambleside				26/10		16/11		05/10		15/03	01/02			14/12	14/09
Cockermouth	29/03			14/12		18/01		16/11				28/09		01/03	26/10
Creighton	04/01	15/03			16/11		05/10		26/10			01/02	14/09		
Egremont			12/10		28/09			01/02	29/03	30/11	02/11				04/01
Furness	30/11	01/02					14/09		05/10			04/01	15/03	02/11	
Greengarth			02/11	14/09	12/10			15/03		04/01	30/11				01/02
Keswick	12/10	30/11		01/03		29/03						02/11	04/01	28/09	
Millom			28/09		29/03		18/01		01/03	02/11	12/10				30/11
Moresby	02/11	04/01				28/09	15/03					30/11	01/02	12/10	
Netherhall		05/10	01/03		18/01		16/11		14/12		29/03		26/10		
Silloth		14/09	18/01		14/12		26/10		16/11			15/03	05/10		
St Benedict's	01/03			16/11		14/12		26/10		14/09				18/01	05/10
Upper Eden	28/09	02/11		18/01		01/03		14/12				12/10		29/03	
Whitehaven			30/11	05/10		26/10		14/09		01/02	04/01				15/03
Windermere			29/03		01/03		14/12		18/01	12/10	28/09		16/11		

South Lancs/ Chesire 1

	Birchfield (Lancs)	Caldy	Leigh	Northwich	Oldershaw	Ormskirk	Southport	Vagabonds (I.O.M.)	Warrington	Widnes	Wigan	Wirral
Birchfield (Lancs)		04/01	07/12	05/10	18/01	14/12	15/03	12/04	14/09	16/11	08/02	26/10
Caldy	02/11		23/11	14/09	08/02	18/01	12/04	21/12	07/12	11/01	15/03	05/10
Leigh	29/03	14/12		26/10	04/01	14/09	08/02	07/09	05/10	30/11	18/01	16/11
Northwich	01/02	01/03	11/01		29/03	30/11	02/11	12/10	21/12	28/09	23/11	07/09
Oldershaw	12/10	28/09	02/11	07/12		15/03	21/12	11/01	23/11	01/02	12/04	01/03
Ormskirk	23/11	12/10	01/03	12/04	07/09		01/02	07/12	11/01	02/11	21/12	28/09
Southport	07/09	30/11	28/09	04/01	16/11	05/10		01/03	18/01	29/03	26/10	14/12
Vagabonds (I.O.M.)	30/11	16/11	15/03	18/01	26/10	29/03	14/09		08/02	14/12	05/10	04/01
Warrington	01/03	29/03	01/02	16/11	14/12	26/10	12/10	28/09		07/09	04/01	30/11
Widnes	21/12	26/10	12/04	08/02	05/10	04/01	07/12	23/11	15/03		14/09	18/01
Wigan	28/09	07/09	12/10	14/12	30/11	16/11	11/01	01/02	02/11	01/03		29/03
Wirral	11/01	01/02	21/12	15/03	14/09	08/02	23/11	02/11	12/04	12/10	07/12	

South Lancs/ Chesire 2

	Anselmians	Ashton on Mersey	Bowdon	Crewe and Nantwich	Dukinfield	Ellesmere Port	Hoylake	Moore	Runcorn	Sandbach	St. Edwards' O.B.	Trentham
Anselmians		01/02	11/01	30/11	07/09	01/03	29/03	12/10	16/11	14/12	02/11	28/09
Ashton on Mersey	05/10		14/09	26/10	16/11	14/12	04/01	15/03	29/03	18/01	08/02	30/11
Bowdon	26/10	01/03		16/11	30/11	29/03	14/12	28/09	05/10	04/01	18/01	07/09
Crewe and Nantwich	12/04	11/01	21/12		28/09	01/02	01/03	02/11	15/03	07/12	23/11	12/10
Dukinfield	15/03	21/12	12/04	08/02		11/01	05/10	23/11	18/01	14/09	07/12	02/11
Ellesmere Port	14/09	23/11	07/12	05/10	26/10		18/01	12/04	04/01	08/02	15/03	21/12
Hoylake	07/12	02/11	23/11	14/09	01/02	12/10		21/12	08/02	15/03	12/04	11/01
Moore	18/01	07/09	08/02	04/01	14/12	30/11	16/11		14/09	26/10	05/10	29/03
Runcorn	21/12	07/12	01/02	07/09	12/10	02/11	28/09	01/03		12/04	11/01	23/11
Sandbach	23/11	12/10	02/11	29/03	01/03	28/09	07/09	11/01	30/11		21/12	01/02
St Edward's O.B.	04/01	28/09	12/10	14/12	29/03	07/09	30/11	01/02	26/10	16/11		01/03
Trentham	08/02	12/04	15/03	18/01	04/01	16/11	26/10	07/12	14/12	05/10	14/09	

South Lancs/ Chesire 3

	Douglas (I.O.M.)	Liverpool Coll. O.B.	Marple	Newton-le-Willows	Orrell Anvils	Prenton	Ruskin Park	Sefton	St Mary's O.B. (Lancs)	Wallasey
Douglas (I.O.M.)		12/04	08/02	28/09	15/03	16/11	02/11	26/10	07/12	01/02
Liverpool Collegiate	30/11		12/10	14/12	02/11	05/10	01/03	14/09	18/01	29/03
Marple	05/10	01/02		14/09	12/04	01/03	07/12	16/11	04/01	26/10
Newton-le-Willows	01/03	16/11	15/03		07/12	04/01	26/10	01/02	12/04	05/10
Orrell Anvils	14/09	04/01	30/11	29/03		26/10	01/02	05/10	16/11	01/03
Prenton	14/12	08/02	28/09	02/11	18/01		14/09	29/03	12/10	30/11
Ruskin Park	04/01	28/09	29/03	18/01	12/10	15/03		30/11	08/02	14/12
Sefton	18/01	15/03	14/12	12/10	08/02	07/12	12/04		28/09	02/11
St Mary's O.B. (Lancs)	29/03	26/10	02/11	30/11	14/12	01/02	05/10	01/03		14/09
Wallasey	12/10	07/12	18/01	08/02	28/09	12/04	16/11	04/01	15/03	

South Lancs/ Chesire 4

	Capenhurst	Congleton	Eagle	Halton	Helsby	Holmes Chapel	Manchester Wanderers	Mossley Hill A.C.	Oswestry	Port Sunlight
Capenhurst		12/10	30/11	29/03	02/11	14/12	18/01	08/02	14/09	28/09
Congleton	01/02		14/09	01/03	30/11	29/03	14/12	26/10	05/10	02/11
Eagle	12/04	15/03		04/01	08/02	12/10	28/09	07/12	16/11	18/01
Halton	07/12	28/09	02/11		12/10	18/01	08/02	15/03	12/04	14/12
Helsby	04/01	12/04	05/10	01/02		01/03	07/12	16/11	26/10	15/03
Holmes Chapel	16/11	07/12	01/02	26/10	28/09		15/03	12/04	04/01	08/02
Manchester Wanderers	26/10	16/11	01/03	05/10	29/03	14/09		04/01	01/02	30/11
Mossley Hill A.C.	05/10	18/01	29/03	14/09	14/12	30/11	02/11		01/03	12/10
Oswestry	15/03	08/02	14/12	30/11	18/01	02/11	12/10	28/09		29/03
Port Sunlight	01/03	04/01	26/10	16/11	14/09	05/10	12/04	01/02	07/12	

South Lancs/ Chesire 5

	Burtonwood	Christleton	Parkonians	Prescot	Sale Amateur	Vulcan
Burtonwood		tba	18/01	14/12	12/10	02/11
Christleton	tba		16/11	14/09	15/03	01/02
Parkonians	05/10	29/03		02/11	01/03	14/09
Prescot	15/03	30/11	28/09		16/11	26/10
Sale Amateur	01/02	14/12	26/10	29/03		05/10
Vulcan	28/09	12/10	30/11	01/03	18/01	

Durham Northumberland 1

	Acklam	Ashington	Billingham	Durham City	Gateshead	Gosforth	Hartlepool	Hartlepool Rovers	Northern	Percy Park	Ryton	West Hartlepool TDSOB
Acklam		12/04	11/01	12/10	14/09	08/02	23/11	15/03	01/02	07/12	21/12	02/11
Ashington	30/11		01/03	07/09	14/12	26/10	12/10	16/11	29/03	04/01	01/02	28/09
Billingham	26/10	14/09		16/11	18/01	14/12	15/03	05/10	04/01	08/02	07/12	12/04
Durham City	18/01	15/03	21/12		05/10	04/01	07/12	08/02	26/10	14/09	12/04	23/11
Gateshead	01/03	23/11	12/10	01/02		15/03	21/12	07/12	28/09	12/04	02/11	11/01
Gosforth	28/09	11/01	23/11	02/11	07/09		01/02	12/04	12/10	21/12	01/03	07/12
Hartlepool	14/12	18/01	07/09	29/03	16/11	05/10		04/01	30/11	26/10	28/09	01/03
Hartlepool Rovers	07/09	21/12	01/02	28/09	29/03	30/11	02/11		01/03	23/11	11/01	12/10
Northern	05/10	07/12	02/11	11/01	08/02	18/01	12/04	14/09		15/03	23/11	21/12
Percy Park	29/03	02/11	28/09	01/03	30/11	16/11	11/01	14/12	07/09		12/10	01/02
Ryton	16/11	05/10	29/03	30/11	04/01	14/09	08/02	26/10	14/12	18/01		07/09
West Hartlepool	04/01	08/02	30/11	14/12	26/10	29/03	14/09	18/01	16/11	05/10	15/03	

Durham Northumberland 2

	Barnard Castle	Blyth	Consett	Guisborough	Houghton	North Shields	Novocastrians	Seaton Carew	Sunderland	Wallsend	Whitby	Winlaton Vulcans
Barnard Castle		01/03	12/10	12/04	02/11	21/12	28/09	01/02	07/12	23/11	07/09	11/01
Blyth	14/09		14/12	26/10	30/11	18/01	16/11	08/02	07/09	29/03	04/01	05/10
Consett	18/01	23/11		14/09	11/01	15/03	05/10	12/04	21/12	02/11	08/02	07/12
Guisborough	30/11	11/01	01/03		28/09	23/11	07/09	02/11	12/10	01/02	29/03	21/12
Houghton	04/01	12/04	26/10	08/02		14/09	18/01	07/12	23/11	21/12	05/10	15/03
North Shields	16/11	12/10	07/09	14/12	01/03		29/03	11/01	01/02	28/09	30/11	02/11
Novocastrians	08/02	21/12	01/02	15/03	12/10	07/12		23/11	02/11	11/01	14/09	12/04
Seaton Carew	05/10	28/09	30/11	04/01	29/03	26/10	14/12		01/03	07/09	16/11	18/01
Sunderland	29/03	15/03	16/11	18/01	14/12	05/10	04/01	14/09		30/11	26/10	08/02
Wallsend	14/12	07/12	04/01	05/10	16/11	08/02	26/10	15/03	12/04		18/01	14/09
Whitby	15/03	02/11	28/09	07/12	01/02	12/04	01/03	21/12	11/01	12/10		23/11
Winlaton Vulcans	26/10	01/02	29/03	16/11	07/09	04/01	30/11	12/10	28/09	01/03	14/12	

Durham Northumberland 3

	Bishop Auckland	Chester le Street	Jarrovians	Medicals	Ponteland	Richmondshire	Seghill	S. Tyneside College	Wearside	West Hartlepool Am.	Whitley Bay Rock.	Yarm
Bishop Auckland		05/10	07/12	14/09	08/02	15/03	12/04	26/10	14/12	18/01	04/01	16/11
Chester le Street	01/02		11/01	21/12	23/11	02/11	12/10	07/09	30/11	29/03	01/03	28/09
Jarrovians	29/03	26/10		05/10	18/01	08/02	07/09	16/11	14/09	04/01	14/12	30/11
Medicals	01/03	16/11	01/02		04/01	12/10	28/09	30/11	26/10	14/12	29/03	07/09
Ponteland	28/09	14/12	12/10	02/11		11/01	01/02	29/03	16/11	30/11	07/09	01/03
Richmondshire	07/09	04/01	28/09	18/01	26/10		01/03	14/12	05/10	16/11	30/11	29/03
Seghill	30/11	18/01	15/03	08/02	05/10	14/09		04/01	29/03	26/10	16/11	14/12
South Tyneside College	11/01	15/03	21/12	12/04	07/12	23/11	02/11		08/02	14/09	01/02	12/10
Wearside	23/11	12/04	01/03	11/01	21/12	01/02	07/12	28/09		07/09	12/10	02/11
West Hartlepool	12/10	07/12	02/11	23/11	12/04	21/12	11/01	01/03	15/03		28/09	01/02
Whitley Bay Rockcliff	02/11	14/09	23/11	07/12	15/03	12/04	21/12	05/10	18/01	08/02		11/01
Yarm	21/12	08/02	12/04	15/03	14/09	07/12	23/11	18/01	04/01	05/10	26/10	

Durham Northumberland 4

	Durham Constabulary	Hartlepool Athletic	Hartlepool B.B.O.B.	Newton Aycliffe	Seaham	Shildon Town	Wensleydale
Durham Constabulary		16/11	26/10	12/10	15/03	30/11	18/01
Hartlepool Athletic	29/03		02/11	28/09	18/01	12/10	01/03
Hartlepool B.B.O.B.	01/03	15/03		30/11	28/09	18/01	12/10
Newton Aycliffe	01/02	14/12	14/09		01/03	02/11	29/03
Seaham	02/11	05/10	14/12	26/10		29/03	14/09
Shildon Town	14/09	01/02	05/10	15/03	16/11		14/12
Wensleydale	05/10	26/10	01/02	16/11	30/11	28/09	

Yorkshire 1

	Bridlington	Dinnington	Huddersfield YMCA	North Ribblesdale	Old Brodleians	Old Crossleyans	Pontefract	Selby	Sheffield Tigers	Wheatley Hills	Yarnbury	York
Bridlington		07/12	18/01	12/04	14/09	15/03	23/11	08/02	05/10	26/10	21/12	04/01
Dinnington	29/03		14/12	28/09	26/10	18/01	01/03	04/01	16/11	30/11	07/09	05/10
Huddersfield Y.M.C.A.	12/10	23/11		21/12	07/12	12/04	02/11	15/03	14/09	01/02	11/01	08/02
North Ribblesdale	30/11	08/02	16/11		18/01	05/10	07/09	26/10	04/01	14/12	29/03	14/09
Old Brodleians	01/03	11/01	29/03	12/10		02/11	01/02	14/12	30/11	07/09	28/09	16/11
Old Crossleyans	07/09	12/10	30/11	01/02	04/01		28/09	16/11	14/12	29/03	01/03	26/10
Pontefract	14/12	14/09	04/01	15/03	05/10	08/02		18/01	26/10	16/11	30/11	29/03
Selby	28/09	02/11	07/09	11/01	23/11	21/12	12/10		29/03	01/03	01/02	30/11
Sheffield Tigers	01/02	21/12	01/03	02/11	12/04	23/11	11/01	07/12		28/09	12/10	15/03
Wheatley Hills	11/01	12/04	05/10	23/11	15/03	07/12	21/12	14/09	08/02		02/11	18/01
Yarnbury	16/11	15/03	26/10	07/12	08/02	14/09	12/04	05/10	18/01	04/01		14/12
York	02/11	01/02	28/09	01/03	21/12	11/01	07/12	12/04	07/09	12/10	23/11	

Yorkshire 2

	Beverley	Heath	Ilkley	Keighley	Leodiensians	Malton and Norton	Northallerton	Pocklington	Ripon	Skipton	West Leeds	West Park Bramhope
Beverley		05/10	08/02	02/11	14/09	12/04	21/12	11/01	18/01	15/03	23/11	07/12
Heath	01/02		14/09	11/01	15/03	23/11	02/11	12/10	08/02	07/12	21/12	12/04
Ilkley	28/09	01/03		12/10	07/12	21/12	11/01	01/02	15/03	12/04	02/11	23/11
Keighley	04/01	26/10	18/01		05/10	15/03	12/04	16/11	14/12	08/02	07/12	14/09
Leodiensians	01/03	07/09	29/03	01/02		02/11	12/10	28/09	30/11	23/11	11/01	21/12
Malton and Norton	30/11	14/12	16/11	07/09	04/01		01/03	29/03	05/10	26/10	28/09	18/01
Northallerton	16/11	04/01	26/10	30/11	18/01	14/09		14/12	29/03	05/10	15/03	08/02
Pocklington	26/10	18/01	05/10	21/12	08/02	07/12	23/11		04/01	14/09	12/04	15/03
Ripon	12/10	28/09	07/09	23/11	12/04	01/02	07/12	02/11		21/12	01/03	11/01
Skipton	07/09	29/03	30/11	28/09	14/12	11/01	01/02	01/03	16/11		12/10	02/11
West Leeds	14/12	16/11	04/01	29/03	26/10	08/02	07/09	30/11	14/09	18/01		05/10
West Park Bramhope	29/03	30/11	14/12	01/03	16/11	12/10	28/09	07/09	26/10	04/01	01/02	

Yorkshire 3

	Bradford Salem	Bramley Phoenix Park	Castleford	Halifax Vandals	Hemsworth	Knottingley	Leeds Corinthians	Moortown	Old Otliensians	Stocksbridge	Wath on Dearne	York R. I.
Bradford Salem		26/10	08/02	29/03	14/12	04/01	30/11	14/09	18/01	05/10	15/03	16/11
Bramley Phoenix Park	11/01		23/11	15/03	01/02	01/03	12/10	21/12	07/12	12/04	02/11	28/09
Castleford	28/09	14/12		26/10	07/09	30/11	01/03	12/10	16/11	04/01	01/02	29/03
Halifax Vandals	07/12	07/09	11/01		02/11	28/09	23/11	01/02	12/04	21/12	01/03	12/10
Hemsworth	23/11	05/10	15/03	04/01		18/01	21/12	07/12	08/02	14/09	12/04	26/10
Knottingley	02/11	14/09	12/04	08/02	12/10		11/01	23/11	15/03	07/12	21/12	01/02
Leeds Corinthians	12/04	18/01	14/09	14/12	16/11	26/10		15/03	05/10	08/02	07/12	04/01
Moortown	01/03	16/11	18/01	05/10	29/03	14/12	07/09		04/01	26/10	28/09	30/11
Old Otliensians	12/10	29/03	21/12	30/11	28/09	07/09	01/02	02/11		23/11	11/01	01/03
Stocksbridge	01/02	30/11	02/11	16/11	01/03	29/03	28/09	11/01	14/12		12/10	07/09
Wath on Dearne	07/09	04/01	05/10	14/09	30/11	16/11	29/03	08/02	26/10	18/01		14/12
York Railway Institute	21/12	08/02	07/12	18/01	11/01	05/10	02/11	12/04	14/09	15/03	23/11	

Yorkshire 4

	Baildon	Barnsley	Doncaster Phoenix	Hessle	Hullensians	Old Modernians	Roundhegians	Sheffield Medicals	Sheffield Oaks	Thornensians	Wakefield Cougars	Wetherby
Baildon		14/12	26/10	30/11	14/09	04/01	05/10	16/11	07/09	08/02	18/01	29/03
Barnsley	23/11		14/09	11/01	18/01	08/02	07/12	05/10	21/12	12/04	15/03	02/11
Doncaster Phoenix	11/01	01/03		28/09	30/11	29/03	21/12	07/09	12/10	02/11	23/11	01/02
Hessle	12/04	26/10	08/02		04/01	05/10	15/03	18/01	23/11	07/12	14/09	21/12
Hullensians	01/03	12/10	12/04	02/11		07/09	11/01	28/09	07/12	01/02	21/12	23/11
Old Modernians	02/11	28/09	07/12	01/02	15/03		23/11	01/03	11/01	21/12	12/04	12/10
Roundhegians	01/02	29/03	16/11	07/09	26/10	14/12		30/11	28/09	12/10	04/01	01/03
Sheffield Medicals	21/12	01/02	15/03	12/10	08/02	14/09	12/04		02/11	23/11	07/12	11/01
Sheffield Oaks	15/03	16/11	18/01	14/12	29/03	26/10	08/02	04/01		14/09	05/10	30/11
Thornensians	28/09	30/11	04/01	29/03	05/10	16/11	18/01	14/12	01/03		26/10	07/09
Wakefield Cougars	12/10	07/09	14/12	01/03	16/11	30/11	02/11	29/03	01/02	11/01		28/09
Wetherby	07/12	04/01	05/10	16/11	14/12	18/01	14/09	26/10	12/04	15/03	08/02	

Yorkshire 5

	Adwick le Street	Aireborough	Hornsea	Knaresborough	Mosborough	Old Rishworthians	Ossett	Stanley Rodillians	Wharfedale Rams	Wibsey
Adwick le Street		26/10	07/12	01/03	01/02	05/10	15/03	12/04	04/01	16/11
Aireborough	18/01		12/10	02/11	30/11	14/12	29/03	08/02	15/03	28/09
Hornsea	29/03	01/02		14/09	05/10	01/03	30/11	16/11	26/10	04/01
Knaresborough	28/09	04/01	15/03		26/10	01/02	08/02	07/12	16/11	12/04
Mosborough	12/10	12/04	08/02	18/01		02/11	14/12	28/09	07/12	15/03
Old Rishworthians	08/02	16/11	28/09	12/10	04/01		18/01	15/03	12/04	07/12
Ossett	14/09	07/12	12/04	05/10	16/11	26/10		04/01	01/03	01/02
Stanley Rodillians	30/11	05/10	14/12	29/03	01/03	14/09	02/11		01/02	26/10
Wharfedale Rams	02/11	14/09	18/01	14/12	29/03	30/11	28/09	12/10		08/02
Wibsey	14/12	01/03	02/11	30/11	14/09	29/03	12/10	18/01	05/10	

Yorkshire 6

	Burley	Garforth	Marist	Pontefract Pythons	Rawmarsh	Rotherham Clifton	Thirsk	Walkington Rovers	Wickersley Exel	Withernsea
Burley		07/12	26/10	12/04	04/01	16/11	01/03	01/02	05/10	14/09
Garforth	29/03		14/12	12/10	08/02	30/11	15/03	28/09	02/11	18/01
Marist	18/01	16/11		28/09	15/03	04/01	12/04	07/12	12/10	08/02
Pontefract Pythons	30/11	01/02	01/03		16/11	05/10	26/10	04/01	14/09	29/03
Rawmarsh	02/11	05/10	14/09	14/12		01/03	01/02	26/10	29/03	30/11
Rotherham Clifton	14/12	12/04	02/11	08/02	28/09		07/12	15/03	18/01	12/10
Thirsk	28/09	14/09	30/11	18/01	12/10	29/03		08/02	14/12	02/11
Walkington Rovers	12/10	01/03	29/03	02/11	18/01	14/09	05/10		30/11	14/12
Wickersley Exel	08/02	04/01	01/02	15/03	07/12	26/10	16/11	12/04		28/09
Withernsea	15/03	26/10	05/10	07/12	12/04	01/02	04/01	16/11	01/03	

NORTHERN REGION

CLUBS

ACKLAM RUFC
Ground Address: Talbot Park, Saltersgill Avenue, Middlesborough, Cleveland
Tel: 01842 321397
Brief Directions: Leave A19 at A174 towards Redcar. Leave Marton slip road and turn left through lights and left again into Broadwell Road.Follow signs to Saltersgill Pavilion.
Club Secretary: K.J.Heath, 43 Ash Green, Coulby Newham, Middlesbrough TS8 0UW. Tel No: 01642 590927
Fixtures Secretary: Jim Ward, 108 Guisborough Road, Nunthorpe, Middlesborough, TS7 0JD.
Tel No : 01642 319302.
Club Colours: Black, green and white
League: Durham/Northumberland 2

ADWICK LE STREET RUFC
Ground Address: Church Lane Playing Fields, Adwick-le-Street, Doncaster, South Yorkshire Tel: 01302 723550 (HQ Foresters Arms)
Email Address: oldshep@compuserve.com
Brief Directions: 4 miles north of Doncaster on A638 Wakefield Road. Just off south bound A1 (Doncaster turn off at Redhouse) Ground directly opposite Adwick Railway Station.
Hon Secretary: J. Sheppard, 23 Finghall Road, Doncaster, DN6 8PB Tel: (H) 01302 724 383 Tel: (M) 07801 537 130 Tel: (W) 01302 724 383
Email: oldshep@compuserve.com
Fixtures Secretary: M. A. Leach-Flanagan, 31 Alexandra Road, Doncaster, South Yorkshire Tel: (H) 01302 872 429
Club Colours: Navy with White/Royal Hoops
League: Yorkshire 5

AIREBOROUGH RUFC
Ground Address: Nunroyd Park, Yeadon, Leeds, LS19 Tel: 01943 878299
Brief Directions: From Leeds follow signs for Airport. Then for Guiseley - Club is approx 1 mile from Jct 600 R/about on the A65 - Leeds/Ilkley Road.
Hon Secretary: M. Harper, 32 Aire View, Leeds, LS19 7TL Tel: (H) 0113 250 4219 Tel: (W) 0113 250 5151
Club Colours: Maroon and white hoops - Black shorts
League: Yorkshire 5

ALDWINIANS RUFC
Ground Address: Audenshaw Park, Droylsden Road, Audenshaw, Manchester, M34 5SN Tel: 0161 301 1001
Brief Directions: East of Manchester, at the junction of the A662 /635 Nr. Snipe Retail Park.
Hon Secretary: Chris Daly, 60 Green Lane, Hyde, Cheshire, SK14 8JQ Tel: (H) 01457 762 402
Email: cldaly@aol.com
Fixtures Secretary: Alan Whalley, 190 Greenside Lane, Manchester, M35 6RR Tel: (H) 0161 355 5922 Tel: (W) 0161 223 1353 ext 246
Club Colours: Red and white narrow hoops. Blue shorts/socks
League: North 2 West

ALNWICK RUFC
Ground Address: Greensfield, St. James, Alnwick, Northumberland, NE66 1BG Tel: 01665 602 342
Email Address: dave.debbage@btinternet.com
Web Address: alnwickrugby.com
Brief Directions: A1 slip (South) of Alnwick signed Alnwick from N/castle, after slip 1st left, club 300 yds on left. From Edinburgh, after slip straight over cross roads, Greensfield Ave as above
Hon Secretary: R. Todd, Linden House, Alnwick, Northumberland, NE66 3QW Tel: (H) 01665 830 898
Fixtures Secretary: John Ainsworth, n/a Tel: (H) 01665 605 196
Club Colours: Royal blue jersey with gold lion rampant badge,white shorts
Brief Directions: M56 J3, take road towards Altrincham, after 3 miles 3rd exit off roundabout, Stelfox Ave 100 yds on right
League: North 2 East

ALTRINCHAM KERSAL RFC
Ground Address: Kersal Drive, Stelfox Avenue, Timperley, Altrincham, Cheshire Tel: 0161 973 9157
Web Address: www.akrfc.co.uk
Hon Secretary: Edward Frankland, 59 Station Road, Goostrey, Cheshire, CW4 8PJ Tel: (W) 0161 833 5215
Email: Edandgail@btopenworld.com
Club Colours: Black, red & white hoops
League: North 2 West

AMBLESIDE RFC
Ground Address: Galava Park, Borrans Road, Ambleside, Cumbria, LA22 0UL Tel: 01539 432 536
Brief Directions: A591 Kendal to Ambleside. Take Coniston, Hawkshead road at Traffic Lights - ground half mile on left after lights.
Hon Secretary: Jeanette Irwin, Flat 2, Orrest Drive, Windermere, LA23 2LF Tel: (H) 01539 442 025
Email: irwinjeanette@hotmail.com
Fixtures Secretary: Nick Fecitt, Hart Head Farm, Ambleside, Cumbria Tel: (H) 01539 433 772
Club Colours: Black & Amber.
League: Cumbria

ANSELMIANS RFC
Ground Address: Malone Field, Eastham Village Road, Eastham, Wirral, Merseyside Tel: 0151 327 1613
Hon Secretary: T. J. Petterson, 27 Queens Drive, Wirral, CH43 0RR Tel: (H) 0151 608 1540 Tel: (W) 0191 225 4368
Email: petterst@email.msn.com
Fixtures Secretary: Tony McArdle, 18 Greenbank Drive, Wirral, CH61 5UF Tel: (H) 0151 342 1470 Tel: (W) 0151 229 4511
Club Colours:
League: South Lancs/Cheshire 2

ASHINGTON J.W. RFC
Ground Address: Recreation Ground, Ellington Road, Ashington, Northumberland
Tel: 01670814123
Brief Directions: 1 mile north west of Ashington town centre on A1068. Map available on request
Club Secretary: Albert Armstrong, 25 Dundale Drive, Cramlington, Northumberland. NE23 2GA. Tel: (H) 01670 736891 (W) 01670 533303
Fixtures Secretary: A Armstrong as above plus:- e-mail: aarmstrong@northumberland.gov.uk
Club Colours: Royal blue and amber hoops, white shorts.
League: Durham/Northumberland 1

ASHTON-ON-MERSEY RFC
Ground Address: Banky Lane (off Carrington Lane), Ashton on Mersey, Sale, Cheshire, M33 5NL Tel: 0161 973 6637
Web Address: www.aomrufc.co.uk
Brief Directions: M63 J63 Carrington Spur, towards Carrington, right at lights, left at T junction, club 300 yards on right
Hon Secretary: Mike McCarthy, 111 Woodhouse Lane, Sale, Cheshire, M33 4LF Tel: (H) 0161 962 7641 Tel: (M) 07970 965 243 Tel: (W) 0161 962 7641
Fixtures Secretary: Pat Stokes, 26 Oldfield Road, Sale, Cheshire, M33 2AQ Tel: (H) 0161 282 3245 Tel: (M) 07711 453 961 Tel: (W) 0161 973 6064
Club Colours: Maroonshirts with navy shorts and maroon and white socks
League: South Lancs/Cheshire 2

ASHTON-UNDER-LYNE RFC
Ground Address: Gambrel Bank, St. Albans Avenue, Ashton-under-Lyne Tel: 0161 330 1361
Web Address: aulrfc@supanet.com
Brief Directions: Town centre, Henrietta Street to Broadoak Hotel, through mini R/about to St Albans Avenue
Hon Secretary: Dennis Gee, 26 Burnedge Lane, Oldham, OL4 4EA Tel: (H) 01457 872 823 Tel: (W) 0161 303 9482
Fixtures Secretary: Paul Newton, 6 The Ladysmith, Ashton-under-Lyme, OL6 9AR Tel: (H) 0161 339 8931
Email: pannewton@aol.com
Club Colours: Red, black and amber hoops,black shorts, red socks
League: North Lancs 1

ASPULL RFC
Ground Address: Woodshaw Park, Woods Road, Aspull, Wigan, WN2 1PJ Tel: 01942 831 611
Brief Directions: M61 Jtn 6, follow signs for Aspull & Wigan on B5239. At T/Jtn turn left onto B5238 to Wigan.1st left is Woods Road - club at the end.
Hon Secretary: Graham Bennett, 11 Prestbury Avenue, Wigan, WN3 6SG Tel: (H) 01942 824 297 Tel: (M) 07977 319 762
Email: gbennett15a@tiscali.co.uk
Fixtures Secretary:
Club Colours: Sky and navy hoops
League: North 2 West

BAE BARROW RUFC
(formerly Vickers Sports)
Ground Address: BAE Systems Sports Club, Hawcoat Lane, Barrow in Furness, Cumbria Tel:01229 825296/823366 Website: www.vcfc.co.uk
Brief Directions: M6 Jct 36. Follow A590 to Barrow. From West Coast A591. Follow signs to Barrow. From west turn left at Strawberry Hotel on Abbey Road. From East turn right - club 300m on left Hancoat Lane.
Club Secretary: Alan Troughton, 188 Yarlside Road, Barrow-in-Furness, Cumbria Tel: 01229 838023
Fixtures Secretary: Norman Smith, 3 Old Farm Close,Barrow-in-Furness, Cumbria. 0EYBarrow in Furness, Cumbria Tel: 01229 828234
Club Colours: Maroon and white shirts.
League: Cumbria

BAILDON RUFC
Ground Address: Heygate Lane, off Jenny Lane, Baildon, BD17 6RS Tel: 01274 582 644
Email Address: baildonrufc@hotmail.com
Brief Directions: A650 to centre of Shipley, follow Baildon signs in village centre, roundabout 3rd exit then left on Jenny Lane
Hon Secretary: F. C. A. Guyers, 10 Wensleydale Rise, Bradford, BD17 6TA Tel: (H) 01274 595 326 Tel: (W) 01274 734 673
Fixtures Secretary: M. Bradney, 4 Vespel Gate Mount, Leeds, LS5 3NN Tel: (H) 0113 278 3698 Tel: (M) 07710 616 814
Club Colours: Red, white and black hoops
League: Yorkshire 4

BARNARD CASTLE RUFC
Ground Address: The Clubhouse, 7 Birch Road, Barnard Castle, Durham, DL12 8JR Tel: 01833 631766
Brief Directions: Head into Town centre. At Market Cross follow signs for Bowes Museum. Take L. turn at Catholic Church (Birch Road). Clubhouse is on left (approx 100 yds)
Hon Secretary: Tim Worley, 17 Newgate, Barnard Castle, Co. Durham, DL12 8NQ Tel: (H) 01833 637 608 Tel: (W) 01833 690 305
Email: tworley@wmsmith.co.uk
Fixtures Secretary: D. Jackson, c/o Headlam Hall Hotel, Nr. Darlington, Co. Durham, DH2 3HA Tel: (H) 01325 730238 Tel: (M) 07905 933710 Tel: (W) 01325 730 238
Club Colours: All black. Change Black & Red
League: Durham/N'thm'land 2

BARNSLEY RUFC
Ground Address: Shaw Lane, Barnsley, South Yorkshire, S70 6HZ Tel: 01226 203 509
Brief Directions: M1 J37, towards Barnsley, through 1st major lights, 2nd turning right into Shaw Lane, ground on right after school
Hon Secretary: Mick Marshall, 4 Westbourne Grove, Barnsley, South Yorkshire, S75 1AE Tel: (H) 01226 321 721 Tel: (M) 07808 918 768
Email: mick.marshall@barnsleyrufc.co.uk
Fixtures Secretary: Steve Lumb, 21 Haigh Moorway, Barnsley, S71 4EG Tel: (H) 01226 726 542
Club Colours: Red, white and blue irregular hoops
League: Yorkshire 4

BEVERLEY RUFC
Ground Address: Beaver Park, Norwood, Beverley, HU17 9HT Tel: 01482 870 306
Brief Directions: Through Beverley centre, follow signs for Hornsea, ground is just before rail level crossing behind Lady Le Gros pub
Hon Secretary: Lee Gallagher, 5 Maple Cottages, Beverley, HU17 8RW Tel: (H) 01482 870 767 Tel: (M) 07740 427 940 Tel: (W) 01482 597 572
Fixtures Secretary: Robert Jenner, 42 Normandy Avenue, Beverley, E. Yorkshire, HU17 8PE Tel: (H) 01482 868 944
Club Colours: Green, brown and white
League: Yorkshire 2

BILLINGHAM RFC
Ground Address: Greenwood Road, Billingham, TS23 4JZ Tel: 01642 563 057
Brief Directions: From A19, leave for A1027 Follow signs to Belasis Hall Technology Park - left at park entrance R/about - beyond Tech. Park on right hand side.
Hon Secretary: John Ker, 4 Anlaby Close, Billingham, TS23 3RA Tel: (H) 01642 560 536 Tel: (M) 0765 291 436
Email: john.ker@ntlworld.com
Fixtures Secretary: Hadyn Beckwith, 5 Gorton Close, Billingham, TS23 2TF Tel: (H) 01642 560 649
Club Colours: Green and thin white hoopsand white shorts.
League: Durham/N'thm'land 1

BIRCHFIELD (LANCASHIRE) RUFC
Ground Address: Birchfield Park Sports Club, Birchfield Road, Widnes, WA8 9ES Tel: 0151 424 3222
Brief Directions: From M62 Junc7 follow A57 (Warrington). Turn right at first set of lights, then at T junction, 1st at roundabout onto Birchfield Rd. Ground is 250 yds on the right.
Hon Secretary: M. H. Cuthbert, 8 Weymouth Drive, Wigan, WN2 4QX Tel: (H) 01942 255 445
Email: ldudgeon@orange.net
Fixtures Secretary: Mac Cuthbert, 8 Weymouth Drive, Hindley Green, WN2 4QX Tel: (H) 01942 255445
Club Colours: Marron & Black
League: South Lancs/Cheshire 1

BIRKENHEAD PARK FC
Ground Address: The Upper Park, Park Road North, Birkenhead. CH41 8AA
Tel: 0151 652 4646
Brief Directions: M53 J1, follow signs for Bidston and Birkenhead centre. Straight on at R/about with church in centre. Take 1st right after Aldi Supermarket into Park Road North. Ground is on left.
Club Secretary: Peter Greville, 2 Howbeck Close, Oxton, Prenton, Birkenhead CH43 6TH
Tel: 0151 653 6070 (W)
Fixtures Secretary: Bob Hardman, 32 Shamrock Road, Claughton, Birkenhead.
Tel: (H) 0151 652 5204
Club Colours: Red, white and blue
League: North 2 West

BISHOP AUCKLAND R.U.F.C.
Ground Address: West Mills Playing Fields, Bridge Road, Bishop Auckland, Co. Durham, DL14 7PA Tel: 01388 602 922
Brief Directions: Follow signs for Crook. Avoid new road over viaduct. Take old road down hill past Newton Cap pub. Turn off left before River Wear.
Hon Secretary: Ajmair Singh, 156 Collingwood Street, Bishop Auckland, Co. Durham, DL14 8LG Tel: (M) 07980 146696
Email: ajmair.singh@emersonprocess.com
Fixtures Secretary: R. Williamson, 19 Waddington Street, Bishop Auckland, Co. Durham, DL14 6HG
Club Colours: Navy & Sky Blue, Red
League: Durham/N'thm'land 3

BLACKBURN RUFC
Ground Address: Ramsgreave Drive, Blackburn, Lancs, BB1 8NB Tel: 01254 247 669
Brief Directions: M6 J31, follow A677 for 5 miles to County Hotel. Turn left (Yew Tree Drive) - Ground is 1.5 miles on left.
Hon Secretary: John Beeston, Forge Cottage, 43 Belthorn Road, Near Blackburn, BB1 2NN Tel: (H) 07855 842 280 Tel: (W) 01254 679 131
Email: John.Beeston@PMM.co.uk
Fixtures Secretary: Andy Whalley, 5 Heys Court, Accrington, Lancs, BB1 2NN Tel: (H) 01772 741 181
Club Colours: Royal Blue shirts + white band
League: North 2 West

BLACKPOOL RUFC
Ground Address: Fleetwood Road, Norbeck, Blackpool Tel: 01253 853 308
Email Address: iansharples@supanet.com
Web Address: www.blackpool-rugby.co.uk
Brief Directions: M55 J4, right onto A583, right onto Whitegate Drive (still A583), bear right onto Devonshire Rd B5214, club on right 0.5 mile past Red Lion pub
Hon Secretary: C Wainscott, 15 Stafford Avenue, Blackpool, FY6 8BJ Tel: (H) 01253 885 151 Tel: (W) 0776 129 2088
Fixtures Secretary: M. Spowart, 3 Plymouth Road, Blackpool, FY3 7JS Tel: (H) 01253 393 448
Club Colours: Red & blue squares
League: North Lancs/Cumbria

BLYTH RFC
Ground Address: Blyth RFC, Plessey Road, Blyth, Northumberland, NE24 3LE Tel: 01670 352 063
Email Address: dave.grey@bt.com
Brief Directions: Take A1 north of Newcastle and turn off onto A19. After 2 miles take A189 (North) and then turn off towards Blyth on A1061. Follow town centre signs and turn left onto A193, turn left into Plessey Rd.
Hon Secretary: D. Grey, 12 Winchester Avenue, Blyth, Northumberland, NE24 2SY Tel: (H) 01670 369 591 Tel: (M) 07860 841 701 Tel: (W) 01977 594 656
Email: dave.grey@bt.com
Fixtures Secretary: A. Raffle, 51 Druridge Drive, Blyth, Northumberland, NE24 4QR Tel: (H) 01670 366 002 Tel: (W) 01670 352 063
Club Colours: Black and green hoops, black shorts
Club Colours: No First Team defined
League: Durham/N'thm'land 2

BOLTON R.U.F.C.
Ground Address: Mortfield Pavilion, Avenue Street (off Chorley Old Road), Bolton, Lancashire, BL1 3AW
Tel: 01204 363 710
Email Address: play@boltonrugby.co.uk
Web Address: www.boltonrugby.co.uk
http://www.multimap.com/map/browse.cgi?pc=bl13aw
Brief Directions: Head out of Bolton on Chorley Old Road, signposted near Morrisons supermarket
Hon Secretary: Robert Killiner, 9 Kittiwake Road, Chorley, Lancashire, PR6 9BA Tel: (H) 01257 268 107 Tel: (M) 07771 665 812 Tel: (W) 0161 491 4990
Email: honsec@boltonrugby.co.uk
Hon Fixtures: Arnie Redmond, 6 Ashdale Avenue, Bolton, BL3 4PH Tel: (H) 01204 409 815
Email: president@boltonrugby.co.uk
Leagues Contact: Les Towler, 18 Moor Lane, Leigh, Lancashire, WN7 5JF Tel: (H) 01942 876 960 Tel: (M) 07836 655 305 Tel: (W) 0151 422 3813
Email: captain@boltonrugby.co.uk
Fixtures Secretary: Kevin Norburn
Email: juniorfixtures@boltonrugby.co.uk
Club Colours: Red and white hoops, black shorts and red socks.
League: North Lancs 1

BOWDON RFC
Ground Address: Clay Lane, Timperley, Altrincham, Cheshire, WA15 7AF Tel: 0161 980 8321
Brief Directions: M56 J6, follow signs to Hale, after 1.5 turn right at lights onto Delahays Rd, through next set of lights, after 0.5 mile up Thorley Lane turn right at Mini R/about on to Clay Lane. Club on left.
Hon Secretary: Myles Kitchiner, 67 Crofton Avenue, Altrincham, Cheshire, WA15 6BZ Tel: (H) 0161 973 3003 Tel: (M) 07887 657 439
Email: kitch@kitchiner.freeserve.co.uk
Fixtures Secretary: Frank Norton, 36 Grrenwalk, Altrincham, Ches. WA15 6JN Tel: (H) 0161 980 8195
Email: frank_norton@hotmail.com
Club Colours: Claret, white and black
League: South Lancs/Cheshire 2

BRADFORD & BINGLEY RFC
Ground Address: Wagon Lane, Bingley, W. Yorkshire, BD16 1LT Tel: 01274 775 441
Email Address: rugby@beesrugby.fsnet.co.uk
Web Address: www.beesrugby.fsnet.co.uk
Brief Directions: From the A650 approx. 1/2mile south of Bingley town centre, turn into Wagon Lane by Beckfoot School.
Hon Secretary: Mick Waterhouse, 15 Villa Grove, Bingley, W. Yorkshire, BD16 4EX
Email: mickwaterhouse@blueyonder.co.uk
Fixtures Secretary: Barry Shinn, 20 Heaton Drive, Eldwick, BD16 3DN Tel: (H) 01274 563 791
Tel: (M) 0776 047 8891
Email: b.j.shinn@tinyworld.co.uk
Club Colours: Red/Amber/Black
League: North 2 East

BRADFORD SALEM RFC
Ground Address: Shay Lane, Heaton, Bradford, West Yorkshire, BD9 6SL Tel: 01274 496430
Email Address: brucestrachan@btinternet.com
Brief Directions: From Bradford centre take A650 (Towards Keighley) along Manningham Lane. Left at 'The Park' (pub) and up hill turn right at top, past shops into Shay Lane. Ground is 100 yds on left.
Hon Secretary: A. Wheeler, 25 Ashwell Road, Bradford, BD9 4BA Tel: (H) 01274 771 210
Club Colours: Royal blue, gold, black hoops, black shorts, blue socks
League: Yorkshire 3

BRAMLEY PHOENIX RFC
Ground Address: The Warrels Grosmont Terrace, Warrels Road, Bramley, Leeds, West Yorkshire, LS13 3NY Tel: 0113 257 7787
Hon Secretary: Mick Ryan, 280 Whitehall Raod, Bradford, BD12 9DX Tel: (W) 01274 727 780
Fixtures Secretary: Chris Parker, 32, Warrals Mount, Leeds, West Yorkshire, LS13 3NU Tel: (M) 07801311034
Club Colours: Green, black and gold, black shorts
League: Yorkshire 3

BRIDLINGTON RUFC
Ground Address: Dukes Park, Queens Gate, Bridlington, Yorkshire, YO16 6TS Tel: 01262 676405
Email Address: rugby@brufc.fsnet.co.uk
Brief Directions: Follow signs to Bridlington, 1st traffic lights keep in n/s lane, right at roundabout, left at next lights, ground is 0.25 mile on right
Hon Secretary: Gordon Morrice, Dukes Park, Bridlington, YO16 7LN Tel: (H) 01262 676 101 Tel: (W) 01262 676 405
Email: gordon@gmorrice.fsbusiness.co.uk
Fixtures Secretary: John Waller, 12 Hustler Road, Bridlington, East Yorks. YO16 Tel: (H) 01262 603476
Club Colours: Navy & Amber Hoops.
League: Yorkshire 1

BROUGHTON PARK FC
Ground Address: Chelsfield Grove, Mauldeth Road West, Manchester, M21 7SU Tel: 0161 881 2481
Brief Directions: From M60 Jct 5 or M56 Jct# get on A5103 towards Manchester. After 21/2 miles turn left at Princess Pub into Mauldeth Road. Ground is 1/2 mile on left .
Hon Secretary: Rob Loveday, 2 Devonshire Road, Stockport, Cheshire, SK4 6LB Tel: (H) 0161 947 9157 Tel: (W) 0161 833 3355
Email: secretary@broughton-park.co.uk
Fixtures Secretary: Tom Barber, 48 Pauldon Road, Manchester, M23 8PD Tel: (H) 0161 998 8936 Tel: (W) 0161 226 2501
Club Colours: Black and white hoops
League: North 2 West

BROUGHTON RUFC
Ground Address: Broughton House, Yew Street, Lower Broughton, Salford, M7 9HL Tel: 0161 792 2920
Email Address: broughtonrugbyclub@angelfire.com
Fixtures Secretary: Peter R. Smith, 33 Kirtley Avenue, Monton Green, Manchester, M30 9PU Tel: (H) 0161 788 8098 Tel: (W) 0161 908 6075
Club Colours: Blue with yellow, red, yellow stripe midway
League: North Lancs 2

BURLEY RFC
Ground Address: The Club House, Abbey Road, Leeds, LS5 3NG Tel: 0113 275 7400
Brief Directions: Travel out of Leeds on the A65 past Kirkstall Abbey. Club House on left after and opposite Vestergate Pub.
Hon Secretary: R. K. N. Jones, 377 Burley Road, Leeds, West Yorkshire, LS4 2SP Tel: (H) 0113 274 2769
Fixtures Secretary: John Sanderson, 3 Southolme Close, Leeds, LS5 3LP Tel: (H) 01132 787 772
Club Colours: No First Team defined
League: Yorkshire 6

BURNAGE RFC
Ground Address: Varley Park, Battersea Road, Stockport, Cheshire, SK4 3EA Tel: 0161 432 2150
Hon Secretary: Rick Hine, 23 Litchfield Street, Stockport, SK5 6BQ Tel: (H) 0161 666 0890 Tel: (W) 07974 643 182
Email: richardatlantean@aol.com
Club Colours: Maroon and white
League: North Lancs 1

BURTONWOOD RFC
Ground Address: Fir Tree Lane, Burtonwood, Warrington Tel: 01925 244 80
Brief Directions: From M6 J22 or M62 J9 proceed to Winwick Island then take A49 towards Newton, at traffic lights turn left onto Hollins Lane and follow road to Burtonwood. Pitches on left hand side.
Hon Secretary: B. Southern, 25 Knight Road, Warrington, WA5 4QQ Tel: (H) 01925 227 611
Club Colours: Red & black quarters
League: South Lancs/Cheshire 5

BURY RUFC
Ground Address: Radcliffe Road, Bury, Lancs Tel: 0161 764 1528
Brief Directions: Leave M602 at J.17 follow A56 towards Bury. After 4 miles turn left at T/lights into Radcliffe Road. Club 20yds on right.
Hon Secretary: G. J. Hilton, 66 Twiss Green Lane, Warrington, Cheshire, WA3 4DQ Tel: (H) 01925 762 119
Fixtures Secretary: M. Kennedy, 14 Beeston Close, Bolton, Lancs Tel: (H) 01204 597 891
Club Colours: Red, gold and blue hoops, navy blue shorts, red stockings
League: North Lancs/Cumbria

CALDER VALE RUFC
Ground Address: Holden Road, Reedley, Burnley, Lancashire, BB10 2LE Tel: 01282 424 337
Brief Directions: M65 J12, right to to Brierfield, through one set of traffic lights, Holden Road on left approxa quarter mile by Oaks Hotel
Hon Secretary: Graham Downey, Plush Laithe, Colne, BB8 7EF Tel: (H) 01282 859300 Tel: (M) 07774 117696
Email: graham.downey.gd@bayer.co.uk
Fixtures Secretary: M. Wilton, 93 Talbot Drive, Burnley, Lancs, BB10 2RT Tel: (H) 01282 457 963
Club Colours: Royal blue and gold hoops
League: North Lancs 1

CALDY RFC
Ground Address: Paton Field, Lower Caldy Cross Road, Telegraph Road, Wirral, CH48 1NZ Tel: 0151 625 8043
Web Address: www.caldyclub.com
Brief Directions: M53-Jcnt 1 - B5139 West Kirby - A540
Hon Secretary: R. B. Flashman, 26 Milton Crescent, Wirral, CH60 5ST Tel: (H) 0151 342 5300 Tel: (W) 0151 653 1700
Email: rbflashman@ukonline.co.uk
Fixtures Secretary: K. Doolan, 40 Woodgate Road, Whitby, South Wirral Tel: (H) 01535 577 30
Club Colours: Sable, Claret, Silver, Gold
League: South Lancs/Cheshire 1

CAPENHURST RUFC
Ground Address: 8 Chichester St, Chester, Cheshire, CH1 4AD Tel: 0151 339 2389
Email Address: ted.roberts@ukgateway.net
Hon Secretary: Ted Roberts, 8 Chichester Street, Chester, CH1 4AD Tel: (H) 01244 378 789 Tel: (W) 0161 200 8849
Email: ted.roberts@umist.ac.uk
Fixtures Secretary: Kristina Roberts, 8 Chichester St, Chester, CH1 4AD Tel: (H) 01244 378789 Tel: (M) 07890225445
Email: ted.roberts@ukgateway.net
Club Colours: Blue & White
League: South Lancs/Cheshire 4

CARLISLE RFC
Ground Address: The Rugby Ground, Warwick Road, Carlisle, Cumbria. Tel: 01228 521300
Web Address: carlislerugby.com
Brief Directions: From North,South and East: From Junction 43 on the M6 follow the A69 into Carlisle for just over a mile. The club entrance is the first right after the main entrance to Carlisle United AFC. From West: Follow signs for A69 to Newcastle. Club entrance is on the left just before Carlisle United AFC.
Hon Secretary: N. J. Laycock, 90 Greystone Road, Carlisle, CA1 2DD Tel: (H) 01228 523 447 Tel: (M) 07951 120 187 Tel: (W) 01228 607 587
Email: nlaycock@freenet.co.uk
Fixtures Secretary: D. D. Morton, 14 Naworth Drive, Carlisle Tel: (H) 01228 515 486
Email: mortwas82@aol.com
Club Colours: Navy Blue and Red
League: North Lancs/Cumbria

CARNFORTH RFC
Ground Address: Carnforth High School, Kellet Road, Carnforth, Lancashire
Email Address: secretary@carnforthrufc.co.uk
Web Address: www.carnforthrufc.co.uk
Hon Secretary: Paul Jackson, 72 Morecambe Road, Lancaster, LA1 5JA Tel: (H) 01524 847 143
Email: jacko@mcbe.fsnet.co.uk
Club Colours: Green and black hoops, black shorts, green socks
League: North Lancs 2

CASTLEFORD RUFC
Ground Address: Willow Bridge Lane, Whitwood, Castleford, West Yorkshire Tel: 01977 554 762
Email Address: gmjswalker@btopenworld.com
Brief Directions: M62E towards Hull, exit J31, 2nd turn left off roundabout, approx 1 mile through traffic lights, ground on right hand side
Hon Secretary: George Walker
Email: Gmjswalker@btopenworld.com
Fixtures Secretary: D. Price, 10 Langdale Avenue, Wakefield, WF1 3TX Tel: (H) 01924 825 434
Club Colours: blue and red
League: Yorkshire 3

CHESTER-LE-STREET RFC
Ground Address: David Owen Clark Centre, Riverside Park, Chester-le-Street, Durham Tel: 0191 387 1995
Brief Directions: Take A1(M) to Chester-Le-Street, follow directions to County Cricket Ground, Rugby Club is situated adjacent to ground in the Donald Owen Clarke Centre.
Hon Secretary: David Kilkenny, 64 Highfield Rise, Chester-le-Street, DH3 3UX Tel: (H) 0191 388 8357 Tel: (W) 0191 492 5209
Fixtures Secretary: Graham Rodger, 3 Fife Avenue, Chester-Le-Street, Co. Durham, DH3 3UX
Tel: (H) 0191 389 1713
Club Colours: Blue shirts and shorts, red socks - Change Yellow Shirts, Blue shorts, Red socks.
League: Durham/N'thm'land 3

CHORLEY RFC
Ground Address: Brookfields, Chancery Road, Astley Village, Chorley, PR7 1XP Tel: 01257 268 806
Brief Directions: Exit M61 J.8 towards Chorley acorss 1st R/about. Right at 2nd R/about past hospital on left. Left at next R/about into Chancery Road. Club on the right after 200 yards.
Hon Secretary: Lynn Spencer, 37 Sandringham Drive, Chorley, Lancashire, PR6 8SU Tel: (H) 01254 832 102 Tel: (W) 01257 278 379
Email: lynn.spencer@btclick.com
Fixtures Secretary: Dave Nickeas, 7 Morris Close, Leyland, Lancs, PR5 2FD Tel: (H) 01772 451 171
Club Colours: Black and white hoops, Red
League: North Lancs 2

CHRISTLETON RFC
Ground Address: Christleton Sports Centre, Plough Lane, Christleton, Chester Tel: 01244 336 664
Hon Secretary: D. Shaw, 65 Greenbank Road, Chester, CH2 3RW Tel: (H) 01244 401 587
Email: dave@shawsee.fsnet.co.uk
Club Colours: No First Team defined
League: South Lancs/Cheshire 5

CLITHEROE RFC
Ground Address: Littlemoor Park, Littlemoor Road, Clitheroe, Lancs Tel: 01200 422 261
Brief Directions: Directions From the M6 junction 31 follow signs for Clitheroe and Skipton along the A59. Follow the A59 for approx. 13 miles, you will come to a roundabout (1 mile after the right turn towards Padiham along the A671), take the 1st exit off the roundabout onto the A671 towards Clitheroe. At the first group of houses, as you enter the 30mph zone, take the 1st on your right onto Littlemoor Road, the club entrance is 200 yards on your left.
Hon Secretary: Philip Isherwood, 160 Chatburn Rd, Clitheroe, Lancs, BB7 2AZ
Tel: (H) 01200 423781 Tel: (M) 07957355245
Email: phil.isherwood@freeserve.co.uk
Hon Fixtures: Andrew Moorby Tel: (M) 07966394474
Leagues Contact: Philip Isherwood, 160 Chatburn Rd, Clitheroe, Lancs, BB7 2AZ
Tel: (H) 01200 423781 Tel: (M) 07957355245
Email: phil.isherwood@freeserve.co.uk
Club Colours: Dark Blue Light Blue Quarters
League: North Lancs 2

COCKERMOUTH RFC
Ground Address: Grasmoor, Strawberry How, Lorton Road, Cockermouth, Cumbria, CA13 9QT
Tel: 01900 824 884 Email Address: gastmoorcentre@cockermouth.fslife.co.uk
Brief Directions: Leave by-pass along Lampugh Rd and Station St. Turn L. 50yards past Shell F/Stn on Right into Lorton Rd. .5 mile pass cemetry oin left turn left into Strawberry How - 100 yds club driveway on right (then open fields!).
Hon Secretary: C. Garrard, Bent Hill, Eaglesfield, Cockermouth, Cumbria, CA13 0SF Tel: (H) 01900 822 835 Tel: (M) 07980 039 492 Tel: (W) 01900 823 592
Email: grassmoorcentre@fslife.co.uk
Club Colours: Black and amber hoops, black shorts
League: Cumbria

COLNE & NELSON RFC
Ground Address: Holt House, Harrison Drive, Colne, Lancashire Tel: 01282 863 339
Email Address: claire.woodhead@calderglen.net
Web Address: www.pendlerugby.co.uk
Brief Directions: At end of M65follow Skipton signs. Through traffic lights and left at large roundabout and on the top of the hill.
Hon Secretary: K. I. Thornton, 261 Brunshaw Road, Burnley, Lancashire, BB10 4QR Tel: (H) 01282 717673 Tel: (W) 01282 415 511
Club Colours: All black
League: North Lancs 2

CONGLETON RUFC
Ground Address: The Woodman, 78 Park Street, Congleton, Cheshire, CW12 1EG Tel: 01260 273 338 (Clubhouse) 01270 878 293 (Hon Sec)
Email Address: dennis.thorley@iclway.co.uk
Web Address: www.congletonrufc.co.uk
Brief Directions: Directions to the Ground: If lost follow the signs to Congleton Leisure Centre in Congleton Park. The senior pitch is alongside the Leisure Centre with the clubhouse and changing rooms 100 metres up the hill in Park Street (limited parking in the cul de sac and small public car park).
Hon Secretary: Dennis Thorley, 46 Bladon Crescent, via Stoke-on-Trent, Cheshire, ST7 2BG
Tel: (H) 01270 878 293
Email: dennis.thorley@iclway.co.uk
Leagues Contact: Richard Burkard, 6 Peel Drive, Congleton, Ches. CW12 4RF Tel: (H) 01260 281206
Email: richard@burkard.freeserve.co.uk

Fixtures Secretary: Ken Williams, 2 Sprink Lane, Congleton, Ches. CW12 3PF Tel: (H) 01260 279202
Club Colours: Red white red black hoops
League: South Lancs/Cheshire 4

CONSETT & DISTRICT RFC
Ground Address: Belle Vue Park, Medomsley Road, Consett, Co Durham
Tel: 01207 590662 (admin) or 503600
Clubhouse: The Demi., Albert Rd., Consett Tel: 01207 590662
Brief Directions: Behind and to the side of Consett Civic Centre only 400m from centre of Consett. Full details on website.
Club website: www.derwntside.org.uk/community/demi
Club Secretary: Barry Cook,37 Queens Road, Blackhill, Co.Durham. DH8 0BL
Tel: 01207 500624 e-mail: cooklbaz@aol.com
Fixtures Secretary: Robert Brough, Sowerby House, St Ives Road, Leadgate, Consett Co Durham. DH8 7PZ
Tel 01207 501951
e-mail: schaboom@hotmail.com
Club Colours: Black and amber hoops with red trim and black shorts and socks
League: Durham/Northumberland 1

CREIGHTON RFC
Ground Address: Carrs Field, Caxton Road (off Newtown Road), Carlisle Tel: 01228 21169
Brief Directions: Follow signs to hospital, 500m past hospital on right - sign to Industrial Estate.
Hon Secretary: Steve Allison, 19 Scotby Gardens, Carlisle, CA1 2XH Tel: (H) 01228 402 720 Tel: (W) 01228 822 203
Email: svallisons@aol.com
Fixtures Secretary: Ian Langley, Kiln Green House, Wigton, Cumbria
Club Colours: Navy blue, red collars and cuffs, white shorts, red sock
League: Cumbria

CREWE & NANTWICH RFC
Ground Address: Crewe Vagrants Sports Club, Newcastle Road, Willaston, Nantwich, CW5 7EP Tel: 01270 569 506
Brief Directions: Situated on A500, opposite The Horseshoe pub, 2 miles east of Nantwich and 6 miles from J16 M6
Hon Secretary: Alan G. Jones, 9 Gingerbread Lane, Nantwich, Cheshire, CW5 6NH Tel: (H) 01270 625 737 Tel: (W) 01270 625 737
Fixtures Secretary: Henry Edwards
Email: Henry.Edwards@collectibleworld.com
Club Colours: Black Jersey with broad white band
League: South Lancs/Cheshire 2

DE LA SALLE (SALFORD) RUFC
Ground Address: Lancaster Road, Salford 6
Tel: 0161 789 2261
Brief Directions: Sth: off M602 Eccles Jcn 2 follow Salford past Hope Hsptl on rt, next lights left onto Lancaster Rd. From Nth: A580 East Lancs Rd towards Salford, right at Lancaster Rd, club halfway on right
Club Secretary: Paul Barrett, 24 Delbooth Avenue, Flixton, Manchester M41 8SD
Tel No: 0161 746 8199
Email: the - barrett @delboothj.fsnet.co.uk
Fixtures Secretary: Jim Collins, 8 Oakwood Drive, Salford Tel: (H) 0161 281 3761 (W) 0161 775 7928
Club Colours: Red and gold quarters
League: North Lancs & Cumbria

DIDSBURY TOC H RFC
Ground Address: Ford Lane, Didsbury, Manchester
Tel: 0161 446 2146
Brief Directions: From A34 follow signs for Didsbury to Shell garage. Left on to Dene Road immediate left to Ford Lane - down to bottom.
Club Secretary: Mrs. Geraldine Harris, 17 Edenhall Avenue, Burnage, Manchester, M19 2BG.
Tel: 0161 224 1251
Fixtures Secretary: Peter Bradley, 8 Barnard Avenue, Heaton Moor, SK4 4EP.
Tel: 0161 432 0496
Club Colours: Black and amber hoops
League: North Lancs 1

DINNINGTON RFC
Ground Address: Lodge Lane, Dinnington, Sheffield, South Yorkshire. S31 7PB
Email Address: bill@thegilbodys.co.uk
Web Address: www.dinningtonrugby.com
Brief Directions: M1 J 31, Take A57 towards Worksop. At 2nd set of lights[2mls] turn left on B6060 signposted N.Anston, Dinnington.Continue on B6060 until miniroundabout, go straight across. Carry on for further 1 mile to top of hill, turn rt at xroads.Club house 1/4 mile on left.
Hon Secretary: W. Gilbody, 16 Devonshire Drive, Sheffield, S25 4AQ Tel: (H) 01909 562 997
Tel: (M) 0797 920 7543 Tel: (W) 0797 920 7543
Email: bill@thegilbodys.co.uk
Fixtures Secretary: W. Gilbody, 16 Devonshire Drive, Sheffield, S25 4AQ Tel: (H) 01909 562 997
Tel: (M) 0797 920 7543 Tel: (W) 0797 920 7543
Email: bill@thegilbodys.co.uk
Club Colours: Blue, gold, black and white hoops.
League: Yorkshire 1

DOUGLAS RFC
Ground Address: Port-E-Che Meadow, Peel Road, Douglas, Isle of Man Tel: 01624 676 493
Brief Directions: Leave Douglas via Peel Road to Quaterbridge, ground on right. FROM AIRPORT. Head for Douglas turn left at Quarterbridge roundabout, ground on the Right.
Hon Secretary: P. E. Garrett, 9 Birch Hill Grove, Isle of Man, IM3 4EJ
Tel: (H) 01624 629 037 Tel: (W) 01624 651 387
Fixtures Secretary: T. Gethin Taylor, 17 Keeil Pharkk Pack, Isle of Man, IM4 4EW Tel: (H) 01624 851 180
Club Colours: Maroon with gold band
League: South Lancs/Cheshire 3

DUKINFIELD RUFC
Ground Address: Blacksages Playing Fields, Blocksages, Birch Lane, Dukinfield, Cheshire
Tel: 0161 343 2592
Brief Directions: On B6170 between Hyde and Ashton-under-Lyne, next to the baths
Secretary: C. Hadley, 3 Milton Close, Dukinfield SK16 5DZ Tel: (H) 0161 338 8003 Tel: (W) 0161 877 8660
Fixtures Secretary: Alan Hilton, Old St. Georges Vicarage, Pennine View, Stalybridge, Cheshire
Tel: (H) 0161 338 3410
Club Colours: Royal blue and gold hoops
League: South Lancs/Cheshire 3

DURHAM CITY RFC
Ground Address: Hollow Drift, Green Lane, Durham, DH1 3JU Tel: 0191 386 1172
Email Address: dcrfc@talk21.com
Web Address: www.durhamcityrfc@freenetname.co.uk
Brief Directions: Leave A1M at Junction 62 Carrville SUNDERLAND / DURHAM. Follow A690 DURHAM CITY CENTRE Signs along Dual Carriageway to City Centre, at 1st roundabout take second junction Sign posted CITY CENTRE, decend hill, keep to left hand lane and take 1st left on roundabout Cross Bridge, Sign posted BOWBURN & COXHOE. Keeping inside lane at Traffic Lights at ROYAL COUNTY HOTEL. Turn left into OLD ELVET. Proceed to the top of OLD ELVET, turn left onto GREEN LANE, 300 metres turn right ionto Car Park, follow road to the left D.C.R.F.C.
Hon Secretary: Rob Elston, 18 Mayorswell Field, Claypath, Durham, DH1 1JW Tel: (H) 0191 386 3245
Club Colours: Blue & Gold irregular hooped Shirts
League: Durham/N'thm'land 1

DURHAM CONSTABULARY RUFC
Ground Address: Durham Constabulary Police HQ, Aykley Heads, Durham.DL1 5TT Tel: 0191 3864929
Brief Directions: Situated to the north of Durham City, follow signs for County Hall and then Police H.Q.
Club Secretary: Mr Peter Davis, 44 Hauxley Drive, Chester-le-Street, Co. Durham, DH2 3TE
Tel: (H) 0191 3890848
Email: peterdavis@bronyaur.fsnet.co.uk
Fixtures Secretary: M.Taylor, 79 Willowtree Avenue, Gilesgate Moor, Durham DH1 1DZ
Tel: 0191 3865562
Club Colours: Royal blue & gold quarters, black shorts
League: Durham/Northumberland 4

EAGLE RUFC
Ground Address: Thornton Road, Great Sankey, Warrington Tel: 01925 632 926
Brief Directions: A57 west from Warrington towards Liverpool onto the dual carriageway, where road splits at roundabout take left hand road (A562) and at lights turn left into Thornton Rd
Hon Secretary: Mark Simmons, 3 Dorchester Road, Warrington, WA5 1XZ Tel: (H) 01925 492 689
Fixtures Secretary: Dave Unsworth, 20 keith Avenue, Warrington Tel: (H) 01925 727 565
Fixtures Secretary: Robert McDonald Smith, 179 Liverpool Road, Warrington, Cheshire, WA5 1QU
Tel: (M) 07976 329955
Club Colours: Black and white
League: South Lancs/Cheshire 4

ECCLES RFC
Ground Address: Gorton Street, Peel Green, Eccles, Manchester, M30 7LZ Tel: 0161 789 2613
Web Address: www.ecclesrfc.org.uk
Brief Directions: M63 J2 towards Eccles, Gorton Street 2nd on left
Hon Secretary: Andy C. Brunt, 12 Woodstock Drive, Manchester, M28 2WW Tel: (H) 0161 794 4114
Email: andybrunt@hotmail.com
Fixtures Secretary: Alan Chettoe, 7 Pelton Avenue, Wardley, Manchester Tel: (H) 0161 661 1158
Tel: (M) 07967 046 077
Club Colours: Navy & white hoops, white shorts
League: North Lancs 1

EGREMONT RFC
Ground Address: Bleach Green, Egremont
Tel: 01946 820 645
Brief Directions: M6 J36, follow A595 north towards Workington, Egremont is approx 4 miles south of Whitehaven
Hon Secretary: Luke Murphy, 13 Sunnyside, Castle Croft, Egremont, Cumbria Tel: (H) 01946 822 261
Tel: (W) 01946 777 114
Email: luke.murphy@bnfl.com
Fixtures Secretary: L. E. Oliver, Melbreak, Egremont
Tel: (H) 01946 822 443
Club Colours: Black and amber
League: Cumbria

ELLESMERE PORT RUFC
Ground Address: Whitby Sports & Social Club, Chester Road, Whitby, Ellesmere Port, Cheshire
Tel: 0151 200 7050 / 200 7080
Brief Directions: M6, M56, M53 J.10. A5117 to Strawberry Pub R/about 4th off. Ground in .75 mile
Hon Secretary: A. R. Dale, 12 Archers Way, Ellesmere Port, Cheshire, CH66 2RY Tel: (H) 0151 200 1860
Tel: (M) 07946 394 204
Fixtures Secretary: G. Fenion, 19 Belgrave Drive, Ellesmere Port, Cheshire Tel: (H) 0151 357 3841
Tel: (W) 01244 283 710 / 281 281
Club Colours: Black w/ 2 single red/yellow hoops
League: South Lancs/Cheshire 2

FLEETWOOD RUFC
Ground Address: Melbourne Avenue, Fleetwood, Lancs, FY5 1SR Tel: 01253 874 774
Brief Directions: M55, J3 (Blackpool) to Fleetwood/Kirkham follow, A585 to Fleetwood, 1st exit off r'about at Nautical Coll., sharp left at tram tracks into the Crescent, round to Melbourne Ave.
Hon Secretary: C. Smith, 46 The Strand, Fleetwood, Lancs, FY7 8NR Tel: (H) 01253 874 725
Tel: (W) 01253 823 241
Email: csmith@cybermail.uk.com
Fixtures Secretary: A. Thompson, 67 Levens Drive, Poulton Le Fylde, Lancs, FY6 8EZ Tel: (H) 01253 882 121 Tel: (W) 01253 392 957
Club Colours: Green and gold hoops
League: North Lancs/Cumbria

FURNESS RFC
Ground Address: Strawberry Gardens, Abbey Road, Barrow-in-Furness, Cumbria Tel: 01229 825 226

Brief Directions: At 3rd R/about on Dalton bypass take L. exit for hospital. At mini R/about turn R. onto Abbey Road after approx 1 mile turn L. into Croslands Park Road, entrance 100 yards on R.
Hon Secretary: Ken Oliver, 5 Trinity Gardens, Ulverston, Cumbria, LA12 7UB Tel: (H) 01229 581569 Tel: (W) 01229 584 546
Fixtures Secretary: Don Troughton, Greystones House, Greystone Lane, Dalton-in-Furness, Cumbria, LA15 8PX Tel: (H) 01229 462 586
Club Colours: Blue and white hoops
League: Cumbria

GARFORTH RUFC
Ground Address: Gaforth Community College, Lidgett Lane, Garforth, Leeds, Ls25 1LJ
Brief Directions: A63 Leeds to Selby Road, left into Lidgett Lane, school on right, thro' main gate, to changing facilities at back of school buildings
Hon Secretary: George Shaw, 34 Rose Court, Leeds, LS25 1NS Tel: (H) 0113 286 7193 (W) 01909 473565
Email: gshawgarforthrfu@yahoo.co.uk
Fixtures Secretary: Jonathan Fallas, 14 Firtree Avenue, Leeds, LS25 2JN Tel: (H) 0113 286 3042 Tel: (M) 07788 591 717
Club Colours: Red, yellow, blue & black quarters
League: Yorkshire 6

GARSTANG RFC
Hon Secretary: M. McGowan
Email: purkisfc@supanet.com
League: North Lancs 2

GATESHEAD RFC
Ground Address: Eastwood Gardens, Low Fell, Gateshead, NE9 5UB Tel: 0191 420 0207
Email Address: dave_rugby@hotmail.com
Web Address: http://www.gatesheadrfc.co.uk
Brief Directions: Travelling north A167 into Gateshead, pass two sets of main lights, turn right into Joicey Road, second left Eastwood Gardens. Travelling south on A167 turn left at Springfield Hotel into Dryden Road turn left at phone box.
Fixtures Secretary: John Davison, 9 Torver Place, Gateshead, NE9 6YL Tel: (H) 0191 4823778
Fixtures Secretary: W. L. Hetherington, 97 Kells Lane, Gateshead, NE9 5XX Tel: (H) 0191 421 9487
Club Colours: Red, pale blue band surrounded by navy blue band,
League: Durham/N'thm'land 1

GOOLE
Ground Address: Westfield Banks Sports Complex, Westfield Banks, Hook, Goole, E. Yorks, DN14 5PW Tel: 01405 762 018
Email Address: jeffb@shopacheck.co.uk
Web Address: www.goolerufc.co.uk
Brief Directions: Exit M62 at Jnc 37 (Signed Howden). At end of sliproad follow signs for Goole (A614). Staight across mini roundabout and over Boothferry Bridge. Turn left at next roundabout (signed Hook). Rugby club is approx 1 mile down the road on the right.
Hon Secretary: I. Higgins, 14 The Meadows, Goole, DN14 7DX Tel: (H) 01430 430 037
Fixtures Secretary: P. Shand, 4 Kings Close, Pontefract, W. Yorkshire, WF8 3PD Tel: (H) 01977 780 652 Tel: (M) 0771 276 3057 Tel: (W) 01977 703 357
Email: phil.shand@btinternet.com
Club Colours: Blue and Gold
League: North 2 East

GOSFORTH RFC
Ground Address: Bullocksteads Sports Ground, Ponteland Road, Kenton Bank Foot, Newcastle-upon-Tyne NE13 8AH Tel: 0191 286 0088
Email Address: rugby@gosforthrfc.fsnet.co.uk
Web Address: www.gosforthrfc.fsnet.co.uk
Brief Directions: Turn off A1 at Airport sign, follow B6918 westwards for approx 1 mile. Ground is on right hand side of Ponteland Road.
Hon Secretary: Trevor Hogg, 11 Launceston Close, Newcastle upon Tyne, NE3 2XX Tel: (H) 0191 2711120
Email: t.hogg@tesco.net
Fixtures Secretary: Malcolm Bell, 3 Lansdowne Gardens, Northumberland, NE62 5LF
Tel: (H) 01670 851 652
Email: malcolmdbell@hotmail.com
Club Colours: Green and white hoops, white shorts
League: Durham/N'thm'land 1

GOSFORTH GREENGARTH RUFC
Ground Address: Shealings, Wasdale Rd., Gosforth, Cumbria Tel: 01946 725 313
Email Address: kensmith6@virgin.net
Fixtures Secretary: Stephen Edgar
Tel: (H) 01946 784 1534
Club Colours: Maroon and gold
League: Cumbria

GUISBOROUGH RUFC
Ground Address: Belmangate, Guisborough, Teesside, TS14 7BB Tel: 01287 632966
Web Address: www.geocities.com/grufc
Brief Directions: Leave A19 at A174 Jctn. to Marton. Turn R. into A171 to Guisborough via Nunthorpe at Swans Corner. Through town to T/lights - Bow St., Whitby Road, Belmangate Jctn - over to club just prior to Bridge.
Hon Secretary: Jonathan Weastell, 18 Sudbury, Middlesbrough, TS6 9XT Tel: (H) 01642 317 220
Tel: (W) 01642 230 800
Email: jweastell@geraldeve.com
Club Colours: Black and amber trim.
League: Durham/N'thm'land 2

HALIFAX VANDALS RUFC
Ground Address: Warley Town Lane, Warley, Halifax, W. Yorkshire Tel: 01422 831 703
Email Address: stephencbeard@hotmail.com
Brief Directions: From Halifax head towards Burnley. At King Cross junction right to Warley. Left at top of road then left to Warley village.Ground opp. Maypole PH.
Hon Secretary: Stephen. C Beard, 107 Haley Hill, Halifax, West Yorkshire, HX3 6EE Tel: (H) 01422 353099 Tel: (W) 01484 719642
Email: stephencbeard@hotmail.com
Hon Fixtures: Ralph Pollard, 16 Willowfield Road
Tel: (H) 01422 321979
Club Colours: Blue & white hoops, navy blue shorts
League: Yorkshire 3

HALTON RUFC
Ground Address: Widnes Recreation Club, Liverpool Road, Widnes, Cheshire
Tel: 0151 424 2355/50
Brief Directions: Frm M62 J7, A57 W'ington, rt at 1st lights, rt at T jcn, rt after 4th pelican, rt at lights, club on lft. Frm R'corn Brge, towncentre slip, under flyover, lft at r'bout, over next r'bout, rt at lights, club on lft
Club Secretary: S.G.Dennett. 267 Lunts Heath Road,Widnews, CheshireWA8 5BB
Tel: 01514243978 (H) 07050 191715 (W)
Email: stedennett@supanet.com
Fixtures Secretary: D.Dyer, 19 Clincton Close, Widnes, Cheshire WA8 8JP
Tel No: 0151 424 6944
Club Colours: Blue with gold and green band.
League: South Lancs & Cheshire 4

HARTLEPOOL RFC
Ground Address: Mayfield Park, Easington Road, Hartlepool Tel: 01429 266 445
Hon Secretary: Dave Jones, 14 Turnberry Grove, Hartlepool, TS27 3PX Tel: (H) 01429 231 125
Email: davjones@supanet.com
Fixtures Secretary: Ken Thompson, 10 Boswell Gorve, Hartlepool Tel: (W) 01642 279 880
Club Colours: Black and White
League: Durham/N'thm'land 1

HARTLEPOOL ATHLETIC RFC
Ground Address: Oakesway Estate, Hartlepool, TS24 0RE Tel: 01429 274 715
Hon Secretary: Jim Ainslie, Archway Cottage, 10 Regent Street, Hartlepool, Co. Durham, TS24 0QN Tel: (H) 01429 260 003 Tel: (M) 07836 258 317
Fixtures Secretary: John Bentham, 22 Tempest Road, Hartlepool, Co Durham, TS24 9QH Tel: (H) 01429 281012
Club Colours: No First Team defined
League: Durham/N'thm'land 4

HARTLEPOOL BOYS BRIGADE OLD BOYS RFC
Ground Address: Old Friarage, Moor Terrace, Headland, Hartlepool, (Field Only / No Corresp.) Tel: 01429 266 420
Hon Secretary: Keith Faint, 11 Nesby Road, Hartlepool, TS24 9NB Tel: (H) 01429 265 674 Tel: (M) 0793 258 5037
Fixtures Secretary: Paddy Mullrooney, 6 Carr Street, Hartlepool, TS26 8RE Tel: (H) 01429 272 254
Club Colours: No First Team defined
League: Durham/N'thm'land 4

HARTLEPOOL ATHLETIC RFC
Ground Address: Oakesway Estate, Hartlepool, Co Durham. TS24 0RE Tel: 01429 274715
Brief Directions: Leave A19 at A179 Hartlepool turn off, follow signs for Headland, ground 3 miles from A19
Club Secretary: Jim Ainslie, 10 Regent Street, Hartlepool, Co Durham. TS24 0QN
Tel: (H) 01429 260003
Fixtures Secretary: John Bentham, 22 Tempest Rd., Hartlepool, Co.Durham.
TS24 9QH Tel: (H) 01429 281012
Club Colours: Sky blue/ white/ royal blue
League: Durham/Northumberland 4

HARTLEPOOL BOYS BRIGADE OLD BOYS RFC
Ground Address: Old Friarage, Headland, Hartlepool (Field only) Tel: 0793 2585037M
Brief Directions: A19 take A179 Hartlepool exit, over 4 R/abouts left at T Jnct, take l eft fork at `Mural', left at Fire Station, right onto seafront, ground on left after tennis courts.
Club Secretary: G K Faint, 11 Nesbyt Road, Hartlepool. TS24 9NB Tel: (H) 01429 265674
Fixtures Secretary: I Mulrooney, 6 Carr Street, Hartlepool, TS26 8RE Tel: 01429 272254
Club Colours: Black with broad white band, black shorts
League: Durham/Northumberland 4

HARTLEPOOL ROVERS RFC
Ground Address: The Friaridge, Low Warren, Westview Road, Hartlepool, TS24 0BP Tel: 01429 26 741
Hon Secretary: John Ainsley, 'Inglethorpe', Elwick Road, Hartlepool, TS26 0DE Tel: (H) 01429 861 793
Fixtures Secretary: Tony Lowe, Alma House, Junciton Road, Stockton-on-Tees, TS22 5D
Tel: (H) 01624 530 697
Club Colours: No First Team defined
League: Durham/N'thm'land 1

HARTLEPOOL RFC
Ground Address: Mayfield Park, Easington Road, Hartlepool. TS24 9BA Tel: 01429 266445
Brief Directions: Leave A19 north of town on A179 over 2 roundabouts, right at 3rd, ground 500m on left
Club Secretary: Dave Jones, 14 Turnberry Grove, Hartlepool TS27 3PX
Tel: (H) 01429 231125
Email: davjones@supanet.com
Fixtures Secretary: Ken Thompson, 10 Boswell Grove, Hartlepool. Tel: (W) 01642 279880
Club Colours: Black and white
Change Colours: Maroon and White
League: Durham/Northumberland 2

HEATH RUFC
Ground Address: North Dean, Stainland Road, Halifax, W. Yorkshire, HX4 8LS Tel: 01422 372 920
Brief Directions: M62 J24, follow Halifax signs at bottom of hill (end of dual c'way), turn left towards Stainland, clubhouse approx 500m on left through used car lot
Hon Secretary: P. Burton, 10 Castle Lane, Sowerby Bridge, W. Yorkshire, HX6 4JY Tel: (H) 01422 824 847
Email: Notrub@btinternet.com
Fixtures Secretary: J. Ingham, 1 George Street, Halifax, W. Yorkshire, HX4 8DH Tel: (H) 01422 371 045
Club Colours: Emerald, gold & claret
League: Yorkshire 2

HEATON MOOR RUFC
Ground Address: Green Lane, Heaton Moor, Stockport, Cheshire, SK4 2NF Tel: 0161 432 3407
Brief Directions: M60 Jct. 1 to Stockport. A5145 towars Didsbury. At top of hill, turn right at T/lights into Bankhall Road. Turn right at next set of lights into Green Lane. Club 250yds on left.
Hon Secretary: D. Todd, 7 Warwick Road, Stockport,

Cheshire, SK4 4NQ
Tel: (H) 0161 432 0943 Tel: (W) 0161 374 3000
Email: davidtodd@lycos.co.uk
Fixtures Secretary: M. J. Jeskins, 5 Hazel Drive, Manchester, M22 5LY
Tel: (H) 0161 436 4807 Tel: (W) 0161 485 4372
Email: john.jeskins@theridge.ac.uk
Club Colours: Black, red and amber
League: North Lancs 1

HELSBY RFC
Ground Address: Helsby Sports and Social Club, Chester Road, Helsby, Frodsham, Cheshire, WA6 0DL
Tel: 01928 722267
Email Address: Chris.J.Johnson@atosorigin.com
Web Address: www.hrufc.co.uk
Brief Directions: From Junction 14 of the M56 take the A556 towards Helsby. Go straight through the traffic lights after one mile (Helsby Arms pub on the left hand side). The club are based at Helsby Sports & Social Club which is a further 400 metres along the road, on the left hand side opposite the petrol station.
Hon Secretary: C. J. Johnson, Greenfields, Primrose Lane, Frodsham, Cheshire, WA6 9BS
Tel: (H) 01928 724180 Tel: (M) 07968 073136
Tel: (W) 01928 59 8584
Fixtures Secretary: A. Ryder, 64 Chester Road, Helsby, Cheshire Tel: (H) 01928 723 733
Club Colours: Black & Amber Hoops, Black shorts, Hooped socks
League: South Lancs/Cheshire 4

HEMSWORTH RUFC
Ground Address: Moxon Fields, Lowfield Road, Hemsworth, Pontefract, W. Yorkshire, WF9 4JT
Tel: 01977 610 078
Brief Directions: From Hemsworth town centre take Pontefract Road. Lowfield Road is on the right just after the left hand bend.
Hon Secretary: Barrie Spencer, 39 Orchid Crest, Upton, West Yorkshire, WF9 1NT
Tel: (H) 01977 648118 Tel: (M) 07788 924768
Email: BrrSpncr@aol.com
Fixtures Secretary: N. Jennings, 8 Churchfield Terrace, Barnsley
Club Colours: Maroon & Blue Quarters
League: Yorkshire 3

HESSLE RUFC
Ground Address: Livingston Road, Hessle, Hull, HU13 0EG Tel: 01482 643 430
Brief Directions: Turm right off clive Sullivan Way at `Sainsburys'. At mini R/about turn right and then left into Livingston Road. Club lm on left.
Hon Secretary: Nick Whitaker, 77 West Grove, Askew Avenue, Hull, HU4 6RQ Tel: (H) 01482 576 091
Fixtures Secretary: Phil Denton, 7 Maplewood Avenue, Hull Tel: (H) 01482561 338
Club Colours: Green, black and white irregular hoops
League: Yorkshire 4

HOLMES CHAPEL RFC
Ground Address: AP Sports and Social Club, Station Road, Holmes Chapel, Cheshire, CW4 8AA
Tel: 01477 532 018
Brief Directions: Ground is on A54 (Holmes Chapel - Congleton Rd) on outskirts of village just beyond Railway Station
Hon Secretary: John Morris, 6 Westbury Close, Middlewich, Cheshire, CW10 0PR
Tel: (H) 01606 834572 Tel: (M) 07748 962 143
Hon Secretary: M. Cummins, 4 Portree Drive, Holmes Chapel, CW4 7JB
Tel: (H) 01477 534 617 Tel: (W) 01477 537 176
Email: martinbrio@aol.com
Fixtures Secretary: John Leary
Tel: (H) 01606 554 614 Tel: (W) 01606 562 816
Club Colours: Royal Blue Shirts with Single Gold Band
League: South Lancs/Cheshire 4

HORDEN WELFARE RFC
Ground Address: Horden Welfare Park, Northumberland Street, Horden, Peterlee, Co. Durham, SR8 4PX Tel: 0191 586 3501
Brief Directions: A19 into Peterlee, follow signs for Horden, left onto Sunderland Rd, turn right at Bell Hotel, 100 yards to club house
Hon Secretary: Joseph Watson, 'Clairemont', Sunderland Road, Peterlee, Co. Durham, SR8 4PF
Tel: (H) 0191 586 1042
Email: joseph.watson1@btinternet.com
Fixtures Secretary: Robert Brownless, 31 Manor Way, Peterlee, Co. Durham Tel: (H) 0191 586 4464
Club Colours: Claret & Blue
League: North 2 East

HORNSEA RUFC
Ground Address: The Hollis Recreation Ground, Westwood Avenue, Hornsea, E. Yorkshire, HU18 1BB
Tel: 01964 534 181
Brief Directions: Leave Hornsea on Atwick and Bridlington road. Turn left after 300m onto Westwood Avenue, opposite school playing fields.
Hon Secretary: I. Rodmell, 100 Parliament Street, Malton, North Yorkshire, YO17 9HE
Tel: (H) 01653 698 605 Tel: (M) 07770 435 406
Email: IanRodmell@msn.com
Fixtures Secretary: Roger McLatchie, 18 Shaftsbury Avenue, Hornsea, E. Yorkshire, HU18 1LX
Tel: (H) 01964 534 497
Club Colours: Black with green and white hoops
League: Yorkshire 5

HOUGHTON RUFC
Ground Address: Dairy Lane, Houghton-Le-Spring, DH4 5BH Tel: 0191 584 1460
Email Address: juliecrowther@aol.com
Brief Directions: Situated on A1052, Houghton to Chester-le-Street road, opposite Houghton Police Station, 0.25 mile west of A690
Hon Secretary: Tom Roberts, Jelta, Gilpin Street, Tyne & Wear, DH4 5DR Tel: (H) 0191 584 0603
Email: enidtom@btinternet.com
Fixtures Secretary: John Felton, 37 Larchwood, Washington, NE33 9BT Tel: (H) 0191 416 1467
Tel: (W) 0191 401 6308
Club Colours: Black shirts with white hoop, black shorts, black socks
League: Durham/N'thm'land 2

HOYLAKE RFC

Ground Address: Melrose Avenue, Hoylake, Wirral, Merseyside, CH47 3BU Tel: 0151 632 2538
Email Address: stirlingdutton@excite.com
Web Address: www.hoylake.net
Brief Directions: Turn at roundabout in Hoylake towards Railway Station. After 500 yards, turn left down Carham Road.
Hon Secretary: Stirling K. Dutton, 10 Hadfield Avenue, Wirral, CH47 3DJ Tel: (H) 0151 632 0379
Tel: (W) 0151 235 3417
Email: stirling.dutton@excite.com
Fixtures Secretary: John Kellaway, 43 Dovedale Road, Wirral, CH47 Tel: (H) 0151 632 5742
Club Colours: Green with red/white hoops
League: South Lancs/Cheshire 2

HUDDERSFIELD YMCA RUFC

Ground Address: Lawrence Batley Sports Centre, Laund Hill, Huddersfield, HD3 4YS Tel: 01484 654 052
Brief Directions: FROM WEST: M62,J23, follow Huddersfield sign, ground 0.5 mile on left.
FROM EAST: M62, J24, follow Rochdale sign at r'bout, along A643 for 1 mile, left at r'bout, follow Huddersfield sign, ground o.5 mile on left.
Hon Secretary: Ian Leask, 3 Cheviot Way, Mirfield, WF14 8HW Tel: (H) 01924 508 642
Tel: (M) 07831 778 623 Tel: (W) 01924 508 641
Email: ian.leask@ntlworld.com
Fixtures Secretary: Gavin Wray, 365 Stainland Road, Stainland, Halifax, Yorkshire, HX4 9HF
Tel: (H) 01422 374368 Tel: (M) 0771 866047
Club Colours: Red & black hoops, black shorts
League: Yorkshire 1

HULL RUFC

Ground Address: Haworth Park, Emmott Road, Beverley Road, Hull, HU6 7AB Tel: 01482 802 119
Email Address: djw@amj.co.uk
Brief Directions: The ground is East of Beverley High road (A1079) and is signed from t he main road.
Hon Secretary: D. J. Ward, 78 St. Margarets' Avenue, Hull, HU16 5NB Tel: (H) 01482 842 292
Tel: (M) 07785 701 223 Tel: (W) 01482 325 242
Email: djw@amj.co.uk
Fixtures Secretary: Norman Angell, "Shelley", Main Street, Burstwick, E. Yorkshire Tel: (H) 01964 622 975
Club Colours: Black with gold and red band
League: North 2 East

HULLENSIANS RUFC

Ground Address: Springhead Lane, Springfield Way, Analby Common, Hull Tel: 01482 505 656
Web Address: www.hullensians.org.uk
Brief Directions: A63 to Hull. Turn off at Ferriby follow signs for Anlaby. Travel along Boothferry Road, left along First Avenue, right at the end, sharp left at R/about 1st right Springhead Lane.
Hon Secretary: P. F. Jones, 5 Sherwood Drive, Hull, HU4 7RG Tel: (H) 01482 354 975
Fixtures Secretary: Tim Robinson, 79 Huntley Drive, Chanterlands Avenue, Hull, HU5 4DP
Tel: (H) 01482 844 707
Club Colours: Red and black
League: Yorkshire 4

ILKLEY RFC

Ground Address: Stacks Field, Denton Road, Ilkley, W. Yorkshire, LS29 0AD Tel: 01943 607 037
Brief Directions: At traffic lights in centre of town (with Church, Star Inn, Crescent Hotel on 3 corners) turn left if coming from Skipton/Silsden, or right if coming from Leeds/Bradford/Otley. Go about 1/4 mile over bridge and club is visible on your right. Turn right down Denton Road. The gates are about 30 yards along on the right.
Hon Secretary: Ken Bernard, 36 Dale View, Ilkley, West Yorkshire, LS29 9BP Tel: (H) 01943 602 945
Email: j.k.bernard@btinternet.com
Leagues Contact: Richard Hey, 28a Leeds Road, Ilkley, West Yorkshire, LS29 8DS
Tel: (H) 01943 816855 Tel: (M) 07747700394
Fixtures Secretary: David Duxbury, 12 Broadfield Way, Ilkley, LS29 0TJ Tel: (M) 07811 331427
Club Colours: Red, Black, White
League: Yorkshire 2

JARROVIANS RFC LTD

Ground Address: Lukes Lane Estate, Hebburn, Tyne & Wear, NE32 5RS Tel: 0191 561 0627
Brief Directions: North end of A1(M)/A194(M), continue north along A194, at 1st roundabout turn left, then immediate right, follow road along full length, ground on right
Hon Secretary: Albert Ritson, 5 Belsfield Gardens, Monkton, Tyne & Wear, NE32 5QB
Tel: (H) 0191 489 3866
Club Colours: Black and amber hoops
League: Durham/N'thm'land 3

KEIGHLEY RUFC

Ground Address: Skipton Road, Utley, Keighley, W. Yorkshire, BD20 6DX Tel: 01535 602 174
Brief Directions: Access to ground is from former A629 from Keighley to Skipton, ground is on right travelling north just on outskirts of town. NB no access from present A629 Aire V'ly rd
Hon Secretary: M. T. Greaves, Holmlea, Summerhill Lane, Keighley, W. Yorkshire, BD20 6RX
Tel: (H) 01535 653 192 Tel: (W) 01535 605 646
Fixtures Secretary: J. Midgley
Tel: (H) 01535 214 545
Club Colours: Scarlet, white and green hoops
League: Yorkshire 2

KESWICK RFC

Ground Address: Davidson Park, Heads Road, Keswick, Cumbria, CA12 5EG Tel: 01768 772 823
Brief Directions: Located between town centre and Derwentwater. Drive past the Lakes Supermarket & take first right. Follow signs within the grounds to allocated parking spaces for rugby cars.
Hon Secretary: David Hume, c/o The Climbing Wall, Southey Hill Trading Estate, Keswick, CA12 5HP Tel: (H) 01768 775 274 Tel: (M) 07780 883 984 Tel: (W) 01768 772 000
Email: pam5@btinternet.com
Fixtures Secretary: Alan F. Gray, 49 Blencathrast, Keswick, Cumbria, CA12 4HX Tel: (H) 01768 773 051
Tel: (W) 01768 773 051
Club Colours: Navy, green & yellow hooped shirts
League: Cumbria

KIRKBY LONSDALE RFC
Ground Address: The Clubhouse, Underley Park, Raygarth, Kirkby Lonsdale, Lancs, LA6 2DS
Tel: 01524 271 780
Email Address: rihardharkness@hackney-leigh.co.uk
Web Address: kirkbylonsdalerufc@.co.uk
Brief Directions: m6,juntion36 approx 5miles signposted kirkby lonsdale.Petrol Station on right,next turn left.At road junction bear left and at bottom of hill turn left..5 miles turn right sin posted KLRUFC.
Hon Secretary: Richard Harkness, Meadowgarth, Fairbank, via Carnforth, Lancs, LA6 2DU
Tel: (H) 01524 271137 (M) 07971 911357
(W) 01524 272111
Fixtures Secretary: Bill Whewell, Field Edge, Burton in Kendal, Lancs Tel: (H) 01524 782049 (W) 01524 782049
Club Colours: Red/black/amber hooped jerseys
League: North Lancs/Cumbria

KNARESBOROUGH RUFC
Ground Address: Hay-A-Park, Park lane (off Chain Lane), Knaresborough, North Yorks. Tel: 01423 866811
Brief Directions: Follow A59 to centre of Knaresborough, at traffic lights by Board Inn turn North, away from Calcutt (signposted), take 2nd right, at school, follow on to end of road. Continue on down lane under bridge. Pitch is 200 yds on right.
Hon Secretary: Antony Merrin, 73 West End Avenue, Harrogate, North Yorkshire, HG2 9BX
Tel: (H) 01423 569245 (M) 07836 708278
(W) 01423 322706
Email: themerrins@westend73.fsnet.co.uk
Fixtures Secretary: Steve McGrail, 33 Westville Oval, Harrogate, N. Yorkshire Tel: (H) 01423 522 521
Club Colours: Blue and gold hooped shirts
League: Yorkshire 5

KNOTTINGLEY RUFC
Ground Address: Knottingley RUFC, Howards Field, Marsh Lane, Knottingley, W. Yorkshire, WF11 9DE
Tel: 01977 672 438
Brief Directions: Onto A645 main road toward Knottingley, turn off at town hall/St Botolophs Church, follow road 500m past Cherry Tree pub, turn left just before lights at bridge to Howards Field
Hon Secretary: Adrian Carley, 50 Womersley Road, West Yorkshire, WF11 0DJ Tel: (H) 01977 677 690
Tel: (W) 01977 677111 ext 249
Fixtures Secretary: John Alexander (H) 07899 732757
Club Colours: Blue & white shirts/ blue/ blue
League: Yorkshire 3

LEEDS CORINTHIANS RUFC
Ground Address: Nutty Slack, Middleton District Centre, Leeds. 10-4RA Tel: 0113 2711574
Brief Directions: M62 J28 to Leeds or M1 city centre to Dewsbury follow signs for A653, turn onto Middleton ringroad at Tommy Wass pub, right at 1st r'bout and go to rear of supermarket onto shale track to club
Club Secretary: Andrew Parker,16 Forsythia Avenue, East Ardsley, Wakefield. WF3 2HT.
Tel: 01924 823675
Fixtures Secretary: Graham Mapplebeck
46 Cranmore Crescent, Belle Isle, Leeds LS10 4AN
Tel: (H) 0113 2704935 (W) 0113 2457205
Club Colours: Black, gold and white.
League: Yorkshire 3

LEIGH RUFC
Ground Address: Round Ash Park, Hand Lane, Leigh, Lancashire, WN7 3NA Tel: 01942 673 526
Email Address: leighrufc@blueyonder.co.uk
Web Address: www.leighrufc.co.uk
Brief Directions: At the top of Hand Lane, which is off St. Helens Road in the Pennington area of Leigh.
Hon Secretary: Michael Hampson, 12 Briar Close, Wigan, Lancashire, WN2 4RH Tel: (H) 01942 523 496
Fixtures Secretary: T. Hughes, 2 Launceston Road, Wigan Tel: (H) 01942 257 427
Club Colours: Black and amber
Brief Directions: Leeds ringroad (outer) to Moortown Sainsburys, from Sainsburys travel away from Leeds on King Lane for 0.75 mile, ground on left hand side
League: South Lancs/Cheshire 1

LEODIENSIAN RUFC
Ground Address: Crag Lane, off King Lane, Alwoodley, Leeds, LS17 5PR Tel: 0113 267 3409
Email Address: leodiensian@yahoogroups.com
Web Address: www.leodiensian.co.uk
Hon Secretary: Iain Batchelor, 1 Sunningdale Green, Leeds, LS17 7SQ Tel: (H) 0113 268 1197
Tel: (M) 07775 546 905 Tel: (W) 0113 296 3264
Email: secretary@leodiensian.co.uk
Fixtures Secretary: Alun Gabriel, 28 Denton Avenue, Leeds, LS8 1LZ Tel: (H) 0113 266 1931
Tel: (M) 07774 114 159 Tel: (W) 01422 322 396
Club Colours: Navy blue and gold
League: Yorkshire 2

LITTLEBOROUGH RUFC
Ground Address: Rakewood, Hollingworth Lake, Littleborough, OL15 0AP Tel: 01706 370 220
Brief Directions: From Littleborough centre, under railway bridge. right turn signs for Hollingworth Lake. Turn between lake and Fisherman Pub, straight down lane 800yds on right.
Hon Secretary: Stephen Blackburn, 2 Mount Avenue, Ridale, Lancs, OL12 9QE Tel: (H) 01706 375 489
Fixtures Secretary: Brent Pollitt, 36 Charlotte Street, Rochdale, OL16 4TJ Tel: (H) 01706 341 732
Club Colours: Black, yellow and green
League: North Lancs 1

LIVERPOOL COLLEGIATE RUFC
Ground Address: Liverpool Cricket Club, Aigburth Road, Grassendale, Liverpool, L19 3QF
Tel: 0151 427 2930
Brief Directions: M62 Follow Queens Drive to Aigburth Road (Ohone secretary if further details are needed)
Hon Secretary: F. Carroll, 10 Mather Avenue, Liverpool, L18 5HS
Tel: (H) 0151 724 4756 Tel: (M) 07876 048 801
Email: frankcarroll@btinternet.com
Fixtures Secretary: T. Mcglouchlin, 12 Redmoor Cresent, Tower Hill, Liverpool, Merseyside, L33 1YF
Tel: (H) 07786937109 Tel: (M) 07786937109 Tel: (W) 01512921801
Club Colours: Light blue, dark blue quarters
League: South Lancs/Cheshire 3

LONSDALE WANDERERS RFC
Ground Address: The Clubhouse, Underley park, Kirkby Lonsdale Tel: 01524 271 780
Hon Secretary: W. Whewell, Field Edge, Heron Syke, Burton-in-Kendall, LA6 1LG Tel: (H) 01524 782 049
Email: wwhewell@aol.com
League: North Lancs 2

LYMM RFC
Ground Address: Beechwood, Crouchley Lane, Warrington, Cheshire, WA13 0AT Tel: 01925 753 212
Email Address: author@lymmrfc.free-online.co.uk
Web Address: www.lymmrfc.free-online.co.uk
Hon Secretary: G. Kennedy, 3 Northway, Lymm, Cheshire, WA13 9AT Tel: (H) 01925 754 995
Fixtures Secretary: C. Monks, 8 Newlands Road, Warrington Tel: (H) 01925 262 904
Club Colours: Black, green, white
League: North 2 West

LYTHAM
Ground Address: Woodlands Memorial ground, Blackpool Road, Ansdell, Lytham St Annes, Lancashire. Fy8 4EL Tel No: 01253 734 733
Brief Directions: Follow Lytham St Annes signs on B5230 at end of M55 then B5261 onto Queensway. Ground is three miles on left opposite 'Blossoms' public house and R.C.church.
Club Secretary: Sean Townsend, 26 Badgers Walk East, Lytham St Annes, Lancashire FY8 4BS
Tel No: 01253 737649
Fixtures Secretary: Grahame Benstead, 19 Wellington St, Lytham St Annes, Lancs. FY8 5BZ
Tel: 01253 736922
Club Colours: Claret, gold and white
League: North Lancs 1

MALTON & NORTON RUFC
Ground Address: The Gannock, Old malton Rd., Malton, Yorks. YO17 7EY. Tel: 01653 694 657
Email Address: laidler@wlaidler.fsnet.co.uk
Web Address: www.malton-norton-rfu.co.uk
Brief Directions: A64 York-Scarborough take first turning for Malton. At traffic lights in town centre carry straight on towards Pickering. Ground is approx 600 yards on right after cricket club.
Hon Secretary: W. Laidler, Ashdale, 8 Second Avenue, Pickering, YO18 8AH
Tel: (H) 01751 472 228 Tel: (M) 07733 335 309
Email: laidler@wlaidler.fsnet.co.uk
Fixtures Secretary: W. Laidler, Ashdale, 8 Second Avenue, Pickering, YO18 8AH Tel: (H) 01751 472 228
Tel: (M) 07733 335 309
Email: laidler@wlaidler.fsnet.co.uk
Club Colours: Red, white & black irregular hoops
League: Yorkshire 2

MANCHESTER WANDERERS RUFC
Ground Address: Grove Park, Grove Lane, Cheadle Hulme, Cheshire, SK8 7NB.
Brief Directions: From North-East: Exit 3 from M60. South on A.34 (signed Wilmslow) for 2.5 miles. At second R/about exist left on B5095. Ground is on the left 400-500 yards. From South-West: M6 to M56 (Manchester Airport). To A.34 South to B5095 Bramhall.
Club Secretary: Peter Luxton, 33 Bowdan Avenue, Hazel Grolve, Stockport, Cheshire, SK7 4LH.
Tel: 0161 2851023
Fixtures Secretary: Cliff Williams, 45 Drive, Marple, Stockport, Cheshire. Tel: 0161 449 8325
Club Colours: Red & white quarters
League: South Lancs & Cheshire 4

MARIST RUFC
Ground Address: Cranbrook Avenue, Cottingham Road, Hull Tel: 01482 859 216
Web Address: www.maristrufc.co.uk
Brief Directions: From M62 follow signs for Universities, then continue to Cranbrook Avenue along Cottingham Road
Hon Secretary: Mick Jones, 52 Ferriby Road, Hull, East Yorkshire, HU13 0HT Tel: (H) 01482 643 362
Email: mickjo@ntlworld.com
Fixtures Secretary: Ralph Ayre, 92 Auckland Avenue, Cottingham Road, Hull, HU6 Tel: (H) 01482 804 166
Club Colours: White Shirt with Blue Band,Navy Shorts
League: Yorkshire 6

MARPLE RUFC
Ground Address: Ridge Sports Pavillion, Wood Lane, Marple, Stockport, Cheshire, SK6 7RE
Tel: 0161 427 7915
Email Address: hopey1@ntlworld.com
Web Address: www.marplerugby.com
Brief Directions: Club House at Wood Lane Playing Fields. A626 into Marple, turn right into Cross Lane at Bowling Green Pub, turn right into Wood Lane. At Otters Lodge pub, go to end of road, club house on left at field.
Hon Secretary: Stuart Budd, 143 Woodville Drive, Stockport, SK6 7RD Tel: (H) 0161 484 5099 Tel: (M) 07968 089 569 Tel: (W) 01925 833 733
Email: stuart.bould@brfc.com
Fixtures Secretary: Neil Hawkley, 43 High Croft, Hyde, SK14 5LD Tel: (H) 0161 366 0110
Club Colours: Red and black
League: South Lancs/Cheshire 3

MEDICALS RFC
Ground Address: Medical Athletic Ground, Carrington Crescent, Newcstle upon Tyne
Tel: 0191 265 6321/ 276 1473 (match days)
Hon Secretary: J. Shawcross, 109 St. Georges Terrace, Newcastle upon Tyne, NE
Tel: (H) 0191 209 3401
Email: j.s.shawcross@ncl.ac.uk
Fixtures Secretary: A. Ramshaw, 19 Douglas Avenue, Newcastle, NE3 4XD
Club Colours: Maroon with white shorts
League: Durham/N'thm'land 3

MIDDLESBROUGH RUFC
Ground Address: Acklam Park, Green Lane, Acklam, Middlesborough, TS5 7SL Tel: 01642 818 567
Web Address: www.mrufc.homepage
Brief Directions: A19, A11330 exit to M'bro, immediate left at fork, right at bollards onto Croft Ave, straight over traffic lights onto Green Lane, club 400yds on right
Hon Secretary: D. Brydon, 20 Westwood Avenue, Middlesborough, TS5 5PY Tel: (H) 01642 819 954

Fixtures Secretary: J. Haddon, 5 Wycherley Avenue, Middlesborough, TS5 5HH Tel: (H) 01642 713048 Tel: (M) 07730 987 682 Tel: (W) 01642 677 181 Email: jh@ls-stairs.co.uk
Club Colours: Maroon shirts, white shorts
League: North 2 East

MILLOM RUFC
Ground Address: WIlson Park, St. Lukes Road, Haverigg, Millom, Cumbria Tel: 01229 774 076
Email Address: secretary@mrufc.co.uk
Brief Directions: Follow the coast road from the Harbour Hotel. Carry on past Inshore Rescue, the club is 150yds on the right
Hon Secretary: Ed Whitfield, 13 Willowside Park, Millom, Cumbria, LA18 4PT Tel: (H) 01229 774 876 Tel: (W) 01229 772 862
Email: secretary@mrufc.co.uk
Hon Secretary: Edward Whitfield, 13 Willowside Park, Haverigg, Millom, Cumbria, LA18 4PT
Tel: (H) 01229 774876 Tel: (W) 01229 772862
Fixtures Secretary: John Irving, 10 Buttermere Drive, Millom, Cumbria, LA18 4PL
Club Colours: Blue and white
League: Cumbria

MOORTOWN RUFC
Ground Address: Moss Valley, King Lane, Alwoodley, Leeds, W. Yorkshire Tel: 0113 267 8243
Web Address: www.moortownrufc.org
Brief Directions: From the ring road turn up past the entrance to Sainsburys, 1.5 miles turn right onto The Avenue, 0.5 mile turn right into Far Moss
Hon Secretary: Graham Spark, 16 Sandal Cliff, Wakefield, WF2 6AU Tel: (H) 01924 242 753 Tel: (M) 07712 911 736 Tel: (W) 0113 2822410
Email: graham@gpspark.screaming.net
Fixtures Secretary: Nick Webb, 8 Adel Wood Drive, Leeds, LS16 8ES
Tel: (H) 0113 267 7833 Tel: (M) 07816 817695
Club Colours: Maroon with green and white hoops
League: Yorkshire 3

MORESBY RUFC
Ground Address: Walkmill Park, Moresby, Whitehaven, Cumbria, CA28 8XW Tel: 01946 695 984
Brief Directions: M6 Junction 40 (Penrith) A66 for 35 miles. Turn left onto A595 for approx 7 miles, then left up Swallow Brow. Ground is approx 2 miles.
Hon Secretary: Ian Johnstone, 41 Hillcrest Avenue, Whitehaven, Cumbria, CA28 6SS Tel: (H) 01946 66713
Fixtures Secretary: Steven Kellett, 26 Mitredale Close, Whitehaven, Cumbria
Tel: (H) 01946 599 344 Tel: (M) 07710 680 786
Club Colours: Red shirts, white shorts
League: Cumbria

MORPETH RFC
Ground Address: Grange House Field, Mitford Road, Morpeth Tel: 01670 512 508
Brief Directions: North from Newcastle on A1 from Morpeth centre travelling north, left after telephone exchange onto Mitford Road, entrance on right past the school
Hon Secretary: Ken. U. Fraser, Solway House, De Merley Road, Morpeth, Northumberland, NE61 1HZ Tel: (H) 01670 511 208 Tel: (W) 01624 800 800
Fixtures Secretary: Bill Hewitt, The Sirches, Lane Head, Felton Tel: (H) 01670 787 757
Club Colours: Red, white & navy irregular hoops
League: North 2 East

MOSBOROUGH RUFC
Ground Address: Mosborough WMC, Station Road, Mosborough, Sheffield, S20 Tel: 0114 248 5546
Brief Directions: M1 J30, take A616 towards Sheffield, at 2nd set of lights turn right, clubhouse on left 50m.
Hon Secretary: Hedley Craney, 14 Hollow Lane, Sheffield, South Yorks. S20 4GF Tel: (H) 0114 2481413
Fixtures Secretary: John Staton, 10 Westfield Crescent, Sheffield, S20 5AQ Tel: (H) 01142 489 705
Email: jstatonuk@yahoo.co.uk
Club Colours: Black and red
League: Yorkshire 5

MOSSLEY HILL RUFC
Ground Address: Mossley Hill Road, Liverpool
Tel: 0151 724 4377
Brief Directions: From M62 take ring road towards Liverpool Airport. Turn left onto Allerton Road, right onto Rose Lane (at Tescos) Ground is behind Mossley Hill Church at top of Rose Lane.
Hon Secretary: Andy Pealing, 48 Heathfield Park, Widnes, WA8 9WY Tel: (H) 0151 423 1821
Email: andrewpealing@btopenworld.com
Fixtures Secretary: Peter Barnett, 49 Ferndale Road, Liverpool, Merseyside, L15 3JY Tel: (H) 0151 280 5794 Tel: (M) 07976 885 318
Email: pete@barno.freeserve.co.uk
Club Colours: Maroon and Gold
League: South Lancs/Cheshire 4

NETHERHALL RFC
Ground Address: Netherhall Park, Netherhall Road, Maryport Tel: 01900 815 833
Brief Directions: A66 to Cockermouth Head to Workington, right at roundabout for Maryport, turn left off bypass head into Maryport, right at lights A596 to Carlisle, club 400yds on right
Hon Secretary: Paul Bartlett, 66 Garborough Close, Maryport, CA15 6RZ Tel: (H) 01900 818 420
Email: p_bartlett2000@hotmail.com
Fixtures Secretary: L. Rumney Tel: (H) 01900 811440
Club Colours: Claret and gold
League: Cumbria

NEWTON AYCLIFFE RUFC
Ground Address: Moore Lane, Newton Aycliffe, Co. Durham, DL5 5AG Tel: 01325 312 768
Brief Directions: Approach Newton Aycliffe on the A167. At the traffic lights at the top of the hill turn onto the B6443, Central Avenue. Turn left at the first r'about onto Shafto Way. Take the third left, Creighton Road then take the first right onto Moore Lane
Hon Secretary: Bob Malvern Tel: (H) 01325 320085
Hon Secretary: Sue Adams, 35 Holly Hill, Durham, DL4 2DB Tel: (M) 07977 306629 (W) 01388 774 669
Email: susan.adams2@btopenworld.com
Hon Fixtures: Bob Malvern Tel: (H) 01325 320085
Club Colours: Green, Maroon & Amber
League: Durham/N'thm'land 4

NEWTON-LE-WILLOWS RUFC
Ground Address: Crow Lane East, Newton-le-Willows, Merseyside. Tel: 01925 224591
Brief Directions: M6 J23, take signs for Newton A49, continue down Ashton Rd (A49) until mini roundabout with Oak Tree pub on right, right into Crow Lane, club 300 yds on right
Club Secretary: David Hughes, 127 Birley St., Newton-le-Willows, Merseyside WA12 9UN.
Tel: 01925 221304
Fixtures Secretary: Steve Kruger, 2 Camelot Close, Newton-le-Willows, Merseyside.
Tel: 01925 221937
Club Colours: Royal blue and gold hoops
League: South Lancs & Cheshire 3

NORTH MANCHESTER & OLDHAM COLLEGES RUFC
Ground Address: Greengate/Victoria Avenue East, Moston, Manchester
Tel: 0161 682 9234
Club Secretary: Brian H Stott, 8 Barlea Avenue, New Moston, Manchester. M40 3WL
Tel: (H) 0161 682 0541 (W) 0161 681 1582
Fixtures Secretary: Jason Malone
Tel: (H) 0161 653 5020
Club Colours: Green, black and white hoops
League: North Lancs 2

NORTH RIBBLESDALE RFC
Ground Address: Grove Park, Lower Greenfoot, Settle, N. Yorkshire, BD24 9QH Tel: 01729 822 755
Email Address: cvsharpe@lineone.net
Brief Directions: leave A65 at roundabout on southskirts of town,into town turning right 1st past falcon manor (signposted "rugby ground) head .25 mile grounds on left proceed along 1st team field entrance on left past large club sign.
Hon Secretary: Christopher Sharpe, 28 Ash Grove, Keighley Road, Keighley, BD20 7RU Tel: (H) 01535 636 694 Tel: (M) 07752 351 820
Email: cvsharpe@lineone.net
Fixtures Secretary: D. Brown, 4 Eastview, Settle, N. Yorks, BD24 9AU
Tel: (H) 01729 824 041 Tel: (M) 07812958940
Club Colours: ROYAL BLUE AND WHITE
League: Yorkshire 1

NORTH SHIELDS RFC
Ground Address: Preston Playing Field, Preston Village, North Shields Tel: 0191 257 7352
Brief Directions: From Tyne Tunnel (south) or A1/A19 (north) take A1058, follow signs for Tynemouth, club is situated next to Tynemouth Swimming Baths
Hon Secretary: G. Siddle, 5 Belsay Ave., Whitley Bay
Tel: (H) 0191 290 2267
Fixtures Secretary: A. G. Shield, 9 Cresswell Avenue, North Shields, Tyne & Wear, NE29 9BQ
Tel: (H) 0191 259 0402
Club Colours: Royal blue and white hoops
League: Durham/N'thm'land 2

NORTHALLERTON RUFC
Ground Address: Brompton Lodge, Northallerton Road, Brompton, Northallerton, N. Yorks. DL6 2PZ
Tel: 01609 773496
Brief Directions: Brompton Road. Left at filling station. Club 1/4 mile on left.
Club Secretary: David Middlemiss, 13 Quaker Lane, Northhallerton, Yorks. Tel: (H) 01609 779945
Email: david.middlemiss@genie.co.uk
Fixtures Secretary: Alan Bradley, 15 Borrowby Ave., Northallerton, N. Yorkshire. Tel: (H) 01609 772743
Club Colours: Green, amber and white
League: Yorkshire 2

NORTHERN RFC
Ground Address: McCracken Park, Great North Road, Newcastle Upon Tyne, NE3 2DG Tel: 0191 236 3369
Email Address: admin@northernfc.co.uk
Web Address: www.northernfc.co.uk
Brief Directions: From south & west, A1 western bypass north, take 'city north/Gosforth B1318' for 0.75 mile, ground on left. From north take B1318 from A1, ground 0.75 mile on left
Hon Secretary: Andy James, c/o Northern FC, McCracken park, Newcastle upon Tyne
Email: andypjames@yahoo.co.uk
Fixtures Secretary: Ian Ramshaw, 7 Chatsworth Cres, Sunderland, SR4 7NP
Tel: (H) 0191 5201176 Tel: (W) 0191 4332463
Club Colours: No First Team defined
League: Durham/N'thm'land 1

NORTHWICH RFC
Ground Address: Moss Farm Recreaction Centre, Moss Farm, Winnington, Northwich, Cheshire, CW8 4BH
Tel: 01606 783335
Email Address: dave.sargeant@tesco.net
Web Address: homepages.tesco.net/~northwich.rfc
Brief Directions: Follow directions from Northwich town centre to swimming pool
Hon Secretary: Dave Sargeant, 12 Sydney Street, Northwich, Cheshire, CW8 4AP Tel: (H) 01606 783335
Tel: (M) 0786 755 3910 Tel: (W) 01204 602300
Email: dave.sargeant@tesco.net
Fixtures Secretary: Paul Hughes, 14 Woodlands Road, Northwich, Cheshire Tel: (H) 01606 768 17
Fixtures Secretary: Trevor Rawling, 49 School Lane, Northwich, Cheshire Tel: (H) 01606 871 636
Club Colours: Black shirts Black shorts
League: South Lancs/Cheshire 1

NOVOCASTRIANS RFC
Ground Address: Sutherland Park, The Drive, Benton, Newcastle upon Tyne, NE7 7SX Tel: 0191 266 1247
Web Address: www.novosrfc.cjb.net
Brief Directions: From either the A19 or Newcastle Central Motorway A6127M, take the sliproads signed Newcastle or Tynemouth onto the A1058. Exit on sliproad A188 to Killingworth. On the left, The Drive, signposted NOVOS RFC. Club is on the left.
Hon Secretary: Angus Forbes Walker, 6 Redesdale Avenue, Newcastle upon Tyne, NE3 3PP
Tel: (H) 0191 213 1084
Fixtures Secretary: Robert Fay, 10 Lyndhurst Crescent, Gateshead, NE9 6BA
Tel: (H) 0191 487 3393 Tel: (W) 0191 386 2714
Club Colours: Red, black and white hoops
League: Durham/N'thm'land 2

OLD BEDIANS RFC
Ground Address: Old Bedians RUFC, Didsbury Sports Centre, Millgate Lane, Didsbury, Manchester, M20 0QT
Tel: 0161 445 8862
Hon Secretary: Ian Wilson, 7 Brooklands Close, Manchester, M34 3PL
Tel: (H) 0161 445 8862 Tel: (W) 0161 287 7760
Club Colours: Navy blue shirts, white shorts
League: North Lancs 1

OLD BRODLEIANS RUFC
Ground Address: Woodhead, Denholme Gate Road, Hipperholme, Halifax Tel: 01422 202 708
Brief Directions: M62 J26, follow A58 signs to Halifax, after 3.75 miles turn right at Hippodrome lights, continue up hill for 0.5 mile, club on left about 250 yds after Shell petrol station
Hon Secretary: Simon Heaton, Sutcliffe Wood Farm, Woodbottom Lane, Brighouse, HD6 2QW
Tel: (H) 01484 721 628 Tel: (W) 01274 700 115
Email: sheaton@heaton-valves.co.uk
Fixtures Secretary: M. Hey, 2 Sunnybank Crescent, Sowerby Bridge, Halifax Tel: (H) 01422 839 614
League: Yorkshire 1

OLD CROSSLEYANS RUFC
Ground Address: Standeven House, Broomfield Avenue, Halifax, West Yorkshire. HX3 0JF
Tel: 01422 363000
Brief Directions: M62 Exit 24. A629 towards Halifax at 4th set of lights. Left at A646 towards Rochdale /Burnley. Left at second mini roundabout. (Birdcage Lane).
Club Secretary: Richard A Davies, 4 Warley Dene, Holme Road, Warley, Halifax, West Yorks. HX2 7RS
Tel: (H) 01422 832218
Fixtures Secretary: Derek Ainley, 1 Savile Heath, Manaor Heath Road, Halifax.
Tel: (H) 01422 368233
Club Colours: Blue, white and amber
League: North 2 East

OLD MODERNIANS RUFC
Ground Address: Cookridge Lane, Cookridge, Leeds, LS16 7ND Tel: 0113 267 1075
Brief Directions: A660 north from Leeds until 1/4 mile past junction with A6120 ring road at Lawnswood. Fork left at Cookridge, ground 2 miles on right
Hon Secretary: John Bracewell, 30 Queen's Gate, North Park Road, Harrogate, HG1 5RQ
Tel: (H) 01423 709 357 Tel: (W) 0113 241 3683
Fixtures Secretary: David Carter, 81 Green Lane, Leeds, LS16 7ET Tel: (H) 0113 267 9718
Club Colours: Red and black hoops shirts and socks, black shorts
League: Yorkshire 4

OLD OTLIENSIANS RUFC
Ground Address: Chaffers Field, Pool Road, Otley, West Yorkshire, LS21 Tel: 01943 461 476
Brief Directions: From Otley town centre, take A659 to Harrogate, turn right at Smiths Garden Centre, follow sign to clubhouse
Hon Secretary: David Beardsley, 5b Birdcage Court, Birdcage Walk, LS21 3HH Tel: (H) 01943 466 362
Fixtures Secretary: Adrian Normanton, 26 Roseberry Crescent, Middlesborough, TS9 6ER
Tel: (H) 01642 723 192 Tel: (W) 01642 467 194
Club Colours: Navy blue, royal blue and white narrow hoops
League: Yorkshire 3

OLD RISHWORTHIAN RUFC
Ground Address: The Clubhouse, Copley, Halifax, W. Yorkshire, HX3 0UG Tel: 01422 353 919
Email Address: orrufc@singlevision.co.uk
Web Address: www.singlevision.co.uk
Brief Directions: Leave the M62 at junction 24 and at the roundabout take second exit and follow signs to Halifax. Follow dual carriageway down the hill until it becomes a single carriageway. After 100 there is a set of traffic lights, turn left at lights and go across mini roundabout. Follow signs for Sowerby Bridge and Copley and at the next set of traffic lights turn left at the Volunteer Arms.Follow the road over the canal bridge and carry on going under the railway bridge. Old Rishworthian RUFC is 50 yards on the left.
Hon Secretary: P.G. Morgan, 18 Woodfield Drive, Saddleworth Road, Halifax, HX4 8NZ
Tel: (H) 01422 373 379 Tel: (M) 07799 338 560
Email: pgm18@aol.com
Fixtures Secretary: Ray Wadsworth, Abbotsroyd Cottage, Rochdale Road, Halifax
Tel: (H) 01422 822 113 Tel: (W) 01484 845 740
Email: ray@wyorks.com
Club Colours: Maroon, white and black hoops
League: Yorkshire 5

OLDERSHAW RFC
Ground Address: Belvidere Field, Belvidere Road, Wallasey, Wirral, CH45 5DE Tel: 0151 638 4379
Brief Directions: J.1 M53 to New Brighton, turn 2nd R. after golf club, 2nd L. into Grove Rd, turn R. at traffic lights. Ground is half mile on right hand side.
Hon Secretary: R. Arrowsmith, 5A Gorsehill Road, Wirral, CH45 9JA Tel: (H) 0151 630 5975
Tel: (M) 07866437118 Tel: (W) 0161 222 2424
Fixtures Secretary: Peter Purland, 63 Croxteth Road, Liverpool, L8 3SF Tel: (H) 0151 733 4854
Club Colours: Navy blue with gold hoops
League: South Lancs/Cheshire 1

OLDHAM RUFC
Ground Address: Manor Park, Bryth Road, Bardsley, Oldham Tel: 0161 624 6383
Brief Directions: Off the main A627 Oldham to Ashton road, behind Bardsley Church
Hon Secretary: T. J. Brown, 12 Tilton Street, Oldham, Lancs, OL1 4JA
Tel: (H) 0161 620 1878 Tel: (W) 0161 624 4167
Fixtures Secretary: T. Park, 79 Crofton Aveue, Timperley, Cheshire
Tel: (H) 0161 962 0781 Tel: (W) 0161 832 6753
Club Colours: Red and white hoops, navy shorts
League: North Lancs/Cumbria

ORMSKIRK RUFC
Ground Address: Green lane, Ormskirk, L39 1ND
Tel: 01695 572 523
Brief Directions: Adjacent A59 at junction with A570 opposite the Fiveways Pub.
Hon Secretary: R. A. Spencer, 62 New Lane, Ormskirk, Lancashire, L39 4UD Tel: (H) 01695 572 523
Fixtures Secretary: A. Barton, n/a Tel: (H) 01257 253 051 Tel: (M) 0771 397 4981
Club Colours: Dark green with light green and navy blue hoops
League: South Lancs/Cheshire 1

ORRELL ANVILS RUFC
Ground Address: Orrell RUFC, Edge Hall Road, Church Street, Wigan, WN5 8TL Tel: 01942 623 193
Brief Directions: M6, Junction 26, follow signs for Orrell club.
Hon Secretary: Eric Wilkinson, 60 Winstanley Road, Wigan, WN5 7XD Tel: (H) 01695 622 813
Email: eric@wilconet.freeserve.co.uk
Fixtures Secretary: Mel Parker, 2 Warrington Road, Newton-le-Willows Tel: (H) 01925 226 679
Club Colours: Black & Amber
League: South Lancs/Cheshire 3

OSSETT RUFC
Ground Address: Ossett Cricket & Athletic Club, Queens Terrace, Ossett, W. Yorkshire, WF5 Tel: 01924 273 618
Email Address: tays@tinyonline.co.uk
Web Address: www.ossett-rufc.com
Brief Directions: Home games played at Springmill,off Queens Drive Ossett. M1 Junction 40, follow A638 to Wakefield.Turn right at 2nd lights into Queens Drive. Go under motorway and after 200 yards turn right at sign for Golf and follow track to ground.
Hon Secretary: P. A. Taylor, 10 Grange Drive, Ossett, West Yorkshire, WF5 0SH Tel: (H) 01924 276 800
Tel: (M) 07771 865 205 Tel: (W) 01924 292 191
Email: tays@tinyonline.co.uk
Fixtures Secretary: I. Whitehead, 20 Westfield Street, Ossett, WF5 8JE Tel: (H) 01924 274 345
Club Colours: Black with narrow red and white hoops.
League: Yorkshire 5

OSWESTRY RFC
Ground Address: Park Hall, Oswestry
Tel: 01691 652949
Brief Directions: From Chester area take the A483/A5. Turn left at the A495, then next left after 150 meteres. Club is at end of lane
Club Secretary: Jim Pickard, 12 Hampton Rise, Oswestry, Shropshire SY11 1ST
Tel No: 01691 654899
Fixtures Secretary: Mark Hemming, Oakfield House, Morda House, Oswestry SY11 2AU.
Tel No : 01691 652912
Club Colours: Black and red hoops, black shorts
League: South Lancs & Cheshire 4

PARKONIANS RFC
Ground Address: Martin Curphey Mem. Ground, Holm Lane, Oxton, Birkenhead, Wirral, Cheshire, CH43 2HU
Tel: 0151 652 3105
Brief Directions: Off M53 at J3 head to B'head on A552. Turn off into Holm Lane at the Swan Hotel. Club is 400m on left - near top of Holm Lane
Hon Secretary: P. L. Mullen, 8 Deerwood Crescent, Ellesmere Port, Cheshire, CH66 1SE
Tel: (H) 0151 339 1270 Tel: (W) 0151 357 5532
Email: mullen@8deerwood.freeserve.co.uk
Hon Fixtures: Peter Evans, 24 Pine Tree Grove, Wirral, Cheshire Tel: (H) 0151 677 3825
Fixtures Secretary: E. Potter, 24 Thornton Rd, Birkenhead, Cheshire Tel: (H) 0151 609 0202
Club Colours: Maroon Blue White Jerseys &Stockings &White Shorts
League: South Lancs/Cheshire 5

PENRITH RFC
Ground Address: Winters Park, Penrith, Cumbria, CA11 8RG Tel: 01768 863 151
Brief Directions: M6 J40, A66 east for 0.5 mile, A686 east for 0,5 mile, PRUFC on left just past Police HQ
Hon Secretary: Keith Davis, Ivy Bank, 59 Lowther Street, Penrith, Cumbria, CA11 7UQ
Tel: (H) 01768 866 089 Tel: (W) 01768 863 151
Fixtures Secretary: Willie Mounsey
Club Colours: Myrtle green and white hoops
League: North Lancs/Cumbria

PERCY PARK RFC
Ground Address: Preston Avenue, North Shields, Tyne & Wear, NE29 Tel: 0191 257 5710
Brief Directions: From A19 (north or south) take A1058 Coast road signed East Tynemouth & North Shields. Turn right onto Preston North Road immediately after Swimming Baths and 3rd left is Preston Avenue where the ground is on the left.
Hon Secretary: A. C. Baker, 30 The Garth, Tyne & Wear, NE21 6BD Tel: (W) 0191 414 8672
Fixtures Secretary: Andy Donaghy, 71 Davison Avenue, Whitley Bay, Tyne & Wear, NE26 3ST
Tel: (H) 0191 253 4689
Club Colours: Black and white hoops
League: Durham/N'thm'land 1

POCKLINGTON RUFC
Ground Address: Percy Road, Pocklington, E. Yorkshire, YO4 2QB Tel: 01759 303 358
Brief Directions: Pocklington is situated 13 miles east of York off the A1079 towards Hull, ground located near town centre
Hon Secretary: Ian Johnston, 1 Northfield Close, Pocklington, East Yorkshire, YO42 2EG
Tel: (H) 01759 302 967 Tel: (M) 07974 103 903
Tel: (W) 01759 301 381
Fixtures Secretary: Adrian Wilson
Tel: (H) 01759 305 014
Club Colours: Navy and white quarters
League: Yorkshire 2

PONTEFRACT PYTHONS
League: Yorkshire 6
For further details contact
Yorkshire 6 League Secretary
Anthony McNally, 28 Cherry Tree Road, Armthorpe, Doncaster, Yorks DN3 2HP
Tel: 01302 834252

PONTEFRACT RFC
Ground Address: Moor Lane, Carleton, Pontefract, W. Yorkshire, WF8 3RX Tel: 01977 702 650
Brief Directions: Exit A1 at Darrington, follow signs for Pontefract, 2 miles to Moor Lane which is 1st left after 30mph sign on outskirts of Pontefract
Hon Secretary: S. J. Trigg, 52 Hadleigh Rise, Pontefract, West Yorkshire, WF8 4SJ Tel: (H) 01977 703 786 Tel: (W) 01302 736459
Fixtures Secretary: D. L. Howdle, 7 Mill Lane Close, Pontefract Tel: (H) 01977 704 615
Club Colours: ROYAL BLUE SHIRTS AND SHORTS
League: Yorkshire 1

PONTELAND RFC
Ground Address: Ponteland Leisure Centre, Callerton Lane, Ponteland, Northumberland, NE20 9EG
Tel: 01661 825 441
Brief Directions: From north or south, enter village via A696, at lights by Diamond Inn turn to follow river, entrance to Sports Centre 150 yards on left just after zebra crossing
Hon Secretary: Daniel Whaley, 'Copelands', 72 Cheviot View, Ponteland, Northumberland, NE20 9BW
Tel: (H) 01661 820 425 Tel: (M) 07885 205 714
Tel: (W) 01661 821 821
Club Colours: Maroon, black & white shirts.
League: Durham/N'thm'land 3

PORT SUNLIGHT RFC
Ground Address: Leverhulme Playing Fields, Green Lane, Bromborough, Wirral Tel: 0151 334 3677
Email Address: secretary@psrfc.co.uk
Web Address: http://www.psrfc.co.uk
Brief Directions: A41 Bromborough at T/light turn into Old Hall Road, at R/about 3rd exit into Riverwood Road, take 1st right into lane signed PSRFC
Hon Secretary: Louise Outram, 30 June Avenue, Wirral, CH62 7HY
Tel: (H) 0151 334 2349 Tel: (W) 0151 630 1700
Email: greystones@tingworld.co.uk
Club Colours: Black and white narrow hoops
League: South Lancs/Cheshire 4

PRENTON RUFC
Ground Address: Prenton Dell Road, Prenton, Birkenhead Tel: 1051 608 1501
Brief Directions: M53 Jct 3 Follow signs to Birkenhead. Pass under railway bridge(A551) 200 yds sign for golf range, Preston Dell Rd with club entrance half a mile on right.
Hon Secretary: C. McHugh, Arrowe Park Road, Wirral, Merseyside, CH 49 0UG Tel: (H) 0151 678 5148 Tel: (W) 0151 350 0382
Email: chrismchugh@tiscarli.co.uk
Fixtures Secretary: Paul Bennett, 2 Aston Wood Road, Birkenhead, L42 6DJ Tel: (H) 0151 7644 9775
Club Colours: Maroon, gold and black
League: South Lancs/Cheshire 3

PRESCOT RFC
Ground Address: Rainhill High School, Warrington Road, Rainhill, Merseyside
Brief Directions: From M62, J7 take road to Rainhill. School is situated on right hand side.
Hon Secretary: K. O'Keeffe, 39 French Street, St. Helens Tel: (H) 01744 616 683
League: South Lancs/Cheshire 5

RAWMARSH RUFC
Ground Address: Rawmarsh Leisure Centre, Barbers Avenue, Rawmarsh, Rotherham, South Yorkshire
Tel: 01709 719 952
Brief Directions: From Sheffield or Doncaster approach the Rotherham ring road.Take A630 and enquire at Mushroom Garage.
Hon Secretary: Eric Perkins, 21 Harding Avenue, Rotherham, South Yorkshire, S62 7ED
Tel: (H) 01709 526 786
Fixtures Secretary: Eric Perkins - as above
Club Colours: Black/amber trim
League: Yorkshire 6

REDCAR RUFC
Ground Address: McKinlay Park, Green Lane, Redcar, Cleveland, TS10 3RW Tel: 01642 482 733
Brief Directions: From A19 take A174 east towards Saltburn, take 2nd left (B1269), over level crossing, 1st right to coast road, continue to Green Lane on right at end of houses
Hon Secretary: J S Fawcett, 1 Stirling Road, Cleveland, TS10 2JU
Tel: (H) 01642 477 201 Tel: (W) 01642 482 424
Fixtures Secretary: D. Pearson, 36 Henry Street, Redcar, Cleveland Tel: (H) 01642 473 786
Club Colours: Black and Red
League: North 2 East

RICHMONDSHIRE RUFC
Ground Address: The Playing Fields, Theakston Lane, Richmond, N. Yorkshire, DL10 4LL Tel: 01748 850 515
Brief Directions: A6136 out of Richmond, pass bus station approx 500 yards turn right, club situated on left approx 100 yards from junction
Hon Secretary: Russell Lord, 12 Whitefields Walk, Richmond, North Yorkshire, DL10 7DE
Tel: (H) 01748 824 273 Tel: (W) 01904 525 844
Fixtures Secretary: Bob Dixon Tel: (H) 01748 825360
Club Colours: Red, yellow and white hoops
League: Durham/N'thm'land 3

RIPON RUFC LTD.
Ground Address: The Clubhouse, Mallorie Park, Ripon, N. Yorkshire, HG4 2QD Tel: 01765 604 675
Email Address: mijovin963@supanet.com
Web Address: www.rugby.ripon.org/
Brief Directions: Mallorie Park is on Pateley Bridge road out of Ripon. Access from the South is via Harrogate Road and Skellbank; from the North via North Road and Pateley Road
Hon Secretary: M. P. P. Viner, Golden Hill House, Barton-le-Willows, York, YO60 7PD Tel: (H) 01653 619 282 Tel: (M) 07799 408 223 Tel: (W) 0113 224 3443
Email: mijovin963@supanet.com
Fixtures Secretary: A. W. Proud, 1 Ure Bank Terrace, Ripon, N. Yorkshire, HG4 1JG Tel: (H) 01765 605 474
Tel: (M) 0467 318 069 Tel: (W) 0113 292 6846
Colours: White, light & dark blue narrow hoops
League: Yorkshire 2

ROCHDALE RUFC
Ground Address: Moorgate Avenue, Bamford, Rochdale, Lancashire, OL11 5LU Tel: 01706 646863
Email Address: club@rrufc.org
Brief Directions: From Rochdale: B6222 to Bury past Cemetary Hotel, Moorgate Ave 3rd on right. From M62: J20 A627(M) to Rochdale, over 2nd r'bout B6452 left into B6222 at Cemetary Hotel
Hon Secretary: Tim Taylor, 61 Augusta Close, Rochdale, OL12 6HT Tel: (H) 01706 345 971
Tel: (M) 07769 886 070 Tel: (W) 0161 828 6456
Email: tim.taylor@eu.joneslanglasalle.com
Fixtures Secretary: Michael Deasey, 405 Shawclough Road, Rochdale, OL12 7H
Tel: (H) 01706 356 094 Tel: (M) 07887 580 043
Email: mikedeasey@aol.com
Club Colours: Maroon and white hoops
League: North 2 West

ROSSENDALE RUFC
Ground Address: Marlpits Sports Centre, Newchurch Road, Rawtenstall, Lancashire Tel: 01706 229 152
Brief Directions: A56, onto Newchurch Road at the market. Ground 1 mile up on the leflt.
Hon Secretary: Alec J. Graham, 636 Newchurch Road, Rossendale, Lancs, BB4 9HG
Tel: (H) 01706 225 078 Tel: (W) 01282 415 515
Fixtures Secretary: Terence Kelly, 111 Broadway, Haslingden, Lancs
Tel: (H) 01706 217 361 Tel: (W) 01706 217 361
Club Colours: Maroon and white
League: North Lancs/Cumbria

ROTHERHAM CLIFTON
Ground Address: Change at Rotherham Rugby Club and play on Hemingthorpe PLaying Fields.
Brief Directions: M1 Jct 33. Follow Rotherway for 1/2 mile to roundabout. Take 2nd exit for Bawtry.AtTraffic lights straight on up hill to roundabout. First left to town centre and ground is 1 mile on right.
Club Secretary: Paul C Richardson, 22 Boswell Street, Broom, RotherhamS65 2ED. Tel: 01709 517823
Fixtures Secretary: As above
Club Colours: Maroon & sky blue hoops, navy shorts
League: Yorkshire 5

ROUNDHEGIANS RUFC
Ground Address: Memorial Ground, Chelwood Drive, Roundhay, Leeds, LS8 2AT Tel: 0113 266 7377
Brief Directions: A61 to junction with Street Lane, follow Street Lane towards Roundhay Park, Chelwood Drive is a road off Street Lane
Hon Secretary: D. J. Matthews, 32 Woodhall Road, Leeds, LS28 5PP Tel: (H) 0113 255 7623
Email: david@flankers.freeserve.co.uk
Fixtures Secretary: Stafford Smart, Laurendene, Harrogate Rd, Leeds W17 0EF Tel: (H) 01423 734803
Club Colours: Green, black and white hoops
League: Yorkshire 4

RUNCORN RFC
Ground Address: Halton Sports, Murdishaw Avenue, Runcorn, WA7 6HP Tel: 01928 714 815
Web Address: www.runcornrfc.co.uk
Brief Directions: M56,A56,A533, Runcorn, Murdishaw, Halton Arms Pub off Murdishaw Avenue.
Hon Secretary: Jeff Gore, 26 Tarnbeck, Norton, Runcorn, Cheshire, WA7 6SF Tel: (H) 01928 712 284
Email: jeffgore@saltunion.com
Fixtures Secretary: Tony Elliot Tel: (H) 01928 715091
Club Colours: Blue & white hoops
League: South Lancs/Cheshire 2

RUSKIN PARK RUFC
Ground Address: Ruskin Drive, St Helens, Merseyside Tel: 01744 22893
Brief Directions: Turn off A580 onto A570 towards St Helens. Travel approx one mile and turn right into Dentons Green Lane. Ruskin Drive is 400 yards on left.
Club Secretary: Brian Ball, 10 Broadway, Eccleston, St.Helens, Lancs WA10 5DE Tel: 01744 611955
Email: b.j.ball@btinternet.com
Fixtures Secretary: Barry Loftus, Prescot Road, St Helens, Merseyside. Tel No: 01744 608578
Email: barry.loftus@btclick.com
Club Colours: Blue with black and white band
League: South Lancs & Cheshire 3

RYTON RFC LTD
Ground Address: Barmoor, Ryton, Tyne & Wear, NE40 3AG Tel: 0191 413 3820
Web Address: www.rytonrfc.co.uk
Brief Directions: On B6317 road to the west of Ryton, B6317 Ryton Road signposted from A695
Club Secretary: Gordon Wright, 57 Middle Row, Stargate, Ryton,Tyne & Wear NE40 3EE
Tel 0191 4131986 Mobile 07931 860858
Email: gordon.wright1@btinternet.com
Fixtures Secretary: Ian Nesbitt, 118 Middle Drive, Ponteland, Newcastle upon Tyne NE20 9DW
Tel: 01661 823629
Club Colours: Royal blue or green
League: Durham/Northumberland 1

SANDBACH RUFC
Ground Address: Bradwall Road, Sandbach, Cheshire, CW11 1RA Tel: 01270 762 475
Web Address: www.sandbachrufc.co.uk
Brief Directions: M6 J17, follow signs for Sandbach, turn right by Texaco garage. Turn right on to Offley Rd, turn right signed Bradwall, club 400 yards on right
Fixtures Secretary: Rob Yates, 135 Heath Road, Sandbach, Cheshire, CW11 2JY Tel: (H) 01270 753931
Tel: (M) 07768 833 406
Email: fixtures@sandbachrufc.co.uk
Club Colours: Green & Red
League: South Lancs/Cheshire 2

SCARBOROUGH RFC
Ground Address: The Club House, Scalby Road, Scarborough, YO12 6EE Tel: 01723 363 039
Brief Directions: Main Whitby road out of Scarborough, approx 2 miles
Hon Secretary: S. E. Hanson, 15 St. Leonards Crescent, Scarborough, YO12 6SR
Tel: (H) 01723 373 599 (W) 01723 363 039
Fixtures Secretary: J. B. Beanland, 34 Ridge Green, Scarborough, YO13 0QF Tel: (H) 01723 367023
Club Colours: Maroon, navy and white
League: North 2 East

SEAHAM RUFC
Ground Address: Seaham Rugby Club, 27 Cornelia Terrace, Seaham, Co. Durham Tel: 0191 581 2331
Brief Directions: Come down A19 or A1, follow signs for Seaham, once in Seaham follow signs for harbour and ask for directions to club (everyone knows where it is)
Hon Secretary: Carol A. Pinder, 37 Stavordale Street, Seaham, Co. Durham, SR7 7LS
Tel: (W) 0191 581 5836
Fixtures Secretary: Alan Mason
Tel: (H) 0191 520 0282 Tel: (W) 0191 279 4342
Club Colours: Red jersey, white shorts, red socks
League: Durham/N'thm'land 4

SEATON CAREW RUFC
Ground Address: Hornby Park, Elizabeth Way, Seaton Carew, Hartlepool Tel: 01429 260 945
Brief Directions: From A19 take A689 to Hartlepool, right at Owton Lodge pub onto B1276 to Seaton Carew seafront area, turn right and go along seafront past golf club, club on right in Elizabeth Way.
Hon Secretary: Paul McManus, 9 Ruswarp Grove, Seaton Carew, Hartlepool, Teesside, TS25 2BA
Tel: (H) 01429 296 327 Tel: (M) 0775 1727958
Tel: (W) 01429 268 821
Fixtures Secretary: Andy Sedgewick, 16 Headingley Close, Hartlepool, TS25 2PD Tel: (H) 01429 261 995
Tel: (M) 07967 173753 Tel: (W) 01429 266 544
Club Colours: Maroon and amber hooped shirts & socks, black shorts
League: Durham/N'thm'land 2

SEFTON RUFC
Ground Address: Thornhead Lane, Leyfield Road, West Derby, Liverpool. L12 9EY
Tel: 0151 228 9092
Brief Directions: End of M62 take A5058 towards Bootle, at A57 turn right, left at lights, right in front of hospital, left at Bulldog pub (Leyfield Road), right into lane by electricity substation
Club Secretary: Roy Spencer, 8 Stoneycroft Close, Liverpool L13 0AT. Tel: (H) 0151 228 9833
Fixtures Secretary: B Houghton
Tel: (H) 0151 428 3740
Club Colours: Red and white hooped shirts & socks, blue shorts
League: South Lancs & Cheshire 3

SEGHILL RFC
Ground Address: Welfare Park, Seghill, Cramlington, Northumberland, NE23 7EZ Tel: 0191 237 0414
Brief Directions: A19 through Tyne Tunnel, take sliproad for Seghill, right at junction, left at next junction, right at mini r'bout then 2nd left, right at T junction, car park 150yds on right
Hon Secretary: Sheila Burgess, 19 Chester Grove, Cramlington, Northumberland, NE23 7TR
Tel: (H) 0191 237 4056 Tel: (M) 07715 972 622
Tel: (W) 0191 226 2222
Email: burgesss@pbworld.com
Club Colours: Scarlet and Black Hooped Shirts, white shorts
League: Durham/N'thm'land 3

SELBY RUFC
Ground Address: Sandhill Lane, Leeds Road, Selby, YO8 4JP Tel: 01757 703 608
Web Address: www.selbyrufc.org
Brief Directions: Situated off Sandhill Lane, 1 mile west of town centre off A63 Leeds road
Hon Secretary: G. Adamson, 70 Parkways, Selby, North Yorkshire, YO8 9BB
Tel: (H) 01757 706 125 Tel: (M) 07715 043 893
Fixtures Secretary: J. C. Philips, Greystones, Chapel Street, Nr Selby
Tel: (H) 01977 680 437 (W) 01757 213 344
Club Colours: Green, red and gold narrow hoops
League: Yorkshire 1

SHEFFIELD MEDICALS RUFC
Ground Address: University Ground, Warminster Road, Norton, Sheffield.
Brief Directions: M1 J33 to Sheffield A630. 2 miles turn left A6102 to Bochum Parkway. Take 3rd Exit off R/about onto Norton Avenue. Over next R/about onto Hemsworth Road, Warminser Road 6th right
Club Secretary: Jonathon Cowley,16 The Nook, Crookesmoor, Sheffield, S10 1EJ
Tel No: 0114 268 3200
Email: jbcowley@hotmal.com
Fixtures Secretary: Adan Hogg, 9 Brick Street, Crookes, Sheffield. S10 1WR
Tel: 0771 235 9442
Club Colours: Navy & sky blue with white hoops.
Change: Navy & Burgundy with white hoops
League: Yorkshire 5

SHEFFIELD OAKS RUFC
Ground Address: Malin Bridge Sports & Social Club, 22a Stannington Road, Malin Bridge, Sheffield, S6 5TA
Tel: 01142 345 349
Brief Directions: M1 J36 into Sheffield (north), A61 to Hillsborough Ground, 1st available right after Hillsborough Ground, Bradfield Rd, to Holme Lane, left at end of Holme Ln, 1st right after petrol station
Hon Secretary: Kay Grayson, 13 Hill Close, Sheffield, S6 6BH Tel: (H) 0114 233 9209
Tel: (M) 07808 264 495 Tel: (W) 0114 249 5501
Fixtures Secretary: Glyn Davies, 12 Malin Road, Sheffield, S6 5TA Tel: (H) 01142 233 5829
Club Colours: Royal blue with gold hoops
League: Yorkshire 4

SHEFFIELD TIGERS RUFC
Ground Address: Dore Moor, Hathersage Road, Sheffield. S17 3AB Tel: 0114 236 0075
Website: www.sheffieldtigers.co.uk
Brief Directions: About 5 miles south west of Sheffield city centre on the A625 signed Hathersage. Ground just after Dore Moor Inn.
Club Secretary: Alick Bush, 210 Bradway Road, Sheffield. S17 4PE
Tel: (H) 0114 2361129 (W) 0114 2716950
e-mail; alickb@chsheff-tr.trent.nhs.uk
Fixtures Secretary: Mick Rothenburg, 65 Westwick Rd.,Sheffield S8 7BU Tel: 0114 274 0378
Email: m.rothenburg@amserve.net
Club Colours: Maroon & gold hoops, black shorts
League: Yorkshire 1

SHEFFIELD RUFC
Ground Address: Abbeydale Park, Totley Rise, Sheffield, South Yorkshire, S17 3LJ Tel: 0114 235 3414
Email Address: admin@sheffieldrufc.co.uk
Web Address: www.sheffieldrugby.com
Brief Directions: From the North via M1 Motorway By Coach 1. Exit M1 at Junction 33. From the r'about follow A630 (Sheffield Parkway) towards city centre. 2. Immed. after 2nd exit, where speed limit drops to 50, take left lane and use slip road signposted Ring Road and Services. 3. At top of slip road go straight across, and remain in the left lane, which brings you onto the slip road beside the Little Chef Services. Stay in the left lane. 4. At r'about at top of slip road, turn left on to Ring Road (Prince of Wales Road) sign-posted A61 Chesterfield. 5. Continue along Ring Road (dual carriage way) for 4/5 miles, following A61 Chesterfield signs, until 3rd r'about. 6. At 3rd r'about take middle lane (A61 Chesterfield is now signposted left) and continue straight on B6054 Holmsfield, taking the right hand lane as you exit the r'about. 7. Turn immed. right, signposted A621 Bakewell and carry on to the first r'about (about 1 mile). 8. At r'about turn left onto Abbey Lane. 9. At traffic lights (Beauchief Hotel is on left just before lights) turn left onto Abbeydale Road South. Abbeydale Sports Club is approximately 1 mile on the right. NOTE: Do not take the entrance to Abbeydale Tennis Club By Car Follow as above 1-5. 4. At 3rd r'about take middle lane (A61 Chesterfield is now signposted left) and continue straight on B6054 Holmsfield. 5. Continue for 1_ miles over one r'about. 6. After passing Dore & Totley Golf Club on left, take first right (signposted Dore) into Twentywell Lane. 7. At the T-Junction at the bottom turn left and Abbeydale Sports Club is 200yds on the right. NOTE: Do not take the entrance to Abbeydale Tennis Club From the South via M1 Motorway By Coach 1. Exit M1 at Junction 29 and take the A617 to Chesterfield. 2. At the r'about turn right onto the A61 to Sheffield and follow for approx. 8 miles, over 3 r'abouts. 3. At 4th r'about turn left onto B6054 Holmsfield, taking the right hand lane as you exit the r'about. 4. Turn immed. right, signposted A621 Bakewell and carry on to the first r'about (about 1 mile). 5. At r'about turn left onto Abbey Lane. 6. At traffic lights (Beauchief Hotel is on left just before lights) turn left onto Abbeydale Road South. Abbeydale Sports Club is approx. 1 mile on the right. NOTE: Do not take the entrance to Abbeydale Tennis Club By Car 1. Exit M1 at Junction 29 and take the A617 to Chesterfield. 2. At the r'about turn right onto the A61 to Sheffield and follow for approx. 8 miles, over three r'abouts. 3. At fourth r'about turn left onto B6054 Holmsfield. 4. Continue for1_ miles over one r'about. 5. After passing Dore & Totley Golf Club on left, take first right (signposted Dore) into Twentywell Lane. 6. At the T-Junction at the bottom turn left and Abbeydale Sports Club is 200yds on the right. NOTE: Do not take the entrance to Abbeydale Tennis Club
Hon Secretary: Chris Wilson
Tel: (H) 0114 267 8891 Tel: (W) 0114 276 7481
Leagues Contact: Richard Fedyk
Tel: (H) 0114 2364785 Tel: (W) 01332 262 916
Fixtures Secretary: Neil Adgie Tel: (H) 0114 2309503
Tel: (W) 0114 2309503 Email: neil@theadgies.co.uk
Club Colours: Blue & White Hoops
League: North 2 East

SHILDON TOWN RUFC
Ground Address: Shildon Sunnydale Leisure Centre
Tel: 01388 777340
Brief Directions: Please phone fixtures secretary
Club Secretary: Patrick Lewis, 11 Co-operative Street, Shildon, Co. Durham DL4 1DA
Tel: 07940 309237
Fixtures Secretary: Peter Plews, 14 Alexandra Street, Shildon, Co. Durham DL4 2EY
Tel: 01388 777334
Club Colours: Red and Green Quarters
League: Durham/Northumberland 4

SILLOTH RUFC
Ground Address: Old Marshalling Yard, Eden Street, Silloth, Cumbria, CA5 4He Tel: 01697 332 299
Brief Directions: Lies in the centre of town
Hon Secretary: Barry Sloan, 15 Waver Street, Silloth
Email: slinkydinky@tinyworld.co.uk
Fixtures Secretary: Richard Smith
Tel: (H) 01697 331936
Club Colours: Green and black hoops
League: Cumbria

SKIPTON RFC
Ground Address: The Coulhurst Memorial Ground, Carleton New Road, Skipton, N. Yorkshire, BD23 2AZ
Tel: 01756 793148
Web Address: www.skiptonrfc.co.uk
Brief Directions: Ground is situated off Engine Shed Lane.Entering from town centre travel along Broughton Road keeping Morrisons on left hand side opposite the railway station is a left turn onto Carleton New Road take this go up onto railway bridge then first right onto Engine Shed Lane first left club is at the bottom. If travelling from A59 (Lancs) take first Skipton turn after sign along Broughton Road past the ambulance station under railway bridge for 25yrds then turn right onto Carleton New Road follow road up onto railway bridge then 1st right onto Engine Shed Lane followed by 1st left which will take you to the clubhouse.
Hon Secretary: Mark Botham, 52 Regent Drive, Skipton, North Yorkshire, BD23 1AY
Tel: (H/M) 07779 128717 (W) 01423 866342
Email: SCROOGE736@aol.com
Fixtures Secretary: Paul Tyson, 24 Rombalds Drive, Skipton, BD23 2SP
Tel: (H) 01756 797 661 Tel: (M) 07796 974612
Email: tysontiny@aol.com
Club Colours: Red shirts,black shorts,red socks
League: Yorkshire 2

SOUTH TYNESIDE COLLEGE RUFC
Ground Address: Grosvenor Road, South Shields, Tyne & Wear Tel: 0191 427 3500
Brief Directions: Travel to south side of Tyne Tunnel, take road to South Shields, travel to Westhoe area of South Shields, ground adjacent to S.T. College
Club Secretary: R Smith, 87 Colman Avenue, South Shields, Tyne & Wear. NE34 9AG
Tel: (H) 0191 4242101 (W) 0191 4273571
Fixtures Secretary: C Moule
Tel: (H) 0191 3887548 (W) 0191 4273577
Club Colours: Black with 2 red and 1 gold hoop
League: Durham/Northumberland 4

SOUTHPORT RUFC
Ground Address: Waterloo Road, HIllside, Southport, PR8 4QW Tel: 01704 569 906
Web Address: www.southportrufc.com
Brief Directions: The Waterloo Road ground is situated on the main A565 Liverpool to Southport Road close to Merseyrail's Hillside station
Hon Secretary: A. Shorrock, 32D Lulworth Road, Southport, PR8 2BQ Tel: (H) 01704 562 340
Email: kshorrock@tinyworld.co.uk
Fixtures Secretary: M. Jackson, 43 Kenilworth Road, Southport, PR8 3PH Tel: (H) 01704 578 362
Club Colours: Red / Amber / Black
League: South Lancs/Cheshire 1

ST. BENEDICTS RFC
Ground Address: Newlands Avenue, Mirehouse, Whitehaven, Cumbria Tel: 01946 61753
Brief Directions: Directions Leave M6 at Junc 40, take A66 towards Keswick. A595 towards Whitehaven. On entering town take left fork past BP Garage. Straight on through 2 sets of lights, roundabout straight on. Next right, T Junc club opposite.
Hon Secretary: Stephen Howse, 12 Castlerigg Close, Mirehouse, Whitehaven, Cumbria, CA28 9RJ Tel: (H) 01946 599 657
Fixtures Secretary: Ian Maguire, 9 Grisedale Close, Whitehaven, Cumbria, CA28 8DF
Club Colours: Grren, Yellow and Black irregular hoops
League: Cumbria

ST. EDWARD'S OB RUFC
Ground Address: St. Edwards College, North Drive, Sandfield Park, West Derby, Liverpool, L12 2AR
Tel: 0151 228 1414
Email Address: simon@mail.cybase.co.uk
Brief Directions: To end of M62, traffic lights, right onto Queens Drive (A5080), downhill through lights, right at next lights onto Alder Rd, left onto Eaton Rd, playing fields on left
Hon Secretary: S. J. Smith, 107 Church Road, Liverpool, L25 6DB
Tel: (H) 0151 428 2799 Tel: (W) 07810 152 341
Email: simon@mail.cybase.co.uk
Club Colours: Royal blue with gold band
League: South Lancs/Cheshire 2

ST. MARY'S COLLEGE OB RUFC
Ground Address: 17 Moor Lane, Crosby, Liverpool, L23
Tel: 0151 924 1774
Hon Secretary: Laurence Doherty, 1 Marlborough Road, Liverpool, L23 3DD
Tel: (H) 0151 931 4200 Tel: (W) 0151 924 3926
Fixtures Secretary: Peter Moore, 77 Freshfield Road, Formby, Lancashire
Tel: (H) 01704 878 537 Tel: (W) 0151 924 4898
Club Colours: Maroon, yellow and blue hoops
League: South Lancs/Cheshire 3

STANLEY RODILLIANS RUFC
Ground Address: Manley Park, Lee Moor Road, Stanley, Wakefield, W. Yorkshire, WF3 4EF
Tel: 01924 823 619
Brief Directions: M62 J30, head towards Wakefield, turn right opposite Gordons Tyres, top of hill turn right, past double junction on left, turn left just after Lee Moor pub
Hon Secretary: M. Thompson, 23 Cyprus Mount, St. John's, Wakefield, WF1 2RJ Tel: (H) 01924 217 969
Email: rodillians@martyn379.idps.co.uk
Fixtures Secretary: I. Young
Tel: (H) 0113 282 6743 Tel: (W) 01742 671 131
Club Colours: Green, white, black hoops, black shorts and socks
League: Yorkshire 5

STOCKPORT RFC
Ground Address: Bridge Lane Memorial Ground, Headlands Rd, Bramhall, Stockport, Cheshire, SK7 3AN
Tel: 0161 439 2150
Brief Directions: Contact Fixture Secretary
Hon Secretary: Michael Drew, c/o Cardwell & Drew, 8 Hawthorn Lane, Wilmslow, SK9 5DD
Tel: (M) 07976 623 361 Tel: (W) 01625 539 037
Email: mike@cardwell-draw.damon.co.uk
Fixtures Secretary: M J. Wroe, 62 Kennerley Road, Stockport, SK2 6EY Tel: (H) 0161 484 0838
Club Colours: Red, white and green hoops
League: North 2 West

STOCKSBRIDGE RFC
Ground Address: 634 Manchester Road, Stocksbridge, Sheffield, Yorkshire, S36 1DY
Tel: 0114 288 5078
Brief Directions:
Ground: Just outside village of Bolsterstone.
Club House: Just outside centre of Stocksbridge, opposite fire station.
Hon Secretary: M. Gribbins, 7 Hole House Lane, Sheffield, S36 1BN
Tel: (H) 0114 288 4995 Tel: (W) 0114 260 2136
Email: mickgribbins@supanet.com
Fixtures Secretary: Keith Moore, 1 Marsden Road, Sheffield, S36 5EE
Tel: (H) 0114 288 6570 Tel: (M) 07946 802 051
Club Colours: Royal blue with two white hoops
League: Yorkshire 3

STOCKTON RUFC
Ground Address: Norton (Teesside) Sports Complex, Station Road, Norton, Stockton, Cleveland, TS20 1PE
Tel: 01642 554 031
Email Address: enquiries@stocktonrfc.freeserve.co.uk
Web Address: www.stockton.freeserve.co.uk
Brief Directions: From A19 take A1027 to Norton, at roundabout turn right into Station Rd, 60 yds on turn right, travel to end, clubhouse on left before Norton Tavern for dressing rooms
Hon Secretary: Keith Kelly, 11 Valley Gardens, Stockton-on-Tees, TS19 8BE
Tel: (H) 01642 867 170 Tel: (W) 01642 522 132
Email: keith_kelly@ici.com
Fixtures Secretary: A. Todd, 21 Harrow Road, Middlesborough, TS5 5NT Tel: (H) 01642 818 507
Email: allyrug@aol.com
Club Colours: Red / white / royal blue
League: North 2 East

SUNDERLAND RFC
Ground Address: West Lawn, Ashbrooke, Sunderland, Tyne & Wear, SR2 7HH Tel: 0191 528 4536
Brief Directions: A19 tow'ds Sunderland, exit Durham/S'land jcn, east 2.5 mls on Durham Rd to Barnes Htl, right then left into Qn Alex'a Rd, over 1st r'bout, 1st left W'bank Rd, left Ashbrk Rd, club 200yds left
Hon Secretary: John C. Martin, 11 Roker Park Terrace, Sunderland, Tyne & Wear, SR6 9LY
Tel: (H) 0191 567 7045
Fixtures Secretary: A. Scott-Gray, 27 Glemesk Road, Sunderland, Tyne & Wear, SR2 9BN
Tel: (H) 0191 522 6188
Club Colours: Red,black & Gold hoops, white shorts
League: Durham/N'thm'land 2

THE GENTLEMEN OF MOORE RUFC
Ground Address: Moss Lane, Moore, Warrington, Cheshire, WA4 6UU Tel: 01925 740 473
Brief Directions: M56 J11 follow A56 towards Warrington, straight over R/about, left at 1st set of traffic lights along Runcorn Road for 2 miles, right on `S' bend into Moss Lane in Moore Village
Hon Secretary: S. J. Woollacott, Mayfield, 2 Knutsford Road, Warrington, Cheshire, WA4 2JZ
Tel: (H)01925 481462 (M)0777 5550767 (W)01565 612799
Email: woolllacotts@bigfoot.com
Club Colours: Black with broad gold band.
League: South Lancs/Cheshire 2

THIRSK RFC
Ground Address:
Hon Secretary: I. McQuade, 21 Herriot Way, Thirsk, North Yorkshire, YO7 1FL
Tel: (H) 01845 524 156 Tel: (W) 01845 521 031
Email: ian.mcquade@teleware.co.uk
League: Yorkshire 6

THORNENSIANS RUFC
Ground Address: Clubhouse, Coulman Road, THorne, Doncaster, S. Yorkshire Tel: 01405 812 746
Brief Directions: M18 J6 signed Thorne, 1 mile to town, left at traffic lights, right at crossroads, left at Church, club on left past school
Hon Secretary: M. Williams, The Clubhouse, Coulman Street, Doncaster, DN8 5JU
Tel: (H) 01405 816 915 Tel: (W) 01405 812 746
Email: maria@womma.freeserve.co.uk
Club Colours: Blue, black and white hoops
League: Yorkshire 4

THORNTON CLEVELEYS RUFC
Ground Address: Fleetwood Road North, Thornton Cleveleys, Lancashire Tel: 01253 854 104
Brief Directions: J3 M55 A585 to Fleetwood, follow A585 for 6 miles to second roundabout take 4th exit into Fleet Road. Ground is 1.5mile on left.
Hon Secretary: P. Horsfield, 336 Fleetwood Road North, Thornton Cleveleys, Lancashire, FY5 4LQ
Tel: (H) 01253 868 537 Tel: (W) 01253 854 321
Email: phorsfield@talk21.com
Club Colours: Black, red, and amber
League: North Lancs 1

TRAFFORD MV RFC
Ground Address: MacPherson Park, Finney Bank Road, Sale, Cheshire, M3 6LR Tel: 0161 973 7061
Brief Directions: M63 J7, head for Altrincham, at 1st traffic lights turn right (Glebelands Rd), Finney Bank Rd is 0.5 mile along on right
Hon Secretary: D. Moore, 19 Gredle Close, Manchester, M41 9RL
Tel: (H) 0161 747 5082 Tel: (W) 0161 877 5797
Email: dave.moore@milla.co.uk
Fixtures Secretary: M. Pringle, Flat 4, 109 Edge Lane, Manchester, M32 8P
Tel: (H) 0161 286 1775 Tel: (W) 0161 877 7760
Club Colours: Black and white hoops
League: North Lancs 1

TRENTHAM RUFC
Ground Address: New Inn Lane, Trentham, Stoke-on-Trent, Staffs. Tel: 01782 642320
Brief Directions: M6 J15, A500 towards Stoke-on-Trent, A34 south signs to Trentham, at Trentham Gardens R/about tunr left onto Longton road, then 4th left into New Inn Lane, Approx 1\3rd mile on right.
Club Secretary: Mrs Jane Procter, Holly House, Barn Court, Clayton, Newcastle, Staffs ST5 4N.
Tel: 01782 623292
Email: michaelpehollyhouse78.freeserve.co.uk
Fixtures Secretary: Mr Michael Procter. As above
Club Colours: Green and white hoops
League: South Lancs & Cheshire 2

TYLDESLEY RUFC
Ground Address: St. George's Park, Astley Street, Tyldesley, Lancashire, M29 8HG Tel: 01942 882 967
Web Address: www.tyldesleyrugby.com
Brief Directions: Follow A572 into Tyldesley centre where Astley Street is the main road facing the town square.
Hon Secretary: H. Hughes, 81 Astley Street, Manchester, M29 7BA Tel: (H) 01942 513 334
Tel: (M) 07710 083 984 Tel: (W) 0161 600 1523
Email: howard.3.hughes@bt.com
Fixtures Secretary: A. W. Jones, 363 Manchester Road, Manchester, M29 7DX
Tel: (H) 01942 876 938 Tel: (W) 01942 883 348
Club Colours: Royal blue shirts, white shorts
League: North Lancs/Cumbria

UPPER EDEN RUFC
Ground Address: Pennine Park, Westgarth Road, Kirkby Stephen, Cumbria, CA17 4DW
Tel: 01768 371 585
Brief Directions: M6 J38, 12 miles to Kirkby Stephen, turn left by Spar shop (Westgarth), straight on to top of estate. A66 turn off at Brough, 4 miles to K. Stephen, right just after shop
Hon Secretary: N. Marston, Meadowbarn, Oxenthwaite, Kirkby Stephen, Cumbria, CA17 4SG
Tel: (H) 01768 341 179
Email: robbosksbh@aol.com
Fixtures Secretary: D. Metcalfe, 17 The Crescent, Kirby Stephen, Cumbria, CA17 4AF
Tel: (H) 01768 371 795
Club Colours: Black and white hoops
League: Cumbria

VAGABONDS RFC
Ground Address: Mike Halewood Centre, Glencruthchley Road, Douglas, Isle of Man
Tel: 01624 661 996
Web Address: www.vagabonds.iofm.net
Brief Directions: From Douglas Promenade head uphill at the T/lights. Across the 1st T/lights, then turn right at the 2nd T/lights. The ground is on the right past the TT Grandstand.
Hon Secretary: Peter Barlow, 22 Berrywoods Avenue, Govenor's Hill, Douglas, Isle of Man, IM2 7DA Tel: (H) 01624 621 324 Tel: (W) 01624 985 043
Email: jugs@ukonline.co.uk
Fixtures Secretary: David Watterson, 7 Castlemere Apartments, Douglas, Isle of Man, IM2 4LJ
Tel: (H) 01624 670 398
Club Colours: White with black & yellow band
League: South Lancs/Cheshire 1

VALE OF LUNE RUFC
Ground Address: Powderhouse Lane, off Torris Holme Road, Lancaster, LA1 2TT Tel: 01524 64029 / 63151
Email Address: webmaster@valeoflune.co.uk
Web Address: www.valeoflune.co.uk
Brief Directions: M6 J34 for Lancaster, follow signs for A589 Morecambe, approx 0.5 mile, turn right down Scale Hall Lane, turn left at T/junction, ground 100yds on right
Hon Secretary: Mike Sheard, 2 Endsleigh Grove, Lancaster, LA1 2TX Tel: (H) 01524 68704
Tel: (M) 07801 315651 Tel: (W) 01524 32933
Email: michael.sheard@btclick.com
Fixtures Secretary: Fred Swarbrick, Oxendale Farm, Wyresdale Road, Lancaster, LA1 3JJ
Tel: (H) 01524 37601
Club Colours: Cherry and white hoops
League: North 2 West

VULCAN RUFC
Ground Address: The Sports Ground, Wargrave Road, Newton-le-Willows, Merseyside Tel: 01925 241 80
Email Address: vulcan_rufc@hotmail.com
Web Address: www.vulcanrufc.co.uk
Brief Directions: Wargrave Rd is a continuation of Victoria Rd which is off Crow Lane West (A572)
Hon Secretary: Ronnie Evans, 132 Park Road South, Newton-le-Willows, WA12 8QD Tel: (H) 01925 270 051
Club Colours: Black and amber/ black / black
League: South Lancs/Cheshire 4

WAKEFIELD COUGARS RUFC
Ground Address: Wakefield Cougars RUFC, College Grove, Eastmoor Road,Wakefield. WF1 3RR
Tel : 01924 374801
Brief Directions: M1 Jct41. Take A650 to City centre. Left at Queen Elizabeth GS to Wakefield Rd.Ground 250 yds.M62 Jct30 .A642 to centre. Rt at Lights after hospital to Eastmoor Rd.Grd 300yds.
Club Secretary: Alex Judson, 2 Windsor Crescent, Wrenthorpe, Wakefield WF1 2BS
Tel: (H) 01924 361358 (M) 0976 976153
Fixtures Secretary: Bill Halstead
Tel: (H) 01274 872710 (Fax) 01274 865975
Club Colours: Black & Gold. Alternative Red.
League: Yorkshire 4

WALKINGTON ROVERS
Ground Address: Walkington Playing Field, Walkington, Beverely, East Yorkshire.
Brief Directions: South or West: Head for Humber Bdg at R'abt turn L. for Beverley A164 stay on this road passed Willerby- Skidby-Cottingham. After Skidby/Cottingham R'abt sign on L. for Walkington (abt 2M) turn L & go to Traffic Lightd turn L into Village. Turn L before pond Autherd Garth follow Signpost to Playing Field. From North head for Beverley Racecourse go up hill to R'abt take 2nd left to Walkington go to Traffic Lights turn R. into village then follow directions as above.
Club Secretary: Dave Lee, 57 Canada Drive, Cherry Burton, East Yorkshire. Tel: 01964 550500
Fixtures Secretary: Andy Taylor,
Dockside House, Earles Road, Hedon Road, Hull, E. Yorks, HU9 1UD. Tel: 07866 372424M
Club Colours: Red & white hoops, blue collar & cuffs
League: Yorkshire 6

WALLASEY RFC
Ground Address: Cross Lane, Leasowe road, Wallasey, CH45 8NS Tel: 0151 638 1486
Web Address: www.rugby-club.org.uk
Brief Directions: Exit 1 on M53 towards Wallasey, take 2nd slip road to A551, turn right at lights
Hon Secretary: John Burton, 14 Seaview Lane, Wirral, CH61 3UL Tel: (H) 0151 648 4341
Tel: (M) 07979 877 448 Tel: (W) 0151 639 6508
Fixtures Secretary: Andy Rae, 8 Inchcape Road, Wirral, CH45 8RJ Tel: (H) 0151 638 6903
Club Colours: Red, black, white hoops
League: South Lancs/Cheshire 3

WALLSEND RFC
Ground Address: Benfield Community Association, Sam Smith's Pavilion, Benfield School Campus, Benfield Road, Walkergate, Newcastle, NE6 4NU
Tel: 0191 265 9357
Web Address: www.wallsendrfc.co.uk
Brief Directions: Just off A1058 Newcastle-Tynemouth (Coast rd), turn on to C127 to Benfield School, club at rear of school
Hon Secretary: Brian. J. Thirlway, 29 Belmont Close, Battle Hill Estate Tel: (H) 0191 234 4877
Fixtures Secretary: Stuart Robinson, 5 Dinsdale Avenue, Wallsend Tel: (H) 0191 262 7485
Club Colours: Myrtle green jerseys with gold trim
League: Durham/N'thm'land 2

WARRINGTON RUFC
Ground Address: Bridge Lane, Appleton, Warrington
Tel: 01925 264 591
Brief Directions: J20 M6. Follow A50 Warrington 2m. At lights turn left, after 1 1/2 mls 2 sets of lights, left at 2nd set, under bridge first right into Bridge Lane, .1/4m on right.
Hon Secretary: G. P. Robinson, 25 Victoria Avenue, Warrington, WA4 2PD Tel: (H) 01925 489 213
Email: gavin.robinson@quista.net
Fixtures Secretary: P. Broadbent, 22 Victoria Avenue, Warrington, WA4 2PE Tel: (H) 01925 261 959
Club Colours: Red white & green
League: South Lancs/Cheshire 1

WATH-UPON-DEARNE RUFC
Ground Address: Moor Road, Wath-Upon-Dearne, Rotherham Tel: 01709 872399
Brief Directions: Moor Road is adjacent to Wath Swimming Baths on the main Rotherham to Barnsley (A630) road
Club Secretary: Mr S Poxton, 19 Packham Way, Wath-upon-Dearne, Rotherham, S Yorks S63 6BR
Tel: (H) 01709 874154 (W) 01226 282549
Fixtures Secretary: Mr S Corns
Tel: (H) 01709 874911
Club Colours: Blue with maroon and gold bands
League: Yorkshire 3

WEARSIDE RUFC
Ground Address: The Grange Hotel, Newcastle Road, Sunderland, Tyne & Wear Tel: 0191 516 3121
Brief Directions: Leave A19, follow A184 (Newcastle Rd) into Sunderland passing Regal Greyhound Stadium on left, turn right at roundabout to changing rooms
Hon Secretary: Stephen Thompson, 87 Beach Road, Tyne & Wear, NE33 2LZ Tel: (H) 0191 497 5013
Fixtures Secretary: William Johnston, 14 Manilla Street, Sunderland Tel: (H) 0191 552 3559
League: Durham/N'thm'land 3

WENSLEYDALE RUFC
Ground Address: Cawkill Park, Wensley Road, Leyburn, North Yorkshire. DL8 5AR
Tel: 01969 623067 Website: wensleydalerufc.com
Brief Directions: Leave Leyburn on the Hawes/Wensley Road (A684) the club is one mile west of Leyburn on the left.
Club Secretary: Graham Jameson, 7 Fearby Rd., Masham, Ripon, N.Yorks. HG4 4ES
Tel: 01765 689185 (H)
Email: graham@bellfieldwest .com
Fixtures Secretary: Brian Carlisle, Hoppers Estate Agents, Central Chambers, Keyburn, N. Yorkshire. DL8 5BD
Tel: 01969 622936 / 01969 663570
Club Colours: Black and yellow hoops
League: Durham/Northumberland 3

WEST HARTLEPOOL AMATEUR RFC
Ground Address: THe Shakespeare, Catcote Road, Hartlepool Tel: 01429 273 737
Brief Directions: Entering Hartlepool on A689 turn left at 1st set of T/lights into Truro Drive. At T/Jnt then left into Catcote Road. Ground Approx. 2 miles on RHS.
Hon Secretary: Tony Wilson, 27 Suggitt Street, Hartlepool, TS26 8PY
Tel: (H) 01429 279 322 Tel: (M) 07788 972 827
Club Colours: Royal blue and scarlet hoops
League: Durham/N'thm'land 3

WEST HARTLEPOOL T.D.S.O.B RFC
Ground Address: Wiltshire Way, Hartlepool, TS26 0TB
Tel: 01429 233 548
Brief Directions: From A19 take A179 towards Hartlepool.At first r'about turn right and continue for approx. 2 miles. Continue straight on at mini r'about (next to Golf course) Take next left turn onto Throston Grange Estate.Turn right at T junction and travel down Wiltshire Way. Club on right after approx 0.5mls.
Hon Secretary: Dave BRAMLEY, 63 Hutton Avenue, Cleveland, TS26 9PP
Tel: (H) 01429 263 157 Tel: (W) 01642 833 761
Email: david.bramley4@btopenworld.com
Fixtures Secretary: Anthony CHESHIRE, 9 Elmwood Place, Hartlepool
Tel: (H) 01429 262 939 Tel: (W) 01429 604661
Club Colours: Blue and white
League: Durham/N'thm'land 1

WEST LEEDS RUFC
Ground Address: The Clubhouse, Bluehill Lane, Leeds, LS12 4NZ Tel: 0113 263 9869
Brief Directions: From M621 to Leeds outer ring road take A6110 and turn right at second roundabout . After Ringways, turn right at lights follow road leftt at Fawcett Lane and club is half a mile on left
Hon Secretary: J. Broadbent, 21 Butterbowl Road, Leeds, West Yorks. LS12 5JE Tel: (H) 0113 279 6220
Tel: (M) 07720 297 873 Tel: (W) 0113 243 6606
Fixtures Secretary: Colin Edwards, 59 Moorfield, Leeds, LS27 7BW
Tel: (H) 0113 252 2487 Tel: (W) 07850 226 393
Club Colours: Navy, old gold and white
League: Yorkshire 2

WEST PARK BRAMHOPE RUFC
Ground Address: The Sycamores, Bramhope, Leeds, West Yorkshire, LS16 9JR Tel: 0113 267 1437
Brief Directions: From Leeds city centre take A660 sign posted Skipton & Otley, at Bramhope village turn left at roundabout direct to Club
Hon Secretary: R. Storey, 7 Moseley Wood Way, Leeds, LS16 7HN
Tel: (H) 0113 267 5266 Tel: (W) 0113 224 3196
Email: bob.storey@leeds.gov.uk
Fixtures Secretary: Phil March, 202 Moseley Wood Gardens, Leeds, LS16 7SE Tel: (H) 0113 226 8246
Club Colours: Black and Gold
League: Yorkshire 2

WEST PARK WARRIORS RUFC
Ground Address: Red Rocks, Prescot Road, St. Helens, WA10 3AG Tel: 01744 261 38
Hon Secretary: M. Barrow, 21 Grnage Park Road, St. Helens, WA10 3EL
Tel: (H) 01744 615 640 Tel: (M) 07748 007 377
League: North Lancs 2

WESTOE RFC
Ground Address: Dean Road, South Shields
Tel: 0191 456 1506
Email Address: kevin@westoerfc.co.uk
Brief Directions: Map available
Hon Secretary: John R. Wells, 240 Mowbray Road, South Shields, NE33 3NW
Tel: (H) 0191 455 2260 Tel: (W) 0191 427 3502
Fixtures Secretary: D. Allen, 118 Harton House Road (E), South Shields, NE34 6DZ
Tel: (H) 0191 456 9531 Tel: (W) 0191 456 115
Club Colours: Red, sky and dark blue hoops
League: North 2 East

WETHERBY RFC
Ground Address: Grange Park, Wetherby, LS22
Tel: 01937 582 461

Web Address: www.wetherbyrugby.com
Brief Directions: From Wetherby town centre head for A1 south, pass Police station on left, to R/about, 2nd exit for A1 south, cross A1 and take left turn into Grange Park.
Hon Secretary: M. Lonsdale, 9 Darnborough Street, York, North Yorkshire, YO23 1AN
Tel: (H) 01904 626 772 Tel: (M) 07747 693 446
Email: mark.lonsdale@scbrew.co.uk
Fixtures Secretary: Richard Watts, 43 St. James Street, Wetherby, W. Yorkshire, LS22 6RS
Tel: (H) 01937 584 446 Email: rpw@fss.co.uk
Club Colours: Red and white hoops, white shorts
League: Yorkshire 4

WHARFEDALE RAMS RUFC
Ground Address: Wharfeside Avenue, Threshfield, Skipton, N. Yorks, BD23 5ND
Tel: 01756 752547
Brief Directions: Take B6265 from Skipton, signed Grassington, after 8 miles turn right after Old Hall Inn in Threshfield, left after 400 metres down Wharfeside Avenue.
Club Secretary: Dave Lovell, 2 Brackenley Crescent, Embsay, Skipton, N. Yorks, BD23 6PO.
Tel: 01756 795804
Fixtures Secretary: Michael Harrison, Old Hall Stables, threshfield, Skipton, N. Yorks, BD23 5PL.
Tel: 01756 752777
Club Colours: Emerald green shirts
League: Yorkshire 5

WHEATLEY HILLS DONCASTER RUFC
Ground Address: Wheatley Hills Sports Ground, Brunel Road, York Road Industrial Estate, Doncaster. DN5 8PT Tel: 01302 781472
Brief Directions: A638, behind B & Q depot, on Wakefield Road, 1 mile from town centre.
Club Secretary: A. R. Dunkerley, 1 Mayfields, Scawthrope, Doncaster, Yorkshire, DN5 7UA. Tel: 01302 782214 (H) 01302729793 (W)
Email: dunk@beargarden.freeserve.co.uk
Fixtures Secretary: Chris Whitehouse, 11A Hillfold, South Elmsall, Pontefract, WF9 2BZ.
Tel No: 01977 644303 (H) 08707 415151 (W)
Club Colours: Maroon, gold & white broad hoops
League: North 2 East

WHITBY RUFC
Ground Address: 'Showfield', Whitleys Road, Whitby, N. Yorkshire, YO21 3PB Tel: 01947 602 008
Brief Directions: North West side of river, towards Sandend off Stakesby Road
Hon Secretary: F. Howarth, 18 Lime Grove, Whitby, North Yorkshire, YO21 1LP Tel: (H) 01947 600 692
Fixtures Secretary: Chris Riddolls, Manor House Farm, Eskdaleside, Whitby, N Yorks, YO22 5ES
Tel: (H) 01947810096 Tel: (M) 07970342787
Email: holiday@whitby.name
Club Colours: Maroon and black
League: Durham/N'thm'land 2

WHITEHAVEN RFC
Ground Address: The Playground, Richmond Terrace, Whitehaven Tel: 01946 695 253
Brief Directions: Behind the Whitehaven Sports Centre and next to Jacksons Timber Yard.
Hon Secretary: E. McConnell, 38 Loop Road South, Whitehaven, Cumbria CA28 7SE Tel: (H) 01946 692225
Club Colours: Maroon and white hoops
League: Cumbria

WHITLEY BAY ROCKCLIFF RFC
Ground Address: Hillheads, Lovaine Avenue, Whitley Bay, Tyne and wear, NE25 8RW Tel: 0191 251 0748
Email Address: martinpage54@hotmail.com
Brief Directions: Travelling downhill on Hillheads Rd. past the Ice rink, turn 2nd right (club signed) along Lovaine Avenue, 2nd right into club.
Hon Secretary: Martin Page, 25 Hillcrest, Whitley Bay, Tyne & Wear, NE25 9AD
Tel: (H) 0191 251 0748 Tel: (W) 0191 200 5062
Email: martinpage54@hotmail.com
Fixtures Secretary: D. Bennett, 4 Millfield Gardens, Tynemouth, Tyne & Wear, NE30 2PX
Tel: (H) 0191 257 2174
Club Colours: Cardinal and gold shirts
League: Durham/N'thm'land 3

WIBSEY RUFC
Ground Address: Northfield Rd, Wibsey, Bradford BD6
Tel: 01274 671643
Brief Directions: From top of M606 take 2nd exit towards Odsal r'about, take 4th exit at side of Police station, 0.75 mile on left joined onto White Swan pub
Club Secretary: Steve Rose,236 Poplar Grove, Great Horton, Bradford BD7 4HU Tel: 01274 406546
Fixtures Secretary: Bob Wood
Tel: 01274 571810 (H) 0794 136 4204 (M)
Club Colours: Red and green hoops
League: Yorkshire 6

WICKERSLEY EXEL
Ground Address: Wickersley Comprehemsive School, Bawtry Road, Wickersley, Rotherham
Brief Directions: M18 Junction 1. Follow sign for Rotherham. Ground on left just before footbridge.
Club Secretary: David Trueman, 12 Larch Road, Maltby, Rotherham, S66 8AZ. Tel: 01709 817971
Fixtures Secretary: Steve Houghton, 150 Pear Tree Ave., Bramley, Rotherham, S. Yorks.S66 2NF
Tel Nos: 01709 531758 (H) 0498 825644(M)
Club Colours: Blue and gold
League: Yorkshire 6

WIDNES RUFC
Ground Address: Heath Road, Widnes, WA8 7NU
Tel: 0151 424 2575
Brief Directions: Directions: M62 J6. Take A5080 to Cronton. Right at Traffic Lights. After 1 mile, take second exit from roundabout. Go over railway, take first left into Heath Road. Clubhouse on left.
Hon Secretary: John Loughnane, 352 Upton Lane, Widnes, WA8 9AQ Tel: (H) 0151 424 0618
Fixtures Secretary: Gary Clare, 7 Claremont Avenue, Widnes, WA8 9NB
Tel: (H) 0151 424 2236 Tel: (M) 07957 242 334
Club Colours: Red and Black hooped jerseys, Black shorts.
League: South Lancs/Cheshire 1

WIGAN RUFC
Ground Address: Douglas Valley, Wingates Lane, Leyland Mill Lane, Wigan, WN1 2SJ Tel: 01942 242556
Brief Directions: M6 J27, follow signs to Standish, take A49 towards Wigan, 2 miles, 1st left after Cherry Gardens Hotel into Leyland Mill Lane, then signposted
Hon Secretary: David Wilkinson
Email: Davorlia@aol.com
Fixtures Secretary: D. Clarke, 224 Billinge Road, Wigan Tel: (H) 01942 207 771
Club Colours: Black and white irregular hoops
League: South Lancs/Cheshire 1

WIGTON RFC
Ground Address: Lowmoor Road, Wigton, Cumbria, CA7 9QT Tel: 016973 42206
Brief Directions: Junction 41, M6, B3505 to Wigton to j/w A595, follow signs to Wigton. Club on right 3/4 mile approx. For vehicles not using motorway follow A595 to j/w as above and follow directions as above.
Hon Secretary: Alan Lynch, Parsonbridge, Wigton, Cumbria, CA7 8NH
Tel: (H) 01697 343 436 Tel: (W) 01228 606 957
Fixtures Secretary: David Allison, 23 Highmoor Bungalows, Wigton, Cumbria, CA7 9LW
Tel: (H) 016973 45330
League: North 2 West

WILMSLOW RFC
Ground Address: Memorial Ground, Kings Road, Wilmslow, Cheshire, SK9 5PZ Tel: 01625 522 274
Email Address: jffletcher@ukonline.co.uk
Web Address: wilmslow-wolves.co.uk
Brief Directions: Kings Road is off the A538 - Wilmslow to Altrincham, approx 4 miles from the M56 junction, on the left as you enter the town.
Fixtures Secretary: J. Harries, 'Gwynant', 39 Wallingford Road, Wilmslow, SK9 3JT
Tel: (H) 01625 524 359
Email: texukltd@dialstart.net
Club Colours: Sky blue w/ maroon & white hoops
League: North 2 West

WINDERMERE RUFC
Ground Address: 3 Meadow Road, Windermere, Cumbria, LA23 2EU Tel: 015394 43066
Email Address: john@jsreid.freeserve.co.uk
Web Address: windermererufc.org.uk
Brief Directions: Drive towards Bowness & the lake from Windermere, coming in to Bowness, right just before cinema, right again past the bowling club, clubhouse is on the right.
Hon Secretary: John Reid, 3 Meadow Road, Windermere, Cumbria, LA23 2EU
Tel: (H) 01539 488 870 Tel: (M) 07997 495 219
Email: john@jsreid.freeserve.co.uk
Fixtures Secretary: Nigel Rimmer, Clayton's Flat, Crescent Road, Windermere, Cumbria, LA23 1EA
Tel: (H) 015394 48971 Tel: (W) 015397 20028
Club Colours: Amber and black
League: Cumbria

WINLATON VULCANS RFC
Ground Address: Axwell View Playing Fields, Winlaton, Blaydon, Tyne & Wear, NE21 6NF
Tel: 0191 414 2502
Email Address: rugby@sapphire-carrel.co.uk
Web Address: www.wilt.co.uk/winlaton
Brief Directions: From A1 take exit past Metro Centre signed Swalwell, take signs for Blaydon, just past Blaydon Pool turn left, continue up Shibdon Bank for 0.5 mile, club on left
Hon Secretary: Paul Maguire, 3 Woodburn Close, Hanover Estate, Blaydon, NE21 6EL Tel: (H) 0191 414 4409 Tel: (M) 07730 979 790 Tel: (W) 0191 414 0448
Email: paul@sapphire-carrel.co.uk
Fixtures Secretary: I. Bilclough, 7a Tyne Street, Wincanton, Tyne & Wear Tel: (H) 0191 414 7723
Club Colours: Black & White
League: Durham/N'thm'land 2

WINNINGTON PARK RFC
Ground Address: Burrows Hill, Hartford, Northwich, Cheshire Tel: 01606 742 42
Web Address: www.wprfc.com
Brief Directions: 1 mile from Hartford turn off A556, signed Hartford, neat BlueWeaver Bridge, turn right at Church, left at the lights, right at T.Jct. Then next left, Barrows Hill Ground 2nd on right.
Hon Secretary: Ian Smith, 12A Church Meadows, Little Leigh, Northwich, Cheshire, CW8 4SB
Tel: (H) 01606 891 936
Email: SydsRugby@aol.com
Fixtures Secretary: C. Gleave, 'Westerley', West Road, Northwich, Cheshire
Tel: (H) 01606 853 999 Tel: (W) 01925 752 016
Email: c.f.gleave@aol.com
Club Colours: Light Blue, Dark Blue and White
League: North 2 West

WIRRAL RUFC
Ground Address: Memorial Ground, Thornton Common Road, Clattebridge, Bebington, Wirral, CH63 4JU Tel: 0151 334 1309
Web Address: www.wirralrugbyclub.com
Brief Directions: M53 J4. Follow signs for Willaston & Naston. Straight ahead at R/about. Left at 1st crossroads.
Hon Secretary: G. E. Roberts, 19 Thornton Road, Wirral, Merseyside, CH63 5PN
Tel: (H) 0151 608 9643 Tel: (W) 0151 334 6226
Email: graeme.roberts@huytonroberts.com
Fixtures Secretary: A. Hignett, 22 Argyle Avenue, Wirral, Merseyside Tel: (H) 0151 327 1309
Email: alan@hignetts.freeserve.co.uk
Club Colours: Maroon and white hoops
League: South Lancs/Cheshire 1

WITHERNSEA RUFC
Ground Address: Clifton Lodge, Seaside Lane, Tunstall, Nr Hull, E. Yorkshire, HU12 0JQ
Tel: 01964 612 049
Email Address: sue.simmonds2@btopenworld.com
Web Address: www.rufc.withernsea.com
Brief Directions: The postcode of the club is HU12 2RS, this will allow you to find us easily using a web based streetmap package
Hon Secretary: A. Ellis, Clifton Lodge, Seaside Lane, Roos (Nr Hull), HU12 0JQ Tel: (H) 01964 671 863 Tel: (W) 01964 670 403

Fixtures Secretary: R. K. Thompson, 3 Oak Avenue, Hull, HU19 2PE Tel: (H) 01964 613 722
Club Colours: Navy and white
League: Yorkshire 6

WORKINGTON RFC
Ground Address: Ellis Sports Ground, Mossbay Road, Workington, CA14 3XZ Tel: 01900 602 625
Email Address: michael@heaslip.fslife.co.uk
Brief Directions: Follow trunk roads to town centre, then follow B5296 (Harrington) for 1/2 mile. Entrance to ground on right 100m after traffic lights at TA Centre.
Hon Secretary: Michael Heaslip, 32 Elizabeth Street, Workington, Cumbria, CA14 4DB Tel: (H) 01900 64493
Tel: (M) 07786 625859 Tel: (W) 01946 852955
Email: Michael@heaslip.fslife.co.uk
Leagues Contact: Kevin Greenhow, 94 Curwendale, Workington, CA14
Tel: (H) 01900 608 075 Tel: (M) 07960 127053
Fixtures Secretary: Kevin Greenhow, 94 Curwendale, Workington, CA14
Tel: (H) 01900 608 075 Tel: (M) 07960 127053
Club Colours: Black & White Hoops, Black shorts.
League: North Lancs/Cumbria

YARM RUFC
Ground Address: c/o 5 Pinewood Road, Eaglescliffe, Stockton on Tees, Cleveland, TS16 0AH
Tel: 07813 328 258
Email Address: john@cosywash.co.uk
Web Address: www.yarmrugbyclub.co.uk
Brief Directions: Clubhouse - Yarm Sports and Social Club, Leven Road, Yarm. Directions - Leave A19 onto A67 towards Yarm, go straight over roundabout onto Thirsk Road past Fire Stn on left, turn right into Leven Road and 2nd right to clubhouse. 1st XV play at Green Ln or Aislaby Rd changing at Yarm School, 2nd XV play and change at Kirklevington Detention Centre.
Hon Secretary: Nick Barfield, 5 Pinewood Road, Stockton -on-Tees, TS16 0AH Tel: (H) 01642 787796
Tel: (M) 07626 454 627 pager
Fixtures Secretary: Ian Betts, 23 Angrove Close, Stockton on Tees
Tel: (H) 01642 789949 Tel: (W) 01642 644 444
Email: ian@ibetts.freeserve.co.uk
Club Colours: Navy & light blue 1/4's, navy shorts
League: Durham/N'thm'land 3

YARNBURY (HORSFORTH) RFC
Ground Address: Brownberrie Lane, Horsforth, Leeds
Tel: 0113 2581346
Brief Directions: Follow signs on Leeds outer ring road (A6120) to Horsforth. Turn north onto Low Lane at T junction turn left then third exit off the roundabout
Club Secretary: Paul Trigg, 3 Moorland Gardens, Moortown, Leeds. LS17 6JT
Tel: (H) 0113 2251389
Fixtures Secretary: John Riley, 65 Broadgate Lane, Horsforth, Leeds, LS18 5AB
Tel: (H) 0113 2589131 (W) 01924 441818
Club Colours: Blue, black & white uneven hoops
League: Yorkshire 1

YORK RAILWAY INSTITUTE RUFC
Ground Address: Railway Institute Sports Ground, New Lane, Acomb, York. YO2 4NU
Tel: 01904 798930
Brief Directions: From A1237 York ringroad, take B1224 signposted Acomb for 1.5 miles, after the Church of the Latter Day Saints on right, take the 1st on the right (New Lane), sports ground at end
Club Secretary: Bryn D Bates, 16 Beech Place, Strensall, York. YO32 5AS
Tel: 01904 491296 (H) 01904 622112 (W)
Fixtures Secretary: W F Cooper, Moorcroft, Lucy Hall Drive, Baildon, Shipley Tel: (H) 01274 584355
Club Colours: Royal blue and white hoops
League: Yorkshire 2

YORK RUFC
Ground Address: Clifton Park, Shipton Road, York, YO30 6RE Tel: 01904 623 602
Brief Directions: Turn south off York outer ring road (A10) towards city centre on A19 from Thirsk, club situated on right after about 1.75 miles
Hon Secretary: Brian McLure, 15 Stubden Grove, York, YO30 4UY Tel: (H) 01904 691026 (M) 07785 951070
Email: bmcc1999@aol.com
Fixtures Secretary: Colin Ventress, 1 Barnfield Way, York, YO23 3RT Tel: (H) 01904 704 793
Club Colours: Green, black and white hoops
League: Yorkshire 1

Trentham RUFC (South Lancs & Cheshire 2) celebrate winning their own 10-a-side competition. Club captain, Phil Milington, is holding the A J Philpott & Sons Ltd. trophy.

Northampton Mens Own (Midlands 3 East South) pictured here with Ercole Rugby Monselice, Padua, on their tour of Italy in May 2002. Mens Own won this particular match 27-7.

MIDLAND REGION

A complete club index appears at the back of the book.
This shows which Division and league each club is in for the 2002-03 season

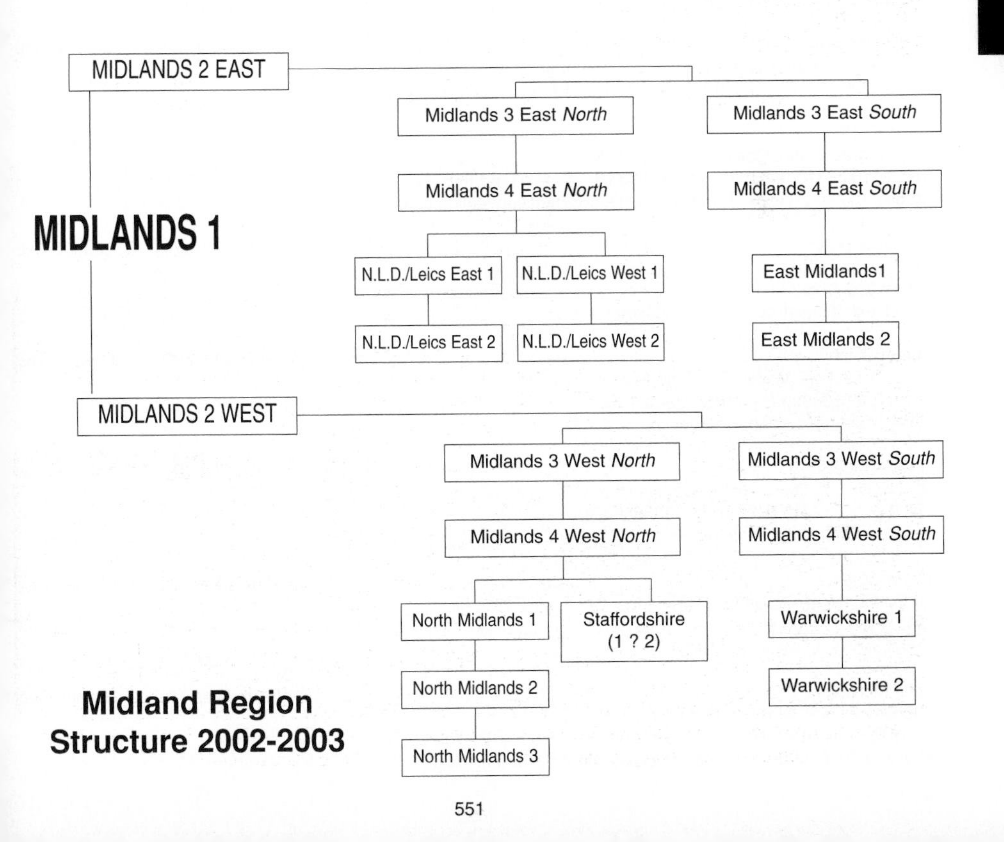

Midland Region Structure 2002-2003

MIDLAND REGION OFFICIALS 2001-2002

Official	Position	Role
David Robins The Clubhouse, Upper Chase Road, Malvern, Worc, WR14 2BU Tel: 01684 564826 (H) 01684 560247 (B) Fax: 01684 893125 Email:dir-int@dir-int.demon.co.uk	Chairman North Mids Rep	
Mike Bracey 19,The Cedars, Dunstable Street, Ampthill, Beds, MK45 2JZ Tel: 01525 840929 (H) Email:Plumtreedeacon@aol.com	Mids 1	League Sec
Stuart Hetherington 87, Church Lane, Backwell, Bristol, BS48 3JW Tel: 01275 463902 (H) 07779 126142 (M) Email:shethers@aol.com	Mids 2 West	League Sec
Bob Ingledew 15 Martin Close, Bedford, Beds, MK41 7JY Tel: 01234 407521 (H) Email:bingledew@ntlworld.com	Mids 2 East East Mids Rep	League Sec
Nigel Banwell 16 Riverside Close, Upton upon Seven, Worc Tel: 01684 592046 (H) Email: Nigel.Banwell@tesco.net	Mids 3 West(N) WR8 0JN	League Sec
Keith Dale 14 St. Anthony's Drive, Newcastle, Staffs, ST5 2JE Tel: 01782 615770 (H)	Mids 3 West(S)	League Sec
Philip Osborne Ashthorne, Teeton Road, Ravensthorpe, Northampton NN6 8EJ Tel: 01604 770772 (H) 01327 705785 (B) Email: annaliz.100@virgin.net	Mids 3 East(N)	League Sec
Clive Elliott 9 Wavertree Close, Cosby, Leic, LE9 1TN Tel: 0116 2841746 (H) 01788 544508 (B) Fax: 01788 568711 Mobile: 07740 205928 Email: cliveelliott56@netscapeonline.co.uk	Mids 3 East(S) Leics Rep	League Sec
Alun Humphreys 26 Low Fold Close, St Johns, Worcester, WR2 5UE Tel: 01905 422522 (H) Email: agh@christopherwhitehead.worcs.sch.uk	Mids 4 West(N)	League Sec
Martin Dolphin 10 Canobie Lea, Madeley, Telford, Shrops, TF7 5RL Tel: 01952 684904 (H) 01952 294424 (B) Email: martin@dolphin-mc.fsnet.co.uk	Mids 4 West(S)	League Sec
David Trubee 42 Charnwood Drive, Ripley, Derbys DE5 3TB Tel: 01773 512719 (H) 01773 835556 (F) Email: dtrubee@dircon.co.uk	Mids 4 East(N)	League Sec
Kevin Curtis 21 Potton Road, St. Neots, Huntingdon, Cambs, PE19 2NP Tel: 01480 390066 (H) Email: kevincurtis@ntlworld.com	Mids 4 East(S)	League Sec
John McNally 490 Brook Lane, Moseley, Birmingham, B13 0BZ Tel: 0121 604 6180 (H) 0121 783 7232 (B) Fax: 0121 789 8306 Mobile: 07976 364234 Email: jmcnally@stberns.bham.sch.uk	North Mids 1	League Sec

Contact	Division	Role
Terry Wheeler 14 Woolescote, Pedmore, Stourbridge, DY9 7JJ Tel: 01384 832647 (H) 0121 423 4000 (B)	North Mids 2	League Sec
Andy Rogers 234 Turves Green, Northfield, Birmingham B31 4BW Tel: 021 603 1364 Email: andyrogers@oldgriffs.com	North Mids 3	League Sec
John Powderley 10,Garman Close, Great Barr, Birmingham, B43 6 NB Tel: 0121 357 4918 (H) Email: powderleyjohn@btinternet.com	Staffs 1&2	League Sec
Henri Ginvert 5 The Paddock, Markfield, Leics, LE6 9RR Tel: 01530 242761 (H) 01534 249621 (B) Fax: 01534 249621 Mobile: 07785 724989 Email: henri.ginvert@uk.zurich.com	NLD/Leics 1 West	League Sec
Tim Bembridge 5,Blackthorn Lane, Boston, Lincs, PE21 9BG Tel: 01205 351973 (H) Fax: 01509 842893 Mobile: 07733 116513 Email: tim@tbembridge.freeserve.co.uk	NLD/Leics 1 East	League Sec
David Miller 7 Rosemary Drive, Alvaston, Derby, DE24 0TA Tel: 01332 755935 (H) 01332 260144 (B) Email: MillerAdmiller@aol.com	NLD/Leics 2 West	League Sec
David Murphy The Old Carpenters Arms, 32 High Street, Little Bytham,Grantham, NG33 4QX Tel: 01780 410692 (H)	NLD/Leics 2 East	League Sec
Peter Howard Caudle View, Church Lane, Thorpe, Langton, LE16 7TR Tel: 01858 545227 (H) 01455 610747 (B)	East Mids 1	League Sec
Chris Rowan 17 Blethan Drive, Huntingdon, Cambs, PE18 6GN Tel: 01480 434959 (H) 01480 892838 (B) Email: chris.rowan1@ntlworld.com	East Mids 2	League Sec
Kevin Price 10 Seagrave Road, Thrussington, Leicester, LE7 4UG Tel: 01664 424388 (H) Fax: 01664 424388 Email: KPKRFC@aol.com	NLD Rep	League Sec
Ray Roberts 261,Alwyn Road, Rugby, Warwickshire, CV22 7RP Tel: 01788 810276 (H) Fax: 01788 816520 Email: Rayrobwark@aol.com	Warks 1&2 Warks Rep Secretary	League Sec
Geoff Payne Spectra Plastics Ltd, Southam Road, Long Itchington, Southam, CV47 9QL Tel: 01926 812195 (B) Fax: 01926 817410	Treasurer	
Andy Rogers 234,Turves Green, Northfield, Birmingham, B31 4BW Tel: 0121 603 1364 (H) Mobile: 07974 733112 Email: andy_rogers@blueyonder.co.uk	North Mids 3	League Sec
Sid Goodman 47,The Avenue, Stone, Staffs, ST15 8DG Tel: 01785 814845 (H)	Staffs Rep	League Sec

MIDLAND ONE

2001-02 LEAGUE TABLE

	P	W	D	L	PF	PA	PD	Pts
Broadstreet	22	18	0	4	573	340	233	36
Walsall	22	15	0	7	524	454	70	30
Longton	22	14	0	8	519	434	85	28
Luctonians	22	13	1	8	421	327	94	27
Leicester Lions	22	12	0	10	543	347	196	24
Kenilworth	22	12	0	10	620	434	186	24
Dunstablians	22	12	0	10	670	499	171	24
Malvern	22	11	0	11	482	467	15	22
Barkers Butts	22	9	0	13	354	521	-167	18
Hereford	22	7	1	14	345	549	-204	15
Camp Hill	22	5	0	17	244	612	-368	10
Banbury (-2)	22	3	0	19	312	623	-311	4

2002-03 FIXTURE GRID

	Barkers Butts	Bromsgrove	Dunstablians	Hinckley	Kenilworth	Leicester Lions	Longton	Luctonians	Malvern	Spalding	Walsall	Whitchurch
Barkers Butts		15/03	01/03	02/11	23/11	01/02	12/04	12/10	07/12	21/12	11/01	28/09
Bromsgrove	07/09		28/09	01/03	11/01	02/11	21/12	23/11	12/04	01/02	07/12	12/10
Dunstablians	14/09	08/02		21/12	12/04	12/10	07/12	11/01	15/03	23/11	02/11	01/02
Hinckley	04/01	14/09	16/11		05/10	30/11	18/01	29/03	26/10	08/02	07/09	14/12
Kenilworth	14/12	26/10	30/11	01/02		07/09	04/01	01/03	16/11	12/10	28/09	29/03
Leicester Lions	05/10	04/01	18/01	12/04	15/03		14/09	21/12	08/02	07/12	23/11	26/10
Longton	30/11	16/11	29/03	12/10	02/11	01/03		28/09	14/12	11/01	01/02	07/09
Luctonians	18/01	14/12	26/10	07/12	14/09	16/11	08/02		05/10	15/03	12/04	04/01
Malvern	29/03	30/11	07/09	11/01	21/12	28/09	23/11	01/02		02/11	12/10	01/03
Spalding	16/11	05/10	14/12	28/09	18/01	29/03	26/10	07/09	04/01		01/03	30/11
Walsall	26/10	29/03	04/01	15/03	08/02	14/12	05/10	30/11	18/01	14/09		16/11
Whitchurch	08/02	18/01	05/10	23/11	07/12	11/01	15/03	02/11	14/09	12/04	21/12	

BARKERS' BUTTS RFC

Founded: 1947

President	R Anderson	22 Washbrook Lane, Coventry CV5 9EG	Tel: 02476 526633
Chairman	R A White	36 Westcotes, Coventry CV4 9BD	Tel: 02476 469875
Sponsorship Sec.	R Berisford	9 Macauley Road, Coventry CV2 5FD	Tel: 02476 441162
Hon. Secretary	H Roberts	84 Keresley Road, Coventry CV6 2JD	Tel: 02476 333244
Fixture Secretary	B Lester	7 Tiverton Road, Coventry CV2 3ED	Tel: 02476 443605
League Contact	R G Coward	c/o Barkers' Butts RFC (see below)	

Ground: Pickford Grange Lane, Allesley, Coventry CV5 9AR Tel: 01676 522192 Fax: 01676 523470
Capacity: 1000 - all uncovered standing. Website: barkersbutts.co.uk

Directions: From Birmingham A45 - take Meriden turn - turn right at 3rd roundabout.
From Coventry A45 - take Meriden slip road, after 200 yds turn left - ground 300 yds on right.
Nearest Railway station: Birmingham International or Coventry

Car Parking: 200 spaces available at ground

Matchday admission: £2

Clubhouse: Open Mon.-Fri. 7-11pm, Sat. 12-11 & Sun 12-4 **Club Shop:** Open 1-5 Sat & 12-2 Sun.

Colours: Royal blue and amber **Change colours:** All red Training Nights: Tuesday & Thursday

Programme: Size: A3 Pages: 32 Price: £1 Editor: J Saltmarsh
Advertising: £125 full page £75 half page

BROMSGROVE RFC

Chairman D W Wellington Tel: 01905 756019 (H)

Hon. Treasurer Phillip A Drew, 42 Oakdene Drive, Barnt Green, Birmingham B45 8LQ
0121 445 5608 (H)

Club Secretary: Robin J Davies, Drovers Barn, 4 Naunton Farm Barns, Holt Heath, Worcester WR6 6NG
Tel: 07966 155686 (M) 01905 621808 (H) 01905 797277 (B) 01905 791300 (Fax)
Email: robin.davies@inter-alliance.com

Fixtures Secretary: Ralph M Gordon, 66 Hanbury Road, Stoke Heath, Bromsgrove, Worcs. B60 4LU
Tel: (H & W) 01527 832003 Email: rmgordon@btclick.com

League Contact: Kenneth J Copson 01527 872955 (H) 0121 454 2323 (B) 07801 649040 (M)

Ground Address: Finstall Park, Finstall Road, Bromsgrove, Worcs. B60 3DH
Tel: 01527 874690
Web address: www.bromsgrovefc.co.uk

Directions: Situated between Aston Fields and Finstall on Finstall Road (B4184), Bromsgrove

Club Colours: White jerseys with red/black/red hoops, white shorts

DUNSTABLIANS RUFC

Founded: 1948

President	Ross Barrington	20 Ringshall, Little Gaddesden, Berkhamsted, Herts HP4 1ND	01442 843464
Chairman	Steve Butler	12 Church Rd., PulloxHill, Beds. MK45 5HE	01525 716343
Secretary	Paul Freeman	36 Lincoln Way, Harlington, Dunstable, Beds., LU5 6NQ.	01525 750852
Treasurer	Tim Allsop	58 Holywell Rd., Studham, Dunstable, Beds. LU6 2PD	01582 873095
Fixtures Secretary	Dai Gabriel	19 Hillyfields, Dunstable, Beds. LU6 3NS	01582 606262
League Contact	Paul Freeman (as above)		

Ground **Address**: Bidwell Park, Bedford Road, Houghton Regis, Dunstable, Beds. LU5 6JW.
Tel: 01582 866555 email: secretary@dunstablians-rufc.org.uk www.dunstablians-rufc.org.uk
Capacity: 400 all uncovered standing
Directions: M1 J12 through Toddington, ground is 2-3 miles on left on double bend before Houghton Regis or North out of Dunstable on A5, turn right after roundabout to Thorn, at end of road, ground is opposite.
Car Parking: 100+ cars at ground Nearest Railway Station: Leagrave, Luton or Harlington
Admission: Matchday £3

Clubhouse: Two bars, changing rooms, kitchen & showers. **Club Shop:** Yes

Training Nights: Tuesday & Thursday

Programme: Size: A5 Price: with admission Pages: 32 Editor: Steve Butler (as above) Advertising: Contact Editor

Colours: Red, black, silver **Change colours:** All black **Nickname**: "Ds"

MIDLAND

HINCKLEY RFC

President	Roy Petty	01455 239254 (H)
Chairman	Peter Wallace	01455 634001 (H)
Hon. Treasurer	Peter Wallace	As Chairman
Club Secretary:	John Bennett	Beechrome, Ivydene Close, Earl Shilton, Leics. LE9 7LR Tel: 01455 843874 Email: john @james-bennett.co.uk
Fixture Secretary:	Trevor Williams	94 Druid Street, Hinckley, Leics. LE10 1QQ. Tel: 07939 351866 - or c/o club numbers
Coach	John Davey	01455 636103 email: johnldavey@hotmail.com

Ground Address: Leicester Road, Hinckley, Leicestershire, LE10 3DR.
Tel: 01455 615010 Fax: 01455 615050

Directions: On the B4668 between Hinckley and Earl Shildon

Club Colours: Black and amber hoops, black shorts.

KENILWORTH R.F.C.

Founded: 1924

President	Chris Holmes	36 Lunn Ave., Kenilworth CV8 2DS 01203 713313
Chairman	Chris Elgar	7 Wordsworth Drive, Kenilworth CV8 2TB 01926 852587
Secretary	Wille Whitesmith	4 Glasshouse Lane, Kenilworth CV8 2AJ 01926 859465 (H) e-mail: willie@iges.co.uk
Treasurer	John Davies	24 Thirlestone Close, Kenilworth CV8 2DW 01926 857962
Fixtures Secretary	Graham Billinger	7 Saville Grove, Kenilworth Kenilworth CV8 2PR 01926 851914

Ground Jack Davies Memorial Ground, Glasshouse lane, Kenilworth CV8 2AJ
Tel: 01926 853945 Fax: 01926 851394 website: www.westmids.co.uk/kenilworthrugby
Capacity: Unknown

Directions A452 off A46. At roundabout take third exit onto Birches lane; ground is about 1/2 mile on the right.
Nearest Railway station: Coventry Car Parking: Plenty at the ground

Admission Charges vary No season tickets are available

Clubhouse Tue, Wed & Thur 7-11pm, Fri 6-11pm, Sat 12-12, Sun 12-3pm **Club Shop:** Open as clubhouse

Colours: Yellow & blue/dark blue **Change colours:** All red

Training Nights: Tues, Wed & Thur. **Nickname:** "Kens"

Programme Size: A5 Pages: 20+ Price: Varies Editor: Chris Holmes 01203 713313
Advertising: Page: £100 Half: £60 Quarter: £35

LEICESTER LIONS R.F.C.

Founded 1999

Westleigh (Founded 1904) & Wigston (Founded 1946) merged 1999

Secretary Haydn Evans, c/o Thirteen Amp Ltd., Units 1-4, Brunel Rd., Hinckley, Leics. LE10 0AA
Tel: 01455 251411 e-mail: hevans@13-amp.co.uk

Fixture Secretary Chris Barker, 29 Oliver Court, 329 London Rd., Leicester LE2 2PQ
Tel: 0116 270 2278 e-mail: chris@barker-leicsfreeserve.co.uk

League Contact Roger Hill, 24 Welford Road., Blaby, Leics. LE8 4FS
Tel: 0116 277 2494 Fax: 0116 278 8089 mob. 07710 645033

Ground: Westleigh Park, Lutterworth Road, Blaby, Leicestershire LE8 3DP Tel: 0116 277 1010

Directions: M1/M69 J21, take B4114 to Narborough, left at Foxhunter r'about (Toby Carvery), right at next r'about, straight over next r'about & left at next (4th) r'about, ground 150 yds on left.

Admission By programme

Programme Price: £2 Size: A5 Pages: 20

Clubhouse Open Mon & Thur, matchdays & Sun am.

Training Nights Monday and Thursday.

Colours Black, white and purple quarters

LONGTON R.F.C.

Founded: 1952

President Martin Hamer Riverside, Church Lane, Broadway WR6 5NQ 01886 822138
Chairman Alan Miller Primrose Cottage, Church Down, Hilderstone, Staffs. 01889 505127
email: chairman@longtonrugby.co.uk
Secretary John Till The Hayloft, Ellenhall, Staffs. ST21 6JQ 01785 859368
email: secretary@longtonrugby.co.uk
Fixture Secretary Ian Wright 41 Sackville St., Basford, Stoke-on-Trent ST4 6HU 01782 616903 (T&Fax)
email: fixtures@longtonrugby.co.uk
Head of Rugby / League Contact Tim Tams 07812 251045 (M) 01283 820740 (H)
Coach Simon Robson
Ground Roughcote Lane, Caverswall, Stoke-on-Trent, Staffs. ST11 9EG 01782 394449
Capacity: 250 - all uncovered standing Web Site: www.longtonrugby.co.uk

Directions: Roughcote Lane is off the A520, 2 miles north of the A50/A520 intersection at Meir, to the east of Stoke-on-Trent.
Nearest Railway station: Stoke-on-Trent Car Parking: Plenty on ground

Admission: £3
Clubhouse: Open matchdays & training nights **Club Shop**: Limited amount of merchandise available from clubhouse
Colours: Black and amber, black shorts **Change colours:** Blue & white
Training Nights: Tuesday & Thursday
Programme: Size: A5 Pages: Vary Price: with admission

MIDLAND

LUCTONIANS RFC

Founded: 1948

Chairman David Thomas, Old Hall, Newtown, Leominster, Herefordshire. 01568 615472 (H) 01568 612977 (B)
Club Secretary Huw Davies, The Bell House, Kingsland, Leominster, Herefordshire. HR6 9RU.
e-mail:club@luctonians.freeuk.co Tel: 01568 708450 (H) 01432 362130 (W)
Treasurer Richard Powell, Lower Newton, Weobley, Hereford. 01544 318340 (H&B)
Fixtures Secretary Simon Green-Price, c/o the club Tel: as ground, plus mobile 07967 806678
League Contact Simon Green-Price (as above)

Ground **Address**: Mortimer Park, Hereford Road, Kingsland, Leominster, Herefordshire. HR6 8JS
Tel: 01568 709080 Fax: 01568 708169 email: cluboffice@luctonians.co.uk Website: luctonians.co.uk
Capacity: Ample, all uncovered standing
Directions: 4 miles north west of Leominster off the A44 in the village of Kingsland, opposite the Monument Inn.
Car Parking: 200+ at ground Nearest Railway Station: Leominster
Admission: £2 including programme
Clubhouse: Open Sat, Sun & training nights **Club Shop:** Yes, within clubhouse.
Programme: Size: A5 Price: £1 (incl. with ground admission) Pages: 20 Advertising: Contact Editor
Editor: Rod Hawnt, Kingsfield Ho., Trevern, Marden, Herefordshire HR1 3EX 01568 797867 (H) 01885 483789 (B)
Training Nights: Tuesday & Thursday **Nickname**: 'Lucs'
Colours: Black with white hoops, black shorts & socks. **Change colours:** All green

MALVERN

Club Secretary Simon Phillips, The Chantry, 2 Camphill Road, Worcester WR5 2HE. Tel: 01905 767887
e-mail: simonphillips@fountaincourt.com
Fixtures Secretary W Pomeroy, 50 Barnards Green Road, Malvern. WR14 3LW
Tel: (H) 01684 562279. e-mail: wpomeroy@dera.gov.uk
GroundAddress: Spring Lane, Malvern Link, Worcester. WR14 1AJ Tel: 01684 573728
Directions: Turn left at Texaco garage on approaching Malvern from Worcester on A449. Ground is on right.
Colours: Maroon, gold and light blue hoops, navy shorts

SPALDING RFC

President	Don Beecham	01775 630590 (H)
Chairman	Geof Nichols	Hethersett House, 4 Redmile Close, Pinchbeck, Spalding, Lincs. PE11 3UT Tel: 01775 769897 (H) 01775 725041 (B) 07730 129268 (M)
Hon. Treasurer	Graham Garrett	01778 425357 email: grahamgarrett@arsenalfc.net
Club Secretary	Peter Jullien	Sunnyside House, 21 The Parkway, Spalding, Lincs. PE11 3EE. Tel: 01775 712376 (H) 07967 807495 (M)
Fixtures Secretary	Martin Beecham	48 West Elloe, Spalding, Lincs. PE11 2BH Tel: 01775 722356 (H) 07887 821173 (M) email: beech@waitrose.com
Marketing Director	Tim Hall	01775 762145 (H)
League Contact	Geof Nichols	see Chairman, above.

Ground Address: Memorial Field, St Thomas' Road, Spalding, Lincs
Tel: 01775 725191

Directions: From the A16 follow Spalding sign at the A1073 roundabout. About 1/2 mile turn left over bridge and immediately right along river. 1/4 mile turn left into Welland Rd.

Club Colours: Maroon and blue hoops

MIDLAND

WALSALL R.F.C.

Founded: 1922

President	D E Horton	c/o Walsall RFC, Broadway Ground, Delves Rd,Walsall WS1 3JY
Chairman	Barry J Bodilly	55A Highgate Road, Walsall. 01922 645330 (H)
Club Secretary	Steve Lewis	15 Coppyhall Grove, Aldrdge WS9 8RP 01922 451569 (H) 01922 613310 (Fax)
Fixtures Secretary	Tim Day	20 Daffodil Place, Walsall. WS5 3DN 01922 611729(H), 01922 613310 (Fax)
Press Officer	Howard Clews	4 Binbrook Rd, Short Heath, Walsall. WV12 4TW 01902 631947 (H), 01922 613310 (F)
Director of Coaching	Arnie Evans	0121 353 1017 (H), 0121 378 1288 (B)

GroundAddress: Broadway Ground, Delves Road, Walsall WS1 3 JY Tel: 01922 626818 Fax 01922 613310
Capacity: 2,250 Seated: 250 Standing: 2,000

Directions: From NE (A38.A461) almost into Town centre, take ring Rd left, ground 2 miles on right.
From NW (M6) Jnc 9, go left and bear right at lights onto ring road, ground on left after 2miles.
From South, head for M6 Jct 7, take A34 Walsall, after 2 miles left onto ring road, ground half mile on right.

Nearest Railway Station: Walsall BR 1.5 miles, hourly bus or taxi.

Car Parking: 100 adjacent to Clubhouse, 200 within 5 mins walk. **Admission**: Match £5, inc programme, Members £3

Clubhouse: Matchdays 12-11. Eves (except Wed), 8-11Sun. 12-4.30. Snacks & bar meals available.

Club Shop: Yes, contact Club Secretary **Training Nights:** Tuesday & Thursday

ProgrammeSize: A5 Price: Included in entryPages: 36 plus coverEditor: Howard Clews 01902 631947

Advertising Rates Mono Full Page £150, Half £75

Colours: Scarlet/black/scarlet **Change colours:** Royal blue & amber/blue/blue & amber

WHITCHURCH RFC

Founded: 1936

President	John Henry Wynn	Fenns Wood, Whitchurch, Shropshire.	01948 780343
Chairman	Paul Kaminski	21 Kingsway, Whitchurch SY13 1EH	01948 662536 (H), 01948 662889 (B)
Treasurer	Mark Smith	25 Smallbrook Rd., Whitchurch SY13 1BT	01948 664894 07971 118980 (M)
Secretary	Graham Kendall	Hibernia, Mile Bank, Whitchurch SY13 4JY	01948 666632 (H), 0151 243 7831 (B) 0151 243 7800 (F) 07930 324524 (M)
Fixture Secretary	Paul Kaminski	21 Kingsway, Whitchurch SY13 1EH	01948 662536(H), 01948 662889 (B)
Marketing	Mike Dixon	Arden Fields, Ridley Hill Farm, Tarporley, Cheshire CW6 9RX	01829 260310

Ground Address: Edgeley Park, Whitchurch SY13 1EU Tel: 01948 663316 Fax: 01948 665508
Capacity: Unlimited Seated: None Standing: Unlimited

Directions: Follow by-pass (A41/A49) to the south of the town.
Opposite Sir John Talbot school, access via Edgeley Road (on right).
Nearest Railway Station: Whitchurch (5 mins walk)

Car Parking: Free parking on ground

Admission: Matchday - Adults £5 Concessions £3 Season Tickets - £40

Clubhouse: Regularly open Functions: Yes. Contact Club **Club Shop:** None

Colours: Red/white/red **Change colours:** White **Training Nights:** Tuesday & Thursday

Programme Size: A5 Price: with entry Pages: 16/20 Editor: Dr. Alan Hares 01630 652135

Advertising Rates - Mono Full page £100 Half £60 Qtr. £35

MIDLAND REGION FINAL LEAGUE TABLES 2001-02

Midlands 2 East

	P	W	D	L	PF	PA	PD	Pts	-
Hinckley	22	18	2	2	729	188	541	38	
Spalding	22	15	2	5	603	326	277	32	
South Leicester	22	15	1	6	603	333	270	31	
Kettering	22	13	1	8	447	368	79	27	
Mansfield	22	13	0	9	392	344	48	26	
Ampthill	22	11	0	11	457	423	34	22	
Syston	22	9	1	12	386	439	-53	19	
Wellingborough	22	9	1	12	437	526	-89	19	
Luton	22	7	3	12	398	432	-34	17	
Ilkeston	22	7	0	15	287	685	-398	14	
Huntingdon	22	6	1	15	368	530	-162	13	
Lincoln	22	3	0	19	266	779	-513	6	

Midlands 3 East (North)

	P	W	D	L	PF	PA	PD	Pts	-
Market Bosworth	18	14	3	1	544	247	297	31	
Nottingham Moderns	18	12	1	5	425	236	189	25	
Matlock	18	11	1	6	301	182	119	23	
Belgrave	18	11	0	7	381	275	106	22	
Newark	18	9	1	8	346	248	98	19	
Melton Mowbray	18	9	1	8	417	433	-16	19	
Loughborough	18	9	0	9	302	384	-82	18	
Stoneygate	18	7	0	11	319	441	-122	14	
Glossop	18	2	2	14	213	499	-286	6	
Market Rasen	18	1	1	16	190	493	-303	3	

Midlands 4 East (North)

	P	W	D	L	PF	PA	PD	Pts	-
Loughborough Students	18	16	0	2	651	192	459	32	
Paviors	18	15	1	2	697	189	508	31	
Kesteven	18	11	2	5	462	219	243	24	
*Ashbourne	18	12	0	6	398	407	-9	22	2
Long Eaton	18	10	0	8	368	330	38	20	
Buxton	18	8	0	10	237	411	-174	16	
Grimsby	18	6	1	11	333	341	-8	13	
Amber Valley	18	3	0	15	144	435	-291	6	
*East Retford	18	4	0	14	194	587	-393	2	6
*Melbourne	18	3	0	15	168	541	-373	-6	1

Midlands 3 East (South)

	P	W	D	L	PF	PA	PD	Pts	-
Northampton Old Scouts	18	15	1	2	653	257	396	31	
Stewarts & Lloyds	18	12	1	5	389	253	136	25	
Long Buckby	18	11	0	7	390	262	128	22	
Northampton Mens Own	18	11	0	7	394	300	94	22	
Leighton Buzzard	18	10	0	8	336	328	8	20	
Towcestrians	18	9	0	9	307	305	2	18	
Peterborough	18	8	1	9	302	247	55	17	
Kibworth	18	8	0	10	299	305	-6	16	
Stockwood Park	18	3	1	14	262	673	-411	7	
Vipers	18	1	0	17	194	596	-402	2	

Midlands 4 East (South)

	P	W	D	L	PF	PA	PD	Pts	-
Lutterworth	18	15	0	3	465	192	273	30	
Old Northamptonians	18	14	1	3	574	223	351	29	
Leicester Forest	18	12	0	6	379	227	152	24	
Old Newtonians	18	10	1	7	277	339	-62	21	
Northampton Casuals	18	10	0	8	266	259	7	20	
Oadby Wyggestonians	18	8	1	9	212	302	-90	17	
Biggleswade	18	8	0	10	283	370	-87	16	
*Coalville	18	5	0	13	151	339	-188	8	2
Bugbrooke	18	3	1	14	221	398	-177	7	
Oakham	18	3	0	15	213	392	-179	6	

Midlands 2 West

	P	W	D	L	PF	PA	PD	Pts	-
Bromsgrove	22	21	0	1	894	245	649	42	
Old Laurentians	22	20	0	2	762	150	612	40	
Stratford-Upon-Avon	22	15	0	7	547	328	219	30	
Stafford	22	14	0	8	506	397	109	28	
Derby	22	13	0	9	430	314	116	26	
Wolverhampton	22	10	0	12	442	416	26	20	
Newbold	22	10	0	12	321	374	-53	20	
Sutton Coldfield	22	7	2	13	279	539	-260	16	
Burton	22	7	1	14	322	422	-100	15	
Shrewsbury	22	6	2	14	306	610	-304	14	
Stoke on Trent	22	5	1	16	280	626	-346	11	
Newport	22	1	0	21	188	856	-668	2	

Midlands 3 West (North)

	P	W	D	L	PF	PA	PD	Pts	-
Dixonians	18	13	3	2	333	185	148	29	
Aston Old Edwardians	18	13	1	4	415	219	196	27	
Kidderminster	18	10	3	5	342	266	76	23	
Lichfield	18	11	0	7	410	270	140	22	
Bridgnorth	18	10	1	7	348	317	31	21	
Old Yardleians	18	7	1	10	264	328	-64	15	
Telford	18	7	0	11	230	279	-49	14	
*Selly Oak	18	6	1	11	229	324	-95	11	2
Old Halesonians	18	5	0	13	285	376	-91	10	
Leek	18	3	0	15	185	477	-292	6	

Midlands 4 West (North)

	P	W	D	L	PF	PA	PD	Pts	-
Burntwood	18	16	1	1	399	131	268	33	
Willenhall	18	14	2	2	332	162	170	30	
Tamworth	18	12	1	5	295	220	75	25	
Ludlow	18	11	1	6	416	257	159	23	
Old Saltleians	18	10	0	8	380	332	48	20	
Wednesbury	18	7	1	10	299	277	22	15	
Newcastle (Staffs)	18	7	1	10	287	352	-65	15	
Handsworth	18	5	1	12	305	363	-58	11	
Cleobury Mortimer	18	3	0	15	197	447	-250	6	
*Wheaton Aston	18	1	0	17	105	474	-369	0	2

Midlands 3 West (South)

	P	W	D	L	PF	PA	PD	Pts	-
Leamington	18	15	1	2	316	146	170	31	
Bedworth	18	14	0	4	329	148	181	28	
Silhillians	18	13	1	4	346	214	132	27	
Pershore	18	8	1	9	245	237	8	17	
*Keresley	18	9	0	9	327	283	44	16	2
Old Leamingtonians	18	7	1	10	341	288	53	15	
Old Coventrians	18	7	1	10	281	345	-64	15	
*Nuneaton Old Edwardians	18	7	1	10	224	220	4	13	2
Evesham	18	4	0	14	193	313	-120	8	
Birmingham Exiles	18	2	2	14	111	519	-408	6	

Midlands 4 West (South)

	P	W	D	L	PF	PA	PD	Pts	-
Ledbury	18	15	0	3	458	192	266	30	
Southam	18	13	1	4	318	196	122	27	
Droitwich	18	11	0	7	357	230	127	22	
Berkswell & Balsall	18	10	2	6	283	220	63	22	
*Earlsdon	18	9	0	9	332	251	81	16	2
Coventry Welsh	18	8	0	10	246	309	-63	16	
Kings Norton	18	6	1	11	239	369	-130	13	
Stourport	18	6	0	12	202	284	-82	12	
Dunlop	18	6	0	12	220	385	-165	12	
Woodrush	18	4	0	14	178	397	-219	8	

East Midlands 1

	P	W	D	L	PF	PA	PD	Pts	-
Northampton BBOB	18	16	0	2	750	195	555	32	
Rushden & Higham	18	16	0	2	678	220	458	32	
Daventry	18	13	1	4	598	216	382	27	
Brackley	18	10	1	7	386	285	101	21	
Bedford Queens	18	9	0	9	383	288	95	18	
Kempston	18	8	0	10	239	360	-121	16	
Westwood	18	7	0	11	228	406	-178	14	
Wellingborough O.G.	18	5	0	13	192	497	-305	10	
St Ives (Midlands)	18	4	0	14	231	539	-308	8	
Deepings	18	1	0	17	139	818	-679	2	

East Midlands 2

	P	W	D	L	PF	PA	PD	Pts	-
Biddenham	14	13	0	1	609	77	532	26	
Bedford Swifts	14	13	0	1	495	64	431	26	
St Neots	14	9	0	5	321	252	69	18	
*Corby	14	6	0	8	236	267	-31	10	2
Vauxhall Motors	14	5	0	9	238	370	-132	10	
Northampton Heathens	14	5	0	9	156	413	-257	10	
Oundle	14	4	0	10	216	404	-188	8	
*Thorney	14	1	0	13	132	556	-424	0	2

NLD/Leics 1East

	P	W	D	L	PF	PA	PD	Pts	-
Mellish	18	16	1	1	668	119	549	33	
West Bridgford	18	15	0	3	538	167	371	30	
Nottinghamians	18	11	2	5	263	307	-44	24	
Southwell	18	10	1	7	267	231	36	21	
Stamford	18	10	0	8	285	264	21	20	
Boston	18	7	1	10	198	281	-83	15	
Keyworth	18	7	1	10	221	319	-98	15	
Sleaford	18	7	0	11	283	276	7	14	
Skegness	18	2	1	15	142	512	-370	5	
North Kesteven	18	1	1	16	168	557	-389	3	

NLD/Leics 2 East

	P	W	D	L	PF	PA	PD	Pts	-
Stamford College	16	15	0	1	681	99	582	30	
Barton & District	16	14	0	2	620	151	469	28	
Ollerton	16	10	0	6	305	305	0	20	
Cleethorpes	16	9	0	7	347	271	76	18	
Appleby Frodingham	16	9	0	7	273	295	-22	18	
Meden Vale	16	7	0	9	206	190	16	14	
Bourne	16	4	0	12	134	411	-277	8	
Gainsborough	16	2	0	14	102	456	-354	4	
Horncastle	16	2	0	14	157	647	-490	4	

NLD/Leics 1 West

	P	W	D	L	PF	PA	PD	Pts	-
Ashfield	18	18	0	0	409	87	322	36	
Nottingham Casuals	18	15	0	3	492	172	320	30	
Bakewell Mannerians	18	11	1	6	421	315	106	23	
Dronfield	18	11	1	6	240	218	22	23	
Belper	18	9	0	9	203	187	16	18	
Worksop	18	7	0	11	214	277	-63	14	
Ashby	18	6	1	11	240	355	-115	13	
Aylestonians	18	5	1	12	168	385	-217	11	
Leesbrook	18	3	0	15	137	241	-104	6	
Aylestone St James	18	3	0	15	143	430	-287	6	

NLD/Leics 2 West

	P	W	D	L	PF	PA	PD	Pts	-
Castle Donington	18	16	0	2	577	98	479	32	
East Leake	18	14	0	4	789	139	650	28	
Anstey	16	12	0	4	660	143	517	24	
*Boots Athletic	18	15	0	3	513	131	382	24	6
Chesterfield	18	8	0	10	296	385	-89	16	
Tupton	17	7	0	10	117	347	-230	14	
Bingham	18	4	1	13	110	486	-376	9	
*Cotgrave	17	6	0	11	178	436	-258	8	4
Rolls Royce	18	3	1	14	141	759	-618	7	
Hope Valley	18	1	2	15	118	575	-457	4	

North Midlands 1

	P	W	D	L	PF	PA	PD	Pts	-
Edwardians	18	12	2	4	420	153	267	26	
Yardley & District	18	13	0	5	341	174	167	26	
Redditch	18	13	0	5	344	248	96	26	
Veseyans	18	12	0	6	402	222	180	24	
Upton On Severn	18	12	0	6	369	251	118	24	
Bromyard	18	9	2	7	286	250	36	20	
Five Ways O.E.	18	5	1	12	228	295	-67	11	
*Bishops Castle & O.V.	18	5	2	11	156	216	-60	10	2
Tenbury	18	4	1	13	227	430	-203	9	
Warley	18	1	0	17	143	677	-534	2	

North Midlands 2

	P	W	D	L	PF	PA	PD	Pts	-
Solihull	16	16	0	0	542	153	389	32	
Worcester Wanderers	16	12	0	4	463	154	309	24	
Old Griffinians	16	10	1	5	445	208	237	21	
Birmingham C.S.	16	10	1	5	250	218	32	21	
Clee	16	6	2	8	241	271	-30	14	
Aldridge	16	7	0	9	238	329	-91	14	
Bloxwich	16	4	0	12	176	365	-189	8	
Harborne	16	3	0	13	143	337	-194	6	
Bournville	16	2	0	14	139	602	-463	4	

North Midlands 3

	P	W	D	L	PF	PA	PD	Pts	-
Bredon Star	14	13	0	1	726	46	680	26	
Birchfield	14	11	0	3	403	133	270	22	
Essington	14	9	0	5	343	169	174	18	
*Chaddesley Corbett	14	8	2	4	282	244	38	16	2
Greyhound	14	4	1	9	117	240	-123	9	
*Kynoch	14	5	0	9	192	389	-197	8	2
*Erdington	14	4	1	9	123	353	-230	7	2
Bewdley	14	0	0	14	76	688	-612	0	

Staffordshire 1	P	W	D	L	PF	PA	PD	Pts	-
Uttoxeter	8	8	0	0	258	51	207	16	
*St Leonards	8	4	0	4	122	135	-13	6	2
Linley	8	3	0	5	118	173	-55	6	
*Cannock	8	3	0	5	83	106	-23	4	2
Whittington	8	2	0	6	85	201	-116	4	

Staffordshire 2	P	W	D	L	PF	PA	PD	Pts	-
Rugeley	12	11	1	0	303	80	223	23	
Stone	12	8	1	3	241	141	100	17	
Gnosall	12	8	0	4	370	131	239	16	
Barton under Needwood	12	6	0	6	223	174	49	12	
Hanford	12	4	0	8	148	233	-85	8	
Market Drayton	12	3	0	9	115	364	-249	6	
Eccleshall	12	1	0	11	83	360	-277	2	

Warwickshire 1	P	W	D	L	PF	PA	PD	Pts	-
Marconi Coventry	18	17	0	1	447	143	304	34	
Shipston On Stour	18	16	0	2	507	94	413	32	
Manor Park	18	9	2	7	285	258	27	20	
Spartans (Midlands)	18	9	1	8	311	283	28	19	
Alcester	18	9	0	9	270	311	-41	18	
Trinity Guild	18	7	2	9	270	401	-131	16	
Old Wheatleyans	18	6	1	11	322	401	-79	13	
Stoke Old Boys	18	5	1	12	220	346	-126	11	
Rugby St Andrews	18	4	1	13	241	427	-186	9	
Standard	18	4	0	14	180	389	-209	8	

Warwickshire 2	P	W	D	L	PF	PA	PD	Pts	-
Harbury	16	15	0	1	548	106	442	30	
Claverdon	16	12	1	3	500	118	382	25	
Coventry Technical	16	11	2	3	559	126	433	24	
Pinley	16	10	0	6	331	239	92	20	
Coventry Saracens	16	9	1	6	399	210	189	19	
*Atherstone	16	7	0	9	355	301	54	12	2
Old Warwickians	16	2	0	14	130	494	-364	4	
Warwick	16	2	0	14	120	652	-532	4	
*Coventrians	16	2	0	14	100	796	-696	0	4

Midlands 2 East

	Ampthill	Banbury	Ilkeston	Kettering	Luton	Mansfield	Market Bosworth	Northampton Old	Nottingham Moderns	South Leicester	Syston	Wellingborough
Ampthill		01/03	07/09	28/09	11/01	02/11	12/10	21/12	23/11	01/02	12/04	07/12
Banbury	14/09		04/01	16/11	05/10	30/11	14/12	18/01	29/03	08/02	26/10	07/09
Ilkeston	15/03	02/11		01/03	23/11	01/02	28/09	12/04	12/10	21/12	07/12	11/01
Kettering	08/02	21/12	14/09		12/04	12/10	01/02	07/12	11/01	23/11	15/03	02/11
Luton	26/10	01/02	14/12	30/11		07/09	29/03	04/01	01/03	12/10	16/11	28/09
Mansfield	04/01	12/04	05/10	18/01	15/03		26/10	14/09	21/12	07/12	08/02	23/11
Market Bosworth	18/01	23/11	08/02	05/10	07/12	11/01		15/03	02/11	12/04	14/09	21/12
Northampton Old	16/11	12/10	30/11	29/03	02/11	01/03	07/09		28/09	11/01	14/12	01/02
Nottingham Moderns	14/12	07/12	18/01	26/10	14/09	16/11	04/01	08/02		15/03	05/10	12/04
South Leicester	05/10	28/09	16/11	14/12	18/01	29/03	30/11	26/10	07/09		04/01	01/03
Syston	30/11	11/01	29/03	07/09	21/12	28/09	01/03	23/11	01/02	02/11		12/10
Wellingborough	29/03	15/03	26/10	04/01	08/02	14/12	16/11	05/10	30/11	14/09	18/01	

Midlands 2 West

	Bedworth	Camp Hil	Derby	Dixonians	Hereford	Leamngtn	Newbold	Old Laurentians	Stafford	Stratford-Upon-Avon	Sutton Coldfield	Wolverhampton
Bedworth		07/09	01/03	01/02	11/01	02/11	28/09	21/12	12/10	23/11	12/04	07/12
Camp Hill	15/03		02/11	21/12	23/11	01/02	01/03	12/04	28/09	12/10	07/12	11/01
Derby	14/09	04/01		08/02	05/10	30/11	16/11	18/01	14/12	29/03	26/10	07/09
Dixonians	05/10	16/11	28/09		18/01	29/03	14/12	26/10	30/11	07/09	04/01	01/03
Hereford	26/10	14/12	01/02	12/10		07/09	30/11	04/01	29/03	01/03	16/11	28/09
Leamington	04/01	05/10	12/04	07/12	15/03		18/01	14/09	26/10	21/12	08/02	23/11
Newbold	08/02	14/09	21/12	23/11	12/04	12/10		07/12	01/02	11/01	15/03	02/11
Old Laurentians	16/11	30/11	12/10	11/01	02/11	01/03	29/03		07/09	28/09	14/12	01/02
Stafford	18/01	08/02	23/11	12/04	07/12	11/01	05/10	15/03		02/11	14/09	21/12
Stratford-Upon-Avon	14/12	18/01	07/12	15/03	14/09	16/11	26/10	08/02	04/01		05/10	12/04
Sutton Coldfield	30/11	29/03	11/01	02/11	21/12	28/09	07/09	23/11	01/03	01/02		12/10
Wolverhampton	29/03	26/10	15/03	14/09	08/02	14/12	04/01	05/10	16/11	30/11	18/01	

Midlands 3 East North

	Belgrave	Glossop	Lincoln	Loughborough	Loughborough Students	Matlock	Melton Mowbray	Newark	Paviors	Stoneygate
Belgrave		15/03	04/01	01/03	16/11	12/04	01/02	05/10	07/12	26/10
Glossop	14/09		01/03	05/10	01/02	04/01	16/11	26/10	12/04	07/12
Lincoln	02/11	28/09		14/12	08/02	12/10	29/03	30/11	18/01	14/09
Loughborough	28/09	08/02	16/11		12/04	07/12	26/10	01/02	15/03	04/01
Loughborough Students	14/12	12/10	05/10	30/11		18/01	14/09	29/03	02/11	01/03
Matlock	30/11	02/11	01/02	29/03	26/10		01/03	14/09	14/12	05/10
Melton Mowbray	12/10	14/12	07/12	18/01	15/03	28/09		02/11	08/02	12/04
Newark	08/02	18/01	12/04	12/10	07/12	15/03	04/01		28/09	16/11
Paviors	29/03	30/11	26/10	14/09	04/01	16/11	05/10	01/03		01/02
Stoneygate	18/01	29/03	15/03	02/11	28/09	08/02	30/11	14/12	12/10	

Midlands 3 East South

	Huntingdon	Kibworth	Leighton Buzzard	Long Buckby	Lutterworth	Northampton Mens	Old Northamptonians	Peterborough	Stewarts & Lloyds	Towcestrians
Huntingdon		14/09	01/03	05/10	01/02	26/10	04/01	16/11	12/04	07/12
Kibworth	15/03		04/01	01/03	16/11	05/10	12/04	01/02	07/12	26/10
Leighton Buzzard	28/09	02/11		14/12	08/02	30/11	12/10	29/03	18/01	14/09
Long Buckby	08/02	28/09	16/11		12/04	01/02	07/12	26/10	15/03	04/01
Lutterworth	12/10	14/12	05/10	30/11		29/03	18/01	14/09	02/11	01/03
Northampton Mens	18/01	08/02	12/04	12/10	07/12		15/03	04/01	28/09	16/11
Old Northamptonians	02/11	30/11	01/02	29/03	26/10	14/09		01/03	14/12	05/10
Peterborough	14/12	12/10	07/12	18/01	15/03	02/11	28/09		08/02	12/04
Stewarts & Lloyds	30/11	29/03	26/10	14/09	04/01	01/03	16/11	05/10		01/02
Towcestrians	29/03	18/01	15/03	02/11	28/09	14/12	08/02	30/11	12/10	

Midlands 3 West North

	Aston OE	Bridgnorth	Burntwood	Burton	Kidderminster	Lichfield	Newport	Shrewsbury	Stoke on Trent	Willenhall
Aston Old Edwardians		14/09	01/03	05/10	01/02	26/10	04/01	16/11	12/04	07/12
Bridgnorth	15/03		04/01	01/03	16/11	05/10	12/04	01/02	07/12	26/10
Burntwood	28/09	02/11		14/12	08/02	30/11	12/10	29/03	18/01	14/09
Burton	08/02	28/09	16/11		12/04	01/02	07/12	26/10	15/03	04/01
Kidderminster	12/10	14/12	05/10	30/11		29/03	18/01	14/09	02/11	01/03
Lichfield	18/01	08/02	12/04	12/10	07/12		15/03	04/01	28/09	16/11
Newport	02/11	30/11	01/02	29/03	26/10	14/09		01/03	14/12	05/10
Shrewsbury	14/12	12/10	07/12	18/01	15/03	02/11	28/09		08/02	12/04
Stoke on Trent	30/11	29/03	26/10	14/09	04/01	01/03	16/11	05/10		01/03
Willenhall	29/03	18/01	15/03	02/11	28/09	14/12	08/02	30/11	12/10	

Midlands 3 West South

	Birmingham Exiles	Evesham	Keresley	Ledbury	Nuneaton Old	Old Coventrians	Old Leamingtonians	Pershore	Silhillians	Southam
Birmingham Exiles		14/09	01/03	05/10	01/02	26/10	04/01	16/11	12/04	07/12
Evesham	15/03		04/01	01/03	16/11	05/10	12/04	01/02	07/12	26/10
Keresley	28/09	02/11		14/12	08/02	30/11	12/10	29/03	18/01	14/09
Ledbury	08/02	28/09	16/11		12/04	01/02	07/12	26/10	15/03	04/01
Nuneaton Old	12/10	14/12	05/10	30/11		29/03	18/01	14/09	02/11	01/03
Old Coventrians	18/01	08/02	12/04	12/10	07/12		15/03	04/01	28/09	16/11
Old Leamingtonians	02/11	30/11	01/02	29/03	26/10	14/09		01/03	14/12	05/10
Pershore	14/12	12/10	07/12	18/01	15/03	02/11	28/09		08/02	12/04
Silhillians	30/11	29/03	26/10	14/09	04/01	01/03	16/11	05/10		01/02
Southam	29/03	18/01	15/03	02/11	28/09	14/12	08/02	30/11	12/10	

Midlands 4 East North

	Ashbourne	Ashfield	Buxton	Grimsby	Kesteven	Long Eaton	Market Rasen	Mellish	Nottingham Casuals	West Bridgford
Ashbourne		14/09	01/03	05/10	01/02	26/10	04/01	16/11	12/04	07/12
Ashfield	15/03		04/01	01/03	16/11	05/10	12/04	01/02	07/12	26/10
Buxton	28/09	02/11		14/12	08/02	30/11	12/10	29/03	18/01	14/09
Grimsby	08/02	28/09	16/11		12/04	01/02	07/12	26/10	15/03	04/01
Kesteven	12/10	14/12	05/10	30/11		29/03	18/01	14/09	02/11	01/03
Long Eaton	18/01	08/02	12/04	12/10	07/12		15/03	04/01	28/09	16/11
Market Rasen	02/11	30/11	01/02	29/03	26/10	14/09		01/03	14/12	05/10
Mellish	14/12	12/10	07/12	18/01	15/03	02/11	28/09		08/02	12/04
Nottingham Casuals	30/11	29/03	26/10	14/09	04/01	01/03	16/11	05/10		01/02
West Bridgford	29/03	18/01	15/03	02/11	28/09	14/12	08/02	30/11	12/10	

Midlands 4 East South

	Biggles	Coalville	Leicester Forest	Northampton BBOB	Northampton Casuals	Oadby Wyggestonians	Old Newtonians	Rushden & Higham	Stockwood Park	Vipers
Biggleswade		01/03	05/10	14/09	26/10	04/01	12/04	01/02	16/11	07/12
Coalville	28/09		14/12	02/11	30/11	12/10	18/01	08/02	29/03	14/09
Leicester Forest	08/02	16/11		28/09	01/02	07/12	15/03	12/04	26/10	04/01
Northampton BBOB	15/03	04/01	01/03		05/10	12/04	07/12	16/11	01/02	26/10
Northampton Casuals	18/01	12/04	12/10	08/02		15/03	28/09	07/12	04/01	16/11
Oadby Wyggestonians	02/11	01/02	29/03	30/11	14/09		14/12	26/10	01/03	05/10
Old Newtonians	30/11	26/10	14/09	29/03	01/03	16/11		04/01	05/10	01/02
Rushden & Higham	12/10	05/10	30/11	14/12	29/03	18/01	02/11		14/09	01/03
Stockwood Park	14/12	07/12	18/01	12/10	02/11	28/09	08/02	15/03		12/04
Vipers	29/03	15/03	02/11	18/01	14/12	08/02	12/10	28/09	30/11	

Midlands 4 West North

	Leek	Ludlow	Newcastle (Staffs)	Old Salteians	Selly Oak	Tamworth	Telford	Uttoxeter	Wednesbury	Yardley & District
Leek		14/09	01/03	05/10	01/02	26/10	04/01	16/11	12/04	07/12
Ludlow	15/03		04/01	01/03	16/11	05/10	12/04	01/02	07/12	26/10
Newcastle (Staffs)	28/09	02/11		14/12	08/02	30/11	12/10	29/03	18/01	14/09
Old Saltleians	08/02	28/09	16/11		12/04	01/02	07/12	26/10	15/03	04/01
Selly Oak	12/10	14/12	05/10	30/11		29/03	18/01	14/09	02/11	01/03
Tamworth	18/01	08/02	12/04	12/10	07/12		15/03	04/01	28/09	16/11
Telford	02/11	30/11	01/02	29/03	26/10	14/09		01/03	14/12	05/10
Uttoxeter	14/12	12/10	07/12	18/01	15/03	02/11	28/09		08/02	12/04
Wednesbury	30/11	29/03	26/10	14/09	04/01	01/03	16/11	05/10		01/02
Yardley & District	29/03	18/01	15/03	02/11	28/09	14/12	08/02	30/11	12/10	

MIDLAND

Midlands 4 West South

	Berkswell & B.	Coventry Welsh	Droitwich	Earlsdon	Edwardians	Kings Norton	Marconi Coventry	Old Halesonians	Old Yardleians	Shipston on Stour
Berkswell & Balsall		08/02	02/11	14/12	29/03	30/11	18/01	28/09	12/10	14/09
Coventry Welsh	05/10		14/12	30/11	14/09	29/03	02/11	12/10	18/01	01/03
Droitwich	04/01	16/11		01/03	01/02	05/10	07/12	15/03	12/04	26/10
Earlsdon	16/11	12/04	28/09		26/10	01/02	15/03	08/02	07/12	04/01
Edwardians	07/12	15/03	12/10	18/01		02/11	08/02	14/12	28/09	12/04
Kings Norton	12/04	07/12	08/02	12/10	04/01		28/09	18/01	15/03	16/11
Marconi Coventry	26/10	04/01	29/03	14/09	05/10	01/03		30/11	16/11	01/02
Old Halesonians	01/03	01/02	14/09	05/10	16/11	26/10	12/04		04/01	07/12
Old Yardleians	01/02	26/10	30/11	29/03	01/03	14/09	14/12	02/11		05/10
Shipston On Stour	15/03	28/09	18/01	02/11	30/11	14/12	12/10	29/03	08/02	

Notts/Lincs/ Derbys/Leic. 1 East

	Barton & District	Boston	East Retford	Keyworth	Nottinghamians	Oakham	Sleaford	Southwell	Stamford	Stamford College
Barton & District		14/12	29/03	08/02	15/03	18/01	30/11	02/11	28/09	12/10
Boston	16/11		18/01	15/03	12/04	08/02	04/01	12/10	07/12	28/09
East Retford	07/12	26/10		04/01	01/03	14/09	16/11	05/10	01/02	12/04
Keyworth	05/10	14/09	02/11		01/02	30/11	01/03	29/03	26/10	14/12
Nottinghamians	14/09	30/11	28/09	12/10		02/11	29/03	14/12	08/02	18/01
Oakham	26/10	05/10	15/03	12/04	04/01		01/02	01/03	16/11	07/12
Sleaford	12/04	02/11	14/12	28/09	07/12	12/10		18/01	15/03	08/02
Southwell	04/01	01/02	08/02	07/12	16/11	28/09	26/10		12/04	15/03
Stamford	01/03	29/03	12/10	18/01	05/10	14/12	14/09	30/11		02/11
Stamford College	01/02	01/03	30/11	16/11	26/10	29/03	05/10	14/09	04/01	

Notts/Lincs/ Derbys/Leic. 1 West

	Amber Valley	Anstey	Ashby	Aylestonians	Bakewell Mannerians	Belper	Castle Donington	Dronfield	East Leake	Melbourne	Worksop
Amber Valley		02/11	15/03	01/03	21/12	28/09	01/02	23/11	12/04	07/12	12/10
Anstey	04/01		14/09	16/11	08/02	14/12	30/11	05/10	18/01	26/10	29/03
Ashby	07/09	01/03		28/09	01/02	12/10	02/11	11/01	21/12	12/04	23/11
Aylestonians	14/09	21/12	08/02		23/11	12/10	12/04	07/12	15/03	11/01	
Bakewell Mannerians	16/11	28/09	05/10	14/12		30/11	29/03	18/01	26/10	04/01	07/09
Belper	08/02	23/11	18/01	05/10	12/04		11/01	07/12	15/03	14/09	02/11
Castle Donington	05/10	12/04	04/01	18/01	07/12	26/10		15/03	14/09	08/02	21/12
Dronfield	14/12	01/02	26/10	30/11	12/10	29/03	07/09		04/01	16/11	01/03
East Leake	30/11	12/10	16/11	29/03	11/01	07/09	01/03	02/11		14/12	28/09
Melbourne	29/03	11/01	30/11	07/09	02/11	01/03	28/09	21/12	23/11		01/02

Notts/Lincs/ Derbys/Leic. 2 East

	Appleby Frodingham	Bourne	Cleethorpes	Gainsborough	Horncastle	Meden Vale	North Kesteven	Ollerton	Skegness
Appleby Frodingham		14/09	01/03	05/10	01/02	26/10	04/01	16/11	12/04
Bourne	15/03		04/01	01/03	16/11	05/10	12/04	01/02	07/12
Cleethorpes	28/09	02/11		14/12	08/02	30/11	12/10	29/03	18/01
Gainsborough	08/02	28/09	16/11		12/04	01/02	07/12	26/10	15/03
Horncastle	12/10	14/12	05/10	30/11		29/03	18/01	14/09	02/11
Meden Vale	18/01	08/02	12/04	12/10	07/12		15/03	04/01	28/09
North Kesteven	02/11	30/11	01/02	29/03	26/10	14/09		01/03	14/12
Ollerton	14/12	12/10	07/12	18/01	15/03	02/11	28/09		08/02
Skegness	30/11	29/03	26/10	14/09	04/01	01/03	16/11	05/10	

Notts/Lincs/ Derbys/Leic. 2 West

	Aylestone Athletic	Aylestone St James	Bingham	Boots Athletic	Chesterfield	Leesbrook	North Derbyshire	Rolls Royce	Tupton	University of Derby
Aylestone Athletic		14/09	05/10	01/02	26/10	04/01	16/11	01/03	12/04	07/12
Aylestone St James	15/03		01/03	16/11	05/10	12/04	01/02	04/01	07/12	26/10
Bingham	08/02	28/09		12/04	01/02	07/12	26/10	16/11	15/03	04/01
Boots Athletic	12/10	14/12	30/11		29/03	18/01	14/09	05/10	02/11	01/03
Chesterfield	18/01	08/02	12/10	07/12		15/03	04/01	12/04	28/09	16/11
Leesbrook	02/11	30/11	29/03	26/10	14/09		01/03	01/02	14/12	05/10
North Derbyshire	14/12	12/10	18/01	15/03	02/11	28/09		07/12	08/02	12/04
Rolls Royce	28/09	02/11	14/12	08/02	30/11	12/10	29/03		18/01	19/10
Tupton	30/11	29/03	14/09	04/01	01/03	16/11	05/10	26/10		01/02
University Of Derby	29/03	18/01	02/11	28/09	14/12	08/02	30/11	15/03	12/10	

East Midlands 1

	Bedford Queens	Bedford Swifts	Biddenham	Brackley	Bugbrooke	Daventry	Kempston	Wellingborough O.G.	Westwood
Bedford Queens		18/01	14/09	14/12	01/03	05/10	30/11	29/03	12/10
Bedford Swifts	26/10		05/10	29/03	01/02	16/11	14/09	01/03	04/01
Biddenham	15/03	08/02		18/01	07/12	12/04	02/11	14/12	28/09
Brackley	16/11	07/12	26/10		04/01	01/03	05/10	01/02	12/04
Bugbrooke	28/09	12/10	29/03	02/11		14/09	14/12	30/11	08/02
Daventry	08/02	14/12	30/11	28/09	15/03		12/10	02/11	18/01
Kempston	12/04	15/03	04/01	08/02	16/11	01/02		26/10	07/12
Wellingborough O.G.	07/12	28/09	16/11	12/10	12/04	04/01	18/01		15/03
Westwood	01/02	02/11	01/03	30/11	05/10	26/10	29/03	14/09	

East Midlands 2

	Corby	Deepings	Northampton Heathens	Oundle	St Ives (Midlands)	St Neots	Thorney	Vauxhall Motors
Corby		01/02	18/01	07/12	14/09	02/11	12/10	12/04
Deepings	28/09		12/10	04/01	07/09	08/02	02/11	18/01
Northampton Heathens	05/10	11/01		01/03	01/02	12/04	04/01	07/12
Oundle	15/03	26/10	07/09		30/11	18/01	08/02	12/10
St Ives (Midlands)	08/02	01/03	28/09	12/04		04/01	18/01	02/11
St Neots	14/12	14/09	30/11	05/10	26/10		15/03	01/02
Thorney	11/01	14/12	26/10	14/09	05/10	07/12		01/03
Vauxhall Motors	30/11	05/10	15/03	11/01	14/12	28/09	07/09	

North Midlands 1

	Bromyard	Cleobury Mortimer	Five Ways O.E	Redditch	Solihull	Stourport	Upton On Severn	Veseyans	Woodrush	Worcs Wanderers
Bromyard		14/09	01/03	05/10	01/02	26/10	04/01	16/11	12/04	07/12
Cleobury Mortimer	15/03		04/01	01/03	16/11	05/10	12/04	01/02	07/12	26/10
Five Ways O.E.	28/09	02/11		14/12	08/02	30/11	12/10	29/03	18/01	14/09
Redditch	08/02	28/09	16/11		12/04	01/02	07/12	26/10	15/03	04/01
Solihull	12/10	14/12	05/10	30/11		29/03	18/01	14/09	02/11	01/03
Stourport	18/01	08/02	12/04	12/10	07/12		15/03	04/01	28/09	16/11
Upton On Severn	02/11	30/11	01/02	29/03	26/10	14/09		01/03	14/12	05/10
Veseyans	14/12	12/10	07/12	18/01	15/03	02/11	28/09		08/02	12/04
Woodrush	30/11	29/03	26/10	14/09	04/01	01/03	16/11	05/10		01/02
Worcester Wanderers	29/03	18/01	15/03	02/11	28/09	14/12	08/02	30/11	12/10	

North Midlands 2

	Aldridge	Birchfield	Birmingham C.S	Bishops Castle & O.V	Bloxwich	Bredon Star	Clee Hill	Old Griffinians	Tenbury	Warley
Aldridge		14/09	01/03	05/10	01/02	26/10	04/01	16/11	12/04	07/12
Birchfield	15/03		04/01	01/03	16/11	05/10	12/04	01/02	07/12	26/10
Birmingham C.S.	28/09	02/11		14/12	08/02	30/11	12/10	29/03	18/01	14/09
Bishops Castle & O.V.	08/02	28/09	16/11		12/04	01/02	07/12	26/10	15/03	04/01
Bloxwich	12/10	14/12	05/10	30/11		29/03	18/01	14/09	02/11	01/03
Bredon Star	18/01	08/02	12/04	12/10	07/12		15/03	04/01	28/09	16/11
Clee Hill	02/11	30/11	01/02	29/03	26/10	14/09		01/03	14/12	05/10
Old Griffinians	14/12	12/10	07/12	18/01	15/03	02/11	28/09		08/02	12/04
Tenbury	30/11	29/03	26/10	14/09	04/01	01/03	16/11	05/10		01/02
Warley	29/03	18/01	15/03	02/11	28/09	14/12	08/02	30/11	12/10	

North Midlands 3

	Bewdley	Bournville	Chaddesley Corb.	Dudley Wasps	Erdington	Essington	Greyhound	Harborne	Kynoch	Stourbridge Lions
Bewdley		12/10	18/01	08/02	28/09	07/12	15/03	14/12	02/11	12/04
Bournville	01/02		01/03	07/12	12/04	04/01	16/11	14/09	05/10	26/10
Chaddesley Corbett	26/10	28/09		15/03	07/12	16/11	12/04	08/02	01/02	04/01
Dudley Wasps	05/10	29/03	14/09		16/11	26/10	04/01	30/11	01/03	01/02
Erdington	01/03	30/11	29/03	14/12		01/02	26/10	02/11	14/09	05/10
Essington	29/03	02/11	14/12	18/01	12/10		08/02	28/09	30/11	14/09
Greyhound	14/09	14/12	30/11	02/11	18/01	05/10		12/10	29/03	01/03
Harborne	16/11	15/03	05/10	12/04	04/01	01/03	01/02		26/10	07/12
Kynoch	04/01	08/02	12/10	28/09	15/03	12/04	07/12	18/01		16/11
Stourbridge Lions	30/11	18/01	02/11	12/10	08/02	15/03	28/09	29/03	14/12	

MIDLAND

Warwickshire 1

	Alcester	Claverdon	Dunlop	Harbury	Manor Park	Old Wheatleyans	Rugby St. Andrews	Spartans (Midlands)	Stoke O.B.	Trinity Guild
Alcester		01/03	26/10	16/11	01/02	14/09	12/04	07/12	05/10	04/01
Claverdon	28/09		30/11	29/03	08/02	02/11	18/01	14/09	14/12	12/10
Dunlop	18/01	12/04		04/01	07/12	08/02	28/09	16/11	12/10	15/03
Harbury	14/12	07/12	02/11		15/03	12/10	08/02	12/04	18/01	28/09
Manor Park	12/10	05/10	29/03	14/09		14/12	02/11	01/03	30/11	18/01
Old Wheatleyans	15/03	04/01	05/10	01/02	16/11		07/12	26/10	01/03	12/04
Rugby St Andrews	30/11	26/10	01/03	05/10	04/01	29/03		01/02	14/09	16/11
Spartans (Midlands)	29/03	15/03	14/12	30/11	28/09	18/01	12/10		02/11	08/02
Stoke Old Boys	08/02	16/11	01/02	26/10	12/04	28/09	15/03	04/01		07/12
Trinity Guild	02/11	01/02	14/09	01/03	26/10	30/11	14/12	05/10	29/03	

Warwickshire 2

	Atherstone	Coventrians	Coventry Saracens	Coventry Technical	Old Warwickians	Pinley	Standard	Warwick
Atherstone		14/09	01/03	05/10	04/01	16/11	26/10	12/04
Coventrians	15/03		04/01	01/03	12/04	01/02	05/10	07/12
Coventry Saracens	28/09	02/11		14/12	12/10	29/03	30/11	18/01
Coventry Technical	08/02	28/09	16/11		07/12	26/10	01/02	15/03
Old Warwickians	02/11	30/11	01/02	29/03		01/03	14/09	14/12
Pinley	14/12	12/10	07/12	18/01	28/09		02/11	08/02
Standard	18/01	08/02	12/04	12/10	15/03	04/01		28/09
Warwick	30/11	29/03	26/10	14/09	16/11	05/10	01/03	

Discussions regarding the structure of Staffs 1 & 2 were still ongoing at the time of going to press and no fixtures' schedule had been finalised. The clubs involved have been listed below in alphabetical order.

Barton under Needwood
Cannock
Eccleshall
GEC St. Leonards
Gnosall
Handsworth
Linley
Market Drayton
Michelin
Rugeley
Stone
Wheaton Aston
Whittington

Staffordshire 1

Staffordshire 2

GIFTS & SOUVENIRS

REPLICA KIT

EQUIPMENT

PROTECTION

LEISUREWEAR

TRAINING KIT

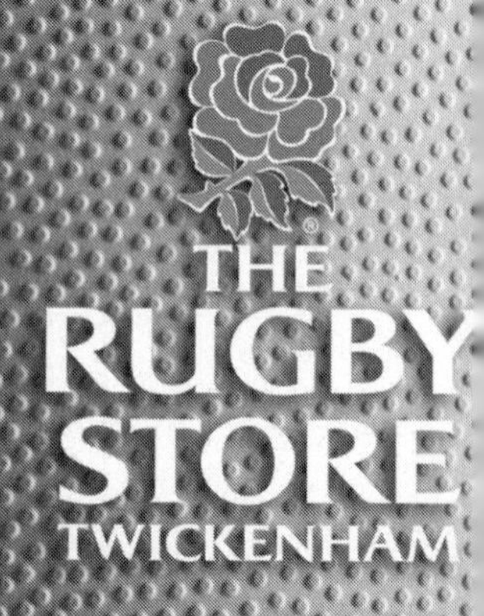

FOOTWEAR

OPEN 7 DAYS A WEEK IN TWICKENHAM'S EAST STAND
CALL 020 8891 4141 FOR YOUR FULL RANGE CATALOGUE
OR VISIT WWW.RFU.COM TODAY

ALCESTER RFC
Ground Address: Birmingham Road, Kings Coughton, Alcester, Warwickshire B49 5QF Tel: 01789 764061
Web Address: www.alcesterrfc.co.uk
Brief Directions: The Ground is situated on the West side of the A435 between Studley and Alcester approx. 1 mile north of Alcester at Kings Coughton.
Hon Secretary: F. D. Billingsley, Foxton House, 4 Willoughby Close, Alcester, Warwickshire B49 5QJ
Tel: (H) 01789 764502 Tel: (M) 07813 731656
Fixtures Secretary: A. Brookes, 20 Alvana Avenue, Alcester, Warks B49 6AN
Tel: (H) 01789 764076 Tel: (W) 01789 761215
Club Colours: Red and black, black shorts
League: Warwickshire 1

ALDRIDGE RFC
Ground Address: Bourne Vale, off Little Hardwick Road, Aldridge, Walsall WS9 0SH Tel: 0121 353 2856
Web Address: www.aldridgerfc.co.uk
Brief Directions: Sign posted off Little Hardwick Road. Situated at the end of Bourne Vale.
Hon Secretary: Jim Chambers, 15 Hidcote Grove, Birmingham B37 7BE Tel: (H) 0121 779 4189
Email: jayelsie@supanet.com
Fixtures Secretary: Alex Reed, 2 Coppice View Road, Sutton Coldfield B73 6UE Tel: (H) 0121 243 8599
Club Colours: Black, maroon & gold hoops
League: North Midlands 2

AMBER VALLEY RUFC
Ground Address: Pye Bridge, Lower Somercotes, Alfreton, Derbys DE55 1NF Tel: 01773 541308
Brief Directions: M1 J28 follow A38 towards Derby, 2 miles B600 to Somerscotes, follow B600 towards Selston club 2 miles on left.
Hon Secretary: Andrew Clarke, 98 Hickton Road, Alfreton, Derbys DE55 1AG Tel: (H) 01773 605755
Tel: (W) 01332 290 550 ext 468
Email: aclarke15@compuserve.com
Fixtures Secretary: Andy Pickworth, 53 Ashton Close, Alfreton, Derbys DE55 1HG Tel: (H) 012773 528845
Club Colours: Black, gold/maroon hoops, Black shorts
League: NLD/Leics 1 West

AMPTHILL & DISTRICT RFC
Ground Address: 8 Meadow Way, Ampthill, Beds MK45 2QX Tel: 01525 403303
Email Address: ampthill@freeuk.com
Web Address: www.ampthillrufc.com
Brief Directions: Ground on right approaching Ampthill from Woburn
Hon Secretary: Helene Wright, 74 Willow Way, Ampthill, Beds MK45 2SP Tel: (H) 01525 754551
Tel: (M) 07979 754721 Tel: (W) 01582 373700
Email: ampthill@freeuk.com
Fixtures Secretary: Glenys Davis
Club Colours: Maroon and amber
League: Midlands 2 East

ANSTEY RFC
Ground Address: Link Road, Anstey, (Next to Anstey Martin School), Leicester
Web Address: www.ansteyrfc.co.uk
Brief Directions: See club website. A5630 into Anstey off A46 (from J21A M1). From town centre roundabout take Bradgate Road. Link Road is 5th right. Park and change at Martin School, half-mile on left. Clubhouse is Old Hare and Hounds, Bradgate Road
Hon Secretary: Alan Chapman, 1 Groby Road, Anstey, Leics LE7 7FN Tel: (H) 0116 221 7727
Tel: (M) 07973 561 289 Tel: (W) 0116 235 5585
Email: ac@alanchapman.com
Fixtures Secretary: Ian Pollock, 14 Pinewood Close, Leicester LE4 1ER Tel: (H) 0116 236 7364
Email: irp@arfc.fsnet.co.uk
Club Colours: Black with red/emerald chevron.
League: NLD/Leics 1 West

APPLEBY FRODINGHAM RFC
Ground Address: Brumby Hall Social Club, Ashby Road, Scunthorpe. Tel: 01724 276279
Brief Directions: Off M180 (Scunthorpe). Right at 1st R/about, 3rd turning off 2nd R/about. Left at next R/about onto Ashby Road, Brumby Hall 100yds on left.
Club Secretary: Rob Garner, 26 Glanville Avenue, Scunthorpe, Lincs DN17 1DE. Tel: 07957 934878
Fixtures Secretary: Andy Graves, 69 Glanville Avenue, Scunthorpe, Lincs DN17. Tel: 01724 276279
Club Colours: Black & white. Change Red & white
League: NLD/Leics 2 East

ASHBOURNE RUFC
Ground Address: The Recreation Ground, Cokayne Avenue, Ashbourne DE6 1EJ
Brief Directions: A52 Derby/Ashbourne. The ground is visible coming down the Derby Hill to your right.
Hon Secretary: P. J. Fuller, Ednaston Lodge Farm, Ednaston, Derbys DE6 3BA Tel: (H) 01335 360381
Email: fullerful4et@supanet.com
Fixtures Secretary: Andrew Bailey, Ednaston Hall, Derby Tel: (H) 01335 343432
Club Colours: Gold & blue hoops
League: Midlands 4 East (North)

ASHBY RFC
Ground Address: Nottingham Road, Ashby, Leicester LE65 1DJ Tel: 01530 413 992
Brief Directions: M42 junction 13, signposted Ashby (A50), right at next roundabout, signposted Lount Breedon (A453)
Hon Secretary: J. Mitchell, 50 Pennine Way, Ashby, Leics LE65 1EW Tel: (H) 01530 415284
Tel: (M) 0783 614 398 Tel: (W) 01302 755222
Fixtures Secretary: J. Grimsley, The White Hart Inn, Market Street, Ashby, Leics LE65 1BE
Tel: (H) 01530 414531
Club Colours: Maroon and sky blue hoops
League: NLD/Leics 1 West

ASHFIELD RFC
Ground Address: Moor Lane Community Centre, Moor Lane, Mansfield, Notts NG15 5SF Tel: 01623 635437
Brief Directions: A38 into Mansfield to McDonalds island, 3rd exit,through three sets of lights. Moor Lane on right just after speed cameras, ground on right.
Hon Secretary: Stephen Trainer, 12 Belfry Close, Broadlands Park, Kirkby in Ashfield, Notts NG17 8NS
Tel: (H) 01623 400411 Tel: (M) 07974 871701
Tel: (W) 01623 622515 ext 4201
Fixtures Secretary: John Chambers, 12 Berry Hill Lane, Mansfield, Notts NG18 4BQ Tel: (H) 01623 641391
Club Colours: Red, navy & amber hoops, black sleeves
League: Midlands 4 East (North)

ASTON OLD EDWARDIANS RFC
Ground Address: Sunnybank Avenue, Perry Common, Birmingham B44 0HP Tel: 0121 373 5746
Email Address: grundyjill@hotmail.com
Web Address: www.astonoldeds.co.uk
Brief Directions: Off College Road (A453) approx half way between A452 and B4138. Seat garage located on corner of A453 and Sunnybank Avenue.
Hon Secretary: G. M. Grundy, 31 Frederick Road, Sutton Coldfield B73 5QN
Tel: (H) 021 354 5840 Tel: (W) 0121 747 6101
Email: grundyjill@hotmail.com
Fixtures Secretary: Tony Stafford, 54 Station Road, Solihull, West Midlands B37 7BA
Tel: (H) 0121 684 2653
Email: a.stafford@blueyonder.co.uk
Club Colours: Green, red and white hooped shirts, white shorts
League: Midlands 3 West (North)

ATHERSTONE RFC
Ground Address: Ratcliffe Road, Atherstone, Warwickshire Tel: 01827 714934
Brief Directions: Drive into town centre, turn at Midland Bank into Ratcliffe Road, clubhouse approx 0.75 mile down on left
Hon Secretary: David Boal, Thurmaston House, 74 South Street, Atherstone, Warwickshire CV9 1DZ
Tel: (H) 01827 713145 Tel: (W) 01827 713145
Email: dave@boaly.fsnet.co.uk
Fixtures Secretary: Nick Cameron, 22 Barnsley Close, Atherstone CV9 2DG Tel: (H) 01827 713857
Tel: (M) 07789 221540
Club Colours: Black/white
League: Warwickshire 2

AYLESTONE ATHLETIC RFC
Ground Address: The Pavilion, Victoria Park, Leicester
Brief Directions: Victoria Park is to the south of the city centre and the Pavilion is on the north side of the park
Hon Secretary: Mark Elliott, 29 Bridgewater, Great Glen, Leicester LE8 9DX Tel: (H) 0116 259 3550
Tel: (M) 07966 249576 Tel: (W) 0116 252 8048
Fixtures Secretary: Mark Walters, 113 Holmfield Road, Stoneygate, Leicester LE2 1SF
Club Colours: Navy and red horizontal stripes, navy shorts
League: NLD/Leics 2 West

AYLESTONE ST. JAMES RFC
Ground Address: The Clubhouse, Covert Lane, Scraptoft, Leicester Tel: 0116 241 9202
Brief Directions: Out of Leicester on A47 Uppingham Rd, left into Scraptoft Lane, top of lane go directly on to Covert Lane, 2nd clubhouse on left
Hon Secretary: C. J. Gamble, 24 Firfield Avenue, Leicester LE4 4DR Tel: (H) 0116 267 2065
Tel: (M) 07885 788 606 Tel: (W) 0116 247 0178
Fixtures Secretary: P. Chapman, 8 Valentine Road, Leicester LE5 2GH Tel: (H) 0116 243 1826
Tel: (W) 0116 260 2475
Club Colours: Blue and white hoops, navy shorts
League: NLD/Leics 2 West

AYLESTONIANS RFC
Ground Address: Knighton Lane East, Leicester
Tel: 0116 283 4899
Hon Secretary: Clive Cooper, 36 Chestnut Road, Glenfield, Leicester LE3 8DB Tel: (H) 0116 225 0610
Email: c.cooper11@ntlworld.com
Fixtures Secretary: Colin Shaw, 95 Bonney Road, New Parks, Leicester LE3 9NL Tel: (H) 0116 232 2258
Tel: (M) 07736 108801
Club Colours: Red, white and navy blue hoops with navy shorts
League: NLD/Leics 1 West
League Contact: As Fixture Secretary

BAKEWELL MANNERIANS RUFC
Ground Address: The Showground, Coombs Road, Bakewell, Derbys.
Brief Directions: Follow the `Agricultural Centre' signs from the A6. Pitch is on the right in front of the centre. Changing is at the Pavilion across the river via the foot-bridge.
Club Secretary: Martin Pearce,Manor House Farm, Over Haddon, Bakewell, Derbys.. DE45 1JE
Tel No: 01629 814706 Email: jmpprop@aol.com
Fixtures Secretary: Rod Bell, Nether Croft, Eaton Place, Baslow DE45 1RW. Tel: 01246 583564
Club Colours: Navy, light blue and white hoops, navy shorts
League: NLD/Leics 1 West

BANBURY RFC
Ground Address: Bodicote Park, Oxford Road, Banbury Tel: 01295 279000
Brief Directions: M40 Jct 11. Follow signs to Town Centre, Hospital, Adderbury A4260. Ground is situated on the A4260 going towards Adderbury on the left 1.5 miles beyond the hospital
Hon Secretary: Bryan A. Davies, 34 Horton View, Banbury OX16 9HP Tel: 01295 262027
Fixtures Secretary: Roger Croft, 1 Daisy Hill Farm Cottage, Duns Tew, Oxford OX6 4JS
Tel: 01869 347124
Club Colours: Navy and white hooped shirts, navy shorts
League: Midlands 2 East

BARTON & DISTRICT RUFC
Ground Address: Mill Lane, Barton, N. Lincs
Tel: 01464 531119
Brief Directions: To Barton, Right at mini roundabout, through Barton market place, out of Barton approx 1 1/2 miles to Barrow, right at roundabout next sharp right into ground.
Hon Secretary: Andy Bontoft, 44 Westfield Road, North Lincolnshire DN18 5AB
Fixtures Secretary: Graham Briggs, 99 Farthings Road, Barton Tel: (H) 01652 634187
Club Colours: Red and white hoops
League: NLD/Leics 1East

BARTON-UNDER-NEEDWOOD RFC
Ground Address: Holland Sports & Social Club, Efflinch Lane, Barton Under Needwood, Staffs
Tel: 01283 712937
Hon Secretary: Nick Rigby, 2 Forest Barn Cottage, Barton Gate, Barton Under Needwood, Staffs DE13 8BP Tel: (H) 01283 716528
Email: nickrigby@forestbarn.freeserve.co.uk
League: Staffordshire 2

BEDFORD QUEENS RUFC
Ground Address: Putnoe Wood, Wentworth Drive, Bedford, Beds MK41 8QA Tel: 01234 350874
Brief Directions: From Bedford City Centre, take A428 Goldington Road towards Cambridge. Take B660 Kimbolton Road towards Kimbolton for 1.75 miles, turn

right onto Wentwoth Drive. Ground .5 mile on left.
Hon Secretary: Jason Cracknell, 105 Dudley Street, Bedford, MK40 3SZ Tel: (H) 01234 309817
Tel: (M) 07976 559506 Tel: (W) 07976 559506
Email: cracks@dialstart.net
Fixtures Secretary: Andy Radnor, No. 133, Ireland, Herts SG17 5QL Tel: (H) 01462 816175
Club Colours: Maroon & white hoops, navy blue, maroon & white topped socks.
League: East Midlands 1
League Contact: As Fixtures Secretary

BEDFORD SWIFTS RUFC
Ground Address: Bedford Athletics Stadium, Barkers Lane/Newham Avenue, Bedford, Beds MK41 9SA
Tel: 01234 351115
Email Address: bedford.swifts@virgin.net
Web Address: www.bedford-swifts.co.uk
Brief Directions: From M1 J.13 A421 signed Cambridge, at end of Bedford By Pass, left to A428 into Bedford, follow signs to Bedford Leisure Centre Aspects or Bedford Athletic Stadium. From A1, A428 west to Birmingham & Northampton on outskirts of Bedford follow the same direction signs to facilities.
Hon Secretary: T. N. Stewart
Tel: (H) 01234 771828 Tel: (W) 01767 681491
Leagues Contact: Richard Harpham, 33, Kimble Drive, Bedford M41 9SX Tel: (H) 01234 403018
Fixtures Secretary: Matthew Norris, Dewberry Cottage, 78, Bedford Road,, Bedford MK43 9JE
Tel: (H) 01234 296669
Club Colours: Gold and royal blue hoops, navy shorts
League: East Midlands 1

BEDWORTH RUFC
Ground Address: Rectory Fields, Smarts Road, Bedworth, CV12 0BP Tel: 02476 312025
Brief Directions: M6 J3. Bedworth turn off A444 Bypass, left at the bottom of slip road then left at Cross Keys pub into Smarts Road
Hon Secretary: N. Brown, 38 Ratcliffe Road, Hinckley, LE10 2SF Tel: (H) 01455 890433
Email: nickbrown_1@hotmail.com
Fixtures Secretary: Tom Murphy, 7 Larkin CLose, Bedworth, CV12 9PB Tel: (H) 02476 315892
Club Colours: Emerald Green jerseys, white shorts
League: Midlands 2 West

BELGRAVE RFC
Ground Address: Belgrave Pastures, Thurcaston Road, Abbey Lane, Leicester Tel: 0116 266 3033
Email Address: belgraverfc@talk21.com
Web Address: belgraverfc.com
Brief Directions: Ground is where A6 Loughborough Rd meets Abbey Lane, opposite Mcdonalds
Hon Secretary: M. J. Goddard, Grange Court, 271A Birstall Road, Birstall, Leics LE4 4DJ
Tel: (H) 0116 267 7383 Tel: (M) 07802 263676
Tel: (W) 07802 263676
Fixtures Secretary: Kevin Hick, 62 Goodes Lane, Syston, Leics Tel: (H) 0116 2608617 (W) 0116 2739501
Club Colours: Red and black hoops, black shorts
League: Midlands 3 East (North)

BELPER RUFC
Ground Address: Herbert Strutt Scholl Fields, Derby Rd, Belper, Derbys. Web Address: www.brufc.freeuk.com
Brief Directions: Ground is off A6 in Belper between Safeways and Babbington Hospital - near town centre.
Hon Secretary: I. S. Davidson, 42 Royston Drive, Derby DE56 0EL Tel: (H) 01773 821112
Tel: (M) 07736 727181 Email: iandavidson@fsmail.net
Fixtures Secretary: Mike Phelan, 5 Derby Road, Belper, Derbys Tel: (H) 01332 780203
Email: mike.caroline@lineone.net
Club Colours: Black and white hoops
League: NLD/Leics 1 West

BERKSWELL & BALSALL RFC
Ground Address: Honiley Road, Meer End, Kenilworth, Warwicks CV8 1NQ Tel: 01676 534862
Email Address: Lesley@dhscontractors.fsnet.co.uk
Brief Directions: From Birmingham or Balsall Common follow main road to Warwick A4111 (Not road to Kennilworth). Ground approx I mile on right with entrance in Honiley Road.
Hon Secretary: Lesley Fahy, 7 Dalmeny Road, Westwood Heath, Coventry CV4 8AX
Tel: (H) 02476 474093 Tel: (W) 01676 533316
Email: lesley@dhscontractors.fsnet.co.uk
Club Colours: Red and black shirts, black shorts
League: Midlands 4 West (South)

BEWDLEY RFC
Ground Address: Bewdley Leisure Centre, Stourport Road, Bewdley DY12 1PS
Tel: 01299 822308
Brief Directions: From Kidderminster head for the safari park and on towards Bewdley. At traffic island take left fork around by-pass. Turn first right at the traffic lights and the leisure centre is 200m down that road on the l/h side
Hon Secretary: Darren Hughes Tel: 07778 846546
Fixtures Secretary: Alan Banks Tel: 07977 135356
Club Colours: Blue with gold and black band, navy shorts
League: North Midlands 3

BIDDENHAM RFC
Ground Address: The Pavilion, Deep Spinney, Biddenham, Beds.
Website: www.biddenham/rugbyclub.co.uk
Brief Directions: Enter Biddenham from A428. R/about turn right follow the road along. Pavilion in front of you.
Hon Secretary: J. C. W. Gambold, 22 Days Lane, Beds MK40 4AE Tel: (H) 01234 347247
Email: jonathan.gambold@btinternet.com
Fixtures Secretary: J. Bird, 24 Banbury Close, Wickingham, Berks, RG41 2YS Tel: (M) 07968 977482
Club Colours: Bottle green and cream quarters
League Contact: Phil Mann, 24 Church End, Renhold, MK41 0LU Tel: 01234 772438
League: East Midlands 1

BIGGLESWADE RUFC
Ground Address: Langford Road, Biggleswade, Beds. SG18 9RA Tel: 01767 312463
Email Address: biggleswade.rugby@ntlworld.com
Web Address: www.biggleswaderfc.tripod.com
Brief Directions: On the A6001 Biggleswade to Henlow Road, approx 1 mile from Biggleswade by the Broom turn off, on the right hand side coming fromBiggleswade
Hon Secretary: Mike Williams, 8 Laurel Way, Hitchin, SG5 3UP Tel: (H) 01462 624925
League Contact: Nigel Aldis Tel: (H) 01767 691333
Email: nigel-adis@supanet.com
Club Colours: Navy blue with broad red band
League: Midlands 4 East (South)

BINGHAM RFC
Ground Address: The Town Pavilion, Brendan Grove, Wynhill, Bingham, Notts Tel: 01949 832874
Brief Directions: A46/A52 roundabout, take Bingham exit then 1st left (town pavilion sign), left at T jct. Down hill, left Brendon Grove still following pavilion signs.
Hon Secretary: J. K. Perry, 29 Cogley Lane, Bingham, Nottinghamshire NG13 8DD Tel: (H) 01949 875231
Tel: (W) 0115 971 2575
Email: jperry.goem@go-regions.gsi.gov.uk
Fixtures Secretary: Graham Mason, 5 Church Close, Bingham, Notts Tel: (H) 01949 875771
Club Colours: Green/red, white
League: NLD/Leics 2 West
League Contact: Barry Stewart, 62 Carnarvon Close, Bingham, Notts. Tel: 01949 875128

BIRCHFIELD RUFC
Ground Address: UCE Sports Ground, Moor Lane, Witton, Birmingham, B6 7AA. Tel: 0121 356 2142
Brief Directions: M6 J7 A34 towards Birmingham, A452 towards Sutton Coldfield, ground on Kiingstanding road B4138 1/2mile from A453 junction. B'ham A-Z Ref 5B page 48
Club Secretary: John Wingate, 9 Eaton Wood, Pype Hayes, Birmingham, B24 0NW. Tel: 07811 864592 (M)
Email: john@jwingate.fsnet.co.uk
Fixtures Secretary: Robert Chapman, 44 Olton Croft, Acocks Green, Birmingham B27 6PG.
Tel: (H) 0121 604 3694
Club Colours: Black with green hoop on arm, black shorts and socks
League: North Midlands 2
League Contact: As Secretary

BIRMINGHAM CIVIL SERVICE RFC
Ground Address: Old Damson Lane, Elmdon, Solihull, West Midlands, B91 3RW Tel: 0121 782 0423
Directions: Opposite Birmingham Airport on A45
Hon Secretary: Dick Webb, 51 Ladbrook Road, Solihull, B91 3RW Tel: (H) 0121 705 2812
Fixtures Secretary: Karl Smith, n/a
Tel: (H) 01526 60251
Club Colours: Red and White shirts, blue socks and red socks
League: North Midlands 2

BIRMINGHAM EXILES RFC
Ground Address: Catherine De Barnes Lane, Bickenhill, Solihull, West Midlands, B92 0DX
Tel: 01675 442995
Brief Directions: Leave M42 at J.6 then leave A45 Coventry Road at Birmingham Airport junction and take Catherine de Barnes Lane exit.
Hon Secretary: Martin Whateley, 19 Wimbourne Road, Birmingham, B76 2SU Tel: (H) 0121 378 3446
Tel: (W) 0121 687 5169
Email: martin.whateley@focus.co.uk
Fixtures Secretary: P. Bates, 69 Woodlands Way, Birmingham, B37 6RN Tel: (H) 0121 788 1081
Tel: (M) 07802 350854
Club Colours: Blue and Red hoops, navy blue shorts
League: Midlands 3 West (South)

BISHOPS CASTLE & ONNY VALLEY RFC
Ground Address: Love Lane, Bishops Castle, Shropshire Tel: 01588 638639
Brief Directions: On Eastern edge of town off the A484 Shrewsbury to Clun Road
Hon Secretary: David Bryan-Jones, c/o 43 Church St, Blishops Castle SY9 5AD
Tel: (H) 01588 63875
Fixtures Secretary: R. Jones, Hayford Farm, Shrewsbury, Shropshire Tel: (H) 01743 884248
Club Colours: Green and red
League: North Midlands 2

BLOXWICH RFC
Ground Address: Bloxwich Sports Club, Stafford Road, Bloxwich, West Midlands, WS3 3NJ
Tel: 01922 405891
Email Address: anthony.allen@talk21.com
Web Address: www.bloxwich.org
Brief Directions: 0.25 mile outside Bloxwich Town on A34 to Cannock, entrance between houses on left marked by black and white posts, 100yds past traffic lights
Hon Secretary: Anthony Allen, 16 Sorrel Close, Featherstone, Staffs Tel: (H) 01902 739835
Email: anthony.allen@talk21.com
Fixtures Secretary: Paul Coyne, c/o Club
Club Colours: Green with black and white chest hoops and black shorts
League: North Midlands 2

BOOTS ATHLETIC RUFC
Ground Address: Boots Athletic Club, Holme Road, Lady Bay, West Bridgford, Nottingham NG2 5BJ
Tel: 0115 949 2388
Brief Directions: Follow signs to either Trent Bridge Cricket or Nottingham Forest, the Athletic Grounds are at the junction of Lady Bay Bridge and Trent Boulevard.
Hon Secretary: Graham Atkinson, 42 Ashness Close, Nottingham, Nottinghamshire NG2 6QW
Tel: (M) 07879 451954
Email: graham.atkinson@bcm-ltd.co.uk
Fixtures Secretary: Pete Webb, 189 Measham Road, Swadlingcote, Derbys DE12 6AJ
Tel: (H) 01530 270422 Tel: (W) 01509 554453
Email: pete_j_webb@yahoo.com
Club Colours: Dark blue and light blue quarters
League: NLD/Leics 2 West

BOSTON RFC
Ground Address: Great Fen Road, Wyberton, Boston, Lincs, PE21 7PB Tel: 01205 362683
Email Address: keightley1@aol.com
Web Address: www.boston-rufc.org
Brief Directions: Quarter of a mile west of Boston on A1121 next to airfield
Hon Secretary: M. Keightley, 25 Manor Gardens, Boston, Lincolnshire, PE21 6JG
Tel: (H) 01205 364755
Fixtures Secretary: T. Bembridge, 5 Blackthorne Lane, Boston, Lincs, PE21 9BG Tel: (H) 01205 351973
Email: t@tbembridge.freeserve.co.uk
Club Colours: Blue and white hoops
League: NLD/Leics 1 East

BOURNE RUFC
Ground Address: Milking Nook Drive, Spalding Road, Bourne, Lincs Tel: 01788 393346
Brief Directions: Take the Spalding road out of Bourne and the ground is on the right after one and a half miles.
Hon Secretary: H. Sherwin, 30 Waterloo Drive, Nr Bourne, Lincolnshire PE10 0PJ
Tel: (H) 01778 571394

Fixtures Secretary: As Secretary.
Club Colours: Navy blue with broad gold band and navy shorts
League: NLD/Leics 2 East

BOURNVILLE RFC
Ground Address: Rowheath, Heath Road, Bournville, Birmingham, West Midlands B30 1HH
Tel: 0121 458 1711
Email Address: tempestharry@hotmail.com
Web Address: www.bournvillerfc.freeserve.co.uk
Brief Directions: A38 out of B'ham city centre, after approx 5 miles turn left into Oaktree Ln and follow signs for Cadbury World, turn right into Maryvale Rd, ground 0.5 mile on left
Hon Secretary: Keith Smith, 1 Witley Road, Birmingham B31 3BD
Tel: (H) 0121 680 1269 Tel: (M) 0775 9 679397
Fixtures Secretary: Eamon Harkin, 18 Lansdowne Road, Studley, Warks, B80 7RB
Tel: (H) 01527 853241 Tel: (W) 07968 440875
Club Colours: Blue, maroon & gold shirts, blue shorts
League: North Midlands 3

BRACKLEY RUFC
Ground Address: Fine Lady Fields, Nightingale Close, Brackley, Northants NN13 6PN Tel: 01280 700685
Email Address: alan.j143@virgin.net
Web Address: www.brackleyrufc.co.uk
Brief Directions: A43 Northampton, go towards Town Centre, take 4th turn right (opp. Bell Inn). Bear right at mini R/about. Turn left at next R/about, then right at nedt R/about - club on left.
Hon Secretary: A. Jukes, 9 Crabtree Close, HARTWELL, Northampton, Northants NN7 2LB
Tel: (H) 01604 864682 Tel: (M) 07940 533910
Email: alan.j143@virgin.net
Fixtures Secretary: Mike Harper, Horwell Farm, Bicester, Oxon OX6 9SQ Tel: (H) 01869 345821
Email: mikey2harper@aol.com
Club Colours: Royal blue & white 1/4s, blue shorts.
League: East Midlands 1

BREDON STAR RFC
Ground Address: Bredon Playing Fields, Kemerton Road, Bredon, Nr. Tewkesbury, Glos.
Tel: 01684 773183
Brief Directions: From Jct 9 of M5 take A46 to Evesham. Left after 2 miles at traffic lights onto B4079. Left at T junction in village and car park is 50 yards on right.
Brief Directions: From Jct 5 of M5 take A46 to Evesham.Left after 2 miles at traffic lights onto B4079. Left at T junction in village and car park is 50 yards on right before Nissan garage.
Hon Secretary: Rachel Gallagher, 21 Pippins Road, Tewkesbury, Glos., GL20 7NJ
Tel: (H) 01684 77206 Tel: (M) 07768 651105
Email: tewkgc@connectfree.co.uk
Fixtures Secretary: Neil Evans, Apple Orchard, Chapel Lane, Tewkesbury, Glos., GL20 8HS
Tel: (H) 01684 772 645 Tel: (W) 07973 171451
Club Colours: Red and black shirts with black shorts
League: North Midlands 2

BRIDGNORTH RFC
Ground Address: The Bull, Bridge Street, Bridgenorth, Shropshire WV15 5LQ Tel: 01746 762796
Email Address: annabeljefferies@hotmail.com
Web Address: www.bridgnorth-rugby.co.uk
Brief Directions: Severn Park off A442 Bridgnorth to Telford Road. Clubhouse adjacent to Old Bridge Low Town. Parking at Falcon Pub car park.
Hon Secretary: Annabel Jefferies, 28 Kings Loade, Bridgnorth, Shropshire WV16 4BT
Tel: (H) 01746 768453 Tel: (M) 07812 573686
Email: annabeljefferies@hotmail.com
Hon Secretary: Sam Rossiter-Stead, 8 Lower Forge, Eardington, Bridgnorth, Shropshire, WV16 5LQ
Tel: (H) 01746 764286 Tel: (W) 01952 811500
Email: samrs@breathemail.net
Fixtures Secretary: Alun Stoll, Ty'r Ysgol, Vicarage Road, Wolverhampton WV4 5HP
Tel: (H) 01902 558355 Tel: (W) 01902 558368
Club Colours: All black
League: Midlands 3 West (North)

BROMYARD RFC
Ground Address: Clive Richards Sports Ground, Tenbury Road, Bromyard, Herefordshire HR7 4LW
Tel: 01885 483 933
Email Address: deborahpiggott@compuserve.com
Brief Directions: From Bromyard, take the B4214 towards Tenbury Wells, the ground is on the right hand side, approx 0.5 mile from the town
Hon Secretary: Deborah J. Piggott, Upper Brockington, Bredenbury, Bromyard, Herefordshire, HR7 4TH
Tel: (H) 01885 483322 Tel: (M) 07770 372233
Email: deborahpiggott@compuserve.com
Fixtures Secretary: Simon Irwin, 2 Pinetree Cottage, Bromyard, Herefordshire, HR7 4QD
Tel: (H) 01885 488322
Club Colours: Green with gold band, black shorts
League: North Midlands 1

BUGBROOKE RUFC
Ground Address: The Playing Fields, Pilgrims Lane, Bugbrooke, Northants Tel: 01604 831137
Email Address: bryn.curtis@ladbrokes.co.uk
Web Address: www.bugbrooke-rugby-club.co.uk
Brief Directions: A45 from Northampton towards J16 M1 at Kislingbury R/abt. Turn L. for Rugbrook. Go through village on same road almost at other end for Bugbrooke Community Centre. Turn left in there.
Hon Secretary: Bryn Curtis, Weedon Road, Northants NN7 3LF Tel: (H) 01327 342798
Tel: (M) 07855 275836 Tel: (W) 07855 275836
Fixtures Secretary: Richard Sherlock, 9 Mount Pleasant, Harpole, Northants NN7 4DL
Tel: (H) 01604 831632 Tel: (M) 07855 974075
Tel: (W) 01604 233101
Club Colours: Bottle green & yellow quarters, green, green & yellow hoops
League: East Midlands 1

BURNTWOOD RUFC
Ground Address: The North Shore, Church Street, Chasetown, Staffs WS7 8XE. Tel: 01543 676651
Brief Directions: From A5 follow directions to Chasetown Clubhouse at end of Church St. Club is next to Chasetown Football Club.
Club Secretary: Kevin Cantrill, 39 Hunter Avenue, Burntwood, Staffs WS79AQ. Tel: 01543 672737
Fixtures Secretary: Mark Bourne, 27 Willett Avenue, Burntwood, Staffordshire WS7 8FJ. Tel: 01543 675918
Club Colours: Scarlet, emerald & white hoops, black shorts.
League: Midlands 3 West (North)

BURTON RFC LTD
Ground Address: Peel Croft, Lichfield Street, Burton-on-Trent, Staffs DE14 3RH Tel: 01283 564510
Email Address: roy.bradley@barbox.net
Web Address: www.burtonrugbyclub.co.uk
Brief Directions: In the centre of Burton, adjacent to Safeways supermarket
Hon Secretary: John D. Lowe, 20 The Chevin, Stretton, Burton-On-Trent, Staffs DE3 0XU
Tel: (H) 01283 534422
Email: johndlowe@ricsonline.org
Fixtures Secretary: John E. French, 193 Newton Road, Burton-Upon-Trent, Staffs DE15 0TU
Tel: (H) 01283 548774
Email: frenchmanjohn@hotmail.com
Club Colours: White - black diagonal sash
League: Midlands 3 West (North)

BUXTON RUFC
Ground Address: Fairfield Centre, Victoria Park Road, Buxton, Derbys Tel: 01298 24081
Brief Directions: Follow A6 Stockport, up Fairfield Road 1st R. Queens Rd becomes Bench Rd, left at T jcn with Victoria Park Rd, Centre on left after Royal Forresters
Hon Secretary: D. J. Robson, 20 Errwood Avenue, Buxton, Derbys SK17 9BD
Tel: (H) 01298 22432 Tel: (W) 01298 26121
Email: davidjrobson@netscapeonline.co.uk
Fixtures Secretary: Lorraine Trevis Brown, 6 New Road, Whaley Bridge, Derbys, SK17 9BD
Tel: (H) 01663 73504 Tel: (W) 01298 23195
Club Colours: Blue, red and gold hoops, blue shorts
League: Midlands 4 East (North)

CAMP HILL RFC
Ground Address: Haslucks Green Road, Shirley, Solihull, W Midlands Web Address: www.chrfc.com
Brief Directions: M42 J4 - A34 towards Birmingham for approx 3m. Thro' Shirley to main traffic lights, turn left, club signposted 400yds on left
Hon Secretary: Karen Gibbons, 29 Acheson Road, Hall Green, Birmingham. B28 0TU
Tel: (H) 0121 745 9349 Tel: (W) 0121 600 3402
Tel: (M) 07956 170829
Email Address: secretary@chrfc.com
Fixtures Secretary: Graham Scutt, 130 Longmore Road, Solihull B90 3EE Tel: (H) 0121 744 4495
Club Colours: Maroon with light blue band
League: Midlands 2 West

CANNOCK RUFC
Ground Address: The Morgan Ground, Stafford Road, Huntingdon, Staffordshire. WS12 4NU
Tel: 01543 467906
Club Secretary: Sarah Sindrey, 22 Coppermill Close, Cannock WS12 4SQ email: sgreen@rmplc.co.uk
Fixtures Secretary: Alan Graham, 23 Stag Drive, Huntington, Cannock WS12 4UJ
Tel: 01543 502679
Club Colours: Blue and gold hoops
League: Staffordshire 1

CASTLE DONINGTON RUFC
Ground Address: The Spittal Pavilion, The Spittal, Castle Donington, Derbys Tel: 01332 812214 (pub)
Brief Directions: Travel into Donington from A6 turning right into the Spittal after the Tudor Inn, ground is situated 400yds on right
Hon Secretary: A. C. E. Hackett, 88 Station Road, Castle Donington, Derbys DE74 2NL
Tel: (H) 01509 856631 Tel: (W) 01332 853344
Email: moose@donington.demon.co.uk
Fixtures Secretary: Alan Hampson, 77 Station Road, Derby Tel: (H) 01332 812314
Club Colours: Red & black quarters, black, red & black
League: NLD/Leics 1 West

CHADDESLEY CORBETT
Ground Address: Chaddesly Corbett Sports Club, Longmore, Fox Lane, Chaddesley Corbett
Website: ccrfc.co.uk
Brief Directions: On A448 between Kidderminster & Bromsgrove. Do not enter village, turning to ground is on sharp corner between The Fox P.H. and Rowberrys farm shop. Signed CCRFC - turn right from Kidderminster, left from Bromsgrove.
Club Secretary: Nigel Evans, Cherry Tree House, Mustow Green, Nr. Kidderminster DY10 4LQ.
Tel: 01562 777070
Fixtures Secretary: M Page, 8 The Green, Chaddesley Corbett DY10 4PZ Tel: 01562 777700
Club Colours: Green & blue Quarters with blue shorts.
League: North Midlands 3

CHESTERFIELD RUFC
Ground Address: The Rugby Field, Stonegravels, Sheffield Road, Chesterfield
Tel: 01246 232321
Brief Directions: M1 J29, follow signs to Chesterfield town centre A61 to Sheffield (old road, not bypass), ground is on left 1 mile from town centre
Hon Secretary: D. J. Taylor, 7 Hallfields Rise, Alfreton, Derbys DE55 6DH Tel: (H) 01773 836138
Tel: (M) 01773 521778 Tel: (W) 0115 989 5223
Email: duncan.taylor@nelsons-solicitors.co.uk
Club Colours: Red and white hoops, white shorts
League: NLD/Leics 2 West

CLAVERDON RFC
Ground Address: Ossetts Hole Lane, Yarningale Common, Claverdon, Warwickshire CV35 8HN
Tel: 01926 843133
Email Address: big@basil.junglelink.co.uk
Web Address: www.clavrfc.co.uk
Brief Directions: Off A4189 Warwick to Henley in Arden.
Hon Secretary: Basil Sayer, Croft Cottage, 162 High Street, Solihull B95 5BN
Tel: (H) 01564 795714
Email: big@basil.junglelink.co.uk
Fixtures Secretary: Lindsay Shaw, 23 Castle Close, Solihull, B95 5LR Tel: (H) 01564 795474
Tel: (W) 01789 41411 ext 4598
Email: ambm49@dial.pipex.com
Club Colours: Red/ white hooped jersey,white shorts
League: Warwickshire 1

CLEE HILL RFC
Ground Address: Golden Lion, 2 Lion Lane, Tenbury Road, Clee Hill, Ludlow, Shropshire
Tel: 01584 890262
Brief Directions: Between Ludlow and Cleobury Mortimer on A4117. Take B4214 to Clee Hill (signposted Tenbury Wells). Ground approx. I mile on R.H.S.
Club Secretary: Mrs. Penny Cooper, Studley Cottage, Clee Hill, Nr. Ludlow, Shropshire SY8 3NP.
Tel: 01584 890990

Fixtures Secretary: Harvey Stevens, 17 Crestwood Avenue, Kidderminster, Worcs. DY11 6JS
Tel: 01562 637384
Club Colours: Maroon & navy blue quarters, blue shorts
League: North Midlands 2

CLEETHORPES RUFC
Ground Address: Lucarleys Club, Wilton Road, Cleethorpes, N.E. Lincs Tel: 01472 812936
Brief Directions: Follow signs for Tesco superstore, ground is first turning right past Tesco.
Hon Secretary: Simon Regan, 3 Robson Road, Cleethorpes, North East Lincolnshire DN35 7UY
Tel: (H) 01472 317 605 Tel: (W) 01472 250010
Email: reganxxxxuk@yahoo.co.uk
Fixtures Secretary: John Walsham, 38 Richmond Road, Cleethorpes, N.E. Lincs Tel: (H) 01472 699322
Club Colours: Blue & Gold hoops
League: NLD/Leics 2 East

CLEOBURY MORTIMER RFC
Ground Address: Cleobury Mortimer Sports & Social Club, Love Lane, Cleobury Mortimer, Kidderminster, Worcs., DY14 8PE Tel: 01299 270364
Email Address: jon@jonredfern.fsnet.co.uk
Brief Directions: To Cleobury along main street, then turn right just before the Three Horseshoes pub, left at mini roundabout, car park and ground 100 yards on left
Hon Secretary: Jon Redfern, 4 Catherton Road, Kidderminster DY14 8EB
Tel: (H) 01297 270364 Tel: (M) 07831 234602
Email: jon@jonredfern.fsnet.co.uk
Fixtures Secretary: Kath Phillips, Orchard House, Ludlow Road, Cleobury Mortimer DY14 8DU
Tel: (H) 01299 270381
Club Colours: Red and green quarters, black shorts
League: North Midlands 1

COALVILLE RFC
Ground Address: 50.Parkdale, Ibstock, Leicester LE67 6JW Tel: 01530 812090
Web Address: www.coalville-rfc.co.uk
Brief Directions: Leave M1 at Junction 22. Coalville is signposted on A511. Go over four roundabouts and then turn left at fifth roundabout and Coalville RFC is 100 yards on right.
Hon Secretary: P. Smith, 50 Parkdalk, Ibstock, Leicester Tel: (H) 01530 262113
Tel: (M) 07903 943148 Tel: (W) 01530 832085
Email: pete@num-leics.fsnet.co.uk
Fixtures Secretary: G. Harding, 115 High St., Leicester
Tel: (H) 01530 262200 Tel: (W) 01530 262200
Club Colours: Navy blue with amber stripe, navy shorts
League: Midlands 4 East (South)

CORBY RFC
Ground Address: Northern Park, Rockingham Road, Corby, Northants NN17 2AE Tel: 01536 204466
Brief Directions: Located at the junction of the A6003 (Corby to Oakham Road) and the A6116 (Rockingham Road) Corby.
Hon Secretary: Clayton Nunn, 20 Dovedale Road, Corby, Northants NN17 1LP Tel: (H) 01536 395933
Email: CLAYTON@corby10.freeserve.co.uk
Fixtures Secretary: Charles Sanders, 21 Brunswick Gardens, Corby NN18 9ER Tel: (W) 01536 269600
Club Colours: Red and white quarters, blue shorts
League: East Midlands 2

COVENTRIANS RFC
Ground Address: The Black Pad, Yelverton Road, Radford, Coventry CV6 4NW (no mail to this address)
Tel: 02476 682885
Brief Directions: M6 J3 onto A444 to Coventry, right at 2nd roundabout to Holbrooks, at next 2nd roundabout Yelverton Road is 50yds on right
Hon Secretary: J. Daniell, 116 Mill Farm Park, Bedworth, Warwickshire CV12 9SF
Tel: (H) 02476 373470 Tel: (M) 07831 896240
Email: jeff.daniell@tesco.net
Fixtures Secretary: J. Daniell, 116 Mill Farm Park, Bedworth, Warwickshire CV12 9SF
Tel: (H) 02476 373470 Tel: (M) 07831 896240
Email: jeff.daniell@tesco.net
Club Colours: Blue and white, quarters
League: Warwickshire 2

COVENTRY SARACENS RFC
Ground Address: Bredon Avenue, Binley, Coventry CV6 2AR Tel: 02476 453557
Brief Directions: From A46 (Eastern bypass) take A428 to Coventry City Centre for approx 1 mile, left into Bredon Ave, ground approx 200 mtrs on left
Hon Secretary: Brian Craner, 71 Westhill Road, Coventry CV6 2AD
Tel: (H) 02476 765884 Tel: (W) 02476 832968
Email: briancraner@supanet.com
Fixtures Secretary: Steven Hancox, 21 Anne Crescent, Coventry CV3 3GX Tel: (H) 02476 306217
Club Colours: Black shirts, red/green "V", black shorts
League: Warwickshire 2

COVENTRY TECHNICAL RFC
Ground Address: Mitchell Avenue, Canley, Coventry, West Midlands CV4 8DW Tel: 02476 471733
Email Address: a.power@warwick.ac.uk
Brief Directions: The club is only 5 mins from A45 Flethhampstead Highway, northbound take right turn into Charter Ave, southbound left at island by Canley fire and police station
Hon Secretary: A. Wallis-Power, 27 Nod Rise, Mount Nod, Coventry CV5 7HU Tel: (H) 02476 474040
Tel: (M) 07932-762813 Tel: (W) 02476 524652
Fixtures Secretary: Maurice Caine, 27 Nod Rise, Coventry, CV5 7HU Tel: (H) 02476 474040
Tel: (M) 07909 906965 Tel: (W) 02476 221743
Club Colours: Dark green, yellow and brown
League: Warwickshire 2

COVENTRY WELSH RFC
Ground Address: Burbages Lane, Exhall, Coventry CV6 6AY Tel: 02476 360303
Web Address: www.coventrywelsh.com
Brief Directions: M6 J3, take bypass road A444 to next roundabout and the right hand turn at roundabout is Burbages Lane
Hon Secretary: J. Hughes, 10 Ladymead Drive, Whitemoor Park, Coventry, CV6 4EL
Tel: (H) 02476 726097
Fixtures Secretary: Gary Greenway, 4 Kings Gardens, Nuneaton, Warwicks CV12 8JG
Tel: (H) 02476 315403 Tel: (M) 07932 773556
Email: gary.greenway@talk21.com
Club Colours: Red shirts, black shorts
League: Midlands 4 West (South)

DAVENTRY RFC
Ground Address: Stefen Hill, Western Avenue, Daventry, Northants NN11 4ST Tel: 01327 703802
Brief Directions: M1 J16, A45 west to Daventry, upon reaching Daventry, straight over roundabout heading for Daventry town centre, 3rd road on left and the ground is facing you
Hon Secretary: P. Weckermann, 3 Portland Close, Daventry, Northants NN11 4SQ
Tel: (H) 01327 311151 Tel: (M) 07971 096782
Fixtures Secretary: Graham Woodliffe, Old Barn House, The Green, Daventry, Northants NN11 3AF
Tel: (H) 01327 703496 Tel: (W) 01327 305137
Email: gwoodlif@ford.com
Club Colours: All black
League: East Midlands 1

DEEPINGS RUFC
Ground Address: Linchfield Road, Deeping St. James, Peterborough PE6 8BS Tel: 01788 345228
Email Address: kirby01.b@care4free.net
Brief Directions: R'bout Market Deeping (Jcn of A15/A16) take A16 towards Spalding, through town until sight footbridge, left at Xroads before bridge, immediate right thro' gates to ground
Hon Secretary: Brian Kirby, 29 Tattershall Drive, Peterborough PE6 8BS Tel: (H) 01778 343048
Tel: (M) 07720 538600 Tel: (W) 01778 381069
Email: kirby01.b@care4free.net
Fixtures Secretary: Colin Astley, 34 Thackers Way, Peterborough PE6 8HP Tel: (M) 07944 985021
Club Colours: Green, black and gold hoops
League: East Midlands 2

DERBY RFC
Ground Address: The Pavillion, Kedleston Road, Derby DE22 2TF Tel: 01332 344341
Web Address: www.derbyrugbyfootballclub.com
Brief Directions: Off A38 at Markeaton Park towards University of Derby campus - ground half a mile further on the left
Hon Secretary: John L. Archer, 5 Dunvegan Close, Derby, Derbys DE24 3AL
Tel: (H) 01332 769300 Tel: (M) 07932 308584
Email: johnlarcher@supanet.com
Fixtures Secretary: John Dickens, 57 Wheeldon Avenue, Derby DE22 1HP
Tel: (H) 01332 341546 Tel: (W) 01332 702502
Email: johnandpam@dickensj.freeserve.co.uk
Club Colours: Black and amber hoops, black shorts
League: Midlands 2 West

DIXONIANS RFC
Ground Address: Ravenhurst Sports Pavillion, Knightlow Road, Harborne, Birmingham, B17 8PX
Tel: 0121 434 3313
Email Address: JT@dixoniansrfc.co.uk
Web Address: www.dixoniansrfc.co.uk
Hon Secretary: Vivian Shingler, Timberhonger House, Worcester B61 9ET Tel: (H) 01527 861686
Tel: (W) 0121 544 4788
Fixtures Secretary: David Hall, Vesey House, 37 Holland Street, Sutton Coldfield B72 1RR
Tel: (H) 0121-354 8333 Tel: (M) 0589 691839
Club Colours: maroon green and black jerseys,black shorts,green
League: Midlands 2 West

DROITWICH RFC
Ground Address: The New Clubhouse, Hanbury Road, Droitwich, Worcs WR9 8PR Tel: 01905 771919
Web Address: www.droitwichfc.co.uk
Brief Directions: M5 J5, A38 towards Droitwich, turn towards town centre. At traffic lights turn left into Hanbury Road, club 2 miles on left.
Hon Secretary: Phillip Hopkins, 15 Avondale, Droitwich, Worcestershire WR9 8PB
Tel: (H) 01905 794950 Tel: (W) 0121 552 4022
Email: philip.hopkins1@virgin.net
Fixtures Secretary: Richard Latham, 3 Isaacs Way, Droitwich, Worcs WR9 8UZ
Tel: (H) 01905 794638 Tel: (W) 0121 585 3033
Club Colours: Black and gold hoops
League: Midlands 4 West (South)

DRONFIELD RUFC
Ground Address: Gosforth School, Carr Lane, Dronfield-Woodhouse, Dronfield
Brief Directions: From north (Sheffield) into Dronfield, right at Coach & Horses, bear right under bridge, follow road at top of hill turn left (Stubley Drive), turn into school car park
Hon Secretary: B. Machin, 2 Hatton Close, Donfield Woodhouse, Derbys S18 8RW
Tel: (H) 01246 411453 Tel: (M) 07836 373554
Email: machin1@btinternet.com
Hon Secretary: John Singleton, 1 Millstone Close, Dronfield Woodhouse, Derbys S18 8ZL
Tel: (H) 01246 417891 Tel: (M) 07711 004824
Tel: (W) 02476 368528
Email: singo1m@dialstart.net
Fixtures Secretary: Verdon McCauliffe, 56 Highfield Road, Dronfield S18 6UW
Club Colours: Red shirts, black shorts
League: NLD/Leics 1 West

DUDLEY WASPS RFC
Ground Address: Heathbrook Stadium, Swindon Road, Wall Heath, West Midlands Tel: 01384 287006
Brief Directions: Just off the A449 at Wall Heath, miday between Kidderminster and Wolverhampton
Hon Secretary: John Taylor, 4 Hayrick Drive, Wall Heath, West Midlands DY6 0DU Tel: 01384 820709
Email: taylorz@supanet.com
Fixtures Secretary: as Secretary above
Club Colours: Red with blue 'V', navy shorts
League: North Midlands 3

DUNLOP RFC
Ground Address: Dunlop Sports and Social Club, Burnaby Road, Radford, Coventry Tel: 02476 662394
Web Address: www.dunloprfc.co.uk
Brief Directions: M6 J3, take 4th exit to Coventry, along bypass, over roundabout, right at 2nd round-about, left at 3rd roundabout, turn right into Burnaby Rd, ground .5 mile on right
Hon Secretary: Kim Challis, 29 James Dawson Drive, Meriden, Nr Coventry CV5 9QJ
Tel: (H) 01676 523522 Tel: (W) 02476 366416
Email: kim@challis1959.fsnet.co.uk
Fixtures Secretary: John Ormsby, 5 Post Bridge Road, Coventry CV3 5AG
Tel: (H) 02476 410313 Tel: (M) 07932 173715
Club Colours: Black and amber hoops, black shorts
League: Warwickshire 1

MIDLAND

EARLSDON RFC
Ground Address: R. F. Brown Pavillion, Mitchell Avenue, Canley, Coventry, West Midlands CV4 8DY
Tel: 02476 464467
Web Address: www.earlsdonrfc.moonfruit.com
Brief Directions: Along A45 to Police and Fire Stations, follow signs to Canley & Warwick University
Hon Secretary: Jim Lorimer, 10 Ludlow Road, Coventry, West Midlands CV5 6JA
Tel: (H) 02476 675957 Tel: (M) 07779 320965
Tel: (W) 02476 852735
Email: jimlorimer@tinyworld.co.uk
Fixtures Secretary: Robert (Bob) Price, 25 Montrose Drive, Nuneaton Tel: (H) 02476 346190
Club Colours: Red and white
League: Midlands 4 West (South)

EAST LEAKE RFC
Ground Address: Costock Road Playing Fields, Costock Road, East Leake, Loughborough, Leics
Brief Directions: A60 N'gham tow'ds L'boro, right at Costock tow'ds E. Leake, ground on right. M1 J24, A6 tow'ds L'boro, left onto A6006 tow'ds Rempstowe, left where signed, thro' village, club on right
Hon Secretary: A. Pridmore, 6 Ashley Road, Kegworth, Derbys DE74 2DH Tel: (H) 01509 670246
Email: audrey100@totalise.co.uk
Fixtures Secretary: Nigel Kendall, 28 Salisbury Avenue, East Leake, Loughborough, Leics LE12 6NJ
Tel: (H) 01509 856735 Tel: (M) 07929 872830
Tel: (W) 0115 924 9924 ext 35150
Club Colours: Maroon and White
League: NLD/Leics 1 West

EAST RETFORD RUFC
Ground Address: Ordsall Road, Retford, Notts
Tel: 01777 703243
Brief Directions: From A1, join B620 from Worksop, past Ranby prison on left, through Babworth cross-roads, right at mini roundabout, ground .5 mile on right
Hon Secretary: E. M. Henderson, 51 Trent Street, East Retford, Nottinghamshire, DN22 6NG
Tel: (H) 01777 706987 Tel: (M) 07779 356886
Email: Tedhenderson@retford510.freeserve.co.uk
Fixtures Secretary: I. H. McComb, 125 Ordsall Road, Retford, Notts Tel: (H) 01777 701092
Club Colours: Emerald & amber hoops, navy shorts
League: NLD/Leics 1 East

ECCLESHALL RUFC
Ground Address: Baden Hall Farm, Nr Eccleshall, Staffordshire Tel: 01785 851495
Brief Directions: From centre of Eccleshall follow A519 (Newcastle), take right fork after leaving town, past Drake Hall then follow signs to Baden Hall on right
Hon Secretary: Kevin Levitt, 46 Old Road, Stone, Staffs ST15 8HR
Tel: (H) 01785 818234 Tel: (W) 01925 836105
Fixtures Secretary: Ian Bradford, 1 Buckmaster Avenue, Newcastle, Staffs ST5 3AJ
Tel: (H) 01782 632256 Tel: (W) 01782 823447
Colours: Yellow with green & black band, black shorts.
League: Staffordshire 2

EDWARDIAN FC
Ground Address: The Memorial Ground, Streetsbrook Road, Solihull, W. Midlands B90 3PE
Tel: 0121 744 6831
Email Address: administrator@edsrugby.com
Web Address: www.edsrugby.com
Brief Directions: M42 J.4. Follow A34 towards Birmingham. Turn right into Olton Road. At lights straight over into ground.
Hon Secretary: Susan Whitehouse, 120 Rumbush Lane, Solihull, West Midlands B90 1SU
Tel: (M) 07970 063109
Fixtures Secretary: Steve Abercrombie, 35 Green Lane, Solihull, W. Mids, B90 1AP
Tel: (H) 0121 608 6195 Tel: (W) 0121 430 7508
League Contact: Paul Price, 88 Stonor Road, Hall Green, Birmingham, B28 0QR Tel: 0121 745 8745
Colours: Old gold, claret and navy irregular hoops
League: Midlands 4 West (South)

ERDINGTON RFC
Ground Address: Spring Lane Playing Fields, Kingsbury Road, Erdington, Birmingham
Tel: 0121 373 7597
Hon Secretary: Derek Owen, 129 Bradbury Road, Solihull B92 8AL
Tel: (H) 0121 706 4699 Tel: (W) 0121 654 4022
Fixtures Sec.: Keith Robinson Tel: (H) 0121 351 2740
Club Colours: White shirts with single blue hoop
League: North Midlands 3

ESSINGTON RUFC
Ground Address: High Hill Centre, High Hill, Essington WV11 2DW Tel: 01922 492795
Brief Directions: M6 J.11 A462 for 3 miles. Traffic lights turn right, Upper Snyde Lane - .75 mile - club on left
Hon Secretary: Michael R. Chandler, 32 Coppice Road, Walsall WS9 9BC
Tel: (H) 01543 820611 Tel: (W) 01909 397777
Fixtures Secretary: Graham Smith, 7 Oakwood Close, Essington, W. Mids. WV11 2DQ Tel: (H) 01922 400222
Club Colours: Black shirts and shorts with red socks.
League: North Midlands 3

EVESHAM RFC
Ground Address: Evesham Sports Club, Albert Road, Evesham, Worcester Tel: 01386 446469
Brief Directions: A435 south - over railway bridge, Albert Road is 2nd right off High Street, Evesham, go to end to Evesham Sports Club
Hon Secretary: Carol Horseman, 3 Green Hill Gardens, Evesham, Worcester
Email: carol@greenhillg.fsnet.co.uk
Fixtures Secretary: Jon Nettell, 43 Princess Road, Evesham, Worcs., WR11 4GQ Tel: (H) 01386 456111
Club Colours: Navy and maroon hoops
League: Midlands 3 West (South)

FIVE WAYS OLD EDWARDIANS FC
Ground Address: Masshouse, Ash Lane, Hopwood, Alvechurch, Birmingham B48 7BD Tel: 0121 445 4909
Web Address: www.fivewaysoe.freeserve.co.uk
Brief Directions: M42 J2, signpost to Birmingham reach roundabout to Birmingham, 100yds before garage on right turn right into Ash Lane, club on right at end of lane
Hon Secretary: Richard Lissiter, 138 Chatsworth Road, West Midlands B62 8TH Tel: (H) 0121 559 6549 Tel: (W) 01384 818640 Email: rlisseter@aol.com
Fixtures Secretary: Derek Earl, 88 Westminster Road, Birmingham B29 7RS Tel: (H) 01222 481222
Club Colours: Navy blue and amber
League: North Midlands 1

GAINSBOROUGH RUFC
Ground Address: Castle Hills School, The Avenue, Gainsborough Tel: 01724 763825
Email Address: anthonygoude@aol.com
Brief Directions: Follow signs for Leisure Centre, the school is next to it
Hon Secretary: A. Lobley, Church View Cottage, Gringle Road, Nr Gainsborough, Lincolnshire
Tel: (H) 01427 890951
Fixtures Secretary: Andre Russell
Tel: (W) 01724 276401
Email: andrerussell@aol.com
Club Colours: Black shirt & shorts
League: NLD/Leics 2 East

GEC ST LEONARDS RUFC
Ground Address: GEC Protection and Control, GEC St Leonards Social Club, St Leonards Avenue, Stafford, Staffs Tel: 01785 258070
Club Secretary: J A Waibley, 26 Hall Close, Stafford, Staffs ST17 4JJ Tel: (H & W) 01785 253201
Fixtures Secretary: Mr I McLeod
Tel: (H) 01889 579365 (W) 0860 694548
Club Colours: Black with a gold hoop
League: Staffordshire 1

GLOSSOP RFC
Ground Address: Hargate Hill Lane, Charlesworth, Glossop SK13 5HG Tel: 01457 864553
Web Address: www.glossop-rugbyufc.co.uk
Brief Directions: Through Glossop on A57, take A626 signed Marple, ground is 1.5 miles on left
Hon Secretary: Alistair May, 6 Kinder Grove, Stockport, Cheshire, SK6 4EU
Tel: (H) 0161 4275774 Tel: (W) 01457 864553
Email: alaistair@shaylor-thompson.co.uk
Fixtures Secretary: Phil Littlewood, Oakmount, Dinting Road, Glossop
Tel: (H) 01457 867168 Tel: (M) 07976 714706
Club Colours: Royal blue shirts, black shorts
League: Midlands 3 East (North)

GNOSALL RUFC
Ground Address: Gnosall Cricket Club, Brookhouse Road, Gnosall, Stafford Tel No: 01785 823500
website: gnosallrugby.org.uk
Brief Directions: A518 (Stafford & Telford road), from Stafford to mini R/about, village centre, straight over is Brookhouse Road, 1st left down track by Play Area.
Club Secretary: Mrs Anne Timmins, Norden Newport Road, Gnosall, Stafford ST20 0BN.
Tel: 01785 823431
Email: anne.timmins@btinternet.com
Fixtures Secretary: Stuart Davies, 27 Cranmore Grove, Aston Lodge, Stafford ST15 XD
Tel No: 01785 817846
Club Colours: Green & black quarters, black shorts.
League: Staffordshire 2

GREYHOUND RFC
Ground Address: Herford City Sports Club, Grandstand Road, Hereford, Herefordshire HR4 9NG
Tel: 01432 354221
Email Address: LizPeel@thevicnp19.fsnet.co.uk
Web Address: www.greyhoundrugby.com
Brief Directions: Turn off A49 Leominster Road. The ground is on the opposite side to the Hereford Leisure Centre.
Hon Secretary: Allan Braithwaite, Victoria Inn, 2 Nash Road, Newport, South Wales NP19 4NG
Tel: (H) 01633 283722 Tel: (M) 07775 724365
Tel: (W) 01633 271482
Email: LizPeel@thevicnp19.fsnet.co.uk
Fixtures Secretary: Nigel Greening, 9 Old School Lane, Hereford HR1 1EU Tel: (H) 01432 356579
Club Colours: Paleblue/navy/red
League: North Midlands 3

GRIMSBY RUFC
Ground Address: The Pavillion, Springfield Road, Scartho, Grimsby DN33 3JF Tel: 01472 878594
Web Address: www.beehive.thisisgrimsby.co.uk
Brief Directions: From M180/A180, take A1136, left at roundabout, right at Toothill roundabout, left at Bradley crossroads, right at Nuns corner, right fork, 1st right
Hon Secretary: Terry Horswood, 5 Fernby Lane, Grimsby, North East Lincolnshire DN33 3NU
Tel: (H) 01472 872416 Tel: (W) 01469 563382
Email: terry-horswood@msn.com
Fixtures Secretary: John Waudby, 25 Park Drive, Grimsby DN32 0EF Tel: (H) 01472 500135
Tel: (W) 01469 565420
Email: john.waudby@conoco.com
Club Colours: Royal blue shirts & black shorts.
League: Midlands 4 East (North)

HANDSWORTH RUFC
Ground Address: Charles Lewis Memorial Ground, 450 Birmingham Road, Walsall West, West Midlands WS5 3JP Tel: 0121 357 6427
Brief Directions: M6 J7, take A34 towards Walsall, ground at bottom of hill at end of dual carriageway on left
Hon Secretary: Alec Hardy , 6 Freemount Square, Birmingham B43 5QT
Tel: (H) 0121 358 6612 Tel: (W) 01902 422399
Email: deamon@thardy.fsnet.co.uk
Fixtures Secretary: Alec Hardy , 6 Freemount Square, Birmingham B43 5QT
Tel: (H) 0121 358 6612 Tel: (W) 01902 422399
Email: deamon@thardy.fsnet.co.uk
Club Colours: Red and white hoops, black shorts.
League: Staffordshire 1

HANFORD RFC
Ground Address: Hanford Cricket & Rugby Club, Church Lane, Hanford, Stoke-on-Trent ST4 8QP.
Tel: 01782 641442
Brief Directions: M6 J.15, A500 towards Stoke, 1st exit (signed Trentham) turn right at R/about. Immediate left after Petrol Station. 1st left into club.
Club Secretary: Craig Boulton, 11 Whatmore St., Smallthorne, Stoke-on-Trent, Staffs ST6 1SH.
Tel: 01782 851281
Fixtures Secretary: Brian Davies, 15 Stanley Grove, Badderley Green, Stoke on Trent, Staffs ST2 7SA. Tel: (H) 01782 545085
Club Colours: Navy Blue & Gold Hoops
League: Staffordshire 2

HARBORNE RFC
Ground Address: Playing Fields, Metchley, Park Road, Harborne, Birmingham Tel: 07970 296833
Brief Directions: From Birmingham city centre follow signs to Harborne (3 miles) Ground to south of High Street
Hon Secretary: Graham Hitchcock, 81 Station Road, BIrmingham B17 9LR Tel: (H) 0121 427 8290

Fixtures Secretary: Simon Parker, 56 Farm Road, Rowley Regis, West Mids Tel: (H) 0121 532 4780
Email: simonparker65@netmail.com
Club Colours: Black & green hoop with red stripe.
League: North Midlands 3

HARBURY RFC
Ground Address: Waterloo Fields, Middle Road, Harbury, Leamington Spa, Warks Tel: 01926 613462
Brief Directions: 1 mile off Fosse Way, 2 miles north of junction of Fosse Way with B4100 (Banbury-Warwick Road) between J.12 and J.13 M40
Hon Secretary: Peter Rollason, 27 Farm Street, Leamington Spa, Warwickshire CV33 9LR
Tel: (H) 01926 613422 Tel: (W) 01327 301771
Email: prollasen@rollasens.com
Fixtures Secretary: Jerry Birbeck, 22 Campion Terrace, Leamington Spa, Warks
Tel: (H) 01926 424053
Colours: Red & white Hoops, black shorts and socks
League: Warwickshire 1

HEREFORD RFC
Ground Address: Belvedere Lane, Wyeside, Hereford, HR4 9UT Tel: 01432 273 410
Email Address: mandy.miles@herefordrfc.com
Web Address: www.herefordrfc.com
Brief Directions: Follow the ring road to Ross-on-Wye, turn right before the bridge over the Wye, first left after The Antelope into Broomy Hill, first left again into a narrow lane, the club is on the riverside.
Hon Secretary: Peter Greenow, Hackford House, Hereford HR2 6PD
Tel: (H) 01432 870874 Tel: (W) 07808 336396
Club Colours: Red and black
League: Midlands 2 West

HORNCASTLE RFC
Ground Address: The Playing Fields, Coronation Walk, Horncastle Tel: 01507 526742
Web Address: horncastlerfc@aol.com
Brief Directions: To centre of Horncastle traffic lights, take Boston direction 200yds turn right follow signs to playing field.
Hon Secretary: Mick Jenkinson, 2 The Crescent, Horncastle, Lincolnshire LN9 6EZ
Tel: (H) 01507 525183 Tel: (W) 07909 542594
Email: horncastlerfc@aol.com
Fixtures Secretary: Dave Stow, 7 Mareham Road, Horncastle, Lincs Tel: (H) 01507 522128
Club Colours: Green and gold quarters black shorts
League: NLD/Leics 2 East

HUNTINGDON & DISTRICT RFC
Ground Address: Hinchingbrooke School, Brampton Road, Huntingdon, Cambs PE18 6BN
website: www.huntingdonrufc.co.uk
Brief Directions: Heading into Huntingdon from A14 or A1, Hinchingbroke School is adjacent to Hinchingbroke Hospital on the left.
Club Secretary: Mrs S Morgan, 17 Pages Way, Brampton, Huntingdon PE28 4UR
Tel: 01480 383625
Fixtures Secretary: Mrs. I. Tack, 37 Egremont Road, Hardwick, Cambridge. Tel: 01954 211140
Email: mrstefiracing.co.uk
Club Colours: Emerald Green shirts, navy blue shorts, green and green socks
League: Midlands 3 East (South)

ILKESTON RUFC
Ground Address: The Stue, Hallam Fields Road, Ilkeston, Derbys DE7 4AZ
Tel: 0115 932 3244
Email Address: tom.egglestone@lineone.net
Web Address: www.ilkestonrufc.co.uk
Brief Directions: M1 Exit 25, A52 to Nott'ham. Left at 2nd round't (A6007) Ilkeston Rd. At mini round't, A6007 now Stapleford Rd. Left at T jct to A609.Left at garage toThurman St/Corpor'n Rd,T jct left
Hon Secretary: Michael Green, 62 Northern Drive, Nottingham NG9 3QL
Tel: (H) 0115 917 0740 Tel: (W) 0115 906 4556
Fixtures Secretary: Colin Fox, 39 Nursery Hollow, Ilkeston, Derbys DE7 4LQ
Tel: (H) 0115-930-8421
Club Colours: Green, blue, white hoops, blue shorts
League: Midlands 2 East

KEMPSTON RFC
Ground Address: Sports Club, 134 High Street, Kempston, Beds MK42 7BN Tel: 01234 852499
Email Address: richard.dell@bt.com
Brief Directions: Head towards Kempston. Find Sainsburys, go down hill past Citroen Garage on right, stay on this road and club is on right before you go out of Kempston
Hon Secretary: Peter Blades, 35 Chestnut Avenue, Bedford, Beds MK43 8GD Tel: (H) 01234 825944
Email: pete.blades@sainsburys.co.uk
Fixtures Secretary: C. Pitts, 34 Park Road, Kempston, Beds, MK42 8NZ Tel: (H) 01234 840921
Club Colours: Red & black quarters
League: East Midlands 1

KERESLEY RFC
Ground Address: The John E. Radford Fields, Burrow Hill Lane, Corley, Nr. Coventry CV7 8BE
Tel: 01676 540082
Email Address: jwfrawley2@ukonline.co.uk
Brief Directions: Situated off Bennetts Road North, just past Keresley Village
Hon Secretary: John Frawley, 37 The Crescent, Coventry CV7 8LB Tel: (H) 02476 337537
Email: jwfrawley@hotmail.com
Fixtures Secretary: A. Atkins, 2 Carpenters Close, Hinckley LE10 2RB Tel: (H) 01455 456956
Club Colours: Royal blue, scarlet and white, navy shorts
League: Midlands 3 West (South)
Leagues Contact: Malcolm Jackson, 119 Bennetts Road Sth, Keresley, Coventry, CV6 2FP
Tel: (H) 02476 334589

KESTEVEN RUFC
Ground Address: Woodnock, Grantham, Lincs NB33 5AA Tel: 01476 564887
Brief Directions: A52 out of Grantham towards Spalding, past the R.A.F. camp then right at roundabout (B6403). Club on right about 400 yards.
Hon Secretary: William Berridge, 60 Belton Grove, Grantham, Lincolnshire NG31 9HH
Tel: (H) 01476 590561 Tel: (M) 07801 905645
Fixtures Secretary: Robert Cole, 7a Long Street, Grantham Tel: (H) 01476 401194
Club Colours: Black shirts, white shorts
League: Midlands 4 East (North)

KETTERING RFC
Ground Address: Waverley Road, Kettering, Northants NN15 6NT Tel: 01536 485588
Brief Directions: A14 J10, turn onto A6 to Kettering, at second traffic lights turn right, first left and first left again into Waverley Road, Ground is at end of road
Hon Secretary: L. Blatchley, c/o Kettering RFC, Waverley Road, Kettering, Northants NN15 6NT
Tel: (H) 01536 501679 Tel: (M) 07967 029975
Email: linda.blatchly@ntlworld.com
Fixtures Secretary: R. Bowley, Messuage Farmhouse, 10 Lower Benefield, Peterborough PE8 5AF
Tel: (H) 01832 205382 Tel: (M) 07980 578177
Tel: (W) 01536 722181
Club Colours: Royal Blue and white irregular hoops, navy shorts
League: Midlands 2 East

KEYWORTH RFC
Ground Address: The Pavillion, Willoughby Lane, Widmerpool, Nottingham NG12 5PU
Tel: 0115 937 5579
Email Address: krfc@keyworthrugby.co.uk
Web Address: www.keyworthrugby.co.uk
Brief Directions: A606 from Nottingham to Melton Mowbray. Turn right at Widmerpool cross roads. Turn left at end of road, then 2nd left to Willoughby, ground is on the right hand side.
Hon Secretary: Robert Baker, 14 Orchard Way, Wymeswold, Leicestershire LE12 6SW
Tel: (H) 01509 881473
Hon Fixtures: Andy Evans, 6 East Close, Nottingham NG12 5GN Tel: (H) 0115 846 0795
Fixtures Secretary: Andy Evans, 6 East Close, Nottingham NG12 5GN Tel: (H) 0115 846 0795
Club Colours: Black with gold hoops, black shorts.
League: NLD/Leics 1East

KIBWORTH RUFC
Ground Address: Northampton Road, Market Harborough, Leics LE16 9HF Tel: 01858 464210
Brief Directions: The Club has agreed to move to an incorporated status. This process is underway with revised rules all now agreed.
Brief Directions: From town centre, follow signs for Leisure Centre, club on right as you enter centre. From M1, M6, A14, follow A508 to Market Harborough, ground on left as entering town
Hon Secretary: Peter Rowbotham, 7 Rhodes Close, Market Harborough, Leics LE16 9FB
Tel: (H) 01858 469869 Tel: (M) 07976 275811
Tel: (W) 01858 821 321
Fixtures Secretary: David Coe, Flat 1, 58/60 Station Road, Desborough, Northants NN14 2RS
Tel: (H) 01536 762482 Tel: (M) 07976 692663
Tel: (W) 01536 464188
Email: david.r.coe@talk21.com
Club Colours: All Black
League: Midlands 3 East (South)

KIDDERMINSTER CAROLIANS RFC
Ground Address: Marlpool Lane, Kidderminster, Worcs DY11 4HP Tel: 01562 740043
Brief Directions: Follow signs from Kidderminster ringroad to Bridgnorth, at end Proud Cross Ringway is Jackson pub, Marlpool Lane is to one side, ground 400m from pub
Club Secretary: Keith Skirving,43 Leawood Grove, Kidderminster, Worcs DY11 6JT.
Tel: (H) 01562 747482
email:san.kela@talk21.com
Fixtures Secretary: Mr Tim Carder, 218 Puxton Drive, Kidderminster, Worcs DY11 5HJ
Tel: (H) 01562 747910 (W) 01902 774217
Club Colours: Black with gold hoops and black shorts
League: Midlands 3 West (North)

KINGS NORTON RFC
Ground Address: Ash Lane, Hopwood, Birmingham B48 7BB Tel: 0121 445 3340
Brief Directions: Near exit 2 from the M42, take Birmingham road and turn down Ash Lane and the ground is on the right
Club Secretary: Jim Williams, 44 Heaton Road, Solihull B91 2DX Tel: 0121 682 8600
email: Williams@44heatonroad.freeserve.co.uk
Fixtures Secretary: Ms R Dalley, 33 Maple Road, Bournville, Birmingham B30 2AE
Tel: (H) 0121 472 2194 (M) 07771 724146
Club Colours: Red and gold hooped shirts, black shorts, red socks
League: Midlands 4 West (South)

KYNOCH RFC
Ground Address: Aston Manor and Lucas Social Club, Church Road, Perry Barr, Birmingham
Tel: 0121 456 8267
Hon Secretary: Carole Gibbs, 46 Church Hill, Wednesbury, West Midlands WS10 9DG
Tel: (H) 0121 556 8796 Tel: (M) 07714 262284
Tel: (W) 0121 456 8267
Email: carole.gibbs@mills-reeve.com
Fixtures Secretary: Ray Jones, 23 Blounts Road, Birmingham B23 7DE Tel: (H) 0121 382 0310
Club Colours: Black and white hoops
League: North Midlands 3

LEAMINGTON RUFC
Ground Address: Moorefields, Kenilworth Road, Leamington Spa, Warwickshire CV32 6RG
Tel: 01926 425584
Email Address: john@lyons99.freeserve.co.uk
Web Address: www.leamingtonrufc.co.uk
Brief Directions: Join A46 Warwick bypass (from North M6, J2, from South M40, J15). Leave bypass at Leamington/Kenilworth junction. Take A452 towards Leamington 1 mile, ground on left
Hon Secretary: John Lyons, 3 Denewood Way, Kenilworth CV8 2NY Tel: (H) 01926 855787
Email: john@lyons99.freeserve.co.uk
Fixtures Secretary: Tony Grimes, The White hall, Rugby CV23 9PU Tel: (H) 01926 813501
Tel: (M) 0970 228755 Tel: (W) 01926 813501
Colours: Royal blue shirt with single red and gold hoop
League: Midlands 2 West

LEDBURY RFC
Ground Address: Ross Road Playing Fields, Ross Road, Ledbury, Hereford, HR8 1LP Tel: 01531 631788
Brief Directions: Get off Exit 2 of the M50. Take A417 to Ledbury for 4 miles. Take left turn at R/about down by-pass. Next R/about take A449 to Ross-on-Wye, 100yds on right.
Hon Secretary: Jill Matthew, Dunbridge Farm, Ledbury, Herefordshire, HR8 2JE
Tel: (H) 01531 633958 Tel: (M) 07989 011237
Tel: (W) 01453 794932 Email: delamoreW@aol.com

Fixtures Secretary: Trevor Humphreys, 10 Challenger Close, Ledbury, Herefordshire HR8 2PW
Tel: (H) 01531 635774 Tel: (M) 07808 987846
Club Colours: Black and white hoops
League: Midlands 3 West (South)

LEEK RUFC
Ground Address: Post & Times Park, St. Edwards, Cheddleton, Leek, North Staffs ST13 8NW
Tel: 01538 361770
Email Address: Achandle@celestica.com
Brief Directions: Leek RFC is located within the grounds of St Edwards Hospital, Cheddleton situated south of Leek on the A520
Hon Secretary: Andrew Chandler, 22 Shirburn Road, Leek, Staffs ST13 6LE
Tel: (H) 01538 381045 Tel: (W) 0467 297880
Email: achandle@celetica.com
Fixtures Secretary: Daniel Hunt, 4 Southbank Street, Leek ST13 5AA Tel: (H) 01538 388526
Club Colours: Blue and white hoops, blue, blue
League: Midlands 4 West (North)

LEESBROOK RUFC
Ground Address: Asterdale Sports Centre, Borrowash Road, Spondon, Derby DE21 7PH Tel: 01332 668656
Brief Directions: M1 J25, 3rd turn marked Spondon. From city centre take A52, take turning marked Spondon (Ntm Old Road)
Hon Secretary: John Burns, 160 Cole Lane, Derbys DE27 3GP Tel: (H) 01332 674216
Email: burns@family123321.fsnet.co.uk
Fixtures Secretary: Peter Dodd, 14 Sunny Crescent, Derby DE21 6QN Tel: (H) 01332 662144
Club Colours: Black, with green and blue band, black shorts and socks.
League: NLD/Leics 2 West

LEICESTER FOREST RFC
Ground Address: Hinckley Road, Leicester Forest East, Leicester LE3 3PJ Tel: 0116 238 7136
Email Address: lfrfc@aol.com
Web Address: www.leicesterforestrfc.com
Brief Directions: Ground is off the main A47 Leicester. Hinckley road 1.5 miles from the Leicester Forest Services on the M1.
Hon Secretary: Kate Bramley, 45 Beechwood Avenue, Leicester LE3 3PL Tel: (H) 0116 233 8881
Email: k.bramley3@ntlworld.com
Fixtures Secretary: Tony Thraves, 5 Lynmouth Drive, Leicester LE16 1BP
Tel: (H) 0116 210 0980 Tel: (M) 07976 259882
Club Colours: Royal & dark blue shirts, dark blue shorts.
League: Midlands 4 East (South)

LEIGHTON BUZZARD RFC
Ground Address: Wright's Meadow, Leighton Road, Leighton Buzzard, Beds LU7 9HR Tel: 01525 371322
Email Address: leighton_buzzard@hotmail.com
Web Address: www.lbrufc.co.uk
Brief Directions: North: M1 J13, A507 through Woburn, South: M1 J9, then A5 to Dunstable, A505 to Aylesbury, 2nd turn right, Club 1 mile on right
Fixtures Secretary: Alan Perrey, 22 The Coppins, Ampthill MK45 2SN Tel: (H) 01525 403812
Club Colours: White with blue hoops
League: Midlands 3 East (South)

LICHFIELD RUFC
Ground Address: Cooke Fields, Tamworth Road, Lichfield WS14 9JE Tel: 01543 263020
Web Address: www.lichfieldrugby.co.uk
Brief Directions: Take A51 from Lichfield to Tamworth for approx one mile. Ground behind Horse & Hockey public house.
Hon Secretary: Roger Fathers, 75 Spring lane, Whittington, Staffs WS14 9NA
Tel: (H) 01543 433118 Tel: (W) 0121 326 1960
Email: Roger@textileassemblies.co.uk
Fixtures Secretary: Steve Barr, 2 Barley Croft, Lichfield, Staffs WS14 9LY Tel: (H) 01543 432605
League Contact: As Fixtures Secretary
League: Midlands 3 West (North)

LINCOLN RFC
Ground Address: Lindum Sports Ground, Wragby Road, Lincoln LN4 2PE Tel: 01522 526592
Brief Directions: Head for Cathedral, club is located on Wragby Road in the `Upilll' area of Lincoln.
Hon Secretary: H. M. Edwards, 60 Bailgate, Lincoln LN1 3AR Tel: (H) 01522 534849 (W) 01522 888555
Email: huw.edwards@langleys.co.uk
Fixtures Secretary: Simon Gregory, 4 St, Johns Road, Lincoln Tel: (H) 01522 829203
Club Colours: Red/green/white bands, green
League: Midlands 3 East (North)

LINLEY & KIDSGROVE RUFC
Ground Address: Ski Centre, Bathpool Park, West Morland Avenue, Kidsgrove, Stoke-on-Trent.
Brief Directions: M6 J16, A500 towards Stoke-on-Trent, 2nd junction A34 Kidsgrove, follow signs for the Ski Centre**Club Secretary:** Jason Swingewood, 48 Appledore Grove, Packmoor, Stoke-on-Trent ST6 6XH
Tel: (H) 01782 816213 Tel: (W) 0151 9556835
e-mail: jason@jswingewood.freeserve.co.uk
Fixtures Secretary: Michael Cunningham.
Tel: 01782 638725
Club Colours: Green and gold quarters
League: Staffordshire 1

LONG BUCKBY RFC
Ground Address: Station Road, Long Buckby, Northampton Tel: 01327 842222
Brief Directions: 0.25 mile from market square, along Station Road towards Daventry
Hon Secretary: Lynn Stratford, 66 Weggs Farm Road, Duston, Northampton, Northants NN5 6HD
Tel: (H) 01604 754555
Fixtures Secretary: Stan Ruddlesden, 37 Rockhill Road, Northampton NN6 7PT Tel: (H) 01327 842 933
Colours: Emerald shirts/navy sleeves, navy shorts
League: Midlands 3 East (South)

LONG EATON RFC
Ground Address: West Park, Long Eaton, Nottingham (Non Postal) Tel: 0115 946 0907
Brief Directions: M1 Jct 25. Follow signs to Long Eaton. Then West Park Leisure Centre. Club is based next to Leisure Centre.
Hon Secretary: P. A. Hickinbottom, PO Box 5830, Long Eaton, Nottingham NG10 1LX Tel: (H) 0115 972 0992
Fixtures Secretary: Chris Brookes, 82 Thoresby Road, Nottingham NG10 3NP
Tel: (H) 0115 946 8485 Tel: (W) 01773 540 707
Colours: Royal blue and white hoops with blue shorts.
League: Midlands 4 East (North)

LOUGHBOROUGH RFC
Ground Address: The Clubhouse, Derby Road Playing Fields, Loughborough (Not a postal address)
Tel: 01509 216093
Brief Directions: Turn onto Bishop Meadow Road. At Bishop Meadow R/about (A6) turn left at Pay Less DIY. First right then first left
Hon Secretary: Steve Hughes, 6 Maclean Avenue, Loughborough, Leics LE11 5XX Tel: (H) 01509 558955
Tel: (W) 007967 668027
Fixtures Secretary: Eddie Blythe, c/o 6 maclean av, Loughborough, Leics LE11 5XX
Tel: (H) 01455 611639 Tel: (M) 07714 159848
Club Colours: Navy blue and old gold
League: Midlands 3 East (North)

LOUGHBOROUGH STUDENTS
Ground Address: Loughborough University, Leics LE11 3TU Tel: 01509 632009 (Athletic Union)
Brief Directions: M1 J21, head towards Loughborough along Ashly Rd, follow directions into University, 1st XV pitch immediately on left
Club Secretary: Mr. J. Saker, Management Develop Centre, Loughborough University, Loughborough, Leicestershire LE11 3TU.
Fixtures Secretary: Glynn James, 31 Melbourne Road, Stamford, Lincs PE9 1UD. Tel: (H) 01780 51793
Club Colours: White and maroon
League: Midlands 3 East (North)

LUDLOW RFC
Ground Address: Ludlow RFC, The Linney, Ludlow, Shropshire SY8 1EE Tel: 01584 875762
Email Address: davidaroberts@beeb.net
Brief Directions: Approaching Ludlow town centre from north, turn R. just after Honda Equipe, follow narrow road for .5 mile, club on right behind football pitch
Hon Secretary: David Roberts, 'Willow Croft', Marden, Herefordshire HR1 3EZ Tel: (M) 07977 541434
Email: davidaroberts@beeb.net
Fixtures Secretary: Ian Townsend, 43, Normandie Close, Ludlow, Shropshire SY8 1UJ
Tel: (H) 01584 875349 Tel: (M) 07870 208663
League contact: as Fixtures Secretary
Club Colours: Red shirts, black shorts
League: Midlands 4 West (North)

LUTON RFC
Ground Address: Newlands Rd, Luton, Beds LU1 4BQ
Tel: 01582 720355
Email Address: info@lutonrugby.com
Web Address: www.lutonrugby.com
Brief Directions: M1 J10, take spur to roundabout, turn right, 200m turn right again, ground 1km on left
Hon Secretary: P. J. Wilson, 17 Burghley Close, Flitwick, Beds MK45 1TF
Tel: (H) 01525 713409 Tel: (W) 01525 713409
Fixtures Secretary: M. Alexander, 9 Glenfield Road, Luton, Beds Tel: (H) 01582 598581
Club Colours: Green, red and black.
League: Midlands 2 East

LUTTERWORTH RFC
Ground Address: Ashby Lane, Bitteswell, Nr. Lutterworth, Leics LE17 4SQ Tel: 01455 557329
Email Address: Colin.hudson@morganest.com
Brief Directions: Approx 1.5 miles north off Lutterworth on A426 take left turn at small cross roads (signed to Lutterworth RFC)
Fixtures Secretary: Chris Payne, Cawder Ghyll, Main Street, Nr. Lutterworth, Leics. Tel: (H) 01788 860442
Club Colours: Red, green and white hoops
League: Midlands 3 East (South)

MANOR PARK RFC
Ground Address: Griff & Coton Sports Club, Heath End Road, Stockingford, Nuneaton, Warwickshire
Tel: 02476 386798
Brief Directions: M1-M6 J3, A444 Nuneaton, keep left at George Elliot Hospital, into Heath End Road, turn into Griff & Coton Sports Ground on right
Hon Secretary: W. J. Newcombe, 489 Heathe End Road, Nuneaton, Warwickshire CV10 7HD
Tel: (H) 02476 374476
Fixtures Secretary: S. Atkinson, 10 East Avenue, Bedworth, Warwickshire Tel: (H) 02476 730606
Colours: Red & black hoops, black shorts & socks
League: Warwickshire 1

MANSFIELD RUFC
Ground Address: Eakring Road, Mansfield, Notts NU18 3EN Tel: 01623 649834
website: www.mansfieldrugby.co.uk
Brief Directions: From Mansfield Town centre take A617 towards Neward. Travel 2 miles, turn left towards Ollerton. Travel 1 mile to T/lights turn right onto Eakring Road.
Hon Secretary: Steven Troman, 44 Leadale Crescent, Nottinghamshire NG19 9HL
Tel: (H) 01623 652993 Tel: (M) 07966 220515
Email: Steven.Troman@toyotauk.com
Fixtures Secretary: Simon Harrison, 20 The Shires, Mansfield, Notts NG19 0QL
Tel: (H) 01623 792145 Tel: (W) 01623 415200
Email: mansfieldrufcfixtures@hotmail.com
Club Colours: Blue & white hoops, blue shorts & socks
League: Midlands 2 East

MARCONI COVENTRY RFC
Ground Address: Marconi Sports Pavilion, Allard Way, Coventry CV2 1HS. Tel: 02476 562831
website: gptrfc.freeserve.co.uk
Brief Directions: From M6 J2 join A46. After approx 2 miles right at r'about. Left at next r'about. Right at lights, right at next lights, then left at 2nd set of lights. Ground 300 yds on the left.
Club Secretary: Brett Naylor, 177 Tennyson Road, Poets Corner, Coventry CV2 3JD.
Tel: 02476 278547 (H)
email: brett.naylor@marconi.com
Fixtures Secretary: Roger Wood, 67 John McGuire Crescent,Coventry CV32 2QH Tel: 02476 459379
Club Colours: Red, green & blue hoops, blue shorts.
League: Midlands 4 West (South)

MARKET BOSWORTH RFC
Ground Address: Cadeby Lane, Cadeby, Market Bosworth, Nuneaton, Warks, CV13 0BE
Tel: 01455 291340
Web Address: www.pdcnet.org.uk/mbrfc
Brief Directions: Off the A447, Hinckley to Ibstock Road, turn at signs for Cadeby and follow lane in direction of Market Bosworth
Hon Secretary: Mike McKay, 20 Occupation Road, Orton-on-the-Hill, Warks CV9 3NE
Tel: (H) 01827 880788
Fixtures Secretary: John Jackson, 10 Cedar Drive, Market Bosworth, Warks Tel: (H) 01455 290044

Club Colours: Blue, white & gold irregular hoops
League: Midlands 2 East

MARKET DRAYTON RFC
Ground Address: Greenfields Sports Ground, Greenfields Lane, Market Drayton, Shropshire
Tel: 01630 655088
Brief Directions: Turn into town centre from the Gingerbread Man pub. Greenfields is signposted 300m from the R/about on the righthand side of the bridge.
Hon Secretary: Derek Partington, Prospect House, 1 Cemetery Road, Market Drayton, Shropshire TF9 3BD
Tel: (H) 01630 657429 Email: Mktdrayton@aol.com
Fixtures Secretary: David Gould, 16 Pendral Close, Tern Hill, Market Drayton, Shropshire, TF9 2ET
Tel: (H) 01630 638777
Club Colours: Black with green trim
League: Staffordshire 2

MARKET RASEN & LOUTH RUFC
Ground Address: Willingham Road, Market Rasen, Lincs LN8 3RE Tel: 01673 843162
Brief Directions: Situated I mile out of Market Rasen heading east towards Louth on A631 on the right hand side, just passed De Aston Secondary School
Hon Secretary: Nicholas Pope, 41 Church Street, Middale Rasen, Market Rasen, Lincolnshire LN8 3TR
Tel: (H) 01673 844793 Tel: (M) 07785 934422
Tel: (W) 01507 600249 Email: popes@btclick.com
Fixtures Secretary: P. Dixon, Springfield, High Street, Glentham, Lincs. LN2 3EA. Tel: 01673 878222 - email: pjbdixon@glentham60.freeserve.co.uk
Club Colours: Red and green hoops
League: Midlands 4 East (North)

MATLOCK RUFC
Ground Address: Cromford Meadows, Cromford, Matlock, Derbys Tel: 01629 822821
Brief Directions: Turn off A6 at Cromford towards Crich/Holloway, ground 300yds on right after public carparks and before river bridge
Hon Secretary: R. E. Grindrod, Primrose Cottage, Upperwood Road, Matlock Bath, Derbys DE4 3PE
Tel: (H) 01629 56741
Fixtures Secretary: D. Pearson, Greyfriars, Bakewell Road, Matlock, Derbys. Tel: (H) 01629 55440
Club Colours: Royal blue, gold & grey quarters, navy blue shorts, royal blue
League: Midlands 3 East (North)

MEDEN VALE RFC
Ground Address: Welbeck Colliery Welfare, Elkersley Road, Meden Vale, Mansfield, Notts
Tel: 01623 842267
Email Address: mikeheaton@edwinstowe.co.uk
Brief Directions: From A60 turn towards Meden Vale, follow road until petrol station then turn left up the hill, take 2nd left into car park
Hon Secretary: Mike Heaton, 50 Mount Crescent, Warsop, Nottinghamshire NG20 0HF
Tel: (H) 01623 847153 Tel: (M) 07931 356675
Tel: (W) 01623 823833
Fixtures Secretary: Eddie Davison, 25 Egmanton Road, Warsop NG20 9DN Tel: (H) 01623 847322
Tel: (M) 0770 2204758 Tel: (W) 01623 424242
Club Colours: Black
League: NLD/Leics 2 East

MELBOURNE RFC
Ground Address: Cockshutt Lane, Melbourne, Derby
Tel: 01332 863785
Email Address: garry@wilsonconsultant.softnet.co.uk
Web Address: www.melbourne-rfc.junglelink.co.uk
Brief Directions: From M1, A453 to Melbourne. From Derby/Uttoxeter, A514 to Melbourne. Then B587 to Recreation Ground
Hon Secretary: Julie Johnson, 21 George Street, Derby DE73 1FS Tel: (H) 01332 863785
Email: philandjulie21@aol.com
Fixtures Secretary: Crawford Fisher
Tel: (H) 01332 863335
Email: minijunior@melbournetown.co.uk
Club Colours: Bottle green and white
League: NLD/Leics 1 West

MELLISH RFC
Ground Address: Memorial Ground, Plains Road, Mapperley, Nottingham NG3 5RT Tel: 0115 926 6653
Brief Directions: Ground situated on west side of B684 opposite The Travellers Rest, 2 miles east of the turn off the A614 and 2 miles north of the Plains squash club (national grid ref: 605463)
Hon Secretary: Bob Knowles, 20 Spring Lane, Lambley, Notts NG4 4PH Tel: (H) 0115 931 2037
Tel: (M) 07753 850 742 Tel: (W) 0115 977 4739
Email: knowles@lambley20.freeserve.co.uk
Fixtures Secretary: Syd Harris, 2 Tilstock Court, Nottingham NG16 1JZ Tel: (H) 0115 938 5456
Tel: (M) 07778 927576 Tel: (W) 0115 975 4222
Email: maisonharris@hotmail.com
Club Colours: Green, black, gold
League: Midlands 4 East (North)

MELTON MOWBRAY RFC
Ground Address: Burton Road, Melton Mowbray, Leics LE13 1DR Tel: 01664 563342
Web Address: www.mmrfc.freeserve.co.uk
Brief Directions: Leave Melton Mowbray via the A606 to Oakham. Access is on the left past King Edward VII Upper School.
Hon Secretary: Hugh Middleton, 10 New Road, Burton Lazars, Melton Mowbray, Leics LE14 2UU
Tel: (H) 01664 563792 Tel: (M) 07812 723534
Tel: (W) 01664 444333
Email: middleton-hugh@hotmail.com
Fixtures Secretary: S. Kerr, 30 Dorothy Avenue, Melton Mowbray, Leics LE13 0LB
Tel: (H) 01664 850954 Tel: (W) 01664 474789
Club Colours: Maroon, white, maroon
League: Midlands 3 East (North)

NEWARK RFC
Ground Address: Kelham Road, Newark, Notts
Tel: 01636 702355
Brief Directions: From A1, A46 Newark bypass, ground is on Kelham Road on the road marked to Kelham on the right. From A46, take Newark bypass, left at roundabout, ground on right
Hon Secretary: J. E. Rimmer, Old Vicarage, Chapel lane, Newark, Nottinghamshire NG24 2PW
Tel: (H) 01636 640352
Email: johnrimmer@sheppardmoscow.com
Fixtures Secretary: Owen Mathias, North Muskham Prebend, Church Street, Southwell, Notts NG25 0HQ
Tel: (H) 01636 815808
Colours: Navy blue with single hoop and white shorts.
League: Midlands 3 East (North)

NEWBOLD-ON-AVON RFC
Ground Address: The Clubhouse, Parkfield Road, Newbold-on-Avon, Rugby CV21 1EZ
Tel: 01788 565811
Web site: www.newboldrfc.co.uk
Brief Directions: M6, J1 to Rugby. After 1/2 mile, at large landscaped r'about turn right (3rd exit) to Newbold village (1.5 miles). At crossroads, Parkfield Road is straight over, clubhouse 100 metres on the right.
Club Secretary: R. Hall, 8 Belmont Road, Rugby CV22 5NZ Tel: 01788 334757
Fixtures Secretary: Paul E Bale, 135 Norman Road, Rugby CV21 1DW. Tel: (H) 01788 560014
Tel: (W) 01788 569750 Email: paul.bale@virgin.net
League Contact: Fixture Secretary as above
Club Colours: Red and black quarters
League: Midlands 2 West

NEWCASTLE (STAFFS) RUFC
Ground Address: Pavilion Ground, Lilleshall Road, Clayton, Newcastle-under-Lyme, Staffs ST5 3BX
Tel: 01782 617042
Brief Directions: M6 J15 to Newcastle, turn L. at 1st R/about, straight over next R/about, R. at next R/about down Stafford Ave. 3rd Rd on L. Lilleshall Road - past Cricket Ground on R.
Club Secretary: Dave Ellerton, 45 The Plaisaunce, Westlands, Newcastle, Staffs ST5 3RZ.
Tel: 01782 614276 e-mail: davidfe@ freenetname.co.uk
Fixtures Secretary: Jeff Scholes, 51 Emery Avenue, West;lands, Newxastle, Staffs ST5 2JF
Tel: 01782 617840
Colours: Maroon & white hoops, black shorts & socks.
League: Midlands 4 West (North)

NEWPORT (SALOP) RUFC
Ground Address: The Old Showground, Forton Road, Newport, Shropshire Tel: 01952 810021
Brief Directions: From the bypass, take turning to Newport on the roundabout that also signs to Shrewsbury, the ground is on the right
Hon Secretary: David Rees, Three Fishes House, Church Square, Newport, Shropshire, TF10 7BH
Tel: (H) 01952 404228 Tel: (W) 01952 810307
Fixtures Secretary: David Vasilionka, 25 Norbroom Drive, Newport, Shropshire, TF10 7TG
Tel: (H) 01952 810755
Fixtures Secretary: David A. Flanagan, 2 The Parks, Bridgnorth, Shropshire
Tel: (H) 01746 787627 Tel: (W) 01746 787627
Club Colours: Maroon and white hoops with white shorts and maroon socks.
League: Midlands 3 West (North)

NORTH DERBYSHIRE RFC
Ground Address: The 'Stoot', Oxcroft Miners Welfare, 55 Clown Road, Stanfree, Chesterfield S44 6AG
Tel: 01246 241394
Brief Directions: Ground is on the B6418 east of the M1 , leave at the M1 Jct 29 if you are coming from the south or at Jct 30 if approaching from the north
Hon Secretary: Arwyn Morgan, 20 Abbeyhill Close, Ashgate, Chesterfield S42 7JL
Tel: (H) 01246 222919 (W) 01246 547638
(M) 07754 588538
Email: arwynmorgan@aoc.com
Fixtures Secretary: Steve Allford, 3 Lincoln Street, Chesterfield S40 2TW
Tel: (H) 01246 297053 (M) 07759 489384
Club Colours: Navy blue shirts with white trim, white shorts
League: NLD/Leics 2 West

NORTH KESTEVEN RUFC
Ground Address: NK RUFC, Hykeham PFA Club, 319 Newark Road, North Hykeham, Lincoln CN6 9RY
Tel: 01522 880035
Brief Directions: From A46 south of Lincoln, go towards Lincoln, look for Memorial Hall sign on left opposite North Kesteven School and Sports Centre
Hon Secretary: Simon Scarth, 5 Crown Mill, Vernon Street, Lincoln, Lincolnshire LN5 7QD
Tel: (M) 07900 586300
Fixtures Secretary: Nigel Thomas, 192 Hykeham Road, Lincoln LN6 8AR Tel: (H) 01522 696666
Club Colours: Black with red,white & green hoops
League: NLD/Leics 2 East

NORTHAMPTON BBOB RFC
Ground Address: St. Andrews mill, St. Andrews Road, Northampton NN1 2PQ Tel: 01604 632460
Brief Directions: M1 J15A, follow signs for town centre, left at 1st lights just past 'Saints' Northampton RFC, cross 3 sets of lights, left into St Andrews Rd, Ground entrance by Texaco garage
Hon Secretary: H. Bolden, 15 Berry Lane, Wootton, Northampton, Northants NN4 6JU
Tel: (H) 01604 766949
Fixtures Secretary: A. C. Bolden, 15 Berry Lane, Wotton, Northhampton NN4 6JU
Tel: (H) 01604 766949
Club Colours: Light blue, dark blue and maroon hoops with black shorts
League: Midlands 4 East (South)

NORTHAMPTON CASUALS RFC
Ground Address: Rush Mills House, Old Bedford Road, Rush Mills, Northampton, Northamptonshire NN4 7AA Tel: 01604 795500
Email Address: bob.barfield@eliteselectionsrvices.co.uk
Brief Directions: At J15 of M1 take A508 to Northampton and then 4th slip road and take A428 to Bedford. At first roundabout go right round and back towards Northampton, then take first left.
Hon Secretary: John Thomas Wearing, 145 Obelisk Rise, Northampton, Northants NN2 8TX
Tel: (H) 01604 844882
Email: john.wearing@virgin.net
Fixtures Secretary: Michael David Askew, 60 Hinton Road, Northampton, Northamptonshire NN2 8NX
Tel: (H) 01604 454283 Tel: (M) 07778 838341
Email: mick@mdaskews.freeserve.co.uk
Club Colours: Black with amber band
League: Midlands 4 East (South)

NORTHAMPTON HEATHENS RFC
Ground Address: The Obelisk Centre, 400 Obelisk Rise, Northampton, Northamptonshire NN2 8UE
Tel: 01604 843032
Email Address: lon.dhodgkinson@cma-cgm.com
Brief Directions: Situated at the top of Obelisk Rise which is located off Cherry Lodge Drive [off the Market Harborough Road A508] - Look for The Obelisk.

Hon Secretary: Derek Hodgkinson, 5 Pine Trees, Northampton, Northants NN3 3ET
Tel: (H) 01604 416442 Tel: (M) 07866 773871
Tel: (W) 020 8532 6724
Email: hodgk@aol.com
Leagues Contact: Derek Hodgkinson, 5 Pine Trees, Northampton, Northants NN3 3ET
Tel: (H) 01604 416442 Tel: (M) 07866 773871
Tel: (W) 020 8532 6724
Email: hodgk@aol.com
Fixtures Secretary: Martin Robson, 8 Rockcroft, Northampton, Northamptonshire NN4 OUB
Tel: (H) 01604 705987 Tel: (W) 01908 522122
Club Colours: Black with amber 'V'
League: East Midlands 2

NORTHAMPTON MENS OWN RFC
Ground Address: Stoke Road, Ashton, Northampton NN7 2JN Tel: 01604 862463
Brief Directions: M1 J15, take A508 to Milton Keynes for 2.5 miles, through Roade village, take next left turning at crossroads, after 1 mile, signed Ashton, ground 0.5 mile on right
Hon Secretary: John Goold, 38 Millway, Northampton NN5 6ES Tel: (H) 01604 756297
Fixtures Secretary: Jacqueline Webb, 23 Amberley Road, Northampton NN7 2JB
Tel: (H) 01604 864266 Tel: (W) 01908 690055
Club Colours: White shirts with blue hoop and black shorts.
League: Midlands 3 East (South)

NORTHAMPTON OLD SCOUTS RFC
Ground Address: Rushmere Road, Northampton NN1 5RY Tel: 01604 633639
Brief Directions: Mi Jct 15 head towards N'ton. Signs to town centre/Bedford.2nd exit off r'about after slip road into Rushmere Rd. Club is first building on left
Hon Secretary: R. Letty, 49 Barley Hill Road, Northampton NN3 5JA Tel: (H) 01604 493727
Tel: (M) 07801 399219 Tel: (W) 01933 400300
Fixtures Secretary: K. Shurville, 41 Churchill Avenue, Northampton NN3 6NY Tel: (H) 01604 494374
Tel: (M) 07721 368477 Tel: (W) 01908 600406
Club Colours: Red, green, gold & navy hooped shirts, navy shorts.
League: Midlands 2 East

NOTTINGHAM CASUALS RFC
Ground Address: Canalside, Meadow Road, Beeston, Nottingham NG9 1JQ Tel: 0115 925 0135
Email Address: casuals@rugby-club.co.uk
Web Address: www.rugby-club.co.uk
Brief Directions: M1 J25, A52 to Nottingham, after 2nd roundabout, right at 2nd lights, straight across 2 crossroads, continue till road makes sharp right, over bridge, turn left
Hon Secretary: A. Crowther, 18 Longleat Crescent, Nottingham NG9 5EU
Tel: (H) 0115 967 8390 Tel: (W) 0115 957 5910
Email: onzc@clara.net
Fixtures Secretary: Lech Kluk, 46 Springfield Avenue, Nottingham NG10 5LZ Tel: (H) 0115 946 2846
Tel: (M) 07713 149399 Tel: (W) 0115 946 2846
Email: lktrain@aol.com
Club Colours: Maroon,black and white with black shorts.
League: Midlands 4 East (North)

NOTTINGHAM MODERNS RFC
Ground Address: Ferryfields, Main Road, Willford Village, Nottingham NG11 7AA Tel: 0115 981 1374
Web Address: www.nottighammodernsrfc.co.uk
Brief Directions: On the banks of the Trent, 10 minutes walk from Nottingham City centre. On A453 by Clifton Bridge.
Hon Secretary: Keith Straughan, 44 Longdale Road, Nottingham NG5 6ES
Tel: (H) 0115 926 2891 Tel: (W) 0115 950 2098
Fixtures Secretary: Alistair Clark, 17 Mountsorrel Avenue, Abbey Park, Nottingham
Tel: (H) 0115 981 9207
Club Colours: Red and white hoops
League: Midlands 2 East

NOTTINGHAMIANS RFC
Ground Address: Adbolton Lane, West Bridgford, Nottingham Tel: 0115 981 1372
Brief Directions: M1 jct 24, A453 to A52, the Nottingham ring road. Follow signs to Holme Pierrepont (National Water Sports centre)
Hon Secretary: David Hampson, 36 Longleat Crescent, Nottingham NG9 5EU
Tel: (H) 0115 925 8395 Tel: (W) 0115 945 6648
Email: hampsond@logica.com
Fixtures Secretary: Matthew Draper, 3 Crescent Avenue, Nottingham NG4 3JQ Tel: (H) 0115 987 4533
Club Colours: Black, white and purple quarters with black shorts and socks.
League: NLD/Leics 1 East

NUNEATON OLD EDWARDIANS RFC
Ground Address: Weddington Road, Nuneaton, Warwickshire CV10 0AL Tel: 02476 386778
Email Address: webmaster@nuneatonoldeds.org.uk
Web Address: www.nuneatonoldeds.org.uk
Brief Directions: Off M6 J3: follow A444 into and through Nuneaton, on left leaving town. Off A5 at A444 junction: A444 into Nuneaton for 2 miles, ground on right
Hon Secretary: Ken McBride
Email: kemac@supanet.com
Fixtures Secretary: John Burdett, 5 Henley Close, Warwickshire CV11 6HF
Tel: (H) 02476 347257 Tel: (W) 02476 341231
Club Colours: Red and white hoops, black shorts
League: Midlands 3 West (South)

OADBY WYGGESTONIAN RFC
Ground Address: Oval Park, Wigston Road, Oadby, Leicester, Leics LE2 5JE
Tel: 0116 271 4848
Email Address: jimkilgallen@aol.com
Web Address: www.owrfc.com
Brief Directions: M1 J21, follow Leicester South and East for 4 miles to A50, turn right, left at roundabout, ground 0.5 mile on left
Hon Secretary: Jim Kilgallen, 75 Leicester Road, Leicester LE2 4DF Tel: (H) 0116 271 3987
Tel: (M) 07803 649854 Tel: (W) 0116 262 6123
Email: jimkilgallen@aol.com
Fixtures Secretary: Tony Bayley, 27 Dover House, Dover Street, Leicester LE1 6PL
Tel: (H) 0116 255 3787
Club Colours: Black, gold and white hooped shirts & balck shorts
League: Midlands 4 East (South)

MIDLAND

OAKHAM RFC
Ground Address: The Showground, Barleythorpe Road, Oakham, Rutland Tel: 01572 724206
Email Address: rut.preservation@btclick.com
Web Address: www.rutnet.co.uk/sportleisure/oakhamrugby
Brief Directions: Take the A606 Oakham to Melton Mowbray and ground is on left.
Hon Secretary: Peter Bateman, 26 Well Street, Oakham, Rutland LE15 7JS Tel: (H) 01572 723850 Tel: (M) 07710 082447 Tel: (W) 01572 756143
Leagues Contact: Jeremy Bryant, 17 Princess Avenue, Oakham, Rutland LE15 6PQ Tel: (H) 01572 722005 Tel: (M) 07944 067015 Tel: (W) 01780 783838 Ext 7392
Email: jerry.bryant@talk21.com
Fixtures Secretary: Peter Bateman, 26 Well Street, Oakham, Rutland LE15 7JS Tel: (H) 01572 723850 Tel: (M) 07710 082447 Tel: (W) 01572 756143
Club Colours: Black shirts with single amber band
League: NLD/Leics 1 East

OLD COVENTRIANS RFC
Ground Address: Tile Hill Lane, Tile Hill, Coventry CV4 9DE Tel: 02476 715273
Web Address: www.ocrfc.freeserve.co.uk
Brief Directions: Old Coventrians RFC is at the junction of the A45 (Fletchamstead Highway) and B4101 (Tile Hill Lane). Coming from Birmingham direction on A45 turn left at the Tile Hill Lane traffic lights and the ground is 50 yards on the left. Coming from South East on A45 filter right at Tile Hill Lane traffic lights and ground is 50 yards on left, through another set of lights.
Brief Directions: Tile Hill Lane is at the Junction of A45 and B4101
Hon Secretary: Phil Gill, 27 Glebe Crescent, Kenilworth CV8 1JA Tel: (H) 01926 858634 Tel: (W) 01926 464679
Email: phil_gill@uk.ibm.com
Fixtures Secretary: Colin Hart, 7 Staverton Close, Coventry CV5 7LF Tel: (H) 02476 469463
Email: colinandjanet@dartsystems.freeserve.co.uk
Club Colours: Red black & gold hoops
League: Midlands 3 West (South)

OLD GRIFFINIANS RFC
Ground Address: WM Travel Transport Stadium, Wheelers Lane, Kings Heath, Birmingham, West Midlands B13 0ST Tel: 0121 687 2465
Email Address: andyrogers@oldgriffs.com
Web Address: www.oldgriffs.com
Brief Directions: M42 J3, take A435 into B'ham, at Kings Heath turn right into Wheelers Lane and follow signs for Indoor Tennis Centre (B'ham A-Z page 106, grid ref C2)
Hon Secretary: Andy Rogers, 234 Turves Green, Birmingham B31 4BW
Tel: (H) 0121 604 1364 Tel: (M) 07974 733112
Email: andyrogers@oldgriffs.com
Fixtures Secretary: Adrian Johnson
Tel: (H) 0121 605 1324
Club Colours: All Black
League: North Midlands 2

OLD HALESONIANS RFC
Ground Address: Old Halesonians, Wassell Grove, Hagley, Stourbridge, West Midlands DY9 9JP
Tel: 01562 883036
Brief Directions: Wassell Grove is signposted on the A456, 4 miles from junction 3 of the M5
Hon Secretary: Mike Churchill, 10 Parkfield close, Halesowen, West. Midlands B62 0HL
Tel: (H) 0121 602 3797 Tel: (M) 07802 890506
Email: ohrfc@aol.com
Fixtures Secretary: Ian Glendinning, 31 Middleacre Road, Bartley Green, West Midlands, B32
Tel: (H) 0121 603 5639
Colours: Royal blue, amber & gold irregular hoops
League: Midlands 4 West (South)

OLD LAURENTIANS RFC
Ground Address: Fenley FIeld, Lime Tree Avenue, Rugby CV22 7QT Tel: 01788 810855
Web Address: www.oldlaurentianrfc.co.fc
Brief Directions: From A45 take A4071 turn right into Alwyn Road. right again into Lime Tree Ave. or M6 Leicester Road, Bilton Road, Bilton Village, left into Alwyn Road and right into Lime Tree Ave.
Hon Secretary: A. Willis, 45 Frobisher Road, Rugby CV22 7QT
Tel: (H) 01788 813481 Tel: (W) 02476 203564
Email: awillis@jaguar.com
Fixtures Secretary: Ray Roberts, 261 Alwyn Rd, Rugby Tel: (H) 01788 810276
Email: rayrobwark@aol.com
Club Colours: Maroon, green and gold
League: Midlands 2 West

OLD LEAMINGTONIANS RFC
Ground Address: The Crofts, Bericote Road, Blackdown, Leamington Spa, Warks CV32 6QP
Tel: 01926 424991
Web Address: www.olrfc.co.uk
Brief Directions: From A46 take A452 towards Leamington Spa, after 600 yards take left fork towards Cubbington, ground .75 mile on right
Hon Secretary: D. Fisher, 14 New Street, Leamington Spa CV32 7LA Tel: (H) 01926 778639
Email: jananden@tesco.net
Fixtures Secretary: Martyn Rawbone, 3 Hampton On The Hill, Warwick CV35 8QR
Tel: (H) 01926 497464 Tel: (W) 0121 698 4024
Club Colours: Blue and gold hoops, navy shorts
League: Midlands 3 West (South)

OLD NEWTONIANS RFC
Ground Address: Hinckley Road, Leicester Forest East, Leicester, Leics LE3 3PJ Tel: 0116 239 2389
Email Address: Alan.Naylor@antools.co.uk
Brief Directions: Follow main A47 to Hinckley out of Leicester, pass Red Cow pub on right, continue along A47 for 1 mile ground on right
Hon Secretary: G. A. Clark, 250 Wigston Lane, Leicester LE2 8DH
Tel: (H) 0116 283 2309 Tel: (W) 0116 2785 288
Fixtures Secretary: Peter Muggleton, 18 ROman Road, Leicester LE4 4BA Tel: (H) 0116 267 6739
Club Colours: Navy (white, green, red) central band, navy shorts
League: Midlands 4 East (South)

OLD NORTHAMPTONIANS RFC
Ground Address: Sports Field, Billing Road, Northampton Tel: 01604 634045
Email Address: mjpipparsons@aol.com
Web Address: www.oldnorthamptonians-rfc.co.uk
Brief Directions: Follow signs for Northants County Cricket Ground and District of Abington
Hon Secretary: M. J. Parsons, 65 Porlock Close,

Northampton, Northants NN5 6BS
Tel: (H) 01604 755887 Tel: (M) 07808 545107
Tel: (W) 01604 755887
Email: mjpipparsons@aol.com
Fixtures Secretary: Simon James, 7 Chipsey Avenue, Northampton NN1 5SE
Tel: (H) 01604 639860 Tel: (M) 07808 364378
Email: simon.james@breathemail.net
Club Colours: Cardinal red,navy and gold hoops-navy shorts
League: Midlands 3 East (South)

OLD SALTLEIANS RFC
Ground Address: Watton Lane, Water Orton, North Warwickshire B46 1PL Tel: 0121 748 3380
Web Address: www.oldsaltleians.com
Brief Directions: Junction of Gilson Road/Watton Lane, off A446, near Coleshill
Hon Secretary: Colin Gardner, 26 Julius Drive, Coleshill, North Warwickshire B46 1HL
Tel: (H) 01675 465050 Tel: (W) 0121 214 3180
Fixtures Secretary: Nik Wilkins, 14 Mercury Close, Daventry NN11 5HW
Tel: (H) 01327 878785 Tel: (W) 01675 432400
Club Colours: Red & gold hoop shirts, navy shorts
League: Midlands 4 West (North)

OLD WARWICKIAN RFC
Ground Address: Sports Ground, Hampton Road, Warwick Tel: 01926 496295
Brief Directions: Follow road out of Warwick towards Henley in Arden pass the Warwick Horse Race Stadium and ground is on the right after bypass
Club Secretary: Patrick Wing, 57 Broadeers Road, Knowle, Solihull, West Midlands. B93 9OG
Tel: (H) 01564 779947
e-mail: patrickwing@yahoo.co.uk
Fixtures Secretary: Andrew Marshall, 33 Borrowoale Rd,Leamington Spa, Warwicks CV32 6AY
Tel: (H) 01926 881499 (M) 07421 556098
Club Colours: Maroon and white hoops
League: Warwickshire 2

OLD WHEATLEYANS RFC
Ground Address: Norman Place Road, Coundon, Coventry Tel: 02476 334888
Brief Directions: At J9 on Coventry ring road, take A4170 (Radford Rd), after 1.5 miles turn left into Norman Place Rd, entrance is at the far end of road, on left
Hon Secretary: Andrew Hibberd, 59 Frilsham Way, Coventry CV5 9LJ Tel: (H) 02476 711955
Email: andy.hibberd@ntlworld.com
Fixtures Secretary: Graham Paine, 2 Craven Street, Chapel Fields, Coventry CV5 8DU
Tel: (H) 02476 679864 Tel: (W) 0121 744 3835
Email: melindapaine@hotmail.com
Club Colours: Navy blue, maroon, gold
League: Warwickshire 1

OLD YARDLEIANS RFC
Ground Address: Tilehouse Lane, Shirley, Solihull, West Midlands B90 1PW Tel: 0121 744 3380
Brief Directions: From north, M42 J4, Stratford Road, Dog Kennel Lane, Dickens Heath Road, Tythebarn Lane, Tilehouse Lane. From south, M42 J3 Alcetter Lane, Station Road, Lowbrook Lane, Tilehouse Lane.
Hon Secretary: Ian Wallace, 54 Geraldine Road, Birmingham B25 8BD Tel: (H) 0121 604 2168
Tel: (M) 07979 387368 Tel: (W) 0121 695 5286
Email: enoch.wallace@virgin.net
Fixtures Secretary: Shannon Killarney, 112 Fabian Crescent, Solihull, W. Midlands B90 2AD
Tel: (H) 0121 733 7116
Email: shannontk@msc.com
Club Colours: Old gold, maroon and green
League: Midlands 4 West (South)

OLLERTON RFC
Ground Address: Boughton Sports Field, Church Lane, Boughton, Newark, Notts NG22 9JU
Tel: 01623 860871
Email Address: daipri@lathkill.freeserve.co.uk
Brief Directions: Ground -Boughton SportsField-Church Lane Boughton From A614 take A6075 thro' New Ollerton towards Tuxford. Under railway bridge-200yds turn left on the APEX of the lefthand bend at the Harrow Inn into Church Rd. In 200yds follow the road to the righthand side of the church into Church Lane . The ground is behind the Church. From the A1, from Tuxford take the A6075 towards Ollerton,thro' the village of Kirton,past Boughton Industrial Estate. On entering Boughton turn right on the APEX of the lefthand bend at the Harrow Inn into Church Road
Hon Secretary: D. G. Price, 'Lathkill' Harrow Farm, Tuxford Road, Newark, Nottinghamshire NG22 9JZ
Tel: (H) 01623 860871 Tel: (M) 07748 261675
Email: daipri@lathkill.freeserve.co.uk
Fixtures Secretary: Clive Ford, 8 Linton Drive, Boughton, Notts NG22 9JH Tel: (H) 01623 862608
Club Colours: Yellow & blue hoops, navy shorts
League: NLD/Leics 2 East

OUNDLE RFC
Ground Address: Occupation Road, Oundle, Peterborough Tel: 01832 273101
Brief Directions: From Peterborough, cross bridge, turn right by garage, turn right then right again down single track road
Hon Secretary: D. Hook, 12 Wyatt Way, Peterborough, Cambs PE8 4HE Tel: (H) 01832 275407
Tel: (M) 07768 154421 Tel: (W) 01733 422238
Email: duncan.hook@farming.co.uk
Fixtures Secretary: Andrew Kendall, 30 Sydons Close, Oundle, Peterborough, Cambs PE8 4QJ.
Tel No: 01832 274760
Club Colours: Red and white hoops on black with black shorts.
League: East Midlands 2

PAVIORS RFC
Ground Address: The Ron Rossin Ground, Burnstump Hill, Arnold, Nottingham NG5 8PG Tel: 0115 963 0384
Web Address: www.paviorsfc.co.uk
Brief Directions: A614 from Nottingham to Doncaster, 2 miles north of city turn left onto Burntstump Hill, first left pass the school on left to Rugby Club
Hon Secretary: R. Boulton, The Barnacles, 40 St. Andrews, Lincolnshire NG31 9PE
Tel: (H) 01476 401977 Tel: (W) 0115 915 4502
Email: tomas_boulton@hotmail.com
Fixtures Secretary: Len Hines, 6 Beverley Gardens, Nottingham NG4 3LF Tel: (H) 0115 956 3379
Club Colours: Green with red bands, green or blue shorts
League: Midlands 3 East (North)

MIDLAND

PERSHORE RFC
Ground Address: Piddle Park, Mill Lane, Wyre Piddle, Nr Pershore, Worcs WR10 2JE Tel: 01386 554105
Email Address: webmaster@prfc.co.uk
Web Address: www.prfc.co.uk
Brief Directions: Between Worcester and Evesham on B4538, turn off main road in middle of village on the corner by the War Memorial, club 0.5 mile down the lane
Hon Secretary: David Snell, 9 Poplar Way, Evesham, Worcs WR11 8JD Tel: (H) 01386 870251
Email: snelly@madasafish.com
Fixtures Secretary: Anthony Perks, 3 Abbewy View Road, Pershore
Club Colours: Black shirts with two scarlet hoops, black shorts
League: Midlands 3 West (South)

PETERBOROUGH RUFC
Ground Address: Second Drove, Fengate, Peterborough PE1 5XA Tel: 01733 69413
Email Address: enquiries@prufc.com
Web Address: www.prufc.com
Brief Directions: Leave A1 or A47.Take Parkways to East of City, following signs for Fengate Industries
Hon Secretary: Barbara Johnson, 4 Middleham Close, Park Farm, Peterborough PE2 8XG
Tel: (H) 01733 894854 Tel: (M) 07780 554490
Email: secretary@prufc.com
Club Colours: Red, silver, gold
League: Midlands 3 East (South)

PINLEY RFC
Ground Address: Wyken Croft, Wyken, Coventry
Tel: 02476 602059
Hon Secretary: Mike Brown, 11 Minton rd, Minton Gardens, Coventry, CV2 2XH
Tel: (H) 02476 622062 Email: pinleyrfc@aol.com
Fixtures Secretary: B. Lester Tel: (H) 01203 443605
Club Colours: Red and black quarters
League: Warwickshire 2

REDDITCH RFC
Ground Address: Bromsgrove Road, Redditch
Tel: 01527 62807
Web Address: www.reditchrugbyclub.com
Brief Directions: Bromsgrove Highway - Birchfield Road - Bromsgrove Road
Hon Secretary: Brian Carr, 60 Wychbury Road, Quarry Bank, Brierley Hill, West Midlands
Tel: (H) 01384 79092 Tel: (W) 01384 422494
Email: bcarr4@aol.com
Fixtures Secretary: Paul Thurston, 18 Crendon Close, Stodley, Warks Tel: (H) 01527 854802
Club Colours: Navy and light blue shirts navy shorts & socks
League: North Midlands 1

ROLLS ROYCE RFC
Ground Address: Merril Way, Allenton, Derby
Brief Directions: Contact Secretary
Hon Secretary: C. Ellans, 39 Keyhaven Close, Derbys S42 6DW Tel: (H) 01332 720844
Tel: (W) 01332 260317
Email: chris.ellans@rolls-royce.com
Fixtures Secretary: T. Jenkins, 5 Woodland Road, Derby DE22 1GF Tel: (H) 01332 298564
Club Colours: Maroon and sky blue quarters,
League: NLD/Leics 2 West

RUGBY ST. ANDREWS RFC
Ground Address: Hillmorton Grounds, Ashlawn Road, Rugby Tel: 01788 542786
Brief Directions: Ashlawn Road runs between Dunchurch (A45) and Hillmorton (M1-Northampton) A428
Hon Secretary: Patricia Lee, 29 Faraday Road, Rugby CV22 5ND
Tel: (H) 01788 333393 Tel: (W) 01788 533708
Email: pat.lee@rugby.gov.uk
Fixtures Secretary: Richard Hobley, 13 Alfred Street, Rugby Tel: (H) 01788 330664
Tel: (M) 07775 714896 Tel: (W) 01788 558518
Email: rhobley@ntlworld.com
Club Colours: Sky & navy quarters navy shorts.
League: Warwickshire 1

RUGELEY RUFC
Ground Address: Hagley Park Field, Burnthill Lane, Rugeley, Staffs WS15 2HS Tel: 07721 449869
Email Address: secretary@rugeleyrugby.co.uk
Web Address: www.rugeleyrugby.co.uk
Brief Directions: A460 towards Hednesford, 1st right into Burnthill Lane. 50 yards on right, Hagley Park Field.
Hon Secretary: Ian McLeod, 6 Raven Road, Burton-on-Trent, Staffs DE13 8PY
Tel: (H) 01543 472864 Tel: (W) 07860 694548
Email: ianmcleod@rugeleyrugby.co.uk
Fixtures Secretary: Ian Bailey
Email: ianbailey@rugeley217.freeserve.co.uk
Club Colours: Gold shirts and black shorts
League: Staffordshire 2

RUSHDEN & HIGHAM RUFC
Ground Address: Manor Park, Bedford Road, Rushden, Northants NN10 0SA Tel: 01933 312071
Web Address: www.rhrufc.co.uk/rugby
Brief Directions: On main A6 Bedford side of Rushden, on the left leaving Rushden and the right when approaching Rushden from Bedford
Hon Secretary: Steve Miles, Kialanga, The Green, Kettering, Northants NN14 1JA Tel: (H) 01933 400123
Tel: (M) 07721 376359 Tel: (W) 01604 545034
Email: stevemiles14@hotmail.com
Fixtures Secretary: Tristan Clee, 121 Torrington Crescent, Wellingborough, Northants
Tel: (H) 01933 675973 Tel: (M) 07803 511180
Email: triatanclee@fedex.com
Club Colours: Black, white and gold
League: Midlands 4 East (South)

SELLY OAK RFC
Ground Address: Holders Lane, Moseley, Birmingham
Tel: 0121 472 0939
Email Address: postmaster@tcsclub.f9.co.uk
Web Address: www.tcsclub.force9.co.uk
Brief Directions: From Edgbaston Cricket Ground turn right into Russell Road, proceed until right turn into Moor Green Lane, Holders Lane is 1st right
Hon Secretary: Simon Walster, 5 Barnsley Road, Edgbaston B17 8EB
Tel: (H) 0121 429 6802 Tel: (W) 0121 625 1407
Fixtures Secretary: Nick Lally, 78 Reservoir Road, Birmingham B28 6TF
Tel: (H) 0121 603 1493 Tel: (M) 07718 926682
Club Colours: Blue and white hoops with red spangles and blue shorts
League: Midlands 4 West (North)

SHIPSTON ON STOUR RFC
Ground Address: Mayo Road, Shipston on Stour, Warwickshire Tel: 01608 662107
Brief Directions: On A3400, through Shipston, turn opposite hospital and follow signs.
Hon Secretary: R. H. Slatter, Woodhills Farm, Moreton In Marsh, Gloucestershire GL56 9PH
Tel: (H) 01608 650453 Tel: (M) 07971 852360
Fixtures Secretary: R. Hawkins, Washbrook Place, Shipston On Stour
el: (H) 01608 682216
Club Colours: All black
League: Midlands 4 West (South)

SHREWSBURY RUFC
Ground Address: Sundorne Castle, Uffington, Shrewsbury SY4 4RR Tel: 01743 353380
Web Address: www.shrewsburyrufc@freeserve.co.uk
Brief Directions: Follow M54/A5 extension from north or south to Shrewsbury, exit bypass at roundabout, marked B5062 Haughmond Abbey, ground 800 mtrs on left
Hon Secretary: Garry Dean, 3 Hardwick Drive, Shrewsbury
Fixtures Secretary: Glyn Jones, 10 Copthorne Park, Shrewsbury Tel: (H) 01743 360194
Club Colours: Sky blue and navy blue narrow hooped shirts, navy shorts
League: Midlands 3 West (North)

SILHILLIANS RUFC
Ground Address: Warwick Road, Copt Heath, Knowle, Solihull, West Midlands B93 9LW Tel: 01564 777680
Web Address: www.silhillians.com
Brief Directions: J5 M42, then towards Knowle, ground 50yds on left hand side
website: www.silhillians.com
Hon Secretary: G. R. Loader, 21 Bantock Gardens, Wolverhampton WV3 9LP Tel: (H) 07702 632219
Tel: (M) 07702 632219 Tel: (W) 01902 382454
Fixtures Secretary: K. Lane, 53 Shelsey Way, Solihull B91 3UZ
Tel: (H) 0121 709 1622 Tel: (M) 07803 246490
Club Colours: Maroon and blue shirts, blue shorts
League: Midlands 3 West (South)

SKEGNESS RUFC
Ground Address: Wainfleet Road, Playing Fields, Skegness Tel: 01754 765699
Web Address: www.skegness-rufc.co.uk
Brief Directions: A153 turn right for town centre, 0.5 mile turn right at Highwayman pub, ground across A52
Hon Secretary: Alan Hawkes, Grunters Grange, East Keal, Lincolnshire PE23 4AY
Tel: (H) 01790 752788 Tel: (W) 01790 754611
Email: skegrufc@aol.com
Fixtures Secretary: John Harris, 13 Jenkins Close, Skegness Tel: (H) 01754 765797
Club Colours: Royal blue and white hooped shirts, navy shorts
League: NLD/Leics 2 East

SLEAFORD RFC
Ground Address: East Road Ground, Ruskington Road, Sleaford, Lincs Tel: 01529 303335
Web Address: www.sleaford-rfc.freeserve.co.uk
Brief Directions: One mile north east of Sleaford on the A153 Skegness road, at the junction with the A17 Sleaford by-pass
Hon Secretary: S. Collyer, Damask, 17 The Sidings, Ruskington, Lincolnshire NG34 9GA
Tel: (W) 01526 833036
Email: rscollyer@aol.com
Fixtures Secretary: George Marsh, 37 Meadow Field, Sleaford, Lincs Tel: (H) 01529 303859
Club Colours: Red and black hooped shirts, black shorts., red socks
League: NLD/Leics 1 East

SOLIHULL RFC
League: North Midlands 1
For further information contact: **North Midlands 1 League Secretary -** John McNally, 490 Brook Lane, Moseley, Birmingham B13 0BZ
Tel: (H) 0121 604 6180
(W) 0121 783 723
(M) 07976 364234
(F) 0121 789 8306
Email: jmcnally@stberns.bham.sch.uk

SOUTH LEICESTER RFC
Ground Address: Welford Road, Wigston, Leicester LE18 1TE Tel: 0116 288 2066
Brief Directions: M1/M69 J21, head east on ringroad towards Oadby & Wigston, take A50 towards Northampton, ground at the final roundabout of the built up area of Wigston
Hon Secretary: Henri Ginvert, 5 The Paddock, Leicester, Leics LE67 9RR
Tel: (H) 01530 242761
Tel: (W) 01530 249621
Email: henri.ginvert@uk.zurich.com
Fixtures Secretary: Jason Pinnock, 197 Little Glen Road, Leicester LE2 9TX Tel: (H) 07050 153252
Club Colours: Green and white hoops
League: Midlands 2 East

SOUTHAM
Ground Address: Kineton Road, Southam, Nr. Rugby, Warwickshire Tel: 01926 813674
Brief Directions: Take Leamington road (A425) off Southam by-pass (A423). Left at next roundabout, past Ind. Estate. Ground on right.
Club Secretary: Ivan Harvey, Rookery Nook, Priors Hardwick, Nr. Rugby, Warwickshire CV23 8SL
Tel: (H) 01327 260709
Fixtures Secretary: Paul Broadway, 37 Barcus Close, Southam, Leamington Spa, Warwicks
Tel: 01926 815118
Club Colours: Navy blue jerseys with white hoops and white shorts.
League: Midlands 3 West (South)

SOUTHWELL RFC
Ground Address: Soutwell RUFC, Park Lane, Southwell, Notts NG25 0QN Tel: 01636 812576
Brief Directions: On entering into Southwell follow signs to the recreation centre. The rugby club is behind the recreation centre.
Hon Secretary: Andrew Smith, 66 Easthorpe, Southwell, Nottinghamshire NG25 0HZ
Tel: (H) 01636 812869 Tel: (M) 07780 956340
Fixtures Secretary: Phil Gordon, Main Street, Notts NG25 0U Tel: (H) 01636 830485
Club Colours: Maroon and navy blue quarters
League: NLD/Leics 1 East

SPARTANS RUFC
Ground Address: Coppice Lane, Middleton, Nr Tamworth, Staffordshire B78 2BS.
Tel: 0121 308 5857
Brief Directions: Club is situated by the junction of A446 and Coppice Lane, 0.25 mile on the Colehill side of the A453 at Bassetts Pole
Club Secretary: Tim Hesketh,108 Somerset Road, Erdington, Birmingham B23 6NH
e-mail: tim.hesketh@willenhallsteel.co.uk
Fixtures Secretary: John Whiting, 33 Whiston Grange, Moorgate, Rotherham. S60 3BG Tel:(H) 01709 372265 (W) 01709 842201 (M) 07831 118191
Club Colours: Black shirts and black shorts
League: Warwickshire 1

ST. IVES RUFC
Ground Address: Somerham Road, St. Ives, Cambs PE27 3LY Tel: 01480 464455
Web Address: www.stivesrufc.co.uk
Brief Directions: Follow signs to St Ives off A14 follow by pass (B1040) to Ramsey and ground is on left approx .5 mile from St Ives.
Hon Secretary: C. Ford, 3 The Aisled Barn, The Green, Cambs PE28 9NA Tel: (H) 01480 831862
Tel: (M) 07802 451130 Tel: (W) 01223 358966
Email: thefords@ic24.net
Fixtures Secretary: G. Price, 32 Laburnum Way, St. Ives, Cambs Tel: (H) 01480 381742
Club Colours: Royal B lue, black
League: East Midlands 2

ST. NEOTS RUFC
Ground Address: The Common, St. Neots, Cambs PE19 1HA Tel: 01480 218727
Email Address: tmradley@aol.com
Web Address: www.stneotsrufc.co.uk
Brief Directions: Follow signs for Little Paxton from town centre, ground on left as you leave St Neots (1 mile from Town centre)
Hon Secretary: S. Radley, 99 High Street, St. Neots, Cambs PE19 6QH
Tel: (H) 01480 218727 Tel: (M) 07796 935505
Email: tmradley@aol.com
Fixtures Secretary: S. Picton, 9 Phillips Gardens, Eynesbury, St Neots, Cambridgeshire
Tel: (H) 01480 390132
Email: pictonsteve@hotmail.com
Club Colours: Light blue with navy blue hoops.
League: East Midlands 2

STAFFORD RUFC
Ground Address: The County Ground, Castlefields, Newport Road, Stafford, Staffs, ST16 1BG
Tel: 01785 211241
Web Address: www.staffordrugbyclub.co.uk
Brief Directions: M6 J13, A449 to Stafford for 1.5 miles, turn on left marked Rowley Park Westway, continue to junction with Newport Rd, turn right, Club 500 yds on left
Hon Secretary: P.L. Hill, 39 Rising Brook, Stafford ST17 9DE Tel: (H) 01785 259583
Fixtures Secretary: B. J. Bowen, 6 Fallowfield, Stafford, Staffs ST17 4QU Tel: (H) 01785 603961
Club Colours: Black and amber hooped jerseys, black shorts
League: Midlands 2 West

STAMFORD RUFC
Ground Address: Hambleton Road, Stamford, Lincs
Tel: 01780 752180
Brief Directions: Take Oakham/Melton Mowbray exit from A1, turn towards Stamford, approx 500 yds right turn into Lonsdale Rd, approx 200 yds fork left into Hambleton Rd
Hon Secretary: A. Jones, 12 College Close, Stamford, Lincolnshire PE9 4AW
Tel: (M) 07967 398838 Tel: (W) 01780 765764
Club Colours: Purple, black and white shirts, black shorts
League: NLD/Leics 1 East
League Contact: As Secretary

STAMFORD COLLEGE OLD BOYS RFC
Ground Address: Stamford College, Drift Road, Stamford, Lincs
Brief Directions: Follow signs to Stamford College, ground behind Leisure Centre
Club Secretary: James Gerever, 77 Radcliffe Road, Stamford,Lincs PE91AU Tel No: 01780 766849
e-mail: james.gerever@adas.co.uk
Fixtures Secretary: Ray Bates. 55 Millfield Road, Deeping St James, Lincs PE6 8QX.
Tel: 01778 348644
e-mail: rbates@aptelecom.com
Club Colours: Red and green hoops
League: NLD/Leics 1 East

STANDARD RFC
Ground Address: The Sports Ground, Tanners Lane off Tile Hill Lane, Coventry CV4 9BD
Tel: 02476 675186
Brief Directions: From A45 to Tile Hill Lane to Tile Hill Village. Tale Tanners Lane and Ground is 100 yds on left.
Hon Secretary: Chris Hughes, 108 Earlsdon Avenue South, Coventry CV5 6DN Tel: (H) 02476 679552
Email: chris.hughes@waa.co.uk
Fixtures Secretary: Melvyn O'Neill, 87 Demontfort Way, Cannon Park, Coventry CV4 7DU
Tel: (H) 02476 690600
Club Colours: Dark blue, sky blue and white hoops with blue shorts
League: Warwickshire 2

STEWARTS & LLOYDS RFC
Ground Address: Occupation Road, Corby, Northants NN17 1EH Tel: 01536 400317
Web Address: www.slrfc.org.uk
Brief Directions: From Kettering, A6003 towards Oakham, right at roundabout at top of Rockingham Hill, .75 mile, turn right past Game Bird Pub into Occupation Rd, 1st right into ground
Hon Secretary: J. M. Thompson, 5 Howe Crescent, Corby, Northants NN17 2RY
Tel: (H) 01536 202433 Tel: (M) 07970 783253
Email: malc.s-l.rfc@talk21.com
Fixtures Secretary: A. Brooks, 22 Lister Close, Corby, Northants NN17 1XR
Tel: (H) 01536 266 01 Tel: (M) 07977 825071
Email: aj.brooks@ntlworld.com
Club Colours: Black shirts and shorts with black & white socks.
League: Midlands 3 East (South)

STOCKWOOD PARK RFC
Ground Address: Stockwood Park, London Road, Luton, Beds LU1 4BH Tel: 01582 728044
Web Address: stockwoodparkrfc.co.uk
Brief Directions: M1 J10, left at end of slip road, left at 1st set of traffic lights into Stockwood Park, Club on right
Hon Secretary: Peter Wise, Dovehouse Farm, Dunstable, Beds LU6 2PQ Tel: (H) 01582 872333 Tel: (M) 07787 526783 Tel: (W) 01582 872333
Email: peterwise14@hotmail.com
Fixtures Secretary: J. Carroll, 41 Wychwood Avenue, Luton, Beds Tel: (H) 01582 655527
Club Colours: Red with yellow hoop, navy, red
League: Midlands 4 East (South)

STOKE OLD BOYS RFC
Ground Address: Albert Gale Field, Brookvale Avenue, Binley, Coventry CV3 2RF Tel: 02476 453631
Brief Directions: Off Binley Road, closest landmark is Binley Fire Station, 40 yards out of town
Hon Secretary: Robert Withers, 3 Conifer Paddock, Binley, Coventry CV3 2RE Tel: (H) 02476 447468
Fixtures Secretary: Dave Henly, 104 Hermitage Road, Coventry CV2 5GE
Club Colours: Maroon and white hoops.
League: Warwickshire 1

STOKE-ON-TRENT RFC
Ground Address: Hartwell Lane, Barlaston, Stoke-On-Trent ST15 8TL Tel: 01782 372807
Web Address: www.stokerugbyclub.co.uk
Brief Directions: From M1: A38 to A50. Left at lights (A520) at town outskirts. Take Rd. to Barlaston after 3m.Club 1m on left. From M6 leaveJ15 (A34 South) to Barlaston, club on right
Hon Secretary: David Potts, Oaks Cottage, Moddershall Oaks, Nr Stone, Staffs ST15 0TR
Tel: (H) 01782 373309 Tel: (W) 01782 715555
Fixtures Secretary: Eric Hardisty, 29 Kingston Drive, Stone, Staffs ST15 0EJ Tel: (H) 01785 813641
Club Colours: Dark blue with light blue hoops
League: Midlands 3 West (North)

STONE RUFC
Ground Address: Bibby's Sports & Social Club, Tilling Drive, Walton, Stone, Staffordhsire ST15 0SJ
Tel: 01785 818319
Brief Directions: From A34 take B5026 to Eccleshall. Take first L. `Tilling Drive', Ground is at end of Tilling Drive.
Hon Secretary: Eric Laroche, 6 Millers Gate, Stone, Staffs, ST15 8ZF Tel: (H) 01785 286963
Fixtures Secretary: Ian Foster, 17 Rowen Close, Stone, Staffordshire ST15 0EP Tel: (H) 01785 814841
Club Colours: Maroon & green quarters, black shorts
League: Staffordshire 2

STONEYGATE RFC
Ground Address: Stoneygate RFC, Covert Lane, Scraptoft, Leics LE7 9SP Tel: 0116 241 9188
Web Address: www.stoneygaterugby.com
Brief Directions: A47 east out of Leicester (Signposted Peterborough), left at lights (Coles Nurseries) into Station La, turn right at bottom onto Covert Lane.
Hon Secretary: Steve Morris, 203 Evington Lane, Leicester LE5 6DJ
Tel: (H) 0116 273 5927 Tel: (W) 0116 262 8596
Fixtures Secretary: Roger Foxon, 33 Buddon Lane, Quorn, Leics LE12 8AD
Tel: (H) 01509 415 529 Tel: (W) 0116 262 5564
Email: foxtayl@quorn.com
Club Colours: Red, white and navy blue.
League: Midlands 3 East (North)

STOURBRIDGE LIONS RFC
Ground Address: Stourton Park, Bridgnorth Road, Stourton DY7 6QZ Tel: 01384 393889
Brief Directions: From A449 Wolverhampton to Kidderminster road take A458 towards Stourbridge town centre, club is on the r/h side
Hon Secretary: Peter Courtis, The Stables, Congreve, Staffs ST19 5QG Tel: 01785 714112
Email: peter@courtis.freeserve.co.uk
Fixtures Secretary: Duncan Laurie, 7 Romany Way, Norton Stourbridge DY8 3JR
Tel: (H) 01384 356789 (M) 07771 651354
Email: duncan.laurie@telewest.co.uk
Club Colours: Green, blue and red, blue shorts
League: North Midlands 3

STOURPORT RFC
Ground Address: Walshes Meadow, Harold Davies Road, Stourport-On-Severn, Worcs Tel: 01299 822210
Brief Directions: From Stourport Town Centre, cross River Severn Bridge, turn immediate left towards Leisure Centre, ground straight ahead at end of road.
Hon Secretary: Richard Gough, 18 Habberley Lane, Kidderminster, Worcs DY11 5JT
Tel: (H) 01562 755271 Tel: (M) 07989 700216
Fixtures Secretary: Eddie Osborn, 52 Stagborough Way, Stourport-on-Severn, Worcs
Tel: (H) 01299 871439
Colours: Yellow chevron on blue, blue shorts & socks
League: North Midlands 1

STRATFORD UPON AVON RFC
Ground Address: Pearcecroft Loxley Road, Stratford upon Avon Tel: 01789 297796
Web Address: www.stratforduponavonrugbyclub.co.uk
Brief Directions: Central Stratford, off Tiddington Road, alongside river on southern bank
Hon Secretary: Charles Beighton, 15 Wetherby Way, Stratford Upon Avon, Warwickshire CV37 9LU
Tel: (H) 01789 415462
Fixtures Secretary: Ian Fathers, 61 Loxley Rd, Stratford upon Avon, Warwicks CV37 7DP
Tel: (H) 01789 205715 (M) 07733 101549
Colours: Black & white hoops, black shorts & socks.
League: Midlands 2 West

SUTTON COLDFIELD RFC
Ground Address: Walmley Road, Walmley, Suitton Coldfield Tel: 0121 351 5323
Email Address: Ian@scrfc.fsnet.co.uk
Brief Directions: M6 J5 take A452 (Brownhills) at Bagot Arms pub, then right onto B4148 to Walmley. Or A38 at A453 to Sutton Coldfield - T/lights left to Walmley.
Hon Secretary: Ken Lewis, 57 Oakwood Road, Boldmere, West Midlands B76 1DY
Leagues Contact: Ian Larsen, 14 Rainscar, Tamworth B77 4LJ Tel: (H) 01827 894292
Email: ian@scrfc.fsnet.co.uk
Fixtures Secretary: John McElhannan, 22 Moor Hall, Sutton Coldfield Tel: (H) 0121 308 0153
Club Colours: Emerald green, white shorts
League: Midlands 2 West

SYSTON RFC
Ground Address: Barkby Road, Quenilborough, Leicester Tel: 0116 260 1223
Brief Directions: Off A607 Melton Mowbray road (Ring secretary for map)
Hon Secretary: M. Scott, 2 Pembroke Avenue, Syston, Leics LE7 2BZ
Tel: (H) 0116 260 3756 Tel: (W) 0116 242 1400
Fixtures Secretary: I. Thorpe, 12 Perseverance Road, Birstall, Leics LE4 4AU
Tel: (H) 0116 267 7950
Club Colours: Navy and saxe (light blue) hooped shirts, navy shorts
League: Midlands 2 East

TAMWORTH RUFC
Ground Address: Wigginton Lodge, Wigginton Park, Tamworth, Staffs Tel: 01827 68794
Brief Directions: Head north out of town towards Burton, left turn into Thackeray Drive, right at T junction, 1st left, 1st left to park
Hon Secretary: Craig Parker, 21 Woodhouse Lane, Tamworth, Staffs
Tel: (H) 01827 709022
Fixtures Secretary: Gordon Penley
Tel: (H) 01827 285211
Club Colours: Maroon, black and white
League: Midlands 4 West (North)

TELFORD HORNETS RFC
Ground Address: Town Park, Hinnshay Road, Dawley, Telford TF4 3NZ
Tel: 01952 505440
Brief Directions: M54, J4 for town centre, 2nd exit at roundabout, 1st exit next roundabout onto A442, continue to Cattlefield, 4th exit at roundabout to Dawley, 4th right, club .75 mile on left
Club Secretary: Mrs Linda Potts, 17 Ellesmere Court, Newport, Shropshire TF10 7SD
Tel No: (H/F) 01952 418801
e-mail; lin@blue yonder.co.uk
Fixtures Secretary: Gareth Evans, 14 Andreas Drive, Muxton, Telford TF2 8SF
Tel: (W) 01952 273888
Club Colours: Black and gold chest band
League: Midlands 4 West (North)

TENBURY RFC
Ground Address: Penlu, Worcester Road, Tenbury Wells, Worcs WR15 8AY Tel: 01584 810456
Brief Directions: Next to Tenbury Hospital
Hon Secretary: Lee Patten, Leamore House, Bromyard road, Tenbury Wells WR15 8DJ
Tel: (H) 01584 819620
Club Colours: Green and black Hoops
League: North Midlands 2

THORNEY RUFC
Ground Address: Crowland Road, Thorney, Peterborough, Cambs
Clubhouse at Thorney Ex-Servicemens Club, Station Road, Thorney, Cambs PE6 0QE.
Tel: 01733 270283
Brief Directions: A47 from Peterborough towards Wisbech, at traffic lights in Thorney Village turn left. Changing rooms situated l.5 miles outside village on Crowland Road.
Hon Secretary: E. Simpson, 9 Kingsline Close, Peterborough PE6 0NR
Tel: (H) 01733 270846 Tel: (M) 07876 053999
Tel: (W) 01945 466666
Email: liz.simpson@pool.net
Fixtures Secretary: L. Deplancke, 7 Headlands Way, Peterborough Tel: (H) 01733 204893
Email: louis@dep135.freeserve.co.uk
Club Colours: Navy and gold quarters
League: East Midlands 2

TOWCESTRIANS RFC
Ground Address: Greens Norton Road, Towcester, Northants NN12 8AW Tel: 01327 350141
Web Address: www.towcestriansrfc.net
Brief Directions: From A43/A5 junction roundabout take exit for Greens Norton and Blakesley, ground situated approx 1 mile on right
Hon Secretary: R. Titmuss, 67 Clare Crescent, Towcester, Northants NN12 6QQ
Tel: (H) 01327 358031 Tel: (M) 0410 835696
Tel: (W) 01327 304 273
Email: r.titmuss@tesco.net
Fixtures Secretary: Ray Chambers, Thorstone, Back Lane, Chapel Brampton, Northants NN6 8AJ
Tel: (H) 01604 843424
Club Colours: Maroon with white edged amber band, black shorts, maroon socks
League: Midlands 3 East (South)

TRINITY GUILD RFC
Ground Address: Rowley Road, Baginton, Coventry, West Midlands Tel: 02476 305928
Email Address: d.h.w@ntlworld.com
Brief Directions: From north, follow A45 west of Coventry, follow airport signs. From south, follow A45 from M45. From west, follow A46 to A45
Hon Secretary: D. H. Williams, 122 Grange Road, Coventry CV6 6DA Tel: (H) 02476 725075
Tel: (W) 02476 666655 ext 2420
Email: David_Williams@dunlop-aviation.co.uk
Fixtures Secretary: K. Lightowler, 37 Oakfield Road, Coventry Tel: (H) 02476 598932
Club Colours: Maroon, old gold and dark navy hoops
League: Warwickshire 1

TUPTON RUFC
Ground Address: The Recreation Ground, North Side, Tupton, Chesterfield, Derbys S42 6DW
Tel: 01246 862441
Web Address: www.rfu.com
Brief Directions: From Chesterfield south A61 to Tupton, left at roundabout into Queen Victoria Road, then 2nd left into North Side
Hon Secretary: R. J. Curry, 190 Queen Victoria Road, Tupton, Derbys S42 6DW
Tel: (H) 01246 862059 Tel: (W) 01773 837222
Email: bobandtracey@clara.co.uk
Fixtures Secretary: Ian Bulloch, 3 Nethercroft Road, Chesterfield S43 1QD
Tel: (H) 01246 238920 Tel: (M) 07977 413389
Club Colours: Navy blue with 3 gold hoops, blue, blue
League: NLD/Leics 2 West

UNIVERSITY OF DERBY RFC
League: NLD/Leics 2 West
For further information contact:
NLD/Leics 2 West League Secretary
David Miller, 37 Rosemary Drive, Alvaston, Derby DE24 0TA Tel: (H) 01332 755935 (W) 01332 260144
Email: MillerAdmiller@aol.com

UPTON-UPON-SEVERN RFC
Ground Address: Sports Club, Old Street, Upton-Upon-Severn, Worcs Tel: 01684 594445
Brief Directions: Opposite Upton-upon-Severn Church in the main street of the town. 10 miles south of Worcester and 7 miles north of Tewkesbury on the A38 trunk road
Hon Secretary: Paul Pickering, 11 The Farrington Suite, Norton Barracks, Worcester, Worcs WR5 2PA
Tel: (H) 01905-355534 Tel: (M) 07979 701115
Tel: (W) 01827 59311
Fixtures Secretary: Nigel Banwell, 16 Riverside Close, Upton-upon-Severn WR8 0JN
Tel: (H) 01684-592046 Tel: (M) 07790-730688
Email: nigel.banwell@tesco.net
Club Colours: Black and white quarters, black shorts
League: North Midlands 1

UTTOXETER RFC
Ground Address: Oldfields Sports Centre, Springfield Road, Uttoxeter, Staffs.
Tel: 01889 564347
Brief Directions: From the centre of Uttoxeter, take Stone Road, after 200 yards right into Springfield Road. After 50 yards turn right.
Club Secretary: Ian Bould, 23 New Road, Uttoxeter, Staffs. ST14 7DD Tel: 01889 564313
email: i.bould@hotmail.com
Fixtures Secretary: Jason Cabrera, 72 Bentley Road, Uttoxeter Staffs ST14 7EN Tel: 01889 564483
email: mel.cabrera@freeserve.co.uk
Club Colours: Navy blue with red, white, yellow hoops, navy, red with blue top
League: Midlands 4 West (North)
League Contact: As Secretary

VAUXHALL MOTORS RUFC
Ground Address: Vauxhall Recreation Club, 20 Gypsy Lane, Luton, Beds LU1 3JH
Tel: 01525 716393 / 01525 713777
Email Address: kevincgreen@aol.com / malcolm.neate@gmacio.com
Brief Directions: Off M1 at J10, follow signs to Luton Airport. Ground on left as you approach 2nd R/about.
Hon Secretary: W. J. Maclaughlan, 242 Poynters Road, Luton, Beds, LU4 0LD Tel: (H) 01582 653380
Fixtures Secretary: M Neate, 32 Gardeners Close, Flitnick, MK45 5BY
Tel: (H) 01525 716393 Tel: (W) 01582 420565
Club Colours: Royal blue and gold hooped shirts, black shorts.
League: East Midlands 2

VESEYANS RFC
Ground Address: Little Hardwick Road, Streetly, Sutton Coldfield, West Midlands Tel: 0121 353 5388
Brief Directions: A452 to Brownhills. Turn left at the Hardwick pub and the ground is 1 mile further on the left.
Hon Secretary: Karl Ward, Claret Wood, Streetly Wood, Sutton Coldfield B74 3DQ
Tel: (H) 0121 353 8115 Tel: (W) 07000 527592
Email: info@sportingclubgroup.com
Fixtures Secretary: Ross Jeffries, 30 Brookes Road, Sutton Coldfield B72 1HP Tel: (M) 07980 647943
Club Colours: Black and white hoops, black shorts
League: North Midlands 1

VIPERS RFC
Ground Address: Blaby Bypass, Whetstone, Leicester
Tel: 0116 286 4777
Web Address: www.vipers-leicester.demon.co
Brief Directions: M1 J21, follow A46 to roundabout at Fosse Park, right onto B4114, straight over next roundabout, next roundabout left, next roundabout right, club on left at end of d/c
Hon Secretary: Andrew Baraclough, 47 Kipling Drive, Enderby, Leics LE9 5QR Tel: (H) 0116 286 5164
Tel: (M) 07889 226898 Tel: (W) 07889 226898
Email: a.baraclough@milesplatts.co.uk
Fixtures Secretary: Ian Reid
Tel: (H) 0116 281 0472 Tel: (M) 07710 110898
Club Colours: Green with gold and black hoops
League: Midlands 4 East (South)

WARLEY RFC
Ground Address: Recreation Ground, St. John Road, West Smethick B67 6BJ Tel: 0121 429 1921
Web Address: www.warleyrugby.co.uk
Brief Directions: From Jt2 on M5, follow A4123 to Birmingham.Turn left at Hen & Chicken Pub, continue to traffic lights, turn right into Warley, then first left is St Johns Road
Hon Secretary: Kevin Jordan, 74 William Road, Smethwick B67 6LW
Tel: (H) 0121 429 1921 Tel: (M) 07801 890014
Email: kvnjrdn@aol.com
Fixtures Secretary: Peter Davies, 23 Holly Road, Warley B68 0AU Tel: (H) 0121 422 0166
Club Colours: Red and white hoops, black shorts
League: North Midlands 2

WARWICK RFC
Ground Address: Hampton Road, Warwick CV34 6RD
Tel: 01926 410972
Brief Directions: Exit M40, follow signs for Warwick, take left into Shakespeare Avenue, club opposite junction, on Hampton Road
Hon Secretary: P. O'Rourke, 35 Moreall Meadows, Coventry CV4 7HL Tel: (H) 02476 697328
Email: psor58@hotmail.com
Fixtures Secretary: John Eley Tel: (H) 01926 403144
Club Colours: Black & purple hoops, black shorts
League: Warwickshire 2

WEDNESBURY RUFC
Ground Address: Woden Road North, Old Park, Wednesbury, West Midlands WS10 9NP
Tel: 0121 502 2477
Email Address: info@wednesbury-rufc.co.uk
Web Address: www.wednesbury-rufc.co.uk
Brief Directions: Leave M6 at Junction 9 - take A461 to Wednesbury - turn right at 1st traffic lights into Myvod Rd - straight on over 2 roundabouts into Woden Road North - Club is 0.5 miles on right.
Hon Secretary: Peter Hughes, 28 Alder Road, Wednesbury WS10 9PX Tel: (H) 0121 556 5005
Tel: (M) 07941 446359 Tel: (W) 0121 687 6005
Email: zorro.hughes@blueyonder.co.uk
Fixtures Secretary: Nigel Belmore, 37 Church Lane, West Bromwich, West Midlands B71 1DB
Tel: (H) 0121 580 4660 Tel: (M) 07715 084226
Tel: (W) 0121 553 2222
Leagues Contact: As Secretary
Club Colours: Black & white hoops, black Shorts
League: Midlands 4 West (North)

WELLINGBOROUGH RFC
Ground Address: Cut Throat Lane, Great Doddington, Wellingborough, Northants NN29 7TZ
Tel: 01933 222260
Email Address: rjstevensonwrfc@aol.com
Web Address: www.wrfc.net
Brief Directions: Leave A45 at Geat Doddington/Earls Barton, turn left at end of slip road, left at small cross-roads in approx 500mtr, clubhouse is at top of hill on right, approx 500 metres
Hon Secretary: Dave Mackintosh, n/a
Email: dave.mackintosh@crowncastle.com
Hon Secretary: R. Stevenson, 12 South Street, Wollaston, Northants NN29 7RX
Tel: (H) 01933 664538 Tel: (M) 07711 562352
Tel: (W) 01933 226077
Email: bobstevenson@btopenworld.com
Fixtures Secretary: Ian Brown, 71 Fulwell Road, Northants, NN29 7LX
Tel: (H) 01933 663622 Tel: (M) 07774 456773
Email: brownbhg@aol.com
Club Colours: White shirts with scarlet hoop
League: Midlands 2 East

WELLINGBOROUGH OLD GRAMMARIANS RFC
Ground Address: New Memorial Sports Field, Sywell Road, Wellingborough, Northants NN8 8BS
Tel: 01933 226188
Brief Directions: From Park Farm North go along Sywell Road, ground is on right.
Hon Secretary: E. Cameron, 8 Hornbeam close, Podington, Northants NN29 7HZ
Tel: (H) 01933 359533 Tel: (W) 01933 409114
Email: carmelandewan@hotmail.com
Fixtures Secretary: T. Keating, 44 Naseby Close, Wellingborough NN8 5XB
Tel: (H) 01933 679424 Tel: (M) 07803 128888
Club Colours: Claret and white hoops, black shorts
League: East Midlands 1

WEST BRIDGFORD RFC
Ground Address: The Memorial Ground, Stamford Road,, West Bridgford, Nottingham Tel: 0115 923 2506
Web Address: www.wbrfc.co.uk
Brief Directions: From the A52 dual carriageway, follow signs for West Bridgford at the major roundabout (Travel Lodge). Take the first exit onto the A60 Loughborough Road. After the cemetry take the right turn onto Boundary Road, proceed to the traffic lights to turn left onto Melton Road (A606). Take the second right onto Stamford Road. WBRFC is at the end of the road on your right.
Hon Secretary: Ian Marriott, 29 Meadowsweet Hill, Bingham, Notts NG13 8TS
Tel: (H) 01949 875986 Tel: (M) 07711 639822
Tel: (W) 0115 945 5211
Email: ian.r.marriott@ntlworld.com
Club Colours: Black shirts with red & gold hoops. Black shorts
League: Midlands 4 East (North)

WESTWOOD DEACONIANS RUFC
Ground Address: Deacon's School, Queens Gardens, Peterborough.
Brief Directions: Head for east side of the City on Dual Carriagway - at R/ablout Jct 5 (Nr. Perkins Engines) go for City centre. Next R/about 3rd exit, straight on at lights, right at mini R/about, 5th right
Club Secretary: Andy Sullivan, 15 Swallowfield, Werrington, Peterborough PE4 5BN
Tel: 01744 324370.
email: apsull@perkins.com
Fixtures Secretary: Mark Middleton, 89 Coniston Road, Gunthorpe, Peterborough PE4 7GU
Tel: 01733 771426
Club Colours: Red, white and hoops
League: East Midlands 1

WHEATON ASTON & PENKRIDGE RUFC
Ground Address: The Monkton Recreation Centre, Pinfold Lane, Penkridge, Staffs Tel: 01785 712264
Email Address: WAPRUFC@aol.com
Brief Directions: M6 J12, A5 towards Telford, at 1st island take A449 to Stafford, when you enter Penkridge take 1st left past Ford dealership, club 800 yds on left
Hon Secretary: Martin P. Donoghue, 3 Sandy Lane, Brewood, Staffs ST19 9ET Tel: (H) 01902 851700
Tel: (M) 07970 120143 Tel: (W) 01902 851700
Email: wheatonastonrufc@aol.com
Fixtures Secretary: Nick Hammond, 1 Primrose Close, Wheaton Aston, Staffs ST19 9PX
Tel: (H) 01785 840907
Club Colours: Black shirts with gold collar and cuffs, black shorts
League: Staffordshire 1

WHITTINGTON RFC
Ground Address: The Pavillion, Whittington Barracks, Whittington, Staffs
Brief Directions: Off A51, between Lichfield and Tamworth
Hon Secretary: Mark Boswell, 14 Columbian Crescent, Burntwood, Staffordshire WS7 8DL
Tel: (M) 07971 864899
Fixtures Secretary: Les Welch
Tel: (M) 07949 083381
Club Colours: Blue and White Hoops
League: Staffordshire 1

WILLENHALL RFC
Ground Address: Bognop Road, Essington, Nr Wolverhampton WV11 2BA Tel: 01922 405694
Brief Directions: From the M6-M54 off at J1, take road towards Wolverhampton. At the second island turn left into Bognop Road. The club house is I mile towards Essington on right.
Hon Secretary: Elfyn Pugh, 9 Five Fields Road, Willenhall, West Midlands WV12 4NZ
Tel: (H) 01902 607747
Email: elfyn.pugh@talkgas.net
Fixtures Secretary: Kevin Richards, 5 Tennscore Avenue, Walsall WS6 7BX Tel: (H) 01922. 412637
Email: kevin.elaine@virgin.net
Club Colours: Maroon and black, with black shorts
League: Midlands 3 West (North)

WOLVERHAMPTON RUFC
Ground Address: Rear of The Castlecroft Hotel, Castlecroft Road, Wolverhampton WV3 8NA
Tel: 01902 763900
Web Address: www.wolverhamptonrugby.co.uk
Brief Directions: Wolverhampton ring road, take A454 Compton Rd/Bridgnorth Rd to traffic lights at Mermaid, turn left, 2nd right into Castlecroft Ave, ground straight ahead, behind hotel
Hon Secretary: D. J. Rutherford, 3 Woodlands Cottages, Wolverhampton WV4 4DG
Tel: (H) 01902 335926 Tel: (W) 01902 424847

Email: duncan@asc-ltd.co.uk
Fixtures Secretary: R. N. Astbury, 1 Hamble Grove, Perton, South Staffs WV6 7QW
Tel: (H) 01902 741495
Club Colours: All Black
League: Midlands 2 West

WOODRUSH RFC
Ground Address: Icknield Street, Forhill, Birmingham, Worcs B38 0EL
Tel: 01564 822 878
Email Address: PJRS@leahyj99.freeserve.co.uk
Brief Directions: M42 J3, take A435 to Birmingham, left to Weatheroak, over crossroads, past Kings Norton Golf Club, left at T junction, 1st right, ground on right
Hon Secretary: Peter Leahy, 8 Burns Close, Headless Cross, Redditch B97 5BS
Tel: (H) 01527 543722 Tel: (W) 01905 352615
Email: pjrs@leahyj99.freeserve.co.uk
Fixtures Secretary: Lee Frogatt, 70 Meadow Road, Birmingham B47 6EQ
Tel: (H) 01564 824302 Tel: (M) 07879 020216
Club Colours: Emerald Green/White Hoops
League: North Midlands 1

WORCESTER WANDERERS RFC
Ground Address: Sixways, Pershore Lane, Hindlip,, Worcester Worcestershire WR3 8ZE
Tel: 01905 454183
Email Address: rugby@wrfc.co.uk
Web Address: www.wrfc.co.uk
Brief Directions: At Junction on the M5, take road to Droitwich (signposted Rugby Centre), the Club is 400 yds on the Left
Hon Secretary: Adrian Harling
Tel: (H) 01905 454900 Tel: (W) 01562 822295
Fixtures Secretary: Mike Clarke, 17 Himbleton Road, Worcester WR2 6BA Tel: 01905 428767
Club Colours: Navy and Old Gold
League: North Midlands 1

WORKSOP RUFC
Ground Address: The Meadows, Stubbing Lane, Worksop, Notts S80 1NF Tel: 01909 484247
Brief Directions: Get onto Worksop bypass at roundabout with Mill House pub, take road to town centre then take 1st left into Stubbing Lane, club and grounds at end of road
Hon Secretary: Ken Thompson, 35 Common Road, Thorpe Salvin, Worksop, Nottinghamshire S80 3JJ
Tel: (H) 01909 771761
Email: kgthompson@tinyworld.co.uk
Fixtures Secretary: John Gibson, 9 Gumber Place, Worksop, Notts S80 1SB
Tel: (M) 07973 453 016
Email: john.gibson@citb.co.uk
Club Colours: Black and white hooped shirts
League: NLD/Leics 1 West

YARDLEY & DISTRICT RFC
Ground Address:
1 Cole Hall Lane, Birmingham B34 6HE
Tel: 0121 789 8450
Brief Directions: B'ham outer ringroad A4040 to Stechford, at T/light jcn of A4040/ A47 take A47 Coleshill Rd, over 1st island, immediate right into H'way, 1st island right, over next island, ground left after bridge
Hon Secretary: Steve Griffiths, 11 Orkney Avenue, Hodge Hill, Birmingham B34 6BY
Tel: (H) 0121 748 2887 Tel: (W) 0121 607 2649
Email: steve.griffiths@capgemini.co.uk
Fixtures Secretary: Andrew Smith, 34 Easthope Road, Birmingham B33 9LJ
Tel: (H) 0121 624 6938
Email: gusanders@aol.com
Club Colours: Royal blue and amber hooped shirts with black shorts
League: Midlands 4 West (North)

LONDON & SOUTH EAST REGION

A complete club index appears at the back of the book.
This shows which Division and league each club is in for the 2002-03 season

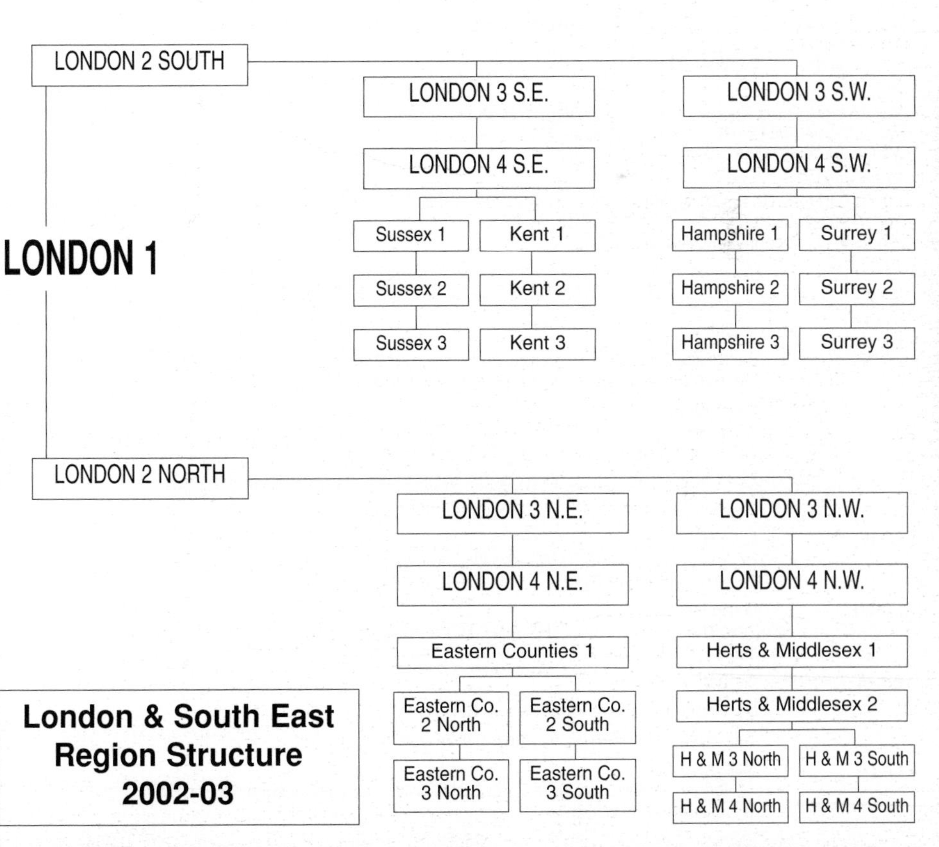

London & South East Region Structure 2002-03

LONDON REGION OFFICIALS 2002-2003

Name / Address	Area	Position
Paul Astbury 32, Kneller Gardens, ISLEWORTH, Middlesex, TW7 7NW Tel: 020-8898-7977 (H) Fax: 020-8898-7977 e-mail: paulnastbury@aol.com	LSE	Chairman
Mike Ward P.O. Box , LOWESTOFT, Suffolk NR32 9HZ Tel: 01502-539345 (H) Fax: 01502-538670 e-mail: londonrfu.competitions@btinternet.com	LSE	Secretary
Mike Stott Brick Kiln Farm, NORTH WALSHAM, Norfolk, NR28 9LH Tel: 01692-409043 (H) Fax: 01692-409043 e-mail: mikestott@tesco.net	Eastern Counties	L.C.C.M.
Neil Hagerty 1, Hodder Close, Chandlers Ford, SOUTHAMPTON, Hampshire, SO53 4QD Tel: 023-8026-3447 (H) e-mail: neilhagerty@scanplan.co.uk	Hampshire	L.C.C.M.
David Williams 7, Sadlers Way, HERTFORD, Hertfordshire,SG14 2DZ Tel: 01992-586744 (H) Fax: 01992-410552	Hertfordshire	L.C.C.M.
Dennis Attwood 6, Somerset Gardens, Lewisham, LONDON, SE13 7SY Tel: 020-8691-2820 (H) Fax: 020-8835-9410 e-mail: dennis.attwood@btinternet.com	Kent	L.C.C.M.
Roger Willingale Fairmile Farm Cottage, Denby Road, COBHAM, Surrey, KT11 1JY Tel: 01932-866927 Fax: 01932-860239 e-mail: willingales@btinternet.com	Middlesex	L.C.C.M.
Paddy Ralston 209, Worple Road, Raynes Park, LONDON, SW20 8QY Tel: 020-8949-8912 (H) Fax: 020-8946-4591 e-mail: paddy@kings.org.uk	Surrey	L.C.C.M.
Brian Vincent 29, St Botolphs Road, WORTHING, West Sussex, BN11 4JS Tel: 01903-206516 (H) Fax:01903-603313 e-mail:brv@vincentfamily.fslife.co.uk	Sussex	L.C.C.M.

LEAGUE SECRETARIES

League	Secretary
L1	Paddy Ralston c/o Village Sports, 209, Worple Road, Raynes Park, LONDON, SW20 8QY Tel: 020-8949-8912 (H) Fax: 020-8946-4591
L2N	David Williams 7, Sadlers Way, HERTFORD, Hertfordshire,SG14 2DZ Tel: 01992-586744 (H) Fax; 01992-410552
L2S	Brian Vincent, 29, St Botolphs Road, WORTHING, West Sussex,BN11 4JS Tel: 01903-206516 (H) Fax: 01903-603313
L3NE	Mike Stott Brick Kiln Farm, NORTH WALSHAM, Norfolk, NR28 9LH Tel: 01692-409043 (H) Fax: 01692-409043
L3NW	David Gerschlick 20a, The Avenue, POTTERS BAR, Hertfordshire,EN6 1EB Tel: 01707-644433 (H) Fax: 01707-644433
L3SE	Gerald Farrow 84, Sedge Crescent, Weedswood, CHATHAM, Kent, ME5 0QD Tel: 01634-666255 (H) Fax: 01634-684301
L3SW	Neil Hagerty 1, Hodder Close, Chandlers Ford, SOUTHAMPTON, Hampshire, SO53 4QD Tel: 023-8026-3447 (H)

L4NE & EC1	Ron Hatch 99, Ernest Road, Wivenhoe, COLCHESTER, Essex, CO7 9LJ Tel: 01206-823548 (H) Fax: 01206-823548
L4NW	Roger Willingale Fairmile Farm Cottage, Denby Road, COBHAM, Surrey, KT11 1JY Tel:01932-866927 (H) Fax: 01932-860239
L4SE & All Kent	John Carley 11, Vlissingen Drive, DEAL, Kent, CT14 6TZ Tel: 01304-381273 (H) Fax: 01304-381273
L4SW	John Collins 4, Neelands Grove, Paulsgrove, PORTSMOUTH, Hampshire, PO6 4QL Tel: 023-9238-0859 (H) Fax: 023-9228-4846
EC 2N	Darryl Chapman 55, Bridge Street, STOWMARKET, Suffolk, IP14 1BP Tel: 01449-672787 (H) Fax: 01449-616309
EC 2S	Beiron Rees 45a, Eastwood Road, Goodmayes, ILFORD, Essex, IG3 8UT Tel: 020-8597-1158 (H) Fax: 020-8597-1158
EC 3N	Ian Forton 183, Middletons Lane, NORWICH, Norfolk, NR6 5SB Tel: 01603-400049 (H) Fax: 01603-400049
EC 3S	Len Hymans 32, Devon Way, CANVEY ISLAND, Essex, SS8 9YD Tel: 01268-693899 (H) Fax:01268-693899
All Hampshire	John Sneezum Bursledon Lodge, Salterns Lane, Old Bursledon, Southampton, SO3 8DH Tel: 023-8040-2286 Fax: 023-8040-2286
HEM 1	Peter Woolgar 114, Elgin Avenue, ASHFORD, Middlesex, TW15 1QG Tel: 01784-259734 (H)
HEM 2	Subhash Kamath 267, Uxbridge Road, Hampton Hill, HAMPTON, Middlesex, TW12 1AR Tel: 020-8979-4339 (H) Fax: 020-8744-2881
HEM 3N	Geoff Payne 16, Brackenbridge Drive, SOUTH RUISLIP, Middlesex, HA4 0NG Tel: 020-8845-0874
HEM 3S	Nick Alway, 20, Herndon Road, LONDON, SW18 2DG Tel: 020-8870-6818 Fax: 020-8870-6818
HEM 4N	John Gregory 58, Luton Road, REDBOURN, Hertfordshire, AL3 7PY Tel: 01582-792798 (H) Fax: 01582-793483
HEM 4S	Brian East 64, Station Road, HARPENDEN, Hertfordshire, AL5 4TL Tel: 01582-762209 (H) Fax: 01582-762209
Sy 1	Ian Johnson 9a, Between Streets, COBHAM, Surrey, KT11 1AA Tel: 01932-860392 (H) Fax: 01932-863528
Sy 2	Paul Tanner 1, Woodland Way, MORDEN, Surrey, SM4 4DS Tel: 020-8540-5784 (H) Fax: 020-8540-5784
Sy 3	Barry Myland Ashtrees, 15, Portley Lane, CATERHAM, Surrey, CR3 5HT Tel: 01883-343319 (H) Fax: 01883-343319
Sx 1	John Thompson 26, Rosehill, BILLINGSHURST, West Sussex, RH14 9QN Tel: 01403-784636 (H)
Sx 2-3	Andy Stephenson 79, Cedar Drive, Southwater, HORSHAM, West Sussex, RH13 9UF Tel: 01403-731138 (H)

LONDON ONE

2001-02 LEAGUE TABLE

	P	W	D	L	PF	PA	PD	Pts
Havant	22	18	0	4	579	239	340	36
Basingstoke	22	16	2	4	648	342	306	34
Sutton & Epsom	22	13	2	7	478	388	90	28
Norwich	22	13	0	9	492	447	45	26
Haywards Heath	22	12	2	8	471	439	32	26
Cheshunt	22	10	1	11	339	453	-114	21
London Nigerians	22	10	0	12	403	400	3	20
Staines	22	9	1	12	404	454	-50	19
Thanet Wanderers	22	8	2	12	435	481	-46	18
Winchester	22	7	0	15	359	477	-118	14
Harlow	22	5	1	16	393	620	-227	11
*Cambridge	22	5	1	16	229	490	-261	(-4) 7

2002-03 FIXTURE GRID	Canterbury	Cheshunt	Harlow	Haywards Heath	Hertford	London Nigerians	Norwich	Southernd	Staines	Sutton & Epsom	Thanet Wanderers	Winchester
Canterbury		18/01	30/11	05/10	14/12	08/02	16/11	14/09	04/01	15/03	26/10	29/03
Cheshunt	12/10		01/02	23/11	28/09	21/12	01/03	02/11	07/09	11/01	29/03	30/11
Harlow	12/04	05/10		08/02	16/11	14/09	04/01	15/03	26/10	07/12	18/01	14/12
Haywards Heath	01/02	14/12	28/09		01/03	02/11	07/09	11/01	29/03	12/10	30/11	16/11
Hertford	23/11	08/02	21/12	14/09		15/03	26/10	07/12	18/01	12/04	05/10	04/01
London Nigerians	28/09	16/11	01/03	04/01	07/09		29/03	12/10	30/11	01/02	14/12	26/10
Norwich	21/12	14/09	02/11	15/03	11/01	07/12		12/04	05/10	23/11	08/02	18/01
Southend	01/03	04/01	07/09	26/10	29/03	18/01	30/11		14/12	28/09	16/11	05/10
Staines	02/11	15/03	11/01	07/12	12/10	12/04	01/02	23/11		21/12	14/09	08/02
Sutton & Epsom	07/09	26/10	29/03	18/01	30/11	05/10	14/12	08/02	16/11		04/01	14/09
Thanet Wanderers	11/01	07/12	12/10	12/04	01/02	23/11	28/09	21/12	01/03	02/11		15/03
Winchester	07/12	12/04	23/11	21/12	02/11	11/01	12/10	01/02	28/09	01/03	07/09	

CANTERBURY

Founded: 1948

Club Secretary Robin Gipson, 1 Maple Close, Rough Common, Canterbury, Kent CT2 9BX.
Tel: 01227 761997 Email: robingipson@hotmail.com

Fixture Secretary Roger Dengate 16 Thornden Close, Greenhill, Herne Bay, Kent CT2 8EG
Tel: 07880 791412 (M)

Ground Address Merton Lane (North), Nackington Road, Canterbury, Kent CT4 7BA
Tel: 01227 761301 Web Site: www.canterbury.co.uk

Directions Exit A2 at sign for Canterbury. At 4th r'about take 3rd exit, (old Dover Rd). Turn right into Nackington Road (B2068) - 9/10ths mile turn right at sign, do not cross bypass.

Colours Black and amber hoops

CHESHUNT RFC

Founded: 1952

President David Bird, 84 Mornington Road, London E4 7DT 0208 529 3467

Chairman Mark Ferris, 44a Harlech Rd., Southgate, London N14 7BX 0208 882 0036 (H) 0208 258 5863 (B)

Club Secretary Stephen Waller, 35 Woodland Mount, Hertford, Herts., SG13 7JD.
01992 302799 (H) 01992 466600 (B)

Fixtures Secretary Mo Phillips, 28 Perram Close, Turnford, Herts. EN10 6AT Tel: 01992 440415 (H)

Director of Coaching Gavin Reynolds, 6 Alexandra Road, St. Albans, Herts. AL1 3AZ Tel: 01727 762219 (H)

League Contact: John Healy, 5 Chatsworth Drive, Bush Hill Park, London EN1 1EX Tel: 0208 363 4820

GroundAddress: Rosedale Sports Ground, Andrews Lane, Cheshunt, Herts. EN7 6TB
Tel: 01992 623983 Fax: 01992 636636 Website: cheshuntrfc.co.uk Email: cheshuntrfc@tesco.net

Directions: M25 J25, head north. At 1st roundabout take first exit along Ellis Way. Straight over next 2 r'abouts, 1st left into Andrews Lane, and club entrance is 200 yds on left

Capacity: Ample - all uncovered standing **Car Parking:** Ample at ground
Nearest Railway Stations: Cuffley (1.5 miles), Cheshunt (1.5 miles) & Theobalds Grove (1 mile)

Admission: £2 incl. programme **Training Nights:** Tuesday & Thursday

Clubhouse: Open every evening except Monday **Club Shop:** Open matchdays and Sunday am

Programme: Size: A5 Price: with admission Pages: 24 Editor: Steve Waller 01992 302799
Advertising: Contact Steve Waller (Editor)

Colours: Green and white hoops, white shorts, red socks **Change colours:** All Blue

HARLOW R.U.F.C.

Founded: 1955

Secretary John Guyton 201 Waterhouse Moor, Harlow, Essex CM18 6BW
Tel: 01279 860590 email: Jr_guyton@tesco.net

Fixture Secretary John Pendleton 56 Priory Court, Harlow, Essex
Tel: 01729 439265 (H)

Treasurer A Webb 33 Peacocks, Harlow, Essex
Tel: 01279 830584 (H)

Ground Ram Gorse, Elizabeth way, Harlow, Essex CM20 2JQ Tel: 01279 426389

Directions Phone Fixtures Secretary

Club Colours: Red shirts, green trimmings and green shorts

HAYWARDS HEATH RFC

Founded: 1958

President The Hon. Nicholas Soames, MP
Chairman Tony Dalby, 109 Western Rd., Hurstepierpoint, W. Sussex BN6 9SY 01273 833736
Club Secretary Neil Milton, 'Littlemead', Albourne Rd., Hurstepierpoint, W. Sussex BN6 9SL 01273 835439
Fixtures Secretary B. Killick, 106 Royal George Rd, Burgess Hill, W. Sussex RH15 9SL Tel: 01444 233361
League Contact Brian Wattam, 18 Priory Rd., Burgess Hill, W. Sussex RH15 9HB 01444 247367
Match Secretary David Kemp, Hammingden Farm, Highbrook, Ardingly, W. Sussex 01444 892292
Coach Steve Heaton, 29 Heath Way, Horsham, W. Sussex 01403 257661

Ground Address: The Clubhouse, Whitemans Green, Cuckfield, Haywards Heath, W. Sussex RH17 5HX.
Tel: 01444 413950 email: neilmilton@eur???.co.uk Web site: www.hhrfc.co.uk
Capacity: Seated: Standing: Covered - Uncovered -
Directions: Left turn off A23 towards Cuckfield on B215. Right at first junction onto B2114 towards Cuckfield. Ground on right about 1/2 mile west of Cuckfield village. Nearest Railway Station: Haywards Heath (3 miles)
Car Parking: Plenty on site **Admission:** No charge - spectators are requested to buy a programme.
Club Shop: Mon - Fri Normal hours @ 18 High St., Cuckfield 01444 416587 **Clubhouse:** Open matchdays
Training Nights: Monday & Thursday
Programme: Size: A5 Price: £1 Pages: 20 Editor: Paul Graham Advertising: Contact Paul Graham 01444 453525
Colours: Red and black quarters, black shorts **Change colours:** Blue & white hoops

HERTFORD RFC

President John Creasey 01992 551715
Chairman Barry Young 01279600768
Club Secretary Nigel Dawes The Old Rectory, Redgrave Rd., South Lopham, Norfolk IP22 2HL
Tel: 01379 688106 (H) Fax: 01379 687789
Fixture Sec./ League Sec. John Atkinson 86 Winterscroft Road, Hoddesdon, Herts. EN11 8RJ
Tel: (H) 01992 462206
Director of Rugby Clive Mann 01920 464 718
Director of Marketing David Baseley 01763 289 241
Hon. Treasurer Tony Burr

Ground Address Highfields, Hoe Lane, Ware, Herts. SG12 9NZ
Tel: 01920 462975 Web Site: hfordrfc@aol.com
Directions Leave A10 at A414 Hertford exit. Take B1502 to Gt. Amwell from roundabout.
First left into Hoe Lane. Club on left at 3-400 yds.
Club colours Black, royal blue and gold, black shorts

LONDON NIGERIANS RFC

Founded: 1991

Chairman Onome Sideso
Chief Executive Tunde Aiyegbusi 131 Dartmouth Road, London NW2 4ES 07976 361607
Secretary Bayo Ogunbufunmi 12 Defiant, Further Acre, Colindale, London NW9 5YT 07947 730976
Treasurer Lakis Kakouris 07956 870911
Fixture Secretary Ola Afuwape 131. Fords Park Road, London E16 1PR 07930 484355
Ground Address: Linford Christie Stadium, Wormwood Scrubs, Off Du Cane Road, London W12
Tel: 020 8740 7379 Website: http://www.londonnigerian.com
Capacity Total - 1000 Covered Seated - 200 Uncovered standing - 800
DIRECTIONS **By Tube:** Central Line to East Acton Station. Out exit & turn left up Erconwald St. Take 2nd rt into Wulfstan St. Walk down to T-Juction & left into Du Cane Rd. Past the prison & left into Artillery Rd. Walk through to Linford Christie Stadium.
By Road: From Baker Street: A40(M) Westway towards Oxford. Turn off as if for Shepherds Bush. At r'about take A40 exit as if rejoining the A40. Stay in left lane and take exit for "Local Traffic". Stay in right hand lane. At the lights, turn right up Wood Lane. First left turn into Du Cane Rd. About 300 yards down and just past Hammersmith Hospital, turn right into Artillery Rd. Drive through to Linford Christie Stadium. **From Hanger Lane:** A40(M) Western Avenue towards Central London. Take the turnoff for Shepherds Bush. At the r'about turn left up Wood Lane. First left into Du Cane Road. Then as above..
Nearest Railway Station: East Acton or White City on the Central Line (London Underground)
Car Parking: Available up to 80 cars **Admission:** Free
Clubhouse: Open Tues & Thur eves and match days. Training Nights: Tues & Thur 7-9.30 pm
Colours: Bottle green & white quarters/green/bottle green with white hoops **Change Colours**: Black/green/green

NORWICH R.F.C.

Founded: 1885

President John Drinkell mail c/o Rugby Office Tel: 01502 731551 (H)
Chairman Mike Srokowski mail c/o Rugby Office Tel: 01603 716961 (H)
Director of Rugby James Sinclair
Community Projects Ed Stead
League Contact James Sinclair
} Norwich RFC, Beeston Hyrne, North Walsham Road, Norwich NR12 7BW
Tel: 01603 426259 Fax: 01603 413670 website: lionrugby.com

Ground Address: Beeston Hyrne, North Walsham Road, Norwich NR12 7BW Tel: 01603 426259 Fax: 01603 413670
Capacity: 1,000 Seated: None Standing: 1,000
Directions: Follow the outer ring road and turn onto the B1150 (signed Coltishall/North Walsham). Over two sets of traffic lights and the ground is 400 yards on the left. **Nearest Railway Station:** Norwich
Car Parking: 500 at ground **Admission:** Matchday tickets £4
Clubhouse: Private Functions, contact rugby office on 01603 426259
Club Shop: Contact rugby office as above.

Programme: Advertising: Contact Roy Bishop 01508 499325
Colours: Maroon, gold & green, **Change colours:** All navy **Nickname:** Lions
Training Nights: Tuesday & Thursday nights (seniors). Wednesday (youth)

STAINES R.F.C.

Founded: 1926

Web site: www.stainesrugby.co.uk

Club Secretary Kevin McMahon, 23 Cherry Orchard, Staines, Middx, TW13 7NB Tel: 01784 463220

Fixture Secretary P Adams, 10 Sutherland Close, Weybridge, Surrey KT13 9EN Tel: 01932 858087

League Contact: R Lawless, 17 Florence Road, Walton on Thames, Surrey KT12 2AL Tel: 01932 247347

Ground The Reeves, Feltham Hill Road, Hanworth, Middlesex, TW13 7NB
Tel 020 8890 3051 e-mail: Dave@stainesrugby.c.uk
Capacity: All uncovered standing
Directions Take Lower Feltham exit from A316 turn left pass Unigate Dairy into Feltham Hill Road, Ground 400yds on left.
Nearest Railway Station: Feltham
Car Parking Yes
Club Shop Yes contact Pam
Training Nights Tuesday & Thursday
Club Colours: Blue & Red Shirts/ White Shorts **Nickname:** Swans

SOUTHEND RFC

President Allan J. Edwards 01702 205 034
Chairman Neil Harding as Secretary, see below
Hon. Fixtures Sec. Frank Dyton 01702 475 075
1 The Coastways, Westcliffe-on-Sea, Essex SS0 0AU
Club Secretary Neil Harding 01702 477799 email: agh477799@aol.com
77 Hillside Crescent, Leigh-on-Sea, Essex SS5 1HH
Hon. Treasurer A. Grace 01702 586 039
Marketing Neil Harding as Secretary, see above
Ground Address Warners Bridge Park, Sumpters Way, Southend-on-Sea. SS2 5RR
Tel: 01702 546682 email: neil@southendrugby.com
Website: wwww.southendrugby.com
Directions A127 to Southend turn left Sutton Road, turn right at r'about into Temple Farm Ind. Estate. Follow road to the end turn left club is 50 yards at end of road.
Club Colours Chocolate brown and white

LONDON & SOUTH EAST

SUTTON & EPSOM R.F.C.

Founded: 1881

President Ian Lovatt 43 Cedar Road, Sutton, Surrey SM2 5DJ 020 7251 6802 (B) 020 8643 5264 (H)
Secretary & League Contact Bob Poole Well Cottage, Loxwood Rd, Wisborough Green, W. Sussex RH14 0DJ 020 8770 6441 (B) 01403 700594 (H)
Fixture Sec. Ian Frazer 111 Benhill Road, Sutton, Surrey SM1 3RR 020 8643 4835 (H) 020 7542 8549 (B)
Rugby Director Peter Hatch 24 Staines Ave., North Cheam, Surrey SM3 9BQ 020 8644 4438 (H) 01372 722999 (B)
1st XV Manager Willie Moore 45 Sutton Grove, Sutton, Surrey SM1 4LP 202 8642 4191 (H) 07776 422313 (B)
Press Officer John Ashton 020 8644 9664 (H) 0403 189661 (M)

Ground: Cuddington Court, Rugby Lane, West Drive, Cheam Surrey SM2 7NF Tel: 0208 642 0280
Web site: www.serfc.freeserve.co.uk
Capacity: 2,000 approx 300 Covered Seats **Car Parking:** 500 spaces at ground
Directions: M25, J8>A217>A240 Reigate road>A24 Ewell by-pass>A232 Cheam road>West Drive, club entrance at junction with Hays Walk. or M25, J10>A3 (London bound)>A240 Kingston road>A232 Cheam road, then as above.
Nearest Railway Station: Cheam BR
Admission: Matchday - £2.50 incl. programme. Season tickets not available
Clubhouse: Yes **Club Shop:** Open league matchdays, training nights & Sunday am.
Colours: Narrow black & white hoops **Change colours:** Peacock blue **Training Nights:** Mon & Thur (1st XV) - others Wed.
Programme Size: A5 Price: with admission Pages: 40 Editor: John Ashton
Advertising Rates Double Page £550, Page £350, 1/2 £200, 1/4 £120

THANET WANDERERS RUFC

Founded: 1886

Secretary / Fixture Secretary / League Contact
Peter Hawkins 51 Park Road, Ramsgate, Kent CT11 9TL
Tel: 01843 593142 (H, B & F) e-mail: peterhawkins2000@yahoo.co.uk

Director of Rugby Geoff Redmond 4 Abbey Grove, Ramsgate, Kent CT11 0JG Tel: 01843 - 595810 (H&B) 852365 (F)
Head Coach Andy Williamson 105 Minnis Road, Minnis Bay, Birchington, Kent CT7 9NY
Tel: 01843 - 845981 (H) 591075 (B) 851907 (Fax)

Ground St Peters Recreation Ground, Callis Court Road, Broadstairs, Kent CT10 3AE Tel: 01843 866763
Capacity: 2000 uncovered standing **Admission** Nil
Directions A2 M2, A299, A256 A255 From Broadstairs Broadway turn left at traffic lights into St Peters Park Road. Take the first right under the railway bridge and the ground is on the left after about 400 metres.
Nearest Railway Station: Broadstairs Car Parking: 50 spaces at the ground, others in the nearby streets.
Clubhouse: Open normal licensing hours. Food available For functions contact Bill May 01843 604376 or 01304 611248 (B)
Club Shop: Open matchdays & Sun. am. Contact Mrs Penny Smith 01843 850904

Programme: Size: A5 Pages: 24 Price: £1.50 Advertising: Full page £450 Half: £300 Quarter: £175
Programme Editor & Director of Marketing: Peter Ruranski 01843 845942 (H) 01843 570044 (B) 01843 570055 (F)
Colours: Blue black & gold hoops **Change colours:** Black & white
Nickname: Wanderers **Training:** Tuesday & Thursday

WINCHESTER R.F.C.

Founded: 1929

President Dai Henley, The Lake House, 64 Mill Lane, Romsey SO51 8EQ
Tel: 01794 512243(H) 01794 512243(F) 07939 034852(M) E-mail:david.henley@dial.pipex.com
Executive Director Paul Beckett, 14 Waverley Drive, South Wonston, Winchester SO21 3EF
Tel: 01962 889492 (H) 01256 867223(B) 01256 867081(F) E-mail:p.beckett@martins.uk.com
Operations Manager Rob Memory, 7 Portal Rd., Highcliffe, Winchester SO23 0PX
Tel: 01962 842251(H) 01962 867021(B) 01962 867045(F) E-mail: office@therugbyclub.fsnet.co.uk
Secretary /League Contact John H Prosser MBE, 10 Princess Court, St Peter St., Winchester SO23 8DN
Tel: 01962 863550 (H) email: jhprosser10@aol.com
Fixture Secretary Godfrey L Toogood, 31 Winslade Rd, Harestock, Winchester SO22 6LN
Tel: 01962 881991 E-mail: 31@toogood8.fsnet.co.uk
Treasurer Fiona Beckett, 14 Waverley Drive, South Wonston, Winchester SO21 3EF
Tel: 01962 889492 (H) 01962 867021(B) E-mail: pgbecks@aol.com
Ground: North Walls Park, off Nuns Road, Winchester SO23 7EF Tel: 01962 867021 Fax: 01962 876045
email: office@therugbyclub.fsnet.co.uk Website: www.winchesterrugby.com
Directions: M3, Junction 9, A34/A33 signed to Basingstoke. After 1 mile fork right then first left onto B3047. Continue for 1.4 miles, left into Russell Rd, right at the end, left into Hillier Way and ground is at the end. **Nearest Rail Station:** Winchester
Capacity: Ample - all unseated Admission: Nil **Programme:** A5 / £2.00 / 10pages **Editor** & Advertising: Contact Operations Manager
Clubhouse: Open every day. Private functions catered for up to 250 - contact Operations Man. **Club Shop:** Contact Operations Man.
Colours: Black with amber band **Change colours:** All red **Training Nights:** Tuesday & Thursday 7.15pm **Nickname:** Winch

LONDON REGION FINAL LEAGUE TABLES 2001-02

London 2 North

	P	W	D	L	PF	PA	PD	Pts	-
Hertford	22	20	0	2	708	169	539	40	
Southend	22	19	0	3	568	245	323	38	
Bishop's Stortford	22	18	1	3	521	260	261	37\	
Woodford	22	14	0	8	443	308	135	28	
*Old Albanians	22	13	0	9	524	350	174	24	2
Twickenham	22	10	1	11	486	534	-48	21	
Thurrock	22	9	1	12	386	379	7	19	
Sudbury	22	7	1	14	317	452	-135	15	
Ipswich	22	7	0	15	351	456	-105	14	
Diss	22	6	0	16	298	463	-165	12	
Old Verulamians	22	3	4	15	306	648	-342	10	
*Metropolitan Police	22	2	0	20	208	852	-644	2	2

London 3 North East

	P	W	D	L	PF	PA	PD	Pts	-
Shelford	18	17	0	1	453	211	242	34	
*Basildon	18	15	1	2	432	229	203	29	2
Brentwood	18	11	0	7	293	293	0	22	
Rochford Hundred	18	9	1	8	352	326	26	19	
Romford & Gidea Park	18	9	1	8	306	285	21	19	
Hadleigh	18	8	0	10	355	283	72	16	
Chingford	18	7	1	10	177	288	-111	15	
Wymondham	18	5	1	12	265	379	-114	11	
Bury St. Edmunds	18	5	0	13	250	368	-118	10	
Chelmsford	18	1	1	16	192	413	-221	3	

London 3 North West

	P	W	D	L	PF	PA	PD	Pts	-
Bank Of England	18	17	0	1	627	218	409	34	
Letchworth Garden City	18	15	0	3	524	210	314	30	
Ealing	18	14	1	3	447	231	216	29	
Barnet Saracens Elizabethans	18	8	1	9	284	373	-89	17	
Ruislip	18	8	1	9	284	376	-92	17	
Imperial Medicals	18	6	1	11	316	393	-77	13	
Harpenden	18	6	0	12	293	415	-122	12	
West London	18	6	0	12	268	513	-245	12	
Finchley	18	4	2	12	263	373	-110	10	
Old Merchant Taylors	18	3	0	15	277	481	-204	6	

London 4 North East

	P	W	D	L	PF	PA	PD	Pts	-
Saffron Walden	18	15	0	3	537	201	336	30	
West Norfolk	18	15	0	3	458	213	245	30	
Campion	18	14	0	4	620	199	421	28	
Thetford	18	11	0	7	345	338	7	22	
Eton Manor	18	10	0	8	415	220	195	20	
Braintree	18	8	0	10	309	344	-35	16	
Upminster	18	7	0	11	297	363	-66	14	
Woodbridge	18	5	0	13	212	445	-233	10	
Lowestoft & Yarmouth	18	3	0	15	156	594	-438	6	
Canvey Island	18	2	0	16	149	581	-432	4	

London 4 North West

	P	W	D	L	PF	PA	PD	Pts	-
London Scottish	18	14	0	4	533	214	319	28	
Fullerians	18	14	0	4	346	314	32	28	
St Albans	18	13	0	5	496	228	268	26	
London New Zealand	18	12	0	6	381	221	160	24	
Grasshoppers	18	11	0	7	358	290	68	22	
Welwyn	18	7	0	11	257	352	-95	14	
Harrow	18	5	1	12	173	308	-135	11	
Hampstead	18	5	0	13	306	428	-122	10	
*Chiswick	18	5	1	12	183	342	-159	9	2
Hemel Hempstead	18	3	0	15	175	511	-336	6	

* denotes points deducted in right hand column

London 2 South

	P	W	D	L	PF	PA	PD	Pts	-
Canterbury	22	19	0	3	778	226	552	38	
Portsmouth	22	18	1	3	769	291	478	37	
Gosport and Fareham	22	14	2	6	542	295	247	30	
Wimbledon	22	15	0	7	508	337	171	30	
Maidstone	22	10	0	12	451	483	-32	20	
Beckenham	22	10	0	12	395	544	-149	20	
*Tunbridge Wells	22	11	0	11	429	582	-153	20	2
Sevenoaks	22	9	0	13	340	559	-219	18	
Effingham & Leatherhead	22	8	1	13	333	469	-136	17	
Old Mid-Whitgiftian	22	7	0	15	308	599	-291	14	
Guildford & Godalming	22	5	0	17	361	557	-196	10	
Gravesend	22	4	0	18	308	580	-272	8	

London 3 South East

	P	W	D	L	PF	PA	PD	Pts	-
Worthing	18	15	1	2	414	133	281	31	
Sidcup	18	14	0	4	450	178	272	28	
East Grinstead	18	11	0	7	447	263	184	22	
Charlton Park	18	9	3	6	322	286	36	21	
Brighton	18	9	2	7	349	282	67	20	
Dartfordians	18	9	1	8	346	342	4	19	
*Tonbridge Juddian	18	8	0	10	369	305	64	14	2
Lewes	18	5	1	12	218	362	-144	11	
Old Dunstonians	18	4	2	12	265	499	-234	10	
Crawley	18	1	0	17	132	662	-530	2	

London 3 South West

	P	W	D	L	PF	PA	PD	Pts	-
Andover	18	17	0	1	491	193	298	34	
Cobham	18	13	1	4	468	216	252	27	
Old Guildfordians	18	13	0	5	472	275	197	26	
Chobham	18	10	0	8	319	349	-30	20	
Jersey	18	10	0	8	370	402	-32	20	
Old Blues	18	7	1	10	396	433	-37	15	
Old Wimbledonians	18	6	0	12	255	452	-197	12	
Alton	18	5	1	12	256	397	-141	11	
Dorking	18	4	0	14	302	404	-102	8	
University Vandals	18	3	1	14	252	460	-208	7	

London 4 South East

	P	W	D	L	PF	PA	PD	Pts	-
Betteshanger	18	17	0	1	434	156	278	34	
Eastbourne	18	14	2	2	508	252	256	30	
Folkestone	18	12	0	6	337	309	28	24	
Bognor	18	10	1	7	304	276	28	21	
Hove	18	8	0	10	284	258	26	16	
Beccehamian	18	8	0	10	297	277	20	16	
*Guy's Hospital	18	7	1	10	325	368	-43	13	2
*Uckfield	18	4	0	14	191	388	-197	6	2
*Cranbrook	18	7	1	10	280	274	6	1	1
Askeans	18	0	1	17	117	519	-402	1	

Cranbrook will be relegated to Kent One next season for a Regulation 9.2.1 offence.

London 4 South West

	P	W	D	L	PF	PA	PD	Pts	-
Richmond	22	22	0	0	1142	115	1027	44	
Barnes	22	19	0	3	962	289	673	38	
Tottonians	22	14	0	8	693	442	251	28	
Farnham	22	14	0	8	574	463	111	28	
Old Emanuel	22	12	1	9	500	504	-4	25	
Purley John Fisher	22	11	0	11	434	527	-93	22	
Trojans	22	9	1	12	359	575	-216	19	
Cranleigh	22	9	0	13	323	622	-299	18	
*Utd. Services, Portsmouth	22	9	0	13	323	519	-196	16	2
Old Reedonians	22	7	0	15	319	667	-348	14	
*Warlingham	22	3	0	19	213	742	-529	4	2
*Farnborough	22	2	0	20	212	589	-377	-2	6

East Counties 1

	P	W	D	L	PF	PA	PD	Pts	-
Mersea Island	18	14	1	3	417	182	235	29	
Beccles	18	13	0	5	462	282	180	26	
Stanford Le Hope	18	12	0	6	365	256	109	24	
Upper Clapton	18	11	1	6	353	235	118	23	
*Maldon	18	12	1	5	269	216	53	21	4
*Holt	18	9	1	8	228	303	-75	17	2
Ely	18	6	1	11	380	321	59	13	
*Billericay	18	5	1	12	227	303	-76	9	2
Newmarket	18	3	2	13	220	399	-179	8	
*Old Edwardians	18	1	0	17	152	576	-424	0	2

East Counties 2 North

	P	W	D	L	PF	PA	PD	Pts	-
Colchester	18	18	0	0	659	55	604	36	
Stowmarket	18	15	1	2	373	167	206	31	
Ipswich Y.M.	18	12	1	5	363	229	134	25	
Cantabrigian	18	12	0	6	372	237	135	24	
Crusaders	18	9	0	9	303	196	107	18	
Thurston	18	7	1	10	324	316	8	15	
*Wisbech	18	6	0	12	262	375	-113	10	2
Lakenham Hewett	18	4	0	14	215	453	-238	8	
Haverhill & District	18	3	0	15	100	559	-459	6	
Harwich & Dovercourt	18	2	1	15	126	510	-384	5	

East Counties 2 South

	P	W	D	L	PF	PA	PD	Pts	-
Wanstead	18	15	1	2	389	117	272	31	
East London	18	14	0	4	410	156	254	28	
Ilford Wanderers	18	11	2	5	365	225	140	24	
Bancroft	18	11	0	7	431	155	276	22	
Westcliff	18	11	0	7	255	183	72	22	
Thames	18	9	0	9	260	308	-48	18	
Old Brentwoods	18	8	1	9	335	256	79	17	
*South Woodham Ferrers	18	7	0	11	256	342	-86	12	2
*Millwall Albion	18	2	0	16	162	619	-457	2	2
*May & Baker	18	0	0	18	72	574	-502	-4	4

East Counties 3 North

	P	W	D	L	PF	PA	PD	Pts	-
Southwold	16	15	0	1	628	126	502	30	
Norwich Union	16	11	1	4	307	188	119	23	
Broadland	16	11	1	4	222	196	26	23	
Brightlingsea	16	9	1	6	367	190	177	19	
Sawston	16	9	0	7	245	237	8	18	
Witham	16	5	1	10	150	286	-136	11	
March BRAZA	16	3	2	11	249	433	-184	8	
Swaffham	16	3	1	12	244	323	-79	7	
Mistley	16	2	1	13	131	564	-433	5	

American Exiles have withdrawn. All fixtures removed. Regulation 12.7 adjustments do not alter the positions of Norwich Union and Broadland and are ignored.

East Counties 3 South

	P	W	D	L	PF	PA	PD	Pts	-
Burnham-On-Crouch	18	15	1	2	476	164	312	31	
*Dagenham	18	12	1	5	406	261	145	23	2
*Loughton	18	11	0	7	433	234	199	20	2
Pegasus	18	9	0	9	253	269	-16	18	
*Ravens	18	9	0	9	287	302	-15	16	2
*Ongar	18	9	0	9	208	317	-109	16	2
*Old Cooperians	18	8	0	10	251	284	-33	14	2
Kings Cross Steelers	18	7	0	11	355	390	-35	14	
*Rayleigh Wyverns	18	5	1	12	241	375	-134	9	2
*Old Bealonians	18	3	1	14	140	454	-314	5	2

Herts/Middlesex 1

	P	W	D	L	PF	PA	PD	Pts	-
Civil Service	18	18	0	0	599	129	470	36	
Old Hamptonians	18	13	0	5	400	225	175	26	
Enfield Ignatians	18	11	0	7	334	243	91	22	
U.C.S. Old Boys	18	9	0	9	276	330	-54	18	
Tring	18	8	0	10	291	312	-21	16	
*Lensbury	18	9	0	9	333	361	-28	16	2
Stevenage Town	18	7	0	11	286	358	-72	14	
Feltham	18	6	0	12	322	392	-70	12	
Uxbridge	18	4	1	13	206	431	-225	9	
*Mill Hill	18	4	1	13	163	429	-266	7	2

Herts/Middlesex 2

	P	W	D	L	PF	PA	PD	Pts	-
Haringey	16	12	0	4	396	219	177	24	
Hitchin	16	12	0	4	370	204	166	24	
Hammersmith & Fulham	16	11	0	5	315	251	64	22	
Old Actonians	16	8	2	6	253	249	4	18	
H.A.C.	16	8	1	7	339	387	-48	17	
Datchworth	16	7	0	9	367	285	82	14	
Old Millhillians	16	5	1	10	299	376	-77	11	
*Kilburn Cosmos	16	5	0	11	222	358	-136	8	2
Old Grammarians	16	2	0	14	209	441	-232	4	

Old Haberdashers withdrew from league. All fixtures and results removed.

Herts/Middlesex 3 North

	P	W	D	L	PF	PA	PD	Pts	-
Chess Valley	14	12	0	2	412	108	304	24	
Hendon	14	11	0	3	369	155	214	22	
Old Tottonians	14	8	0	6	236	148	88	16	
Cuffley	14	8	0	6	308	295	13	16	
Q.E.II Hospital	14	7	0	7	328	236	92	14	
Northolt	14	7	0	7	217	187	30	14	
Hatfield	14	2	0	12	124	607	-483	4	
Watford	14	1	0	13	140	398	-258	2	

Herts/Middlesex 3 South

	P	W	D	L	PF	PA	PD	Pts	-
Wasps	14	12	0	2	490	113	377	24	
Old Isleworthians	14	9	0	5	298	144	154	18	
Old Abbotstonians	14	8	0	6	355	259	96	16	
*Belsize Park	14	8	1	5	267	208	59	15	2
London French	14	6	0	8	280	314	-34	12	
Osterley	14	5	2	7	249	326	-77	12	
St Nicholas O.B.	14	5	1	8	263	301	-38	11	
*Wembley	14	1	0	13	35	572	-537	-4	6

Herts/Middlesex 4 North

	P	W	D	L	PF	PA	PD	Pts	-
Old Streetonians	10	9	0	1	250	109	141	18	
Royston	10	7	1	2	380	109	271	15	
Old Ashmoleans	10	5	1	4	245	143	102	11	
Southgate	10	4	2	4	297	209	88	10	
Pinner & Grammarians	10	3	0	7	135	388	-253	6	
Ware	10	0	0	10	46	395	-349	0	

Hackney and Millfield Old Boys withdrawn from league - failure to play matches. All fixtures and results removed.

Herts/Middlesex 4 South

	P	W	D	L	PF	PA	PD	Pts	-
Sudbury & London Springboks	12	11	0	1	262	93	169	22	
London Tribes	12	9	0	3	409	110	299	18	
British Airways	12	9	0	3	349	111	238	18	
Quintin	12	7	0	5	219	171	48	14	
G.W.R.	12	3	0	9	132	270	-138	6	
Hayes	12	3	0	9	110	412	-302	6	
Thamesians	12	0	0	12	69	383	-314	0	

Orleans FP have withdrawn from League. All fixtures removed.

* denotes points deducted in right hand column

Kent 1	P	W	D	L	PF	PA	PD	Pts	-
Bromley	18	16	0	2	501	141	360	32	
Whitstable	18	15	0	3	420	256	164	30	
Ashford	18	11	1	6	418	268	150	23	
Lordswood	18	10	0	8	371	273	98	20	
Gillingham Anch.	18	9	1	8	366	243	123	19	
New Ash Green	18	9	0	9	331	392	-61	18	
Erith	18	7	0	11	229	275	-46	14	
Park House	18	6	0	12	252	495	-243	12	
Medway	18	5	0	13	151	390	-239	10	
Brockleians	18	1	0	17	197	503	-306	2	

Kent 2	P	W	D	L	PF	PA	PD	Pts	-
Aylesford	18	17	0	1	494	118	376	34	
Sheppey	18	16	0	2	526	162	364	32	
Sittingbourne	18	12	1	5	501	204	297	25	
Old Gravesendians	18	10	1	7	450	293	157	21	
Old Elthamians	18	9	2	7	287	325	-38	20	
Nat. West. Bank	18	8	0	10	281	387	-106	16	
Bexley	18	5	1	12	153	390	-237	11	
Dover	18	4	1	13	218	471	-253	9	
HSBC	18	3	2	13	215	364	-149	8	
*Darenth Valley	18	2	0	16	220	631	-411	2	2

Kent 3	P	W	D	L	PF	PA	PD	Pts	-
Shooters Hill	20	18	0	2	601	121	480	36	
Old Olavians	20	15	1	4	581	186	395	31	
Vigo	20	13	2	5	350	167	183	28	
Edenbridge	20	11	0	9	376	294	82	22	
Greenwich	20	11	0	9	330	316	14	22	
Met. Police, Hayes	20	10	1	9	323	430	-107	21	
Old Williamsonians	20	8	1	11	349	414	-65	17	
Orpington	20	7	1	12	208	330	-122	15	
Foots Cray	20	6	0	14	227	428	-201	12	
Deal Wanderers	20	6	0	14	240	547	-307	12	
*Faversham	20	2	0	18	155	507	-352	2	2

Hampshire 1	P	W	D	L	PF	PA	PD	Pts	-
Petersfield	18	17	0	1	865	120	745	34	
Southampton	18	16	0	2	664	142	522	32	
Guernsey	18	14	0	4	601	214	387	28	
Romsey	18	10	0	8	358	398	-40	20	
Millbrook	18	9	1	8	350	320	30	19	
Sandown & Shanklin	18	8	1	9	340	363	-23	17	
*Fareham Heathens	18	7	1	10	279	331	-52	13	2
Hamble	18	4	1	13	212	695	-483	9	
*Nomads	18	2	0	16	171	588	-417	2	2
Fawley	18	1	0	17	123	792	-669	2	

Hampshire 2	P	W	D	L	PF	PA	PD	Pts	-
New Milton & District	18	15	1	2	551	266	285	31	
Eastleigh	18	13	1	4	400	184	216	27	
Isle Of Wight	18	11	2	5	249	231	18	24	
Ventnor	18	9	2	7	340	233	107	20	
Portcastrians	18	9	2	7	336	257	79	20	
*Fordingbridge	18	10	0	8	263	223	40	18	2
Fleet	18	7	0	11	235	303	-68	14	
Lytchett Minster	18	5	0	13	131	323	-192	10	
Kingsclere	18	3	1	14	177	395	-218	7	
Overton	18	3	1	14	171	438	-267	7	

Hampshire 3	P	W	D	L	PF	PA	PD	Pts	-
Ellingham & Ringwood	12	10	0	2	308	105	203	20	
Alresford	12	10	0	2	266	71	195	20	
Paxton Pumas	12	10	0	2	233	121	112	20	
A.C. Delco	12	5	0	7	113	158	-45	10	
Verwood	12	3	0	9	204	290	-86	6	
*Chineham	12	3	0	9	94	192	-98	4	2
*Brockenhurst	12	1	0	11	108	389	-281	0	2

Regulation 12.7 adjustments apply to Alresford, Ellingham & Ringwood and Paxton Pumas. The effect is to reverse the placings of Alresford and Ellingham with Paxton unaffected.

* denotes points deducted in right hand column

Surrey 1	P	W	D	L	PF	PA	PD	Pts	-
London Irish Amateur	16	14	0	2	587	187	400	28	
K.C.S. Old Boys	16	13	0	3	624	175	449	26	
Old Paulines	16	13	0	3	417	203	214	26	
Old Wellingtonians	16	11	0	5	441	254	187	22	
Old Reigatian	16	9	1	6	335	162	173	19	
Old Rutlishians	16	9	1	6	331	239	92	19	
Battersea Ironsides	16	9	0	7	331	243	88	18	
Old Tiffinians	16	8	0	8	343	278	65	16	
Old Whitgiftians	16	8	0	8	261	353	-92	16	
Old Caterhamians	16	6	1	9	187	376	-189	13	
Law Society	16	6	0	10	366	383	-17	12	
Kingston	16	6	0	10	206	290	-84	12	
Merton	16	6	0	10	251	339	-88	12	
Old Cranleighans	16	6	0	10	295	394	-99	12	
Old Alleynian	16	6	0	10	249	372	-123	12	
Raynes Park	16	4	1	11	196	381	-185	9	
Old Walcountians	16	0	0	16	54	845	-791	0	

Surrey 2	P	W	D	L	PF	PA	PD	Pts	-
London Exiles	14	12	1	1	533	161	372	25	
Old Freemens	14	12	0	2	343	117	226	24	
Mitcham	14	11	0	3	275	160	115	22	
Streatham-Croydon	14	9	1	4	288	152	136	19	
Old Amplefordians	14	9	0	5	288	222	66	18	
Old Haileyburians	14	8	0	6	255	228	27	16	
Woking	14	7	0	7	241	220	21	14	
Teddington	14	7	0	7	171	300	-129	14	
London Media	14	6	1	7	196	288	-92	13	
Shirley Wanderers	14	6	0	8	186	283	-97	12	
Old Abingdonians	14	4	1	9	214	282	-68	9	
Lightwater	14	3	2	9	194	247	-53	8	
London Fire Brigade	14	4	0	10	135	315	-180	8	
Haslemere	14	3	1	10	180	352	-172	7	
Chipstead	14	0	1	13	150	322	-172	1	

Surrey 3	P	W	D	L	PF	PA	PD	Pts
London Cornish	8	7	0	1	315	70	245	14
Reigate & Redhill	8	7	0	1	263	36	227	14
Bec Old Boys	8	7	0	1	196	92	104	14
Wandsworthians	8	4	0	4	189	119	70	8
Worth Old Boys	8	4	0	4	216	170	46	8
Egham	8	4	0	4	162	232	-70	8
Old Bevonians	8	1	0	7	78	250	-172	2
Old Suttonians	8	1	0	7	79	260	-181	2
Croydon	8	1	0	7	37	306	-269	2

Economicals withdrawn from league for failure to fulfil fixtures.

Sussex 1	P	W	D	L	PF	PA	PD	Pts	-
Chichester	18	17	0	1	723	130	593	34	
Heathfield & Wald'n	18	15	0	3	555	116	439	30	
Horsham	18	13	0	5	580	297	283	26	
Hastings & Bexhill	18	13	0	5	477	258	219	26	
*Crowborough	18	10	0	8	575	278	297	18	2
Chichester IHE	18	7	1	10	328	449	-121	15	
Hellingly	18	6	0	12	265	579	-314	12	
Rye	18	3	1	14	125	596	-471	7	
*Sussex Police	18	3	1	14	219	575	-356	3	4
*St Francis	18	1	1	16	163	732	-569	-3	6

Sussex 2 East									
Seaford	12	12	0	0	482	69	413	24	
Newick	12	9	0	3	316	127	189	18	
Burgess Hill	12	8	0	4	320	184	136	16	
*Old Brightonians	12	6	0	6	256	175	81	8	4
Ditchling	12	3	1	8	137	351	-214	7	
Robertsbridge	12	2	1	9	180	425	-245	5	
Plumpton	12	1	0	11	123	483	-360	2	

Sussex 2 West									
Pulborough	14	14	0	0	520	27	493	28	
Royal Sun Alliance	14	11	0	3	428	128	300	22	
Norfolk Arms	14	10	1	3	407	151	256	21	
Midhurst	14	7	0	7	220	312	-92	14	
Barns Green	14	5	0	9	175	408	-233	10	
*B.A. Wingspan	14	4	0	10	101	380	-279	4	4
*Shoreham	14	2	1	11	155	351	-196	3	2
*Arun	14	2	0	12	119	368	-249	0	4

London 2 North

	Bank of England	Bishop's Stortford	Cambridg	Diss	Ipswich	Letchwort G.C.	Old Albanians	Shelford	Sudbury	Thurrock	Twickenham	Woodford
Bank Of England		12/10	01/02	23/11	28/09	21/12	01/03	02/11	07/09	11/01	29/03	30/11
Bishop's Stortford	18/01		30/11	05/10	14/12	08/02	16/11	14/09	04/01	15/03	26/10	29/03
Cambridge	05/10	12/04		08/02	16/11	14/09	04/01	15/03	26/10	07/12	18/01	14/12
Diss	14/12	01/02	28/09		01/03	02/11	07/09	11/01	29/03	12/10	30/11	16/11
Ipswich	08/02	23/11	21/12	14/09		15/03	26/10	07/12	18/01	12/04	05/10	04/01
Letchworth Garden	16/11	28/09	01/03	04/01	07/09		29/03	12/10	30/11	01/02	14/12	26/10
Old Albanians	14/09	21/12	02/11	15/03	11/01	07/12		12/04	05/10	23/11	08/02	18/01
Shelford	04/01	01/03	07/09	26/10	29/03	18/01	30/11		14/12	28/09	16/11	05/10
Sudbury	15/03	02/11	11/01	07/12	12/10	12/04	01/02	23/11		21/12	14/09	08/02
Thurrock	26/10	07/09	29/03	18/01	30/11	05/10	14/12	08/02	16/11		04/01	14/09
Twickenham	07/12	11/01	12/10	12/04	01/02	23/11	28/09	21/12	01/03	02/11		15/03
Woodford	12/04	07/12	23/11	21/12	02/11	11/01	12/10	01/02	28/09	01/03	07/09	

London 2 South

	Andover	Beckenham	Cobham	Effingham & Leatherhead	Gosport and Fareham	Maidstone	Old Mid-Whitgiftian	Portsmouth	Sevenoaks	Tunbridge Wells	Wimbledon	Worthing
Andover		18/01	30/11	05/10	14/12	08/02	16/11	14/09	04/01	15/03	26/10	29/03
Beckenham	12/10		01/02	23/11	28/09	21/12	01/03	02/11	07/09	11/01	29/03	30/11
Cobham	12/04	05/10		08/02	16/11	14/09	04/01	15/03	26/10	07/12	18/01	14/12
Effingham & Leatherhead	01/02	14/12	28/09		01/03	02/11	07/09	11/01	29/03	12/10	30/11	16/11
Gosport and Fareham	23/11	08/02	21/12	14/09		15/03	26/10	07/12	18/01	12/04	05/10	04/01
Maidstone	28/09	16/11	01/03	04/01	07/09		29/03	12/10	30/11	01/02	14/12	26/10
Old Mid-Whitgiftian	21/12	14/09	02/11	15/03	11/01	07/12		12/04	05/10	23/11	08/02	18/01
Portsmouth	01/03	04/01	07/09	26/10	29/03	18/01	30/11		14/12	28/09	16/11	05/10
Sevenoaks	02/11	15/03	11/01	07/12	12/10	12/04	01/02	23/11		21/12	14/09	08/02
Tunbridge Wells	07/09	26/10	29/03	18/01	30/11	05/10	14/12	08/02	16/11		04/01	14/09
Wimbledon	11/01	07/12	12/10	12/04	01/02	23/11	28/09	21/12	01/03	02/11		15/03
Worthing	07/12	12/04	23/11	21/12	02/11	11/01	12/10	01/02	28/09	01/03	07/09	

London 3 North East

	Basildon	Brentwood	Bury St. Edmunds	Chingford	Hadleigh	Rochford Hundred	Romford & Gidea Park	Saffron Walden	West Norfolk	Wymondham
Basildon		12/10	30/11	08/02	14/12	28/09	02/11	15/03	18/01	29/03
Brentwood	01/02		05/10	16/11	01/03	04/01	14/09	26/10	29/03	30/11
Bury St. Edmunds	12/04	08/02		28/09	02/11	15/03	18/01	07/12	12/10	14/12
Chingford	05/10	14/12	01/03		14/09	26/10	29/03	01/02	30/11	02/11
Hadleigh	16/11	28/09	04/01	15/03		07/12	12/10	12/04	08/02	18/01
Rochford Hundred	01/03	02/11	14/09	18/01	29/03		30/11	05/10	14/12	12/10
Romford & Gidea Park	04/01	15/03	26/10	07/12	01/02	12/04		16/11	28/09	08/02
Saffron Walden	14/09	18/01	29/03	12/10	30/11	08/02	14/12		02/11	28/09
West Norfolk	26/10	07/12	01/02	12/04	05/10	16/11	01/03	04/01		15/03
Wymondham	07/12	12/04	16/11	04/01	26/10	01/02	05/10	01/03	14/09	

London 3 North West

	Barnet Saracens	Ealing	Fullerians	Harpenden	Imperial Medicals	London Scottish	Metropolitan Police	Old Verulamians	Ruislip	West London
Barnet Saracens		05/10	16/11	01/03	04/01	01/02	14/09	26/10	29/03	30/11
Ealing	08/02		28/09	02/11	15/03	12/04	18/01	07/12	12/10	14/12
Fullerians	14/12	01/03		14/09	26/10	05/10	29/03	01/02	30/11	02/11
Harpenden	28/09	04/01	15/03		07/12	16/11	12/10	12/04	08/02	18/01
Imperial Medicals	02/11	14/09	18/01	29/03		01/03	30/11	05/10	14/12	12/10
London Scottish	12/10	30/11	08/02	14/12	28/09		02/11	15/03	18/01	29/03
Metropolitan Police	15/03	26/10	07/12	01/02	12/04	04/01		16/11	28/09	08/02
Old Verulamians	18/01	29/03	12/10	30/11	08/02	14/09	14/12		02/11	28/09
Ruislip	07/12	01/02	12/04	05/10	16/11	26/10	01/03	04/01		15/03
West London	12/04	16/11	04/01	26/10	01/02	07/12	05/10	01/03	14/09	

London 3 South East

	Betteshanger	Brighton	Charlton Park	Dartfordians	East Grinstead	Eastbourne	Gravesend	Lewes	Sidcup	Tonbridge Juddian
Betteshanger		12/10	30/11	08/02	14/12	28/09	02/11	15/03	18/01	29/03
Brighton	01/02		05/10	16/11	01/03	04/01	14/09	26/10	29/03	30/11
Charlton Park	12/04	08/02		28/09	02/11	15/03	18/01	07/12	12/10	14/12
Dartfordians	05/10	14/12	01/03		14/09	26/10	29/03	01/02	30/11	02/11
East Grinstead	16/11	28/09	04/01	15/03		07/12	12/10	12/04	08/02	18/01
Eastbourne	01/03	02/11	14/09	18/01	29/03		30/11	05/10	14/12	12/10
Gravesend	04/01	15/03	26/10	07/12	01/02	12/04		16/11	28/09	08/02
Lewes	14/09	18/01	29/03	12/10	30/11	08/02	14/12		02/11	28/09
Sidcup	26/10	07/12	01/02	12/04	05/10	16/11	01/03	04/01		15/03
Tonbridge Juddian	07/12	12/04	16/11	04/01	26/10	01/02	05/10	01/03	14/09	

London 3 South West

	Alton	Barnes	Chobham	Dorking	Guildford	Jersey	Old Blues	Old Wimbledonians	Richmond	University Vandals
Alton		12/10	30/11	08/02	14/12	28/09	02/11	18/01	29/03	15/03
Barnes	01/02		05/10	16/11	01/03	04/01	14/09	29/03	30/11	26/10
Chobham	12/04	08/02		28/09	02/11	15/03	18/01	12/10	14/12	07/12
Dorking	05/10	14/12	01/03		14/09	26/10	29/03	30/11	02/11	01/03
Guildford	16/11	28/09	04/01	15/03		07/12	12/10	08/02	18/01	12/04
Jersey	01/03	02/11	14/09	18/01	29/03		30/11	14/12	12/10	05/10
Old Blues	04/01	15/03	26/10	07/12	01/02	12/04		28/09	08/02	16/11
Old Wimbledonians	26/10	07/12	01/02	12/04	05/10	16/11	01/03		15/03	04/01
Richmond	07/12	12/04	16/11	04/01	26/10	01/02	05/10	14/09		01/03
University Vandals	14/09	18/01	29/03	12/10	30/11	08/02	14/12	02/11	28/09	

London 4 North East

	Beccles	Braintree	Campion	Chelmsford	Eton Manor	Lowestoft & Yarmouth	Mersea Island	Thetford	Upminster	Woodbridge
Beccles		12/10	30/11	08/02	14/12	28/09	02/11	15/03	18/01	29/03
Braintree	01/02		05/10	16/11	01/03	04/01	14/09	26/10	29/03	30/11
Campion	12/04	08/02		28/09	02/11	15/03	18/01	07/12	12/10	14/12
Chelmsford	05/10	14/12	01/03		14/09	26/10	29/03	01/02	30/11	02/11
Eton Manor	16/11	28/09	04/01	15/03		07/12	12/10	12/04	08/02	18/01
Lowestoft & Yarmouth	01/03	02/11	14/09	18/01	29/03		30/11	05/10	14/12	12/10
Mersea Island	04/01	15/03	26/10	07/12	01/02	12/04		16/11	28/09	08/02
Thetford	14/09	18/01	29/03	12/10	30/11	08/02	14/12		02/11	28/09
Upminster	26/10	07/12	01/02	12/04	05/10	16/11	01/03	04/01		15/03
Woodbridge	07/12	12/04	16/11	04/01	26/10	01/02	05/10	01/03	14/09	

London 4 North West

	Civil Service	Finchley	Grasshoppers	Hampstead	Harrow	London New Zealand	Old Hamptonians	Old Merchant Taylors	St Albans	Welwyn
Civil Service		12/10	30/11	08/02	14/12	28/09	02/11	15/03	18/01	29/03
Finchley	01/02		05/10	16/11	01/03	04/01	14/09	26/10	29/03	30/11
Grasshoppers	12/04	08/02		28/09	02/11	15/03	18/01	07/12	12/10	14/12
Hampstead	05/10	14/12	01/03		14/09	26/10	29/03	01/02	30/11	02/11
Harrow	16/11	28/09	04/01	15/03		07/12	12/10	12/04	08/02	18/01
London New Zealand	01/03	02/11	14/09	18/01	29/03		30/11	05/10	14/12	12/10
Old Hamptonians	04/01	15/03	26/10	07/12	01/02	12/04		16/11	28/09	08/02
Old Merchant Taylors	14/09	18/01	29/03	12/10	30/11	08/02	14/12		02/11	28/09
St Albans	26/10	07/12	01/02	12/04	05/10	16/11	01/03	04/01		15/03
Welwyn	07/12	12/04	16/11	04/01	26/10	01/02	05/10	01/03	14/09	

London 4 South East

	Beccehamian	Bognor	Bromley	Chichester	Crawley	Folkestone	Guy's Hospital	Heathfield & Wald.	Hove	Old Dunstonians
Beccehamian		12/10	30/11	08/02	14/12	28/09	02/11	15/03	18/01	29/03
Bognor	01/02		05/10	16/11	01/03	04/01	14/09	26/10	29/03	30/11
Bromley	12/04	08/02		28/09	02/11	15/03	18/01	07/12	12/10	14/12
Chichester	05/10	14/12	01/03		14/09	26/10	29/03	01/02	30/11	02/11
Crawley	16/11	28/09	04/01	15/03		07/12	12/10	12/04	08/02	18/01
Folkestone	01/03	02/11	14/09	18/01	29/03		30/11	05/10	14/12	12/10
Guy's Hospital	04/01	15/03	26/10	07/12	01/02	12/04		16/11	28/09	08/02
Heathfield & Wald'n	14/09	18/01	29/03	12/10	30/11	08/02	14/12		02/11	28/09
Hove	26/10	07/12	01/02	12/04	05/10	16/11	01/03	04/01		15/03
Old Dunstonians	07/12	12/04	16/11	04/01	26/10	01/02	05/10	01/03	14/09	

London 4 South West

	Cranleigh	Farnham	London Irish Amateur	Old Emanuel	Petersfield	Purley John Fisher	Southampton	Tottonians	Trojans	Und Services, Portsmouth
Cranleigh		12/10	30/11	08/02	14/12	28/09	02/11	15/03	18/01	29/03
Farnham	01/02		05/10	16/11	01/03	04/01	14/09	26/10	29/03	30/11
London Irish Amateur	12/04	08/02		28/09	02/11	15/03	18/01	07/12	12/10	14/12
Old Emanuel	05/10	14/12	01/03		14/09	26/10	29/03	01/02	30/11	02/11
Petersfield	16/11	28/09	04/01	15/03		07/12	12/10	12/04	08/02	18/01
Purley John Fisher	01/03	02/11	14/09	18/01	29/03		30/11	05/10	14/12	12/10
Southampton	04/01	15/03	26/10	07/12	01/02	12/04		16/11	28/09	08/02
Tottonians	14/09	18/01	29/03	12/10	30/11	08/02	14/12		02/11	28/09
Trojans	26/10	07/12	01/02	12/04	05/10	16/11	01/03	04/01		15/03
United Services,	07/12	12/04	16/11	04/01	26/10	01/02	05/10	01/03	14/09	

Eastern Counties 1

	Billericay	Canvey Island	Colchester	Ely	Holt	Maldon	Stanford Le Hope	Stowmarket	Upper Clapton	Wanstead
Billericay		12/10	30/11	08/02	14/12	28/09	02/11	15/03	18/01	29/03
Canvey Island	01/02		05/10	16/11	01/03	04/01	14/09	26/10	29/03	30/11
Colchester	12/04	08/02		28/09	02/11	15/03	18/01	07/12	12/10	14/12
Ely	05/10	14/12	01/03		14/09	26/10	29/03	01/02	30/11	02/11
Holt	16/11	28/09	04/01	15/03		07/12	12/10	12/04	08/02	18/01
Maldon	01/03	02/11	14/09	18/01	29/03		30/11	05/10	14/12	12/10
Stanford Le Hope	04/01	15/03	26/10	07/12	01/02	12/04		16/11	28/09	08/02
Stowmarket	14/09	18/01	29/03	12/10	30/11	08/02	14/12		02/11	28/09
Upper Clapton	26/10	07/12	01/02	12/04	05/10	16/11	01/03	04/01		15/03
Wanstead	07/12	12/04	16/11	04/01	26/10	01/02	05/10	01/03	14/09	

Eastern Counties 2 North

	Cantabrigian	Crusaders	Haverhill & District	Ipswich Y.M.	Lakenham Hewett	Newmarket	Norwich Union	Southwold	Thurston	Wisbech
Cantabrigian		12/10	30/11	08/02	14/12	28/09	02/11	15/03	18/01	29/03
Crusaders	01/02		05/10	16/11	01/03	04/01	14/09	26/10	29/03	30/11
Haverhill & District	12/04	08/02		28/09	02/11	15/03	18/01	07/12	12/10	14/12
Ipswich Y.M.	05/10	14/12	01/03		14/09	26/10	29/03	01/02	30/11	02/11
Lakenham Hewett	16/11	28/09	04/01	15/03		07/12	12/10	12/04	08/02	18/01
Newmarket	01/03	02/11	14/09	18/01	29/03		30/11	05/10	14/12	12/10
Norwich Union	04/01	15/03	26/10	07/12	01/02	12/04		16/11	28/09	08/02
Southwold	14/09	18/01	29/03	12/10	30/11	08/02	14/12		02/11	28/09
Thurston	26/10	07/12	01/02	12/04	05/10	16/11	01/03	04/01		15/03
Wisbech	07/12	12/04	16/11	04/01	26/10	01/02	05/10	01/03	14/09	

Eastern Counties 2 South

	Bancroft	Burnham-on-Crouch	Dagenham	East London	Ilford Wanderers	Old Brentwoods	Old Edwardians	South Woodham Ferrers	Thames	Westcliff
Bancroft		12/10	30/11	08/02	14/12	28/09	02/11	15/03	18/01	29/03
Burnham-On-Crouch	01/02		05/10	16/11	01/03	04/01	14/09	26/10	29/03	30/11
Dagenham	12/04	08/02		28/09	02/11	15/03	18/01	07/12	12/10	14/12
East London	05/10	14/12	01/03		14/09	26/10	29/03	01/02	30/11	02/11
Ilford Wanderers	16/11	28/09	04/01	15/03		07/12	12/10	12/04	08/02	18/01
Old Brentwoods	01/03	02/11	14/09	18/01	29/03		30/11	05/10	14/12	12/10
Old Edwardians	04/01	15/03	26/10	07/12	01/02	12/04		16/11	28/09	08/02
South Woodham	14/09	18/01	29/03	12/10	30/11	08/02	14/12		02/11	28/09
Thames	26/10	07/12	01/02	12/04	05/10	16/11	01/03	04/01		15/03
Westcliff	07/12	12/04	16/11	04/01	26/10	01/02	05/10	01/03	14/09	

Eastern Counties 3 North

	Brightlingsea	Broadland	Felixstowe	Harwich & Dovercourt	March BRAZA	Sawston	Swaffham	Witham
Brightlingsea		01/03	12/10	14/12	30/11	08/02	05/10	12/04
Broadland	02/11		08/02	12/10	18/01	28/09	12/04	30/11
Felixstowe	01/02	26/10		18/01	28/09	12/04	30/11	01/03
Harwich & Dovercourt	28/09	01/02	05/10		12/04	30/11	01/03	26/10
March BRAZA	15/03	05/10	14/12	07/12		01/03	26/10	01/02
Sawston	26/10	14/12	07/12	15/03	02/11		01/02	05/10
Swaffham	18/01	07/12	15/03	02/11	08/02	12/10		14/12
Witham	07/12	15/03	02/11	08/02	12/10	18/01	28/09	

Eastern Counties 3 South

	Kings Cross Steelers	Loughton	May & Baker	Millwall Albion	Old Bealonians	Old Cooperians	Ongar	Pegasus	Ravens	Rayleigh Wyverns
Kings Cross Steelers		12/10	30/11	08/02	14/12	28/09	02/11	15/03	18/01	29/03
Loughton	01/02		05/10	16/11	01/03	04/01	14/09	26/10	29/03	30/11
May & Baker	12/04	08/02		28/09	02/11	15/03	18/01	07/12	12/10	14/12
Millwall Albion	05/10	14/12	01/03		14/09	26/10	29/03	01/02	30/11	02/11
Old Bealonians	16/11	28/09	04/01	15/03		07/12	12/10	12/04	08/02	18/01
Old Cooperians	01/03	02/11	14/09	18/01	29/03		30/11	05/10	14/12	12/10
Ongar	04/01	15/03	26/10	07/12	01/02	12/04		16/11	28/09	08/02
Pegasus	14/09	18/01	29/03	12/10	30/11	08/02	14/12		02/11	28/09
Ravens	26/10	07/12	01/02	12/04	05/10	16/11	01/03	04/01		15/03
Rayleigh Wyverns	07/12	12/04	16/11	04/01	26/10	01/02	05/10	01/03	14/09	

Hampshire 1

	Eastleigh	Fareham Heathens	Farnborough	Guernsey	Hamble	Millbrook	New Milton & Dist.	Nomads	Romsey	Sandown & Shanklin
Eastleigh		12/10	30/11	08/02	14/12	28/09	02/11	29/03	15/03	18/01
Fareham Heathens	01/02		05/10	16/11	01/03	04/01	14/09	30/11	26/10	29/03
Farnborough	12/04	08/02		28/09	02/11	15/03	18/01	14/12	07/12	12/10
Guernsey	05/10	14/12	01/03		14/09	26/10	29/03	02/11	01/02	30/11
Hamble	16/11	28/09	04/01	15/03		07/12	12/10	18/01	12/04	08/02
Millbrook	01/03	02/11	14/09	18/01	29/03		30/11	12/10	05/10	14/12
New Milton & District	04/01	15/03	26/10	07/12	01/02	12/04		08/02	16/11	28/09
Nomads	07/12	12/04	16/11	04/01	26/10	01/02	05/10		01/03	14/09
Romsey	14/09	18/01	29/03	12/10	30/11	08/02	14/12	28/09		02/11
Sandown & Shanklin	26/10	07/12	01/02	12/04	05/10	16/11	01/03	15/03	04/01	

Hampshire 2

	Alresford	Ellingham & Ringwood	Fawley	Fleet	Fordingbridge	Isle Of Wight	Lytchett Minster	Portcastrians	Ventnor
Alresford		12/10	30/11	08/02	14/12	28/09	02/11	18/01	29/03
Ellingham &	01/02		05/10	16/11	01/03	04/01	14/09	29/03	30/11
Fawley	12/04	08/02		28/09	02/11	15/03	18/01	12/10	14/12
Fleet	05/10	14/12	01/03		14/09	26/10	29/03	30/11	02/11
Fordingbridge	16/11	28/09	04/01	15/03		07/12	12/10	08/02	18/01
Isle Of Wight	01/03	02/11	14/09	18/01	29/03		30/11	14/12	12/10
Lytchett Minster	04/01	15/03	26/10	07/12	01/02	12/04		28/09	08/02
Portcastrians	26/10	07/12	01/02	12/04	05/10	16/11	01/03		15/03
Ventnor	07/12	12/04	16/11	04/01	26/10	01/02	05/10	14/09	

Hampshire 3

	Brockenhurst	Chineham	Kingsclere	Overton	Paxton Pumas	Southampton Inst.	Verwood
Brockenhurst		18/01	28/09	12/04	30/11	26/10	01/03
Chineham	05/10		12/04	30/11	01/03	01/02	26/10
Kingsclere	14/12	07/12		01/03	26/10	05/10	01/02
Overton	07/12	15/03	02/11		01/02	14/12	05/10
Paxton Pumas	15/03	02/11	08/02	12/10		07/12	14/12
Stoneham Park	08/02	12/10	18/01	28/09	12/04		30/11
Verwood	02/11	08/02	12/10	18/01	28/09	15/03	

Herts & Middlesex 1

	Chiswick	Enfield Ignatians	Feltham	Haringey	Hemel Hempstead	Hitchin	Lensbury	Stevenage Town	Tring	U.C.S. Old Boys
Chiswick		12/10	30/11	08/02	14/12	28/09	02/11	15/03	18/01	29/03
Enfield Ignatians	01/02		05/10	16/11	01/03	04/01	14/09	26/10	29/03	30/11
Feltham	12/04	08/02		28/09	02/11	15/03	18/01	07/12	12/10	14/12
Haringey	05/10	14/12	01/03		14/09	26/10	29/03	01/02	30/11	02/11
Hemel Hempstead	16/11	28/09	04/01	15/03		07/12	12/10	12/04	08/02	18/01
Hitchin	01/03	02/11	14/09	18/01	29/03		30/11	05/10	14/12	12/10
Lensbury	04/01	15/03	26/10	07/12	01/02	12/04		16/11	28/09	08/02
Stevenage Town	14/09	18/01	29/03	12/10	30/11	08/02	14/12		02/11	28/09
Tring	26/10	07/12	01/02	12/04	05/10	16/11	01/03	04/01		15/03
U.C.S. Old Boys	07/12	12/04	16/11	04/01	26/10	01/02	05/10	01/03	14/09	

Herts & Middlesex 2

	Chess Valley	Datchworth	H.A.C.	Hammersmith & Fulham	Mill Hill	Old Actonians	Old Isleworthians	Old Millhillians	Uxbridge	Wasps
Chess Valley		12/10	30/11	08/02	14/12	28/09	02/11	15/03	18/01	29/03
Datchworth	01/02		05/10	16/11	01/03	04/01	14/09	26/10	29/03	30/11
H.A.C.	12/04	08/02		28/09	02/11	15/03	18/01	07/12	12/10	14/12
Hammersmith &	05/10	14/12	01/03		14/09	26/10	29/03	01/02	30/11	02/11
Mill Hill	16/11	28/09	04/01	15/03		07/12	12/10	12/04	08/02	18/01
Old Actonians	01/03	02/11	14/09	18/01	29/03		30/11	05/10	14/12	12/10
Old Isleworthians	04/01	15/03	26/10	07/12	01/02	12/04		16/11	28/09	08/02
Old Millhillians	14/09	18/01	29/03	12/10	30/11	08/02	14/12		02/11	28/09
Uxbridge	26/10	07/12	01/02	12/04	05/10	16/11	01/03	04/01		15/03
Wasps	07/12	12/04	16/11	04/01	26/10	01/02	05/10	01/03	14/09	

Herts & Middlesex 3 North

	Cuffley	Hendon	Old Grammarians	Old Haberdashers	Old Steetonians	Old Tottonians	Q.E.II Hospital	Royston
Cuffley		01/03	12/10	08/02	14/12	30/11	05/10	12/04
Hendon	02/11		08/02	28/09	12/10	18/01	12/04	30/11
Old Grammarians	01/02	26/10		12/04	18/01	28/09	30/11	01/03
Old Haberdashers	26/10	14/12	07/12		15/03	02/11	01/02	05/10
Old Streetonians	28/09	01/02	05/10	30/11		12/04	01/03	26/10
Old Tottonians	15/03	05/10	14/12	01/03	07/12		26/10	01/02
Q.E.II Hospital	18/01	07/12	15/03	12/10	02/11	08/02		14/12
Royston	07/12	15/03	02/11	18/01	08/02	12/10	28/09	

Herts & Middlesex 3 South

	Belsize Park	Harlequin Amateur	Kilburn Cosmos	London French	London Tribes	Northolt	Old Abbotstonians	Osterley	Sudbury & London
Belsize Park		05/10	16/11	01/03	04/01	14/09	26/10	29/03	30/11
Harlequin Amateur	08/02		28/09	02/11	15/03	18/01	07/12	12/10	14/12
Kilburn Cosmos	14/12	01/03		14/09	26/10	29/03	01/02	30/11	02/11
London French	28/09	04/01	15/03		07/12	12/10	12/04	08/02	18/01
London Tribes	02/11	14/09	18/01	29/03		30/11	05/10	14/12	12/10
Northolt	15/03	26/10	07/12	01/02	12/04		16/11	28/09	08/02
Old Abbotstonians	18/01	29/03	12/10	30/11	08/02	14/12		02/11	28/09
Osterley	07/12	01/02	12/04	05/10	16/11	01/03	04/01		15/03
Sudbury & London	12/04	16/11	04/01	26/10	01/02	05/10	01/03	14/09	

Herts & Middlesex 4 North

	Hackney	Hatfield	Old Ashmoleans	Pinner & Grammarians	Southgate	Ware	Watford	Wembley
Hackney		01/03	14/12	30/11	08/02	05/10	12/04	12/10
Hatfield	02/11		12/10	18/01	28/09	12/04	30/11	08/02
Old Ashmoleans	28/09	01/02		12/04	30/11	01/03	26/10	05/10
Pinner &	15/03	05/10	07/12		01/03	26/10	01/02	14/12
Southgate	26/10	14/12	15/03	02/11		01/02	05/10	07/12
Ware	18/01	07/12	02/11	08/02	12/10		14/12	15/03
Watford	07/12	15/03	08/02	12/10	18/01	28/09		02/11
Wembley	01/02	26/10	18/01	28/09	12/04	30/11	01/03	

Herts & Middlesex 4 South

	British Airways	G.W.R.	Hayes	Millfield O.B.	Quintin	St. Nicholas O.B.	Thamesians
British Airways		08/02	12/10	30/11	18/01	28/09	12/04
G.W.R.	26/10		18/01	01/03	28/09	12/04	30/11
Hayes	01/02	05/10		26/10	12/04	30/11	01/03
Millfield O.B.	15/03	02/11	08/02		12/10	18/01	28/09
Quintin	05/10	14/12	07/12	01/02		01/03	26/10
St Nicholas O.B.	14/12	07/12	15/03	05/10	02/11		01/02
Thamesians	07/12	15/03	02/11	14/12	08/02	12/10	

Kent 1

	Ashford	Askeans	Aylesford	Cranbrook	Erith	Gillingham Anch.	Lordswood	New Ash Green	Sheppey	Whitstable
Ashford		12/10	30/11	08/02	14/12	28/09	02/11	15/03	18/01	29/03
Askeans	01/02		05/10	16/11	01/03	04/01	14/09	26/10	29/03	30/11
Aylesford	12/04	08/02		28/09	02/11	15/03	18/01	07/12	12/10	14/12
Cranbrook	05/10	14/12	01/03		14/09	26/10	29/03	01/02	30/11	02/11
Erith	16/11	28/09	04/01	15/03		07/12	12/10	12/04	08/02	18/01
Gillingham Anch.	01/03	02/11	14/09	18/01	29/03		30/11	05/10	14/12	12/10
Lordswood	04/01	15/03	26/10	07/12	01/02	12/04		16/11	28/09	08/02
New Ash Green	14/09	18/01	29/03	12/10	30/11	08/02	14/12		02/11	28/09
Sheppey	26/10	07/12	01/02	12/04	05/10	16/11	01/03	04/01		15/03
Whitstable	07/12	12/04	16/11	04/01	26/10	01/02	05/10	01/03	14/09	

Kent 2

	Bexley	Brockleians	Medway	Nat. West. Bank	Old Elthamians	Old Gravesendians	Old Olavians	Park House	Shooters Hill	Sittingbourne
Bexley		12/10	30/11	08/02	14/12	28/09	02/11	15/03	18/01	29/03
Brockleians	01/02		05/10	16/11	01/03	04/01	14/09	26/10	29/03	30/11
Medway	12/04	08/02		28/09	02/11	15/03	18/01	07/12	12/10	14/12
Nat. West. Bank	05/10	14/12	01/03		14/09	26/10	29/03	01/02	30/11	02/11
Old Elthamians	16/11	28/09	04/01	15/03		07/12	12/10	12/04	08/02	18/01
Old Gravesendians	01/03	02/11	14/09	18/01	29/03		30/11	05/10	14/12	12/10
Old Olavians	04/01	15/03	26/10	07/12	01/02	12/04		16/11	28/09	08/02
Park House	14/09	18/01	29/03	12/10	30/11	08/02	14/12		02/11	28/09
Shooters Hill	26/10	07/12	01/02	12/04	05/10	16/11	01/03	04/01		15/03
Sittingbourne	07/12	12/04	16/11	04/01	26/10	01/02	05/10	01/03	14/09	

Kent 3

	Darenth Valley	Deal Wanderers	Dover	Edenbridge	Foots Cray	Greenwich	H.S.B.C.	Old Williamsonians	Orpington	Vigo
Darenth Valley		12/10	30/11	08/02	14/12	28/09	02/11	15/03	18/01	29/03
Deal Wanderers	01/02		05/10	16/11	01/03	04/01	14/09	26/10	29/03	30/11
Dover	12/04	08/02		28/09	02/11	15/03	18/01	07/12	12/10	14/12
Edenbridge	05/10	14/12	01/03		14/09	26/10	29/03	01/02	30/11	02/11
Foots Cray	16/11	28/09	04/01	15/03		07/12	12/10	12/04	08/02	18/01
Greenwich	01/03	02/11	14/09	18/01	29/03		30/11	05/10	14/12	12/10
HSBC	04/01	15/03	26/10	07/12	01/02	12/04		16/11	28/09	08/02
Old Williamsonians	14/09	18/01	29/03	12/10	30/11	08/02	14/12		02/11	28/09
Orpington	26/10	07/12	01/02	12/04	05/10	16/11	01/03	04/01		15/03
Vigo	07/12	12/04	16/11	04/01	26/10	01/02	05/10	01/03	14/09	

Surrey 1

	Battersea Ironsides	K.C.S. Old Boys	Kingston	Law Society	London Exiles	Merton	Old Caterhamians	Old Cranleighans	Old Freemens	Old Paulines	Old Reedonians	Old Reigatian	Old Rutlishians	Old Tiffinians	Old Wellingtonians	Old Whitgiftians	Warlingham
Battersea Ironsides				12/04	28/09	07/12	01/03		12/10						18/01	04/01	02/11
K.C.S. Old Boys	14/09			26/10			05/10	07/12		04/01		15/03	08/02	18/01			
Kingston	15/03	12/10					14/09	02/11		07/12		08/02	18/01	04/01			
Law Society			05/10		02/11	18/01			07/12		14/09				15/03	08/02	04/01
London Exiles		30/11	26/10			08/02			04/01		05/10				14/09	15/03	18/01
Merton		01/02	11/01					01/03		12/04	14/12			28/09	30/11	26/10	
Old Caterhamians				28/09	12/10	04/01			02/11		15/03				08/02	18/01	07/12
Old Cranleighans	05/10			30/11	14/12		26/10			18/01		14/09	15/03	08/02			
Old Freemens		14/12	30/11			15/03		11/01			26/10				05/10	14/09	08/02
Old Paulines	26/10			14/12	11/01		30/11		01/02			05/10	14/09	15/03			
Old Reedonians	08/02	28/09	12/04					12/10		02/11		18/01	04/01	07/12			
Old Reigatian	11/01			01/03	12/04	02/11	01/02		28/09							07/12	12/10
Old Rutlishians	14/12			01/02	01/03	12/10	11/01		12/04			30/11					28/09
Old Tiffinians	30/11			11/01	01/02		14/12		01/03			26/10	05/10				12/04
Old Wellingtonians		12/04	01/03					28/09		12/10	01/02	04/01	07/12	02/11			
Old Whitgiftians		01/03	01/02					12/04		28/09	11/01		02/11	12/10	14/12		
Warlingham		11/01	14/12			14/09		01/02		01/03	30/11				26/10	05/10	

Surrey 2

	Lightwater	London Cornish	London Media	Mitcham	Old Abingdonians	Old Ampleforians	Old Ampleforians	Old Haileyburians .	Old Walcountians	Raynes Park	Reigate & Redhill	Shirley Wanderers	Streatham-Croydon	Teddington	Woking
Lightwater		08/02					15/03	18/01		07/12	12/10	28/09		02/11	
London Cornish							12/10			01/02	07/12	02/11	14/09	11/01	01/03
London Media	05/10	30/11				14/09	14/12	26/10	01/03			18/01			
Mitcham	14/09	26/10	11/01			01/03	30/11	05/10	01/02						
Old Abingdonians	01/03	05/10	07/12	02/11		01/02		14/09	11/01						
Old Alleynian	30/11	18/01					08/02	14/12			28/09	15/03		12/10	
Old Amplefordians					26/10					01/03	11/01	07/12	05/10	01/02	14/09
Old Haileyburians		15/03					28/09			11/01	02/11	12/10		07/12	01/02
Old Walcountians	26/10	14/12				05/10	18/01	30/11			15/03	08/02			
Raynes Park			28/09	15/03	08/02	02/11			12/10				18/01		14/12
Reigate & Redhill			08/02	18/01	14/12					05/10			30/11	14/09	26/10
Shirley Wanderers				14/12	30/11					14/09	01/02		26/10	01/03	05/10
Streatham-Croydon	01/02		02/11	12/10	28/09	11/01		01/03	07/12						
Teddington			15/03	08/02	18/01				28/09	26/10			14/12		30/11
Woking	11/01		12/10	28/09	15/03	07/12			02/11				08/02		

Surrey 3

	Bec Old Boys	Chipstead	Croydon	Egham	Haslemere	London Fire Brigade	Old Bevonians	Old Suttonians	Wandsworthians	Worth Old Boys
Bec Old Boys				01/02	14/12				12/10	02/11
Chipstead	26/10		01/02			28/09		14/12	30/11	
Croydon	30/11					26/10			18/01	08/02
Egham		12/10	02/11			14/12	08/02			
Haslemere		08/02	12/10	30/11			18/01			
London Fire Brigade	18/01				02/11				08/02	12/10
Old Bevonians	28/09	02/11	14/12			01/02		12/10		
Old Suttonians	08/02		28/09	18/01	26/10	30/11				
Wandsworthians				28/09	01/02		26/10	02/11		14/12
Worth Old Boys		18/01		26/10	28/09		30/11	01/02		

Sussex 1

	Chichester IHE	Crowborough	Hastings & Bexhill	Hellingly	Horsham	Pulborough	Rye	Seaford	Uckfield
Chichester IHE		05/10	16/11	01/03	04/01	14/09	26/10	29/03	30/11
Crowborough	08/02		28/09	02/11	15/03	18/01	07/12	12/10	14/12
Hastings & Bexhill	14/12	01/03		14/09	26/10	29/03	01/02	30/11	02/11
Hellingly	28/09	04/01	15/03		07/12	12/10	12/04	08/02	18/01
Horsham	02/11	14/09	18/01	29/03		30/11	05/10	14/12	12/10
Pulborough	15/03	26/10	07/12	01/02	12/04		16/11	28/09	08/02
Rye	18/01	29/03	12/10	30/11	08/02	14/12		02/11	28/09
Seaford	07/12	01/02	12/04	05/10	16/11	01/03	04/01		15/03
Uckfield	12/04	16/11	04/01	26/10	01/02	05/10	01/03	14/09	

Sussex 2 East

	Barns Green	Burgess Hill	Midhurst	Newick	Norfolk Arms	Royal Sun Alliance	St Francis	Sussex Police
Barns Green		01/03	12/10	14/12	30/11	08/02	05/10	12/04
Burgess Hill	02/11		08/02	12/10	18/01	28/09	12/04	30/11
Midhurst	01/02	26/10		18/01	28/09	12/04	30/11	01/03
Newick	28/09	01/02	05/10		12/04	30/11	01/03	26/10
Norfolk Arms	15/03	05/10	14/12	07/12		01/03	26/10	01/02
Royal Sun Alliance	26/10	14/12	07/12	15/03	02/11		01/02	05/10
St Francis	18/01	07/12	15/03	02/11	08/02	12/10		14/12
Sussex Police	07/12	15/03	02/11	08/02	12/10	18/01	28/09	

Sussex 2 West

	Arun	Ditchling	Old Brightonians	Plumpton	Robertsbridge	Shoreham
Arun		28/09	18/01	26/10	01/03	30/11
Ditchling	14/12		26/10	01/03	30/11	12/10
Old Brightonians	12/10	08/02		30/11	14/12	01/03
Plumpton	08/02	02/11	15/03		12/10	14/12
Robertsbridge	02/11	15/03	28/09	18/01		08/02
Shoreham	15/03	18/01	02/11	28/09	26/10	

ALRESFORD RFC
Ground Address: Bighton Cricket Club, Bighton Hill, Bighton, Nr Alesford, Hampshire Tel: 01962 733169
Web Address: www.alresford.rufc.org
Brief Directions: On entering Bighton from the A31,turn left after Three Horseshoes public house. Ground is on the right.
Hon Secretary: Chris Day, 3 The Spinney, Wood Lane, Bramdean, Hants SO24 9EU Tel: (H) 01962 793106 Tel: (M) 07721 564882 Tel: (W) 020 7357 4640
Fixtures Secretary: Robin Howard, 12 Manor Road South, Hinchley Wood, Surrey KT10 0UL
Tel: (H) 020 8398 1560 Tel: (M) 07946 221862
Club Colours: Gold, green and black
League: Hampshire 2

ALTON RFC
Ground Address: Anstey Park, Anstey Road, Alton, Hants GU34 2RL Tel: 01420 82076
Web Address: www.alton-rfc.com
Brief Directions: From A31 take A339 towards Alton Town. After approx half a mile ground on right.
Hon Secretary: Sian Mills, 12 Waterside Court, Alton, Hants GU34 2PQ Tel: (H) 01420 543241
Tel: (M) 07831 707377 Tel: (W) 01483 482216
Email: nicksianmills@aol.com
Fixtures Secretary: Martin Simpson, 10 Gauvain Close, Alton, Hants GU34 2SB Tel: (H) 01420 868 80
Email: martin.simpson@london-fire.gov.uk
Club Colours: Red & black irregular hoops
League: London 3 South West

ANDOVER RFC LTD
Ground Address: The Goodship Ground, Foxcotte Park, Charlton Down, Andover, Hants SP11 0TA
Tel: 01264 339 518
Web Address: www.andoverrfc.com
Brief Directions: From town centre take ring road to Portway Ind Estate, turn into Goch Way, right onto Hatherden Rd, follow road for 0.75 mile to roundabout, turn into Sports Centre
Hon Secretary: Charles Bacon, Vittoria Place, Penton Grafton, Andover, Hants SP11 0RR Tel: (H) 01264 772420 Tel: (M) 07802 463654 Tel: (W) 01793 655978
Email: charlesb@vplace.fsnet.co.uk
Fixtures Secretary: Rod Smith, 17 Longstock Close, Andover, Hampshire SP10 3UN Tel: (H) 01264 359491
Tel: (W) 01264 332299
Club Colours: Black. Change: Green
League: London 2 South

ARUN RUFC
Ground Address: The Littlehampton School, Hill Road, Littlehampton, West Sussex Tel : 01903 713944
Brief Directions: Off Horsham Road, Littlehampton
Club Secretary: S White, 66 Holmes Lane, Rustington, West Sussex. BN16 3PU
Tel : (H) 01903 774434
Fixtures Secretary: P Best Tel : (H) 01903 723969
Club Colours: Red, white and navy quarters
League: Sussex 3

ASHFORD RFC
Ground Address: Kinneys Field, Canterbury Road, Bybrook, Ashford, Kent TN24 9QQ Tel: 01233 624693
Email Address: jennyarfc@aol.com
Web Address: www.ashfordrugby.com
Brief Directions: M20 Junction 9 follow signs for Canterbury. Turn right just after the Post House. Southern Water sign at entrance.
Hon Secretary: Jenny Lake, 6 Wellesley Road, Ashford, Kent TN24 8EL Tel: (H) 01233 624795
Tel: (M) 07714 437943
Email: jennyarfc@aol.com
Fixtures Secretary: Simon Hall, 1 Patterson Cottage, Nr Ashford, Kent TN25 8BG Tel: (H) 01233 720174
Club Colours: Red, amber and black hoops
League: Kent 1

ASKEAN RFC
Ground Address: Ground share:Blackheath Rugby Club, Rectory Field, Charlton Road, London SE3
Tel: 020 8858 1578
Email Address: connon@supanet.com
Web Address: www.askeans.co.uk
Brief Directions: Multi sited club - contact Ian Lunn - fixture secretary for full details.
Train to Blackheath Station - Bus 54 or 75 to Charlton Road, entrance to Rectory Field.
Hon Secretary: Alison Gaze
Email: connon@supanet.com
Fixtures Secretary: Ian Lunn, 58 Longton Grove, London SE26 6QE Tel: (H) 020 8778 4823
Email: ianlunn@hotmail.com
Club Colours: Blue, black, white
League: Kent 1

AYLESFORD RFC
Ground Address: Ferry Field Ground, Hall Road, Aylesford, Kent ME20 7DS Tel: 01622 790380
Email Address: aylesfordrfc@yahoo.co.uk
Web Address: www.aylesfordruby.co.uk
Brief Directions: Leave M20 at J5. Head westwards on A20. Turn R. at the second set of traffic lights (Hall Road). Turn R. into Ground after motorway bridge.
Hon Secretary: Mike Parker, 'Parkdale', Leeds Road, Maidstone, Kent ME17 3JG Tel: (H) 01622 861405 Tel: (M) 07970 483011
Email: michaelparker@btinternet.com
Fixtures Secretary: David Bracewell, 1 Hillside Cottages, Malling Road, Maidstone, Kent ME18 5AN
Tel: (H) 01622 813772
Club Colours: Red and navy hoops, thin silver/grey line between
League: Kent 1

BANCROFT RFC
Ground Address: Buckhurst Way, Buckhurst Hill, Essex IG9 6JD Tel: 020 8504 0429
Email Address: admin@bancroft-rfc.fsnet.co.uk
Web Address: www.bancroftrfc.co.uk
Brief Directions: Mid way between Woodford and Buckhurst Hill Stations. Adjacent Roding Valley Central Line Station.
Hon Secretary: Stephen Thirsk, 4 Bentley Way, Essex IG8 0SE Tel: (H) 020 8504 1468
Tel: (M) 07968 945541 Tel: (W) 020 8559 7640
Email: stephen.thirsk@whiskers.co.uk
Fixtures Secretary: David Patterson
Tel: (M) 07968 817308
Club Colours: Blue, black, claret, light blue hoops
League: East Counties 2 South

BANK OF ENGLAND RFC
Ground Address: Bank of England Sports Centre, Priory Lane, Roehampton, London SW15 5JQ
Tel: 020 8876 8417
Brief Directions: Turn off A205 South Circular Road into Priory Lane (along side Rosslyn Park). Turn right into Bank Lane after .25 mile entrance on right.
Hon Secretary: M. Anderson, 4 Charles Street, London SW13 0NZ Tel: (H) 020 8878 1341
Club Colours: Old gold, blue & white
League: London 2 North

BARNES RFC
Ground Address: 53 Stanhope Gardens, Kensington, London SW7 5RF Tel: 020 7373 0120
Email Address: Barnes.RFC@ntlworld.com
Web Address: www.barnesrfc.org
Brief Directions: From Hammersmith and Kensington cross Hammersmith Bridge, proceed down Castlenau three-quarters mile, left into Queen Elizabeth Walk at Red Lion Pub. Clubhouse 50 yards on left. Ground and changing rooms half mile at end of road. Large car park available for coaches and cars.
Hon Secretary: Paul Kirby, 53 Stanhope Gardens, London SW7 5RF Tel: (H) 020 7373 0120
Tel: (M) 07860 365 544 Tel: (W) 020 7602 5678
Email: Barnes.RFC@ntlworld.com
Fixtures Secretary: Christy Pickering, Cornermead, 21 Downs Avenue, Epsom, Surrey KT18 5HQ
Tel: (H) 01372 749523 Tel: (M) 07798 602900
Email: barnesrfc@zoom.co.uk
Club Colours: Green/Gold
League: London 3 South West

BARNET SARACENS ELIZABETHANS RFC
Ground Address: Byng Road, Barnet, Herts EN5 4NP
Tel: 020 8449 0040 Web Address: www.barnetrfc.com
Brief Directions: From M25 (Jct 23) on A1081 to Barnet. At pedestrian crossing, right into Alston Rd., through restriction, third right (Wentworth Road, then left (Byng Road), ground at end.
Hon Secretary: Peter Yates, Woodlands, 19 Homefield Road, Ware, Herts SG12 7NG Tel: (H) 01920 484382
Tel: (M) 07887 708 388 Tel: (W) 01992 503 304
Fixtures Secretary: Peter Glenister, 47 Bury Lane, Hitchin, Herts SG4 8XX Tel: (H) 01438 820 692
Club Colours: Dark blue with maroon hoops
League: London 3 North West

BARNS GREEN RFC
Ground Address: Christ's Hospital School, Horsham, West Sussex.
Club Secretary: Miss Sue Blanchard, 42 Finians Field,Barns Green, West Sussex. RH13 7PW.
Tel:(H) 01403 731652
Fixtures Secretary: Mr P A Bailey,
Tel: (H) 01403 730058 (W)020 8667 5504
Club Colours: Gold & green quarters.
League: Sussex 2 West

BASILDON RFC
Ground Address: Gardiners Close, Basildon, Essex. SS14 3AW Tel: 01268 533136
Website: www.basildonrfc.com
Brief Directions: Frm wst: A127 London/S'thend arterial rd, past 1st signs for B'don, rt A132, rt at 2nd r'bout A1235, rt at 1st lights (not Zebra) Gardiners Lane south is first left-ground at end.
Club Secretary: Errol Knott, 25 The Knares, Basildon, Essex SS16 5SB Tel: 01268 543911
Email: eknott@btinternet.com
League Contact: Scott Liebenberg, 72 Beridge Road, Halstead, Essex CO9 1LB. Tel: 01787 477806
Email: basrugby@aol.com
Fixtures Secretary: Gary Clinton, 39 Luncies Road, Basildon, Essex SS14 1SG Tel: 01268 472257
Club Colours: Bottle green & white stripes, green shorts, green & white socks
League: London 3 North East

BATTERSEA IRONSIDES RFC
Ground Address: Openview, London SW17
Hon Secretary: Paul Tanner, 1 Woodland Way, Morden, Surrey SM4 4DS Tel: (H) 020 8540 5784
Club Colours: Green jerseys with white band, white shorts, red socks
League: Surrey 1

BEC OLD BOYS RFC
Ground Address: Sutton Manor Sports & Social Club, Northey Avenue, Cheam SM2 7HJ. Tel: 020 8642 3423
Brief Directions: Right off of A217 into Northey Avenue
Hon Secretary: Andy Rolt, 20 Lime Court, Lewis Road, Mitcham CR4 3LS Tel: (M) 07903 188721
Club Colours: Green jerseys with white band, white shorts, red socks
League: Surrey 3

BECCEHAMIAN RFC
Ground Address: Sparrows Den, Corkscrew Hill, West Wickham, Kent Tel: 020 8777 8105
Brief Directions: Corner of Corkscrew Hill and Addington Road (A2022)
Hon Secretary: S. Corcoran, c/o Goodwill & Corcoran, Shaftesbury House, Bromley, Kent BR1 2RL Tel: (H) 020 8466 6730 Tel: (W) 0208-4669111
Email: simon@gandc.net

Fixtures Secretary: C. Putner Tel: (H) 020 8777 6307
Club Colours: Maroon, black and silver hoops
League: London 4 South East

BECCLES RUFC
Ground Address: Beef Meadow, Common Lane, Beccles, Suffolk Tel: 01502 712016
Web Address: www.beclesrugbyclub.co.uk
Brief Directions: Into Beccles from Safeway roundabout, over mini roundabout, follow road left over railway crossing 1st left is Common Lane
Hon Secretary: Kerry Smy, 38 School Road, Beccles, Suffolk NR34 8NZ
Tel: (M) 077881 488779 Tel: (W) 01986 893137
Fixtures Secretary: Simon Clarke, 16 Grove Road, Beccles, Suffolk Tel: (H) 01502 710121
Email: fix.sec@becclesrugbyclub.co.uk
Club Colours: Black and emerald quarters
League: London 4 North East

BECKENHAM RFC
Ground Address: Balmoral Avenue, Elmers End, Beckenham, Kent BR3 3RD Tel: 020 8650 7176
Brief Directions: Entrance in Balmoral Ave which runs between Eden Park Ave & Upper Elmers End Rd (A214). From bottom of Beckenham High St take Croydon Rd (A222), left into Eden Park Avenue
Fixtures Secretary: J. M. Arger, 15 Thatcher Road, Staplehurst, Kent TN12 0ND Tel: (H) 01580 891550
Club Colours: Royal Blue & Old Gold
League: London 2 South

BELSIZE PARK RFC
Ground Address: Club House, The Chester Arms, 87 Albany Street, London NW1 4BT Tel: 020 7681 6017
Email Address: roche-chesters@onmail.co.uk
Web Address: www.belsizerugby.com
Hon Secretary: Brian East, 64 Station Road, Harpenden, Hertfordshire AL5 4TL
Tel: (H) 01582 762209
Email: the.easts@ntlworld.com
Fixtures Secretary: John Roche, The Chester Arms, 87 Albany Street, London NW1 4BT Tel: (H) 020 7681 6017 Tel: (W) 020 7681 6017
Club Colours: Black & Lavender
League: Herts/Middlesex 3 South

BETTESHANGER RFC
Ground Address: The Welfare Ground, Cavell Square, Deal, Kent CT14 9HR Tel: 01304 372080
Brief Directions: Dover - Deal road A258. Left at Q8 Garage. Continue approx I mile. Right down Mill Hill, 1st left Redsull Avenue, 2nd left, Douglas Road, next left - Sports Gound
Hon Secretary: Cliff Davies, 46 Mongehan Road, Deal, Kent CT14 9HR Tel: (H) 01304 379088
Email: cliff-davies@hotmail.com
Fixtures Secretary: Bob Sykes, 232 Reculver Road, Herne Bay, Kent CT6 6QB Tel: (H) 01227 374246
Club Colours: Red and white hoops, blue shorts
League: London 3 South East

BEXLEY RFC
Ground Address: Bexley Hospital Social Club Ground, Bexley Park, Old Bexley Lane, Bexley, Kent DA5 2BW
Email Address: info@bexleyrfc.co.uk
Web Address: www.bexleyrfc.co.uk
Hon Secretary: Peter Butler, 194 Claremont Road, Hextable, Kent BR8 7QU Tel: (H) 01322 664389
Fixtures Secretary: Paul Herbert, 68 Palmeira Road, Bexleyheath, Kent DA7 4UX Tel: (H) 020 8303 3035
Tel: (M) 07786 115874 Tel: (W) 020 8694 3255
Email: herbert.paul@ntlworld.com
Club Colours: Royal blue & white hoops, blue shorts
League: Kent 2

BILLERICAY RFC
Ground Address: Willowbrook Sports & Social Club, Stock Road, Billericay, Essex Tel: 01277 841442
Email Address: jarv.10@virgin.net
Hon Secretary: Dawn Jones, 1 Broadwater Green, Laindon West, Basildon, Essex SS15 6BG
Tel: (H) 01268 442167 Tel: (W) 01708 794033
Email: jarv.10@virgin.net
Fixtures Secretary: Juan Nel Tel: (H) 01277 630905
Tel: (M) 07884 476124
Email: nel_juan@hotmail.com
Club Colours: Black with gold band, black shorts, black and gold socks
League: East Counties 1

BISHOPS STORTFORD RFC
Ground Address: Silver Leys, Hadham Road, Bishop's Stortford, Herts CM23 2QE Tel: 01279 652092
Web Address: www.bsrfc.co.uk
Brief Directions: From North/South use M11 Junction 8 and A120. From East/West use A120 to the Tesco Roundabout. At Roundabout head towards Town Centre on Hadham Road. Club and Ground 400 yards on the left. Alternatively see the map on the website.
Hon Secretary: Jim Smith, 16 Millcroft, Bishop's Stortford CM23 2BP Tel: (H) 01279 831667
Tel: (W) 01279 836058
Email: jim.smith5@ntlworld.com
Hon Fixtures: Terry Ellis Tel: (H) 01279 461186
Email: the@stort7.fsnet.co.uk
Club Colours: Royal Blue and White Hoops
League: London 2 North

BOGNOR RFC
Ground Address: The Clubhouse, Hampshire Avenue, Bognor Regis, West Sussex. PO21 5JY.
Tel: 01243 824000
Brief Directions: Head west on A259 from the centre of Bognor. Turn left into Hampshire Avenue (marker for club on lamp post). Take 1st turn on left.
Club Secretary: John Donoghue, 62 Victoria Drive, Bognor Regis PO21 2TG.
Tel: 01243 823287 (H) 07971 052857 (M)
Fixtures Secretary: Ian Misselbrook.
Tel: 01243 866354.
Club Colours: Purple, emerald and silver hoops
League: London 4 South East

BRAINTREE RFC
Ground Address: The Clubhouse, Robbswood, Beckers Green Road, Braintree, Essex
Tel: 01376 322282
Email Address: corinneaw@aol.com
Web Address: www.braintreerugbyclub.co.uk
Brief Directions: From Braintree bypass A120 exit at Galleys Corner roundabout to Braintree East (B1018 Cressing Road), 300 metres turn right into Beckers Green Road, Ground at end of road.
Hon Secretary: Adrian Hanson, 'La Cachette', 28 Bridport Way, Braintree, Essex CM7 9FJ
Tel: (H) 01376 328545 Email: hertsref@aol.com
Fixtures Secretary: Chris Copsey, 1 Chelsea Mews, Braintree, Essex Tel: (H) 01376 348 219
Email: chris.bri@ukgateway.net
Club Colours: Black & amber quarters
League: London 4 North East

BRENTWOOD RFC
Ground Address: King Georges Playing Fields, Ingrave Road, Brentwood, Essex CM13 2AQ
Tel: 01277 210267
Brief Directions: M25 Jct28.Follow A1023 towards Brentwood town centre along High street to double mini roundabout. Rt. into Ingrave Road ground .75 mile on right opposite `Masons Restaurtant'.
Hon Secretary: Peter McMullan, Turnstile House, 25 Hutton Village, Brentwood, Essex CM13 1RT
Tel: (H) 01277 200 420
Email: petermcmullan@ukgateway.net
Fixtures Secretary: Nick Priddle, Foxhurst, Loxes Farm Road, Billericay, Essex CM11 2UA
Tel: (H) 01277 656685
Club Colours: Claret, grey & white hoops, black shorts
League: London 3 North East

BRIGHTLINGSEA RFC
Ground Address: Colne Community School, Church Road, Brightlingsea, Essex Tel: 01206 302432
Email Address: www.brfcuk.com
Brief Directions: Colne School is on the main road as you enter the town
Hon Secretary: Roger Kemble, 8 Duke Street, Brightlingsea, Essex CO7 0EA Tel: (H) 01206 302432
Tel: (M) 07720 846 299
Email: rogerkemble@fetchmail.co.uk
Fixtures Secretary: I. Polley, 9 Bellfield Avenue, Brightlingsea, Essex CO7 0NT Tel: (H) 01206 303549
Email: rogerkemble@fetchmail.co.uk
Club Colours: Red, black shorts
League: East Counties 3 North

BRIGHTON RFC
Ground Address: Waterhall Playing Fields, Mill Road, Patcham, Brighton, E. Sussex BN1 8YN
Tel: 01273 562729
Brief Directions: From London A23 to Patcham roundabout, round roundabout, turn into Mill Rd, underneath Railway arch, 1st right, 1st left, straight up to clubhouse
Hon Secretary: Cheryl Vivian, 32 Princep Road, Hove, E. Sussex BN3 7AD Tel: (H) 01273 720458
Email: cheryl.vivian@csfb.com
Fixtures Secretary: R. Greenwood, 11 Lyminster Ave., Brighton, Sussex BN1 8JL Tel: (H) 01273 502898
Club Colours: Blue shirts, shorts, red socks
League: London 3 South East

BRITISH AIRWAYS RFC
Ground Address: Concorde Centre, Crane Lodge Road, High Street, Cranford, Middx TW5 9RQ
Tel: 020 8562 0291
Brief Directions: Take M4, Jct 3 follow A312 to Feltham. At 1st lights turn left, then left at lst mini R'about. Clubhouse is right at 2nd mini R'about
Hon Secretary: Andy Lord, 'Oxford Villas', 143 High Street, Teddington, Middlesex TW11 8HH
Tel: (H) 020 8977 4815 Tel: (M) 07770 574754
Tel: (W) 0161 489 2624
Email: andylord@ukgateway.net
Fixtures Secretary: Peter Attard, 460 Redford Close, Feltham, Middx TW13 4TP Tel: (H) 020 8384 8489
Tel: (M) 07956 511460
Email: p_attard@hotmail.com
Club Colours: Red, white and blue quarters
League: Herts/Middlesex 4 South

BROADLAND RFC
Ground Address: Cobham Playing Field, Cobham, Great Yarmouth, Norfolk Tel: 01493 445692
Brief Directions: From Norwich A47. 1st R/about take 3rd exit over bridge. 400 yards on right.
Hon Secretary: Susan Watson, 44a Southtown Road, Gt. Yarmouth, NR31 0DT
Tel: (H) 01493 733698 Tel: (W) 01493 657052
Fixtures Secretary: D. Todd Tel: (H) 01502 512671
Club Colours: Red, white and blue hoops
League: East Counties 3 North

BROCKENHURST COLLEGE RFC
Ground Address: Brockenhurst College, Lyndhurst Road, Brockenhurst, Hants Tel: 01590 625555
Brief Directions: M27 J.1 signs to Brockenhurst turn L. just prior to Rose & Crown Pub. Ground on Left.
Club Secretary: Mark Bloodworth, Brockenhurst College, Lyndhurst Road, Hants SO41 0FG.
Tel: 01590 625555 Ext. 314
Club Colours: Black & white
League: Hampshire 3

BROCKLEIANS RFC
Ground Address: Eltham Palace Road, Eltham, London SE9 5LX Tel: 020 8850 8650
Email Address: wout.daenen@brockleians.co.uk
Web Address: www.brockleians.co.uk
Brief Directions: A20 to junction with South Circular, turn into Eltham Palace Road at World of Leather.
Hon Secretary: Paul Parish, 38 Cobham Road, London SE25 5NX Tel: (H) 020 8656 0790
Email: paul.parish@skillbase.net
Club Colours: Chocolate, emerald and old gold
League: Kent 1

LONDON & SOUTH EAST

BROMLEY RFC
Ground Address: Warman Trust Ground, Barnet Wood Road, Hayes, Bromley, Kent
Tel: 020 8462 3430 Website: bromleyrfc.org
Brief Directions: M25 J.4 & A21 towards Bromley. At Locksbottom filter left at lights on A232. .5 mile to next lights then right & 1st left to Barnet Wood road.
Hon Secretary: Stephen Wardingley, Fourways, 108 West Common Road, Hayes, Kent BR2 7BY
Tel: (H) 020 8325 6276 Tel: (M) 07710 582327
Email: stephen.wardingley@halliburton.com
Fixtures Secretary: Roger Simpson, 24 Lakeside, WIckham Road, Bromley, Kent BR3 6LX
Tel: (H) 020 8402 5123 Tel: (M) 07885 966372
Email: rogero@18shortlands.fsnet.co.uk
Club Colours: Black/amber, black
League: London 4 South East

BURGESS HILL RFC
Ground Address: Poveys Close, Burgess Hill, West Sussex RH15 0BW Tel: 01444 232221
All mail to be addressed to the Secretary's address - not the ground address
Website: www.bhrfc@freeserve.co.uk
Brief Directions: Royal George Road turn into Southway at Weald public house right into Poveys Close - ground at end.
Club Secretary: Mike Bushell, 4 Kirdford Close, Burgess Hill, West Sussex. RH15 0BW
Tel: (H) 01444 246795
Email: mj@bushell75.freeserve.co.uk
Fixtures Secretary: Tony Balsdon, 102 Marlborough Drive, Burgess Hill, West Sussex. RH15 0EU
Tel: (H) 01444 246170 (W) 01273 273234
Email: gillandtony@tesco.net
Club Colours: All black
League: Sussex 2 East

BURNHAM-ON-CROUCH RUFC
Ground Address: Dengie Hundred Sports Centre, Millfields, Station Road, Burnham On Crouch, Essex CM0 8HS Tel: 01621 784633
Email Address: Info@brufc.org.uk
Web Address: www.brufc.org.uk
Brief Directions: From all main routes continue east (north of River Crouch), pick up B1010 into B-o-Crouch, right at T jctn, over rail bridge into town centre, library on right entrance to ground immediate right
Hon Secretary: Simon Bouch, 13 Willow Close, Burnham-on-Crouch, Essex CM0 8DJ
Tel: (H) 01621 786683 Tel: (M) 07808 255500
Tel: (W) 01206 202308
Email: dinny@bluecarrots.com
Fixtures Secretary: Warwick Bridge, 12 Glendale Road, Burnham On Crouch, Essex CM0 8LY
Tel: (H) 01621 783 807
Email: whbridge@hotmail.com
Club Colours: Navy blue
League: East Counties 2 South

BURY ST. EDMUNDS RUFC
Ground Address: The Haberden, Southgate Green, Bury St. Edmunds, Suffolk IP33 2BL
Tel: 01284 753920
Email Address: enquiries@bserfc.freeserve.co.uk
Web Address: www.bserfc.freeserve.co.uk
Brief Directions: Leave A14 on A134 (B.S.E. East & Sudbury), ground is 400 yards on right, next to BP Petrol Station
Hon Secretary: Roger Pierson
Email: roger.jan.pierson@tinyworld.co.uk
Fixtures Secretary: S. Lord, Ashtrees, 32 Bury Road, Barrow IP29 5AB
Tel: (H) 01284 811189 Tel: (W) 01245 490886
Club Colours: Green and gold bands
League: London 3 North East

CAMBRIDGE RFC
Ground Address: Tel: 01223 312437
Web Address: www.crufc.co.uk
Directions: M11, J12 (A603) to Cambridge. Take 1st right into Granchester Road (opp. Wolfson College). Ground 300 yds on right, just past the last house.
Hon Secretary: David J. Martin, 45 York Street, Cambridge, Cambs CB1 2PZ
Tel: (H) 01223 314705 Tel: (W) 01223 314705
Fixtures Secretary: A. Dockerill, 10 Church Leys, Huntingdon, Cambs PE26 9QD
Tel: (H) 01480 468317 Email: alan.dockerill@virgin.net
Club Colours: Blood and sand
League: London 2 North

CAMPION RFC
Ground Address: Cottons Park, Cottons Approach, Romford, Essex RM7 7AA Tel: 01708 753209
Brief Directions: Frm W. exit A12 at lights after Moby Dick pub, rt -Mawney Rd, before T jnct rt -Marks Rd, ground 1st left. Frm E., A12 thro' 3 lights after Gallows Crnr, lt-Hawney Rd before T Jct. Rt. Marks Road
Hon Secretary: Peter O'Brien, 68 Lancaster Drive, Hornchurch, Essex RM12 5ST Tel: (H) 01708 446680
Fixtures Secretary: M Chapman, 37 Monkwood Close, Romford, Essex RM1 2NQ Tel: (H) 01708 727683
Email: mattewchapman@ubs.com
Club Colours: Red and black hoops
League: London 4 North East

CANTABRIGIAN RFC
Ground Address: Sedley Taylor Road, Cambridge
Tel: 01223 516061
Brief Directions: Leave M11 exit 11(A1309) to Cambridge. Right at 2nd traffic lioghts into Long Rd.,. Left after railway bridge into Sedley Taylor Rd.Ground down narrow entrance immediately on left.
Hon Secretary: Robin Ladds, 4 Flamsteed Road, Cambridge CB1 3QU Tel: (H) 01223 249008
Tel: (W) 01223 555398 Email: ladds.r@ucles.org.uk
Fixtures Secretary: J.. Edmonds, 25 Granta Terrace, Great Shelford, Cambs CA2 5DJ
Tel: (H) 01223 563256 Tel: (W) 01223 506606
Club Colours: Navy blue and white hoops
League: East Counties 2 North

CANVEY ISLAND RFC
Ground Address: Tewkes Creek, Dovervelt Road, Canvey Island, Essex Tel: 01268 681881
Brief Directions: A130 to Sports Centre (Waterside Farm) Keep complex on right and Castle View School on left. Take 1st left after school. Ground 300yds on left
Hon Secretary: Stephen Clarke, 26 Thelma Avenue, Canvey Island, Essex SS8 9DT Tel: (H) 01268 699858 Tel: (M) 07775 703445 Tel: (W) 020 8858 6910
Email: steveclarke_@hotmail.com
Fixtures Secretary: Michael Smith, 6 Elsinir Avenue, Canvey Island, Essex Tel: (H) 01268 690756
Tel: (M) 07775 506717
Club Colours: Red and blue
League: East Counties 1

CHARLTON PARK RFC
Ground Address: 60A Broad Walk, Blackheath, London SE3 8NB Tel: 020 8856 1025
Email Address: doug@cprfc.fsnet.co.uk
Web Address: www.charltonpark.org.uk
Brief Directions: A2 to Kidbrooke then followRochesrter Way eastbound for 250 yds. Broad Walk is on left. Entrance to club on right after 200 yds.
Hon Secretary: Andy Potts, 37 Beechill Road, London SE9 1HJ Tel: (H) 020 8859 8775
Tel: (W) 020 8303 5696
Fixtures Secretary: Murray Rowland, 23 Thaxted Road, London Tel: (H) 020 8859 6776
Tel: (M) 07410 172195 Tel: (W) 01399 049754
Email: murray.rowland@virginnet.co.uk
Club Colours: Red & White Hoops, blue shorts.
League: London 3 South East

CHELMSFORD RFC
Ground Address: Timsons lane, Springfield, Chelmsford, Essex CM2 6AF Tel: 01245 261159
Brief Directions: A12 - take Boreham/North Springfield turning, head for Chelmsford, over 1st roundabout, 2nd roundabout 3rd exit, over roundabout, 1st turning after Plough pub Timsons Lane
Hon Secretary: Lawrence Crispin, 33 Jenner Mead, Chelmer Village, Chelmsford, Essex CM2 6SJ
Tel: (H) 01245 465021 Email: lcrispin@talk21.com
Fixtures Secretary: Clare St. John Coleman, 139 Pollards Green, Chelmsford, CM2 6UX
Tel: (H) 01245 602239 Tel: (M) 07885 344367
Club Colours: Navy Blue shirts & shorrts
League: London 4 North East

CHESS VALLEY RFC
Ground Address: Rickmansworth Sports Club, Park Road, Rickmansworth, WD3 1HU Tel: 01923 445040
Web Address: www.chessvalleyrfc.co.uk
Brief Directions: M25 Jct 18 follow A404 to Rickmansworth. Club between town and Croxley Green and is signposted at bottom of Scots Bride Hill.
Hon Secretary: Graeme Coles, 3 Gordon Way, Chalfont St. Giles, Buckinghamshire Tel: (H) 01494874 655 Tel: (M) 07881 518796 Tel: (W) 01494 876312
Email: sarahgraemeboo@zoom.co.uk
Club Colours: Bottle green shirts with pink collars
League: Herts/Middlesex 2

CHICHESTER RFC
Ground Address: Oaklands Park, Wellington Road, Chichester, W. Sussex Tel: 01243 779820
Email Address: mbesteee@aol.com
Brief Directions: Oaklands Park is near The Festival Theatre in Broyle Road to the north of Chichester centre. (Chichester to Midhurst road)
Hon Secretary: Mike Best, 14 The Avenue, Chichester, West Sussex, PO19 4PU Tel: (H) 01243 779566
Tel: (W) 02392 682204
Email: mbesteee@aol.com
Fixtures Secretary: F. Corby, Caretakers Cottage, School Lane, Selsey, W. Sussex PO20 9EH
Tel: (H) 01243 602354
Club Colours: Dark blue and light blue hoops
League: London 4 South East

CHINEHAM RFC
Ground Address: Old Basing Recreation Ground, Old Basing, Basingstoke, Hampshire
Email Address: chinehamrfc@lycos.co.uk
Web Address: www.chineham.rugbyclub.org.uk
Brief Directions: Directions to Old Basing Recreation ground Take the A30 out of Basingstoke towards Hook/London. After about 1 mile you will see an Esso garage & Oliver's Chip shop on your left- Turn Left into Byfleet Avenue at the lights. Carry on down the road and over the lights into Milkingpen Lane go straight over every junction and under the Railway Bridge. When you reach the next junction, turn right. The recreation is on the right, just after the Bolton Arms.
Hon Secretary: Dave Andrews - as above
Fixtures Secretary: Dave Andrews, 8 Fountains CLose, Basingstoke, RG24 9EZ Tel: (H) 01256 841662
Tel: (M) 07971 161093
Club Colours: Amber Shirt with Black Hoops
League: Hampshire 3

CHINGFORD RFC
Ground Address: Lea Valley Playing Fields, Waltham Way, Chingford, London E4 8AQ Tel: 020 8529 4879
Brief Directions: M11 to A406 westbound, approx 3 miles to Cook's ferry junction.Then A1009 over mini roundabout. Ground 1 mile on left.
Hon Secretary: Peter Wilton, 39 College Gardens, London E4 7LN Tel: (H) 07713 412761
Fixtures Secretary: David Butler, c/o Chingford RFC
Tel: (H) 020 8529 4879
Club Colours: Black with royal blue & white hoops
League: London 3 North East

CHIPSTEAD RFC
Ground Address: The Meads, High Road, Chipstead, Surrey Tel: 01737 553035
Brief Directions: Opposite The white Hart pub. Entrance to the ground is between the White Hart and the pond.
Hon Secretary: Phil Gibson, 23 The Chase, Coulsdon, Surrey CR5 2EJ Tel: (H) 020 8770 3637

Club Colours: Blue and Gold jerseys
League: Surrey 3

CHISWICK RFC

Ground Address: The Boat House, Riverside Lands, Chiswick, London W4. Tel: 020 8994 6956
Brief Directions: From London A316 to Richmond. Turn left immediately before Chiswick Bridge, follow river to The Boat House.
Hon Secretary: David Samuel, 39 Weavers Close, Ilseworth, Middlesex TW7 6ET Tel: (H) 020 8569 8691
Club Colours: Maroon and blue
League: Herts/Middlesex 1

CHOBHAM RFC

Ground Address: Fowlers Wells, Windsor Road, Chobham, Woking, Surrey GU24 8NA
Tel: 01276 858616
Email Address: chobhamrfc@lineone.net
Web Address: www.chobham-rugby.co.uk
Brief Directions: 1. From M25 At Junction 11 (Woking, Chertsey) take A320 to Woking and at next roundabout take 1st exit, A320 to Woking. At next roundabout ("The Otter" Harvester Restaurant) take 3rd exit, A319 to Chobham and go along this road for about 3.5 miles, passing Fairoaks Airport on the left, until T-junction in Chobham.Turn right into Windsor Road (B383). Take the first right after about 0.2 mile, opposite a swimming pool supplies shop and the entrance to the club is on the right after about 100 metres. 2. From M3 At Junction 3 take A322 to Woking, Lightwater and Guildford. At next roundabout take 1st exit, A319, passing Gordons School on the right and go along this road for about 2.5 miles until mini-roundabout in Chobham. Turn left (A319, B383) into High Street/Windsor Road. Turn right after about 0.5 mile, opposite a swimming pool supplies shop and the entrance to the club is on the right after about 100 metres.
Hon Secretary: Nigel Heslop, 98 Broad Street, Guildford, Surrey GU3 3BE Tel: (H) 01483 535840
Tel: (M) 07787 523878 Tel: (W) 01483 850345
Email: nigel@heslop6.demon.co.uk
Fixtures Secretary: Andy Harris, 6 BLoomfield, Knaphill, Woking GU21 2BL Tel: (H) 01483 480895
Colours: Blue with red & gold hoops, green shoulders
League: London 3 South West

CIVIL SERVICE FC

Ground Address: Civil Service Sports Club, Dukes Meadows, London W4 Tel: 020 8994 1202
Email Address: info@civilservicerugby.co.uk
Web Address: www.civilservicerugby.co.uk
Brief Directions: Directions: By road: coming from the West, Staveley Gardens leads into Riverside Drive, on the right off the A316 Chertsey Road before it meets the A4 at Hogarth Roundabout; coming from Central London or the East, take A316 Exit off A4 at Hogarth Roundabout, Staveley Gardens is on the left. By rail: nearest station is Barnes Bridge - NOT Barnes - cross the Thames by the railway bridge.
Hon Secretary: Nick Alway, 20 Herndon Road, London SW18 2DG Tel: (H) 020 8870 6818 Tel: (M) 07831 142666 Tel: (W) 020 7 242 2022
Email: nickalwaysrugby@hotmail.com
Hon Fixtures: B. Dougherty, 34 Belmont Road, Sutton, Surrey SM2 6DW Tel: (H) 020 8296 8722
Tel: (M) 0771 3329874
Leagues Contact: Mike Lee, New Place, 43 Onslow Road, Walton-on-Thames, Surrey
Tel: (H) 01932 228771 Tel: (M) 07768 026472
Tel: (W) 01932 840440
Fixtures Secretary: Ralph Hulme, 4 Beech Way, Blackmore End, Wheathamstead, Herts AL4 8LY
Tel: (H) 01438 832054
Club Colours: White
League: London 4 North West

COLCHESTER RFC

Ground Address: Mill Road, Mile End, Colchester, Essex CO4 5JF Tel: 01206 851610
Email Address: colchester.rfc@ntlworld.com
Web Address: www.colchester-rugby.co.uk
Brief Directions: Turn off A12 onto A1232, right at roundabout into business park, right at next roundabout, straight over next roundabout into Mill Road, ground is 400yds on right
Hon Secretary: Bill Anslow, 22 Fairways, Colchester, Essex CO4 5TX Tel: (H) 01206 841994
Tel: (W) 01206 841994 Email: bill@greyowlgolf.com
Fixtures Secretary: Jon Roberts, 5 Spencers Close, Maldon CM9 6BX Tel: (H) 01621 854043
Club Colours: All Black
League: East Counties 1

CRANBROOK RFC

Ground Address: Tomlin Ground, Angley Road, Cranbrook, Kent TN17 3LB Tel: 01580 712777
Brief Directions: Off A229 Hastings road, 14 miles south of Maidstone, 4 miles north of Hawkhurst at junction of Cranbrook bypass with Whitewell Lane
Hon Secretary: Nick Reed, 6 Northridge, Northian, E. Sussex TN31 6PG Tel: (H) 01797 252374
Fixtures Secretary: Simon Haydon, 1 Church Cottages, Beckley, E. Sussex Tel: (H) 01797 260345
Club Colours: Magenta and white
League: Kent 1

CRANLEIGH RFC

Ground Address: Wildwood Lane, Cranleigh, Surrey GU6 8JR Tel: 01483 275843
Web Address: cranleighrfc.co.uk
Brief Directions: From Guildford take A281 towards Horsham, after 9.5 miles, before Alford crossroads, turn left at Wildwood Lane (signed Cranleigh RFC) 400 yards.
Hon Secretary: Kevin Maxted, 16 Taylors Crescent, Cranleigh, Surrey GU6 7EL Tel: (H) 01483 278551
Tel: (W) 01483 278551
Email: kevin.maxted@royalmail.co.uk
Club Colours: Red and blue quarters, red socks
League: London 4 South West

CRAWLEY RFC
Ground Address: The Clubhouse, Willoughby Fields, Ilford Avenue, Crawley RH11 7LX Tel: 01293 533995
Email Address: pschap@tesco.net
Web Address: www.crawleyrugbyclub.co.uk
Brief Directions: Off A23 Crawley bypass from north take M23 J10 onto A23 bypass, 1.5 miles pass Sainsburys, right at next roundabout into Ifield Ave towards Charlwood, ground approx 0.75 mile on right
Hon Secretary: Paul Chapman, 19 Longwood View, Crawley RH10 6PB Tel: (H) 01293 446961
Tel: (M) 0403 218761 Tel: (W) 01273 493557
Email: pschap@tesco.net
Fixtures Secretary: Monz (John) Monahgan, 40 Oak Way, Crawley, W.Sussex RH10 8UH Tel: (H) 01293 430550 Tel: (M) 07980 392550
Email: monz@eurobell.co.uk
Club Colours: Maroon and blue hoops
League: London 4 South East

CROWBOROUGH RFC
Ground Address: Steel Cross, Crowborough, E. Sussex Tel: 01892 654832
Email Address: gavin.tyler@dial.pipex.com
Brief Directions: South on A26 from Tunbridge Wells, Club signposted at roundabout after village of Boarshead
Hon Secretary: Gavin Tyler, Hornbeam Lodge, Harlequin Lane, Crowborough TN6 1HT
Tel: (H) 01892 665153 Tel: (M) 07971 149323
Tel: (W) 01892 506155
Email: gavin.tyler@dial.pipex.com
Fixtures Secretary: Paul Astill, c/o Club Address
Club Colours: Red with graduated white hoops, blue shorts
League: Sussex 1

CROYDON RFC
Ground Address: Latham Road, Keyton, Bromley, Kent Tel: 01959 573409
Email Address: www.croydonrfc.org
Web Address: ttrevdavies@aol.com
Brief Directions: A2022 to Addington Village, at r'bout 200yds beyond Gravel Hill, fork south to New Addington as signed up Lodge Ln, left at next r'bout into King Henry's Drive, left at end into Latham Rd
Hon Secretary: Trevor Davies, Woodside, 51a Chaldon Common Road, Caterham, Surrey CR3 5DH
Tel: (H) 01883 345288 Email: ttrevordavies@aol.com
Fixtures Secretary: Alan Doe, 16 Cherry Hill Garden, Croydon, Surrey CR3 5DH Tel: (H) 020 8681 0793
Tel: (W) 020 8668 3661 x 6138
Club Colours: Black, magenta & white hoops
League: Surrey 3

CRUSADERS RFC
Ground Address: Beckhythe, Litlle Melton, Nr. Hethersett, Norwich, Norfolk Tel: 01603 811157
Brief Directions: Situated in Little Melton, S.E. of Norwich. From southern bypass take Watton Rd (B1108), turn left past the garden centre, thro' village, pass village inn, next left, 1st right, club 400yds right
Hon Secretary: Steven Dack, 7 Willis Street, Norwich, Norfolk NR3 1SW Tel: (H) 01603 613785
Tel: (M) 07786 031857 Tel: (W) 01603 612311
Email: stevedack@yahoo.co.uk
Fixtures Secretary: Michael Bridgman Tel: (H) 01603 250926
Club Colours: Gold and emerald green hoops
League: East Counties 2 North

CUFFLEY RFC
Ground Address: Cheshunt School, College Road, Cheshunt, Herts EN8 9LY
Brief Directions: Approx. 2 miles North of Junction 25 of M25 on the A10. Turn left at first lights into College Road. School 100 yds on the left opposite Crocodile PH.
Hon Secretary: Chris Palmer, 10 Connaught Road, Harpenden, Herts AL5 4TW Tel: (H) 01582 768152
Tel: (W) 020 7911 2142
Fixtures Secretary: P. Cushing, 10 Lilac Drive, Lutterworth, Leics LE17 4FP Tel: (H) 01455 557658
Club Colours: Red with Black/Red band
League: Herts/Middlesex 3 North

DAGENHAM RUFC
Ground Address: The Pavillion, Central Park, Rainham Road North, Dagenham, Essex RM11 2GT
Tel: 020 8593 8202
Email Address: drufc@yahoo.co.uk
Web Address:
www.geocities.com/mjrogers74/DRUFC.html
Brief Directions: From A13 turn into Ballards Rd, jctn of Princess Bowl/ McDonalds. On to Bull r'about take1st L. Pass Dagenham East R'stn. Over Eastbrook P.H. jctn. Ground 300yds jright thro' park gates
Hon Secretary: Ben Fowler, 4 The Limes, Hornchurch, Essex RM11 2GT Tel: (H) 01708 479249
Tel: (M) 07932 790561 Tel: (W) 020 7588 8085
Email: ben.fowler@ubsw.com
Fixtures Secretary: Marc Randall, 8 Cambeys Road, Dagenham, Essex RM10 8YA Tel: (H) 020 8592 6642
Tel: (M) 07769 942387 Tel: (W) 020 7977 4852
Email: marc@innovationinternational.co.uk
Club Colours: Red and white quarters
League: East Counties 2 South

DARENTH VALLEY RFC
Ground Address: Leigh City Tech, Green Street, Green Road, Dartford, Kent Tel: 07980 683415
Email Address: darenthvalley.rfc@btinternet.com
Brief Directions: No clubhouse. Club plays at Leigh City Tech and moves on to local pub afterwards, The Litten Tree Dartford. Changing/parking facilities at college where pitches are.
Hon Secretary: Ken Parr, 98 High Road, Dartford, Kent DA2 7DW Tel: (H) 01322 287716
Tel: (M) 07980 683415
Email: jaffaparr@btinternet.com
Fixtures Secretary: Pete Murray Snr, 21 Sundridge Hill, Cuxton Rochester, Kent ME2 1LH
Tel: (H) 01634 712289 Tel: (M) 07973 419278
Email: pete@murray76.freeserve.co.uk

Club Colours: Black shirts with white V and black shorts
League: Kent 3

DARTFORDIANS RFC
Ground Address: War Memorial Club House, Bourne Road, Bexley, Kent DA5 1LW Tel: 01322 524176
Web Address: www.dartfordians.co.uk
Hon Secretary: Jack Morris, 7 Irving Way, Swanley, Kent B8 7EP Tel: (H) 01322 669817
Email: jackmorris@supanet.com
Fixtures Secretary: D. Rapley Tel: (H) 020 8857 6198
Email: dave@drapley.freeserve.co.uk
Club Colours: Maroon and old gold.
League: London 3 South East

DATCHWORTH RFC
Ground Address: Datchworth Green, Datchworth, Herts SG3 6TL Tel: 01438 812490
Web Address: www.datch.com
Brief Directions: Leave A1(M) at J6 (Welwyn) on B197 north towards Stevenage, at Woolmer Green turn right towards Datchworth, pitches and clubhouse behind tennis courts
Hon Secretary: Diane Wyatt, 7 Hazeldell, Hertford SG14 3SL Tel: (H) 01920 830407
Tel: (M) 07779 660902 Email: dianew@datch.com
Fixtures Secretary: N. Bennett, 6 Brockwell Shott, Walkern, Herts SG2 7PJ Tel: (H) 01438 861153
Email: nigelb@datch.com
Club Colours: Navy blue, green and white.
League: Herts/Middlesex 2

DEAL WANDERERS RFC
Ground Address: Western Road, Deal, Kent
Tel: 01304 365892
Brief Directions: The ground is located at the junction of West Street and Western Avenue to the North West of the town centre
Hon Secretary: D. Hambrook, 106 Mongeham Road, Nr. Deal, Kent CT14 9LJ Tel: (H) 01304 381676
Tel: (W) 01304 380574
Fixtures Secretary: A. Bodman, 49 Telegraph Road, Deal, Kent Tel: (H) 01304 375750
Club Colours: Blue & Amber Hoops
League: Kent 3

DISS RFC
Ground Address: Bellrope Lane, Roydon, Diss, Norfolk
Tel: 01379 642891
Brief Directions: 1 mile west of Diss on A1066 through Roydon village, at end of 40mph limit turn into Bellrope Lane opposite White Hart pub, club 150 yards on left
Hon Secretary: N. Kingsley, c/o Newman & Co., 104 Victoria Road, Diss, Norfolk IP22 4SG
Tel: (W) 01986 892721
Email: enquiries@newman-co.fsnet.co.uk
Fixtures Secretary: Paul Mitchell, 19 Denmark Street, Diss, Norfolk IP22 3LE Tel: (H) 01379 650638
Tel: (M) 07714 397050 Tel: (W) 01953 715410
Email: mitchdiss@aol.com
Club Colours: Royal blue and white
League: London 2 North

DITCHLING RFC
Ground Address: The Playing Fields, Lewes Road, Ditchling, East Sussex Tel: 01273 843423
Brief Directions: From the village crossroads, head east on the Lewes Road and the ground is approx 0.25 mile down on the left
Club Secretary: Craig Rixon, 2C Plaistow Lane, Bromley, Kent. BR1 4DS Tel No: 020 8 4666159
Fixtures Secretary: Chris Atkinson, 61 St Andrews Road, Burges Hill RH15 0PJ Tel No: 01444 248199
Club Colours: Myrtle green shirts, white shorts
League: Sussex 2 East

DORKING RFC
Ground Address: The Pavillion, The Big Field, Brockham, Betchworth, Surrey RH3 7LZ Tel: 01737 844282
Web Address: www.dorkingrugbyclub.co.uk
Brief Directions: From Dorking take A25 to Reigate after 2miles turn right to Brockham, then 1st left into Kiln Lane
Hon Secretary: Tim Hawkins, 24 Ansell Road, Dorking, Surrey RH4 1QN Tel: (H) 01306 888193
Tel: (M) 07748 703566 Tel: (W) 01293 507758
Email: timhawkins717@hotmail.com
Fixtures Secretary: Mark Bell, 117 Gatton Park Road, Reigate, Surrey RH1 2EB Tel: (H) 01737 766987
Tel: (M) 07939 047 127
Club Colours: Red & white hoops, blue shorts
League: London 3 South West

DOVER RFC
Ground Address: Crabble Athletic Ground, Crabble Road, River, Dover, Kent Tel: 01304 210 296
Email Address: rjc@doverrfc.co.uk
Web Address: www.doverrfc.co.uk
Brief Directions: From M2/A2, at Esso garage take River exit, left at mini r'bout, sharp right at lights, 300m on left. From M20/A20 leave Dover on Canterbury Rd, fork left at lights on Crabble Hill, 300m on left
Hon Secretary: Ian Dean, 102 Templesie, Dover CT16 3BA
Fixtures Secretary: P. Batty-Smith, 46 Lower Road, Dover, Kent CT17 0QY Tel: (H) 01304 823163
Club Colours: Light and dark blue hoops
League: Kent 3

EALING RFC (TRAILFINDERS)
Ground Address: Trailfinders Sports Ground, Vallis Way, Ealing W13 0DD Tel: 020 8998 7928
Email Address: ealingrugby@hotmail.com
Web Address: www.ealingrugby.co.uk
Brief Directions: Take B452 (Argyle Road) towards Ealing at junction with A40 and after two sets of lights turn right at mini roundabout into Vallis Way
Hon Secretary: Lawson Mayer, 32 Wyredale Crescent, Greenford, Middlesex UB6 8TH Tel: (H) 020 8997 7330
Tel: (M) 07887 566627 Email: Lawson@lawsonmayor.co.uk
Fixtures Secretary: Paul Monteith, 5 Bullfinch Close, Oakham, Leicester, LE15 6BS Tel: (H) 01572 757 021
Tel: (W) 020 77204 2932
Club Colours: Green and white hoops, white shorts.
League: London 3 North West

EAST GRINSTEAD RFC
Ground Address: Saint Hill Road, East Grinstead, West Sussex RH19 4JU Tel: 01342 322338
Email Address: rugby@egrfc.co.uk
Web Address: www.egrfc.com
Brief Directions: On Minor Road to Horsted Keynes off B2110 Turners Hill Road
Hon Secretary: Bob Russell, 1 Rose Cottages, Plaistow Street, Lingfield, Surrey RH7 6AU
Tel: (H) 01342 834648 Email: rugby@EGRFC.com
Fixtures Secretary: N. Ward, 46 Hackenden Close, West Sussex RH19 3DS Tel: (H) 01342 322701
Club Colours: White with varied blue hoops.
League: London 3 South East

EAST LONDON RFC
Ground Address: Holland Road, West Ham, London E15 3BP Tel: 020 7474 6761
Brief Directions: From Canning Town roundabout proceed down Manor Road, turn right before West Ham tube station follow road round and turn right at Holland Road
Fixtures Secretary: Rob Williams
Tel: (H) 020 8558 8651 Tel: (W) 020 8556 3322
Club Colours: Maroon and navy hoops
League: East Counties 2 South

EASTBOURNE RFC
Ground Address: Park Avenue, Hampden Park, Eastbourne, East Sussex BN22 9QN
Tel: 01323 503076
Web Address: www.eastbounerugby.co.uk
Brief Directions: 500yds north of Eastbourne District General Hospital, clearly signposted.
Hon Secretary: Peter Lloyd, 51 Burton Road, Eastbourne, East Sussex BN21 2RF
Tel: (H) 01323 723905 Tel: (M) 07866 039993
Tel: (W) 01323 723905 Email: pblloyd@tinyworld.co.uk
Fixtures Secretary: Charles Wise, 128 Wannock Lane, Lower Willington, East Sussex BN20 9SJ
Tel: (H) 01323 482435 Tel: (M) 07831 264717
Tel: (W) 01892 833344
Email: charles@wise128.freeserve.co.uk
Club Colours: Navy blue with gold hoops.
League: London 3 South East

EASTLEIGH RFC
Ground Address: Bishopstoke Pavilion, Bishopstoke Road, Eastleigh Tel: 02380 641312
Brief Directions: From Eastleigh Railway Station take turning over railway bridge to Fair Oak and ground is approx 600 yards up on the left
Hon Secretary: Mark Jones, 71 St. Ronans Road, Portsmouth PO4 0PP Tel: (H) 02392 715069
Tel: (M) 07860 686637 Tel: (W) 01329 229700
Email: m.jones@ashford-colour-press.co.uk
Fixtures Secretary: J. S. Sneezham, Bursledon Lodge, Salterns Lane, Southampton SO31 8DH
Tel: (H) 02380 402286
Club Colours: Black with Red and amber hoops
League: Hampshire 1

EDENBRIDGE RFC
Ground Address: The Pavillion, Lingfield Road Recreation Ground, Edenbridge, Kent TN8 Tel: 01732 862435
Brief Directions: From Edenbridge High Street travelling south, turn right into Stangrove Road, left into Crouch House Road, right into Lingfield Road.
Hon Secretary: Nick Martin, Little Acre, Swan Lane, Edenbridge, Kent TW8 6AJ Tel: (H) 01732 862761
Tel: (M) 0468 125382
Fixtures Secretary: John Martin, Little Acre, Swan Lane, Edenbridge, Kent TN8 6AJ
Tel: (H) 01732 862761
Club Colours: Black and yellow hoops
League: Kent 3

EFFINGHAM & LEATHERHEAD RFC
Ground Address: King George V Hall, Browns Lane, Effingham, Surrey KT24 5ND Tel: 07010 704136
Email Address: info@eaglesrugby.co.uk
Web Address: www.eaglesrugby.co.uk
Brief Directions: M25 J.10. Effingham signpost left on slip road south bound from M25 to A3, follow road until Lord Howard pub on R. go R. then L. forward until lights, then L. and 1st L.
Hon Secretary: Robin Page, 20 Southfields Road, London SW18 1QN Tel: (H) 020 8877 1428
Tel: (M) 07812 240206 Tel: (W) 020 7067 4528
Email: rojopage@aol.com
Fixtures Secretary: Edward Newton, 42 Milner Road, Kingston-Upon-Thames, Surrey KT1 2AU
Tel: (H) 020 8549 8213 Tel: (W) 020 7628 3700
Email: ed@42milnerrd.freeserve.co.uk
Club Colours: Emerald green and amber hoops
League: London 2 South

EGHAM RFC
Ground Address: Kings Lane, Englefield Green, Egham, Surrey Tel: 01784 432983
Brief Directions: From A30 into Englefield Green. St. Judes Road, left at R/about to Bond Street to Kings Lane, club on left.
Hon Secretary: R.B.W. Hayes, 7 Albert Road, Englefield Green, Surrey TW20 0RQ
Tel: (H) 01784 431 299
Club Colours: Mid blue with gold hoop
League: Surrey 3

ELLINGHAM & RINGWOOD RFC
Ground Address: Picket Post, Ringwood, Hants
Tel: 01425 476668
Web Address: www.errfc.fsnet.co.uk
Brief Directions: On A31 eastbound after leaving Ringwood behindShell garage next to Burley turning.
Hon Secretary: Steve Benson, 50 Lin Brook Drive, Ringwood, Hampshire BH24 3LJ
Tel: (H) (01425) 474991 Tel: (M) (07714) 899956
Tel: (W) (01202) 864204 Email: bensonx4@talk21.com
Fixtures Secretary: Michael Riordan, 29 Bennett Road, Bournemouth, Dorset BH8 8QG
Tel: (H) (01202) 398686

Club Colours: Navy blue with amber hoop
League: Hampshire 2

ELY RFC
Ground Address: The Playing Fields, Downham Road, Ely, Cambs Tel: 01353 662156
Web Address: elyrufc.co.uk/index.html
Brief Directions: Just North of Ely. L.H.S. of A10 bypass signed Downham Market, King's Lynn.
Hon Secretary: Christopher Ormerod, 14 Points Hill, Cambridgeshire CB6 1PZ Tel: (H) 01353 863425
Tel: (W) 07767 248056
Fixtures Secretary: Martin Hammond, 110 Bexwell Road, Downham Market, Norfolk PE38 9LH
Tel: (H) 01366 384990
Club Colours: Gold and black hoops, black shorts
League: East Counties 1

ENFIELD IGNATIANS RFC
Ground Address: Enfield Playing Fields, Queen Elisabeth Stadium, Donkey Lane, Off Carterhatch Lane, Enfield, Middlesex Tel: 020 8363 2877
Web Address: www.enfieldignatiansrfc.co.uk
Hon Secretary: Glynn Jones, 45 Halifax Road, Enfield, Middlesex EN2 0PR
Tel: (H) 020 8366 3207 Tel: (M) 07903 969862
Email: kgjones_uk@yahoo.co.uk
Fixtures Secretary: Phil Beschizza, 61 Munster Gardens, London N13 5PU Tel: (H) 020 8807 3887
Tel: (W) 01483 882497
Club Colours: Blue and Gold
League: Herts/Middlesex 1

ERITH RFC
Ground Address: Northumberland Heath Playing Fields, Sussex Road, Erith, Kent
Tel: 01322 432295
Web Address: www.erithrfc.co.uk
Brief Directions: A2 towards London Black Prince turn off towards Erith, turn left into Brook St and left into Sussex Road
Hon Secretary: Perry Francis Tel: (H) 01322 434332
Tel: (W) 020 7533 6078
Email: pelandang@netscapeonline.co.uk
Fixtures Secretary: Chris McGurk, 13 Winifred Road, Erith, Kent DA8 2AJ Tel: (H) 01322 447673
Email: chris@chrismcgurk.idps.co.uk
Club Colours: Light and dark blue hoops, blue shorts
League: Kent 1

ETON MANOR RFC
Ground Address: Wanstead Sports Ground, Nutter Lane, Wanstead, London E11 2JA Tel: 020 8532 2946
Web Address: www.etonmanor.net
Brief Directions: From north A12-eastern Ave.right into Wanstead High St.. Rt into Grove Park, rt in to Avenue and rt again into Leicester Rd. Left to end of Ritter Lane
Hon Secretary: J. H Ayling, 44 Lytton Road, London E11 1JA Tel: (H) 020 8558 1800 Tel: (M) 07941 400244
Tel: (W) 020 7417 3114
Email: jhayling@hotmail.com
Fixtures Secretary: Martin Gibbons, 34 Burnham Road, Dagenham, Essex RM9 4RA
Tel: (H) 020 8595 7092 Tel: (M) 07903 649817
Club Colours: Dark blue with light blue hoops
League: London 4 North East

FAREHAM HEATHENS RFC LTD
Ground Address: Cams Alders Recreation Ground, Palmerston Bus. Pk, 41.North Lane, Buriton,, Petersfield, Hants GU31 5RS
Tel: 01329 221793
Email Address: dirobdaisy@yahoo.co.uk
Web Address: www.farehamheathens.co.uk
Brief Directions: From Fareham centre A27 west signed S'hampton, at Fire station r'about, stay on A27 for 100m, right at lights Redlands Lane, right at next junction by pub/church, Sports Centre next left
Hon Secretary: Rob Townsend, St. Mary's House, 41 North Lane, Petersfield GU31 5RS
Tel: (H) 01730 269390 Tel: (W) 01730 269390
Email: dirobdaisy@yahoo.co.uk
Fixtures Secretary: W. Smith Tel: (H) 01489 578356
Tel: (M) 07866 805793 Tel: (W) 07866 805793
Club Colours: Red and black quarters
League: Hampshire 1

FARNBOROUGH RUFC
Ground Address: Tilebarn Close, Cove, Farnborough GU14 8LS Tel: 01252 542750
Web Address: www.farnboroughrugby.com
Brief Directions: M25 J4, follow road signs to A325 Farnborough, follow signs to Rugby Club
Hon Secretary: Adrian Hathaway, 2 Tees Close, FARNBOROUGH, Hampshire GU14 9NA
Tel: (H) 01252 653502 Tel: (M) 07703 339991
Email: adrian.hathaway@ntlworld.com
Fixtures Secretary: A. B. MacKay, 43 The Grove, Farnborough GU14 6QS Tel: (H) 01252 512363
Club Colours: Dark and light blue hoops
League: Hampshire 1

FARNHAM RUFC
Ground Address: Westfield Lane, Wrecclesham, Farnham, Surrey. GU10 4QP
Tel: 01252 721138
Brief Directions: Take A325 to Petersfield from A31 Farnham bypass, after 0.75 mile pass Bear & Ragged Staff pub on right turn next right into Riverdale, 1st left onto recreation ground
Club Secretary: Derek R Wall, 22 Hope Lane, Farnham, Surrey GU9 0HZ
Tel: (H) 01252 710476
Fixtures Secretary: Bob Smith, 21 Riverside Close, Farnborough, Hants GU14 8Q5.
Tel: 01252 650719 (H) 01256 484185(W)
Club Colours: Black & yellow with one white hoop
League: London 4 South West

FAWLEY RFC
Ground Address: Waterside Sports and Social Club, 179-181 Long Lane, Long Lane, Holbury, Southampton SO45 1PA Tel: 02380 893750
Email Address: secretary@fawley.co.uk
Web Address: www.fawleyrfc.co.uk
Brief Directions: From M27 J2 (271)) follow A326 to Fawley for approx 8 miles. Ground on right after Hardley Roundabout.
Hon Secretary: David Blackmore, 4 Valley Close, Southampton SO45 1WU Tel: (H) 02380 243550 Tel: (W) 02380 871344 Email: secretary@fawleyrfc.co.uk
Fixtures Secretary: Ray Lewis, 2 Sherwood Way, Southampton SO45 1ZQ Tel: (H) 02380 898 391 Email: fixtures@fawleyrfc.co.uk
Club Colours: Scarlet shirts and socks, blue shorts,
League: Hampshire 2

FELIXSTOWE RFC
Ground Address: Coronation Sports Ground, Mill Lane Felixstowe Tel: 01394 270 150
Email Address: chris@frufc.co.uk
Web Address: www.frufc.co.uk
Hon Secretary: Danny Cain, 16 Berners Road, Felixstowe, Suffolk IP11 7LF Tel: (H) 01394 278112 Tel: (W) 01473 217261
League: East Counties 3 North

FELTHAM RFC
Ground Address: Park Road, Hanworth, Middlesex Tel: 020 8894 3609
Brief Directions: Off Hounslow Road, Hanworth adjacent to A316 (Chertsey Road)
Hon Secretary: Keith Tullett, 9 Hall Road, Isleworth, Middlesex TW7 7PA
Email: keith@mfcs99.freeserve.co.uk
Club Colours: Dark blue, light blue and gold
League: Herts/Middlesex 1

FINCHLEY RFC
Ground Address: Summers Lane, Finchley, London N12 0PD Tel: 020 8445 3746
Website: finchleyrfc.co.uk
Brief Directions: From North Circular Rd (A406) take A1000 (High Road Finchley), to Summers Lane.
Hon Secretary: Carl Elliott Tel: (M) 07710 362890
Hon Secretary: Geoff Ottley, 1 Orchard Court, Clifford Road, New Barnet, Hertfordshire EN5 5PQ
Club Colours: Scarlet and white 55mm hoops
League: London 4 North West

FLEET RUFC
Ground Address: Southwood Sports Ground, Southwood, Farborough, Hants
Web Address: www.fleet.rugbyclub.org.uk
Brief Directions: Leave M3 at junction4A follow signs for Farnborough Sports Ground opposite Nokia entrance via Kennels Lane.
Hon Secretary: Merrik Knight, 31 Osborne Road, Farnborough, GU14 6AE Tel: (H) 01252 654818 Tel: (M) 07801 883111 Tel: (W) 020 8877 1331
Email: merrikpih@aol.com
Fixtures Secretary: Lauren Batchelor, Twisell Thorne, Fleet GU13 0YT Tel: (H) 01252 623701
Club Colours: Red,white and blue.
League: Hampshire 2

FOLKESTONE RFC
Ground Address: New Burlington Field, Bargrove, Newington, Folkestone, Kent CT18 8BU
Tel: 01303 266887
Email Address: alex.ruddock@talk21.com
Web Address: www.folkestonerugby.co.uk
Brief Directions: Take the Hythe Road (B2065) from the A20 (Ashford to Folkestone Road), 1 m on left. From London M20 Exit J12 (Cheriton).Follow A20 for 1m then B2065 to Hythe.1/4m on Rt.
Hon Secretary: Ian Russell, 10, Hardwick Road,, Folkestone, Kent CT20 2NX Tel: (H) 01303 253081
Fixtures Secretary: Alex Ruddock, 40 Langdon Road, Folkestone, Kent CT19 4HY Tel: (H) 01303 276530 Tel: (W) 01303 252131
Email: alex.ruddock@talk21.com
Club Colours: Green and white hooped shirts
League: London 4 South East

FOOTSCRAY RUFC
Ground Address: 239a Footscray Road, New Eltham, London SE9 2EL Tel: 020 8850 4698
Email Address: webmaster@footscray.free-online.co.uk
Web Address: www.footscray.org
Brief Directions: Please contact Fixtures Secretary
Hon Secretary: Sue Ward, 56 Blendon Road, Bexley, Kent DA5 1BS Tel: (H) 020 8303 8204
Tel: (M) 07765 156 842
Fixtures Secretary: Tony Codd, 74 Felthampton Road, London SE9 3NX Tel: (H) 020 8857 6040
Club Colours: Royal blue and gold hoops
League: Kent 3

FORDINGBRIDGE RFC
Ground Address: The Recreation Ground, Fordingbridge, Hants Tel: 01425 652047
Brief Directions: Off A338 (12 miles south of Salisbury and 8 miles north of Ringwood) alongside by- pass, western side adjacent to River Avon.
Club Secretary: Mr K.A.Young, 1 Elmwood Avenue, Fordingbridge, Hants SP6 1DL
Tel: 01425 652681
Email: kenalf.rosewood@virgin.net
Fixtures Secretary: John Trim, Trees, Fryern Court Road, Fordingbridge, Hants SP6 1NG
Tel: (H) 01425 655156 (W) 01202 664781
Club Colours: Sky blue with black shorts
League: Hampshire 2

FULLERIANS RFC
Ground Address: Fullerians Sports Facilities, Coningesby Drive, Watford, Herts WD17 3PB
Tel: 01923 224483
Email Address: Fullerians@supanet.com
Web Address: www.fullerians.demon.co.uk
Brief Directions: Watford Grammar School New Field, Coningesby Drive (end of Parkside Drive), Watford.

WD1 3BD. From Hunton Bridge roundabout on A41 (J19/M25) follow Hempstead Road - beware of the speed cameras (A411) towards Watford town centre. At traffic lights turn right into Langley Way. Turn right at end into Coningesby Drive. You are strongly advised not to go through Watford town centre - the ring road is the nearest thing to a black hole known to man!
Hon Secretary: Chris Windsor, 11 Nascot Street, Watford, Herts WD17 4YB Tel: (H) 01923 819124 Tel: (W) 020 7943 6169
Leagues Contact: Kevin Brind, 36 Orchard Drive, Watford, Herts WD17 3DY Tel: (H) 01923 254921 Tel: (M) 07932 628883
Email: kevin@croxleyphysio.co.uk
Fixtures Secretary: Nick Thomas, 11 Ashridge Close, Bovingdon, Herts HP3 0QG Tel: (H) 01442 831386 Tel: (M) 07970 499452 Tel: (W) 020 7430 8300
Email: nickthomas99@hotmail.com
Club Colours: Black, red & green jerseys & stockings
League: London 3 North West

GILLINGHAM ANCHORIANS RFC

Ground Address: Anchorians Clubhouse, Darland Avenue, Gillingham, Kent ME7 3AN Tel: 01634 376891
Web Address: www.anchorians.co.uk
Brief Directions: Leave M2 by A278, turn left at terminal roundabout (signed A2 Gillingham), across new roundabout, left at 2nd traffic lights at Darland Ave, ground 200 yards on left
Hon Secretary: Michael Niven, 62 Trevale Road, Rochester, Kent ME1 3PA Tel: (H) 01634 313309 Tel: (M) 07799 572627
Email: niven_michael@hotmail.com
Club Colours: Purple, black & white hoops, black shorts
League: Kent 1

GOSPORT & FAREHAM RFC

Ground Address: Gosport Park, Dolphin Crescent, Gosport PO12 2HE Tel: 02392 353235
Email Address: iainr@motorcare.co.uk
Web Address: www.gosportandfarehamrfc.co.uk
Brief Directions: Exit M27 at J11 Signposted Fareham / Gosport A32. Follow road undr viaduct towards Gosport A32. Stay in nearside lane, as pass Esso Garage road forks left. This is Gosport Road then Fareham Road. At 2.3 miles you pass DARA Fleetlands (Helicopter) outside. At 4.3 miles you approach double r/about, straight over in nearside lane into Brockhurst Road then Forton Road. Follow road to Ferry Port / Bus Station 6.7 miles.Road is now South Street, past Police Station to mini r/about, straight over past Dock Road on left, approx 500metres turn left into Kensington Road, down to the end, turn right 500 metres turn left over bridge then first left into Dolphin Crescent. Follow road all the way round inyo car park.
Hon Secretary: Iain Rackham, 265 Hawthorn Crescent, Portsmouth PO6 2TL Tel: (H) 07818 417218 Tel: (M) 07818 41 218 Tel: (W) 01489 898574
Email: iainrack@cwcom.net
Fixtures Secretary: Peter Tomlinson, 18 Freemantle Road, Gosport, PO12 4ZD Tel: (H) 02392 617 673
Club Colours: Royal blue and old gold. Change Red
League: London 2 South

GRASSHOPPERS RFC

Ground Address: Ground Address: Macfarlane Sports Field, Macfarlane Lane, off Syon Lane, Middlesex Tel: 020 8891 0053
Hon Secretary: Andrew Dean
Club Colours: Green, gold and black hoops, black shorts and socks
League: London 4 North West

GRAVESEND RFC

Ground Address: Rectory Fields, Donald Biggs Drive, Milton Road, Gravesend, Kent DA12 2TL Tel: 01474 534840
Brief Directions: M25 A2 intersection, head towards Dover, leave A2 at Gravesend East (Valley Drive), follow 1.75 mile to end, right at roundabout, 1st left, ground 0.75 miles on left
Hon Secretary: R. C Bardell, 18 Parrock Avenue, Gravesend, Kent DA12 1QQ Tel: (H) 01474 743285
Email: rbardell@ukgateway.net
Fixtures Secretary: J. Ramsey, Peach Tree Cottage, Cranbrook TN17 2EJ Tel: (H) 01580 852346
Club Colours: Four inch black and white hoops
League: London 3 South East

GREAT WESTERN RAILWAY RFC

Ground Address: G. W. Railway (London) RFC, Castle Bar Park, Vallis Way, West Ealing W13. Tel: 020 8998 7928
Brief Directions: By train to Ealing Broadway, then to Castle Bar Park Halt via E1, E2 or E9 buses.
Club Secretary: Peter Allsop, 41 Lyncroft Avenue, Pinner, Middlesex HA5 1JU. Tel: (H) 020 8866 0532
Fixtures Secretary: Roy Sullivan, Tel: (H) 020 8575 6074
Club Colours: Cardinal and black jerseys.
League: Hertfordshire & Middlesex 4 South

GREENWICH RFC

Ground Address: The Pavilion, Old Mill Road, Plumstead, London SE18 Tel: 020 8854 8637
Email Address: anthony.j2.smith@bt.com
Brief Directions: Off Plumstead Common opposite Old Mill public house.
Club Colours: Red and Black Quarters
League: Kent 3

GUERNSEY RUFC

Ground Address: Footes Lane, St. Peter Port, Guernsey Tel: 01481 254590
Email Address: guernseyrugby@gtonline.net
Brief Directions: Centre of the Island, 1/2 mile from airport.
Hon Secretary: Barry Mildon, PO Box 181, Guernsey, GY1 2AA
Tel: (H) 01481 265493 Tel: (W) 01481 715055
Club Colours: Green and white
League: Hampshire 1

GUILDFORD RFC

Ground Address: Broadwater, Guildford Road (A3100), Godalming, Surrey GU7 3BU. Tel: 01483 416199
Web Address: www.ggrugby.co.uk
Brief Directions: A3100 from Guildford to Godalming-beside Broadwater lake. Or From London by-pass Guildford on A3. 1 mile past town, fork left on to B3000 through Compton for 3 miles-right at T jctn-300 yards on right.
Hon Secretary: David Gambold, 10 Treebys Avenue, Guildford, Surrey GU4 7NT Tel: (H) 01483 566304
Tel: (W) 01483 565771
Fixtures Secretary: Len Bodill, 4 Orchard Road, Guildford, Surrey GU4 7JH Tel: (H) 01483 570580
Club Colours: Blue, White & Gold
League: London 3 South West

GUY'S & ST. THOMAS' HOSPITAL RFC

Ground Address: Honor Oak Park, London SE23 1NW
Tel: 020 8690 1612
Web Address: www.guysrugby.com
Brief Directions: From London A2 along Old Kent Road to New Cross. Follow directions to Brockley going down Brockley High Street, pass Crofton Park Station on your left, over mini-roundabout then on to traffic lights at top of hill. Turn sharp left at traffic lights onto Brockley rise (one way). Ground is half way down Brockley Rise on right.
Fixtures Secretary: James Jackson, 12 Ethnard Road, Peckham, London Greater London SE1 1RU
Tel: (H) 020 7358 0414 Tel: (M) 07932 692382
Club Colours: Navy Blue and gold 4" hoops
League: London 4 South East

H.A.C. R.F.C.

Ground Address: Artillery Ground, Armoury House, City Road, London. EC1Y 2BQ. Tel: 020 7606 4644
Brief Directions: Metropolitan/Northern & Circle lines to Moorgate station, proceed north, towards Finsbury Square on City Road, entrance to ground 200m on left
Hon Secretary: John Bennett, Coram Street Farm, Hadleigh, Suffolk IP7 5NR Tel: (H) 020 8693 8959
Club Colours: Maroon/Dark Blue Hoops
League: Herts/Middlesex 2

HACKNEY RFC

Ground Address: Spring Hill, Stamford Hill, London. E5
Tel: 020 8806 5289
Hon Secretary: David Clarke, 31 Cowley Road, London E11 2HA
Club Colours: Green, blue, yellow & light blue quarters
League: Herts/Middlesex 4 North

HADLEIGH RFC

Ground Address: Layham Road Sports Ground, Hadleigh, Suffolk Tel: 01473 823231
Brief Directions: From Hadleigh High St turn into Layham Rd (flanked by library and chemist), over bridge and go on round bends, ground is on the left
Hon Secretary: Jane Stannard, 21 Kersey Close, Stowmarket, Suffolk IP14 2BG Tel: (H) 01449 774960
Tel: (W) 01449 726901 Email: janel.stannard@virgin.net
Fixtures Secretary: Nick Bray, 28 Wheatfields, Ipswich, Suffolk IP7 6RB Tel: (H) 01473 823661
Tel: (W) 01473 830013
Club Colours: Maroon and gold
League: London 3 North East

HAMBLE RFC

Ground Address: Hamble School, Satchell Lane, Hamble, Southampton
Web Address: www.hamblerugby@btinternet.co.uk
Brief Directions: Take Jct 8 off M27, Satchell Lane is a left off Hamble lane Approx. 2 miles from jct 8
Hon Secretary: Helen Adams, 48 Woolwich Close, Southampton, SO31 8GE Tel: (H) 02380 406465
Tel: (W) 01794 521094
Fixtures Secretary: Gary Camfield
Tel: (H) 02380 437664
Club Colours: Navy & sky blue,with navy, sky and white hoops
League: Hampshire 1

HAMMERSMITH & FULHAM RFC

Ground Address: Hurlingahm Park, Hurlingham Road, Fulham, London SW6 Tel: 020 7854 1432
Email Address: info@hfrfc.co.uk
Web Address: http://www.hfrfc.co.uk/
Brief Directions: From the North side of Putney Bridge turn into New Kings Road (A308). After 100 metres turn right under the railway bridge into Hurlingham Road. Ground is 300 metres on right.
Hon Secretary: Chris Cuthbertson, 17 Wheatsheaf Wharf, Wheatsheaf Lane, London SW6 6LS
Tel: (H) 020 7381 5064
Email: chris.cuthbertson@hfrfc.co.uk
Fixtures Secretary: Lyndon Walters, Flat 1, 22 Adelina Grove, London E1 3BX Tel: (H) 020 7790 1233
Tel: (W) 020 7962 8047
Email: lyndon.walters@hfrfc.co.uk
Club Colours: Red with white and navy bands
League: Herts/Middlesex 2

HAMPSTEAD RFC

Ground Address: Hampstead Heath Extension, Hampstead Way, London. NW11
Tel: 020 8458 4548
Email Address: spilsresearch@aol.com
Web Address: www.hampsteadrugbyclub.co.uk
Brief Directions: North Circular to Finchley Road, left into Millfield Way, cross Meadway, enter Hampstead Way. Look for posts and changing rooms on the left.
Hon Secretary: Mark Spilsbury, 39 Langbourne Avenue, Holly Lodge, London N6 6PS
Tel: (M) 020 8347 7178
Email: SPILSRESEARCH@aol.com
Fixtures Secretary: Courtney Chatterton, 64 Chepstow Road, London W2 5BE
Tel: (H) 020 7229 8615 Tel: (M) 07711 558551
Tel: (W) 020 7291 7136
Club Colours: Maroon and gold halves separated by white band
League: London 4 North West

HARINGEY RFC
Ground Address: New River Sports Centre, White Hart Lane, Wood Green, London N22 5QW
Tel: 020 8888 9299
Email Address: p.a.wilson0@talk21.com
Web Address: www.haringeyrugby.co.uk
Brief Directions: By tube to Wood Green, then W3 bus to White Hart Lane. By road: New River Sports Centre is positioned towards the Wood Green end of White Hart Lane
Fixtures Secretary: Nick J. Critchlow, 28 Coleman Mansions, Crouch Hill, London N8 9EJ
Tel: (H) 020 7281 0246 Tel: (M) 07860 368351
Tel: (W) 07860 368351
Email: nick.critchlow@bt.com
Club Colours: Green, scarlet and white
League: Herts/Middlesex 1

HARPENDEN RFC
Ground Address: Redbourn Lane, Harpenden, Herts AL5 2BA Tel: 01582 460711
Email Address: enquiries@harpendenrfc.net
Web Address: www.harpendenrfc.net
Brief Directions: Take B487 off A1081 (was A6) on south side of Harpenden Ground is 400 metres past entrance to Golf Club
Hon Secretary: Andy Bianchi, 9 Regent Street, Dunstable, Beds, LU6 1KP Tel: (H) 01582 615708
Email: gandy.bianchi@ntlworld.com
Fixtures Secretary: P. Thompson, 7 Kirkdale Road, Harpenden, Herts AL5 2PT Tel: (H) 01582 622103
Tel: (M) 07771 530 756
Email: p.thompson1@ntlworld.com
Club Colours: All black with white trim
League: London 3 North West

HARROW RFC
Ground Address: Grove Field, Wood Lane, Stanmore, Middlesex HA7 4LF Tel: 020 8954 2615
Email Address: harrowrfc@hotmail.com
Brief Directions: From A41, take A5 signed Edgware (Brockley Hill). Turn Right into wood Lane (Past Orthopaedic Hospital). Ground 400m on Right - Junction with Warren Lane.
Hon Secretary: Lesley Wyatt, 17 Rocklands Drive, Stanmore, Middlesex HA7 2JD Tel: (H) 020 8907 1191
Tel: (W) 01923 812834
Email: harrowsrfc@hotmail.com
Fixtures Secretary: Chris Green, 26 Anmersh Grove, Stanmore, Middx HA7 1PA Tel: (H) 020 8537 9544
Email: harrowrfc@hotmail.com
Club Colours: Navy blue with white hoops
League: London 4 North West

HARWICH & DOVERCOURT RFC
Ground Address: Wick Lane, Dovercourt, Harwich, Essex CO12 4XF Tel: 01255 240255
Brief Directions: A120 to Ramsey roundabout, 3rd exit, right at War Memorial into Fronks Rd, 2nd right into Hall Lane, left into Wick Lane, right towards swimming pool, clubhouse past pool
Hon Secretary: Kieran Coyles, 4 Acorn Close, Harwich, Essex CO12 4XF Tel: (H) 01255 504432
Tel: (W) 01255 244813
Email: coyles@harwichessex.freeserve.co.uk
Fixtures Secretary: Barry Male, 28 Mayes Lane, Nr. Harwich, Essex CO12 5EJ Tel: (H) 01255 886165
Tel: (W) 01255 244926
Club Colours: Black shirts, one white hoop, black shorts.
League: East Counties 3 North

HASLEMERE COMMUNITY RUGBY CLUB
Ground Address: Woolmer Hill Sports Ground, Woolmer Hill, Haslemere, Surrey GU27 3QN
Tel: 01428 643272
Web Address: www.haslemererugby.com
Brief Directions: Off A3 turn down Sandy Lane at Bramshott Chase towards Hammer Vale, turn left to Woolmer Hill and then left to Woolmer Hill Sports Ground and school
Hon Secretary: Martin Coakley, 3 St. Mary's Terrace, Mill Lane, Guildford, Surrey GU1 3TZ
Tel: (H) 01428 722966 Tel: (M) 07711 562071
Tel: (W) 01483 562434
Email: martincoakley@aol.com
Club Colours: Light blue and white hoops
League: Surrey 3

HASTINGS & BEXHILL RFC
Ground Address: William Parker Lower School site, Park Avenue, Hastings, E. Sussex
Tel: 01424 444255
Web Address: www.hastingsrugby-org.uk
Brief Directions: Take London road out of Hastings town centre and then into St Helens Road adjacent to Alexander Park and follow signs to Rugby Club.
Hon Secretary: Len Bolton, 180 Harrow Lane, St. Leonards-on-Sea Tel: (H) 01424 755612
Email: elbow@totalise.co.uk
Fixtures Secretary: K. Nichols, 189 St. Helens Road, Hastings, East Sussex Tel: (H) 01424 423614
Club Colours: Blue and white hoops.
League: Sussex 1

HATFIELD RFC
Ground Address: Roe Hill, Briars Lane, Hatfield Tel: 01707 269814
Brief Directions: Take exit for Briars Lane from roundabout by swimming pool and Asda in town centre. Up hill 1st left and ground is on the right.
Hon Secretary: Robin Nicholson, 18 Brocket Road, Welwyn Garden City, AL8 7TY
Tel: (H) 01707 258372
Fixtures Secretary: Graham Waddingham, 9 Stable Mews, Queenswood, Hatfield, AL9 6NX
Tel: (H) 01707 663 659 Tel: (M) 07880 565 626
Tel: (W) 01707 602 613
Email: waddingham5@tesco.net
Club Colours: Green, white, brown and gold
League: Herts/Middlesex 4 North

HAVERHILL AND DISTRICT RFC
Ground Address: Castle Playing Fields, School Lane, Haverhill, suffolk CB9 9DE Tel: 01440 702871
Email Address: secretary@haverhillrugbyclub.com
Web Address: www.haverhillrugbyclub.com
Brief Directions: From Haverhill bypass. take the R/about exit signed Clements Estate. Take 2nd left up School Lane. Map & details on website.
Hon Secretary: Ian Stewart, 7 Minster Road, Haverhill, suffolk CB9 0DR Tel: (H) 01440 706076
Tel: (M) 07714 696708 Tel: (W) 01279 442611
Email: iandmstewart@btinternet.com
Fixtures Secretary: Calum Stewart, 14 Cramswell Close, Haverhill, Suffolk CB9 9QL
Tel: (H) 01440 713182 Tel: (W) 07773 226275
Email: calum.s@virgin.net
Club Colours: Maroon with Blue Banding
League: East Counties 2 North

HAYES RFC
Ground Address: Grosvenor Playing Fields, Kingshill Avenue, Hayes, Middlesex Tel: 020 8723 9786
Brief Directions: From A40, off at "Target" R/about head south, at next R/about (White Hart) take Yeading Lane, at 1st major set of lights turn right into Kingshill Ave, ground is 1 mile on right
Hon Secretary: Neil Fretwell, 15 Sandgate House, Queens Walk, London W5 1TN Tel: (H) 020 8723 9786
Tel: (M) 07956 304909 Tel: (W) 020 7230 2717
Email: fretwellneil@aol.com
Fixtures Secretary: as Hon Secretary above
Club Colours: Navy and Gold
League: Herts/Middlesex 4 South

HEATHFIELD & WALDRON RFC
Ground Address: Hardy Roberts Recreation Ground, Cross in Hand, Heathfield, East Sussex, TN21 0TA
Tel: 01435 868747
Web Address: www.hwrfc.co.uk
Brief Directions: Adjacent to Cross in Hand public house in centre of village opposite Esso garage
Hon Secretary: Peter Mercer, 'Mapsedge', Cross in Hand, Heathfield, TN21 0TA Tel: (H) 01435 863396
Email: mercer@mapsedge.fsnet.co.uk
Fixtures Secretary: Paul Jarvis, Cookoos Rest, Hailsham Road, E. Sussex Tel: (H) 01435 866669
Tel: (M) 0770 915774 Tel: (W) 01435 866666
Email: pauljarvis@nepex.co.uk
Club Colours: Green and white quarters, green shorts.
League: London 4 South East

HELLINGLY RFC
Ground Address: Hellingly Sports Club, Horsebridge, Nr. Hailsham, E. Sussex Tel: 01323 845498
Email Address: roger.white@euphony.net
Brief Directions: Turn east off A22 onto A271, ground half mile on right opposite White Hart pub and before Kings Head.
Hon Secretary: Roger White, 5 Lansdowne Crescent, Hailsham, E Sussex BN27 1LN Tel: (H) 01323 845498
Email: roger.white@euphony.net
Leagues Contact: Roger White - as above
Fixtures Secretary: Jim Bedford, 3 Goodwin Close, Halisham, E. Sussex, BN27 3DE
Tel: (H) 01323 845660
Club Colours: Black with Amber Hoop
League: Sussex 1

HEMEL HEMPSTEAD (CAMELOT) **RFC**
Ground Address: Club House, Chaulden Lane, Hemel Hempstead, Hertfordshire HP1 2BS
Tel: 01442 230353/213408
Email Address: jonathan.clapham@which.net
Web Address: www.camelot-rfc.co.uk
Brief Directions: from main roundabout in town centre take Station road left of Kodak Tower, then Second right into St Johns Road, over Moor, Through Boxmoor Village, over small roundabout into Northridge Way. The club/Chaulden Lane 250yds on left.
Hon Secretary: Jon Clapham, 49 Brook Court, Watling Street, WD7 7JA Tel: (H) 01923 852104
Tel: (W) 01442 258666
Email: jonathan.Clapham@which.net
Fixtures Secretary: Bob Skinner, 137 Fern Drive, Hemel Hempstead, HP3 9ET Tel: (H) 01442 246586
Tel: (M) 07970 006336
Club Colours: Shirts Royal Blue & White Quarters.
League: Herts/Middlesex 1

HENDON RFC
Ground Address: Copthall Playing Fields, Great North Way, Hendon, London NW4 1PS Tel: 020 8954 7060
Email Address: tomann@tbrownsell.freeserve.co.uk
Brief Directions: Directions From M1 southbound take Exit 2 onto A1 & Ground is on left approx 500 yards From A41 at 5 Ways Corner take A1 southbound & Ground is on left approx 500 yards
Hon Secretary: Tom Brownsell, 9 Winscombe Way, Stanmore, Middlesex HA7 3AX Tel: (H) 020 8954 7060
Tel: (M) 07771 860931
Email: tomann@tbrownsell.freeserve.co.uk
Fixtures Secretary: Craig Silver, 1 Gyles Park, Stanmore, Middlesex HA7 1AN Tel: (H) 020 8952 0806
Tel: (M) 07712 677400 Tel: (W) 020 7359 0922
Email: silvercd@aol.com
Club Colours: Green Black and White unequal hoops
League: Herts/Middlesex 3 North

HITCHIN RFC
Ground Address: King George V Playing Fields, Old Hale Way, Hitchin, Herts SG5 1XL Tel: 01462 432679
Web Address: www.hitchinrfc.com
Brief Directions: At Angel Reply pub turn into Bearton Road, take 2nd left into Old Hale Way, turn into ground by phone box
Hon Secretary: Gerallt Morgan, 209 Cambridge Road, Hitchin, Herts SG4 0JP Tel: (H) 01462 635197
Tel: (W) 01462 444 633
Fixtures Secretary: Roger Hood, 1 Tithe Close, Hitchin, Herts SG4 8UX Tel: (H) 01438 820534
Club Colours: Maroon & white shirts, white shorts.
League: Herts/Middlesex 1

HOLT RFC
Ground Address: Bridge Road, High Kelling
Tel: 01263 712191
Brief Directions: Take Cromer Road (A148) from Holt, after approx 1.5 miles turn left into Bridge Road (signposted Holt RFC)
Hon Secretary: Ken Bessent, 4 The Street, Dereham NR20 4RD Tel: (H) 01362 668210
Tel: (W) 01603 662403
Email: sec@holtrfc.fsnet.co.uk
Club Colours: All black
League: East Counties 1

HORSHAM RUFC
Ground Address: Coolhurst Ground, Hammer Pond Road, Coolhurst, Horsham, W. Sussex. RH13 6PJ
Tel: 01403 265027
Brief Directions: From centre of Horsham take A251 to Brighton. At St. Leonards Arms pub turn left. Take 2nd right signed Bucks Head and ground is 600m on left.
Club Secretary: Barry Johnson, 5 Riverside, Storrington, Pulborough, W. Sussex, RH20 4NN
Tel: 01903 744357
Email: johnson.barry@talk21.com
Fixtures Secretary: John Goode, 24 Oakhill Road, Horsham, West Sussex RH13 5SF. Tel: 01403 243496
Email: john.goode@abspumps.com
Club Colours: Emerald green and white
League: Sussex 1

HOVE RFC
Ground Address: Hove Recreation Ground, Shirley Drive, Hove, E Sussex BN3 6LX Tel: 01273 505103
Email Address: admin@hoverfc.com
Web Address: www.hoverfc.com
Hon Secretary: James Angus, 28 Lyndhurst Road, Hove, Sussex, BN3 6FA
Tel: (H) 01273 726309 Tel: (M) 07074 726309
Email: jangushove@aol.com
Fixtures Secretary: Mike Richardson, 6 Wayside, Brighton, BN1 5HL Tel: (H) 01273 500512
Tel: (M) 07860 638092 Tel: (W) 020 7377 1777
Email: mr@railex.pemon.co.uk
Club Colours: Maroon and sky blue hoops.
League: London 4 South East

HSBC RFC
Ground Address: HSBC Group Sports & Social Club, Lennard Road, Beckenham, Kent BR3 1QW
Tel: 020 8919 4366
Brief Directions: Adjoining new Beckenham British Rail Station
Hon Secretary: Mike Brooks, 54 Oaklands Avenue, West Wickham, Kent BR4 9LF Tel: (H) 020 8777 3257
Tel: (W) 07831 686629
Email: sharon@brooks2169.freeserve.co.uk
Fixtures Secretary: Derek Smith, 2 Hurst Gardens, Hurstpierpoint, W. Sussex, BN6 9ST
Tel: (H) 01273 835791 Tel: (M) 07850 505722
Club Colours: Red, white & black hoops
League: Kent 3

ILFORD WANDERERS RFC
Ground Address: Forest Road, Barkingside, Ilford, Essex Tel: 020 8500 4622
Email Address: fullback@ilfordwanderers.co.uk
Web Address: www.ilfordrfu.co.uk
Brief Directions: By road: A12 to Gants Hill r'bout take Cranbrook Rd to Barkingside High St, into Forest Rd at Fulwell Cross R/A Fairlop Oak pub, ground 1 mile left, signposted
Hon Secretary: Steve Ward, 37 Sedley Rise, Loughton, Essex IG10 1LS Tel: (H) 020 8508 0891
Tel: (W) 020 8508 0891
Email: stephenward@realemail.co.uk
Club Colours: Red, green and white hoops
League: East Counties 2 South

IMPERIAL MEDICALS RFC
Ground Address: Imperial College Athletic Ground, Udney Park Road, Teddington, Middlesex TW11 1BB Tel: 020 89773100
Brief Directions: Exit Teddington Station into Station Road, Turn right into Cromwell Road. Udney Park Road is third on left.
Club Secretary: Ral Young FRCS, West Middlesex Hospital, Twickenham Road, Isleworth, Middlesex TW7 6AF Tel:020 8565 5768 (W)
Email: youngral@breathemail.net
League Contact: Justin Vale FRCS, Dept of Urology, St. Mary's Hospital, Praed Street, London W2 1NY
Tel: 020 8991 2389 Email: jvale@ic.ac.uk
Fixtures Secretary: Prof P Sever FRCP, St Mary's Hospital, Praed St., Paddington, London. W2 1NY.Tel: (W) 020 7886 1117 (F) 020 7886 6145
Email: p.sever@ic.ac .uk
Club Colours: Navy blue with a red & yellow astide light blue hoop. Badge Phoenix
League: London 3 North West

IPSWICH RFC
Ground Address: Humber Doucy Lane, Ipswich, suffolk IP4 3PZ Tel: 01473 724072
Email Address: club@ipswich-rugby.co.uk
Web Address: www.ipswich-rugby.co.uk
Brief Directions: A12 ToysRus r'bout straight over towards Ipswich at 3rd traffic light garage on L&R Turn L. go over 2 sets lights. 2 r'bouts. Over bridge turn L. at end T.Junction
Hon Secretary: Roy Bouch, Sunnyside, School Road, Ipswich, IP6 9PS Tel: (H) 01449 760 252
Email: roy_boy45@hotmail.com
Fixtures Secretary: Lisa Greetham, c/o Club Address
Tel: (H) 01473 409 086 Tel: (W) 01473 724 072
Email: club@ipswich-rugby.co.uk
Club Colours: Black and Amber
League: London 2 North

IPSWICH YM RFC
Ground Address: The Street, Rushmere, Ipswich, IP5 1DG Tel: 01473 713807
Brief Directions: From Colchester Road turn Right/Left into Rushmere Road. Straight across cross road past church on left. Club 50 metres on right.
Hon Secretary: Dick Daniels, 85 Western Avenue, Felixstowe, suffolk IP11 9NT Tel: (H) 01394 283907 Tel: (W) 01473 553325
Fixtures Secretary: Bob Hullis, 2 Godbold Close, Ipswich, IP5 2FE Tel: (H) 01473 625027 Tel: (M) 07711 793815 Tel: (W) 01473 335102
Club Colours: Amber and Maroon hoops
League: East Counties 2 North

ISLE OF WIGHT RFC
Ground Address: Wootton Recreation Ground, Footways, Wootton, Isle of Wight PO33 4NQ
Tel: 01983 883 240 Email Address: iwrfc@hotmail.com
Brief Directions: Right at the Cedars, Wootton, into Church Rd, left into Footways, left onto Recreation Ground
Hon Secretary: Nigel Harris
Fixtures Secretary: Dave Metcalfe, Afton View, Blackridge Road, Freshwater, IOW PO4 09Q
Tel: (H) 01983 755339
Email: davidmetcalfechs@hotmail.com
Club Colours: Navy, gold hoops
League: Hampshire 2

JERSEY RFC
Ground Address: Rue des Landes, St. Peters, Jersey JE3 7BG Tel: 01534 499929
Brief Directions: Opposite airport
Hon Secretary: Chris Lynch, 3 Ville de L'Eglise, Jersey JE3 7AR Tel: (H) 01534 482304
Fixtures Secretary: K. Adams Tel: (H) 01534 484509 Tel: (M) 07797 748826 Tel: (W) 01534 613072
Club Colours: Red shirts, white shorts
League: London 3 South West

KCS OLD BOYS RFC
Ground Address: Arthur Road, Motspur Park, New Malden, Surrey KT3 6NA Tel: 020 8336 2512
Email Address: paddy@kings.org.uk
Web Address: www.kings.org.uk
Brief Directions: 5 minutes walk from Motspur Park station, mailine BR from Waterloo. From A3, New Malden underpass, south on A2043, approx 400m left into Motspur Park (Rd) cto Arthur Road, 2nd right after level crossing.
Hon Secretary: Rob Dembitz, 2A Chivalry Road, London SW11 1HT Tel: (M) 07711 648079
Club Colours: Navy, Red, Old Gold
League: Surrey 1

KILBURN COSMOS RFC
Ground Address: Tiverton Green Playing Fields, Aylestone Avenue, London NW6 Tel: 020 8960 1940
Hon Secretary: Julien Laugenie, 29 Holland Road, London NW10 5AH Tel: (H) 020 8960 1940
Tel: (M) 07961 181 210 Tel: (W) 020 7678 3776
Email: jlll@bloomberg.net
Fixtures Secretary: Peter Bigwood, 9b Blenheim Gardens, London NW2 Tel: (H) 020 8450 7726
Tel: (W) 020 7728 2273
Email: peter.bigwood@gtuk.com
Club Colours: Black,gold, blue & green quarters.
League: Herts/Middlesex 3 South

KINGS CROSS STEELERS RFC
Ground Address: Holland Road, West Ham, London E15 3BP. Tel: 020 7474 6761 Website:kxrfc.com
Brief Directions: Turn off A13 just before CanningTown Hyover, turn north on A1011, (Manor Road), turn right just before West Ham tube station into Memorial Avenue.
Club Secretary: Chris Galley, 25 Richart House Drive, Royal Albert Dock, London E16 3RF. Tel: 0161 499 4994. Email: london@compuserve.com
Fixtures Secretary: Julian Kiely Tel: (H) 020 8679 9286 Tel: (M) 07960 764789
Email: julian.kiely@hmce.gov.ukH)
Colours: Irish green & royal blue inverse quarters
League: Eastern Counties 3 South

KINGSCLERE RFC
Ground Address: Field Gate Centre, Foxes Lane, Kingsclere, Newbury, Berks Tel: 01635 298497
Brief Directions: From A339 follow signs to village centre then follow signs to the Field Gate Centre.
Hon Secretary: Chris Smith, 30 Oakfields Close, Newbury, RG20 4UT Tel: (H) 01635 298006
Tel: (W) 01189 811671
Email: chrisandwendy@tiscali.co.uk
Fixtures Secretary: D. Barton, 'The Gables', Tadley, Hants RG26 5TW Tel: (H) 01256 782383
Club Colours: Red and white hoops or All Black
League: Hampshire 3

KINGSTON RFC
Ground Address: Rear of Clubhouse, King Edward Recreation Ground, Hook Road, Chessington, Surrey KT9 2JB Tel: 020 8397 8385
Email Address: nick.deere@chyp.com
Brief Directions: Leave A3 at Hook roundabout, follow sign for A243 Chessington, entrance approx 200 yards on the right
Hon Secretary: Nick Deere, 14 Bolton Road, Chessington, Surrey KT9 2JB Tel: (M) 07885 321123
Fixtures Secretary: Ian Ockenden
Club Colours: Maroon & white hooped shirts, blue shorts
League: Surrey 1

LAKENHAM-HEWETT RFC
Ground Address: Hilltop Sports Ground, Main Road, Swardeston Tel: 01508 78826
Brief Directions: Approach Norwich on the Southern bypass, leave on the Norwich/Ipswich exit (A140), head towards Norwich, turn 1st left (B1113), ground is on right about 1.25 miles
Hon Secretary: Gavin Willoughby, 20 Blackwell Avenue, Norwich, norfolk NR7 8XN
Tel: (H) 01603 414445 Tel: (W) 01603 766 388
Email: gav_willoughby@hotmail.com

Club Colours: Red shirts & socks, black shorts.
League: East Counties 2 North

LAW SOCIETY RFC
Ground Address: C /O Bevonians RFC, Ballard Coombe, Robin Hood way, London SW15 3QF Hill, Wimbledon, London SW20 Tel: 020 8946 3156
Brief Directions: A3 London bound between Robin Hood roundabout & New Malden
Hon Secretary: Peter Watts, 16 Bedford Street, London WC2E 9HF Tel: (M) 07770 747 457
Tel: (W) 020 7395 3000
Email: pwatts@wedlakebell.co.uk
Club Colours: Purple and black
League: Surrey 1

LENSBURY RFC
Ground Address: St Mary's Sports Ground, opposite Teddington Studios, Broom Road, Teddington, Middlesex. TW11 9NU
Brief Directions: By rail: Teddington Station, through High St towards River, over traffic lights into Broom Road
Hon Secretary: Andy Brampton, 29 Admiralty Way, Teddington, Middlesex TW11 0NL
Tel: (H) 020 8977 5219
Email: abrampton@hotmail.com
Club Colours: Black
League: Herts/Middlesex 1

LETCHWORTH GARDEN CITY RFC
Ground Address: Baldock Road, Letchworth Garden City, Hertfordshire SG6 2EN Tel: 01462 682 554
Brief Directions: Turn off A1 to Letchworth (jct 9), at 2nd R/about turn right on to the A505 towards Baldock. Ground situated behind North Herts Laisure Centre.
Hon Secretary: John Donegan, 24 Westholm, Letchworth, Hertfordshire SG6 4JB
Tel: (H) 01462 647721 Tel: (W) 01462 687777
Email:(H) john.donegan@ntlworld.com
Email:(W) john.donegan@siac.co.uk
Leagues Contact: Graham Steele, 11 Rookes Close, Letchworth Garden City, Hertfordshire SG6 2SN
Tel: (H) 01462 676985
Fixtures Secretary: Peter Marsden, 23 Coppice Mead, Nr Hitchin, Beds SG5 4JX Tel: (H) 01462 835163
Club Colours: Black & amber hoops, black shorts
League: London 2 North

LEWES RFC
Ground Address: Stanley Turner Ground, Kingston Road, Lewes, E. Sussex, BN7 1SB
Tel: 01273 47 37 32 (Club)
CLUB INFORMATION LINE 01 483 483937
Email Address: alan@greaterpaddock..demon.co.uk
Web Address: www.lewesrfc.org.uk
Brief Directions: From railway station take old road to Newhaven, passing Swan Inn on right, cross bypass bridge and entrance is on the left
Hon Secretary: Alan Page, 13 Greater Paddock, Ringmer, E. Sussex, BN8 5LH Tel: (H) 01273 813 419
Email: alan@greaterpaddock.demon.co.uk
Fixtures Secretary: Steve Rhodes, 12 Harrow Close, Seaford, E. Sussex, BN25 3PE
Tel: (H) 01323 492462
Club Colours: Blue and white hoops
League: London 3 South East

LIGHTWATER RFC
Ground Address: Lightwater Sports Centre, The Avenue, Lightwater, Surrey Tel: 01276 472662
Brief Directions: Leave the M3 at Junction 3 and turn left at the roundabout.Turn right across the dual carriageway and enter Lightwater Village. Take 2nd. right The Avenue [Large Sign for Lightwater Country Park]and follow this road into the park.The club is based within the sports centre.
Hon Secretary: Mike Keeley, 14 Gloucester Road, Bagshot, Surrey GU19 5LR Tel: (H) 01276 476732
Tel: (M) 07798 658947 Tel: (W) 01932 592212
Email: keeleymichael@hotmail.com
Fixtures Secretary: David Forsaith, 87 Wordsworth Avenue, Yateley, Hants GU46 6YR
Tel: (H) 01252 665387 Tel: (M) 07775 544904
Email: david.forsaith@ntlworld.com
Club Colours: Emerald, purple &white hoops, black shorts.
League: Surrey 2

LONDON CORNISH RFC
Ground Address: Richardson Evans Playing Fields, Roehampton Vale, London SW15
Tel: 020 8744 7100
Email Address: david.fletcher@concordelogistics.com
Brief Directions: Ground located 100 yards north of Robin Hood roundabout on A3 before Asda store
Hon Secretary: Dave Fletcher, 27 Riverbank, Laleham Road, Staines, Middlesex TW18 2QE
Tel: (H) 01784 461927 Tel: (W) 020 8744 7130
Email: dave.fletcher@concordelogistics.com
Hon Fixtures: Dave Fletcher - as above
Club Colours: Black with narrow gold hoops
League: Surrey 2

LONDON EXILES RUFC
Ground Address: Barn Elms Playing Field, Queen Elizabeth Walk, Barnes, London. SW15.
Tel: 020 8876 7685
Brief Directions: A205 (S. Circular) to Junction with A306 turn towards Barnes Bridge. Q. Elizabeth Walk is a small turning on R. at second set of Traffic Lights by the Red Lion Public House.
Club Secretary: Tim Edghill, 65 Ravenswood Road, Balham, London SW12 9PN.
Tel: 020 8673 2628
Fixtures Secretary: Chris Pearse, 11 Martindale Road, Balham, London SW12 9PW.
Tel: 020 8673 2115
Club Colours: Claret, navy blue and white hoops
League: Surrey 1

LONDON FIRE BRIGADE
Southern Command (Moosehead)
Ground Address: Priest Hill Sports Ground, Banstead Road, Ewell, Surrey KT17 3HG Tel: 020 8394 1946
Brief Directions: Junction of Cheam Road and Banstead Road, Ewell, next to Ewell East railway station
Hon Secretary: Charile Gilbert, 15 Park Road, Banstead, Surrey KT17 3HG Tel: (H) 01737 362191
Fixtures Secretary: Steve Russell, 8 Kings Road, Belmont, Surrey SM2 6DG Tel: (H) 020 8287 0638 Tel: (W) 020 8661 3356
Club Colours: Flame, ember, charcoal
League: Surrey 3

LONDON FRENCH RFC
Ground Address: Barn Elms Sports Ground, Castelmau/ Rocks Lane, Barnes, London. SW20
Email Address: trepelac@hotmail.com
Web Address: londonfrenchrfc.co.uk
Brief Directions: From North over Hammersmith Bridge, down Castelnau to junction with Red Lion pub. Ground is on the corner.
Hon Secretary: Andre Trepel, 67 Lant Street, London SE1 1QN Tel: (H) 020 7357 0701
Tel: (M) 07956 962720 Tel: (W) 020 7357 0701
Email: trepelac@hotmail.com
Club Colours: French (Royal) blue shirt, white shorts, red socks
League: Herts/Middlesex 3 South

LONDON IRISH AMATEURS RFC
Ground Address: London Irish Amateurs RFC, The Avenue, Sudbury-On-Thames, Middlesex TW16
Web Address: www.london-irish-amateur.co.uk
Hon Secretary: Bart O'Connell, 8 Furzewood, Sunbury-on-Thames, Middlesex TW16 6SJ
Tel: (H) 01932 786306 Tel: (M) 07711 528473
Email: bart@rocit.freeserve.co.uk
Fixtures Secretary: John Scannell, 26 Burtons Road, Middlesex TW12 1DA Tel: (H) 020 8943 4133
Email: jscan@aol.com
Club Colours: Greenshirts & socks, white shorts
League: London 4 South West

LONDON MEDIA RFC
Ground Address: Battersea Park, London
Brief Directions: Albert Bridge Road entrance to Battersea Park (near Albert Bridge)
Club Secretary: Nick Field, 315a Cavendish Road, Balham, London. SW12 0PQ.
Tel: (H) 020 8673 3809 (W) 020 7734 5358
Club Colours: Black and white quarters
League: Surrey 2

LONDON NEW ZEALAND RFC
Ground Address: c/o Birbeck Sports Ground, Birbeck Avenue, Greenford, Middlesex Tel: 020 8578 1930
Email Address: wendy@charterhouseifa.com
Web Address: www.lnzrugby.co.uk
Brief Directions: BY TUBE: Underground Central Line to GREENFORD. From station turn right, then take 2nd right into Birkbeck Ave. Ground entrance is 50 yds. on left. BY ROAD: On the A40 avoid the Greenford flyover. From the roundabout take the A4127 north. Take 1st left (Ingram Way) then 1st right into Oldfield Lane. Birkbeck Ave is 1st left, ground entrance 50 yds on left.
Hon Secretary: Wendy Whitchurch, 25 Canbury Avenue, Kingston-upon-Thames, Surrey KT2 6JP
Tel: (H) 020 8546 3647 Tel: (W) 020 7631 1311
Email: wendy@charterhouseifa.com
Fixtures Secretary: Richard Peacock, Oakfell, High Wycombe, Bucks Tel: (H) 01494 448 157
Tel: (M) 07957 858670
Email: peacockrichard@hotmail.com
Club Colours: Black shirts, black shorts
League: London 4 North West

LONDON SCOTTISH RFC
Ground Address: Richmond Athletic Ground, Kew Foot Road, Richmond, Surrey TW9 2SS Tel: 020 8892 3162
Web Address: www.london-scottish.co.uk
Brief Directions: From Richmond station (BR and underground) turn right to large R'about, turn left down A316 to Twickenham. Ground 150 yards on right.
Hon Secretary: Iain Young, 51 Cross Deep Gardens, Twickenham, Middlesex TW1 4QZ
Tel: (H) 020 8892 3162 Tel: (M) 07721 631311
Tel: (W) 020 7785 1373
Fixtures Secretary: Jack Knox Tel: (H) 020 8894 9359
Club Colours: Navy blue, white, red
League: London 3 North West

LONDON TRIBES
League: Hertfordshire & Middlesex 3 South
for further information contact League Secretary

LORDSWOOD RFC
Ground Address: Lordswood Sports &Social Club, Lordswood, Chatham, Kent ME5 9YE
Tel: 01634861924
Email Address: sam@wellings.zzn.com
Web Address: lordswoodRFC.co.uk
Brief Directions: At the moment major roadworks are on going at the M2, leave the M2 at junc/aA229 and follow signs for walderslade & lordswood turn right at T/lights, follow signs for lordswood straight over 1st r/about take 2nd turnoff at2nd r/about this is lordswood lane,3rd exit at 3rd R/about this Albermarle Rd, proceed to end of road, turn left into North Dane way and ground is 500 yds on right
Club Colours: Black with gold collars, blackshorts, amber & black socks
League: Kent 1

LOUGHTON RFC
Ground Address: Squirrels Lane, Hornbeam Road, Buckhurst Hill, Essex. Tel: 020 7504 0065
Brief Directions: A11 out of NE London to Woodford Green, turn right following police station into Monkhams Lane, follow to end and straight over crossroads into Chesnut Avenue, continue onto Squirrels Lane.
Club Secretary: Craig Clark, 15 Herenard Green, Coughton, Essex. Tel: (H) 020 8502 4854

LONDON & SOUTH EAST

Fixtures Secretary: Brian Westley,
Tel: (H) 01689 819365 Tel: (W) 020 7777 2883
Club Colours: White with one green and two black hoops.
League: Eastern Counties 3 South

LOWESTOFT & YARMOUTH RFC

Ground Address: Gunton Park, Old Lane, off Corton Long Lane, Corton, Nr Lowestoft, Suffolk.
Tel: 01502 730350
Brief Directions: From south A12 through Lowestoft. Just before dual carriageway turn right into Corton Long Lane. 300yds turn right into Old Lane. Ground at end on right.
Hon Secretary: June Nelson, 70 Upper Cliff Road, Gt. Yarmouth, Norfolk NR31 6AJ
Tel: (H) 01493 653095 Tel: (W) 01493 416207
Email: thenel@aol.com
Club Colours: Blue and white hoops
League: London 4 North East

LYTCHETT MINISTER RFC

Ground Address: South Manor Drive, Lytchett Minster, Poole
Email Address: hazel@warrenh4.fsnet.co.uk
Web Address: www.lmrufc.freeserve.co.uk
Brief Directions: The pitches for Lytchett Minster Rugby Club can be found next to the St. Peters Finger Pub in Lytchett Minster. For detailed directions please visit our website at www.lmrufc.freeserve.co.uk
Hon Secretary: Hazel Warren, 4 Dacombe Drive, Poole, Dorset, BH16 5JL Tel: (H) 01202 623694
Email: hazel@warrenh4.fsnet.co.uk
Club Colours: Blue and Red
League: Hampshire 2

MAIDSTONE FC

Ground Address: The William Day Mem. Ground, The Mote, Willow Way, Maidstone, Kent ME15 7RN
Tel: 01622 754159
Email Address: info@maidstonerugby.org.uk
Web Address: www.MaidstoneRugby.org.uk
Brief Directions: From M20 J.7 Proceed 1-2 miles on A249 towards Maidstone at R/about keep L. onto A20. 100 yds to traffic lights turn R to Square Hill turn L at mini R/about into Mote Avenue
Hon Secretary: Tom Challis, 72 Roseacre Lane, Maidstone, Kent ME14 4JG Tel: (H) 01622 631083
Tel: (M) 07990 891068 Tel: (W) 01322 297000
Email: challis7@aol.com
Fixtures Secretary: Brian McKeon, Questam, Weavering Street, Maidstone, Kent ME14 5JP
Tel: (H) 01622 735572
Club Colours: Red, white and black hoops
League: London 2 South

MALDON RFC

Ground Address: Drapers Farm Sports Club, Heybridge Tel: 01621 852152
Brief Directions: A414 to Maldon. Then northern by-pass to Heybridge.Follow signs to Goldhanger. Half a mile up Goldhanger road on left.
Hon Secretary: Steve Harris, 40 Colchester Road, Maldon, Essex CM9 4AN
Tel: (H) 01621 851755
Email: steve.mrufc@virgin.net
Club Colours: Royal blue and white hoops
League: East Counties 1

MARCH BRAZA RFC

Ground Address: Elm Road, March, Cambs
Tel: 01354 661 398
Email Address: litchfieldcs@btopenworld.com
Web Address: www.marchbears.co.uk
Brief Directions: Follow signs for HMP Whitemoor Sportsfield, on junction off side road to prison.
Club Secretary: Miss Andria Mills, 2 Broad Alder Farm, Mount Pleasant, Chatteris PE16 6XL
Tel: 01354 661398
Fixtures Secretary: Colin Buck Tel: 01354 650074
Club Colours: Maroon and White
League: East Counties 3 North

MAY & BAKER RFC

Ground Address: May & Baker Club, Dagenham Road, Dagenham, Essex
Tel: 020 8919 3156
Brief Directions: A13 to oprds, from Londonleft at McDonalds to roundabout. First exit past Dagenham East Station to traffic lights. Right and right again at mini
Hon Secretary: Terry Simmons, 14 Causton Square, Broad Street, Dagenham, Essex RM10 9HP Tel: (H) 020 8593 1788 Tel: (W) 020 8919 2579
Fixtures Secretary: Mike Parnell, The Old Post Office, Chelmsford, Essex Tel: (H) 01245 231302
Email: mikeparnell@msn.com
Club Colours: Black with single red band., black shorts and red socks.
League: East Counties 3 South

MEDWAY RFC

Ground Address: Priestfield, Rochester, Kent ME1 3AD
Tel: 01634 847737
Email Address: mikburford@blueyonder.co.uk
Web Address: www.mrfc.net
Hon Secretary: Mick Burford, 20 Wouldham Road, Rochester, Kent ME1 3LB Tel: (H) 01634 319013
Email: mikburford@blueyonder.co.uk
Email: gerald6@btinternet.com
Club Colours: Scarlet and Old Gold.
League: Kent 2
Leagues Contact: Gerald Farrow, 84 Sedge Crescent, Chatham, Kent Tel: (H) 01634 666255

MERSEA ISLAND RFC
Ground Address: East Mersea Activity Centre, East Road, East Mersea, Colchester, Essex.
Website: www.mersearugby.co.uk
Brief Directions: Turn left over Causeway coming onto Island (check tide is not over road). Centre is the 3rd road on the right, follow road to the centre
Hon Secretary: Graham Marfleet, The Gables, 10 Yorick Avenue, Colchester, Essex CO5 8HZ
Tel: (H) 01206 385218 Tel: (M) 07973 829550
Tel: (W) 01376 340403
Email: g.n.marfleet@leyford.co.uk
Fixtures Secretary: Graham Woods, 24 Churchfield, Colchester, Essex CO5 8QJ Tel: (H) 01206 383525
Club Colours: Light Blue
League: London 4 North East

MERTON RFC
Ground Address: Morden Recreation Ground, Faversham Road, Morden, Surrey SM4 6RE
Tel: 020 8646 5192
Web Address: www.merton-rugbyclub.com
Brief Directions: From Rose Hill roundabout take St Helier Ave (A297), 1st left into Middleton Rd, then 4th exit from roundabout into Faversham Rd, entrance to ground is 100 yards on left
Hon Secretary: Terry Clouter, 14 Park Crescent, Twickenham, Middlesex TW2 6NT
Tel: (H) 020 8898 5286 Tel: (M) 07803 230666
Email: Terry@clouter.com
Fixtures Secretary: Paul Webster, 39 Elthiron Road, London SW6 4BW Tel: (H) 020 7736 0149
Email: margewebster@hotmail.com
Club Colours: Black
League: Surrey 1

METROPOLITAN POLICE (HAYES) RFC
Ground Address: The Annexe, St. Dunstans Lane, West Wickham, Kent Tel: 020 8462 1266
Web Address: www.mphayesrfc.co.uk
Brief Directions: From Bromley Station tr@ATS Westmorland Rd. TR atnext ATS Hayes Lane.2nd left Bradbourne Rd at bottom of St beside Old Dunstonians RFC DunstansLane
Hon Secretary: Gary Morant, 57 Orchard Way, Croydon, CR0 7NQ Tel: (H) 020 8777 3700
Tel: (W) 020 8248 5924 Email: gary.morant@talk21.com
Fixtures Secretary: Ken Carvalho, Willow, 3 The Mead, West Wickham, Kent Tel: (H) 020 8289 1761
Email: kendob@ukonline.co.uk
Club Colours: Maroon shirts and black shorts
League: Kent 3

METROPOLITAN POLICE RFC
Ground Address: Imber Court, Ember Lane, E. Molesey, Surrey Tel: 020 8398 1267
Email Address: danny@imbercourt.com
Brief Directions: M25 Jnc 12, M3 towards London Jnc 1, take A308 to Hampton Court, turn right over bridge A309 to next roundabout, turn right into Ember Court Rd, club at end.
Hon Secretary: Neil Sinclair, Met. Police RFC, White House, 7 Trinder Mews, Teddington, Middlx. TW11 8HY
Tel: (H) 020 8977 4569 Tel: (M) 07971 048966
Email: neilsinclair@supanet.com
Fixtures Secretary: Simon Gill, 10 Prestbury Crescent, Woodmansterne, Surrey SM7 3PJ
Tel: (H) 01737 353184 Tel: (M) 07989 400239
Email: simonfgill@aol.com
Club Colours: Blue & white hoops
League: London 3 North West

MIDHURST RFC
Ground Address: Cowdray Ruins, Cowdray Park, Midhurst, West Sussex. Tel: 01730 816658
Brief Directions: At mini roundabout junction of A286 and A272 take entrance to Cowdray Park, turn left 200 yards along drive
Club Secretary: Simon Flint, Broadoak, Chichester Road, Midhurst, West Sussex. GU29 9PF
Tel: (H) 01730 816465 (W) 020 8390 1144
Fixtures Secretary: Simon Jenkins, 40 Osborne Road, Petersfield, Hampshire 2AE Tel: (H) 01730 260540
Club Colours: Gold with royal blue hoop.
League: Sussex 2 West

MILL HILL RFC
Ground Address: Copthall Playing Fields, Page Street, Mill Hill, NW7 2EJ Tel: 020 8203 0685
Email Address: ian-webster@ic24.net
Brief Directions: Next to J2 of M1, follow signs for Barnet Copthall and club is top of Page Street at entrace road to Stadium
Hon Secretary: Ian Webster, 76 Grants Close, London NW7 1DE Tel: (H) 020 8346 8136 (M) 07866 893124
Email: ianwebster76@hotmail.com
Hon Fixtures: Martyn Lewis Tel: (H) 020 8958 1237
Email: lewis.martyn@talk21.com
Club Colours: Chocolate and old gold hoops
League: Herts/Middlesex 2

MILLBROOK RFC
Ground Address: Lordshill Recreation Ground, Redbridge Lane, Lordshill, Southampton
Tel: 02380 739759
Brief Directions: M27 J3 to M271 to J1, A3051, 1st left into Redbridge Lane, 1 mile on right
Hon Secretary: Jackie Ings, 27 Gemini Close, Southampton SO16 8BG Tel: (H) 02380 345559
Tel: (M) 07941 968177 Email: chrisjackie@ings.fsnet.co.uk
Fixtures Secretary: Wayne Renwick, 12 Dean Lane, Bishops Waltham, SO32 1SX Tel: (H) 01489 892231
Club Colours: Emerald and scarlet hoops
League: Hampshire 1

MILLFIELD OLD BOYS RFC
Ground Address: Harrow RFC, Grove Field, Wood Lane, Stanmore, Middx HA7 4LF Tel: 020 8945 2615
Email Address: millfield.academy@virgin.net
Brief Directions: From A41, take A5 signed Edgware (Brockley Hill). Turn Right into wood Lane (Past Orthopaedic Hospital). Ground 400m on Right - Junction with Warren Lane.

Hon Secretary: Angela Leslie, Westmill Fisheries, P.O. Box 24, Ware, Hertfordshire SG12 0YN
Tel: (H) 01920 486534 Tel: (W) 01920 486534
Email: millfield.academy@virgin.net
Fixtures Secretary: Alan Burns, Westmill Trout Farm Fishery, Westmill Road, Ware, SG12 0YN
Tel: (H) 01920 486534 Tel: (W) 01920 486534
Club Colours: Red, green and blue hoops, white shorts
League: Herts/Middlesex 4 South

MILLWALL RFC
Ground Address: Victoria Park, Parnell Road, Bow, London E3 Tel: 08007 830675
Email Address: secretary@millwallrugby.com
Web Address: www.millwallrugby.com
Brief Directions: A13 off at Old Ford slip. Right at top of slip into Wick Lane. Follow to R/about, last exit. Straight to Cadagon Terrace. Car Park opposite Top of the Morning Public House.
Hon Secretary: Olly Arthey, 3 Whitton Walk, Bow, E3 2AF
Tel: (H) 020 8983 0242 Tel: (M) 07773 371655
Tel: (W) 07773 371655 Email: oa@lineone.net
Fixtures Secretary: Nigel Webb, 2 Macquarie Way, London E14 3AU Tel: (H) 020 7987 0575
Tel: (W) 020 7623 4481 Email: nwebb@lineone.net
Club Colours: Red, Black, White and Blue
League: East Counties 3 South

MITCHAM RFC
Ground Address: Bishopsford Cottage, Poulter Park, Bishopsford Road, Morden, Surrey Tel: 020 8648 3567
Web Address: www.mitchamrufc.co.uk
Brief Directions: The ground can only be entered from Bishopsford Road(The main Sutton to Mitcham Road).
Hon Secretary: Conrad Murray
Email: conradmurray@yahoo.com
Fixtures Secretary: Richard Tapley, 101 Peaches Close, Sutton, Surrey SM2 7BL Tel: (H) 020 8643 0650
Tel: (M) 0796 7092691 Tel: (W) 020 8871 0803
Club Colours: Lavender & Green Hoops
League: Surrey 2

NATIONAL WESTMINSTER BANK RFC
Ground Address: Copers Cope Road, Beckenham, Kent. BR3 1NZ Tel: 020 7772 6767
Email Address: rugby@nwbrfc.com
Web Address: www.nwbrfc.com
Brief Directions: Freq trains to Charing X and London Bridge to Lower Sydenham. Out of Station on down side. Turn right at bottom into Worsley Bridge Rd. 1st Right (100yds) into Coopers Cope Rd, on right.
Club Secretary: Nigel Adam, 40 Montana Gardens, London SE26 5BF Tel: (H) 020 8461 4056
Tel: (W) 020 7462 2003
Club Colours: Light and dark blue hoops
League: Kent 2

NEW ASH GREEN RFC
Ground Address: Punch Croft, New Ash Green, Kent.
Tel: 01474 874660
Brief Directions: Contact Secretary
Club Secretary: Tracy Shopland, 57 Wellington Street, Gravesend, Kent DA12 1JQ. Tel: (H) 01474 567263
Email: tracy-tonka@hotmail.com
Fixtures Secretary: Rod Banks, 14 Over Minnis, New Ash Green, Longfield, Kent DA3 8JA
Tel No: 01474 873699
Club Colours: Dark green and black quarters, black shorts.
League: Kent 1

NEW MILTON & DISTRICT RFC
Ground Address: Ashley Sports Ground, Ashley Road, Ashley, New Milton, Hants Tel: 01425 610401
Email Address: nmrfc@talk21.com
Web Address: www.newmiltonrugby.co.uk
Brief Directions: From town centre, head towards Ashley. About 1 mile from centre there is a Right turn marked Sports Club. It is immediately after a junior school.
Hon Secretary: Nick Hanmer, Walshingham, Andrew Lane, New Milton, Hants BH25 5QD
Tel: (H) 01425 612613 Tel: (W) 02380 663437
Fixtures Secretary: A. Williams, 57 Oakwood Avenue, New Milton, Hants BH25 5DZ Tel: (H) 01425 628428
Email: akwilliams@talk21.com
Club Colours: Green with band of blue, gold, blue.
League: Hampshire 1

NEWICK RFC
Ground Address: King George V Playing Fields, Allington Road, Newick, East Sussex.
Brief Directions: A272 from Haywards Heath, right at village green, 2nd right, playing field Allington Road, on first bend, left into field
Club Secretary: Mrs. Diane Thomas, Pinecroft, Allington Rd., Newick, East Sussex BN8 4NA.
Tel: (H) 01825 723824
Email: diane.pinecroft@ic24.net
Fixtures Secretary: Martin Barling, Cairn Cottage,41 Western Road, Newick. Tel: 01825 724054
Club Colours: Dark blue and maroon hooped jerseys and socks.White shorts
League: Sussex 2

NEWMARKET RFC
Ground Address: Sports Pavillion, Scaltback Middle School, Elizabeth Avenue, Newmarket, Suffolk CB8 0DJ
Tel: 01638 663082
Brief Directions: A14 (Newmkt bypass), A142 towards Newmkt, right at Tesco r'bout, left at T junction, past 3 factories on right, turn right into Elizabeth Ave, clubhouse at rear of school
Hon Secretary: Robert Voss, 58 King Edward VII Road, Newmarket, Suffolk CB8 0EU
Tel: (H) 01638 669596 Tel: (M) 07751 743580
Tel: (W) 01763 264629
Email: robert.voss@btinternet.com
Fixtures Secretary: John D. Taylor, 32 High Street, Newmarket, Suffolk CB8 9TJ Tel: (H) 01638 507483
Email: john.taylor1@ntlworld.com
Club Colours: Black shirts with emerald cuffs & collar
League: East Counties 2 North

NOMADS RFC
Ground Address: Farlington's Recreation Ground, Eastern Road, Portsmouth, Hampshire.
Tel: 02392 383538
Email Address: ken@walkerk84.fsnet.co.uk
Web Address: www.nomadsrfc.co.uk
Brief Directions: North side of A27, behind Hilton International Hotel.
Hon Secretary: Ken Walker, 5 Panton Close, Portsmouth, Hampshire, PO10 7XW Tel: (H) 01243 371646 Tel: (M) 07831 812262 Tel: (W) 01243 375543
Email: ken@walkerk84.fsnet.co.uk
Fixtures Secretary: Adrian Bold, 16 Oldenburg, Fareham, Hampshire, PO15 7ES
Tel: (H) 01489 880694
Club Colours: Red and black irregular hoops.
League: Hampshire 1

NORFOLK ARMS
Ground Address: Steyning Grammar School, Shooting Field, Steyning. Tel No: (Norfolk Arms) 01903 812215
Website: www.norfoilk armsfc.co.uk
Brief Directions: Locate Steyning Grammar School coach park on Horsham Road, Steyning. The pitches are on school playing fields.
Club Secretary: Graham Wilkins, 4 Roman Road, Steyning. BN44 3FN Tel No: 01903 814950
Fixtures Secretary: Mark Kentell, Flat 3, Glenview, Station Road, Steyning. BN44 3YL
Tel No: 01903 814303
Club Colours: Red shirts with black shorts
League: Sussex 2

NORTHOLT RFC
Ground Address: Cayton Green Park, Cayton Road, Greenford, Middlesex. UB6 8BJ. Tel: 020 8813 1701
Brief Directions: A40 Western Av to Greenford (Bridge Htl jcn/A4127 G'ford Rd), go as if to join A40 to London but stay lft & join slip parallel with A40 (R'mede Gdns), to end, left into Cayton Rd, ground at end
Club Secretary: Mr. Geoff Payne, 16 Brackenbridge Drive, South Ruislip, Middlesex HA4 0NG.
Tel: 020 8845 0874 (H) 07775 714357 (M)
Email: nrfc geoff@aol.com
Fixtures Secretary: Geoff Payne as above
Club Colours: Sky and navy blue hoops
League: Hertfordshire & Middlesex 3 South

NORWICH UNION RFC
Ground Address: Pinebanks, White Farm Lane (off Harvey) Lane, Thorpe St. Andrew, Norwich, NR7 0EA
Tel: 01603 824125
Web Address: www.nurfc.com
Brief Directions: Approach city from S.E. A47 bypass, at end enter city towards Thorpe St Andrew, right into Pound Ln, immediate left before lights onto B1150, 1st left at r'bout Harvey, 4th left, club at end
Hon Secretary: Steve Knights, 14 Avenue Road, Norwich, norfolk NR2 3HL Tel: (H) 01603 477467
Tel: (M) 07787 572 657 Tel: (W) 01603 686727
Email: steve@sknights.fsnet.co.uk
Fixtures Secretary: Craig Davies, 68 Vane Close, Thorpe St. Andrew, Norwich, NR7 0UF
Tel: (H) 01603 257 927 Tel: (M) 07801 034233
Tel: (W) 07801 034233
Email: nofrills@btopenworld.com
Club Colours: Green and white quarters
League: East Counties 2 North

OLD ABBOTSTONIANS RFC
Ground Address: Pole Hill Open Spaces, Raeburn Road, Hayes, Middlesex Tel: 020 8845 1452
Brief Directions: A40 exit for Hillingdon Long Lane towards Uxbridge Rd, left at BP station, left into Pole Hill Rd (Midland Bank at corner), round bend, 1st left after bus stop, club at end
Hon Secretary: Denis Halloran, 8 Swallow Drive, Northolt, Middlesex UB5 6UH Tel: (H) 020 8842 2154
Fixtures Secretary: Vic Deevers, 102 Clarkes Drive, Hillingdon, UB8 3UN Tel: (H) 01895 437396
Club Colours: Blue and red
League: Herts/Middlesex 3 South

OLD ABINGDONIANS RFC
Ground Address: c/o Old Cranleighans, Old Portsmouth Rd, Thames Ditton, Surrey KT7 0HB
Tel: 01582 460844
Email Address: oarfc@hotmail.com
Brief Directions: Same as Old Cranleighans.
Hon Secretary: Richard Wright, 8 Riverbanks Close, Harpenden, Hertfordshire AL5 5EJ
Tel: (H) 01582 460844 Tel: (M) 07930 414540
Email: Richard.Wright2@astrazeneca.com
Fixtures Secretary: Scott Milne, 23 Strickland Row, London SW18 3JD
Tel: (M) 0777 5654445 Tel: (W) 020 8941 2411
Club Colours: Black, cerise & white hoops
League: Surrey 2
Leagues Contact: Richard Wright - as above

OLD ACTONIANS RFC
Ground Address: Old Actonians Sports Club, Gunnersbury Drive, London W5 4LL
Web Address: www.oldactoniansrfc.co.uk
Brief Directions: Coming west from Acton Town tube station, cross North Circular Rd, take 1st right (opposite Gunnersbury Park main entrance), ground 50yds on left of G'sbury Drive
Hon Secretary: Wojtek Swistak,4 Cavendish Avenue, London W13 0JG Tel: (H) 020 8997 1410
Tel: (M) 0771 395106
Email: wojtek.swistak@db.com
Club Colours: Royal blue with three white hoops and red collar
League: Herts/Middlesex 2

OLD ALBANIAN RFC
Ground Address: Woollams, Harpenden Road, St Albans, Herts
Tel: 01727 864476
Email Address: teamsec_oa@hotmail.com
Web Address: www.oarugby.com

Brief Directions: Take turning to Harpenden off ring road to north of City. Turn immediately right down Old Harpenden Road. Ground on right.
Hon Secretary: John Kilvington, 7 Garden City, Edgware, Middlesex Tel: (H) 020 8951 1396
Fixtures Secretary: Elliot Newmarsh, n/a
Email: fixturesec@oarugby.com
Club Colours: Red, blue and yellow hoops, blue shorts
League: London 2 North

OLD ALLEYNIANS RFC
Ground Address: Old Alleynian Club, Dulwich Common, Dulwich, London. SE21 7HA
Email Address: mail@alleynian.org
Web Address: www.alleynian.org/oafc.html
Brief Directions: Situated on the South Circular Road between College Road and Lorsdhip Lane. 10 minutes walk from West Dulwich Train Station.
Hon Secretary: Chris Lomas, 1448B London Road, London SW16 4BD Tel: (H) 01342 717030
Tel: (M) 07710 351505 Tel: (W) 020 8239 0666
Email: chrislomas@aol.com
Club Colours: Dark blue, light blue and black hoops
League: Surrey 2

OLD AMPLEFORDIANS RFC
Ground Address: Old Alleynians RFC, Dulwich Common, Dulwich, London SE21 7HA
Tel: 020 8693 2402
Email Address: honsec@oarfc.org.uk
Web Address: www.oarfc.org.uk
Brief Directions: The address of our home ground is shown above. Directions to the Ground: Situated on the South Circular Road between College Road and Lordship Lane. 10 minutes walk from West Dulwich Station.
Hon Secretary: Nick Hughes, 29 Rectory Grove, London SW4 0DX Tel: (H) 020 7498 4509
Tel: (M) 07801 141550 Tel: (W) 020 7658 7889
Fixtures Secretary: Toby Codrington, 4 Hayes Court, Camberwell New Rd, SE5 0TQ Tel: (H) 020 7708 1390
Tel: (M) 07768 558051 Tel: (W) 020 7820 5769
Club Colours: Black with Red Collar and Cuffs
League: Surrey 2
Leagues Contact: Toby Codrington, asabove

OLD ASHMOLEANS RFC
Ground Address: Ashmole School, Burleigh Gardens, Southgate, N14 Tel: 020 8886 3344
Web Address: www.oarfc.co.uk
Brief Directions: Directions to pitch: at Southgate roundabout turn into Ashfield Parade, bear right into Burleigh Gardens, school entrance 250 metres on left. Directions to clubhouse: At Southgate roundabout turn into The Bourne, turn into entrance to Grovelands Priory Hospital, on junction of Queen Elizabeth's Drive. Clubhouse is 2nd on right.
Hon Secretary: Geoff Bull, 60 Ladysmith Road, Enfield, EN1 3AA Tel: (H) 020 8363 5991 Tel: (M) 07970 828802
Email: geoff.bull01@btinternet.com
Club Colours: Black with red & green hoops, black shorts
League: Herts/Middlesex 4 North

OLD BEALONIANS RFC
Ground Address: C/O Ilford C.C. Valentines Park, Cranbrook Road, Ilford, Essex Tel: 020 8554 8381
Email Address: jastyles@lineone.net
Web Address: www.oldbealsrugby.freewire.co.uk/
Brief Directions: Cranbrook Road is off Gants Hill Roundabout with the ground entrance opposite Redcliffe Gardems.
Hon Secretary: John Styles, 8 Ryecroft Avenue, Barkingside, Ilford, Essex IG5 0UQ
Tel: (H) 020 8550 0304 Tel: (M) 07711 582 050
Tel: (W) 020 7309 5414 Email: jastyles@lineone.net
Club Colours: Red, Black and Gold
League: East Counties 3 South

OLD BEVONIANS RFC
Ground Address: Ballard Coombe, Robin Hood Way, London SW15 3QF Tel: 020 8942 2907
Email Address: bevonians@hotmail.com
Brief Directions: Along A3, London bound side between New Malden & Robin Hood R'about.
Hon Secretary: Ann Lefevre, 100 Longfellow Road, Surrey KT4 8BE Tel: (H) 020 8330 2278
Tel: (M) 07778 370910 Tel: (W) 020 8286 9674
Email: bevonians@hotmail.com
Fixtures Secretary: Ben Line, 6 Highdown, Surrey KT4 7HX Tel: (H) 020 8330 1712 Tel: (M) 07974 978 971
Tel: (W) 020 8974 2460
Club Colours: Black with Green and Amber Hoops
League: Surrey 3

OLD BLUES RFC
Ground Address: Dornan Fields, Arthur Road, Motspur Park, Nr New Malden, Surrey Tel: 020 8336 2566
Website: oldblues.com/rugby-club/index.htm
Brief Directions: From London A3, along Kingston bypass, take sliproad signed Worcester Pk & Cheam, 1st left after pillarbox into Motspur Pk, over levelcrossing into W. Barnes Ln, 2nd right
Hon Secretary: Giles Simons, 66B Gowrie Road, SW11 5NR Tel: (H) 020 8378 1604 Tel: (W) 020 7786 6954
Club Colours: Navy blue, cardinal red & old gold
League: London 3 South West

OLD BRENTWOODS RFC
Ground Address: Old Brentwoods Club, Ashwells Road, Bentley, Nr Brentwood, Essex CM15 9SE
Tel: 01277 374 070 Web Address: www.obrfc.org
Brief Directions: Take the Onger road from Brentwood and after 2 1/'2 miles turn right at the end of the "straight mile" into Ashwells Rd. Ground 1/4 mile on left.
Hon Secretary: Tim Faiers, Archdale, 1 Woodway, Brentwood, Essex CM15 8LP Tel: (H) 01277 214503
Tel: (W) 020 8270 4567
Email: office@eastbrook.bardaglea.org.uk
Fixtures Secretary: Roger Seaman, 5 The Knoll, Rayleigh, Essex SS6 7HD Tel: (H) 01268 774 113
Club Colours: Dark blue/light blue hoops
League: East Counties 2 South

OLD BRIGHTONIAN RFC
Ground Address:
Share with Brighton FC (RFU), Waterhall Playing Fields, Mill Road, Patcham, Brighton. Tel: 01273 562729
Brief Directions: From London & north- A23 turn right at 1st roundabout entering Brighton, past garage under railway bridge, 100 metres sign post, turn right
Club Secretary: C D Loadsman, 20 Meadow Close, Hove, Sussex Tel: (H) 01273 552988
Tel: (W) 01273 736000
Fixtures Secretary: P Rumney Tel: (H) 01273 504981
Club Colours: Light blue and magenta hoops on navy
League: Sussex 3

OLD CATERHAMIANS RFC
Ground Address: Park Avenue, Caterham, Surrey CR3 6AH Tel: 01883 343488
Brief Directions: From Caterham Station up Church Hill, 1st left into Stanstead Rd, Park Avenue 1st on right
Hon Secretary: Lesley Myland, Ash Trees, 15 Portley Lane, Caterham CR3 5HT Tel: (H) 01883 343 319
Tel: (M) 07958 994 572 Tel: (W) 01883 343 319
Email: lesley.myland@btinternet.com
Fixtures Secretary: M. Rowland, 70 Reed Drive, Redhill, Surrey RH1 6TB Tel: (H) 01737 771 605
Tel: (M) 07802 274 320 Tel: (W) 01737 775 045
Email: rowland@furnesswithy.uk.com
Club Colours: Black, amber, silver, mauve with black shorts
League: Surrey 1

OLD COOPERIANS RFC
Ground Address: Coopers Coborn School, St Mary's Lane, Upminster, Essex Tel: 020 8592 9450
Email Address: chrisocc@bigfoot.com
Web Address: www.ocrufc.co.uk
Hon Secretary: John Green, Greenlow House, Royston Rd, Melbourn, Herts SG8 6DG Tel: (H) 01763 260 624
Hon Fixtures: Chris Nicholls, 25 manning road, Dagenham, Essex RM10 9QT Tel: (H) 02085929450
Tel: (W) 02078947005 Email: chrisocc@lineone.net
Club Colours: Light blue with thin navy and gold hoops
League: East Counties 3 South

OLD CRANLEIGHIANS RFC
Ground Address: Old Portsmouth Road, Thames Ditton, Surrey. KT7 0HB Tel: 020 8398 3092
Brief Directions: Please phone Secretary
Hon Secretary: Mark Lubbock, 51 Balham Park Road, London SW12 8DX Tel: (H) 020 8673 4458
Tel: (W) 020 7638 1111
Email: mark.lubbock@ashursts.com
Club Colours: Blue white and gold hoops
League: Surrey 1

OLD DUNSTONIANS RFC
Ground Address: St. Dunstan's Lane, Langley Park, Beckenham, Kent BR3 3SS Tel: 020 8650 1799
Brief Directions: Frm Bromley Sth station, rt at lights Westmoreland Rd, rt at next lights Hayes Ln, 2nd lft Brabourne Rs, at the bottom entrance to St D'stans Ln is almost opp. between no's 114/6 Wickham Way
Hon Secretary: Mike Rogers, 'Aboyne', Pickhurst Lane, Kent BR4 0HN Tel: (H) 020 8462 3064
Tel: (M) 0779 004 0091 Tel: (W) 020 7447 2238
Fixtures Secretary: Tony Greenwood, 5 Silverstone Court, Wanstead Road, Bromley, Kent BR1 3DZ
Tel: (H) 020 8464 7459 Tel: (M) 07980 082 002
Tel: (W) 020 8626 3118
Email: tgreenwood@ssrgroup.com
Club Colours: Navy blue with white hoop
League: London 4 South East

OLD EDWARDIANS RFC
Ground Address: Westlands Playing Fields, London Road, Romford, Essex
Brief Directions: On A118 towards London from Romford (known locally as London Road)
Hon Secretary: Graham Roberts, 7 Lampern Close, Billericay, Essex CM12 0FF Tel: (H) 01277 631240
Tel: (W) 01277 633789
Email: glr@glrnet.plus.com
Club Colours: Navy blue shirts, white shorts or red and white
League: East Counties 2 South

OLD ELTHAMIANS RFC
Ground Address: Old Elthamians Sports Club, Foxbury Avenue, Chislehurst, Kent BR7 6HA
Tel: 020 8467 1296
Web Address: www.old-elthamians-rfc.org.uk
Brief Directions: From M25 (S.E.) take A20 towards Londontake second exit (A222) towards Bromley and Chislehurst. Then second right is Foxbury Avenue.
Hon Secretary: Ian McKinnon, 25 The Gardens, Beckenham, Kent BR3 2PH Tel: (H) 020 8650 1936
Email: mckinnon-ian@hotmail.com
Fixtures Secretary: David Organ, 33 St. Mary's Ave, Bromley, Kent BR2 0PU Tel: (H) 020 8464 2542
Club Colours: Royal blue and amber hoops
League: Kent 2

OLD EMANUEL RFC
Ground Address: Blagdons, Blagdon Lane, New Malden, Surrey Tel: 020 8942 3857
Brief Directions: In London A-Z find where Burlington Rd crosses A3 at New Malden. Using north bound slip road to London ground is situated 200 yards on left
Hon Secretary: Ian Blair, 12 Moor Lane, Chessington, Surrey KT9 1BS Tel: (H) 020 8397 1272
Tel: (W) 020 7848 6917
Email: ian.blair@kcl.ac.uk
Club Colours: All white.
League: London 4 South West

OLD FREEMENS RFC
Ground Address: City of London Freemen's School, Ashtead Park, Ashtead, Surrey. KT21 1ET.
Tel: 01372 274158
Web Address: oldfreemens.co uk
Brief Directions: From Epsom Leatherhead A24 road turn into Park Lane Epsom end of Ashstead take 1st left through gates into park. Entrance to school ground 400 yards on right.

Hon Secretary: Peter Ling, 74 Woodlands Road, Bookham, Surrey KT23 4HH Tel: (H) 01372 459172
Club Colours: Dark blue, maroon & gold shirts, dark blue shorts
League: Surrey 1

OLD GRAMMARIANS RFC
Ground Address: The Sports Field, Corner of Worlds End Lane/Green Dragon Lane, Winchmore Hill, Enfield, Middlesex. - Tel: 020 8364 2459.
Brief Directions: M25 J24 (Potters Bar), A1005 towards Enfield, after about 3 miles right down Slades Hill, 4th left into Bincote Rd to Worlds End Ln, L turn to Green Dragon Ln entrance 80yds on left.
Hon Secretary: Barry White, 239 Chase Side, Enfield, Middlesex EN2 0RA Tel: (H) 020 8350 4179
Email: barrywhite@barrywhite.co.uk
Club Colours: Navy Blue with red and light blue hoops, navy blue shorts
League: Herts/Middlesex 3 North

OLD GRAVESENDIANS RFC
Ground Address: Fleetway Sports Ground, Bronte View, Parrock Road, Gravesend, Kent DA12 1PX
Tel: 01474 365503
Email Address: rugby@ogrfc.freeserve.co.uk
Web Address: www.ogrfc.freeserve.co.uk
Brief Directions: A2 to Gravesend (not Gravesend East), take A227 (Tolgate) towards town.Turn right at lights at 2nd Road Jct. First turning at roundabout into Parrock Rd.. Ground third of mile on right
Hon Secretary: Jeremy Strike, 33 Portland Road, Gravesend, Kent DA12 1DL Tel: (H) 01474 534438
Tel: (W) 01322 392849
Email: jstrike@blueyonder.co.uk
Fixtures Secretary: Stuart Hodge, 61 Parrock Avenue, Gravesend, Kent DA12 1GQ Tel: (H) 01474 569214
Tel: (M) 0850 498552 Tel: (W) 020 7803 5002
Email: stuart@shodge.freeserve.co.uk
Club Colours: Sky and navy blue hoops - Emerald & Scarlet Hoops
League: Kent 2

OLD HABERDASHERS RFC
Ground Address: Croxdale Road, Borehamwood, Herts Tel: 020 8953 1987
Brief Directions: Borehamwood & Elstree Station at R/about take Theobald Street towards Radlett. Croxdale Road on Right after .5 mile. Ground on Left.
Hon Secretary: Martin Baker, Rookwood, Hedsor Road, Bucks SL8 5EE Tel: (H) 01628 529952
Fixtures Secretary: A. Gray, 10 Trovvere Park, Hemel Hemstead, Herts HP1 3HY Tel: (H) 01442 400319
Tel: (W) 020 8801 0101 Email: graya@msdw.com
Club Colours: Blue, white and magenta hooped shirts with blue shorts.
League: Herts/Middlesex 3 North

OLD HAILEYBURIANS RFC
Ground Address: 24 Tonsley Hill, Wandsworth, London SW18 1BB Email Address: ohrfc@hotmail.com
Web Address: www.ohrfc.co.uk
Hon Secretary: Roderick Sheen, I.P.R, 31 Chelsea Wharf, London SW10 0QJ Tel: (W) 020 7782 0990
Email: rodericks@aol.com
Fixtures Secretary: Phil Jones Tel: (M) 07740 088166
Email: Philip.Jones@exodus.net
Club Colours: Magenta and white hoops
League: Surrey 2

OLD HAMPTONIANS RFC
Ground Address: The Pavilion, Dean Road, Hampton, Middlesex. TW12 1AQ Tel: 020 8943 1945
Brief Directions: Leave A316 (London to M3) at signs for A316 Hampton proceed on Uxbridge Road for half mile. R. into Hanworth Road pass 3 schools on R. before turning R into Dean Road
Hon Secretary: B. Robinson, 208 Elm Road, Kingston, Surrey K12 6HP
Club Colours: Gold, silver and black hoops
League: London 4 North West

OLD ISLEWORTHIANS RFC
Ground Address: Memorial Ground, Wood Lane, Isleworth, Middlesex Tel: 020 8898 5924
Brief Directions: A4 (Great West Road) or London Road to Isleworth
Hon Secretary: H. Davies
Hon Secretary: Tony Hawkes, 60 Cranston Close, Hounslow, Middlesex TW3 3DQ
Tel: (H) 020 8570 6143 Tel: (W) 020 8564 2311
Club Colours: Blue jersey with a horizontal red band and grey stripe
League: Herts/Middlesex 2

OLD MERCHANT TAYLORS' FC
Ground Address: Durrants, Lincoln Way, Croxley Green, Herts. WD3 3ND Tel: 01923 773014
Email Address: mrkfost@aol.com
Web Address: www.omtrugby.com
Brief Directions: From Junction 18 of the M25 take signs to Rickmansworth until you reach a roundabout opposite Rickmansworth station. Take first exit to Watford and Croxley Green. At next mini r'bout take l/h exit, towards Watford up Scots Hill. At next mini r'bout (SportsmanPH on left) take first exit onto Croxley Green. After Coach and Horseson left, take r/h fork towards T-junction with Baldwins Lane. Turn right. After small parade of shops on r/h side, turn left into Manor Way at mini-r'bout. Take first right into Kenilworth Drive then first left into Rochester Way. At end of Rochester Way road turns sharp right into Lincoln Way. Entrance to Durrants is straight in front. Please beware of traffic from left before entering the grounds of Durrants.
Hon Secretary: Mark Foster, 199 Uxbridge Road, Rickmansworth, Hertfordshire WD3 8DP
Tel: (M) 07973 657412
Email: mrkfost@aol.com
Fixtures Secretary: Geoff Shilling, The Lodge, Wellingrove, Rickmansworth, Hertfordshire WD3 1PT
Tel: (H) 01923 774506
Club Colours: Black shirts, black shorts
League: London 4 North West

OLD MID-WHITGIFTIAN RFC
Ground Address: Lime Meadow Avenue, Sanderstead, Surrey CR2 9AS Tel: 020 8657 2014
Email Address: theoldmids@yahoo.co.uk
Web Address: OMWRFC.CO.UK
Brief Directions: M25 to junction 6, signposted to Godstone and Caterham (A22). Go north on to the Caterham by-pass. Follow the by-pass to the roundabout at which you need to take the third exit (straight on). This takes you to Whyteleafe. At the mini roundabout by the Whyteleafe Tavern, take third exit. Follow this road until you get to a junction at approximately 45 degrees left. This is Tithepit Shaw Lane. At the end of this road is a "T" junction at which you need to turn left into Limpsfield Road. Follow this road for about a mile and a half when you will come to a set of pedestrian lights close to a Methodist church on the left, and a car sales showroom on the right. Turn right at the Adam Salmon car showroom and then right at "T" junction after about 100 yards. At the end of this road is the Old Mid-Whitgiftian ground.
Hon Secretary: John Crate, 16 Mallard Way, Wallington, Surrey SM6 9LZ Tel: (H) 020 8647 9081
Tel: (M) 07974 974126
Email: johncrate@16mallard.freeserve.co.uk
Fixtures Secretary: Andy Hillburn, 47a Foxearth Road, Selsdon, Surrey CR2 8EL Tel: (H) 020 8657 1825
Tel: (W) 020 7917 8888 ext. 4571
Club Colours: Black shirts with irregular silver & blue hoops
League: London 2 South

OLD MILLHILLIANS RFC
Ground Address: Millhillian Sports Club, Headstone Lane, Harrow, Middlesex HA2 6BR Tel: 020 8349 3637
Brief Directions: Entrance to ground 20 yds to left of Headstone Lane station, exit on opposite side, 5 minutes walk from station
Hon Secretary: Andrew Mortimer, 16a Park View Road, London N3 2JB Tel: (H) 020 8349 3637
Tel: (W) 020 7226 1593 Email: mortimer@btinternet.com
Hon Secretary: Judith Jolleys, 110 Canopus Way, Northwood, Middlesex UB6 8TH
Email: judithjolleys@yahoo.co.uk
Fixtures Secretary: D. G. Penson, 43 Wesley Square, London W11 1TS Tel: (H) 020 7243 3544
Tel: (W) 020 7681 5330
Club Colours: Chocolate and white hoops, black shorts
League: Herts/Middlesex 2

OLD OLAVIANS RFC
Ground Address: St. Olave's School, Goddington Lane, Orpington, Kent Tel: 01689 830744
Email Address: oorfc_info@yahoo.co.uk
Web Address: www.oorfc.co.uk
Directions: Join A224, either from A20 at Crittals Corner or M25 at J.4. Follow signs to Orpington and Goddington Lane is near Volvo BP Garage.
Hon Secretary: Chris Stanbridge, 52 Elgar Way, Horsham, W. Sussex, RH13 6RH
Tel: (H) 01403 248 177
Fixtures Secretary: Les Fairhurst, 9 Ruskin Walk, Bromley, Kent BR2 8EP Tel: (H) 020 8462 8992
Club Colours: Purple, black and white hoops
League: Kent 2

OLD PAULINES RFC
Ground Address: St Nicholas Road, off Speer Road, Thames Ditton, Surrey. KT7 0PW
Tel: 020 8398 1858
Brief Directions: From r'bout in Hampton Court Way (A309) turn east, 400m to Thames Ditton Station, after railway arch 1st left into Speer Rd, 2nd right into St Nicholas Rd
Hon Secretary: Derek Etherton, 25 Kenton Avenue, Sunbury-on-Thames, Middlesex TW16 5AS
Tel: (H) 01932 779030 Tel: (W) 01932 771180
Club Colours: Red, white and black hoops
League: Surrey 1

OLD REEDONIANS
Ground Address: North Avenue, Whiteley Village, Walton-on-Thames KT12 4DX. Tel: 01932 849616
Brief Directions: From A3/A245 junction towards Woking. After 1/4 mile turn right on B365 (Seven Hills Road). At 1st r'about turn right into Burwood Rd. Enter village & ground is 1/4 mile on right.
Club Secretary: John B Rogers, 8 Model Cottages, East Sheen, London. SW14 7PH.
Tel: (H & W) 020 8876 1512
Fixtures Secretary: David Nash, 41 Kennel Road, Fetcham, Surrey. KT12 2JR
Tel: (H) 01372 452601 (W) 020 8560 4111
Club Colours: Dark blue, light blue, red & white hoops.
League: Surrey 1

OLD REIGATIANS RFC
Ground Address: Park Lane, Reigate, Surrey RH2 9DL. Tel: 01737 245634
Web Address: www.reigatiansrufc.org.uk
Directions: Park Lane on A25 Reigate 3/4 mile on RHS
Hon Secretary: David Forsyth, 76 Station Road, Redhill, Surrey RH1 1PL Tel: (W) 01737 773533
Email: david.forsyth@goodhandandforsyth.co.uk
Club Colours: Green and Blue
League: Surrey 1

OLD RUTLISHIANS RFC
Ground Address: The Club House, Poplar Road, Merton Park, London SW19 3JS Tel: 020 8542 3678
Email Address: Enquiries@old-ruts-rugby.co.uk
Web Address: www.old-ruts-rugby.co.uk
Brief Directions: Kingston Rd Merton to Dorset Rd by Merton Park level crossing, proceed along Dorset Rd to Melrose Ave, take left fork for Poplar Road.
Hon Secretary: Simon Englefield, 11 Williams Lane, Morden, Surrey SM4 6EY Tel: (H) 020 8646 1704
Club Colours: Gold, silver, azure and black
League: Surrey 1

OLD STREETONIANS RFC
Ground Address: Play at : East Marsh, Hackney Marshes, Homerton Road E9 Tel: 020 8858 1213
Email Address: lynn@richardhay.demon.co.uk

Web Address: www.oldstreetrugby.com
Brief Directions: From North approach from A106 (Eastway).From South approach from A102 (M)
Hon Secretary: Lynn Hay, 73 Swallowfield Road, London SE7 7NT Tel: (H) 020 8858 1213
Email: lynn@richardhay.demon.co.uk
Club Colours: Blue with red stripe or blue and red qtrs
League: Herts/Middlesex 3 North

OLD SUTTONIANS RFC
Ground Address: 76 Northey Avenue, Cheam, Sutton, Surrey SM2 7HJ Tel: 020 8642 3423
Email Address: oldsutts.rfc@ntlworld.com
Web Address: www.oldsutts-rfc.co.uk
Brief Directions: On A232 between Cheam & Ewell take exit on St Pauls church roundabout into Northey Avenue. Ground is 1/4 mile on the right.
Hon Secretary: Stuart Udall, 91 Beresford Road, Sutton, Surrey SM2 6ES Tel: (H) 020 8642 9892
Tel: (M) 07799 075410 Tel: (W) 020 8606 5410
Email: stuart.udall@aspect.com
Fixtures Secretary: I. Connell, 3 Blacksole Road, Nr. Sevenoaks, Kent TN15 7DB
Tel: (H) 01732 882032 Tel: (W) 020 8224 6696
Email: imc@43grove.fsnet.co.uk
Club Colours: Red, white and black hoops
League: Surrey 3

OLD TIFFINIANS RFC
Ground Address: Grist Memorial Ground, Summer Road, off Hampton Court Way, East Molesey, Surrey KT8 9LU Tel: 020-8942-7194
Email Address: andy.r.green@talk21.com
Brief Directions: Hampton Court roundabout along Hampton Court way (A309).To turn into Summer Road you have to go to roundabout and come back, it is then first left.
Hon Secretary: Andy Green, 28 Amberwood Rise, New Malden, Surrey KT3 5JF Tel: (H) 020-8942-7194
Email: andy.r.green@talk21.com
Fixtures Secretary: Greer Kirkwood, 63 Shaftesbury Way, Strawberry Hill, Middlesex TW2 5RW
Tel: (H) 020-8898-1767
Club Colours: Violet, white & navy blue hoops
League: Surrey 1

OLD TOTTONIANS RFC
Ground Address: Churchfields Playing Fields, Great Cambridge Rd/Harrow Drive, Edmonton, London. N9
Tel: 020 8364 3099
Club website: www.oldtottonians.co.uk
Brief Directions: "Churuhfields" is located on the main A10 (Southbound) at Enfield between the Bury Street and Church Street junctions.
Club Secretary: Trevor De La Salle, 55 Welsummer Way, Le Motte Chase, Cheshunt, Herts. EN8 0UG
Tel: (H) 01992 638492
Fixtures Secretary: John Cockrill, 7 Sutherland Way, Cuffley, Herts EN6 4EG Tel: (H) 01707 872507
Tel: (W) 020 7870 9239
Email:john@cockrillf.freeserve.co.uk
Club Colours: Blue and amber hooped shirts
League: Hertfordshire & Middlesex 3 North

OLD VERULAMIAN RFC
Ground Address: Cotlandswick, North Orbital Road, London Colney, St. Albans, AL2 1DW
Tel: 01727 822929
Web Address: www.ovrugbyrc.co.uk
Brief Directions: Just off North Orbital Road (A414) ground opposite nursery
Hon Secretary: Tony Charlwood, 3 Prior Bolton Street, Canonbury, London N1 2NX Tel: (H) 020 7226 9779
Tel: (M) 07831 386281 Tel: (W) 020 7809 6703
Email: tony@charlwood.org.uk
Fixtures Secretary: Ron Winder, 10 Caenswood House, Chaucer Avenue, Weybridge, Surrey KT13 0SS
Tel: (H) 01932 820467 Tel: (M) 07747 608939
Email: ronlizw@homemail.com
Club Colours: Royal blue with gold 'V'
League: London 3 North West

OLD WALCOUNTIANS RFC
Ground Address: Carshalton Road, Woodmansterne, Surrey Tel: 01737 354348
Email Address: glynjeanette@whsmithnet.co.uk
Web Address: www.oldwalcountians.co.uk
Brief Directions: Carshalton Rd is approx 2 miles from A217, off Croydon Lane, the clubhouse is approx 0.5 mile along Carshalton Rd on the left
Hon Secretary: Paul Woolett, 3 Barrow Ave., Carshalton Beeches, Surrey SM5 4NY Tel: (H) 020 8770 0037
Club Colours: Black with blue and gold hoops.
League: Surrey 2

OLD WELLINGTONIANS RFC
Ground Address: 27 Ruxley Lane, Kingston Road, Ewell, Surrey (Shared with Old Haileyburians RFC).
Tel: 020 8393 3901
Brief Directions: East off the A3 from Tolworth Roundabout.
Hon Secretary: Nick Dennis, 24 Coleford Road, London SW18 1AD Tel: (H) 020 8874 8486
Tel: (W) 020 7600 2801
Colours: Black with orange, light blue & yellow stripes
League: Surrey 1

OLD WHITGIFTIAN RFC
Ground Address: Croham Manor Road, South Croydon, Surrey. CR2 7BG
Tel: 020 8686 2127 (office) 020 8688 3248 (bar)
Brief Directions: 1 mile south of Central Croydon on A235, fork left at The Swan & Sugarloaf pub into Selsdon Rd, 300 yds mini r'bout 2nd exit into Croham Rd, ground 0.5 mile on right
Club Secretary: Huntley Norman, 'St. Dorothys', 52 Croham Manor Rd., South Croydon, Surrey CR2 7BE .
Tel: (H&W) 020 8688 7199
Email: Huntley norman@aol.com
Fixtures Secretary: As Secretary above.
Club Colours: Red, black and blue hooped shirts
League: Surrey 1

OLD WILLIAMSONIANS RFC
Ground Address: Maidstone Road, Rochester, Kent
Tel: 01634 842883
Hon Secretary: Mark Ian Smith, 43 Holland Road, Chatham, Kent ME5 9TW Tel: (H) 01634 669458
Fixtures Secretary: Linton Stickings, 2 Cornwallis Cottages, Heath Road, Maidstone, Kent
Tel: (H) 01622 743994
Club Colours: Navy blue shirts with gold chest hoop
League: Kent 3

OLD WIMBLEDONIANS RFC
Ground Address: 143 Coombe Lane, London SW20 0NQ Tel: 020 8879 0700
Brief Directions: From Raynes Park station follow Coombe Lane towards Kingston. Cross traffic lights at West Barnes Lane junction, ground approx 800 yds on lefthand side.
Hon Secretary: Margaret Parsons, Hawth, Glaziers Lane, Guildford, Surrey GU3 2EA
Tel: (H) 01483 811103 Tel: (M) 07774 705317
Email: m.parsons@talk21.com
Fixtures Secretary: Richard Brayne-Nicholls, 76 Camberley Avenue, London SW20 0BQ
Tel: (H) 020 8946 8487 Tel: (M) 07850 830992
Tel: (W) 020 8813 7990
Email: richard.brayne-nicholls@aquapurge.com
Club Colours: Bottle green, maroon & gold hoops
League: London 3 South West

ONGAR RFC
Ground Address: Love Lane, High Street, Ongar
Tel: 01277 363 838
Brief Directions: To Ongar from Brentwood A128, turn right into town, proceed along High St, before tube station on left turn right into Love Lane, ground 300 metres
Hon Secretary: Nigel Doubleday, 31 Rochford Avenue, Waltham Abbey, Essex EN9 1SL
Tel: (H) 01992 768950 Tel: (W) 01992 769840
Email: ndoubleday@lineone.net
Club Colours: Blue with amber band
League: East Counties 3 South

ORPINGTON RFC
Ground Address: Hoblingwell Wood, Recreation Ground, Leesons Way, St. Paul's Cray, Orpington, Kent BR5 2QB Tel: 01689 823 913
Email Address: mark.hopkins@btclick.com
Web Address: www.orpy.demon.co.uk
Brief Directions: From M25 Jct 3, take A20 towards London. Take first exit, A224 Orpington, then first right, third left and third right into Leesons Way.
Hon Secretary: Mark Hopkins, PO Box 145, Orpington, Kent BR5 2ZY Tel: (H) 01689 815412
Tel: (M) 07957 823641
Email: mark.hopkins@btclick.com
Fixtures Secretary: Dave Corry, c/o PO Box 145, Orpington, Kent BR5 2ZY Tel: (H) 01689 811 396
Club Colours: Amber & Black
League: Kent 3

OSTERLEY RFC
Ground Address: Brunel Univ. Sports Ground, Jersey Road, Osterley, Middx TW5 0TP Tel: 020 8428 5797
Web Address: www.osterley-rigby.co.uk
Brief Directions: On A4 take Stucley Road, west of Osterley Tube Station,into Jersey Road and look for Brunel University Sports Ground.
Hon Secretary: Richard Evans, 111 Rowlands Avenue, Hatch End, Pinner, Middlesex HA5 4AW
Tel: (H) 020 8428 5797
Email: r.evans@nabarro.com
Fixtures Secretary: John Green, 92 Roxborough Avenue, Isleworh, Middx Tel: (H) 020 8568 5557
Club Colours: Black and white hoops
League: Herts/Middlesex 3 South

OVERTON RFC LTD
Ground Address: The Old Cricket Ground, Laverstock Park, Watch Lane, Laverstoke, Nr. Overton, Hants
Web Address: www.overtonrugbyclub.com
Hon Secretary: Roger Filbey, 101 Old Winton Road, Andover, Hants SP10 2DR Tel: (H) 01264 365529
Email: rogerfilbey@waitrose.com
Fixtures Secretary: Alex Cole, 18 Rochford Road, Basingstoke, Hants RG21 7TQ Tel: (H) 01256 410836
Club Colours: Royal blue
League: Hampshire 3

PARK HOUSE FC
Ground Address: Barnet Wood Road, Hayes, Kent Br2 7AA Tel: 020 8462 7318
Brief Directions: A21 to Bromley (or from M25 J4), turn off on A233 (Oakleigh Rd) towards Biggin Hill, Barnet Wood Road is a turning on the right
Hon Secretary: Robert D. Elves, 47 Ramillies Road, Sidcup, Kent DA15 9JA Tel: (H) 020 8304 9170
Fixtures Secretary: G. Bunnage, 48 Southborough Road, Bickley, Kent BR1 2EL
Tel: (H) 020 8467 1447 Tel: (W) 020 8401 0111
Club Colours: Black shirts with red circlet
League: Kent 2

PAXTON PUMAS RFC
Ground Address: Brookfield School, Brook Lane, Sarisbury Green
Web Address: www.abshot.org.com
Brief Directions: Barns Lane leads to Brook Lane and enter through Park Gate.
Hon Secretary: Sue Moorhouse, Formax Farm, Southampton Road, Fareham, PO14 4AX
Tel: (H) 01329 842 303 Tel: (M) 07836 276 689
Fixtures Secretary: Tim Moorhouse, Formax Farm, Titchfield, Hants PO14 4AX
Tel: (H) 01329 842 303
Club Colours: Yellow & green
League: Hampshire 3

PEGASUS RFC
Club Secretary: Mr. R. Tomlinson, 7 Golf Ride, South Benfleet, Essex SS7 1EQ
Fixtures Secretary: As above
League: Eastern Counties 3 South

PETERSFIELD RFC
Ground Address: The Clubhouse, Penns Place, Petersfield, Hants GU31 4EP Tel: 01730 264588
Email Address: glitch1@btopenworld.com
Brief Directions: East edge of town, co-located with E Hants District Council Offices and Taro Leisure Centre
Hon Secretary: Geoff Litchfield, 13 Copse Close, Petersfield, Hants GU31 4DL Tel: (H) 01730 265072
Tel: (M) 07855 216466 Tel: (W) 020 7460 7915
Email: glitch@tinyworld.co.uk
Fixtures Secretary: Albert Winterbottom, 6 Woodbury Avenue, Petersfield, Hants GU32 2EE
Tel: (H) 01730 261860 Tel: (W) 01730 234271
Club Colours: Red with white hoop
League: London 4 South West

PINNER & GRAMMARIANS RFC LTD.
Ground Address: Shaftesbury Playing Fields, Grimsdyke Rd, Hatch End, Middx Tel: 020 8864 0787
Email Address: mail@pinner-rugby-club.co.uk
Web Address: www.pinner-rugby-club.co.uk
Brief Directions: By rail: Hatch End (NSG & B'loo), west A410 Uxbrge Rd to Hatch End B'way Shps, rt G'sdyke Rd, 2nd rt H'view, 1st lt C'burn Ave, club lt. Road: frm E. same, frm W. A410 Uxbrg Rd, lt G'dyke Rd
Hon Secretary: Robin Greenwood, 4 South Drive, Middlesex HA4 8EX Tel: (H) 01895 677764
Tel: (M) 07803 143137 Tel: (W) 020 8339 2725
Fixtures Secretary: Jon Blowers, 38 Dawlish Drive, Pinner, Middlesex HA5 5LN Tel: (H) 020 8866 5127
Tel: (M) 07989 399141 Tel: (W) 020 8868 0982
Email: mail@pinner-rugby-club.co.uk
Club Colours: Navy and 1" scarlet hoops
League: Herts/Middlesex 4 North

PLUMPTON RFC
Ground Address: The Racecourse, Plumpton Green, East Sussex
Brief Directions: Plumpton Racecourse opposite railway station in village of Plumpton Green
Club Secretary: Chris Woodward, 2 Monks Way, Lewes, East Sussex. BN7 2EX Tel: (H) 01273 476219
Fixtures Secretary: Mark Slade, 2 Park Close, Burgess Hill, W Sussex.RH15 8HC Tel: 01444 343792
Club Colours: Maroon and amber hoops
League: Sussex 3

PORTCASTRIAN RFC
Ground Address: Ilford Lane Playing Fields, Iford Lane, Bournemouth, Dorset Tel: 01202 519406
Brief Directions: Turn towards Southbourne off A228 (Wessex Way) into Iford Lane, past Bournemouth Hospital to Iford Lane, playing fields on left
Hon Secretary: Martin Davis, 64 Withermoor Road, Bournemouth, Dorset, BH9 2PD Tel: (H) 01202 519406
Tel: (M) 07801 431320
Email: davismartin1@talk21.com
Fixtures Secretary: Gary Fretton
Tel: (M) 07796 682327
Club Colours: Royal blue, yellow and red hoops
League: Hampshire 2

PORTSMOUTH RFC
Ground Address: Norway Road, Hilsea, Portsmouth, Hants PO3 5EP Tel: 02392 660610
Brief Directions: From A27 take A2030 towards Southsea. at first lights take right turn and continue over bridge. Ground is on left.
Hon Secretary: Iain Wilson, 116 Rowner Road, Gosport, Hants PO13 9RG Tel: (H) 01329 230752
Tel: (W) 01329 813286
Email: iain@portsmouthrugby.freeserve.co.uk
Fixtures Secretary: Will Arnold Tel: (H) 02392 821109
Club Colours: Black jersey with white and yellow bands
League: London 2 South

PULBOROUGH RFC
Ground Address: Sports & Social Club, Rectory Lane, Pulborough, W Sussex Tel: 01798 873020
Web Address: www.prfc.fsnet.co.uk
Brief Directions: Approach by Rectory Lane branching north off east end of Lower St opposite Arundale School
Hon Secretary: Chris Brazier, 2 Heather Farm Cottages, Chobham Road, Woking, GU21 4XY
Tel: (M) 07712 527006 Tel: (W) 01903 881364
Email: fubs@secondrow.fsnet.co.uk
Fixtures Secretary: Michael Ford, 14 Ravenscroft, Storrington, W. Sussex Tel: (H) 01903 745697
Club Colours: Black and white hoops
League: Sussex 1

PURLEY JOHN FISHER RFC
Ground Address: Parsons Pightle, Coulsdon Road, Old Coulsdon, Surrey. CR5 1EE. Tel: 01737 553042
Brief Directions: M25 J7 - M23-A23, turn right in Coulsdon to Marl Pit Lane, to end turn right, Coulsdon Road, ground 0.5 mile on right
Club Secretary: Simon Witham, 2 Kingswood Avenue, Sanderstead, Surrey. CR2 9DQ
Tel: (H) 020 8657 2089 (W) 020 7247 4466
Fixtures Secretary: Martin Bazley
Tel: (H) 020 8660 2157 (W) 020 7377 5423
Club Colours: Black and white
League: London 4 South West

QUEEN ELIZABETH II HOSPITAL RFC
Ground Address: Hatfield Hyde Sports Club, King George V Playing Fields, Beehive Lane, Welwyn Garden City, Herts. Al7 4BP Tel: 01707 326700
Brief Directions: From A1 take WGC exit, follow signs to QE II Hospital, when in the road "Howlands" turn into Beehive Lane, turn left past Beehive public house
Club Secretary: Adan Bowe, 1 Drycroft, Welwyn Garden City, Herts. AL7 4PH Tel: 01707 332303 (H)
E-mail: abowe@ikon.com
Fixtures Secretary: Rod Ibbinson, 29 The Moors, Welwyn Garden City, Herts .
Tel: (H) 01707 331341 Tel: (M) 0374 980145
e-mail; ribinson@ ruberoid.com.uk
Club Colours: Myrtle green and amber shirts, black shorts and green socks
League: Hertfordshire & Middlesex 3 North

QUINTIN RFC
Ground Address: Quintin Hogg Memorial Ground, Cavendish Road, Chiswick, London W4
Tel: 01628 675899
Email Address: nigel.smith4@which.net
Web Address: www.quintinrfc.org.uk
Brief Directions: Club plays at The Quintin Hogg Memorial Ground (part of Westminster University), Chiswick, London W 4. Ground is located just north of the River Thames by Chiswick Bridge. From the A4 (Great West Road, at the Hogarth Roundabout) (by the Fullers Brewery) take the A316 south towatds Mortlake and Richmond. Follow for approx 1 1/2 km. Just before you get to Chiswick Bridge, at traffic lights, turn right in to Harington Road. Pitches are on the left backing on to the river. For Club House, carry along Hartington Road and take first right into Cavendish Road. Entrence to Club House is on the right.
Hon Secretary: Nigel Smith, 4 Australia Avenue, Maidenhead, Berks SL6 7DJ Tel:(H) 01628675899
Email Address: nigel.smith4@which.net
Club Colours: Scarlet and green hoops, blue shorts
League: Herts/Middlesex 4 South

RAVENS RFC
Ground Address: Ford Sports & Social Club, Aldborough Road South, Newbury Park, Ilford, Essex
Tel: 020 8590 3797
Brief Directions: Off Eastern Avenue (A12) Newbury Park
Hon Secretary: Albert Rowley, Willow Lodge, 169 Kiln Road, Thundersley, Essex SS7 1SJ
Tel: (H) 01702 558389 Tel: (W) 01702 558389
Email: alltherowleys@btopenworld.com
Fixtures Secretary: Trevor Moss, 38 Levett Gardens, Ilford, Essex IG3 9BT Tel: (H) 020 8590 5290
Tel: (W) 020 8590 5180
Club Colours: Black
League: East Counties 3 South

RAYLEIGH WYVERNS RFC
Ground Address: Runwell Hospital Sports and Social Club, Runwel Chase, Wickford, Essex SS11 7PJ
Tel: 01268 732453
Email Address: rayleighwyvens.co.uk
Web Address: www.rayleighwyverns.co.uk
Hon Secretary: Neil McQuire Tel: (H) 01268 558879
Tel: (W) 07775 568728
Email: neil@mcquire.totalserve.co.uk
Fixtures Secretary: Mark Priest, 14 Love Lane, Rayleigh, Essex
Tel: (H) 01268 742 961 Tel: (M) 07770 594 852
Club Colours: Scarlet and emerald quarters
League: East Counties 3 South

RAYNES PARK RFC
Ground Address: Raynes Park Sports Ground, Taunton Avenue, Raynes Park, London. SW20
Brief Directions: Shannon Corner exit A3 to Raynes Park, last turning left (Camberley Ave) before Coombe Lane/West Barnes Lane traffic lights
Hon Secretary: Russell Price, 101 Belmont Avenue, New Malden, Surrey KT3 6QE Tel: (H) 020 8949 2448
Tel: (W) 020 8339 1831
Email: russell.price@encodasystems.com
Club Colours: Blue and gold quarters, blue shorts and socks
League: Surrey 2

REIGATE RFC
Ground Address: Eric Hodgkins Memorial Grond, Colley Lane, Reigate, Surrey RH2 9JL
Tel: 01737 221110
Web Address: www.rrrfc.co.uk
Brief Directions: M25 J8 south on Reigate Hill, turn right before level crossing, to end of road turn right then keep left into Colley Lane, club 200m on right
Hon Secretary: Norman Phillips, 28 Hurstleigh Drive, Redhill, Surrey RH1 2AA Tel: (H) 01737 212912
Fixtures Secretary: Bob Collingbourne, 18 West View Close, Redhill, Surrey RH1 6ST Tel: (H) 01737 772562
Club Colours: Royal blue with white hoops
League: Surrey 2

RICHMOND FC
Ground Address: The Athletic Ground, Kew Foot Road, Richmond, Surrey TW9 2SS Tel: 020 8332 7112
Email Address: andrewg@richmondfc.co.uk
Web Address: www.richmondfc.co.uk
Brief Directions: The Athletic Ground lies on the North side of the A316 just West of Richmond Circus roundabout and adjacent to Royal Mid Surrey Golf Club and the swimming pool, Pools on the Park.
Hon Secretary: Andrew Gordon, The Athletic Ground, Kew Foot Road, Richmond, Surrey TW9 2SS
Tel: (H) 020 8332 7112
Email: andrew.j.gordon@btinternet.com
Leagues Contact: Andy Quigley, 46 Coval Road, London SW14 7RL Tel: (H) 020 8878 2838
Email: quigas@aol.com
Fixtures Secretary: Vic Balchin, 11 Troutbeck Close, Berks RG10 9DA Tel: (H) 0118 934 5765
Club Colours: Old Gold, Red and Black
League: London 3 South West

ROBERTSBRIDGE RFC
Ground Address: Robertsbridge Community College, Knelle Road, Robertsbridge, East Sussex. TN32 5EA
Brief Directions: From the village follow signs to the railway station, go over the level crossing, take the 2nd right then go straight up to the college
Club Secretary: Bernard Davies, 12 Ridgeway, Hurst Green, East Sussex TN19 7PJ. Tel: 01580 860325
Fixtures Secretary: Paul Strovell, 12 Ridgeway, Hurst Green, East Sussex TN19 7PJ
Tel:(M) 07944 653204 Tel: (H) 01959 515915
Club Colours: Blue and Black Quarters
League: Sussex 3

ROCHFORD HUNDRED RFC
Ground Address: Magnolia Road, Hawkwell, Rochford
Tel: 01702 544021
Brief Directions: Please phone Secretary

Hon Secretary: Simon Wakefield, 54 Parklands Drive, Chelmsford, Essex CM1 7SP Tel: (H) 01245 266158 Tel: (W) 01277 844800
Email: swakefield@contechs.co.uk
Club Colours: Black shirt and shorts, black socks with white hoops
League: London 3 North East

ROMFORD & GIDEA PARK RFC
Ground Address: Crowlands, Crow Lane, Romford, Essex RM7 0EP Tel: 01708 760068
Brief Directions: A12 to Moby Dick pub, from London right, into Whalebone Lane Nth,at lights left London Rd, 0.5 mile into Jutsums Ln,underbridge,(unsuitable for coaches) left into Crow Ln, ground 100yds on right
Hon Secretary: Keneth Dungate, 186 Lancaster Drive, Elm Park, Essex RM12 5SL Tel: (H) 07967 203632 Tel: (M) 07967 203632 Tel: (W) 020 8271 1280
Fixtures Secretary: Tony Healey, 27 Lansbury Avenue, Chadwell Heath, Essex Tel: (H) 020 8599 6451
Club Colours: Black, purple and white hoops with black shorts.
League: London 3 North East

ROMSEY RUFC
Ground Address: Romsey Sports Centre, Lower Southampton Road, Romsey, Hants SO51 8AF
Tel: 01794 519400
Email Address: www.romseyrfc.co.uk
Brief Directions: On A27 into Romsey, Sports centre is next to Romsey Rapids Swimming centre on Southampton Road.
Hon Secretary: Ian Messenger, 12A The Harrage, Romsey, SO51 8AE Tel: (H) 01794 514 638
Email: mesiai@lineone.net
Fixtures Secretary: Malcolm Pain, 2 Nursery Road, Bitterne Park, Southampton, SO18 1NS
Tel: (H) 02380 557 572
Club Colours: Royal blue with gold hoops, blue shorts, gold topped blue socks
League: Hampshire 1

ROYAL & SUN ALLIANCE
Ground Address: Royal & Sun Alliance Club, North Heath Lane, Horsham, West Sussex RH12 4PJ.
Tel: 01403 352404
Website: www.rsarugby-fsnet.co.uk
Brief Directions: Leave A264 at roundabout for Roffey, 3rd exit at next roundabout, go half mile and turn left into North Heath Lane at mini roundabout, ground is half mile on LHS.
Club Secretary: K. J. Reed, 12 Dale Close, Horsham, West Sussex RH12 4JD Email: keith.reed@uk.royalsun.com
Tel: 01403 242929 (H) 01903 233765 (W)
League Contact: Email: brian@lewsec.clara.net
Fixtures Secretary: C. Nicholas, 44 Cissbury Close, Horsham, West Sussex RH12 5JT.
Tel: 01903 275393 Email: carl.nicholas@esure.com
Colours: Navy with yellow, green & white chevron
League: Sussex 2 West

ROYSTON RFC
Ground Address: The Heath Sports Club, Therfield Heath, Baldock Road, Royston, SG8 5BG
Tel: 01763 243 613
Brief Directions: A10 north or south to roundabout by cinema, turn west through town centre, past golf club on left, A505 from Baldock turn right at Little Chef, club on right
Hon Secretary: Colin Dacey, 4 Valley Rise, Royston, SG8 9EY Tel: (H) 01763 223144
Tel: (W) 01223 427828
Club Colours: Black and white hoops, black shorts, black socks
League: Herts/Middlesex 3 North

RUISLIP RFC
Ground Address: West End Road, Ruislip, Middlesex. HA4 6DR Tel: 01895 633102
Email Address: stephen.aldcroft@wa-a.co.uk
Web Address: www.RuislipRFC.co.uk
Brief Directions: M25, J16 oto M40 towards London and onto A40. After Northolt Airport turn left into West End Road A4180. Ground 3 miles on left. Nearest station is Ruislip Underground.
Hon Secretary: Stephen Aldcroft, 30 Elmbridge Drive, Middlesex HA4 7UT
Tel: (H) 01895 622793 Tel: (M) 07973 313380
Tel: (W) 01895 232234
Email: stephen.aldcroft@wa-a.co.uk
Club Colours: Maroon and white hooped shirts, white shorts, maroon socks
League: London 3 North West

RYE RFC
Ground Address: New Road, Rye, E. Sussex
Tel: 01797 224 867
Brief Directions: Situated east of main town on the A259 coast road
Hon Secretary: Helen Pearce, 1 Martells Plasce, Tram Road, Rye Tel: (H) 01797 224 753
Fixtures Secretary: D. Ramus, Moat Farm, Moat Lane, Iden, E Sussex, TN31 7UU
Tel: (H) 01797 280 049
Email: daveram@cwcom.net
Club Colours: Red and white quarters, black shorts, black socks
League: Sussex 1

SAFFRON WALDEN RFC
Ground Address: Springate, Henham, Nr. Bishops Stortford, Hertfordshire
Tel: 01279 850 791
Email Address: enquiries@swrfc.co.uk
Web Address: www.swrfc.co.uk
Hon Secretary: Brian Peachey, 2 Gloucester Place, Clare, suffolk CO10 8QR
Tel: (H) 01787 278464 Tel: (W) 01708 335600
Email: peachey.bryan@briggsandstratton.co.uk
Club Colours: Myrtle green
League: London 3 North East

SANDOWN & SHANKLIN RFC
Ground Address: The Fairway, Lake, Sandown, Isle of Wight, PO36 9ES Tel: 01983 404707
Email Address: kendouch@yahoo.co.uk
Web Address: www.ssrfc.co.uk
Brief Directions: By rail: Pitch is adjacent to Sandown Station. Use underpass to reach club. By road: Follow main Sandown Shanklin road to Lake, take `The Fairway' - Pitch on right opposite high school.
Hon Secretary: Nigel Stotesbury, 25 Albany View, Camphill, Isle of Wight, PO30 5PF
Tel: (H) 01983 521981 Tel: (W) 01983 529 704
Fixtures Secretary: Colin Bond, 8 St. Johns Crescent, Sandown, IOW PO36 Tel: (H) 01983 402374
Club Colours: Dark blue with red, white and blue hoops
League: Hampshire 1

SAWSTON RFC
Ground Address: Swaston Village College, Swaston Tel: 01223 836615
Brief Directions: M11 J10, take A505 to Sawston, next r'bout take A1301 to Sawston/Cambridge, after 1 mile turn right to Sawston then 1st left New Rd, College on left
Hon Secretary: Paul Clerke, 1 Cross Ways, Linton, Cambridgeshire, CB1 6NO Tel: (H) 01223 891365 Tel: (W) 01223 822360 Email: P28557@aol.com
Club Colours: Black, navy and white quarters
League: East Counties 3 North

SEAFORD RFC
Ground Address: Salts Recreation Ground, Richmond Road (off Dane Road), Seaford Tel: 01323 892 355
Brief Directions: On the sea front just off the A259
Hon Secretary: Andy Smith, 11 Chichester Road, Seaford, E. Sussex, BN25 2DJ Tel: (H) 01323 490993
Tel: (M) 07752 980206 Tel: (W) 01323 891623
Email: andy.smith20@virgin.net
Fixtures Secretary: Paul Joy, 4 Kingston Close, Seaford, E Sussex Tel: (H) 01323 894042
Tel: (W) 01323 894019
Club Colours: Scarlet shirts with navy blue shorts
League: Sussex 1

SEVENOAKS RFC
Ground Address: Knole Paddock, Plymouth Drive, Sevenoaks, Kent TN13 Tel: 01732 452027
Web Address: www.sevenoaks-rugby.org.uk
Brief Directions: J.5 M25. Follow signs to Sevenoaks. At Riverhead R/about turn R. up Amhersa Hill. L. after BR station R. at top then L. around Cricket Ground - Plymouth Drive on right.
Hon Secretary: Howard Pearl, Nearly Corner, Heaverham, Sevenoaks, Kent TN15 6NQ
Tel: (H&W) 01732 763431 Tel: (M) 07979 355109
Email: pearl.corner@tesco.net
Fixtures Secretary: Nick Wagstaff, 34 Garth Road, Sevenoaks, Kent TN13 1RU Tel: (H) 01732 461742
Tel: (W) 020 7805 5000
Email: nick.wagstaff@seacontainers.com
Club Colours: Navy & Gold
League: London 2 South

SHELFORD RFC
Ground Address: Davey Field, Cambridge Road, Gt. Shelford, Cambridge Tel: 01233 843357
Brief Directions: M11 J11 heading into Cambridge, right at traffic lights into Shelford Rd, continue for 1 mile, club is on the right opposite Scotsdale Garden Centre
Hon Secretary: Sue Sutcliffe, 22 The Lane, Cambs, CB2 5HP Tel: (H) 01223 874008
Tel: (M) 07762 375097
Email: sue@succo.fslife.co.uk
Club Colours: Maroon and white hoops, blue shorts
League: London 2 North

SHEPPEY RFC LTD
Ground Address: The Clubhouse, Scocles Field, Lower Road, Minster, Sherness, Kent ME12
Tel: 01795 872082
Email Address: Lin2dave@aol.com
Brief Directions: From M2 or M20 take A249 turnoff for Sheerness/Sittingbourne. Follow A249 onto Island. At first roundabout turn right. Club half a mile on the right, just past traffic lights.
Hon Secretary: Linda Neal, 16 New Road, Minster, Sherness, Kent ME12 3PX Tel: (H) 01795 873983
Tel: (W) 01795 580028 Email: Lin2Dave@aol.dot.com
Fixtures Secretary: Linda Neal, 16 New Road, Minster, Sherness, Kent ME12 3PX Tel: (H) 01795 873983
Tel: (W) 01795 580028
Email: Lin2Dave@aol.dot.com
Club Colours: white jersey with singled broad red band
League: Kent 1

SHIRLEY WANDERERS RFC
Ground Address: 135 Addington Road, West Wickham, Kent BR4 9BF Tel: 020 8777 5298
Brief Directions: From West Wickham, go down Corkscrew Hill and turn right at bottom. Club about 1/4 mile on left.
Hon Secretary: John Pound, 4 Tanglewood Close, Croydon, Surrey CR0 5HX Tel: (H) 020 8656 4336
Fixtures Secretary: G. Jeffcoat, 96 Woodland Way, West Wickham, Kent BR4 9LT Tel: (H) 020 8777 5174
Club Colours: All white
League: Surrey 2

SHOOTERS HILL RFC
Ground Address: 123/125 Mayday Gardens, London SE3 8NP Tel: 020 8856 1511
Web Address: www.shootershillrfc.co.uk
Brief Directions: From Well Hall r'bout take signs for Woolwich & Ferry, over lights at top of hill, next left Broadwalk, over 4 humps, left into Mayday Gdns, follow road to green on left, entrance to ground in corner
Hon Secretary: B. A. C. Kennett, 18 Elmwood Drive, Bexley, Kent DA5 3PT Tel: (H) 020 8304 4982
Email: backennett@yfi.co.uk
Fixtures Secretary: I. Trevett, 76 Southwood Road, London SE9 3QT Tel: (H) 020 8859 6693
Club Colours: Red, blue, green and yellow
League: Kent 2

SHOREHAM RFC
Ground Address: Kings Manor School, Kingston Lane, Shoreham-by-Sea, West Sussex
Tel: 01273 597625
Brief Directions: Take A27 to Shoreham (Old Shoreham Road) westward Kingston Lane is on left at traffic lights before Holmbush shopping centre r'bout, Kings Manor School 0.5 mile on right
Club Secretary: Simon Edgar, 17 Newtimber Gardens, Shoreham-by-Sea, West Sussex BN43 5GQ.
Tel: (H) 01273 701618 (W) 07831 236918
Fixtures Secretary: Mrs Sandy Beal
Tel: (H) 01273 884827
Club Colours: Amber and bottle green quarters
League: Sussex 3

SIDCUP RFC
Ground Address: Crescent Farm, Sydney Road, Sidcup, Kent DA14 6RA
Tel: 020 8300 2336
Email Address: clubofficers@sidcuprfc.co.uk
Web Address: www.sidcuprfc.co.uk
Brief Directions: A20-A222 towards Sidcup (Chislehurst Rd), proceed to 1st traffic lights (Police Station), left into Main Road, left just past fire station into Sydney Rd, ground 200mtrs on left
Hon Secretary: Allan Jones, 53 Goodwin Drive, Sidcup, Kent DA14 4NX Tel: (H) 020 8302 2382
Tel: (W) 020 8302 2382
Fixtures Secretary: Malcolm J. Leamon, 43 Glenhouse Road, London SE9 1JH Tel: (H) 020 8859 5598
Tel: (W) 020 8859 5598
Club Colours: White shirts, blue cuffs/collars. Maroon shorts.
League: London 3 South East

SITTINGBOURNE RFC
Ground Address: Gore Court Sports Club, The Grove, Key Street, Sittingbourne, Kent ME10 1YT
Tel: 01795 423813
Email Address: info@srufc.com
Web Address: www.srufc.com
Brief Directions: From M2 eastbound, A249 to Sittingbourne & Sheerness, after 2 miles take A2 towards Sittingbourne, after 0.5 mile turn left just after Sports ground, left again into club car park
Hon Secretary: Steve Smith, 34 Crouch Hill Court, Lower Halstow, Sittingbourne, Kent ME9 7EJ
Tel: (M) 07710 425195 Tel: (W) 01795 844104
Email: steve.smith@swalenet.co.uk
Club Colours: Blue and gold hoops
League: Kent 2

SOUTH WOODHAM FERRERS RFC
Ground Address: Saltcoats Playing Fields, South Woodham Ferrers, Chelmsford, Essex CM3
Tel: 01245 320 041
Brief Directions: From A127 take A130 to Chelms Road at Rettenden Turnpike take A132 to South Woodham Ferrers. On entering town follow signs to Saltcoats Ind. Est.. Ground on left after 3rd R/about. From A12 Chelms Road take A130 Southend at Rettenden Turnpike A132 as above.
Hon Secretary: David Parkinson, 43 Clements Green Lane, South Woodham Ferrers, Essex CM3 5JS
Tel: (H) 01245 321376 Tel: (M) 07778 010980
Email: nosnikrap4@btinternet.com
Fixtures Secretary: P. Gregory, 1 Maydene, South Woodham Ferrers, Essex CM3 5ND
Tel: (H) 01245 328930 Tel: (M) 07714 705593
Club Colours: All black
League: East Counties 2 South

SOUTHAMPTON RFC
Ground Address: Test Playing Fields, Lower Brownhill Road, Southampton, Hants SO15 4HH
Tel: 02380 737777
Web Address: www.southamptonrfc.co.uk
Brief Directions: M27 onto M271, take 1st slip road, 1st exit towards Lordshill, after 150 yds turn right into Lower Brownhill Road
Hon Secretary: C. Wilmore, 48 Ethelburt Avenue, Swaythling, Southampton, Hants SO16 3DD
Tel: (M) 07900 228165
Fixtures Secretary: Rob Swain
el: (H) 02380 367140
Club Colours: Red and white hoops
League: London 4 South West

SOUTHGATE RFC
Ground Address: Nortel, Oakleigh Road, New Southgate, London N11
Tel: 020 8945 2655
Web Address: www.southgate-rfc.clara.co.uk
Brief Directions: A406 frm E., exit for Arnos Grove, pass Arnos Grve stn to r'bout, 2nd exit for Oakl'gh Rd Sth. A406 frm W., left for New Southgate stn, right at Turrets pub, 1st exit r'bout for Oakl'gh Rd Sth
Hon Secretary: David Hockey, 5 The Vineries, Enfield, Middlesex EN1 3DQ Tel: (H) 020 8342 0202
Tel: (M) 07901 971954 Tel: (W) 020 7270 1551
Fixtures Secretary: Simon Shutler, 60 Exeter Road, London N14 5JX Tel: (H) 020 8368 5325
Tel: (W) 020 8446 8324
Email: simon@ipa.org.uk
Club Colours: Dark blue, light blue and gold irregular hoops
League: Herts/Middlesex 4 North

SOUTHWOLD RFC
Ground Address: Elms Cottages, Elms Lane, Wangford Beccles, Suffolk NR34 8AX
Web Address: www.southwoldrugbyclub.co.uk
Hon Secretary: Clare Webb, 34 Elms Lane, Langford, Suffolk NR34 8BA Tel: (H) 01502 578578
Tel: (W) 01502 578578
Fixtures Secretary: Jeremy Taylor, 27 The Firs, Suffolk IP18 6YS Tel: (H) 01502 724 476
Tel: (M) 07787 548724
Club Colours: Black with Gold hoop.
League: East Counties 2 North

ST. ALBANS RFC
Ground Address: Boggymead Spring, Oaklands Lane, Smallford, St. Albans AL4 0HR Tel: 01727 869945
Web Address: www.st-albans-rfc.com
Hon Secretary: Carole Peel, All Correspondence to Chairman, 39 Watford Road, St. Albans, AL1 2AX
Club Colours: Royal blue and gold hoops, navy shorts
League: London 4 North West

ST FRANCIS RFC
Ground Address: Southgate Playing Fields, Southgate Avenue, Crawley, West Sussex. Tel: 01293 616941
Website: ww st-francis -rugby.com
Brief Directions: M23 J11, take A23 to Crawley, right at roundabout into Southgate Ave, ground approx 1 mile on right hand side
Club Secretary: Mark Eastman, 182 Buckswood Dr, Gossops Green, Crawley, RW11 8PS Tel: 07968 803171
Email: mark.eastman @st.albans-church.co.uk
Fixtures Secretary: Vince McGahan, 83 Winchester Road, Tilgate, Crawley, West Sussex.
Tel: (H) 01293 547194 Tel: (W) 01293 503389
Club Colours: Black with blue and two white hoops
League: Sussex 2

ST. NICHOLAS OLD BOYS RFC
Ground Address: Ickenham Cricket Club, Oak Avenue, Ickenham, Middx UB10 8LP Tel: 01895 673146
Web Address: www.snobrfc.com
Brief Directions: A40 exit Hillingdon Circus, follow signs toIckenham, turn left to Oak Avenue past Total Garage.
Hon Secretary: Alison Summerfield, 13 Paignton Road, Ruislip, Middlesex HA4 0BU Tel: (H) 01895 673146
Email: sgm@summerfieldg.fsnet.co.uk
Hon Fixtures: Nick Reeves, Flat 65, Longcroft, Maple Cross, Herts WD3 9TT Tel: (H) 01923 776363
Tel: (M) 07956 560095 Email: ndr291170@aol.com
Club Colours: Red shirts with black & white hoops, black shorts
League: Herts/Middlesex 4 South

STANFORD LE HOPE RFC
Ground Address: Stanford Rec Ground, Corringham Road, Stanford-le-Hope, Essex Tel: 01375 640 957
Web Address: www.stanford-le-hope-rufc.co.uk
Brief Directions: A13 to Stanford-Le-Hope then turn off at A1014. Right at roundabout into Corringham Rd. First left Rainbow Lane, First Right Billet Lane. Clubhouse at far end on right.
Hon Secretary: Darren Watkins, 169 London Road, Grays, Essex RM17 5YP Tel: (H) 01375 374776
Email: watto@cableinet.co.uk
Fixtures Secretary: Kyran McDonald, 3 St. James Avenue East, Stanford-Le-Hope, Essex
Tel: (H) 01375 403 520
Club Colours: Red and White
League: East Counties 1

STEVENAGE TOWN RFC
Ground Address: Muddy Lane, North Road, Old Stevenage, Herts SG1 4BB Tel: 01438 359 788
Email Address: muddy.1@ntlworld.com
Web Address: www.results.com
Brief Directions: Take A1M Stevenage North Jcn 7, take road towards Graveley, 1st right (past garden centre) towards St'age, ground 400yds on right, parking on access road by pitches
Hon Secretary: Ben Tranter, 30 Ivel Road, Stevenage, Herts SG1 4SD Tel: (H) 01438 317734
Fixtures Secretary: Fred McCarthy, 48 Kennel Drive, Biggleswade, Beds, SG18 8WD Tel: (H) 01767 221243
Tel: (W) 01438 767231
Club Colours: Black shirts with green hoop, black shorts, green socks
League: Herts/Middlesex 1

STONEHAM PARK RUFC
(Formerly AC Delco)
Ground Address: Stoneham Park Sports and Social Club, Sports Ground, Stoneham Lane, Eastleigh, Southampton, Hants. Tel: 02380 613334
Brief Directions: M27 Jct 5. Stoneham Lane Northbound. Ground on left just after Concorde club on right.
Club Secretary: Steve Lines, 18 Mead Road Chandlers Ford, SO53 2EZ Tel: 02380 273166
Email: stevielines@aol.com
Fixtures Secretary: John Hunter, 100 Newton Road, Weston, Southampton Tel: 02380 396688
Club Colours: Navy blue and red quarters or navy blue and light blue hoops
League: Hampshire 3

STOWMARKET RUFC
Ground Address: Chilton Fields Sports Club, Chilton Way, Stowmarket, Suffolk IP14 1SZ Tel: 01449 613181
Email Address: EWright64@aol.com
Brief Directions: From Bury St Edmonds direction along A14, take exit marked Stowmarket, 2nd exit at roundabout, left onto housing estate, follow road, last road on the right
Hon Secretary: Elaine Wright Email: EWright64@aol.com
Fixtures Secretary: Darryl Chapman, 55 Bridge Street, Stowmarket, IP14 1BP
Tel: (H) 01449 672787 Tel: (M) 07803 59957
Email: darryl.chapman@dowcorning.com
Club Colours: Navy blue, white and red
League: East Counties 1

STREATHAM-CROYDON RFC
Ground Address: Rosevale, 159 Brigstock Road, Thornton Heath, Surrey. CR7 7JP. Tel: 020 8684 1502
Brief Directions: A23 turn off at Thornton Heath Pond, 1st left is Brigstock Road, club 400 yards on right
Hon Secretary: Dick Towers, 24 Ernest Grove, Beckenham, Kent BR3 3JF Tel: (H) 020 8658 2333
Club Colours: Maroon shirts, white shorts
League: Surrey 2

SUDBURY & LONDON SPRINGBOKS RFC
Ground Address: Tel: 020 7284 0333
Email Address: johnconway@londonspringboks.com
Web Address: www.londonspringboks.com

Hon Secretary: John Conway, Sudbury & London Springboks FC, 38 Courthope Road, London NW3 2LD Tel: (H) 020 7284 0333 Tel: (M) 07710 227376
Email: john.conway@jcal.co.uk
Fixtures Secretary: Dave Keeling, 17 Nunnery Lane, Luton, Beds, LU3 1XA Tel: (H) 01582 652417
Tel: (M) 07879 843174 Tel: (W) 01582 707200
Email: davidkdragon@aol.com
Club Colours: Green, gold, red, white and blue shirts with black shorts and socks.
League: Herts/Middlesex 3 South

SUDBURY RFC
Ground Address: Moorsfield, Great Conrad, Sudbury, Suffolk CO10 0JR Tel: 01787 377547
Brief Directions: Ground on B 1508 Colchester, Bures, Sudbury road, 1.5 miles from Sudbury town centre in Great Cornard. From town centre left after Kings Head, 1st right into Rugby Rd
Hon Secretary: Mike Maddocks, 8 Nether Court, Halstead, Essex CO9 2HE Tel: (H) 01787 473027
Fixtures Secretary: G. Underwood, 11 Bures Road, Sudbury, Suffolk CO10 0EJ Tel: (H) 01787 373045
Fixtures Secretary: Sandra Mackay, 33 Suffolk Road,, Sudbury, Suffolk CO10 1UN Tel: (H) 07870 545224
Club Colours: Blue jersey and wide white hoop
League: London 2 North

SUSSEX POLICE RFC
Ground Address: Brighton Rugby Club, Patcham, Waterhall, Brighton, Sussex Tel: 01273 562729
Brief Directions: A23 London to Brighton road, turn right at Patcham along Mill Road, then left into Waterhall ground
Club Secretary: P Johnson, Police Station, Kingsham Road, Chichester, Sussex. Tel: (H) 01243 825408
Tel: (W) 01243 520230
Fixtures Secretary: C Gale
Tel: (H) 01444 458482 Tel: (W) 01444 451555
Club Colours: Blue and gold quarters, blue shorts, blue socks
League: Sussex 2

SWAFFHAM RUFC
Ground Address: Swaffham RUFC, North Pickenham Road, Swaffham, Norfolk PE37 7NX
Tel: 01760 724829
Email Address: swaffhamrufc@aol.com
Brief Directions: From East or West continue along A47 bypass and turn off at MacDonalds Drive Thru' into Swaffham. Just after 30 mph sign turn LEFT at Lydney House Hotel. Club is 200 yards on right. From A1065 South take first right AFTER junction with B1077 (South Pickenham)down Whitecross Road.Continue to end and turn right. Clubhouse 150 yards on right.
Hon Secretary: Hugh Green, Gemini Cottage, Kings Lynn, Norfolk PE32 2TD Tel: (H) 01328 838 269 Tel: (W) 01760 721 281
Fixtures Secretary: Eric J. Nye, 7 Warstade Way, Swaffham, Norfolk PE37 7NX Tel: (H) 01760 723377
Email: EJKLN@aol.com
Club Colours: Black and Amber shirts
League: East Counties 3 North

TEDDINGTON RFC
Ground Address: Bushy Park, Teddington, Middlesex
Tel: 020 8977 4989
Web Address: www.teddingtonrfc.co.uk
Brief Directions: Ground adjacent to Teddington Cricket Club in Bushy Park, at the rear of N.P.L.
Hon Secretary: Peter Woolgar, 114 Elgin Avenue, Ashford, Middlesex TW15 1QG Tel: (H) 01784 259734
Email: pjwoolgar@hotmail.com
Club Colours: Dark blue
League: Surrey 2

THAMES RFC
Ground Address: Garron Lane, South Ockendon, Essex Tel: 01708 852907
Brief Directions: Turn off Tunnel Junction, down Ship Lane, right at T junction, second off roundabout. First left, second left.
Hon Secretary: Tony Smith, 67 St. Michaels Close, Aveley, Essex RM15 4SY Tel: (H) 01708 868331
Tel: (M) 07966 422494 Tel: (W) 020 7318 3033
Fixtures Secretary: Paul Brett, 10 Oakdene Road, Orpington, Kent Tel: (H) 01689 836463
Tel: (M) 07860 315381
Club Colours: Emerald Green and black hoops
League: East Counties 2 South

THAMESIANS RFC
Ground Address: The Pavillion, Twickenham Green, Twickenham, Middx Tel: 020 8894 3110
Email Address: theclub@thamesians.com
Web Address: www.thamesians.com
Hon Secretary: Mark de Brett, 89 Lime Grove, New Malden, Surrey KT3 3TR Tel: (H) 020 8942 1314
Tel: (M) 07860 440 892 Tel: (W) 020 8607 4800
Email: mdebrett@aol.com
Fixtures Secretary: Shane Kelly, Flat2, No. 1 The Barons, Twickenham, Middx TW1 2AN
Tel: (H) 020 8744 1707 Tel: (M) 07711 823 093
Tel: (W) 020 7863 5930 Email: Shelly@colt.net
Club Colours:
League: Herts/Middlesex 4 South

THETFORD RFC
Ground Address: Two Mile Bottom, Munford Road, Thetford, Norfolk Tel: 01842 755176
Email Address: iainharper@aol.com
Brief Directions: From Thetford by-pass at top R/about take A134 King's Lynn Road. 1.5 miles down at bottom of hill on right hand side - concealed entrance.
Hon Secretary: Iain Harper, 15 Anna Sewell Close, Thetford, norfolk IP24 1TN Tel: (H) 01842 765369
Tel: (W) 01842 755711
Email: ish87@hotmail.com
Fixtures Secretary: Gordon Hodgkinson, 48 Nunnery Drive, Thetford, Norfolk Tel: (H) 01842 754667
Club Colours: Red and white hooped shirts, white shorts, red & white socks.
League: London 4 North East

THURROCK RFC
Ground Address: Oakfield, Long Lane, Grays, Essex RM16 2QH Tel: 01375 374877/380641
Email Address: bootsy@nasuwt.net
Web Address: www.thurrockrfc.co.uk
Brief Directions: M25 from north J31/A13 direction Southend, 2nd exit (Grays), 4th exit from 2nd roundabout, off 1st left (Long Lane), 3 miles east to above address, left at flats.
Hon Secretary: Mike Stephenson
Email: bootsy@nasuwt.net
Club Colours: Black with white hoops
League: London 2 North

THURSTON RUFC
Ground Address: Robinson Field, Ixworth Road, Thurston, Suffolk IP31 3QE Tel: 01359 232450
Email Address: Lincoln@assureweb.com
Web Address: www.trufc.co.uk
Brief Directions: Exit A14 Thurston and follow Thurston signs, along Thurston Rd past Cracknells garage on right, under railway bridge, head out of village (school on left), ground 200 yards on right
Hon Secretary: Paul Wreathall, 14 Gardiner Close, Bury St. Edmunds, Suffolk IP33 2UB
Tel: (H) 01284 769545 Tel: (W) 07768 930965
Fixtures Secretary: Jeremy Kendall, 1 Harrington Close, Bury St. Edmunds, Suffolk
Tel: (H) 01284 703043 Tel: (W) 01842 754151
Club Colours: Navy blue shirts with red collar & cuffs, blue shorts, stockings
League: East Counties 2 North

TONBRIDGE JUDDIANS RFC
Ground Address: Tonbridge Juddian Clubhouse, The Slade, Tonbridge, Kent TN9 1HR Tel: 01732 358548
Web Address: www.tonbridge-juddians.co.uk
Brief Directions: In Tonbridge High Street, turn opposite Rose & Crown Hotel into Castle Street. Follow signs to swimming pool but turn right at bottom of Slade into club car park
Hon Secretary: Peter Darbyshire, North Cottage, Capel Grange Farm, Tonbridge, Kent TN12 6QX
Tel: (H) 01892 833103 Tel: (M) 07932 000356
Tel: (W) 01892 833608
Email: CDARBYSHIRE@tinyworld.co.uk
Fixtures Secretary: David Carver, 50 Pennington Place, Tunbridge Wells, Kent TN4 0AQ
Tel: (H) 01892 543 736
Club Colours: Red, white & blue hooped shirts
League: London 3 South East

TOTTONIANS RFC LTD
Ground Address: Totton College, Water Lane, Totton, Southampton, Hants SO40 3ZX Tel: 02380 663810
Brief Directions: From centre of Totton follow directions to Totton College/Recreation Centre. The club is located next door.
Hon Secretary: Graham Searle, Meadow End, Romsey Road,, Stockbridge, SO20 6PR Tel: (H) 01794 388779
Tel: (M) 07980 582736 Tel: (W) 01256 482572
Fixtures Secretary: Stephen Anderson, 2 Redwood Gardens, Larchwood, Southampton, SO40 8SY
Tel: (H) 02380 873 565
Club Colours: Green, black and white hoops
League: London 4 South West

TRING RUFC
Ground Address: Pendley Sports Ground, Cow Lane, Tring, Herts HP23 5NT Tel: 01442 825 710
Web Address: www.tringrufc.co.uk
Brief Directions: Turn north into Cow Lane from A4251 (old A41) east of Tring. Pendley Sports Centre is 500m on the right
Hon Secretary: Paul Lamberth, 85 Lawn Lane, Hemel Hempstead, Herts HP3 9HW
Tel: (H) 01442 212148 Tel: (M) 07767 247264
Email: paul_lamberth@hotmail.com
Fixtures Secretary: Malcolm Rose, 5 Grenadine Way, Tring, Herts HP23 5EA Tel: (H) 01442 381110
Tel: (M) 0783 6665975
Club Colours: Mainly black with gold hooped sleeves
League: Herts/Middlesex 1
Leagues contact: Paul Lamberth, as above

TROJANS RFC
Ground Address: Stoneham Park, Stoneham Lane, Eastleigh, Hants SO50 9HT Tel: 02380 613068
Web Address: www.trojansrugby.co.uk
Brief Directions: M27 J5, proceed south signed Southampton on A335 to 1st lights, right into Bassett Green Rd, right at next lights into Stoneham Ln, under motorway and immediate left
Hon Secretary: John Mist, Westbury House, 14 Bellevue Road, Southampton, SO15 2AY Tel: (H) 02380 583450 Tel: (W) 02380 332844
Email: j.mist@matthewsmist.datanet.co.uk
Fixtures Secretary: C. G. Holt, The Chase, 338 Hill Lane, Southampton, SO15 7PH Tel: (W) 02380 771195
Club Colours: Blue with narrow red hoops
League: London 4 South West

TUNBRIDGE WELLS RFC
Ground Address: St Marks Recreation Ground, Frant Road, Tunbridge Wells Tel: 01892 527448
Website: www.twrfc.com
Brief Directions: Southern outskirts of town, 0.5 miles along the A267 (Frant Road) l/h side at brow of hill
Club Secretary: Steve Bassi, Myringa, Broom Park, Langton Green, Tunbridge Wells, Kent. TN3 0RF
Tel: 01892 863619 Email: stev@bassij.fsnd.co.uk
Fixtures Secretary: Colin Sharples, White Craigs, Stonewall Park Road, Langton Green, Tunbridge Wells.Kent. TA3 0HG Tel: 01892 862580
Club Colours: Navy blue and white quarters
League: London 2 South

TWICKENHAM RFC
Ground Address: Park Fields, South Road, Hampton, Middlesex TW12 3PE
Tel: 020 8979 2427
Email Address: jerry.francis@crowfield.ltd.uk
Web Address: www.twickenhamrugby.com

Brief Directions: A316 to A312; head towards The Hamptons and Kingston; straight across first mini roundabout; right at next mini roundabout into Broad Lane; across a number of spped bumps to next mini roundabout; right into Oak Aveneue; left at Royal Oak PH; straight on to end of South Road
Hon Secretary: Jerry Francis, 50 Hatherop Road, Hampton, Middlesex TW12 2RF
Tel: (H) 020 8941 0877
Club Colours: Red and Black irregular hoops
League: London 2 North

U.C.S. OLD BOYS RFC
Ground Address: UCS Sports Ground, Ranulf Road, London NW2 Tel: 020 8830 6376
Email Address: paul.gee5@btinternet.com
Web Address: ucsobrfc.co.uk
Brief Directions: Please phone fixture secretary
Hon Secretary: Paul Gee, 63 Blackhorse Lane, South Mimms, Herts EN6 3PS Tel: (H) 01707 662748
Tel: (M) 07949 082068 Tel: (W) 020 8900 6702
Email: paul.gee5@btinternet.com
Fixtures Secretary: Simon Dickinson, 48 Riffel Road, London NW2 4PH Tel: (H) 020 8208 4617
Tel: (M) 07930 412298
Email: simondickinson@hotmail.com
Club Colours: Maroon, black and white
League: Herts/Middlesex 1

UCKFIELD RFC
Ground Address: Hempstead Playing Fields, Nevill Road, Manor park, Uckfield Tel: 01825 768956
Brief Directions: The Manor Park Estate is on northern outskirts of the town, turn into Browns Ln entrance & take 2nd road on left, the ground is at the end of the 3rd road on the right
Hon Secretary: Peter Dunn, 9 North Row, Uckfield, TN22 5BN Tel: (H) 01825 760785
Fixtures Secretary: Maureen Poole, Pentlands, 9 Keld Avenue, Uckfield, TN22 5BN Tel: (H) 01825 761151
Club Colours: Amber with purple and white hoops
League: Sussex 1

UNITED SERVICES PORTSMOUTH RFC
Ground Address: United Services Sports Club, Burnaby Road, Portsmouth Tel: 01705 830125
Brief Directions: Enter Portsmouth via M275, follow signs to Isle of Wight Car Ferries, ground on right under railway bridge
Club Secretary: Tex.Houston, 36 Leifgh Road, Fareham, Portsmouth, Hants Tel: 01329 280589
Fixtures Secretary: High Wrightson, USRFC Portsmouth, Burnaby Road, Portsmouth
Tel: (W) 02392 547195 Tel: (M) 07778 935010
Club Colours: Navy blue & red hoops, navy shorts
League: London 4 South West

UNIVERSITY VANDALS RFC
Ground Address: Walton Lane, Walton on Thames, Surrey KT12 1QP Tel: 01932 227 659
email address: bruce@vandalsrugby.freeserve.co.uk
Web Address: www.vandals.co.uk
Hon Secretary: Rob Webb, 52 Carleton Road, Walton-on-Thames, Surrey KT12 2DG Tel: (H) 01932 889550
Tel: (M) 07710 817335
Email: robwebb14@hotmail.com
Fixtures Secretary: John Farrow, 26 Oakdene Court, Walton on Thames, Surrey Tel: (H) 01932 220247
Tel: (M) 07870 642877
Club Colours: Black, purple and emerald green
League: London 3 South West

UPMINSTER RFC
Ground Address: Hall Lane Playing Fields, Hall Lane, Upminster, Essex Tel: 01402 220320
Brief Directions: From M25 take A127 towards Romford, take Upminster turn off, ground 0.5 mile on left over mini roundabout
Hon Secretary: Mick Eve, 142 Cranston Park Avenue, Upminster, Essex RM14 3XJ
Tel: (H) 01708 225383
Fixtures Secretary: James Wilkins, 4 Courtenay Gardens, Upminster, Essex RM14 1DD
Tel: (H) 01708 780630 Tel: (M) 07887 832335
Tel: (W) 020 7268 8722
Club Colours: Yellow and blue hoops
League: London 4 North East

UPPER CLAPTON RFC
Ground Address: Uplands Road, Thornwood Common, Epping, Essex CM16 6NL
Tel: 01992 572588
Brief Directions: M11 north, jct 7.Follow signs to B1393 to Epping. Uplands Rd. on right after 500yds after Rooky Garage.
Hon Secretary: David Miller, 13 Ushfield, Sawbridgeworth, Hertfordshire CM21 9NF
Tel: (H) 01279 724849
Email: dwofclapton@aol.com
Club Colours: Red and white 7inch hoops, white shorts, red & white socks
League: Eastern Counties 1

UXBRIDGE RFC
Ground Address: Uxbridge Cricket Club, Gatting Way, Park Road, Uxbridge, Middlesex. UB8 1RN
Tel: 01895 237571
Website: www.uxbridgerfc.co.uk
Brief Directions: Car: Turn off A60 Uxbridge B483 into Park road - entrance to club .5 mile onleft - Gatting Way. Train: Metropolitan & Piccadilly Line - Uxbridge
Club Secretary: Tony Mahood, 20 Highfield Road, Flackwell Heath, Bucks. HP10 9AN
Tel: 01628 528233
Email: tony.j.mahood@britishairways.com
Fixtures Secretary: Bob McPherson, 44 Campden Road, Ickenham, Middlesex UB10 8EU
Tel: (H) 01895 852065
Email: bob.mcpherson@barclays.net
Club Colours: Black, white & red, horizontal hoops, black, red
League: Hertfordshire & Middlesex 2

VENTNOR RFC
Ground Address: Watcombe Bottom, Whitwell Road, Ventnor, Isle of Wight Tel: 01983 854155
Email Address: ventnorrfc@aol.com
Brief Directions: Approach Ventnor via Wroxall and take Whitwell road, ground next to end of speed limit
Hon Secretary: Tony Flower, 2 Stone Bowe Gardens, Nilton, Isle of Wight PO38 2AU Tel: (H) 01983 730567 Tel: (M) 07970 009766 Tel: (W) 01983 823263
Email: stonebowe@aol.com
Fixtures Secretary: J Adams, B1-1K, Avenue Road, Wroxall, IOW Tel: (H) 01983 854201
Club Colours: Navy Blue with White Hoop, Navy Blue Shorts & Socks
League: Hampshire 2

VERWOOD RUFC
Ground Address: Cranemoor House, Manor Road, Verwood, Dorset, BH31 6EE Tel: 01202 826858
Email Address: admin@verwoodrufc.org.uk
Web Address: www.verwoodrufc.org.uk
Hon Secretary: Andrew Hoggins, 17 Shelley Close, Ashley Heath, Ringwood, Hampshire BH24 2JA
Tel: (H) 01425 475963 Tel: (M) 07986 391905
Tel: (W) 01425 471424
Email: AHoggins@verwoodrufc.org.uk
Fixtures Secretary: Neil Scarisbrick, 32 Acacia Avenue, Verwood, Dorset, BH31 6LQ
Tel: (H) 01202 823351 Tel: (W) 01202 824077
Email: NeilScarisbrick@verwoodrufc.org.uk
Club Colours: Red and white quarters
League: Hampshire 3

VIGO RFC
Ground Address: Swanswood Field, Vigo Village, Havvel Road, Vigo, Kent Tel: 01732 823830
Email Address: press@vigorfc.com
Web Address: www.vigorfc.com
Brief Directions: Please phone Fixture Secretary
Hon Secretary: David Wells, Evenden House, Meopham, Kent DA13 0JE Tel: (H) 01474 813133
Fixtures Secretary: John Taylor, Sandon, Burnt House Lane, Hawley, Kent DA2 7SP Tel: (H) 01322 227363
Tel: (W) 020 7488 0733
Club Colours: Black shirts with red V, black shorts
League: Kent 3

WANDSWORTHIANS RFC
Ground Address: Kings College Sports Ground, Windsor Avenue, New Malden, Surrey. KT3 5HA.
Tel: 020 8942 0495
Brief Directions: Please phone Secretary
Hon Secretary: Graham Sparkes, 21 Nursery Close, Ravenna Road, London SW15 6AS
Tel: (H) 020 8789 3097 Tel: (W) 020 7983 4543
Club Colours: Maroon, white and gold hoops
League: Surrey 3

WANSTEAD RFC
Ground Address: The Sports Ground, Roding Lane North, Woodford Bridge, Ilford, Essex
Tel: 020 8550 1561
Web Address: www.wansteadrfc.com
Brief Directions: From Charlie Brown's roundabout immediately under M11 and North Circular Road, take the eastern carriage way of the Southend Road,left at Harvesters Pub-ground 400 yds on left.
Hon Secretary: Julian Greatrex, 15 Grange Avenue, Woodford Green, Essex IG3 9JT
Tel: (H) 020 8504 0191
Email: julian.greatrex@btinternet.com
Fixtures Secretary: Gill Denton, 18 Hornbeam Close, Essex IG9 6JS Tel: (H) 020 8559 2457
Tel: (M) 07940 462410
Club Colours: Blue and white hoops.
League: East Counties 1

WARE RFC
Ground Address: Wodson Park, Ware, Herts
Tel: 01920 487091
Web Address: www.warefc.co.uk
Brief Directions: From A10 take Ware (North) turn off. Continue along Watton Road to R/about in Ware. Turn Left - Wodson Park is .5 mile on right.
Hon Secretary: Ian Williams, Pond House, Back Lane, Essex EN9 2DD Tel: (H) 01992 892925
Tel: (M) 07810 204280 Tel: (W) 01992 713033
Email: i-a-n@lineone.net
Fixtures Secretary: Martin Warner, 37 Clarks Close, Ware, Herts Tel: (H) 01920 464617
Club Colours: Red, white & blue hoops. Blue shorts.
League: Herts/Middlesex 4 North

WARLINGHAM RFC
Ground Address: 87 Church Way, Sanderstead, Surrey CR2 0JU Tel: 01883 622825
Email Address: warlinghamrfc@btopenworld.com
Web Address: www.warlingham-rfc.com
Brief Directions: Directions: From M25, take junction 6 - A22 towards Caterham. After @ 4 miles at the large concrete roundabout take the third exit up a steep winding road (Succombs Hill.)At the top(T junct) turn right to the village green. Turn left- this is Limpsfield Road. Warlingham RFC is @ 1 mile along on the left hand side. (if you get to the Good Companions pub then you've gone @200 yards too far!)
Hon Secretary: Peter Upton, 87 Church Way, Sanderstead, Surrey CR2 0JU Tel: (H) 020 8657 8844
Tel: (M) 07899 067563 Tel: (W) 020 7548 3112
Email: pju@uptonp.co.uk
Club Colours: Light blue/ white hooped shirts, blue shorts
League: Surrey 1

WASPS FC
Ground Address: Twyford Avenue Sports Ground, Twyford Avenue, Acton, London W3 9QA
Tel: 020 8993 0236 Web Address: www.wasps.co.uk
Brief Directions: Twyford Avenue is on the North side of Uxbridge Road (A4020) about half a mile east of the junction with the North Circular Road (A406)at Ealing Common. Twyford Avenue is opposite the Tesco/Esso Garage on Uxbridge Road. The closest London Underground staion is Ealing Common.
Hon Secretary: Graham Wynde, 94 Stapleton Hall Road, London N4 4QA Tel: (H) 020 8347 9240
Tel: (M) 07887 550 372
Email: grimwynde@yahoo.co.uk
Fixtures Secretary: John Jarvis Tel: (H) 07951 953626
Club Colours: ALL Black with gold badge & bands
League: Herts/Middlesex 2

WATFORD RFC
Ground Address: Knutsford Playing Fields, Radlett Road, Watford, Herts Tel: 01923 243292
Brief Directions: From A41 (M1 J5) take Watford/ town centre link road, right at 1st roundabout, over bridge, car park on left, ground on right.
Fixtures Secretary: B. Cox, 10 Sherbourne Way, Rickmansworth, WD3 3PF Tel: (H) 01923 497834
Club Colours: Red, white and blue hoops/ black/red
League: Herts/Middlesex 4 North

WELWYN RFC
Ground Address: Handside Playing Fields, Hobbs Way, Colgrove, Welwyn Garden City, AL8 6HX
Tel: 01707 329116
Web Address: www.welwynrugby.co.uk
Brief Directions: A1(M) J4, follow signs to Gosline sports park, bear left into Parkway, left at next r'bout into Turmore Dale, 1st left into Colgrove, 30 yds right into Hobbs Way
Hon Secretary: John Sargeant, 67 Woodhall Lane, Welwyn Garden City, AL7 3TG Tel: (H) 01707 331186
Club Colours: Maroon, blue and white hoops, blue shorts, maroon socks
League: London 4 North West

WEMBLEY RFC
Ground Address: Roger Bannisters Playing Fields, Uxbridge Road, Harrow Weald, Middlesex
Tel: 020 8420 1789
Brief Directions: From Harrow on Hill take Harrow View to roundabout, ground on right. From Watford take Oxley Lane, ground on left
Club Secretary: Mrs. Nicola McKeon, 16 Brinsley Road, Harrow Weald, Middlesex HA3 5NY
Tel: (H) 020 8427 0900
Email: tish@08002go.com
Fixtures Secretary: John Conlon, 17 Cleverley Cres., Ealing W5 1DZ Tel. 020 8992 2169
email: johnconlon@moose.co.uk
Club Colours: Black & white quarters
League: Herts/Middlesex 4 North

WEST LONDON RFC
(An amalgamation of three clubs Old Gaytonians, Kingsburians, and Roxeth Manor Old Boys. (2000))
Ground Address: South Vale, Sudbury Hill, Middlesex HA1 3PN Tel: 020 8423 4133
Email Address: westlondonrfc@aol.com
Web Address: www.westlondonrfc.com
Brief Directions: A4127 Greenford Road to Sudbury Hill. South Vale opposite Rising Sun pub. Ground 200 yards on right.
Hon Secretary: Stuart Taffs, 17 Hill Grove, Harrow, Middlesex HA1 3PR
Tel: (H) 020 8423 3120
Club Colours: Red & Black Shirt with broad White band & Black
League: London 3 North West

WEST NORFOLK RUFC
Ground Address: Gatehouse Lane, North Wootton, King's Lynn, Norfolk PE30 3RJ
Tel: 01553 631307
Web Address: www.westnorfolkrugby.com
Brief Directions: A149 to K. Lynn to Hunstanton bypass A148 to K. Lynn r'bout at top of hill, right at lights in Castle Rising Rd, left at T junction to North Wootton, through village to green, left at Gatehouse Lane
Hon Secretary: Roy Hewson, Grange Meadow, Manor Road, King's Lynn, Norfolk PE30 3PZ
Tel: (H) 01553 631660 Tel: (M) 07836 655340
Tel: (W) 01553 631464
Email: royhewson@aol.com
Fixtures Secretary: M. H. Ballman, 1 Thornhill Cottages, Great Heath Road, Dereham, NR20 5EY
Tel: (H) 01362 668935 Tel: (M) 0370 664345
Tel: (W) 01553 773393
Colours: French grey / broad cerise band, navy shorts
League: London 3 North East

WESTCLIFF RFC
Ground Address: The Gables, Aviation Way, Southend-on-Sea, Essex SS2 6UN
Tel: 01702 541499
Brief Directions: A127 turn left at Perrys Ford Garage at Kent Elms corner about .5 mile from Southend. After 200yds turn R. in to Snakes Lane go to end turn R and L at 4th r'about to Aviation Way . Ground 600yds.
Hon Secretary: John Duncombe, 6 The Approach, Rayleigh, Essex SS6 9AA
Tel: (H) 01268 785852 Tel: (W) 01245 294600
Email: john.duncombe@btinternet.com
Club Colours: Maroon and old gold hoops, blue shorts
League: East Counties 2 South

WHITSTABLE RFC
Ground Address: Reeves Way, Chestfield, Whitstable, Kent CT5 3QS Tel: 01227 794343
Brief Directions: A299 Thanet Way to Whitstable, by Chestfield roundabout. The ground is opposite Chestfield & Swalecliffe Railway Station
Hon Secretary: Alistair Russell, Meadow Lea, Herne Common, Herne Bay, Kent CT6 7LB
Tel: (H) 01227 375569 Tel: (M) 07802 711281
Tel: (W) 020 7267 9688
Email: sayer@dircon.co.uk
Fixtures Secretary: Roger Dengate, 70 Regent Street, Whitstable, Kent CT5 1JQ Tel: (H) 01227 264604
Club Colours: Blue and white.
League: Kent 1

WIMBLEDON RFC
Ground Address: Beverley Meads, Barham Road, Copse Hill, Wimbledon, SW20 0ET
Tel: 020 8946 3156
Email Address: terence.bagworth@btinternet.com
Brief Directions: Barham Rd off Copse Hill, off Coombe Lane which is off A3. Nearest train station Raynes Park (BR, Network SE), take No 57 bus to Copse Hill, club at end of Barham Rd
Hon Secretary: Terry Bagworth, 38 Chase Side Avenue, London SW20 8LU Tel: (H) 020 8543 5386
Email: terence.bagworth@btinternet.com
Fixtures Secretary: Richard Baker, 19 Chartwell Place, Epsom, Surrey KT18 5JH
Tel: (H) 01372 729331
Club Colours: Maroon and Cambridge blue
League: London 2 South

WISBECH RFC
Ground Address: Chapel Road, Wisbech
Tel: 01945 636 66
Brief Directions: Along South Brink, (from A47) proceed to Old Market Place, turn left, ground approx 200 yards on right next to garage
Hon Secretary: John Mathew, Chapel Road, Harecroft Road, Wisbech, Cambs, PE1 1RG
Email: john@blowline.co.uk
Club Colours: Red shirts, blue shorts
League: East Counties 2 North

WITHAM RUFC
Ground Address: Spa Road, Witham, Essex CM8 1UN
Tel: 01376 511066
Email Address: webmaster@withamrugby.com
Web Address: www.withamrugby.com
Brief Directions: Leave A12, through Witham to lights at Spinks Lane (signed), turn right under railway bridge, left into private road to club house.
Hon Secretary: Pamela Whelan, 34 Highfields Road, Wtiham, Essex CM8 2HJ
Tel: (H&W) 01376 515871
Email: tomardpam@supanet.com
Fixtures Secretary: Grahaem Ball, 9 Juniper Crescent, Witham, Essex CM8 2NX Tel: (H) 01376 516505
Club Colours: Brown & White Shirts, Navy Shorts & Socks
League: East Counties 3 North

WOKING RFC
Ground Address: Woking RFC, 142 Blackmore Crescent, Sheerwater Woking, Surrey GU 21 5NY
Tel: 01483 836817
Hon Secretary: Ian Vousden Tel: (M) 07973 806621
Email: ian_vousden@veeder.co.uk
Club Colours: Blue and gold hoops, black shorts
League: Surrey 2

WOODBRIDGE RFC
Ground Address: Hatchley Barn, Orford Road, Bromeswell, Woodbridge, Suffolk IP12 2PP
Tel: 01394 460630
Email Address: orcor'demon.co.uk
Brief Directions: From N.or S. A12 take B1084 to Orford R/about, L. straight on past turning to Eyke, entrance half mile on right.
Hon Secretary: Brendan J. Owens, 5 Orwell Court, California, Woodbridge, Suffolk IP12 4DF
Tel: (H) 01394 385314 Tel: (M) 07881 844981
Fixtures Secretary: Michael Fisher, Two Gates, The Street, Woodbridge, Suffolk IP12 2QG
Tel: (H) 01394 460494
Email: twogates@lineone.com
Club Colours: Sky Blue/Black Shorts
League: London 4 North East

WOODFORD RFC
Ground Address: Highhams, High Road, Woodford Green, Essex IG8 9LB
Tel: 020 8504 6769
Brief Directions: Woodford tube station, north via Snakes Ln to Woodford High Rd, turn left for 500yds, club entrance on right 25 yds off main road next to Woodford High School
Hon Secretary: Paul James, 46 Suffield Road, London E4 9TA Tel: (H) 020 8524 9658
Email: pedeja@waitrose.com
Fixtures Secretary: Graham Kane, 134 Hallwood Road, London E11 1AN Tel: (H) 020 8539 0390
Club Colours: White, Lavender, Black and Purple
League: London 2 North

WORTH OLD BOYS SOCIETY RFC
Ground Address: North Avenue, Whiteley Village, Walton On Thames.
Brief Directions: From A3 take A245 to Byfleet.B365, rt into Seven Hills Rd. At roundabout take rt into Burnwood Rd to Whiteley Village on rt.
Club Secretary: Jon Nickel, 65A Burlington Road, London SW6 4NBH Tel: 07970 544825
Emai;l jonathon.nichell@yestelevision.com
Fixtures Secretary: Paul Kozary 21 Hampton Road, Teddington, Middlesex TW11 0JN
Tel: (H) 020 8977 1925 Tel: (W) 0207475 3976
Club Colours: Blue and gold quarters
League: Surrey 3

WORTHING RFC
Ground Address: The Rugby Park, Roundstone Lane, Angmering, West Sussex, BN16 4AX
Tel: 01903 784706
Email Address: rugby@wrfc.co.uk
Web Address: www.worthingrfc.co.uk
Brief Directions: A27 Worthing to Arundel Road, leave at Clapham follow signs to Angmering and A259 Worthing to Littlehampton Road, Turn north at Roundstone Pub R/about, quarter mile on right.
Hon Secretary: Robin White, 12 Ferring Street, Ferring
Tel: (H) 01903 242574
Fixtures Secretary: Nigel Lyons, 48 Brookbarn Way, Worthing, West Sussex
Tel: (H) 01903 506880 Tel: (M) 07776 194001
Club Colours: Blue, chocolate and gold hoops
League: London 2 South

WYMONDHAM RFC
Ground Address: Foster Harrison Memorial Ground, Tuttles Lane, Wymondham, Norfolk
Tel: 01953 607332
Brief Directions: Northern exit A11 by-pass follow signs B1135 to Dereham - Tutles Lane starts at second R/about adjacent Summerfields, 200yds on right behind trees.
Hon Secretary: Martin Warren, 14 Newark Close, Norwich, Norfolk NR7 0YJ
Tel: (H) 01603 437 805 Tel: (W) 01603 616 112
Email: mwarren@lawrence-wood.com
Club Colours: Red and black hooped shirts, black shorts and socks
League: London 3 North East

SOUTH WEST REGION

A complete club index appears at the back of the book.
This shows which Region and league each club is in for the 2002-03 season

South West Region Structure 2002-03

SOUTH WEST 1

- SOUTH WEST 2 EAST
  - SOUTHERN COUNTIES NORTH
    - Berks., Bucks. & Oxfordshire 1
      - Berks, Bucks & Oxon 2
  - SOUTHERN COUNTIES SOUTH
    - Dorset & Wiltshire 1
      - D & W 2 North
      - D & W 2 South
- SOUTH WEST 2 WEST
  - WESTERN COUNTIES WEST
    - Devon & Cornwall
      - Devon 1
        - Devon 2
          - Devon 3
      - Cornwall 1
        - Cornwall 2
  - WESTERN COUNTIES NORTH
    - Gloucestershire Premier
      - Gloucesters.1
        - Gloucesters.2
          - Glos. 3 North
          - Glos. 3 South
    - Somerset Premier
      - Somerset 1
        - Somerset 2

SOUTH WEST LEAGUE OFFICIALS 2002/2003

(South West website – www.swrugby.co.uk)

Chairman of Competition Sub-Committee

A. Boyer, 11 Christopher Court, Boundary Road, NEWBURY, Berks, RG14 7PQ
H 01635 40574. EMAIL: chairman@swrugby.co.uk

Deputy Chairman

N.J. Barber, 2, The Crescent, Alexandra Road, ST IVES, Cornwall, TR26 1BY
H/F 01736 796861 B 01752 665951. EMAIL: co1@swrugby.co.uk

League Co-ordinating Secretary

M. Gee, Foxglove Cottage, 70 Halsetown, ST IVES, Cornwall, TR26 3LZ
H/F 01736 797777 EMAIL secretary@swrugby.co.uk

Deputy League Co-ordinating Secretary

B.L. Flanders, The Cottage, Bishops Green, NEWBURY, Berks, RG20 4HS
H/F 01635 269646. EMAIL sw2e@swrugby.co.uk

South West 1

A. Townsend, 2 Kencourt Close, Kenilworth Avenue, GLOUCESTER, GL2 0QL
H/F 01452 522721 EMAIL: sw1@swrugby.co.uk
Deputy: J. Lipscomb

South West 2 West

J. Lipscomb, 16 Main Road, Western Zoyland, BRIDGWATER, Somerset, TA7 0EB
H/F 01278 691345 EMAIL: sw2w@swrugby.co.uk
Deputy: A. Townsend

South West 2 East & Berks/Bucks & Oxon 1 & 2

B. Flanders, The Cottage, Bishops Green, NEWBURY, Berks, RG20 4HS
H/F 01635 269646. EMAIL EMAIL sw2e@swrugby.co.uk
Deputy: (SW2E) D. McAteer
(BB01&2) N. North, 27 Brocks Way, Shiplake, HENLEY-ON-THAMES, Oxfordshire
RG9 3JG. Tel H 0118 9404196

Cornwall/Devon League

Mrs B. Davis, 3 Kernow House, New Road, ST COLUMB, Cornwall, TR9 6AZ
H/F 01637 881879 B 01209 215620 EMAIL cd@swrugby.co.uk
Deputy: G. Simpson

Cornwall 1 & 2

N.J. Barber, 2, The Crescent, Alexandra Road, ST IVES, Cornwall, TR26 1BY
H/F 01736 796861 B 01752 665951. EMAIL: co1@swrugby.co.uk
Deputy: D. Jenkins

Devon 1

J. D Irvine, 1 Great Rea Road, BRIXHAM, Devon, TQ5 9SW
H 01803 882219 EMAIL: dv1@swrugby.co.uk
Deputy: G. Simpson

Devon 2

P. Harris, 15 Blagdon Close, CREDITON, Devon, EX17 1EL
H 01363 772847 F 01363 775499 M 079 6810 4524 EMAIL: dv2@swrugby.co.uk
Deputy: J. D Irvine

Devon 3

G. Simpson, 108 Pattinson Drive, Mainstone, PLYMOUTH, PL6 8RU
H/F 01752 206662 EMAIL: dv3@swrugby.co.uk
Deputy: P. Harris,

Dorset & Wilts 1

N. Stafford, 5 Windsor Drive, TROWBRIDGE, Wilts, BA14 0JZ
H 01225 345305 EMAIL dw1@swrugby.co.uk
Deputy: K. Jones

Dorset & Wilts 2 North

K. Jones, 13 Stratfield Road, BASINGSTOKE, Hants, RG21 5RS
H 01256 410461 B 0118 982 6750: EMAIL dw2n@swrugby.co.uk
Deputy: D. McAteer

Dorset & Wilts 2 South

D. Beck, 101 Sycamore Close, POOLE, Dorset, BH17 7YH
H: 01202 603936 EMAIL dw2s@swrugby.co.uk
Deputy: C. Drake, Folly's End, Wyke, GILLINGHAM, Dorset, SP8 4NA
H 01747 825856 B 01747 826505 EMAIL tcldrake@follys.freeserve.co.uk

Gloucester Premier, 1, 2, 3N & 3S

K. Plain, Foxhole Farm, Kinsham, TEWKESBURY, Gloucestershire, GL20 8HU
H/B/F 01684 772096. EMAIL: gloucestershire@swrugby.co.uk
Deputy: Mrs W. Bunce, County Office, Foxhole Farm, Kinsham, TEWKESBURY, Glos. GL20 8HU.
B 01684-773900 on Monday, Wednesday and Friday mornings from 9am to 1pm

Southern Counties North

D. McAteer, 38 Silchester Road, Pamber Heath, TADLEY, Hants, RG26 3EF
H:0118 970 1245 B:0118 9303066 BF:0118 9303 411 M: 079 7667 0365
EMAIL: scn@swrugby.co.uk
Deputy: B. Flanders,

Southern Counties South

M. Wild, 46 Castleview Road, Langley, SLOUGH, SL3 7NQ
H/F 01753 770870 B 01628 604311. EMAIL: scs@swrugby.co.uk
Deputy: N. Stafford

Somerset Premier, 1 & 2

C. MacDonald, 8 Sycamore Drive, CREWKERNE, Somerset, TA18 7BT
H/B 01460 78959 F 01460 78293 EMAIL: somerset@swrugby.co.uk
R. Fisher, 20 Rookery Road, Knowle, BRISTOL, BS4 2DS
H 0117 983 6325. EMAIL: Rafisherkb@aol.com

Western Counties North

W. Bishop, Helvellyn, 1 Wiltshire Place, Kingswood, BRISTOL, BS15 4XA
H 0117 957 5729 B 0117 935 2017 F 0117 940 1290 EMAIL: wcn@swrugby.co.uk
Deputy: R. Fisher

Western Counties West

D. Jenkins, Albaston Post Office, Albaston, GUNNISLAKE, Cornwall, PL18 9HQ
H/F 01822 832785 EMAIL: wcw@swrugby.co.uk
Deputy: D. Preece, King William IV PH, Church Road, Madron, PENZANCE, Cornwall, TR20 8SS
H/B 01736 363022 EMAIL: denis_preece@lineone.net

Other Committee Members

J. Dance, Birch Cottage, Padworth Common, READING, RG7 4QG
H 0118 970 0288/0118 970 1246 F 0118 970 1237. EMAIL JonathanDance@therfu.com

B. Morrison, First Eleven Sports Agency, P O BOX 11, READING, RG6 3DT
B 0870 741 5117 F 0870 741 5119 EMAIL: rugby@firsteleven.co.uk

R. G. Wildash, 25 Marina Gardens, WEYMOUTH, Dorset, DT4 9QZ
H/F 01305 773286 EMAIL: wwildash@aol.com

SOUTH WEST ONE

2001-02 LEAGUE TABLE

	P	W	D	L	PF	PA	PD	Pts
Weston-Super-Mare	22	19	0	3	479	259	220	38
Dings Crusaders	22	15	0	7	409	315	94	30
Barnstaple	22	14	0	8	404	328	76	28
Reading	22	12	2	8	480	345	135	26
Cheltenham	22	12	0	10	462	427	35	24
Bridgwater & Albion	22	11	1	10	489	426	63	23
Chinnor	22	11	0	11	421	372	49	22
Keynsham	22	11	0	11	401	358	43	22
Stroud	22	10	1	11	439	478	-39	21
Maidenhead	22	9	0	13	463	511	-48	18
Swanage & Wareham	22	3	2	17	250	458	-208	8
Dorchester	22	2	0	20	258	678	-420	4

2002-03 FIXTURE GRID	Barnstaple	Berry Hill	Bridgwater & Albion	Cheltenham	Chinnor	Cinderford	Clifton	Dings Crusaders	Keynsham	Marlow	Reading	Truro
Barnstaple		12/10	07/09	01/03	28/09	02/11	23/11	01/02	11/01	12/04	21/12	07/12
Berry Hill	18/01		08/02	23/11	05/10	11/01	02/11	12/04	07/12	14/09	15/03	21/12
Bridgwater & Albion	15/03	28/09		02/11	01/03	01/02	12/10	21/12	23/11	07/12	12/04	11/01
Cheltenham	14/09	14/12	04/01		16/11	30/11	29/03	08/02	05/10	26/10	18/01	07/09
Chinnor	08/02	01/02	14/09	21/12		12/10	11/01	23/11	12/04	15/03	07/12	02/11
Cinderford	04/01	26/10	05/10	12/04	18/01		21/12	07/12	15/03	08/02	14/09	23/11
Clifton	14/12	04/01	18/01	07/12	26/10	16/11		15/03	14/09	05/10	08/02	12/04
Dings Crusaders	05/10	30/11	16/11	28/09	14/12	29/03	07/09		18/01	04/01	26/10	01/03
Keynsham	26/10	29/03	14/12	01/02	30/11	07/09	01/03	12/10		16/11	04/01	28/09
Marlow	30/11	01/03	29/03	11/01	07/09	28/09	01/02	02/11	21/12		23/11	12/10
Reading	16/11	07/09	30/11	12/10	29/03	01/03	28/09	11/01	02/11	14/12		01/02
Truro	29/03	16/11	26/10	15/03	04/01	14/12	30/11	14/09	08/02	18/01	05/10	

BARNSTAPLE R.F.C.

Founded: 1877

President K Abrahams c/o Barnstaple R.F.C., Pottington Road, Barnstaple EX31 1JH Tel: 01271 345627
Chairman E Gubb c/o Barnstaple R.F.C as above
Secretary C Jones Lilac Cottage, Velator, Braunton, Devon EX33 2BG
Fixture Secretary S Swanson 5 Church Cottages, Swimbridge, Barnstaple, Devon EX32 0PP Tel. 01271 830514
League Contact Secretary

Ground **Address:** Pottington Road, Barnstaple, EX31 1JH Tel/Fax: 01271 345627
Capacity: 3,000 Covered Seats: 500 Uncovered Standing: 2,500
Website: www.beehive.thisisnorthdevon.co.uk/barnstaplerfc

Directions Take the A361 from Banstaple to Ilfracombe, then go left at the second set of traffic lights after Rolle Quay Bridge in Barnstaple.
Nearest Railway Station: Barnstaple **Car Parking:** Plenty at the ground

Admission: Matchday: £4.00 OAPs £2.00 Children Free Season tickets: Not available.
Clubhouse: Yes **Club Shop:** Yes **Colours**: Red/white/red **Change colours:** Black/white/red
Nickname: Barum **Training Nights:** Tuesday & Thursday 7pm
Programme **Size**: A5 **Pages**: 32 **Price**: Free **Editor**: C Jones **Advertising**: Contact Secretary

BERRY HILL R.F.C.

Founded: 1893

President Nick Jenkins c/o Berry Hill RFC
Chairman John Evans Three Jays, Brecon Way, Edge End, Coleford, Glos. GL16 7EW Tel: 01594 836421
Secretary David Pitaway Ty Mai, Crow Ash Road, Berry Hill, Coleford, Glos. GL16 7RB Tel: 01594 836372 (H)
Fixture Secretary G R Goddard 71a Cheltenham Road, Gloucester. GL2 0JG Tel: 01452 306749 (B)
League Contact: John Cole 2 The Close, Broadwell, Coleford, Glos. GL16 7DJ Tel: 01594 835351

Ground: Lakers Road, Berry Hill, Coleford, Glos. GL16 7YL Tel: 01594 833295 email: hjcole@btinternet.com

Capacity: 200 - all uncovered standing
Directions: From M4 Severn Bridge, M48 to Chepstow, B422B to Coleford, follow signs to Berry Hill.
From M50 to Ross, A40 to Monmouth then A4136 to Berry Hill.

Car Parking: On site **Nearest Railway Station:** Lydney/Gloucester **Admission**: £2.50

Clubhouse: Closed Monday & Wednesday 01594 833295 **Club Shop:** None

Colours: Black and amber quarters **Change colours:** All red **Training Nights:** Tuesday & Thursday

Programme: **Editor:** John Cole as above **ADVERTISING:** Contact John Cole

BRIDGWATER & ALBION R.F.C.

Founded: 1875

President Mike Berry c/o Maxwells, King Square, Bridgwater Tel: 01278 423008
Chairman Bob Hudson 10 Cypress Drive, Puriton, Bridgwater Tel: 01278 683525
Club Secretary Tony Pomeroy Hafod-Y-Gan, Newton Road, North Petherton, Somerset TA6 6SN
Tel: 01278 662181 Fax: 01278 662178 email: apomeroy@ukgateway.net
General Manager Tim Fanning c/o the club office Tel: 01278 423900 (Club) Fax: 01278 446608
Fixtures Secretary Ralph Sealey Cape House, Stawell, Bridgwater, Som. Tel: 01278 722934

Ground Address: Bath Road, College Way, Bridgwater, Somerset. TA6 4TZ. Website: barfc.co.uk
Tel: 01278 423900 Fax: 01278 446608 email: timfanning@barfc.co.uk
Capacity: 5,000 Seated: 630 Standing - Covered: 500 Uncovered: 3,870
Directions: The ground is sign-posted from the A38 and A39 **Car Parking:** 400 spaces available at ground
Nearest Railway Station: Bridgwater (BR) (Bristol to Exeter line). 10 minute walk to the ground.
Club Shop: Matchdays only 12-5. Contact Ben Carp c/o the club
Clubhouse: Open normal licensing hours, snacks available. Function capacity 300, contact Tim Fanning 01278 423900

Training Nights: Tuesday & Thursday **Nickname**: 'Bridgey'
Programme: Size: A5 Price: £1 Pages: 8/12 Editor: Tony Pomeroy Advertising: Contact Tim Fanning c/o the club
Colours: Black with red & amber hoops **Change colours:** Scarlet with black & amber inserts

CHELTENHAM RFC

Founded: 1889

President Keith Plain, Foxhole Farm, Kinsham, Tewkesbury. GL20 6JG 01684 772096 (H & Fax)
Chairman Stephen Ratcliffe, 10 Waterside Close, Andoversford, Cheltenham, Glos. 01242 820824 (H), 01242 233430 (B)
Fixtures Secretary Mike Edwards, 2 Greenbank, Guiting Power, Cheltenham. GL54 5UU 01451 850232 (H), 01452 412444 (B)
Press Officer Tom Parker, 39 Long Mynd Avenue, Cheltenham GL51 5QT 01242 694299 (H & Fax)
Club Secretary David Evans, Cliff Cottage, Leckhampton Hill, Cheltenham GL53 9QG 01242 514519 (H), 01452 509555 (B)
Ground Address: Prince of Wales Stadium, Tommy Taylors Lane, Cheltenham, Glos GL50 4NJ Tel: 01242 525393/522085
Capacity: 2500 Seated: 500 Standing: Uncovered 2000

Directions: From North: M5 J10, 1.5 miles A4019, over lights to r'about, left into Kingsditch Lane. 1st right over bridge then 1st left into Windyridge Rd.. At end turn right and after 400 yds right again into Tommy Taylors Lane. Ground .5 mile on right. **From South:** M5 J11, towards Cheltenham. Pass Golden Valley Hotel and GCHQ to next r'about. Turn left along Princess Elizabeth Way for 1.5 miles to r'about, straight over into Kingsditch Lane - then as above. **From East:** Enter Cheltenham on A40 and proceed thro' Charlton Kings, to lights at junction with Hewltt Rd. Turn right (signed Evesham) and along All Saints Rd, Pittville Circus and Wellington Rd. and turn right onto A435. Continue to r'about at racecourse. Turn left into Swindon Lane and 3rd left into Tommy Taylors Lane.
Nearest Railway Station: Cheltenham (Taxi or bus) **Car Parking:** 300 on ground no charge
Admission: Season - Adults Member £45, V-P £60, Matchday - Adults £4 Children/OAPs £2
Clubhouse: Normal Licensing hours, snacks available. **Club Shop:** Open match-days, Manager J G Pitman 01242 525393
Programme: Size: A5 Price: 50p Pages: 24 + cover Editor: T Parker 01242 694299
Colours: Red & black shirts. **Change colours:** Blue **Training Nights:** Tuesday & Thursday

CHINNOR RFC

Founded: 1963

President	Ken Vaughan	The Old Barn, Brook Street, Watlington, Oxon. 01491 612788
Chairman	Richard John	March House, Mill Lane, Chalgrove, Oxon. 01865 400623
Club Secretary	Gary Porter	16 Haddenham Rd., Kingsey, Bucks. HP17 8LS 01844 291807
Treasurer	Mike Thompson	5 Yeates Close, Thame, Oxon. 01844 261454
Fixtures Secretary		01844 213735
League Contact	Secretary as above	

Ground Address: The Pavilion, Kingsey Road, Thame, Oxon. OX9 3PB Website: chinnor-rfc.com
Tel: 01844 213735 Fax: 01844 213907
Capacity: Ample - all uncovered seating
Directions: Situated on the Thame Western bypass at the junction with the A4129 Thame-Princes Risborough road
Car Parking: 100 plus Nearest Railway Station: Thame / Haddenham Parkway
Admission: Matchday £3 No season tickets available
Club Shop: Yes
Clubhouse: Open 7-11.30pm Mon - Fri, all day Sat & Sun.
Training Nights: Tuesday & Thursday
Programme: Size: A5 Price: with entry Pages: 40 Editor: Sue O'Donnell
Colours: Wide black and narrow white hooped jersey, black shorts Change colours: Gold/black

CINDERFORD

Founded: 1886

President Dave Field
Chairman Rob Worgan
Treasurer Barry Holmes
Club Administrator Dennis Hargreaves Tel/Fax: 01594 825503
Director of Rugby Dennis Hargreaves
Press Officer Nigel Wilce 25, The Oakfield, Cinderford, Glos. GL14 2DA 01594 824017
Ground Address The Recreation Ground, Dockham Rd., Cinderford, Glos. GL14 2AQ
Tel: 01594 822673 **Tel/Fax:** 01594 822400
Capacity 2,000 Covered Seats: 300 Uncovered Standing: 2,700
Directions From the A48 or A40 follow signs for Cinderford. In town centre, at mini-r'about, turn into Dockham Rd., towards the County Store supermarket & ground is just past the car park on left.
Car Parking 100 free spaces at the ground
Admission: Matchday: £4.00
Clubhouse Open 7-11pm weekdays & 12-11pm weekends **Club Shop:** Open clubhouse hours
Training Nights Monday, Tuesday & Thursday evenings
Colours: Red, black & amber **Change colours:** Black with red & amber centre hoops.
PROGRAMME **Size:** A5 **Pages:** 26 **Price:** 50p **Advertising:** Contact Club Administrator

CLIFTON

Founded: 1877

Chairman Richard Clifton 24 Springwood Drive, Henbury, Bristol BS10 7PU
0117 950 6214 (H) 0117 950 0070 (B & Fax) 0385 220436 (M)

Secretary Roger Bealing 13 Frobisher Road, Ashton, Bristol. BS3 3AU. 0117 963 1532 (H & Fax)

Rugby Chairman John Raine 1 Shumack House, High Street, Pensford BS18 4NN
01761 490717 (H) 01761 221190 (B) 01761 221950 (Fax)

Fixtures & Press Secretary Brian Ben Jordan 17 RoyalClose, Henbury, Bristol BS10 7XP e-mail: brainjordan@cableinet.co.uk
0117 950 - 4723 (H), 2855 (Fax), 0117 903 1532 (B - Tue -Thu)

Ground Address: Station Road, Cribbs Causeway, Henbury, Bristol BS10 7TP. Tel: 0117 950 0445 Fax: 0117 950 2855
Capacity: 2,500 Seated: 250 Standing: 2,250 e-mail: brainjordan@cableinet.co.uk

Directions: Leave M5 at J17, taking dual carriageway A4018 towards Bristol (ignore signs to Regional Shopping Centre). Coaches go to 2nd r'about and take bus lane. Entrance to ground on right. Cars go on to next r'about (Old Crow P.H.) & return down other side of dual carriageway. Pass BP petrol station & take next left (signed Clifton RFC). Right at end of lane & ground entrance is on left. The way to ground is signed on dual carriageway. Nearest Railway Station: Bristol Parkway, taxi 15 minutes

Car Parking: 250 spaces on the ground. **Admission**: Matchday - Adults £5, OAPs £2.50, Children Free

Clubhouse: Normal licensing hours, bar meals available. Functions: Capacity 150

Club Shop: Manager Stephanie Batterbury 01275 837523 or Mike Anderton

Colours: Lavender, black and white hoops. **Change colours:** White **Training Nights:** Monday & Wednesday

Programme Size: A5 Price: £1 Pages: 40 + cover Editor: Ben Jordan 0117 950 4723 Advertising Rates: contact club.

DINGS CRUSADERS RFC

Founded: 1897

Club Secretary Rob Stevens , 4 Fonthill Way, Bitton, Bristol BS30 6JY 0117 9329 128 (H) 0117 9881 564 (B)
email: rob.stevens@tinyworld.co.uk

League Contact Gary James, 17 Quantock Close, North Common, Bristol BS15 5UR 0117 961 2397 (H)

GroundAddress: Landseer Avenue, Lockleaze, Bristol. BS7 Tel: 0117 969 1367
Capacity: 1000 Standing: Covered - 5 Uncovered - 995

Directions: M4, J19 > M32 J2 (B4469) towards Horfield.
Turn right at second set of traffic lights before railway bridge towards Lockleaze.
After about a mile turn left into Hogarth Walk and right at the end into Landseer Avenue.

Car Parking: Spaces for 50 cars Nearest Railway Station: Bristol Parkway

Admission: Matchday £2 including programme

Club Shop: None

Clubhouse: Large clubhouse and bar with gym attached

Training Nights: Tuesday & Thursday 7pm

Programme: Size: A5 Price: with admission Pages: 10 Advertising: Contact Club Secretary

Colours: Royal blue and black hoops **Change colours:** Blue and grey hoops

KEYNSHAM R.F.C.

Founded: 1923

President Dennis Cockbaine 'Somercourt', Homefield Rd., Saltford, Bristol 01225 873118

Chairman Jon Bishop 89 Albert Rd., Keynsham, Bristol BS31 1AE 0117 986 0867 (H) 0117 921 8713 (B)

Hon. Secretary Ian Tweedie 1 Oakfield Road, Keynsham, Bristol BS31 1JQ 0117 986 2645
e-mail: Ian@Tweedie32.freeserve.co.uk

Hon. Treasurer Colin Murrin 50 Dunster Rd., Keynsham, Bristol BS31 1WZ 0117 986 5331 (H)

Hon. Coach Jerry Barnes 60 Frome Rd., Radstock, Bath BA3 3LF 07885 925181 (M)

Fixture Secretary David Veal 118 Harrington Rd., Stockwood, Bristol BS14 8JR 01275 543416

League Contact Eric Slater 4 Castle Rd., Kingswood, Bristol BS15 1PF 0117 961 5718 (H)

Ground **Address:** Crown Fields, Bristol Rd., Keynsham BS31 2BE **Tel:** 0117 987 2520
Capacity: All uncovered standing **Car Parking:** Unlimited
Nearest Railway Station: Keynsham, 10 mins walk

Directions Follow A4 from Bristol city centre, follow signs for Keynsham & Keynsham town centre.
As you enter Keynsham the rugby club is on the left hand side.

Admission: Matchday: £3.00, incl programme. Season tickets: Not available.

Clubhouse: Open lunch & evening every day. Available for hire, contact Liz Way at the club.

Club Shop: open matchdays & sun. am

Colours: Amber & black **Change colours:** Black **Training Nights:** Tuesday & Thursday

Programme **Size**: A5 **Pages**: 10 **Price**: With admission **Advertising**: Contact Jim Brooks 01761 470229

MARLOW R.U.F.C.

Club Secretary Graham Cutts, 6 Eastern Dene, Hazlemere, Bucks. HP15 7BT
Tel: (H) 01494 711391 (W) 01494 431717
Fixtures Secretary Graham Cutts, as above

Ground Address Riverwoods Drive, Marlow, Bucks
Tel: 016284 77054/83911
Club Colours: Black and white hoops, black shorts

READING R.F.C.

Founded: 1898

President	Ted Goodhew	10 Lamplighters Walk, Fords Farm, Reading RG31 7YU	01189 451015
Chairman	Hugh Crabtree	Ashleigh House, 236 Wokingham Rd., Reading RG6 1JS	01189 261236
Club Secretary	Tim Gilbert	130 St Peters Rd., Reading RG6 1PH	01189 668077
Commercial Manager	Mark Richards	c/o Reading RFC	01189 696592
Publicity	Dave Parish	19 Doddington Close, Lower Earley RG6 4BJ	01189 313321
Operations	Andrew Green	23 Tennyson Rd., Woodley, Berks. RG5 3RH	01189 697733
Rugby Administrator	Phil Betts	7 Sherwood Rd., Winnersh, RG41 5NH	01189 78706

Ground: Holme Park, Sonning Lane, Reading RG4 6ST Tel: 01189 696592 Fax: 01189 696593
Capacity: 2,500 Seated: 200 Standing: 2,300 e-mail: enquiries@readingrfc.co.uk
Directions: A4 Reading to Maidenhead Road, turn left 2.5 miles out of Reading, sign posted Sonning.
Nearest Railway Station: Reading Mainline, by short taxi journey (10 mins). **Car Parking:** 250 at ground, 200 nearby
Admission: Matchday: Standing Adults £5, including programme
Club Shop: Open Sat 1-5 plus training times Contact Andrew Green, c/o Club
Clubhouse: Open daily depending upon club activitiesSnacks & bar meals available.
Functions: Capacity 150 - contact Andy Weller 01189 696592
Training Nights: Tuesdays & Thursdays (Seniors) **Nickname**: Green Machine
PROGRAMME Size: A5 Pages: 72 Price: with admission Editor: Mark Richards Advertising: Contact Mark Richards
Colours: Myrtle & white 'V'/myrtle. **Change colours:** Yellow with myrtle 'V', collar & cuffs

TRURO R.F.C.

Founded: 1890

President	Paul Charnaud	14 Broad st., Truro TR1 1SA	Tel: 01872 270098
Chairman	Alan Milliner	29 Redannick Cres., Truro. TR1 2DQ	Tel: 01872 240788
Vice Chairman	Nigel Whitford	47 College Way, Gloweth, Truro	Tel: 01872 279735
Hon. Secretary	John Collier	1 Bishop Temple Road, Truro TR1 1YP	Tel: 01872 225632
Fixture Sec.	Mike Woolcock	9 Green Close, Truro TR1 2DD	Tel: 01872 262020
Head Coach / League Contact	Steve Enoch	16 Woodlands Ct., Tremorvah Wood Lane, Truro TR1 1SA	Tel: 01872 242289

Ground Address St. Clements Hill, Truro, Cornwall TR1 1NY Tel: 01872 274750
Capacity: 2,000 all uncovered standing
Directions: A30, leave at signpost for Trispen A39 to Truro at large roundabout, enter left St. Clements Hill next to Police station - ground on right at the top of the hill
Car Parking: 150 spaces available at the ground
Admission: Matchday £4 Season tickets: By VIP membership only
Clubhouse: open Tues-Thur eves, all day Sat. & Sun. morning during the season. **Club Shop:** Yes
Colours: Royal blue & amber **Change colours:** Black & gold **Training Nights:** Tuesday & Thursday
Programme: **Size**: A5 **Pages**: 20 **Price**: with admission **Editor**: contact Secretary
Advertising: Contact Paul Barnes 7 Bedruthan Ave.,Truro 01872 242018

SOUTH WEST

SOUTH WEST REGION FINAL LEAGUE TABLES 2001-02

South West 2 East

	P	W	D	L	PF	PA	PD	Pts	-
Marlow	22	21	0	1	787	197	590	42	
Chippenham	22	19	0	3	610	245	365	38	
Abbey	22	17	0	5	640	233	407	34	
Amersham & Chiltern	22	11	1	10	458	327	131	23	
Windsor	22	11	1	10	267	383	-116	23	
Salisbury	22	10	0	12	385	440	-55	20	
Stow-on-the-Wold	22	9	2	11	304	379	-75	20	
Aylesbury	22	9	0	13	306	496	-190	18	
Tadley	22	8	0	14	339	528	-189	16	
Slough	22	6	1	15	208	437	-229	13	
Redingensians	22	6	0	16	334	517	-183	12	
Olney	22	2	1	19	206	662	-456	5	

South West 2 West

	P	W	D	L	PF	PA	PD	Pts	-
Truro	22	18	1	3	683	255	428	37	
Berry Hill	22	18	1	3	555	244	311	37	
Brixham	22	15	1	6	657	367	290	31	
Cleve	22	14	1	7	527	312	215	29	
Matson	22	10	2	10	384	409	-25	22	
Gloucester Old Boys	22	10	0	12	362	438	-76	20	
Hornets	22	9	1	12	424	476	-52	19	
*Taunton	22	10	0	12	497	543	-46	18	2
*Crediton	22	9	1	12	436	413	23	17	2
Torquay Athletic	22	7	0	15	329	514	-185	14	
Camborne	22	4	0	18	288	664	-376	8	
*Cheltenham North	22	4	0	18	276	783	-507	6	2

Southern Counties North

	P	W	D	L	PF	PA	PD	Pts	-
Oxford Harlequins	18	17	0	1	933	163	770	34	
Grove	18	15	0	3	631	192	439	30	
Witney	18	11	0	7	376	274	102	22	
Beaconsfield	18	11	0	7	396	365	31	22	
High Wycombe	18	10	0	8	330	345	-15	20	
Swindon	18	9	1	8	398	349	49	19	
Buckingham	18	8	1	9	340	397	-57	17	
Chipping Norton	18	4	0	14	180	525	-345	8	
Milton Keynes	18	2	0	16	156	570	-414	4	
Oxford	18	2	0	16	179	739	-560	4	

Southern Counties South

	P	W	D	L	PF	PA	PD	Pts	-
Wimborne	18	17	0	1	511	116	395	34	
Oakmeadians	18	13	0	5	548	269	279	26	
Bournemouth	18	12	0	6	555	277	278	24	
Devizes	18	9	0	9	321	325	-4	18	
Ivel Barbarians	18	9	0	9	321	421	-100	18	
Wootton Bassett	18	8	1	9	369	335	34	17	
Frome	18	8	0	10	284	396	-112	16	
Swindon College	18	6	1	11	351	559	-208	13	
Corsham	18	6	0	12	287	435	-148	12	
Cooper Avon Tyres	18	1	0	17	241	655	-414	2	

Western Counties North

	P	W	D	L	PF	PA	PD	Pts	-
Clevedon	22	20	1	1	780	200	580	41	
St Mary's O.B. (SW)	22	20	1	1	695	233	462	41	
Coney Hill	22	15	0	7	603	398	205	30	
Walcot	22	13	1	8	601	439	162	27	
*Old Richians	22	12	1	9	454	409	45	23	2
Gordon League	22	9	1	12	337	421	-84	19	
Old Redcliffians	22	9	0	13	390	414	-24	18	
Thornbury	22	8	0	14	431	460	-29	16	
Whitehall	22	8	0	14	259	458	-199	16	
Old Centralians	22	8	0	14	394	609	-215	16	
Chew Valley	22	5	1	16	261	608	-347	11	
North Bristol	22	2	0	20	235	791	-556	4	

Western Counties West

	P	W	D	L	PF	PA	PD	Pts	-
Exmouth	22	20	0	2	869	213	656	40	
Penryn	22	19	0	3	812	240	572	38	
Bideford	22	13	0	9	473	359	114	26	
Hayle	22	12	1	9	526	392	134	25	
Withycombe	22	12	0	10	427	337	90	24	
Newton Abbot	22	11	0	11	537	361	176	22	
St Just	22	10	1	11	348	459	-111	21	
Tiverton	22	10	0	12	375	554	-179	20	
Ivybridge	22	9	0	13	403	372	31	18	
Okehampton	22	6	1	15	319	669	-350	13	
South Molton	22	5	1	16	250	796	-546	11	
St Austell	22	2	2	18	284	871	-587	6	

Cornwall/Devon	P	W	D	L	PF	PA	PD	Pts	-
Paignton	18	12	1	5	473	270	203	25	
St Ives (SW)	18	12	1	5	437	308	129	25	
Wellington	18	11	0	7	311	317	-6	22	
Devonport Services	18	10	1	7	365	307	58	21	
Wessex	18	9	2	7	367	274	93	20	
Wadebridge Camels	18	10	0	8	396	330	66	20	
Newquay Hornets	18	8	1	9	209	268	-59	17	
Old Plymothian & Mann.	18	7	1	10	371	363	8	15	
Torrington	18	5	3	10	267	440	-173	13	
Saltash	18	1	0	17	227	546	-319	2	

Cornwall 1	P	W	D	L	PF	PA	PD	Pts	-
Bude	16	15	0	1	674	110	564	30	
Mounts Bay	16	13	0	3	339	191	148	26	
Perranporth	16	11	0	5	592	190	402	22	
St Agnes	16	7	0	9	423	408	15	14	
*Liskeard-Looe	16	8	0	8	320	341	-21	14	2
Bodmin	16	7	0	9	227	285	-58	14	
Falmouth	16	6	0	10	269	374	-105	12	
Helston	16	5	0	11	155	340	-185	10	
*Callington	16	0	0	16	112	872	-760	-2	2

Cornwall 2	P	W	D	L	PF	PA	PD	Pts	-
St Day	14	13	0	1	548	91	457	26	
Redruth Albany	14	11	0	3	359	95	264	22	
Veor	14	10	0	4	221	176	45	20	
Illogan Park	14	9	0	5	334	155	179	18	
Roseland	14	7	0	7	372	138	234	14	
*Camborne S o M	14	3	0	11	194	318	-124	4	2
*Stithians	14	3	0	11	193	367	-174	2	4
*Lankelly Fowey	14	0	0	14	22	903	-881	-6	6

Devon 1	P	W	D	L	PF	PA	PD	Pts	-
Kingsbridge	18	18	0	0	693	98	595	36	
Teignmouth	18	14	0	4	427	274	153	28	
Honiton	18	13	0	5	455	242	213	26	
Sidmouth	18	11	0	7	396	258	138	22	
Cullompton	18	7	1	10	291	334	-43	15	
Devonport HSOB	18	7	0	11	229	359	-130	14	
Tamar Saracens	18	7	0	11	214	364	-150	14	
Tavistock	18	6	0	12	258	431	-173	12	
*Old Public Oaks	18	4	1	13	196	536	-340	7	2
*Old Technicians	18	2	0	16	143	406	-263	2	2

Devon 2	P	W	D	L	PF	PA	PD	Pts	-
Topsham	14	11	0	3	379	189	190	22	
Exeter Saracens	14	10	0	4	344	151	193	20	
Ilfracombe	14	10	0	4	232	186	46	20	
Dartmouth	14	9	0	5	302	220	82	18	
Totnes	14	8	0	6	294	225	69	16	
*Marjons	14	6	0	8	214	196	18	8	4
Plymouth Civil Service	14	2	0	12	139	325	-186	4	
Plympton Victoria	14	0	0	14	143	555	-412	0	

Devon 3	P	W	D	L	PF	PA	PD	Pts	-
Prince R/Woodland F	10	10	0	0	330	93	237	20	
North Tawton	10	4	2	4	132	195	-63	10	
Plymouth Argaum	10	3	3	4	136	226	-90	9	
Buckfastleigh	10	4	0	6	162	155	7	8	
Salcombe	10	4	0	6	172	177	-5	8	
*St Columba & Torpoint	10	2	1	7	141	227	-86	3	2

Gloucester Premier	P	W	D	L	PF	PA	PD	Pts	-
Spartans	18	15	2	1	561	226	335	32	
Drybrook	18	13	2	3	445	217	228	28	
Barton Hill	18	13	0	5	482	264	218	26	
Cirencester	18	10	2	6	328	256	72	22	
Avonmouth OB	18	10	1	7	537	301	236	21	
Chosen Hill F. P.	18	10	1	7	495	313	182	21	
Longlevens	18	8	0	10	342	394	-52	16	
Hucclecote	18	4	0	14	238	552	-314	8	
Bristol Saracens	18	2	0	16	206	459	-253	4	
*Chipping Sodbury	18	1	0	17	161	813	-652	0	2

Gloucester 1	P	W	D	L	PF	PA	PD	Pts	-
Aretians	18	16	0	2	692	222	470	32	
Painswick	18	15	1	2	551	246	305	31	
Old Bristolians	18	12	0	6	385	305	80	24	
Ashley Down Old Boys	18	9	0	9	402	378	24	18	
Bream	18	7	2	9	267	353	-86	16	
Tewkesbury	18	7	0	11	368	294	74	14	
*Frampton Cotterell	18	7	1	10	244	469	-225	13	2
Brockworth	18	5	1	12	275	437	-162	11	
Old Cryptians	18	5	1	12	265	449	-184	11	
Westbury on Severn	18	4	0	14	198	494	-296	8	

Gloucester 2	P	W	D	L	PF	PA	PD	Pts	-
Bishopston	16	13	1	2	480	200	280	27	
Southmead	16	13	1	2	336	172	164	27	
Widden Old Boys	16	10	0	6	347	350	-3	20	
Cheltenham Saracens	16	7	2	7	200	262	-62	16	
Kingswood	16	7	1	8	237	322	-85	15	
Old Elizabethans	16	5	2	9	238	372	-134	12	
*Cheltenham Civil Service	16	6	0	10	350	301	49	10	2
Old Colstonians	16	5	0	11	366	352	14	10	
Dursley	16	2	1	13	182	405	-223	5	

St Brendans OB have withdrawn and their results have been removed.

Gloucester 3 North	P	W	D	L	PF	PA	PD	Pts	-
Ross On Wye	12	11	0	1	230	70	160	22	
Smiths (Industries)	12	10	0	2	337	88	249	20	
Gloucester All Blues	12	6	0	6	125	225	-100	12	
Fairford	12	5	1	6	170	194	-24	11	
Gloucester Civil Service	12	4	2	6	103	196	-93	10	
*Newent	12	2	1	9	97	222	-125	-1	6
*Tredworth	12	2	0	10	90	157	-67	-4	1

Gloucester 3 South	P	W	D	L	PF	PA	PD	Pts	-
Minchinhampton	12	11	0	1	345	138	207	22	
Cainscross	12	10	0	2	240	100	140	20	
Bristol Telephones	12	8	0	4	234	217	17	16	
Bristol Aeroplane Co	12	4	0	8	116	206	-90	8	
*Cotham Park	12	4	1	7	214	230	-16	7	2
*Tetbury	12	3	1	8	173	233	-60	5	2
*Wotton	12	1	0	11	105	303	-198	-6	8

Somerset Premier	P	W	D	L	PF	PA	PD	Pts	-
Bristol Harlequins	22	19	1	2	544	179	365	39	
Yatton	22	19	0	3	543	270	273	38	
Tor	22	15	0	7	413	366	47	30	
Gordano	22	14	0	8	536	215	321	28	
Wiveliscombe	22	13	2	7	447	315	132	28	
Midsomer Norton	22	13	0	9	473	315	158	26	
St Bernadettes Old Boys	22	10	1	11	324	337	-13	21	
Avon	22	8	1	13	409	477	-68	17	
Oldfield Old Boys	22	6	0	16	328	452	-124	12	
*Old Culverhaysians	22	5	1	16	361	521	-160	9	2
*Minehead Barbarians	22	5	0	17	305	647	-342	8	2
*Wells	22	2	0	20	156	745	-589	0	4

Somerset 1	P	W	D	L	PF	PA	PD	Pts	-
Nailsea & Backwell	22	19	0	3	870	131	739	38	
North Petherton	22	19	0	3	888	182	706	38	
Stothert & Pitt	22	16	2	4	517	261	256	34	
Combe Down	22	15	0	7	631	337	294	30	
Imperial	22	10	1	11	386	446	-60	21	
Chard	22	10	0	12	411	412	-1	20	
Avonvale	22	9	1	12	390	536	-146	19	
*Crewkerne	22	10	0	12	391	383	8	18	2
*Broad Plain	22	10	0	12	372	458	-86	18	2
Old Sulians	22	7	0	15	267	559	-292	14	
Old Ashtonians	22	5	0	17	266	671	-405	10	
Burnham on Sea	22	0	0	22	144	1157	-1013	0	

Somerset 2	P	W	D	L	PF	PA	PD	Pts	-
Bristol Barbarians	14	13	0	1	492	104	388	26	
Bath Old Edwardians	14	11	1	2	339	153	186	23	
Winscombe	14	10	1	3	448	118	330	21	
Blagdon	14	8	0	6	292	274	18	16	
Bath Saracens	14	6	0	8	271	344	-73	12	
Castle Cary	14	5	0	9	212	301	-89	10	
Morganians	14	2	0	12	115	357	-242	4	
*Cheddar Valley	14	0	0	14	75	593	-518	-4	4

Berks/Bucks & Oxon 1	P	W	D	L	PF	PA	PD	Pts	-
Bicester	18	16	0	2	595	141	454	32	
Wallingford	18	14	1	3	466	231	235	29	
Henley Wanderers	18	13	2	3	411	207	204	28	
Phoenix	18	10	1	7	306	263	43	21	
Drifters	18	10	0	8	311	341	-30	20	
Thatcham	18	7	2	9	286	310	-24	16	
Pennanians	18	8	0	10	182	323	-141	16	
Bletchley	18	6	1	11	306	401	-95	13	
Chesham	18	2	1	15	176	395	-219	5	
*Wheatley	18	0	0	18	111	538	-427	-2	2

Berks/Bucks & Oxon 2	P	W	D	L	PF	PA	PD	Pts	-
Littlemore	12	10	0	2	345	109	236	20	
Aldermaston	12	8	1	3	207	150	57	17	
Gosford All Blacks	12	7	0	5	184	127	57	14	
*Berkshire Shire Hall	12	7	1	4	210	172	38	13	2
Abingdon	12	4	2	6	179	169	10	10	
Harwell	12	2	1	9	115	264	-149	5	
*Winslow	12	1	1	10	64	313	-249	1	2

Didcot have withdrawn from the League - their results and fixtures have been removed.

Dorset & Wilts 1	P	W	D	L	PF	PA	PD	Pts	-
Westbury	14	11	0	3	392	197	195	22	
Calne	14	10	0	4	253	166	87	20	
Trowbridge	14	8	0	6	296	186	110	16	
Blandford	14	8	0	6	265	211	54	16	
Minety	14	6	0	8	205	187	18	12	
North Dorset	14	5	1	8	213	275	-62	11	
Martock	14	5	0	9	160	310	-150	10	
Bridport	14	2	1	11	137	389	-252	5	

Dorset & Wilts 2 North	P	W	D	L	PF	PA	PD	Pts	-
Bradford on Avon	12	11	1	0	554	62	492	23	
Supermarine	12	8	1	3	398	166	232	17	
Hungerford	12	7	1	4	247	165	82	15	
Cricklade	12	7	1	4	192	121	71	15	
Marlborough	12	4	0	8	204	292	-88	8	
Colerne	12	3	0	9	224	432	-208	6	
Pewsey Vale	12	0	0	12	34	615	-581	0	

Dorset & Wilts 2 South	P	W	D	L	PF	PA	PD	Pts	-
Sherborne	10	10	0	0	364	68	296	20	
Weymouth	10	8	0	2	387	116	271	16	
Wincanton	10	6	0	4	197	114	83	12	
Puddletown	10	4	0	6	174	266	-92	8	
Warminster	10	2	0	8	97	414	-317	4	
*Poole	10	0	0	10	10	251	-241	-6	6

South West 2 West

	Brixham	Cleve	Clevedon	Crediton	Exmouth	Gloucester O. B.	Hornets	Matson	St Mary's O.B. (SW)	Stroud	Taunton	Torquay Athletic
Brixham		21/12	15/03	28/09	02/11	23/11	01/02	12/04	01/03	11/01	12/10	07/12
Cleve	16/11		05/10	30/11	28/09	18/01	29/03	26/10	14/12	01/03	07/09	04/01
Clevedon	07/09	01/02		12/10	01/03	11/01	02/11	21/12	28/09	07/12	23/11	12/04
Crediton	08/02	12/04	18/01		23/11	07/12	11/01	15/03	05/10	21/12	02/11	14/09
Exmouth	04/01	08/02	14/09	14/12		05/10	30/11	18/01	16/11	07/09	29/03	26/10
Gloucester Old Boys	14/12	12/10	26/10	29/03	01/02		07/09	04/01	30/11	28/09	01/03	16/11
Hornets	05/10	07/12	04/01	26/10	12/04	15/03		14/09	18/01	23/11	21/12	08/02
Matson	30/11	11/01	16/11	07/09	12/10	02/11	01/03		29/03	01/02	28/09	14/12
St Mary's O.B. (SW)	14/09	23/11	08/02	01/02	21/12	12/04	12/10	07/12		02/11	11/01	15/03
Stroud	26/10	14/09	29/03	16/11	15/03	08/02	14/12	05/10	04/01		30/11	18/01
Taunton	18/01	15/03	14/12	04/01	07/12	14/09	16/11	08/02	26/10	12/04		05/10
Torquay Athletic	29/03	02/11	30/11	01/03	11/01	21/12	28/09	23/11	07/09	12/10	01/02	

South West 2 East

	Abbey	Amersham & Chiltern	Chippenham	Dorchester	Grove	Maidenhead	Oxford Harlequins	Salisbury	Stow-on-the-Wold	Swanage & Wareham	Wimborne	Windsor
Abbey		07/09	28/09	01/03	01/02	12/10	11/01	02/11	23/11	12/04	21/12	07/12
Amersham & Chiltern	15/03		01/03	02/11	21/12	28/09	23/11	01/02	12/10	07/12	12/04	11/01
Chippenham	08/02	14/09		21/12	23/11	01/02	12/04	12/10	11/01	15/03	07/12	02/11
Dorchester	14/09	04/01	16/11		08/02	14/12	05/10	30/11	29/03	26/10	18/01	07/09
Grove	05/10	16/11	14/12	28/09		30/11	18/01	29/03	07/09	04/01	26/10	01/03
Maidenhead	18/01	08/02	05/10	23/11	12/04		07/12	11/01	02/11	14/09	15/03	21/12
Oxford Harlequins	26/10	14/12	30/11	01/02	12/10	29/03		07/09	01/03	16/11	04/01	28/09
Salisbury	04/01	05/10	18/01	12/04	07/12	26/10	15/03		21/12	08/02	14/09	23/11
Stow-on-the-Wold	14/12	18/01	26/10	07/12	15/03	04/01	14/09	16/11		05/10	08/02	12/04
Swanage & Wareham	30/11	29/03	07/09	11/01	02/11	01/03	21/12	28/09	01/02		23/11	12/10
Wimborne	16/11	30/11	29/03	12/10	11/01	07/09	02/11	01/03	28/09	14/12		01/02
Windsor	29/03	26/10	04/01	15/03	14/09	16/11	08/02	14/12	30/11	18/01	05/10	

Western Counties West

	Bideford	Camborne	Hayle	Ivybridge	Newton Abbot	Okehampton	Paignton	Penryn	St. Ives (SW)	St Just	Tiverton	Withycombe
Bideford		07/09	01/03	28/09	01/02	12/10	02/11	11/01	23/11	21/12	12/04	07/12
Camborne	15/03		02/11	01/03	21/12	28/09	01/02	23/11	12/10	12/04	07/12	11/01
Hayle	14/09	04/01		16/11	08/02	14/12	30/11	05/10	29/03	18/01	26/10	07/09
Ivybridge	08/02	14/09	21/12		23/11	01/02	12/10	12/04	11/01	07/12	15/03	02/11
Newton Abbot	05/10	16/11	28/09	14/12		30/11	29/03	18/01	07/09	26/10	04/01	01/03
Okehampton	18/01	08/02	23/11	05/10	12/04		11/01	07/12	02/11	15/03	14/09	21/12
Paignton	04/01	05/10	12/04	18/01	07/12	26/10		15/03	21/12	14/09	08/02	23/11
Penryn	26/10	14/12	01/02	30/11	12/10	29/03	07/09		01/03	04/01	16/11	28/09
St Ives (SW)	14/12	18/01	07/12	26/10	15/03	04/01	16/11	14/09		08/02	05/10	12/04
St Just	16/11	30/11	12/10	29/03	11/01	07/09	01/03	02/11	28/09		14/12	01/02
Tiverton	30/11	29/03	11/01	07/09	02/11	01/03	28/09	21/12	01/02	23/11		12/10
Withycombe	29/03	26/10	15/03	04/01	14/09	16/11	14/12	08/02	30/11	05/10	18/01	

SOUTH WEST

Cornwall/ Devon

	Bude	Devonport Services	Kingsbridge	Newquay Hornets	South Molton	St. Austell	Teignmouth	Wadebridge Camels	Wellington	Wessex
Bude		28/09	14/12	02/11	30/11	08/02	12/10	29/03	18/01	14/09
Devonport Services	01/03		05/10	14/09	26/10	01/02	04/01	16/11	12/04	07/12
Kingsbridge	16/11	08/02		28/09	01/02	12/04	07/12	26/10	15/03	04/01
Newquay Hornets	04/01	15/03	01/03		05/10	16/11	12/04	01/02	07/12	26/10
South Molton	12/04	18/01	12/10	08/02		07/12	15/03	04/01	28/09	16/11
St Austell	05/10	12/10	30/11	14/12	29/03		18/01	14/09	02/11	01/03
Teignmouth	01/02	02/11	29/03	30/11	14/09	26/10		01/03	14/12	05/10
Wadebridge Camels	07/12	14/12	18/01	12/10	02/11	15/03	28/09		08/02	12/04
Wellington	26/10	30/11	14/09	29/03	01/03	04/01	16/11	05/10		01/02
Wessex	15/03	29/03	02/11	18/01	14/12	28/09	08/02	30/11	12/10	

Cornwall 1

	Bodmin	Falmouth	Helston	Liskeard-Looe	Mounts Bay	Perranporth	Saltash	St Agnes	St. Day
Bodmin		05/10	01/02	26/10	04/01	16/11	01/03	12/04	14/09
Falmouth	08/02		12/04	01/02	07/12	26/10	16/11	15/03	28/09
Helston	12/10	30/11		29/03	18/01	14/09	05/10	02/11	14/12
Liskeard-Looe	18/01	12/10	07/12		15/03	04/01	12/04	28/09	08/02
Mounts Bay	02/11	29/03	26/10	14/09		01/03	01/02	14/12	30/11
Perranporth	14/12	18/01	15/03	02/11	28/09		07/12	08/02	12/10
Saltash	28/09	14/12	08/02	30/11	12/10	29/03		18/01	02/11
St Agnes	30/11	14/09	04/01	01/03	16/11	05/10	26/10		29/03
St Day	15/03	01/03	16/11	05/10	12/04	01/02	04/01	07/12	

Cornwall 2

	Callington	Camborne S o M	Illogan Park	Lankelly Fowey	Redruth Albany	Roseland	Stithians	Veor
Callington		02/11	12/10	12/04	08/02	14/09	18/01	30/11
Camborne S o M	01/03		14/09	18/01	12/10	08/02	30/11	12/04
Illogan Park	01/02	04/01		01/03	28/09	30/11	12/04	26/10
Lankelly Fowey	07/12	28/09	02/11		15/03	12/10	08/02	04/01
Redruth Albany	26/10	01/02	18/01	30/11		12/04	14/09	01/03
Roseland	04/01	26/10	15/03	01/02	07/12		02/11	28/09
Stithians	28/09	15/03	07/12	26/10	04/01	01/03		01/02
Veor	15/03	07/12	08/02	14/09	02/11	18/01	12/10	

Devon 1

	Cullompton	Devonport HSOB	Exeter Saracens	Honiton	Old Plymothian	Sidmouth	Tamar Saracens	Tavistock	Topsham	Torrington
Cullompton		14/09	05/10	01/03	01/02	04/01	16/11	12/04	26/10	07/12
Devonport HSOB	15/03		01/03	04/01	16/11	12/04	01/02	07/12	05/10	26/10
Exeter Saracens	08/02	28/09		16/11	12/04	07/12	26/10	15/03	01/02	04/01
Honiton	28/09	02/11	14/12		08/02	12/10	29/03	18/01	30/11	14/09
Old Plymothian &	12/10	14/12	30/11	05/10		18/01	14/09	02/11	29/03	01/03
Sidmouth	02/11	30/11	29/03	01/02	26/10		01/03	14/12	14/09	05/10
Tamar Saracens	14/12	12/10	18/01	07/12	15/03	28/09		08/02	02/11	12/04
Tavistock	30/11	29/03	14/09	26/10	04/01	16/11	05/10		01/03	01/02
Topsham	18/01	08/02	12/10	12/04	07/12	15/03	04/01	28/09		16/11
Torrington	29/03	18/01	02/11	15/03	28/09	08/02	30/11	12/10	14/12	

Devon 2

	Dartmouth	Ilfracombe	Marjons	North Tawton	Old Public Oaks	Old Technicians	Prince R/Woodland F	Totnes
Dartmouth		18/01	12/10	14/09	08/02	01/03	30/11	12/04
Ilfracombe	28/09		15/03	02/11	12/10	07/12	08/02	04/01
Marjons	01/02	30/11		18/01	12/04	26/10	14/09	01/03
North Tawton	04/01	01/03	28/09		30/11	01/02	12/04	26/10
Old Public Oaks	26/10	01/02	07/12	15/03		04/01	02/11	28/09
Old Technicians	02/11	12/04	08/02	12/10	14/09		18/01	30/11
Prince R/Woodland F	15/03	26/10	04/01	07/12	01/03	28/09		01/02
Totnes	07/12	14/09	02/11	08/02	18/01	15/03	12/10	

Devon 3

	Buckfastleigh	Plymouth Argaum	Plymouth C.S.	Plympton Victoria	Salcombe	St Columba & Torpoint
Buckfastleigh		18/01	14/09	12/10	01/03	08/02
Plymouth Argaum	28/09		02/11	15/03	07/12	12/10
Plymouth Civil Service	04/01	01/03		28/09	01/02	30/11
Plympton Victoria	01/02	30/11	18/01		26/10	12/04
Salcombe	02/11	12/04	12/10	08/02		14/09
St Columba & Torpoint	26/10	01/02	15/03	07/12	04/01	

Western Counties North

	Bristol Harlequins	Cheltenham North	Coney Hill	Gordon League	Old Centralians	Old Redcliffians	Old Richians	Spartans	Thornbury	Walcot Old Boys	Whitehal	Yatton
Bristol Harlequins		07/09	01/03	28/09	12/10	11/01	02/11	01/02	23/11	12/04	07/12	21/12
Cheltenham North	15/03		02/11	01/03	28/09	23/11	01/02	21/12	12/10	07/12	11/01	12/04
Coney Hill	14/09	04/01		16/11	14/12	05/10	30/11	08/02	29/03	26/10	07/09	18/01
Gordon League	08/02	14/09	21/12		01/02	12/04	12/10	23/11	11/01	15/03	02/11	07/12
Old Centralians	18/01	08/02	23/11	05/10		07/12	11/01	12/04	02/11	14/09	21/12	15/03
Old Redcliffians	26/10	14/12	01/02	30/11	29/03		07/09	12/10	01/03	16/11	28/09	04/01
Old Richians	04/01	05/10	12/04	18/01	26/10	15/03		07/12	21/12	08/02	23/11	14/09
Spartans	05/10	16/11	28/09	14/12	30/11	18/01	29/03		07/09	04/01	01/03	26/10
Thornbury	14/12	18/01	07/12	26/10	04/01	14/09	16/11	15/03		05/10	12/04	08/02
Walcot	30/11	29/03	11/01	07/09	01/03	21/12	28/09	02/11	01/02		12/10	23/11
Whitehall	29/03	26/10	15/03	04/01	16/11	08/02	14/12	14/09	30/11	18/01		05/10
Yatton	16/11	30/11	12/10	29/03	07/09	02/11	01/03	11/01	28/09	14/12	01/02	

Somerset Premier

	Avon	Chew Valley	Gordano	Midsomer Norton	Minehead Barbarians	Nailsea & Backwell	North Petherton	Old Culverhaysians	Oldfield Old Boys	St Bernadettes O. B.	Tor	Wiveliscombe
Avon		07/09	01/03	28/09	01/02	23/11	07/12	12/10	11/01	02/11	21/12	12/04
Chew Valley	15/03		02/11	01/03	21/12	12/10	11/01	28/09	23/11	01/02	12/04	07/12
Gordano	14/09	04/01		16/11	08/02	29/03	07/09	14/12	05/10	30/11	18/01	26/10
Midsomer Norton	08/02	14/09	21/12		23/11	11/01	02/11	01/02	12/04	12/10	07/12	15/03
Minehead Barbarians	05/10	16/11	28/09	14/12		07/09	01/03	30/11	18/01	29/03	26/10	04/01
Nailsea & Backwell	14/12	18/01	07/12	26/10	15/03		12/04	04/01	14/09	16/11	08/02	05/10
North Petherton	29/03	26/10	15/03	04/01	14/09	30/11		16/11	08/02	14/12	05/10	18/01
Old Culverhaysians	18/01	08/02	23/11	05/10	12/04	02/11	21/12		07/12	11/01	15/03	14/09
Oldfield Old Boys	26/10	14/12	01/02	30/11	12/10	01/03	28/09	29/03		07/09	04/01	16/11
St Bernadettes Old	04/01	05/10	12/04	18/01	07/12	21/12	23/11	26/10	15/03		14/09	08/02
Tor	16/11	30/11	12/10	29/03	11/01	28/09	01/02	07/09	02/11	01/03		14/12
Wiveliscombe	30/11	29/03	11/01	07/09	02/11	01/02	12/10	01/03	21/12	28/09	23/11	

Somerset 1

	Avonvale	Bath Old Edwardians	Bristol Barbarians	Broad Plain	Chard	Combe Down	Crewkerne	Imperial	Old Ashtonians	Old Sulians	Stothert & Pitt	Wells
Avonvale		01/03	02/11	07/09	28/09	01/02	12/10	11/01	23/11	12/04	07/12	21/12
Bath Old Edwardians	14/09		30/11	04/01	16/11	08/02	14/12	05/10	29/03	26/10	07/09	18/01
Bristol Barbarians	04/01	12/04		05/10	18/01	07/12	26/10	15/03	21/12	08/02	23/11	14/09
Broad Plain	15/03	02/11	01/02		01/03	21/12	28/09	23/11	12/10	07/12	11/01	12/04
Chard	08/02	21/12	12/10	14/09		23/11	01/02	12/04	11/01	15/03	02/11	07/12
Combe Down	05/10	28/09	29/03	16/11	14/12		30/11	18/01	07/09	04/01	01/03	26/10
Crewkerne	18/01	23/11	11/01	08/02	05/10	12/04		07/12	02/11	14/09	21/12	15/03
Imperial	26/10	01/02	07/09	14/12	30/11	12/10	29/03		01/03	16/11	28/09	04/01
Old Ashtonians	14/12	07/12	16/11	18/01	26/10	15/03	04/01	14/09		05/10	12/04	08/02
Old Sulians	30/11	11/01	28/09	29/03	07/09	02/11	01/03	21/12	01/02		12/10	23/11
Stothert & Pitt	29/03	15/03	14/12	26/10	04/01	14/09	16/11	08/02	30/11	18/01		05/10
Wells	16/11	12/10	01/03	30/11	29/03	11/01	07/09	02/11	28/09	14/12	01/02	

Somerset 2

	Bath Saracens	Blagdon	Burnham on Sea	Castle Cary	Cheddar Valley	Morganians	Somerton	Winscombe
Bath Saracens		01/03	04/01	30/11	01/02	12/04	28/09	26/10
Blagdon	02/11		28/09	12/10	07/12	08/02	15/03	04/01
Burnham on Sea	14/09	18/01		08/02	01/03	30/11	12/10	12/04
Castle Cary	15/03	01/02	26/10		04/01	02/11	07/12	28/09
Cheddar Valley	12/10	12/04	02/11	14/09		18/01	08/02	30/11
Morganians	07/12	26/10	15/03	01/03	28/09		04/01	01/02
Somerton	18/01	30/11	01/02	12/04	26/10	14/09		01/03
Winscombe	08/02	14/09	07/12	18/01	15/03	12/10	02/11	

Gloucestershire Premier

	Aretians	Avonmouth OB	Barton Hill	Chosen Hill F. P.	Cirencester	Drybrook	Hucclecote	Longlevens	North Bristol	Painswick
Aretians		28/09	02/11	08/02	30/11	12/10	29/03	18/01	14/12	14/09
Avonmouth OB	01/03		14/09	01/02	26/10	04/01	16/11	12/04	05/10	07/12
Barton Hill	04/01	15/03		16/11	05/10	12/04	01/02	07/12	01/03	26/10
Chosen Hill F. P.	05/10	12/10	14/12		29/03	18/01	14/09	02/11	30/11	01/03
Cirencester	12/04	18/01	08/02	07/12		15/03	04/01	28/09	12/10	16/11
Drybrook	01/02	02/11	30/11	26/10	14/09		01/03	14/12	29/03	05/10
Hucclecote	07/12	14/12	12/10	15/03	02/11	28/09		08/02	18/01	12/04
Longlevens	26/10	30/11	29/03	04/01	01/03	16/11	05/10		14/09	01/02
North Bristol	16/11	08/02	28/09	12/04	01/02	07/12	26/10	15/03		04/01
Painswick	15/03	29/03	18/01	28/09	14/12	08/02	30/11	12/10	02/11	

Gloucestershire 1

	Ashley Down O. B.	Bishopston	Bream	Bristol Saracens	Brockworth	Chipping Sodbury	Frampton Cotterell	Old Bristolians	Southmead	Tewkesbury
Ashley Down Old Boys		15/03	04/01	12/04	01/03	01/02	16/11	05/10	26/10	07/12
Bishopston	14/09		01/03	04/01	05/10	16/11	01/02	26/10	07/12	12/04
Bream	02/11	28/09		12/10	14/12	29/03	08/02	30/11	14/09	18/01
Bristol Saracens	30/11	02/11	01/02		29/03	01/03	26/10	14/09	05/10	14/12
Brockworth	28/09	08/02	16/11	07/12		26/10	12/04	01/02	04/01	15/03
Chipping Sodbury	12/10	14/12	07/12	28/09	18/01		15/03	02/11	12/04	08/02
Frampton Cotterell	14/12	12/10	05/10	18/01	30/11	14/09		29/03	01/03	02/11
Old Bristolians	08/02	18/01	12/04	15/03	12/10	04/01	07/12		16/11	28/09
Southmead	18/01	29/03	15/03	08/02	02/11	30/11	28/09	14/12		12/10
Tewkesbury	29/03	30/11	26/10	16/11	14/09	05/10	04/01	01/03	01/02	

Gloucestershire 2

	Cheltenham Saracens	Kingswood	Minchinhampton	Old Cryptians	Old Elizabethans	Ross On Wye	Smiths (Industries)	Widden Old Boys	Westbury on Severn
Cheltenham Saracens		08/02	28/09	02/11	12/10	14/12	30/11	18/01	14/09
Kingswood	05/10		12/10	14/12	18/01	30/11	29/03	02/11	01/03
Minchinhampton	01/03	01/02		14/09	04/01	05/10	26/10	12/04	07/12
Old Cryptians	04/01	16/11	15/03		12/04	01/03	05/10	07/12	26/10
Old Elizabethans	01/02	26/10	02/11	30/11		29/03	14/09	14/12	05/10
Ross On Wye	16/11	12/04	08/02	28/09	07/12		01/02	15/03	04/01
Smiths (Industries)	12/04	07/12	18/01	08/02	15/03	12/10		28/09	16/11
Westbury on Severn	26/10	04/01	30/11	29/03	16/11	14/09	01/03		01/02
Widden Old Boys	15/03	28/09	29/03	18/01	08/02	02/11	14/12	12/10	

Gloucestershire 3 North

	Cheltenham C. S.	Dursley	Fairford	Gloucester All Blues	Gloucester Civil Service	Newent	Tredworth
Cheltenham Civil Service		04/01	26/10	15/03	01/02	07/12	02/11
Dursley	14/09		02/11	12/10	12/04	08/02	18/01
Fairford	08/02	01/03		14/09	18/01	12/10	30/11
Gloucester All Blues	30/11	01/02	04/01		01/03	28/09	12/04
Gloucester Civil Service	12/10	07/12	28/09	02/11		15/03	08/02
Newent	12/04	26/10	01/02	18/01	30/11		14/09
Tredworth	01/03	28/09	15/03	07/12	26/10	04/01	

Gloucestershire 3 South

	Bristol Aeroplane Co	Bristol Telephones	Cainscross	Cotham Park	Old Colstonians	Tetbury	Wotton-under-Edge
Bristol Aeroplane Co		14/09	18/01	12/10	08/02	01/03	30/11
Bristol Telephones	04/01		01/03	28/09	30/11	01/02	12/04
Cainscross	28/09	02/11		15/03	12/10	07/12	08/02
Cotham Park	01/02	18/01	30/11		12/04	26/10	14/09
Old Colstonians	26/10	15/03	01/02	07/12		04/01	02/11
Tetbury	02/11	12/10	12/04	08/02	14/09		18/01
Wotton	15/03	07/12	26/10	04/01	01/03	28/09	

Southern Counties South

	Bournemouth	Calne	Devizes	Frome	Ivel Barbarians	Oakmeadians	Redingensians	Tadley	Westbury	Wootton Bassett
Bournemouth		14/09	05/10	01/02	26/10	04/01	01/03	16/11	12/04	07/12
Calne	15/03		01/03	16/11	05/10	12/04	04/01	01/02	07/12	26/10
Devizes	08/02	28/09		12/04	01/02	07/12	16/11	26/10	15/03	04/01
Frome	12/10	14/12	30/11		29/03	18/01	05/10	14/09	02/11	01/03
Ivel Barbarians	18/01	08/02	12/10	07/12		15/03	12/04	04/01	28/09	16/11
Oakmeadians	02/11	30/11	29/03	26/10	14/09		01/02	01/03	14/12	05/10
Redingensians	28/09	02/11	14/12	08/02	30/11	12/10		29/03	18/01	14/09
Tadley	14/12	12/10	18/01	15/03	02/11	28/09	07/12		08/02	12/04
Westbury	30/11	29/03	14/09	04/01	01/03	16/11	26/10	05/10		01/02
Wootton Bassett	29/03	18/01	02/11	28/09	14/12	08/02	15/03	30/11	12/10	

Dorset & Wiltshire 1

	Blandford	Bradford on Avon	Cooper Avon Tyres	Corsham	Sherborne	Swindon Coll.	Trowbridge	Weymouth
Blandford		14/09	18/01	12/10	08/02	01/03	30/11	12/04
Bradford on Avon	04/01		01/03	28/09	30/11	01/02	12/04	26/10
Cooper Avon Tyres	28/09	02/11		15/03	12/10	07/12	08/02	04/01
Corsham	01/02	18/01	30/11		12/04	26/10	14/09	01/03
Sherborne	26/10	15/03	01/02	07/12		04/01	02/11	28/09
Swindon College	02/11	12/10	12/04	08/02	14/09		18/01	30/11
Trowbridge	15/03	07/12	26/10	04/01	01/03	28/09		01/02
Weymouth	07/12	08/02	14/09	02/11	18/01	15/03	12/10	

Dorset & Wiltshire 2 North

	Colerne	Cricklade	Hungerford	Marlborough	Minety	Pewsey Vale	Supermarine
Colerne		01/03	28/09	30/11	04/01	01/02	12/04
Cricklade	02/11		15/03	12/10	28/09	07/12	08/02
Hungerford	18/01	30/11		12/04	01/02	26/10	14/09
Marlborough	15/03	01/02	07/12		26/10	04/01	02/11
Minety	14/09	18/01	12/10	08/02		01/03	30/11
Pewsey Vale	12/10	12/04	08/02	14/09	02/11		18/01
Supermarine	07/12	26/10	04/01	01/03	15/03	28/09	

Dorset & Wiltshire 2 South

	Bridport	Martock	North Dorset	Poole	Puddletown	Warminster	Wincanton
Bridport		14/09	18/01	12/10	08/02	01/03	30/11
Martock	04/01		01/03	28/09	30/11	01/02	12/04
North Dorset	28/09	02/11		15/03	12/10	07/12	08/02
Poole	01/02	18/01	30/11		12/04	26/10	14/09
Puddletown	26/10	15/03	01/02	07/12		04/01	02/11
Warminster	02/11	12/10	12/04	08/02	14/09		18/01
Wincanton	15/03	07/12	26/10	04/01	01/03	28/09	

Southern Counties North

	Aylesbury	Beaconsfield	Bicester	Buckingham	High Wycombe	Olney	Slough	Swindon	Wallingford	Witney
Aylesbury		28/09	14/12	02/11	08/02	30/11	12/10	18/01	29/03	14/09
Beaconsfield	01/03		05/10	14/09	01/02	26/10	04/01	12/04	16/11	07/12
Bicester	16/11	08/02		28/09	12/04	01/02	07/12	15/03	26/10	04/01
Buckingham	04/01	15/03	01/03		16/11	05/10	12/04	07/12	01/02	26/10
High Wycombe	05/10	12/10	30/11	14/12		29/03	18/01	02/11	14/09	01/03
Olney	12/04	18/01	12/10	08/02	07/12		15/03	28/09	04/01	16/11
Slough	01/02	02/11	29/03	30/11	26/10	14/09		14/12	01/03	05/10
Swindon	26/10	30/11	14/09	29/03	04/01	01/03	16/11		05/10	01/02
Wallingford	07/12	14/12	18/01	12/10	15/03	02/11	28/09	08/02		12/04
Witney	15/03	29/03	02/11	18/01	28/09	14/12	08/02	12/10	30/11	

Berkshire Buckinghamshire & Oxfordshire 1

	Aldermaston	Chipping Norton	Drifters	Henley Wanderers	Littlemore	Milton Keynes	Oxford	Pennanians	Phoenix	Thatcham
Aldermaston		14/09	05/10	01/02	01/03	12/04	07/12	26/10	04/01	16/11
Chipping Norton	15/03		01/03	16/11	04/01	07/12	26/10	05/10	12/04	01/02
Drifters	08/02	28/09		12/04	16/11	15/03	04/01	01/02	07/12	26/10
Henley Wanderers	12/10	14/12	30/11		05/10	02/11	01/03	29/03	18/01	14/09
Littlemore	28/09	02/11	14/12	08/02		18/01	14/09	30/11	12/10	29/03
Milton Keynes	30/11	29/03	14/09	04/01	26/10		01/02	01/03	16/11	05/10
Oxford	29/03	18/01	02/11	28/09	15/03	12/10		14/12	08/02	30/11
Pennanians	18/01	08/02	12/10	07/12	12/04	28/09	16/11		15/03	04/01
Phoenix	02/11	30/11	29/03	26/10	01/02	14/12	05/10	14/09		01/03
Thatcham	14/12	12/10	18/01	15/03	07/12	08/02	12/04	02/11	28/09	

Berkshire Buckinghamshire & Oxfordshire 2

	Abingdon	Berkshire Shire Hall	Bletchley	Chesham	Gosford All Blacks	Harwell	Wheatley	Winslow
Abingdon		18/01	14/09	12/10	08/02	01/03	30/11	12/04
Berkshire Shire Hall	28/09		02/11	15/03	12/10	07/12	08/02	04/01
Bletchley	04/01	01/03		28/09	30/11	01/02	12/04	26/10
Chesham	01/02	30/11	18/01		12/04	26/10	14/09	01/03
Gosford All Blacks	26/10	01/02	15/03	07/12		04/01	02/11	28/09
Harwell	02/11	12/04	12/10	08/02	14/09		18/01	30/11
Wheatley	15/03	26/10	07/12	04/01	01/03	28/09		01/02
Winslow	07/12	14/09	08/02	02/11	18/01	15/03	12/10	

ABBEY RFC
Ground Address: Rosehill, Peppard Road, Emmer Green, Reading, Berks, RG4 8XA Tel: 0118 972 2881
Web Address: www.abbeyrfc.org
Brief Directions: From Reading take the B481 Peppard road. Ground is half a mile north of the Reading boundary.
Hon Secretary: M Lee, Cotswold, Behoes Lane, Reading, Berks, RG8 0PP Tel: (H) 01491 680102
Email: meirion.lee@virgin.net
Fixtures Secretary: Lynne Lee, Cotswold, Behoes Lane, Reading RG8 0PP Tel: (H) 01491 680102
Club Colours: Navy blue with green and white hoops
League: South West 2 East

ABINGDON RFC
Ground Address: Southern Sports Park, Lambrick Way, Abingdon OX14 5TJ Tel: 01235 553810
Email Address: help@abingdonrufc.com
Web Address: www.abingdonrufc.com
Brief Directions: Exit Abingdon on the B4017, Drayton Road, Just prior to leaving the town limits, take left into Preston Road. Lambrick Way is 3rd turning on the right.
Hon Secretary: Tim Davies, Stonehill Cottage, Oday Hill, Abingdon, OX14 4AA Tel: (H) 01235 527973
Tel: (W) 01235 526 012
Email: tdavies.graphictech@virgin.net
Leagues Contact: Xavier Lecocq, 22 Summerfields, Abingdon, Oxon, OX14 2PG Tel: (H) 01235 526 392
Fixtures Secretary: Simon North, The Gatehouse, Farringdon Rd, Abingdon, Oxon, OX14 1BG
Tel: (H) 01235 206254 Tel: (M) 07932 005387
Club Colours: Green and gold hooped shirts
League: Berks/Bucks & Oxon 2

ALDERMASTON RFC
Ground Address: Recreation Ground, A.W.E., Aldermaston, Berkshire Tel: 0118 981 7233
Brief Directions: From Basingstoke follow directions for Tadley on A340, then for Awe Aldermaston, then for Recreational Society.
Hon Secretary: R Hawkins Tel: (H) 0118 981 4615
Email: randthawkins@hotmail.com
Club Colours: Scarlet shirts, black shorts
League: Berks/Bucks & Oxon 1

AMERSHAM & CHILTERN RFC
Ground Address: Ash Grove, Weedon Lane, Chesham Bois, Amersham, Bucks HP6 5QU Tel: 01494 725161
Email Address: mail@chilternrugby.com
Web Address: www.chilternrugby.com
Brief Directions: From Amersham/Chesham road, take Copperkings Lane (signed Hyde Heath), Weedon Lane is 2nd left
Hon Secretary: Ian McKenzie, 17 Highover Park, Amersham, Bucks HP7 0BN Tel: (H) 01494 431966
Tel: (W) 01494 497657
Email: cmckenzie@tesco.net
Fixtures Secretary: Roger Cook, 12 Bois Lane, Amersham, BucksHP6 6BP Tel: (H) 01494 433144
Club Colours: Maroon & White
League: South West 2 East
League Contact: as Secretary

ARETIANS RFC
Ground Address: Station Road, Little Stoke, Bristol BS34 6HW Tel: 01454 888069
Email Address: aretians@bg-mor.demon.co.uk
Brief Directions: M5 J16, A38 into Bristol, at flyover turn left signed Yate (Gypsy Patch Ln), along road to railway bridge, directly left past bridge, ground approx 600yds on right on Station Rd
Hon Secretary: Andy Vaughan, 42 Elm Close, Bristol BS34 6RQ Tel: (H) 01179 756513
Tel: (M) 07771 562213 Tel: (W) 01179 557767
Fixtures Secretary: Glyn Griffiths, 44 Mead Road, Bristol Tel: (M) 07970 975152 Tel: (W) 01453 812118
Club Colours: Black
League: Gloucester Premier

ASHLEY DOWN OLD BOYS RFC
Ground Address: Lockleaze Combination Ground, Bonnington Walk, Lockleaze, Bristol
Tel: 0117 931 2642
Brief Directions: From Filton Avenue, into Bonnington Walk, left at railway bridge, 0.25 mile along lane
Hon Secretary: Paul Golding, 29 Blackhorse Road, Kingswood, Bristol, South Gloucestershire, BS15 8EF
Tel: (H) 0117 987 1343 Tel: (M) 07818 241271
Tel: (W) 0117 953 6487
Email: prgolding@blueyonder.co.uk
Fixtures Secretary: Pat Donovan, 38 Memorial Road, Bristol BS15 3JQ Tel: (H) 0117 967 9649
Club Colours: Purple and white
League: Gloucester 1

AVON RFC
Ground Address: Hicks Field, London Road East, Batherston, Bath, Somerset Tel: 01225 852446
Email Address: Enquiries@AvonRFC.co.uk
Web Address: www.avonrfc.co.uk
Brief Directions: From the A46 take the exit for Bath. At the r-a-b the club is signposted (heading for Batheaston) approx a quarter mile fromtthe r-a-b on the right hand side just at the end of the rank of houses.
Hon Secretary: Dave Loader, 114 Southdown Road, Bath, Somerset BA2 1JJ Tel: (H) 01225 316864
Tel: (M) 07900 055911 Tel: (W) 01249 713218
Email: daveloader@aventeng.co.uk
Fixtures Secretary: Wayne Griffiths, 4 Lower Stoke, Bath Tel: (H) 01225 722433 Tel: (M) 07780 997506
Email: wayne.griffiths@capgemini.co.uk
Club Colours: Black & Amber
League: Somerset Premier

AVONMOUTH OLD BOYS RFC
Ground Address: Barracks Lane, Avonmouth, Bristol
Tel: 0117 982 9093
Brief Directions: Exit M5 J.18 to Bristol. Left at roundabout to Shirehampton, then 2nd left (opp. shops) and continue for 400 yards.
Hon Secretary: Rodney Kennett, 41 Woodland Grove, Bristol BS9 2BD Tel: (H) 0117 968 3598
Email: chris.rodkennett@btinternet.com
Club Colours: Red / Black
League: Gloucester Premier

AVONVALE RFC
Ground Address: Bathford Playing Fields, Bathford Playing Fields, Bathford, Bath Tel: 01225 858295
Website: www.avonvalerfc.co.uk
Brief Directions: A4 out of Bath, through Batheaston, right at next roundabout, under railway bridge and next left, clubhouse is along a track next to phone box 200yds up Bathford Hill. See website for maps
Club Secretary: Paul Beazer, 1 Tropenell Close, Corsham, Wilts SN13 9UG. Tel No: 01249 716135 (H)
Email: beez@totalise.co.uk
Fixtures Secretary: Steve Vowles, 77 Lockswood Road, Lower Weston, Bath BA1 3ES
Tel: (H) 01225 333852 (W) 01225 766451
Club Colours: Navy blue & white
League: Somerset 1
Contact: as Secretary

AYLESBURY RFC
Ground Address: Ostlers Field, Brook End, Weston Turville, Aylesbury, Bucks. HP22 5RN
Tel: 01296 612556 / 614786 Website: www.arfc.org.uk
Brief Directions: A413 from Wendover to Aylesbury. 2 miles rt to B4544 - thro. - ground is on left Weston Turville. Or A41 from Aylesbury, turn rt after 3 miles before Aston Clinton, club is then on right.
Club Secretary: Derek Spence, 2 Dennis Close, Aston Clinton, Bucks. HP22 5US Tel: 01296 631882
E-mail: Secretary-ARFC@cwcom.net
Fixtures Secretary: James P Williams, Tumbleweed, Winslow Rd., Granborough, Bucks MK18 3NJ
Tel: (H) 01296 670798
Club Colours: Black and magenta hooped shirts, black shorts and socks
League: Southern Counties North
Contact: Mark Rose, Skippings Farm NSE, Chesham Lane, Chalfont St. Peter Tel: 01494 876114

BARTON HILL RFC
Ground Address: Duncombe Lane, Speedwell, Bristol
Tel: 01179 872 895
Email Address: ian.lepetit@blueyonder.co.uk
Brief Directions: Follow roads to Lodge Causeway, Fishponds. At lights half way up Causeway turn right opp St. Josephs and take 2nd left into Duncombe Lane.
Hon Secretary: Ian Le Petit, 6 Blackhorse Road, Bristol, BS15 8EF Tel: (H) 0117 9604317
Tel: (M) 07788418119 Tel: (W) 0117 9604317
Email: ian.lepetit@blueyonder.co.uk
Fixtures Secretary: Rob Porter, 13 North Park, Bristol
Tel: (H) 01179 083965 Tel: (M) 0775 690291
Club Colours: White with Cherry Band
League: Gloucester Premier

BATH OLD EDWARDIANS
Ground Address: King Edwards School Field, Bathampton Tel: 01255 462354
Directions: M4 J18, A46 to Bath, London Rd towards Batheaston then follow signs to Bathampton village.Ground is opp. church. From Bath take A36.
Hon Secretary: Daniel Miller, 7 Herbert Road, Oldfield park, Bath, BA3 3PP Tel: (H) 01225 319424
Tel: (M) 01225 445060 Tel: (W) 01225 462871
Email: Miller@Bathnes.gov.uk
Club Colours: Gold, maroon and blue hoops
League: Somerset 1

BATH SARACENS RFC
Ground Address: Sulis Sports Ground, Claverton Down, Bath Tel: 01225 837259
Brief Directions: From Bath take A367 to Frys Garage mini roundabout.Take first left, then straight on for 2 miles and turn right immediately after Ralph Allen School.
Hon Secretary: Mike York, 2 Linden Gardens, Bath, BA1 2YB Tel: (H) 01225 424613
Email: mike@yorkcom.freeserve.co.uk
Fixtures Secretary: R Lawrence, 91 Englishcombe Lane, Bath, BA2 2EH Tel: (H) 01225 427356
Tel: (W) 07802 797756
Club Colours: Blue with red and gold hoops.
League: Somerset 2

BEACONSFIELD RFC
Ground Address: Oak Lodge Meadow, Windsor End, Beaconsfield, Buckinghamshire, HP9 2SQ
Tel: 01494 673 783
Email Address: godrich@lineone.net
Web Address: www.brfc.org.uk
Brief Directions: Exit M40 at Junction 2 and follow signs to Beaconsfield,at the centre of the Old Town (roundabout at Parish Church) turn left,signposted local traffic only, and the club is 800metres and on your left.
Hon Secretary: Jamie Godrich, West Witheridge, The Fourth House, Beaconsfield, Bucks HP9 2TW
Tel: (H) 01494 674329
Email: godrich@lineone.net
Club Colours: Green and gold hoops, green shorts
League: Southern Counties North

BERKSHIRE SHIRE HALL RUFC
Ground Address: Royal County of Berkshire Sports & Social Club, Sonning Lane, Sonning, Reading
Tel: 01734 691340
Brief Directions: From Reading head towards A4 up Sheppards House Hill, pass Mobil garage on right, take left Sonning Lane, 2nd turning on the right
Club Secretary: Mark Porter
105 Severn Way,Reading RG30 4HW
Tel No: 07785 265412
E mail: mark.porter@interservefm.com

Fixtures Secretary: Steve Bentey Tel: (H) 118 954 2030
Club Colours: Royal Blue & gold.
League: Berks/Bucks & Oxon 2

BICESTER RUFC
Ground Address: Bicester Sports Club, Oxford Road, Bicester Tel: 01869 241993
Brief Directions: Approaching Bicester from south (A34) ground is on right on edge of town just past Tescos
Hon Secretary: George Davies, 166 Barry Avenue, Bicester OX26 2HB Tel: (H) 01869 241993
Club Colours: Amber, red and brown hooped shirts, navy shorts
League: Southern Counties North

BIDEFORD RFC
Ground Address: King George's Field, Bideford Tel: 01237 474049
Brief Directions: N.D. link road, left end of Bideford New Bridge, into town until reach river, immediate left at Charles Kingsley statue, proceed River Bank Road to Bideford RFC car park
Hon Secretary: R. G. Booth, 41 Goodwood Park Road, Bideford EX39 2RR Tel: (H) 01237 421259
Email: bobooth@sudburys-gloves.co.uk
Club Colours: Red & white hooped shirts, white shorts
League: Western Counties West

BISHOPSTON RFC
Ground Address: Bonnington Walk, Lockleaze, Bristol Tel: 0117 969 1916
Hon Secretary: Jim Hockley, 21 Pinewood Close, Bristol BS9 4AJ Tel: (H) 0117 962 3509
Tel: (M) 07752 132314 Email: jim@jhockley.fsnet.co.uk
Fixtures Secretary: S. Brain, 46 Clarence Avenue, Bristol BS16 5SX Tel: (H) 01779 109834
Club Colours: Black with red hoop edged with centenary gold
League: Gloucester 1

BLAGDON
Ground Address: The Mead, Blagdon
Tel: 01761 463196
Brief Directions: Turn left off the A38 at Churchill traffic lights and follow road for approx 3 miles into Blagdon
Hon Secretary: Claire Allan, 26 Long Cross, Bristol BS40 9YH
Tel: (H) 01275 472228 Tel: (M) 07796 954912
Email: claire996@hotmail.com
Club Colours: Green, Black and white hoops
League: Somerset 2

BLANDFORD RFC
Ground Address: Blandford School Ground at the Milldown Leisure Centre, Milldown Road, Blandford.
Brief Directions: From town centre, follow signs to Sturminster Newton, Pitches situated at Melldown Leisure Centre opposite hospital.
Hon Secretary: Owen Griffiths, 1 Old Oak Way, Blandford Forum, Dorset DT11 9PG
Tel: (H) 01258 881380 Tel: (M) 07973 898571
Tel: (W) 01202 628 334
Email: owen.griffiths@southernprint.co.uk
Club Colours: Red, Yellow & Brown
League: Dorset & Wilts 1

BLETCHLEY RUFC
Ground Address: Manor Fields, Bletchley, Milton Keynes, Bucks Tel: 01908 372298
Web Address: www.bletchleyrugby.com
Brief Directions: On B488 from Leighton Buzzard, fork right at 'The Plough', from this fork take 3rd right - Manor Road, proceed down road over bridge to ground
Hon Secretary: Paul Morrison, 2 Sheepcoat Close, Milton Keynes MK5 6JL Tel: (H) 01908 506743
Tel: (W) 01604 543 000
Email: paul.morrison@shoosmiths.co.uk
Fixtures Secretary: Ian Punter, 24 Home Close, Milton Keynes MK3 6JE Tel: (H) 01908 642994
Club Colours: Navy shirts with maroon/white hoops. Navy shorts
League: Berks/Bucks & Oxon 2

BODMIN RFC
Ground Address: Clifden Park, Carmminow Cross, Bodmin, Cornwall PL31 4AW Tel: 01208 74629
Email Address: andy.richards@connexions-cd.org.uk
Brief Directions: Directions: Off A38 before flyover at A30. Take B road signed posted to Lanhydrock 400yds turn right down private lane.
Hon Secretary: Andy Richards, Chy Kensa, Robartes Road, Bodmin, Cornwall PL31 1JG
Tel: (H) 07979 718355 Tel: (M) 07979 718355
Tel: (W) 01566 777672 ext 203
Leagues Contact: Andy Richards, Chy Kensa, Robartes Road, Bodmi, Cornwall PL31 1JG
Tel: (H) 07979 718355 Tel: (M) 07979 718355
Tel: (W) 01566 777672 ext 203
Fixtures Secretary: Keith Richardson, Youmes-Den, Westheath Road, Bodmin, Cornwall PL31 1QG
Tel: (H) 01208 77643 Tel: (M) 07833 730724
Email: Keithlr@supanet.com
Club Colours: Light Blue with Dark Blue hoops edged with white.
League: Cornwall 1

BOURNEMOUTH RFC
Ground Address: Chapel Gate, Parley Lane, Christchurch, Dorset BH23 6BD Tel: 01202 581933
Email Address: secretary@bournemouthrfc.org.uk
Web Address: www.bournemouthrfc.org.uk
Brief Directions: Take Bournemouth spur road (A338 Ringwood-Bournemouth). Follow signs to Hurn Airport. Ground is just to west of the airport.
Hon Secretary: Alistair Raworth, Flat 2, 2 St. Anthony's Road, Bournemouth, Dorset BH2 6PD
Tel: (H) 01202 252 188 Tel: (M) 07771 901812
Email: alistair.raworth@btinternet.com
Fixtures Secretary: Alan Coe, 7 Siskin Close, Dorset BH22 9RB Tel: (H) 01202 877219
Email: alandhow@hotmail.com
Club Colours: Black & Gold
League: Southern Counties South

BRADFORD-ON-AVON RFC
Ground Address: St Lawrence School, Ashly Road, Bradford on Avon, Wiltshire BA15 1DZ
Brief Directions: Take Winsley Road out of Boa. Then 2nd right into churches. St Lawrence School car park on right through gates.
Hon Secretary: John Pendrey, 6, Fitzmaurice Close, Bradford-on-Avon, Wiltshire, BA15 1UE
Tel: (H) 01225 864186 Tel: (W) 01454 281779
Email: john@pendrey.fsbusiness.co.uk
Club Colours: Red & Black
League: Dorset & Wilts 1

BREAM RFC
Ground Address: High Street, Bream, Nr. Lydney
Tel: 01594 562320
Brief Directions: Approx 3 miles off main A48 Gloucester to Chepstow road, turn right after Westbury Homes Site on right hand side
Hon Secretary: Graham Moxey, Homestead, New Road, Glos GL15 6HJ Tel: (H) 01594 564547
Fixtures Secretary: As Secretary
Club Colours: Red and black
League: Gloucester 1

BRIDPORT RFC
Ground Address: Bridport Leisure Centre, Skilling Hill Road, Bridport, Dorset. DT6 3LN
Tel: 01308 420555
Brief Directions: Take A35 Bridport By-Pass, at R'bout south of Town turn R. (North). After 300yds turn L. at Traffic Lights opp. Safeway store.
Hon Secretary: Adrian Butler, The Homestead, 101 West Bay Road, Bridport, Dorset DT6 4 AY
Tel: (H) 01308 423338 Tel: (W) as above
Email: adrian.butler@whsmithnet.co.uk
Club Colours: Blue and white quarters
League: Dorset & Wilts 2 South

BRISTOL AEROPLANE COMPANY RFC
Ground Address: Bristol Aerospace Welfare Association Sports Ground, 589 Southmead Road, Filton, Bristol. BS12 7DG
Tel: 0117 976 8066
Brief Directions: Travel south along A38, right at the roundabout at top of Filton Hill into Southmead Road, ground on the right
Club Secretary: Julian Mason-Flucke, 42 Quarrington Road, Horfield, Bristol
Tel: 0117 951 4573 (H) 0117 979 5920 (W)
Fixtures Secretary: Mark Dewhurst,10 Kendon Drive, Westbury-on-Trym, Bristol BS10 5BP.
Tel: 0117 962 4240 (H) 0117 936 4899(W)
Club Colours: Red, white and blue hoops
League: Gloucester 3 South

BRISTOL BARBARIANS
(FORMERLY BRITISH GAS BRISTOL)
Ground Address: Norton Lane, Whitchurch, Bristol BS14 0BT Tel: 01275 833514
Brief Directions: On A37 from Bristol, past Black Lion pub, over bridge, right by playground. 1st gate on right.
Hon Secretary: Colin Rowland, 57 Fitzgerald Road, Bristol BS3 3NB Tel: (H) 01179 775200
Tel: (M) 07979 562457
Email: rcolin@blueyonder.co.uk
Club Colours: Black & White hoops
League: Somerset 1

BRISTOL HARLEQUINS RFC
Ground Address: Valhalla, Broomhill Road, Brislington, Bristol. BS4
Tel: 0117 972 1650
Brief Directions: The ground is situated behind St.Brendan College on the A4 between Bath and Bristol.
Club Secretary: Ian Nunnerly, 17 Warmington Road,Knowle, Bristol BS14 9HG
Tel: 0117 971 1597
Fixtures Secretary: Ed Morrison, 4 Lowbourne,Whitchurch, Bristol BS14 0AN
Tel: (H) 01275 832580
Club Colours: Blue, black and white hoops
League: Western Counties North

BRISTOL SARACENS RFC
Ground Address: Station Road, Cribbs Causeway, Henbury, Bristol, BS10 7TT Tel: 0117 950 0037
Brief Directions: M5 J17 towards Bristol city centre, approx 1000 metres at 2nd roundabout on right
Hon Secretary: Tony Swash, 6 Downs Road, Bristol, BS9 3TX Tel: (H) 0117 962 9047
Tel: (M) 07974 431272 Tel: (W) 07974 431 272
Email: aeswash@bak2.mu.co.uk
Club Colours: Myrtle green and white hooped shirts, black shorts
League: Gloucester 1

BRISTOL TELEPHONE AREA RFC
Ground Address: BT Sports Ground, Stockwood Lane, Whitchurch
Brief Directions: Take A37 (Wells Road) for approx 4 miles from city centre, left at Black Lion pub at Whitchurch, ground approx 1 mile on right
Hon Secretary: Mark Morgan, 21 Durville Road, Bristol BS13 7PS Tel: (H) 0117 964 2331
Tel: (M) 07968 507961 Tel: (W) 0117 966 93150
Email: organm99@hotmail.com
Club Colours: Blue with red & white V neck.
League: Gloucester 3 South

BRIXHAM RFC
Ground Address: Astley Park, Rae Barn Road, Brixham, TQ5 9EA Tel: 01803 882 162
Email Address: brixrugby@netscapeonline.co.uk
Web Address: www.brixhamrugby.org
Brief Directions: Follow signs for Torbay then Brixham, then for Berry Head. Club opposite Police Station.
Hon Secretary: Bob Houston, Astley Park, Rae Barn Road, Brixham, TQ5 9EA Tel: (H) 01803 550427
Tel: (W) 01548 85500
Email: brixrugby@netscapeonline.co.uk
Club Colours: Black with 6" white band
League: South West 2 West

BROAD PLAIN RFC
Ground Address: Hengrove School, Patherton Rd., Hengrove, Bristol Tel No: 0117 955 2782
Brief Directions: Take A37,the Wells Road out of Bristol, two miles from city centre turn right at 'Happy Landings' pub then left at 'The Glass Cutter'.Follow signs for Hengrove school in Petherton Road.
Club Secretary: Don Collins, 77 Lake Road, Henleaze, Bristol. BS10 5JE
Tel: (H) 0117 9622094 (W) 0117 9248051
Fixtures Secretary: Bob Slocombe, 113 Hayward Road, Redfield, Briistol.B55
Club Colours: Blue, maroon and gold hoops
League: Somerset 1

BROCKWORTH RFC
Ground Address: Mill Lane, Brockworth, Glos
Tel: 01452 862 556
Directions: From south: M5 turn off at junct. 11A, follow signs to Gloucester, 1st left to Blockworth at roundabout, straight over next, past Du-Pont, left at lights into Vicarage Lane, straight over small roundabout, 1st right into Mill Lane, 400 metres on LHS.
Hon Secretary: Dave Alden, 37 Boverton Avenue, Glos GL3 4ER Tel: (H) 01452 551353 (W) 01452 711306
Email: dabr23668@blueyonder.co.uk
Club Colours: Black shirts with white 'V'
League: Gloucester 1

BUCKFASTLEIGH RAMBLERS RFC
Ground Address: The Cricket Ground, Buckfastleigh
Tel: 01364 643 895
Hon Secretary: Sue Farley, 6 Holne Road, Buckfastleigh, TQ11 0BE Tel: (H) 01364 643 696
Email: sue@millwood.uk.com
Club Colours: Black and gold
League: Devon 3

BUCKINGHAM RUFC
Ground Address: The Floyd Field, Maids Moreton, Nr Buckingham, Bucks MK18 1RF Tel: 01280 815474
Email Address: piers.b@talk21.com
Web Address: www.buckinghamrugby.co.uk
Brief Directions: From Buckingham town centre take A413 towards Towcester. After approx 0.5 miles, ground is on the right as you approach Maids Moreton village
Hon Secretary: Finlay Gemmell, 22 Elmfields Gate, Buckingham, BucksMK18 3JG Tel: (H) 01296 714 640
Tel: (M) 07881 988 380 Tel: (W) 01753 704 131
Hon Fixtures: Paul Carr, 17 Sandhurst Dr, Buckingham, Bucks Tel: (H) 01280 816373 Tel: (M) 07764 651140
Leagues Contact: Jack Skelton, 4 Pound Lane, Buckingham, MK18 4LX Tel: (H) 01280 848610
Tel: (M) 07949 768579
Club Colours: Green, white hoops
League: Southern Counties North

BUDE RFC
Ground Address: Bencoolen Meadow (off Kings Hill), Bude, Cornwall. EX23 8DG Tel: 01288 354795
Brief Directions: Into Stratton Rd and turn left at bottom of hill then first right turn and right again into club.
Hon Secretary: Anne Troke, Kiama, Church Path, Bude, Cornwall Tel: (H) 01288 354826
Fixtures Secretary: John Boundy, "Linhays", Butterbeare Cross, Bridgerule, Devon
Tel: (H) 01288 381296
Club Colours: Maroon and sky blue hoops
League: Cornwall/Devon

BURNHAM-ON-SEA
Ground Address: Burnham Association of Sports Clubs, Stoddens Road, Burnham-on-Sea
Tel: 01278 788355
Brief Directions: Signposted from M5, J22.
Hon Secretary: Jonathan WIlson, 10 Enmore Close, Burnham-on-Sea TA8 2FB Tel: (H) 01278 784128
Club Colours: Blue and white hoops
League: Somerset 2

CAINSCROSS RFC
Ground Address: Victory Park, Cainscross
Tel: 01453 766707
Brief Directions: Take 2nd exit from Horse Trough R'about. Westward round Ebley into Church Road (on left just before Imo carwash). When travelling from M5
Hon Secretary: Dave Roberts, 24 Upper Church Road, Stroud, Gloucester Tel: (H) 01453 757181
Club Colours: Amber and blue
League: Gloucester 3 North

CALLINGTON RFC
Ground Address: Duchy College, Stoke Climsland, Callington, Cornwall Tel: 01579 382328
Email Address: kim.campbell@ginsters.co.uk
Directions: Callington to Launceston Road, turn off at Kelly Brayy to Stoke Climsland. At Stoke Climsland follow signs to Ventodon then Duchy Coll.
Hon Secretary: Sean Francey, 3 Mawes Court, St. Annes Chapel, Gunnislake, Cornwall PL18 9AX
Tel: (H) 01822 834769 Tel: (M) 07779 636845
Tel: (W) 01579 386408
Fixtures Secretary: John Pritchard, Pinewood, Gunnislake, Cornwall PL18 9AX Tel: (H) 01822 833371
Tel: (W) 01579 386241
Club Colours: Red & black quarters, black shorts
League: Cornwall 2

CALNE RFC
Ground Address: The Recreation Ground, Anchor Road, Calne, Wiltshire. SN11 8DX
Brief Directions: Turn into Bank Row opposite Lansdowne Strand Hotel, past Somerfields into Mill St, follow road uphill into Anchor Rd, car park on left after 500 yards
Hon Secretary: Leigh Martin, 12 Brewer Mead, Chippenham, Wilts SN15 3FB Tel: (H) 01249 443284
Email: leighmartin@tinyonline.co.uk
Leagues Contact: as Hon. Secretary
Fixtures Secretary: Ian West, 23 Tern Close, Calne, Wiltshire, SN11 8NG Tel: (H) 01249 813737
Email: ian.denise.west@ic24.net
Club Colours: Blue with red & white hoop
League: Southern Counties South

CAMBORNE RFC
Ground Address: The Recreation Ground, Crane Park Clubhouse, Cranberry Road, Camborne, TR14 7PW
Tel: 01209 712684
Email Address: simon_moyle @hotmail.com
Web Address: http://www.camborne-rugby.com
Brief Directions: Leave the A30 at Camborne West junction(A3047). Then left at roundabout and right after 200 yds.Then first right after cul de sac.Pass school on right and take left where road divides.
Hon Secretary: Stephen West, 21 Holman Avenue, Cornwall PR14 7JQ Tel: (H) 01209 716665
Tel: (M) 07775 856316 Tel: (W) 01209 712428
Email: wnorthbywest@aol.com
Fixtures Secretary: David Smith, 65 Hughville St., Camborne, TR14 8TS Tel: (H) 01209 716992
Club Colours: Cherry and white
League: Western Counties West

CAMBORNE SCHOOL OF MINES RFC
Ground Address: The Memorial Ground, Boundervean Lane, Penponds, Camborne (not a postal address)
Tel: 01209 612959 - Clubhouse Tel: 01209 711935
Brief Directions: Off Pendraves Road, Camborne, B3303 to Helson, turn right into Boundervean Lane. Before railway bridge, ground is 250m on right.
Hon Secretary: Patrick Foster, 22 Gwarth an Drae, Helston, Cornwall TR13 0BS Tel: (H) 01326 560310
Email: p.j.foster@csm.ex.ac.uk
Club Colours: Navy, gold and silver hoops
League: Cornwall 2

CASTLE CARY RFC
Ground Address: Brookhouse Field, Nr. Alhampton, Ditcheat, Castle Cary, Somerset BA7 7AF
Tel: 01963 351178
Email Address: castlecaryrufc@hotmail.com
Brief Directions: A371 to Castle Cary from Shepton Mallet, turn right at Brookhouse Inn, 2nd on right
Fixtures Secretary: John Franklin, 17 Clothier Meadows, Castle Cary, Somerset BA7 7HA
Tel: (H) 01963 351193
Club Colours: Red and black hoops.
League: Somerset 2

CHARD
Ground Address: The Park, Essex Close, Chard
Tel: 01460 62495
Brief Directions: Bottom of Chard High Street (by Cerdic), 100 yards up Essex Close.
Hon Secretary: N. J. Urch, 2 South View, Ilminster, TA19 0EJ Tel: (H) 01460 57864
Tel: (W) 01935 702913
Email: treasurer@chardrfc.co.uk
Club Colours: Black, red and gold
League: Somerset 1

CHEDDAR VALLEY RFC
Ground Address: Sharpham Road, Cheddar
Tel: 01934 743623
Hon Secretary: Tim Rowlands, c/o 16 Round Oak Grove, Cheddar, BS27 3BW Tel: (H) 01934 712926
Club Colours: Sky blue and scarlet hoops
League: Somerset 2

CHELTENHAM CIVIL SERVICE RFC
Ground Address: Civil Service Sports Ground, Tewkesbury Road, Uckington, Cheltenham, Glos Tel: 01242 680847/680424
Web Address: www.ccsrfc.ndo.co.uk
Brief Directions: 2 miles from Cheltenham on the main road to Tewkesbury (A4019)
Hon Secretary: Brian Didlick, 15 Stoneville Street, Cheltenham, Glos GL51 8PH Tel: (H) 01242 519285
Fixtures Secretary: Kas Dabrowski, 2 Genista Way, Cheltenham, Glos GL51 5XZ Tel: (H) 01242.863040
Email: kdabro@2genistaway.freeserve.co.uk
Club Colours: Navy blue shirts & shorts, red socks
League: Gloucester 3 North

CHELTENHAM NORTH RFC
Ground Address: Stoke Orchard Road, Bishops Cleve, GL52 4RT Tel: 01242 675968
Brief Directions: Junction 10 or 11 Cheltenham, head out of Cheltenham past racecourse on A435 towards Bishops Cleeve, turn toward Stoke Orchard village, 500 yards on left
Hon Secretary: Andy Page, 15 Cheriton Close, Cheltenham, GL51 3NR Tel: (H) 01242 510932
Tel: (W) 01242 822508
Email: andrew_d.page@virgin.net
Fixtures Secretary: J. Creswell, 177 New Barn Lane, Cheltenham, Glos GL52 3LH
Tel: (H) 01242 269811
Club Colours: Black with red band, black shorts.
League: Western Counties North

CHELTENHAM SARACENS RFC
Ground Address: King George V Playing Fields, Brooklyn Road, St Marks, Cheltenham, Glos.
Tel: 01242 520529
Email Address: sport@chelt-saracens.fsnet.co.uk
Web Address: under construction
Brief Directions: Left off A40 Gloucester Road at GCHQ, head up to Coronation Square (PE Way), take the 4th exit and the club is at the end of the road in front of you.
Hon Secretary: David Millar, 11 Scott House, Princess Elizabeth Way, Cheltenham, Glos GL51 0HF
Tel: (H) 01242 700726 Tel: (M) 07986 054938
Tel: (W) 01242 580480
Email: ozziedmillar@hotmail.com
Fixtures Secretary: Jim Earle, 36 Stanwick Gardens, Cheltenham, Glos GL50 9LF Tel: (H) 01242 700479
Tel: (M) 07909 857269 Tel: (W) 01242 690006
Club Colours: Royal blue with gold circle
League: Gloucester 2

CHESHAM RUFC
Ground Address: Chesham Park Community College, Chatridge Lane, Chesham, BucksHP5 2RG
Tel: 01494 793827
Email Address: cheshamrufc@btconnect.com
Web Address: www.cheshamrugbyclub.com

Brief Directions: Location: Follow dual carriage way (St Mary's Way) to centre of Chesham. At r'about take exit into Park Rd/Chartridge Lane with park on the left. Entrance to Club is the furthest college gate on the left.
Hon Secretary: Jane Morris, 109 Chartridge Lane, Chesham, Bucks HP5 2RG Tel: (H) 01494 784951
Tel: (M) 07939 570686 Tel: (W) 01494 783677
Fixtures Secretary: Richard King, 75 Darvell Drive, Chesham, BucksHP5 2QN Tel: (H) 01494 786 056
Tel: (M) 07710 011633
Email: dick@kingr5.freeserve.co.uk
Club Colours: Blue and claret hoops
League: Berks/Bucks & Oxon 2

CHEW VALLEY RFC
Ground Address: Lobbingtons, Chew Lane, Chew Stoke, Bristol BS40 8UE Tel: 01275 333660
Email Address: jimgethin@aol.com
Web Address: www.chewvalleyrfc.co.uk
Brief Directions: Between Chew Stoke and Chew Magna, next to Chew Valley School.
Hon Secretary: Jim Gethin, April Cottage, Top Sutton, Bristol, BS39 5UW Tel: (H) 01275 332080
Tel: (M) 07831 835935 Tel: (W) 07831 835935
Email: jimgethin@aol.com
Fixtures Secretary: Ian Hall, 2 Chalk Farm Close, Norton Malreward, Bristol, BS39 4HQ
Tel: (H) 01275 837987
Club Colours: Green & white
League: Somerset Premier

CHIPPENHAM RFC
Ground Address: Allington Field, Sheldon Corner, Frogwell, Chippenham, Wilts SN14 0YZ
Tel: 01249 446 997
Web Address: www.chippenhamrfc.co.uk
Brief Directions: A420 twoards Bristol. Turn left by Allington Farm shop for Corsham & Sheldon Manor. After 600 yards turn sharp left, entrance on left. NB Now no entrance from Frogwell.
Hon Secretary: Stuart Murrow, 34 Park Lane, Chippenham, Wilts SN15 1LN Tel: (H) 01249 657720
Tel: (M) 07870 193785 Tel: (W) 01249 442125
Email: stuartmurrow@btopenworld.com
Leagues Contact: Robbie Spiers, 42 Willow Bank, Chippenham, Wilts SN14 6QG Tel: (H) 01249 444410
Email: robbie@spiers42.fsnet.co.uk
Fixtures Secretary: Adrian Lloyd, 27 Lords Mead, Chippenham, Wilts SN14 0LL Tel: (H) 01249 656 793
Email: adie.lloyd@ukonline.co.uk
Club Colours: Black & white irregular hoops
League: South West 2 East

CHIPPING NORTON RFC
Ground Address: 14 The Spinneys, Enstone OX7 4LD
Tel: 01608 641182 Email Address: ttc@connectfree.co.uk
Web Address: www.cnrufc.co.uk
Fixtures Secretary: Tony Cripps, 20 Rowell Way, Chipping Norton, OX7 5BD Tel: (H) 01608 641182
Tel: (M) 07773 446 517 Tel: (W) 01608 643 224
Email: ttc@connectfree.co.uk
Club Colours: Red and black hoops
League: Berks/Bucks & Oxon 1

CHIPPING SODBURY RFC
Ground Address: The Ridings, Wickwar Road, Chipping Sodbury, S. Glos
Tel: 01454 312852
Web Address: www.csrfc.com
Brief Directions: Take Wickwar Road out of Chipping Sodbury, ground .5 mile on left hand side.
Hon Secretary: A. C. Richards, 12 Tyning CLose, Bristol BS37 5PN Tel: (H) 01454 882284
Tel: (M) 07968 827333
Email: A.Richards@Cableinet.co.uk
Fixtures Secretary: T. Windsor, School Bungalow, Kes, Sunridge Park, Bristol Tel: (H) 01454 4862640
Club Colours: Black
League: Gloucester 1

CHOSEN HILL FORMER PUPILS RFC
Ground Address: Brookfield Road, Chuchdown, Glos
Tel: 01452 712384
Brief Directions: Equi-distant between Cheltenham/Gloucester on edge of village of Churchdown towards Cheltenham
Hon Secretary: Dave Morris, 20 Moselle Drive, Glos GL3 2RY Tel: (H) 01452 856955
Email: davemorris@micron2.freeserve.co.uk
Club Colours: Myrtle green and white
League: Gloucester Premier

CIRENCESTER RFC
Ground Address: The Whiteway, Cirencester, Gloucester, GL7 1EP Tel: 01285 654434
Brief Directions: Positioned at traffic lights on main Gloucester to Swindon A419 road, approx 1 mile from town centre
Hon Secretary: Henry Church, 38 Purley Road, Cirencester, Gloucester, GL7 1EP
Tel: (H) 01285 6433373
Email: henry.church@crfc.co.uk
Club Colours: Red and black hoops, black shorts.
League: Gloucester Premier

CLEVE RFC
Ground Address: The Hayfields, Cossham Street, Mangotsfield, Bristol, BS16 6HY
Tel: 0117 957 5775
Email Address: rugby@cleverugby.com
Web Address: www.cleverugby.com
Brief Directions: M4 onto M32, M32 J1, carry straight through traffic lights to next roundabout, follow directions to Downend, then to Mangotsfield, turn into Cosasham St. Ground 300yds on Rt.
Hon Secretary: Paul Jones, 43, Bromley Heath Road, Bristol, BS16 6HY Tel: (H) 0117 949 1727
Tel: (M) 07789 374120 Tel: (W) 0117 966 4590
Email: emrys@hotmail.com
Fixtures Secretary: S. Williams, 15 Lincombe Road, Bristol Tel: (H) 0117 9402159 Tel: (M) 07949 287118
Club Colours: Maroon.
League: South West 2 West

CLEVEDON RFC
Ground Address: Coleridge Vale Playing Fields, Southey Road, Clevedon, North Somerset BS21 6PF
Tel: 01275 877772
Web Address: www.clevedonrfc.co.uk
Brief Directions: M5 J20, straight across two R/abouts, turn lest at T/lights, turn left at Arrifa garage. Follow signs there after.
Hon Secretary: Mark Hawkes, 102 Canons Gate, Clevedon, North Somerset BS21
Tel: (H) 01275 877961
Leagues Contact: Mike Thomas, 46 Treefield Road, Clevedon, North Somerset Tel: (H) 01275 875497
Fixtures Secretary: John Evans, 79 Kenn Road, Clevedon, North Somerset BS21 6HE
Tel: (H) 01275 871443
Club Colours: Royal blue and gold
League: South West 2 West

COLERNE RFC
Ground Address: Northwood Farm, Colerne, Chippenham, Wilts SN14 8EP Tel: 01225 742328
Email Address: ben.harraway@dial.pipex.com
Hon Secretary: Ben Harraway, Northwood Farm, Chippenham, Wilts SN14 8QP Tel: (H) 01225 742328
Tel: (M) 07762 823844
Email: ben.harraway@dial.pipex.com
Club Colours: Black
League: Dorset & Wilts 2 North

COMBE DOWN
Ground Address: Holly's Corner, North Road, Combe Down Tel: 01225 832075
Brief Directions: Follow A3062 out of Bath to Combe Down
Hon Secretary: P. Bird, 83 Corston View, Bath, BA2 2PQ Tel: (H) 01225 835153 Tel: (W) 07774 191245
Club Colours: Black and amber
League: Somerset 1

CONEY HILL RFC
Ground Address: Metz Way, Coney Hill, Glos
Tel: 01452 306239
Brief Directions: Gloucester ring road (Eastern Ave) to Texas DIY store, turn into Metz Way, club is 0.25 mile on left
Hon Secretary: David Veale, 13 Stanway Road, Glos GL4 4RE Tel: (H) 01452 306510
Club Colours: Amber & Black
League: Western Counties North

COOPER AVON TYRES RFC
Ground Address: Cooper Avon Sports & Social Club, Melksham House, Market Place Melksham, Wiltshire
Email Address: pat@63stone.freeserve.co.uk
Web Address: melkshamrfc.co.uk
Brief Directions: Follow signs to football club at Melksham market place,
Hon Secretary: Pat Holtom, 63 Foresters Park Road, Melksham, Wiltshire, SN12 7RW
Tel: (H) 01225 703396
Email: pat@63stone.freeserve.co.uk
Fixtures Secretary: Marc Bound Tel: (H) 01225 700889
Club Colours: Navy blue and sky blue hoops
League: Dorset & Wilts 1

CORSHAM RFC
Ground Address: Corsham RFC, Lacock Road, Corsham, Wiltshire, SN13 9QG
Tel: 01249 701064
Email Address: rory@corsham@rfc.net
Web Address: corsham@rfc.net
Brief Directions: .5 mile outside Corsham on road to Lacock
Hon Secretary: John Wiltshire, 84 Springfield Close, Corsham, Wiltshire, SN13 0JR Tel: (H) 01225 810800
Fixtures Secretary: R. Slade, 46 Paul Street, Corsham, Wiltshire, SN13 9DG Tel: (H) 01249 712683
Club Colours: Red,white,black hoops
League: Dorset & Wilts 1

COTHAM PARK RFC
Ground Address: Beggar Bush Lane, Failand, Bristol
Tel: 0117 939 2501
Brief Directions: M5 J19, A369 towards Bristol, left on A3129 (Beegar Bush Lane)
Hon Secretary: Mark Chappell, Garden Flat, 289 Hotwell Road, Bristol, BS8 4HQ Tel: (H) 0117 908 6710
Email: mchappellu@cableinet.co.uk
Club Colours: Black and white hoops
League: Gloucester 3 South

CREDITON RFC
Ground Address: Blagdon, Exhibition Road, Crediton, Devon, EX17 1BY Tel: 01363 772784
Email Address: paulrharris@tinyonline.co.uk
Brief Directions: M5 to Exeter, A377 to Crediton then A3072 towards Tiverton, club on left hand side of road
Hon Secretary: Marilyn Daw, Clotworthy, Coldridge, Crediton, Devon, EX17 6AR Tel: (H) 01363 83446
Tel: (W) 01363 775871(Term time)
Email: cllrjohndaw@netscapeonline.co.uk
Fixtures Secretary: M. Leyman, Pepperlake, New Buildings, Crediton, EX17 4PW Tel: (H) 01363 85092
Club Colours: Black and amber
League: South West 2 West

CREWKERNE RFC
Ground Address: Henhayes, Crewkerne, Somerset TA18 7JJ Tel: 01460 76422
Email Address: crfc@jennandnigel.f9.co.uk
Web Address: www.crewkernerugby.co.uk
Brief Directions: Head for Crewkerne town centre. Follow signs to the Aqua Centre or Henhayes, situated besides car park. Park in main car park. Clubhouse/ field are visible from car park.
Hon Secretary: Jeanette Gollings, 59 Sycamore Close, Taunton, Somerset TA1 2QJ Tel: (H) 01823 279837
Tel: (M) 07855 646801 Tel: (W) 01823 285301
Email: crfc@jennandnigel.f9.co.uk
Fixtures Secretary: Trevor Boyer, 55 St. James, Beaminster, Dorset DT8 3PW Tel: (H) 01308 863169
Club Colours: Scarlet & black Hoops
League: Somerset 1

CRICKLADE RFC
Ground Address: 4 Collett Place, Latton, Wiltshire, SN6 6EH Tel: 01793 751589
Email Address: gardinerpa@x-stream.co.uk
Hon Secretary: Philip Gardiner, 4 Collett Place, Swindon, Wiltshire, SN6 6EH Tel: (H) 01793 751589
Tel: (W) 01285 713913
Email: gardinerpa@x-stream.co.uk
Fixtures Secretary: Ron Price, 70 Hallsfield, Cricklade, Wiltshire SN6 6LS Tel: (H) 01793 752204
League: Dorset & Wilts 2 North

CULLOMPTON RFC
Ground Address: Stafford Park, Knowle Lane, Cullompton, Devon EX15 Tel: 01884 32480
Brief Directions: M5 J28 town centre, turn right by Manor Hotel, past fire station turn left to Langlands Rd, turn right at end of road, club at top of lane
Hon Secretary: Russell Burrows, Westgate House, orpington Court, Devon, EX15 7DD
Tel: (H) 01884 821326 Tel: (M) 07970 478467
Email: Russnsar@aol.com
Fixtures Secretary: K. Ballantyne, 34 New Street, Cullompton, Devon EX15 1HA Tel: (H) 01884 35379
Club Colours: Scarlet and black hoops
League: Devon 1

DARTMOUTH RFC
Ground Address: Roseville Pavilion, Roseville Street, Dartmouth, Devon, TQ6 9QH Tel: 01803 833994
Brief Directions: Milton Lane: Enter Dartmouth from Totnes. First right, past Park& Ride, Dartmouth School and Community College
Hon Secretary: Nigel Boyd, 100 Victoria Road, Dartmouth, Devon, TQ6 9EF Tel: (H) 01803 834474
Tel: (W) 01803 834031 Email: boydhypostop@aol.com
Fixtures Secretary: Steven Atkins, 125 Victoria Road, Dartmouth, Devon, TQ6 9DY Tel: (H) 01803 832381
Tel: (M) 07790 261986 Email: ackey@btinternet.co.uk
Club Colours: Red & green irregular hoops, black shorts
League: Devon 2

DEVIZES RFC
Ground Address: Chivers Ground, The Sports Club, London Road, Devizes, Wilts SN10 2DL
Tel: Sports Club - 01380 723763
Email Address: nick.dark@lineone.net
Web Address: http://www.intheteam.com/Saddlebacks
Brief Directions: Found at the Sports Club, London Road, Devizes. Approaching from the East, we're just after the Police HQ before the canal bridge. From the West, we're immediately after the canal bridge and before the Police HQ.
Hon Secretary: Nick Dark, Ashleigh, Salisbury Street, Devizes, Wilts SN10 1QA Tel: (H) 01380 721429
Tel: (M) 07779 793057 Tel: (W) 01249 812086
Email: nick.dark@lineone.net
Fixtures Secretary: Clive Meaney, 10 Park Road, Devizes, Wilts SN10 4ED Tel: (H) 01380 818 735
Tel: (M) 0797 661 0547
Club Colours: Broad black and white hoops; white shorts
League: Southern Counties South
Leagues Contact: Nick Dark - as above.

DEVONPORT HIGH SCHOOL OLD BOYS RFC
Ground Address: Devonport High School for Boys, Paradise Road, Millbridge, Plymouth, Devon.
Tel: 01752 564682 Website: msn.co.uk
Brief Directions: A38 to Home P"k,along Outland Rd,to Mllehouse traffic lights. Into Mllehouse Rd,left at top of hill ights into Molesworth Rd. Right at bottom of hill lights then top of hill left to DHS
Club Secretary: Geoff Simpson, 108 Pattinson Drive, Mainstone, Plymouth, Devon. PL6 8
Tel: (H) 01752 206662 Email: gks49@hotmail.com
Fixtures Secretary: Chris Hill,7 Hats Hill Close, Mainstone, Plymouth PL6 8RU Tel: (H) 01752 776792
Club Colours: Green & white hoops, black shorts
League: Devon 1

DEVONPORT SERVICES RFC
Ground Address: The Rectory, 2nd Avenue, Devonport, Plymouth. PL1 5QE. Tel: 01752 50559
Brief Directions: Maps are issued to visiting clubs
Club Secretary: Allan Berry, 36 Beechwood Avenue, Plymouth, Devon PL4 6PW Tel: 01752 662443
Fixtures Secretary: G Kelly, 24 Youldon Way, Morrabridge, Yelverton PL20 7SN Tel: 01822 854251
Club Colours: Navy shirts, blue shorts
League: Cornwall/Devon

DORCHESTER RFC
Ground Address: Coburg Road, Dorchester, Dorset DT1 2HX Tel: 01305 - 265692
Email Address: webmaster@dorchester-rfc.co.uk
Web Address: www.dorchester-rfc.co.uk
Directions: From the by-pass follow signs to "West Dorset Leisure Centre"
Hon Secretary: Graham Aspley, 5 Nappers Court, Charles Street, Dorchester, Dorset DT1 1EE
Tel: (H) 01305 814 802 Tel: (W) 01305 269 944
Email: aspley@dorch.freeserve.co.uk
Club Colours: Green & white hoops/navy blue
League: South West 2 East

DRIFTERS RFC
Ground Address: Farnham Common Sports CLub, One Pin Lane, Farnham Common, Bucks SL2 3QY
Tel: 01753 644 190
Email Address: chrisashton@btconnect.com
Web Address: www.fcsc.org.uk/drifters2.htm
Brief Directions: Directions:M4 J6 head north on A355, or M40 J2 head south on A355 One Pin Lane half mile north of Farnham Common village
Hon Secretary: John Flower, Ceadel House, 49 Kings Road, Chalfont St Giles, Bucks HP8 4HP
Tel: (H) 07831 236532 Tel: (M) 07831 236532
Email: johnnflower@aol.com
Fixtures Secretary: Alan Pearce, 9 Stevenson Rd, Hedgerley, Bucks SL2 3YP Tel: (H) 01753 645973
Tel: (M) 07957 692131 Email: fiercepearce@hotmail.com
Club Colours: Black, with gold and magenta hoops
League: Berks/Bucks & Oxon 1

DRYBROOK RFC
Ground Address: Mannings Ground, Drybrook, Glos Tel: 01594 542595
Brief Directions: Gloucester to Mitcheldean via Huntley, ground is on outskirts of village on Mitcheldean Road
Hon Secretary: Glyn Tingle, 16 Woodland Road, Glos GL17 9HE Tel: (H) 01594 544334 Tel: (W) 01594 542769
Club Colours: Green with black on white band
League: Gloucester Premier

DURSLEY RFC LIMITED
Ground Address: Stinchcombe Stragglers, The Avenue, Stinchcombe, Dursley, Glos GL11 6AJ Tel: 01453 543693
Brief Directions: Located on Dursley to Wotton-under-Edge road (B4060), on the right just before entering Stinchcombe village if travelling from Dursley
Hon Secretary: Phil Case, 2 Coach Close, Berkeley, Glos GL13 9EJ Tel: (H) 01453 819055
Fixtures Secretary: Tony Powell, 55 Oakfield Way, Glos GL13 9UT Tel: (H) 01453 811484
Club Colours: Maroon with amber hoop (change colours green)
League: Gloucester 3 North

EXETER SARACENS RFC
Ground Address: Exhibition Field, Summer Lane, Whipton, Exeter, EX4 8NN Tel: 01329 462651
Email Address: rugby@exetersaracens.co.uk
Brief Directions: From M5 follow signs for Exeter Arena or from other direction follow Whipton signs then Exeter Arena signs
Hon Secretary: David Mortimore, 39 Lonsdale Road, Exeter, EX1 3DP Tel: (H) 01392 433 305
Colours: Red shirts with white collar, black shorts
League: Devon 1

EXMOUTH RFC
Ground Address: Imperial Recreation Ground, Royal Avenue, Exmouth, EX8 1DG Tel: 01395 263665
Email Address: enquiries@exmouthrugby.co.uk
Web Address: www.exmouthrugby.co.uk
Brief Directions: M5 to Sandy Gate-Exeter, exit here, follow Exmouth signs 8 miles, enter Exmouth on town bypass from which ground can be seen by River Exe
Hon Secretary: Peter Appleby, 18 Hulham Road, Exmouth, Devon, EX8 3LB Tel: (H) 01395 272110 Tel: (M) 07785 256289 Tel: (W) 01395 222665
Email: peter.appleby@virgin.net
Fixtures Secretary: Gerry Williams, 40 Bapton Close, Exmouth, Devon, EX8 3LQ Tel: (H&W) 01395 271373 Tel: (M) 07811 582061
Club Colours: Heliotrope&white hoops, white shorts
League: South West 2 West

FAIRFORD RFC
Ground Address: Coln House School, Fairford
Hon Secretary: Christopher Jackson, The Flat, 35 London Road, GL7 4QA Tel: (H) 01285 713991 Tel: (M) 07974 686 067 Email: chris@inFinity-it-co.uk
Club Colours: Emerald and Black Hoops.
League: Gloucester 3 North

FALMOUTH RFC
Ground Address: The Recreation Ground, Dracaena Avenue, Falmouth, Cornwall Tel: 01326 311304
Brief Directions: Right at traffic lights on A39 (by SAAB Garage) and left into and along Dracaena Avenue, visible from main road. Ground at junction of Tregenver and Killigrew roads.
Hon Secretary: Hugh Murton, 3 Wellington Place, Truro, Cornwall TR3 6LF Tel: (H) 01872 863679 Tel: (M) 07771 595593
Email: hughmurtoncd@aol.com
Fixtures Secretary: G. U. Wilkes, 33 Carrine Road, Truro, Cornwall TR1 3XB Tel: (H) 01872 223487
Club Colours: Black with white hoops
League: Cornwall 1

FRAMPTON COTTERELL RFC
Ground Address: Crossbow House,School Road, Frampton Cotterell, Bristol, (Avon) Tel: 01454 856628
Email Address: jerry.c.boaden@uktransco.com
Web Address: www.fcrfc.com
Brief Directions: Off B3058 Winterbourne to Chipping Sodbury road
Hon Secretary: Steve Buckley, 125 Ratcliffe Drive, Bristol BS34 8TZ Tel: (H) 0117 907 0344 Tel: (W) 0117 979 1234 ext 93798 Tel: (M) 07812 202760 Email: stevebucks@supanet.com
Fixtures Secretary: Nathan Cole, 29 Robel Avenue, Frampton Cotterell, Bristol, South Glos., BS36 2BY Tel: (H) 01545 778875 Tel: (M) 07971 616287
Email: nathan_cole_ee@hotmail.com
Club Colours: Green, black and gold shirts
League: Gloucester 1

FROME RFC
Ground Address: Gypsy Lane, Frome, Somerset. BA11 2NA Tel: 01373 462506
Brief Directions: Follow signs for Leisure Centre, Frome RFC is signposted from the Bath Road/Princess Anne Road traffic lights
Club Secretary: Ray Harding, 93 Dakfield Road, Frome, Somerset BA11 4JH
Tel: 01373 461638 (H) 01373 456410 (W)
Email: ray.harding@which.net
Fixtures Secretary: Symon Crouch 7Alder Walk, Frome, Somerset Tel: 01373 465600
Club Colours: Red, black & white hoops.
League: Southern Counties South

GLOUCESTER ALL BLUES RFC
Ground Address: Westgate Bridge, Oxleaze, Westgate, Gloucester, GL1 2TH Tel: 01452 306984
Email Address: info@ironmansports.co.uk
Web Address: www.gabrfc.co.uk
Brief Directions: South Wales road out of Gloucester (signposted to Ross-on-Wye, Chepstow and Ledbury) then first left after crossing River Severn (Westgate Bridge)

SOUTH WEST

Hon Secretary: Robert Hart, The Uplands, Minsterworth, Gloucester, Glos GL2 8JH
Tel: (H) 01452 750223 Tel: (M) 07880 791865
Tel: (W) 01452 425656
Club Colours: Navy blue shirts, shorts and socks.
League: Gloucester 3 North

GLOUCESTER CIVIL SERVICE TIGERS RFC
Ground Address: Estcourt Road, Gloucester, Glos
Tel: 01452 528317
Brief Directions: M5 J11, A40 to Gloucester, continue on A40 to Longford roundabout, left at Longford Inn (Beefeater), left at next roundabout, ground is on immediate right
Hon Secretary: R. W. Sheppard, 95 Lavington Drive, Gloucester GL20 0HR Tel: (H) 01452 532802
Club Colours: Blue, red, white hoops, white shorts
League: Gloucester 3 North

GLOUCESTER OLD BOYS RFC
Ground Address: Horton Road, Gloucester
Tel: 01452 302390
Brief Directions: M5 J11A, follow signs to city centre, 3rd exit at roundabout adjacent to Wall's ice cream factory, 2nd left is Horton Road
Hon Secretary: Ray Ellis, 15 Armscroft Way, Gloucester GL2 0ST Tel: (H) 01452 525375
Tel: (W) 01452 416033
Email: russ.ellis@btclick.com
Fixtures Secretary: S. J. Turner, 19 St. Marks Street, Gloucester Tel: (H) 01452 422973
Tel: (W) 01242 277203
Club Colours: Claret, gold and navy
League: South West 2 West

GORDANO
Ground Address: Gordano RFC, Caswell lane, Portbury, Bristol, BS20 9UF Tel: 01275 373486
Brief Directions: Jct 19 at M5, take A369, head into village of Portbury and bear left at the village green.
Hon Secretary: Caroline Goddard, 6 Clayton Close, Portishead, BS20 6YU
Tel: (H) 01275 817340
Tel: (W) 01275 375361 ext 2238
Club Colours: Red and black shirts, black shorts.
League: Somerset Premier

GORDON LEAGUE RFC
Ground Address: Hempsted Lane, Gloucester, Glos GL2 6JN Tel: 01452 303434
Email Address: gordonleague@yahoo.co.uk
Web Address: gordonleague.com
Brief Directions: Contact Hon Secretary for detailed instructions
Hon Secretary: Martin Gamston, 20 Robinson Road, Gloucester Tel: (H) 01452 521719
Club Colours: White, red sash, black socks
League: Western Counties North

GOSFORD ALL BLACKS RFC
Ground Address: Stratford Brake Sports Ground, Langford Lane, Kidlington, Oxon
Tel: 01865 373994
Brief Directions: Take A44 Evesham road from Oxford, follow signs to Oxford Airport, club is opposite airport.Or take A4260 to Kidlington roundabout and follow signs to Stratford Brake Sports ground.
Club Secretary: Martin Lambert,57 Brunstock Beck,Didcot, Oxon. OX11 7YG
Tel: 01235 810405
e-mail:martin@manor-didcot.oxon.sch.uk
Fixtures Secretary: Dave Duthie, 10 Lovell Close, Duckington, Witney, Oxon, OX8 7YQ
Tel: (H) 01993 702261
Club Colours: All Black
League: Berks/Bucks & Oxon 2

GROVE RFC
Ground Address: Recreation Ground, Cane Lane, Grove, Wantage, Oxfordshire
Tel: 01235 762750
Brief Directions: Frm Oxford (A338), turn right into village, rt at r'bout, lft at r'bout (Brereton Dv), lft at end to Cane Ln. Frm sth enter vlge at lights, lft at r'bout into D'worth Rd, follow as above
Club Secretary: Mrs Sylvia Morrison, 19 Hardwell Close, Grove, Oxon.
Tel No: 01235 223903
Fixtures Secretary: Wayne Latimer, 30 Mallard Way, Grove, Wantage, Oxon.
Tel: 01235 771004
Club Colours: Red, white and blue hoops, navy shorts and red socks
League: South West 2 East

HARWELL RUFC (50th Anniversary Season)
Ground Address: Central Sports Field, A.E.A. Harwell Laboratory, Nr Didcot, Oxon
Brief Directions: To the left of main gate at Harwell Laboratory on old Newbury-Abingdon road (A4185)
Club Secretary: Douglas Bosley,55 West Lockinge, nr Wantage,Oxon. OX12 8QE. Tel: 01235 833688
Email: dougbosley@btinternet.com
Fixtures Secretary: Jenny Bosley
Tel: (H) 01235 833688
Club Colours: Royal blue, light blue and white hooped shirts
League: Berks/Bucks & Oxon 2

HAYLE RFC
Ground Address: Memorial Park, Marsh Lane, Hayle, Cornwall TR27 4PS
Tel: 01736 753 320
Brief Directions: Take A30 to first roundabout, ground immediately in front
Hon Secretary: Rod Porter, 3 Greenbank, Hayle, Cornwall TR27 5DA Tel: (H) 01736 757 203
Email: gwinear-gpc@ruralnet.org.uk
Fixtures Secretary: Mike Gee, Lowenna, 70 Halsetown, St. Ives, Cornwall TR26 3LX Tel: (H) 01736 797 168 Tel: (M) 0468 910 556
Email: swrfu@aol.com
Club Colours: Green, black and white
League: Western Counties West

HELSTON RFC
Ground Address: King George V Memorial Playing Fields, Clodgey Lane, Helston
Tel: 01326 573742
Brief Directions: A394 into north of town past Tesco superstore, 0.25 mile on right, before Flambards Theme Park
Hon Secretary: Alison Dodd, 78 Bulwark Road, Helston, Cornwall Tel: (H) 01326 564 785
Club Colours: Navy and white hoops
League: Cornwall 1

HENLEY WANDERERS
Ground Address: Dry Leas, Marlow Road, Henley on Thames RG9 2JA
Tel No: 01491 413156
Brief Directions: Leave Henley on the Oxford Road and fork right into Marlow Road. Dry leas is on the left ater 100 yardy
Club Secretary: David Shove, 201 Greys Road, Henley on Thames, Oxon RG9 1QU Tel No: 01491 576541
Email: dave@shove.fsnet.co.uk
Fixtures Secretary: Alan Richardson.
Tel: 01491 574664 (H) 01628 487755(W)
Club Colours: Bottle Green with gold collar, blue shorts and green socks.
League: Berks/Bucks & Oxon 1

HIGH WYCOMBE RUFC
Ground Address: Kingsmead Road, High Wycombe, Bucks. HP11 1JB. Tel: 01494 532024
Brief Directions: M40, J4 to A404 (Amersham) into town centre. A40 ((Beaconsfield). After 3rd mini r'about right into Abbey Barn Rd. After 800 yds sharp left into Kingsmead Rd.
Club Secretary: Don Dickerson, 3 Talbot Ave., High Wycombe, Bucks. HP13 5HZ.
Tel: (H) 01494 532024 (B) 01494 479722
Fixtures Secretary: George Brown,
Deerleap, Primrose Hill, Widmerend, High Wycombe, Bucks. HP15 6NU. Tel: (H) 01494 716700
Club Colours: Broad green and narrow black & white hoops
League: Southern Counties North

HONITON RFC
Ground Address: Allhallows Playing Fields, Northcot Lane, Honiton, Devon Tel: 01404 41239
Brief Directions: From traffic lights in High St, turn into Dowell St, continue for 0.5 mile, turn right at the Fire station into Northcote Lane, follow road around to the Sports Centre
Hon Secretary: Jeremy Rice, 184 High Street, Honiton, EX14 1LA Tel: (H) 01404 46820
Tel: (M) 07971 995048
Email: jeremy.rice@btinternet.com
Fixtures Secretary: Adrian Wilson, Hindscott, Hind Street, Whimple, Devon, EX5 2TB
Tel: (M) 07816297926
Club Colours: Red black & amber hoops, black shorts.
League: Devon 1

HORNETS RFC
Ground Address: Hutton Moor Park, Hutton Moor Road, Weston-super-Mare, Somerset BS22 8LX
Tel: 01934 621433
Brief Directions: J.21 M5 dual carriage way to Weston-super-Mare. Straight across two r'abouts - turn right at filter light - Ground on right.
Hon Secretary: Keith Powell, 103 Sunnyside Road North, Weston-super-Mare BS23 3PZ
Tel: (H) 01934 625750
Fixtures Secretary: John Wilson, 6 Blackberry Drive, Weston-Super-Mare, Somerset Tel: (H) 01934 513543
Club Colours: Black and amber
League: South West 2 West

HUCCLECOTE RFC
Ground Address: The Old School Field, Churchdown Lane, Hucclecote, Gloucester, GL3 3QH
Tel: 01452 621 281
Web Address: www.hucclecoterfc.co.uk
Brief Directions: Exit M5 (north) Jct 11A, To Glos take left at Zoons Ct round't to Glos Trading Estate roundabout. Rt. to Hucclecote.Rt. at lights to Churchdown Lane. Club on right past school.
Hon Secretary: John Ring, 9 Conway Road, Gloucester, GL3 3PD Tel: (H) 01452 618920
Tel: (W) 01452 857367
Fixtures Secretary: Len Taylor, 41 Larkhay Road, Gloucester, GL3 3NR Tel: (H) 01452 619718
Club Colours: Black and amber
League: Gloucester Premier

HUNGERFORD RFC
Ground Address: The Triangle Field, Priory Road, Hungerford, Berks Tel No: 01488 684662
Brief Directions: A4 to Hungerford. Turn into High Street at Bear Hotel junction. Travel through town and up high street, until left into Priory Road after 3/4 mile. Signposted to Football Club and Coombe. After mile pitch is on left after John O'Gaunt School.
Club Secretary: Adrian Chapman.
Tel No: 0780 2281837
Fixtures Secretary: Simon Ford, 28 Shalbourne Close, Hungerford,Berks RG17 0QH
Club Colours: Claret and porter hoops, black shorts.
League: Dorset & Wilts 2 North

ILFRACOMBE RFC
Ground Address: Brimlands, Hillsborough Road, Ilfracombe, Devon Tel: 01271 864249
Brief Directions: From town centre take road to east signed Combe Martin, look out for swimming pool, club on left close by
Hon Secretary: John Williams, 5 Castle Hill Villas, Ilfracombe, Devon EX34 9HT
Tel: (H) 01271 865198 Tel: (M) 07803 723986
Tel: (W) 01271 814999
Fixtures Secretary: R. Crabb, 43 Oak Tree GArdens, Ilfracombe, Devon Tel: (H) 01271 863 011
Club Colours: Blue and white hoops
League: Devon 2

ILLOGAN PARK RFC
Ground Address: Illogan Park, Paynters Lane End,Illogan, Redruth, Cornwall
Brief Directions: Turn off A30 at Portrath and head for Pool.Turn right down Cheriot Road for one mile . Ground is on left.
Hon Secretary: Nigel Bowden, Copperhaven, Perranporth, Corwall, TR6 0JY
Tel: (H) 01872 571719 Tel: (M) 07836 798019
Email: bowdenn@tycohealth.com
Club Colours: Yellow and black
League: Cornwall 2

IMPERIAL
Ground Address: Bristol Imperial Club, West Town Lane, Knowle, Bristol, Somerset
Tel: 01275 546000
Brief Directions: From Wells road (A37) and Bath road (A4), turn into West Town Lane
Hon Secretary: Andy Buckle, 227 Headley Lane, Headley Park, Bristol, BS13 7QB
Tel: (M) 07967 467333 Tel: (W) 0117 963 6636
Club Colours: Myrtle and amber shirts, blue shorts
League: Somerset 1

IVEL BARBARIANS RFC LTD
Ground Address: Yeovil Showground, Dorchester Road, Yeovil, Somerset BA22 9RA
Tel: 01935 474591
Web Address: www.ivelbarbarians.fsnet.co.uk
Hon Secretary: Elizabeth Maunder, 2 Church View, Great Street, North-sub-Hamdon, Somerset TA14 6SG
Tel: (H) 01935 881152 Tel: (M) 07790 513878
Email: Stuartandliz.Maunder@talkgas.net
Fixtures Secretary: Keith Smith, 39 Welbeck Road, Yeovil, BA21 5PH Tel: (H) 01935 420206
Club Colours: Black and white quarters with black shorts
League: Southern Counties South

IVYBRIDGE RFC
Ground Address: Cross-in-Hand, Exeter Road, Ivybridge, Devon PL21 0TH Tel: 01752 894392
Email Address: rugby@ivybridgerugby.co.uk
Web Address: www.ivybridgerugby.co.uk
Brief Directions: From A38 Exeter/Plymouth main road, follow the `Park & Ride' signs. The ground is almost opposite the station entrance.
Hon Secretary: Simon Arthurs, 9 Wellstones Close, Ivybridge, Devon PL21 0FE
Tel: (H) 01752 698815 Tel: (M) 07754 791070
Tel: (W) 01752 305471
Email: sra@sleepy-1.fsnet.co.uk
Fixtures Secretary: Jim Edington, Cramond Lodge, Ivybridge, Devon PL21 0DJ Tel: (H) 01752 696 330
Club Colours: Green shirts and black shorts
League: Western Counties West

KINGSBRIDGE RFC
Ground Address: High House, Kingsbridge, Devon. TQ7 1JL Tel: 01548 852051
Web Address: www.kingsbridgerfc.co.uk
Brief Directions: From centre of Kingsbridge take Dartmouth road alongside estuary, take first left and first right to the top of the hill
Hon Secretary: Martin Newman, 46 Saffron Park, Kingsbridge TQ7 1RL Tel: (H) 01548 853976
Tel: (M) 07974 803735
Email: martinnewman@kingsbridegerfc.freeserve.co.uk
Club Colours: Blue and white hoops
League: Cornwall/Devon

KINGSWOOD RFC
Ground Address: Deanery Road Playing Field, Grimsbury Road, Kingswood
Brief Directions: Bristol on A420, turn right into Grimsbury Rd immediately before Tennis Court pub, ground is 1st left
Hon Secretary: Mark Phillips, 5 Cloverdale Drive, Bristol Tel: (H) 0117 932 5334
Email: markphillips@tinyworld.co.uk
Club Colours: Sky blue and chocolate brown
League: Gloucester 2

LANKELLY-FOWEY RFC
Ground Address: Lankelly Farm, Lankelly Lane, Lankelly, Fowey, Cornwall
Web Address: www.lankellyfoweyrfc.com
Brief Directions: On entering Fowey, turn right into Lankelly Lane, follow road until T junction, turn left, ground is 100yds on right
Hon Secretary: Geoff Rew, 123 Creak-a-Vose, St. Stephen, St. Austell, Cornwall PL26 7NB
Tel: (H) 01726 821471
Email: geoff_rew@hotmail.com
Club Colours: Navy blue and white hoops
League: Cornwall 2

LISKEARD-LOOE RFC
Ground Address: Lux Park, Coldstyle Road, Liskeard, Cornwall Tel: 01579 342665
Brief Directions: Ask for the Leisure Centre, near town centre
Hon Secretary: Dave Williams, 9 Clifton Terrace, New Road, Liskeard, Cornwall PL14 4HN
Tel: (H) 01579 344082
Club Colours: Red and black hoops
League: Cornwall 1

LITTLEMORE RFC
Ground Address: Peers School, Sandy Lane, Oxford, OX4 6JY Tel: 01865 715776
Email Address: lrfc@littlemorerfc.org.uk
Brief Directions: Oxon ring road to Cowley (eastern bypass A4142), past the Rover plant on left, left turn and signpost to Peers School
Hon Secretary: G. Wakeham, 124 Church Way, Court Place Gardens, Oxford, OX4 4PQ
Tel: (H) 01865 749374
Fixtures Secretary: C. Wright, 37 Ock Drive, Wallingford OX10 7PP Tel: (H) 01865 341720
Club Colours: Royal Blue and White
League: Berks/Bucks & Oxon 1

LONGLEVENS RFC
Ground Address: Longford Lane, Longlevens, Gloucester, GL2 9EU Tel: 01452 306880
Brief Directions: M5 J11 - Golden Valley bypass towards Gloucester, right at 2nd lights into Old Cheltenham Rd, Church Rd then Longford Ln. Or A38 T'kesbury rd turn right into Longford Ln past Queens Head
Hon Secretary: Colin Dunford, 66 Estcourt Road, Gloucester GL1 3LG Tel: (H) 01452 522795 Tel: (W) 01452 529751
Club Colours: Red
League: Gloucester Premier

MAIDENHEAD RUFC
Ground Address: Braywick Park, Braywick Road, Maidenhead, Berkshire Tel: 01628 629663
Web Address: www.maidenheadrfc.com
Directions: From M4 junct 8/9 follow signs A308(M) Maidenhead Town Centre. A308(M) to r'about, left on A308 towards Maidenhead. After 1/2 mile filter right across dual carriageway & club is directly opposite.
Hon Secretary: R.M. Brown, 49 Bannard Road, Maidenhead, Berkshire, SL6 4NP Tel: (H) 01628 670586 Tel: (M) 07850 294005 Tel: (W) 01628 670816
Fixtures Secretary: Chris G. Reeves, 21 Belmont Road, Maidenhead, Berks SL6 6JL Tel: (H) 01628 620601
Club Colours: Magenta, violet & black
League: South West 2 East

MARLBOROUGH RFC
Ground Address: The Common, Free's Avenue, Marlborough, Wiltshire, SN8 1DL Tel: 01672 514717
Email Address: rodneyandjoyce@supanet.com
Brief Directions: Take Swindon road out of Marlborough then left at Common and right into Frees Avenue.
Hon Secretary: Joyce Adams, 10 Ailesbury Way, Marlborough, Wilts SN8 3TD Tel: (H) 01672 810718
Email: rodneyandjoyce@supanet.com
Fixtures Secretary: Alec Thomas, 2 Dando Drive, Barton Park, Marlborough, Wilts SN8 1TT Tel: (H) 01672 512296
Club Colours: Black & amber hoops.
League: Dorset & Wilts 2 North

MARTOCK RFC
Ground Address: Registered Office is, 3A North Street, Martock, Somerset
Hon Secretary: Philip Jackson, Church Lodge Cottage, Church Street, Martock TA12 6JL Tel: (H) 01935 823514
Fixtures Secretary: Peter Cockle, 19 Birch Road, Martock, Somerset TA12 6DR Tel: (H) 01935 823198 Tel: (W) 01454 272050 Email: pmc1@mead.com
Club Colours: Green and black quarters
League: Dorset & Wilts 2 South

MATSON RFC
Ground Address: Redwell Road, Matson, Gloucester Tel: 01452 528 963
Brief Directions: Three miles south of city centre on B4073, adjacent to dry ski slope
Hon Secretary: Don Danter, c/o Matson Rugby CLub Tel: (H) 01452 612808
Club Colours: Black shirts and white shorts
League: South West 2 West

MIDSOMER NORTON RFC
Ground Address: Norton Down Playing Fields, Stratton-on-the-Fosse, Bath, Somerset BA3 2RW Tel: 01761 412827
Brief Directions: From town centre follow Shepton Mallet road (B3355) for approx 800 yards
Hon Secretary: Corrine Edwards, Hillview, Mendip Road, Stoke St. Michael, Somerset BA3 5JU Tel: (H) 01749 841425 Tel: (M) 07968 058847
Fixtures Secretary: Rob Porter, Upper Lentley Farm, Kilmersdon, Bath, BA3 5SL Tel: (H) 01761 432325 Tel: (W) 01761 420042
Email: rob@wessexifa.co.uk
Club Colours: Red and white hoops, black shorts
League: Somerset Premier

MILTON KEYNES RUFC
Ground Address: Sam Coster Pavilion, Field Lane, Greenleys, Wolverton, Milton Keynes, Bucks. MK12 6AZ Tel: 01908 313858
Brief Directions: Travel from Stony Stratford town centre towards Wolverton, rt at double r'bout into Gt Monics St (V5), proceed across r'bout, rt into Field Ln, rt at T j'tion, next left to clubhouse
Club Secretary: Gary Spinks, Harley House, Bow Brickhill, Bucks. MK17 9LH Tel No: 01908 277138
Fixtures Secretary: David Eales. Tel: 01296 714422
Club Colours: Black and white hoops, black shorts
League: Berks/Bucks & Oxon 1

MINCHINHAMPTON RFC
Ground Address: Minchinhampton Sports and Social Club, Tobacconist Road, Minchinhampton, Glos Tel: 01453 882636
Email Address: mrfc@minchinhamptonrfc.com
Web Address: www.minchinhamptonrfc.com
Brief Directions: From centre of village take Tetbury road (Tetbury Street), 1st left, clubhouse straight ahead
Hon Secretary: Robert Edmonds, Woodlands Cottage, 205 Slad Road, Gloucester, GL5 1RJ Tel: (H) 01453 766662 Tel: (M) 07932 385453 Tel: (W) 01452 872420
Email: mrfc@minchinhamptonrfc.com
Fixtures Secretary: Mike Evans, 66 Glebe Road, Minchinhampton, Glos GL6 9LQ Tel: (H) 01453 731982
Club Colours: Green White & Black
League: Gloucester 2

MINEHEAD BARBARIANS RFC
Ground Address: The Tom Stewart Field, Ellicombe Lane, Ellicombe, Minehead, Somerset TA24 6TR Tel: 01643 707155
Brief Directions: A39 to Minehead from Taunton/Bridgwater, left at roundabout signed Ellicombe, ground 100 metres

Hon Secretary: Jonathan Sweetland, Bramley, Higher Orchard, Minehead, TA24 8SD Tel: (H) 01643 705283
Fixtures Secretary: C. Ford, 13 Samford Brett, Williton, Somerset TA4 4LA Tel: (H) 01984 633237
Club Colours: Black and white hoops
League: Somerset Premier

MINETY RFC
Ground Address: The Playing Fields, Silver Street, Minety, Nr Malmesbury, Wiltshire
Tel: 01666 860802
Web Address: http://www.minetyrfc.com
Brief Directions: From Swindon take A419 to Cirencester, turn off at Cricklade, thro' Cricklade to Minety, right at Q8 garage to the playing fields
Hon Secretary: Kevin Vancil, 12 Essex Walk, Swindon, Wilts SN3 3EY Tel: (H) 01793 525898
Tel: (W) 01793 504945
Email: kevin.vancil@uk.zurich.com
Fixtures Secretary: Mark Turner, 11 Cantors Way, Malmesbury, Wilts SN16 9QZ Tel: (H) 01666 860680
Tel: (M) 07775 232150 Tel: (W) 01666 860923
Email: mturner@atrenta.com
Club Colours: Green and purple hoops
League: Dorset & Wilts 2 North
Leagues Contact: Mark Turner - as above

MORGANIANS RFC
Ground Address: The Clubhouse, Chedzoy Lane, Bridgwater Tel: 01278 423434
Brief Directions: On A39 Bridgwater to Glastonbury road, over M5 motorway, 1st right into Chedzoy Lane opposite Mole Valley Farms
Hon Secretary: Peter Donnachie, 28 Almond Tree Close, Bridgwater TA6 4EB Tel: (M) 07974 235071
Tel: (W) 01278 425310
Email: pete@donnachie63.fsnet.co.uk
Club Colours: Navy shirts with gold and red hoops
League: Somerset 2

MOUNTS BAY
League: Cornwall 1
For further information contact League Secretary

NAILSEA & BACKWELL
Ground Address: West End Park, West End Lane, Nailsea Tel: 01275 810818
Brief Directions: Directions signed from Town Centre
Hon Secretary: Anita Heappy, Wareham Lodge, Whitsfield Road, Nailsea, BS48 2UF
Tel: (H) 01275 851478 Tel: (M) 07973 499778
Email: anita@familyheappy.fsnet.co.uk
Club Colours: Black/White
League: Somerset Premier

NEWENT RFC
Ground Address: Recreation Ground, Watery Lane, Newent, Glos
Brief Directions: Drive into centre of town, turn right into Watery Lane by the library/health centre, ground is on the right about 400 metres along Watery Lane
Hon Secretary: Mark Smith, 2 Winfield, Newent, Glos GL18 1QB Tel: (H) 01531 822 410
Club Colours: Green and gold
League: Gloucester 3 North

NEWQUAY HORNETS RFC
Ground Address: Newquay Sports Centre, Tretvenson Road, Newquay, Cornwall Tel: 01637 875533
Website: newquayhornetsrfc.co.uk
Directions: Newquay via A3058, lft Chester Rd, 2nd lft Whitegate Rd, lft at T jcn, club 50 yds lft. Frm Redruth, N'quay via A392, across mini r'bouts into Edgcumbe Ave, rt Hilgrove Rd, 1st rt, club at end
Hon Secretary: J. G. Grindle, 1 Polwhele Road, Newquay, Cornwall TR7 2SJ Tel: (H) 01637 874540
Tel: (W) 01637 878787
Email: grindle@jeal64.freeserve.co.uk
Club Colours: Green and white hoops
League: Cornwall/Devon

NEWTON ABBOT RFC
Ground Address: Rackerhayes, Newton Road, Kingsteignton, Newton Abbot, TQ12 3AD
Tel: 01626 354150/352030
Brief Directions: Follow signs for Racecourse, ground is opposite the course behind Fairway Furniture
Hon Secretary: Maurice Young, 51 Lime Tree Walk, Newton Abbot, TQ12 4LF Tel: (H) 01626 206776
Tel: (W) 01803 529529
Club Colours: White shirts & shorts, black socks with gold, red & white trim
League: Western Counties West

NORTH BRISTOL RFC
Ground Address: Oaklands, Gloucester Road, Almondsbury, Bristol, BS32 4AG Tel: 01454 612740
Club Secretary: L.Hayward, 51 Brdeman Grove, Filton, Bristol BS34 7HP
Tel No: 0117 969 8905
Hon Secretary: L. Hayward, 51 Bridgman Grove, Bristol, BS34 7HP Tel: (H) 0117 968 905
Fixtures Secretary: M. Cottle, 33 Clavell Road, Bristol, BS10 7EJ Tel: (H) 0117 950 6182
Club Colours: Royal & scarlet 2" hoops
League: Gloucester Premier

NORTH DORSET RFC
Ground Address: Slaughtergate, Longbury Hill Lane, Gillingham, Dorset SP8 5SY Tel: 01747 822748
Email Address: jimwhite@jimwhitesmortgages.com
Brief Directions: Take Wincanton Road (B3081) from town centre, Longbury Hill Lane is on right about 1 mile from the town, 300 yds after the end of 30mph zone
Hon Secretary: Jim White, Lime Tree House, Queen Street, Gillingham, Wiltshire, SP8 4DY
Tel: (H) 01747 826351
Email: jimwhite@jimwhitesmortgages.com
Fixtures Secretary: Clive Drake, Folly's End, Wyke Street, Gillingham, Dorset SP8 4NA
Tel: (H) 01747 825856 Tel: (M) 07967 808515
Tel: (W) 01747 826 505
Email: tcldrake@follys.freeserve.co.uk
Club Colours: Emerald Green and navy
League: Dorset & Wilts 2 South

NORTH PETHERTON
Ground Address: Beggars Brook, North Petherton
Tel: 01278 663028
Brief Directions: M5 J24, A38 Taunton, through North Petherton, layby on left at exit of North Petherton
Hon Secretary: C. Facey, Duckhams Cottage, Rhode, North Petherton, TA5 2AD Tel: (H) 01278 663315
Tel: (W) 01278 435 334
Club Colours: Black and white hooped shirt, black shorts
League: Somerset Premier

NORTH TAWTON RFC
Ground Address: Taw Meadows, Fore Street, North Tawton, Devon. Tel: 01837 82907
Brief Directions: Directions to Club;- If coming into town from Exeter or Okehampton direction enter town and keep to left hand side of clock tower in square, follow road until just before bridge - Club is on right hand side. If entering town from Cheese Factory side go over bridge and turn left into Club.
Hon Secretary: Gill Hoggins, The Old Forge, 33 North Street, North Tawton, Devon EX20 2DE
Tel: (H) 01837 82516
Email: peter.hoggins@talk21.com
Fixtures Secretary: Sarah Quick, 7 Victoria Cottages, North Tawton, Devon EX20 2DF Tel: (H) 01837 82704
Email: sequick.ntawton@virgin.net
Club Colours: Black & amber
League: Devon 2

OAKMEADIANS RFC
Ground Address: Meyrick Park Pavilion, Central Drive, Meyrick Park, Bournemouth, Dorset BH10 6JX
Tel: 01202 789497
Web Address: www.oakmeadians.com
Brief Directions: Directions to the Ground. Leave the A31 by the A338 dual carriageway to Bournemouth off the Ashley Heath roundabout after passing Ringwood. Continue over the Cooper Dean Flyover (approx. 5 miles) to St Pauls roundabout – straight over. Leave the A338 at the next elevated roundabout - Richmond Hill, via a slip road (signposted to Wimborne) on the A347. Take the 3rd exit off this roundabout into Wimborne Road. 1st left into Braidley Road 3rd right at the T-junction into Central Drive and follow the road around until you see the clubhouse and grounds on your right. Vehicles are NOT allowed into the park.
Hon Secretary: S Dimmer, Meyrick Park Cricket Pavilion, Central Drive, Bournemouth, Dorset BH2 6LJ
Tel: (H) 01202 789497 Tel: (W) 01202 789497
Hon Fixtures: Steven Warrington
Tel: (H) 01202 763799 Tel: (M) 07752 791065
Email: steven.warrington@virgin.net
Leagues Contact: George Edward Jones,
1B, Ullswater Crescent, Weymouth, Dorset DT3 5HE
Tel: (H) 01305 771284 Tel: (M) 07929 258976
Tel: (W) 01305 206328 Email: gejones60@hotmail.com
Club Colours: Green, blue and white hoops, black shorts.
League: Southern Counties South

OKEHAMPTON RFC
Ground Address: Showfield, Oaklands, Okehampton
Tel: 01837 52508
Hon Secretary: Max Sansom, 20 Fore Street, Moretonhamstead TQ13 8LL Tel: (H) 01647 441134
Club Colours: Maroon and amber unequal hoops
League: Western Counties West

OLD ASHTONIANS RFC
Ground Address: Ashton Park School, Blackmoors Lane, Bower Ashton, Bristol Tel: c/o 0117 987 7796
Brief Directions: From city follow signs for Portishead, school is indicated at 1st roundabout (turn left)
Hon Secretary: Ian Reed, 42 Stockwood Crescent, Knowle, Bristol, BS4 1AW Tel: (H) 0117 983 3942
Tel: (M) 07970 666 365
Email: ianreed@blueyonder.co.uk
Fixtures Secretary: T. Excel, 18 Perrycroft Road, Bristol, BS13 7RY Tel: (H) 0117 964 2352
Club Colours: Blue shirt, yellow band, black shorts
League: Somerset 1

OLD BRISTOLIANS RFC
Ground Address: Memorial Playing Field, Longwell Lane, Failand, Bristol Tel: 01275 392137
Brief Directions: M5 junction 19 head for Bristol, turn right at main lights onto B3129 for Failand, turn left after country club into Longwood Lane.
Hon Secretary: Charles van der Lande, 12 Palmerston Road, Bristol BS6 7RH Tel: (H) 0117 942 1908
Tel: (W) 0117 917 4434
Fixtures Secretary: Oliver Early, 14 Pleasant Road, Bristol BS16 5JD Tel: (H) 0117 956 1332
Email: oearly@vwl.co.uk
Club Colours: Maroon, gold and green hoops.
League: Gloucester 1

OLD CENTRALIANS RFC
Ground Address: Saintbridge Sports Centre, Painswick Road, Gloucester, GL4 9QX
Tel: 01452 303768
Brief Directions: Follow B4073 from Gloucester Ring Road. Approx 400m on right just before traffic lights
Hon Secretary: Matthew Vye, 27 Farmington Close, Gloucester, GL4 4XA Tel: (H) 01452 623801
Tel: (M) 07787 133631 Tel: (W) 01452 429299
Email: mathewvye@egcarter.co.uk
Fixtures Secretary: Fred Crowther, 9 Richmond Gardens, Gloucester Tel: (H) 01452 415810
Club Colours: Navy blue & royal blue quarters with gold trimmimgs.
League: Western Counties North

OLD COLSTONIANS RFC
Ground Address: Colstons School, Bell Hill, Stapleton, Bristol, BS16 1BJ Tel: 0117 965 5207
Brief Directions: M32 Eastville roundaboutuphill towards Stapleton.Enter school gates at top of hill
Hon Secretary: John Hall, 94 Nightingale Gardens, Bristol, BS48 2BN Tel: (H) 01275 854195
Tel: (M) 07803 855446
Email: John.C.Hall@guinnessudv.com

Fixtures Secretary: Steve Back, 9 Wellsford Road, Bristol, BS16 1BW Tel: (H) 0117 939 0456
Email: f@rbj.demon.co.uk
Club Colours: Blue, black & gold Hoops
League: Gloucester 3 South

OLD CRYPTIANS RFC
Ground Address: Memorial Ground, Tuffley Avenue, Glos Tel: 01452 532002
Brief Directions: Off Bristol Road to Tuffley Avenue, ground 1 mile on right before Stroud Road
Hon Secretary: Alan Roberts, 1 Ardea Close, Gloucester Tel: (H) 01452 728573 Tel: (M) 07715 602768
Email: alan_r@lincone.net
Fixtures Secretary: D. Howell, 255c Stroud Road, Gloucester GL1 5JZ Tel: (H) 01452 414010
Club Colours: Gold, maroon and navy blue
League: Gloucester 2

OLD CULVERHAYSIANS
Ground Address: The Glasshouse, Bradford Road, Combe Down, Bath. Clubhouse: Old Fosse Road, Odd Down, Bath, BA2 2SS Tel: 01225 832 081
Brief Directions to Ground: Take Wells road out of Bath.Approx 1 mile, turn left at roundabout opposite Red Lion pub, across next junction, 200 yards on right
Hon Secretary: Dick Stevens, 43 Inverness Road, Bath, BA2 3RX Tel: (H) 01225 422433 Tel: (W) 01225 422433
Fixtures Secretary: Martin Lynch, 2 Lyme Road, Bath, BA1 3LN Tel: (H) 01225 448511
Club Colours: Black
League: Somerset Premier

OLD ELIZABETHANS RFC
Ground Address: Severn Road, Hallen, Bristol BS10 7RZ Tel: 0117 959 1071
Brief Directions: M5 J17, turn towards Pelning at roundabout then 1st left, continue for 2-3 miles until junction with King William IV pub on right, turn right, club 200 yards on left
Hon Secretary: David Perkins, 855 Filton Avenue, Bristol, BS34 7HJ Tel: (H) 0117 969 2545
Fixtures Secretary: P. Abel, 2 Dublin Crescent, Bristol, BS9 4NA Tel: (M) 07973 194508
Email: pabel@ceravision.net
Club Colours: Blue, white and old gold hoops
League: Gloucester 2

OLD PLYMOTHIAN & MANNAMEDIAN RFC
Ground Address: King George V Playing Fields, Elburton, Plymouth
Brief Directions: A38 take 1st Plymouth junction to Marsh Mills roundabout, follow signs for Kingsb'dge for 3-4 miles, at r'bout (Plympton signed to left) 1st left, ground 0.25 mile on right
Hon Secretary: Ernest Bolster, 22 Carlton Close, Plymouth, PL3 6JS Tel: (H) 01752 296327
Email: bolster@eurobell.co.uk
Fixtures Secretary: Simon Matthews, 16 Trevannion Close, Plymouth, PL6 5NW Tel: (H) 01752 780114 Tel: (W) 01752 304 562
Email: simon.matthews@plymouth.gov.uk
Club Colours: Claret and blue quarters
League: Devon 1

OLD PUBLIC OAKS RFC
Ground Address: 13 St George's Avenue, Plymouth, Devon PL2 3PW Tel: 01752 251708
Email Address: opo.rugbyclub@virgin.net
Web Address: www.oporfc.org.uk
Brief Directions: Leave A38 at Marsh Mills r'about, take A374 towards city, turn left onto A379 Billacombe Rd, left at 3rd roundabout into Haye Rd, ground on right
Hon Secretary: Richard Yarwood, 13 St Georges Ave, Plymouth, Devon PL2 3PW
Tel: (H) 01752 770140
Tel: (M) 07761 641755
Fixtures Secretary: Keith Potter
Email: keith@119ruskin.freeserve.co.uk
Club Colours: Green and gold hoops
League: Devon 2

OLD REDCLIFFIANS
Ground Address: Stockwood lane, Brislington, Bristol Tel: 0117 977 8501
Brief Directions: A34 from Bristol, turn right at McDonalds/Park & Ride, travel for 0.25 mile, ground on right hand side
Hon Secretary: Richard Yandell, 11 Imperial Walk, Bristol, BS14 9AD Tel: (H) 0117 977 7657
Tel: (W) 0117 903 0395
Club Colours: Red and black hoops.
League: Western Counties North

OLD RICHIANS RFC
Ground Address: Sandyleaze, Longlevens, Gloucester, GL2 0PX
Tel: 01452 524649
Brief Directions: Turn into Nine Elms Road from Cheltenham Rd and follow to Sir Thomas Rich's School
Hon Secretary: Josie Collier, 5 Foxleigh Crescent, Gloucester, GL2 0XW Tel: (H) 01452 386 808
Tel: (M) 07714 260 905
Email: westway@blueyonder.com
Fixtures Secretary: Steve Collier, 5 Foxleigh Crescent, Gloucester, GL2 0XW Tel: (H) 01452 386808
Tel: (M) 07941 365473
Email: westway@blueyonder.com
Club Colours: Royal blue and gold
League: Western Counties North

OLD SULIANS RFC LTD
Ground Address: Lansdown Road, Bath
Tel: 01225 310201
Brief Directions: Follow Lansdown Road from city centre, ground is on left 400 m past MOD site
Hon Secretary: Terry Haines, 24 Rockliffe Avenue, Bath, BA2 6QP Tel: (H) 01225 465107
Tel: (W) 0117 979 7540
Email: terryhaines@24rockliffe.freeserve.co.uk
Fixtures Secretary: Tony Slee, 8 Heathfield Close, Bath Tel: (H) 01225 317256
Club Colours: Blue with red band
League: Somerset 1

OLD TECHNICIANS RFC
Ground Address: Weston Mill Oak Villa, Ferndale Road, Weston Mill, Plymouth, Devon
Tel: 01752 363352
Brief Directions: A38 turn off onto B3396 to Devonport, left at 1st traffic lights, club approx 100 yards on left
Hon Secretary: John Pengilley, 338 Beaumont Road, Plymouth, PL4 9EN Tel: (H) 01752 308217
Email: otrfc@pengers.freeserve.co.uk
Leagues Contact: John Pengilley - as above
Email: otrfc@pengers.freeserve.co.uk
Fixtures Secretary: Simon Raymont, 1 Roberts Road, Plymouth, Devon Tel: (H) 01752 368854
Club Colours: Black with white circlet
League: Devon 2

OLDFIELD OLD BOYS
Ground Address: Shaft Road, Coombe Down, Bath
Tel: 01225 834135
Brief Directions: Into Bath, follow signs for University, follow on towards Combe Down, turn down Shaft Road.
Hon Secretary: Steve Godwin, 12 Lime Grove Gardens, Bath, BA2 4HE Tel: (H) 01225 318612
Tel: (W) 01258 486635
Email: stevegodwin36@hotmail.com
Fixtures Secretary: Gary Paul, 1 Down Avenue, Bath
Tel: (H) 01225 836121 Tel: (W) 01249 658090
Club Colours: Maroon and gold.
League: Somerset Premier

OLNEY RFC
Ground Address: Recreation Ground, East Street, Olney, Bucks Tel: 01234 712880
Brief Directions: From Newport Pagnell & Milton Keynes take A509, on entering Olney past church & right at market place, left into East St, ground 300 yards on right
Club Secretary: Laurence O'Connor, 6 Crabtree Close, Olney, Bucks. MK46 5DO Tel: 01234 713390
e-mail: laurence@jo'connor3.fsnet.co.uk
Fixtures Secretary: Alec Tebby
Tel: (H) 01933 663385 (W) 07850 560660
Club Colours: Cerise and french grey
League: Southern Counties North

OXFORD RFC
Ground Address: Southern by pass, North Hinksey Village, Oxford
Tel: 01865 243984
Brief Directions: Ground can only be approached from A34 going south, turn left off A34, sign posted
Club Secretary: Mrs Kay Honner, 361 Woodstock Road, Oxford. OX2 8AA
Tel No: 01865 438655
Email: kevin.honner@ntlworld.com
Fixtures Secretary: Roger Mountford, 28 Crecy Walk, Woodstock, Oxford OX20 1US
Tel: (H) 01993 812389
Club Colours: Green, black and silver hoops
League: Berks/Bucks & Oxon 1

OXFORD HARLEQUINS RFC
Ground Address: Horspath Road, Marston Ferry Road, Oxford, Oxfordshire Tel: 01865 775765
Email Address: info@oxfordharlequins.com
Web Address: www.oxfordharlequins.com
Brief Directions: Off the Eastern ring road sign-posted to Horspath or follow signs to Summertown, north Oxford, go towards city centre and left at Marston Ferry Road.
Hon Secretary: Keith Latham, 29 Churchill Way, Long Hanborough, Witney, Oxon, OX29 8JJ
Tel: (H) 01993 881985 Tel: (M) 07967 206098
Tel: (W) 01295 754560
Email: keith.latham@tinyworld.co.uk
Club Colours: Blue, White, Maroon & Yellow
League: South West 2 East

PAIGNTON RFC
Ground Address: Queens Park, Queens Road, Paignton, Devon TQ4 6AT Tel: 01803 557715
Email Address: paigntonrugby@yahoo.co.uk
Web Address: www.paigntonrugby.co.uk
Brief Directions: PRFC has the use of the clubhouse and grounds from 1st Sept. to 30th April. For info outside these months contact Secretary - as below 01803 524212
Hon Secretary: Graham Nelson-Smith, 1 St. Andrews Road, Paignton, TQ4 6HA Tel: (H) 01803 524212
Email: gjnelsonsmith@aol.com
Fixtures Secretary: John Hogan, 5 Courtland Road, Paignton, Devon TQ4 6AT Tel: (H) 01803 529442
Club Colours: Red and white hoops
League: Western Counties West

PAINSWICK RFC
Ground Address: Broad Ham Field, Painswick
Tel: 01452 813735
Brief Directions: Situated adjoining the A46 on the southern edge of the village on the Stroud side of Painswick
Hon Secretary: Peter Haines, Savannah, Church Road, Stroud, GL5 4JE Tel: (H) 01453 765003
Club Colours: Cherry and white hoops, navy shorts
League: Gloucester Premier

PENNANIANS RFC
Ground Address: Farnham Sports Field, Beaconsfield Road, Farnham Royal, Buckinghamshire
Tel: 01753 646252
Email Address: pennsrugbyclub@btinternet.com
Web Address: www.pennsrufc.org.uk
Hon Secretary: Tony James, 345 Farnham Road, Slough, Berkshire, SL2 1HU Tel: (H) 01753 644474
Tel: (M) 07971 036661 Tel: (W) 01628 819022
Email: tony_James@hotmail.com
Fixtures Secretary: Ian Thompson, 39a Pevensey Road, Slough, Berks SL2 1UG Tel: (H) 01753 538753
Tel: (M) 07958 579877 Tel: (W) 020 8818 8516
Email: ithompson@gb.dhl.com
Club Colours: Black shirt with 2 white hoops
League: Berks/Bucks & Oxon 1

PENRYN RFC
Ground Address: The Memorial Ground, Kernick Road, Penryn, Cornwall TR10 8HE
Tel: 01326 372239
Web Address: www.penryn-rfccornwall.eu.org
Brief Directions: From ExeterA38to Plymouth, head towards Liskeard, follow signes for Truro. From truro A39 to Falmouth, continueto the distributer road,atroundaboutturn to industrial estate (ASDA)ground second left.
Hon Secretary: Peter Webber, Avallen, Penryn, Cornwall TR10 8HE Tel: (H) 01326 376613
Tel: (M) 07811 824989
Email: sam@webber44.fsnet.co.uk
Fixtures Secretary: Mike Gregory, 20 Penvale Crescent, Penryn, Cornwall
Tel: (H) 01326 373820
Club Colours: Red and black hoops
League: Western Counties West

PERRANPORTH RFC
Ground Address: Ponsmere Valley, Perranporth, Cornwall Tel: 01872 572968
Email Address: glyn.b@ic24.net
Brief Directions: From Newquay turn right at Goonhavern roundabouts, continue for approx 2 miles, past Golf Club on right, down steep hill, 1st turning left
Club Secretary: Glyn Barnicoat, Tresavean Farm
Ho**Hon Secretary**: Glyn Barnicoat, Tresavean Farm House, Tresavean Farm, Redruth, Cornwall TR16 6AL
Tel: (H) 01209 214680 Tel: (M) 07989 088791
Tel: (W) 01326 370811
Email: glyn.b@ic24.net
Club Colours: Green and yellow
League: Cornwall 1

PEWSEY VALE RFC
Ground Address: Pewsey Vale School Playing Fields, Wilcot Road, Pewsey, Wilts SN9 5
Tel: 01672 562218
Brief Directions: A345 to Pewsey, into Wilcot Road, 2nd left into Pewsey Vale School car park, change at the adjacent Sports Centre, pitches are to the back of the school
Hon Secretary: David Aroskin, 47 Swan Meadow, Pewsey, Wiltshire, SN9 5HP Tel: (H) 01672 562218
Tel: (M) 07976 882103 Tel: (W) 07976 882103
Hon Fixtures: Robinson Alison, 4 Stratton Road, Pewsey, Wiltshire, SN9 5AY
Tel: (H) 01672 562989
Club Colours: Red, white, royal blue and black quarters
League: Dorset & Wilts 2 North

PILNING RFC
Ground Address: Pilning RFC, Beach Road, Severn Beach Tel: 01454 633549
Hon Secretary: Geraldine Sloman, 14 Riverside Park, Bristol, BS35 Tel: (H) 01454 631568
Email: geraldine.slowman@orange.co.uk
League: Gloucester 3 South

PHOENIX RFC
Ground Address: Institute Road, Taplow, Bucks
Tel: 01628 664319
Brief Directions: M4 J7, take A4 towards Maidenhead, after Sainsburys superstore take next right (0.5 mile) then 1st left after the bridge is Institute Road
Hon Secretary: Neil Bennett, 29 Belgrave Road, Slough, Berks SL1 3RG Tel: (H) 01753 570341
Tel: (W) 020 7238 0723
Email: neil.bennett2@tinyworld.co.uk
Club Colours: Red & Black Quarters, black shorts, black socks with red trim
League: Berks/Bucks & Oxon 1

PLYMOUTH ARGAUM RFC
Ground Address: Bickleigh Down, Roborough, Plymouth, Devon PL6 7AD Tel: 01752 772156
Email Address: secretary@argaum.org.uk
Web Address: www.argaum.org.uk
Brief Directions: At Roborough village turn down Bickleigh Down Rd, pass Medlands and carry on down lane, clubhouse on the right
Hon Secretary: Richard Belli, 7 Lincoln Avenue, Plymouth, PL4 7NT Tel: (H) 01752 316926
Tel: (M) 07711 441599 Tel: (W) 01752 725394
Email: secretary@argaum.org.uk
Fixtures Secretary: Andy Rees, 38 Huxham Close, Plymouth, PL6 5LH Tel: (H) 01752 516675
Email: fixtures@argaum.org.uk
Club Colours: Black, bottle green, white
League: Devon 3

PLYMOUTH CIVIL SERVICE RFC
Ground Address: 8 longwood close, chaddlewood, Plymouth, Devon PL72HD Tel: 01752 221576
Email Address: chris.travers@talk21.com
Brief Directions: Ground directly behind Plymouth Albion's ground at Beacon Park. Top of Ham Drive.
Hon Secretary: Chris Travers, c/o Club Address
Email: chris.travers@talk21.com
Fixtures Secretary: Paul Routley, c/o the club
Club Colours: Red & white hooped shirts, black shorts., red socks
League: Devon 3

PLYMPTON VICTORIA RFC
Ground Address: Ground Address: King George V Playing Fields, Elburton, Plymstock, Plymouth, Devon.
Email Address: pvrfcsec@freemail.eurobell.co.uk
Hon Secretary: Alan Dibble, 8 Wolridge Way, Plymouth, Devon PL7 2RU Tel: (H) 01752 519512
Tel: (M) 07786 842744 Tel: (W) 01752 323066
Email: dibbs@eurobell.co.uk
Fixtures Secretary: Chris Mayne
Tel: (H) 01752 311147 Tel: (M) 07713 501280
Club Colours: Red, gold and black.
League: Devon 3

PLYMSTOCK RFC
Club Colours: Royal Blue
League: Devon 2
For further information contact League Secretary

POOLE RFC
Ground Address: Hamworthy Recreation Ground, Turlin Moor, Blandford Road, Hamworthy, Poole, Dorset Tel: 01202 241993
Email Address: tessa.inglefinch@btinternet.com
Brief Directions: From Poole quay, follow directions for Hamworthy, over the lifting bridge and continue for 2 miles.
Hon Secretary: Tessa Ingle-Finch, 6 Mansfield Avenue, Poole, Dorset BH14 0DQ Tel: (H) 01202 241993
Tel: (M) 07812 455653 Tel: (W) 01202 241993
Email: tessa.inglefinch@btinternet.com
Fixtures Secretary: Karen Lambert, 12 Goldfinch Road, Poole, Dorset BH17 7TD Tel: (H) 01202 658714
Email: karenl@accanet.com
Club Colours: Blue and amber
League: Dorset & Wilts 2 South

PRINCE ROCK WOODLAND FORT RFC
Ground Address: Woodland Fort Community Centre, Crownhill Road, Plymouth, Devon PL5 3SQ
Tel: 01752 367853
Email Address: chris@dbarrett3.fsnet.co.uk
Brief Directions: On leaving A38 Plymouth City Centre, at Marsh Mills, take third exit Plympton B3416. Pass MacDonalds take left onto Coypool Road. Follow road around over railway line, under bridge, back over railway line, sharp 2nd left to ground, small car park.
Hon Secretary: Chris Barrett, 3 Budshead Road, Plymouth, PL5 2QY Tel: (H) 01752 367853
Email: chris@dbarrett3.fsnet.co.uk
Fixtures Secretary: Les Fowdon, 1 Hayes Road, Plymouth, PL9 7QA Tel: (H) 01752 405 018
Club Colours: Green & Amber Quarters
League: Devon 2

PUDDLETOWN RFC
Ground Address: Greenfields, Puddletown, Dorchester, Dorset. Tel: 01305 848808
Brief Directions: Leave Dorchester on A35 east, after 1/4 mile turn left on B3143, 3 miles on RHS, old army camp club.
Hon Secretary: Dick Corbett-Winder, St. Martins House, Dorchester, Dorset DT2 9JP
Tel: (H) 01305 889410 Tel: (W) 01703 333501
Fixtures Secretary: Phil Smeeth, 21 London Close, Dorchester, Dorset DT2 7QT Tel: (H) 01300 348310
Club Colours: Red shirts, black shorts, red socks
League: Dorset & Wilts 2 South

REDINGENSIANS RFC
Ground Address: Old Redingensians Sports Ground, Old Bath Road, Sonning, Reading, Berkshire RG4 6TQ
Tel: 0118 969 5259
Email Address: information@redingensians.org
Web Address: www.redingennians.org
Brief Directions: On the A4 east of Reading, next to Sonning Golf Club
Hon Secretary: J. H. Cook, 95 Century Court, Grove End Road, London NW8 9LD Tel: (H) 020 7289 1887
Tel: (W) 020 7953 2280
Fixtures Secretary: G. F. Nattriss, 64 Broadwater Rd, Reading, Berks RG10 0EU Tel: (H) 0118 934 0685
Email: george@natts.com
Club Colours: Dark blue, light blue & white hooped shirts
League: Southern Counties South

REDRUTH ALBANY RFC
Ground Address: Trewirgie Hill, Redruth, Cornwall.(Post to Clubhouse, 2 Station Hill, Redruth, Cornwall. TR15 2PP) Tel: 01209 216945
Brief Directions: Adjacent to Redruth Cricket Club behind Trewirgie School, Falmouth Rd, Redruth, 0.5 mile from train station. Or ring club house for directions.
Hon Secretary: Mark Stevens, 32 Bellevue, Redruth, Cornwall TR15 1LF Tel: (H) 01209 215904
Email: tankster.hufflepuff@tiscari.co.uk
Club Colours: Royal blue shirts, black shorts
League: Cornwall 2

ROSELAND RFC
Ground Address: Philleigh, Truro, Cornwall. TR2 5ET
Brief Directions: 15 miles from Truro on the Roseland Peninsula, signed via Tregony and Towary, St Mawes.
Hon Secretary: Iwan Lemoine, 10 The Square, Gerrans, Truro TR2 5EB Tel: (H) 01872 580059
Club Colours: Navy and scarlet
League: Cornwall 2

ROSS ON WYE RFC
Ground Address: Ross-on-Wye Sports Centre, Wilton Rd, Ross-on-Wye. Tel: 01989 563256
Brief Directions: End of M50 stay on Bypass A40 to Monmouth. 3rd R/about left for town centre by Esso garage. Turn right by car park.
Club Secretary: Miss Sarah Bourne, 1 Prospect Terrace, Homs Road, Ross on Wye HR9 7DE
Tel: 01989 562081
Fixtures Secretary: David Cooke, 22 Brampton Avenue, Ross on Wye HR9 7EW. Tel: 01989 564626
Club Colours: Royal blue and white hoops
League: Gloucester 2

SALCOMBE RFC
Ground Address: Two Meads, Camperdown Road, Salcombe Tel: 01548 842639
Brief Directions: On entering Salcombe take 1st left, 1st right, 2nd left
Hon Secretary: Graham Jacobs, Highleigh, Grenville Road, Salcombe, TQ8 8BJ Tel: (H) 01548 842521
Club Colours: Red shirts, white shorts, white shorts, red and white socks
League: Devon 3

SALISBURY RFC
Ground Address: C/O Salisbury RFC, Castle Rd, Salisbury, Wiltshire, SP1 3SA Tel: 01722 325317
Email Address: enq@salisburyrfc.org
Web Address: www.salisburyrfc.org
Brief Directions: On A345 Salisbury to Amesbury Road, just to the south of Old Sarum
Hon Secretary: George. W. Jack, 14 Windlesham Road, Salisbury, Wilts SP1 3PY Tel: (H) 01722 335542
Tel: (W) 01980 612388 Email: g.w.jack@talk21.com

Hon Fixtures: Jayne Roderick, 39 Lindford Rd, Bishopdown Farm, Salisbury, Wiltshire, SP1 3WX
Tel: (H) 01722 410589 Tel: (M) 07866 743706
Tel: (W) 01722 344295
Email: fixtures@salisburyrfc.org
Club Colours: Green and white
League: South West 2 East

SALTASH RFC
Ground Address: Moorlands Lane, Saltash, Cornwall Tel: 01752 847227
Brief Directions: From A38 westward over Tamar Bridge, through tunnel, left at 1st roundabout, right at lights, then 2nd right into Moorlands Lane, clubhouse at end of lane
Hon Secretary: W. T. Ryan, 7 Clear View, Saltash, Cornwall Tel: (H) 01752 843565
Fixtures Secretary: W. T. Ryan, as above
Club Colours: Black, gold and red hoops
League: Cornwall 1

SHERBORNE RFC
Ground Address: The Terrace Playing Fields, Sherborne, Dorset Tel: 01935 812478
Email Address: srfc@sherbornerugby.freeserve.co.uk
Web Address: www.sherbornerugby.freeserve.co.uk
Brief Directions: The ground is on the A352, half a mile south of the town centre going towards Dorchester.
Hon Secretary: Tim Berry, 71 Granville Way, Sherborne, Dorset DT9 4AT Tel: (H) 01935 389259
Email: tim@clarencepaper.fsnet.co.uk
Fixtures Secretary: Kevin Hunt, 5 Mill Lane, Sherborne, Dorset DT9 6ND Tel: (H) 01935 873641
Email: nicki.hunt@tesco.net
Club Colours: Black with graduated white hoops.
League: Dorset & Wilts 1

SIDMOUTH RFC
Ground Address: The Blackmore Field, Heydon's Lane, Sidmouth, EX10 8NJ Tel: 01395 516816
Brief Directions: (Via footpath), behind Sidmouth/ Victoria Cottage Hospital.(Follow signs to Hospital)
Hon Secretary: Paul Rossiter, 'Gulls', Kings Lane, Sidmouth, EX10 8DU Tel: (H) 01395 516414
Tel: (W) 01803 863 260
Fixtures Secretary: T. J. O'Brien, 2 Rivolet Cottages, Church St, Sidmouth EX10 9RD Tel: (H) 01395 577403
Club Colours: Green, white shorts
League: Devon 1

SLOUGH RFC
Ground Address: Tamblyn Fields, Upton Court Park, Upton Court Road, Slough, Berkshire, SL3 7LT
Tel: 01753 522107/692115
Email Address: mikewild_srfc@yahoo.co.uk
Web Address: www.sloughrugbyclub.com
Brief Directions: Exit M4 junction 5 towards Slough. At 2nd lights (fire station to left) turn left into Upton Court Road. Club entrance drive approx 700 metres on left, signposted. Club at end of drive. If arriving by coach or high vehicle phone for code to anti-traveller height restriction gate!
Hon Secretary: Mike Wild, 46 Castleview Road, Slough, Berkshire, SL3 7NQ Tel: (H) 01753 770870
Tel: (W) 01628 604311
Email: mikewild_srfc@yahoo.co.uk
Hon Fixtures: Clive Blackman
Colours: Sage green jersey with single white hoop
League: Southern Counties North

SMITHS (INDUSTRIES) RFC
Ground Address: The Newlands, Evesham Road, Bishops Cleeve, Cheltenham, Glos Tel: 01242 672752
Brief Directions: 2 miles north of Cheltenham on A435
Hon Secretary: Gerald Owen, Jasmine Cottage, 79 Station Road, Cheltenham, Glos GL52 4HJ
Tel: (H) 01242 676345 Tel: (W) 01242 673333
Fixtures Secretary: Carl Slatter, 54 Mandrin Way, Cheltenham, Glos Tel: (H) 01242 232269
Tel: (M) 07980 933789
Club Colours: Royal Blue and White
League: Gloucester 2

SOMERTON RFC
League: Somerset 2
For further information contact the League Secretary

SOUTH MOLTON RFC
Ground Address: Unicorn Park, Station Road, South Molton Tel: 01769 572024
Brief Directions: Taking Pathfields exit on the North Devon link road when reading signs for South Molton, take first right then first left
Hon Secretary: A. White, 8 Duke Street, EX36 4AL
Tel: (H) 01769 573 471 Tel: (W) 01769 573 294
Email: annie_kingdon@hotmail.com
Club Colours: All Black
League: Cornwall/Devon

SOUTHMEAD RFC
Ground Address: Greenway Sports Centre, Greystoke Avenue, Southmead, Bristol Tel: 0117 959 3060
Brief Directions: A38 to Filton, Southmead Road into Doncaster Road, Southmead
Hon Secretary: Mike Davies, 90 Twenty Acres, Bristol, BS10 6PR Tel: (H) 0117 949 7017
Club Colours: Blue shirt with emerald green hoop
League: Gloucester 1

SPARTANS RFC
Ground Address: St. Catherines Meadow, Cattlemarket, Gloucester Tel: 01452 410 552
Brief Directions: M5 J12 for Gloucester, into Glos take signs for docks, past docks, veer right just before Esso g'ge, take l/h lane, under railbridge, 1st left at Bell & Gavel, down as far as can go
Hon Secretary: Barry Stokes, 66 Elderwood Way, Gloucester, GL4 0RD Tel: (H) 01452 546238
Tel: (M) 07787 170489
Fixtures Secretary: P. Minns, 63 Henry Road, Gloucester, GL1 3DX Tel: (H) 01452 500122
Tel: (M) 07790 248903
Club Colours: Red and black
League: Western Counties North

ST. AGNES RFC
Ground Address: Enys Park, West Polberro, St. Agnes, Cornwall Tel: 01872 553673
Brief Directions: Turn left opposite church, turn right after 800 yards, Enys Park is 200 yards on right
Hon Secretary: Allison Thompson, 4 Tregease Road, St. Annes, Cornwall TR5 0SL
Tel: (H) 01872 553719
Email: actionken@aggie4.freeserve.co.uk
Fixtures Secretary: Allison Thompson, 4 Tregease Road, St. Annes, Cornwall TR5 0SL
Tel: (H) 01872 553719
Email: actionken@aggie4.freeserve.co.uk
Club Colours: Black and red hoops
League: Cornwall 1

ST. AUSTELL RFC
Ground Address: Tregorrick Park, Tregorrick Lane, St Austell, Cornwall. PL26 7AG Tel: 01726 76430
Brief Directions: Located on the road behind Asda superstore and next to Mount Edgecumbe Hospice. From St Austell By-Pass take turning to Penrice Hopital.First right before Hospital.
Hon Secretary: Amanda Kellow, 27 Polmarth Close, St. Austell, Cornwall PL25 3TW Tel: (H) 01726 76294
Tel: (W) 01726 291224
Fixtures Secretary: Bernie Shepherd, 128 Landreath Place, Par, PL24 2LA Tel: (H) 01726 816995
Tel: (M) 07979 321324 Tel: (W) 01726 76430
Club Colours: Red and white hoops
League: Cornwall/Devon

ST. BERNADETTE'S OLD BOYS
Ground Address: Hengrove Park, Bamfield Road, Whitchurch, Bristol Tel: 01275 891500
Brief Directions: A37 out of town, turn right at Airport Rd traffic lights, turn left 0.5 mile by The Happy Cock pub, club is 0.25 mile on right
Hon Secretary: Brian Murphy, 4 Rookery Way, Bristol, BS14 0DT Tel: (H) 01275 837702
Fixtures Secretary: Tony Aldridge, 44 Savoy Road, Bristol, BS4 3SY Tel: (H) 01179 770075
Tel: (M) 07973 427340
Club Colours: Green and blue hoops
League: Somerset Premier

ST. BRENDANS'S OLD BOYS RFC
Ground Address: Combination Ground, Filton, Bristol BS34 7QG Tel: 0117 969 2793
Brief Directions: J. 15 M5 connect to A38 towards Bristol - opposite BAC runway on the left.
Hon Secretary: Richard Kolanko, 91 Church Road, Bristol, BS7 Tel: (H) 0117 924 1390
Email: richard.kolanko@btinternet.com
Hon Fixtures: Larry Brien, 67, Luckwell Road, Ashton, Bristol BS3 3ES Tel: (M) 07788 744112
Club Colours: Maroon and Old Gold Hoops
League: Gloucester 3 South

ST. COLUMBA & TORPOINT RFC
Ground Address: Defiance Field, Torpoint, Cornwall
Email Address: honsec@stcoltorpointrfc.freeserve.co.uk
Brief Directions: From Torpoint ferry follow the A374 towards Antony for approx.1 mile the club is situated on the left hand side of the road with a hidden entrance.
Hon Secretary: B. Mumford, 51 Hamoaze Road, Torpoint, Cornwall PL11 2EF
Tel: (H) 01752 814612
Fixtures Secretary: B. Mumford, as above
Club Colours: Scarlet with thin royal blue hoops and black shorts
League: Devon 3

ST. DAY RFC
Ground Address: The Playing Matters, St. Day, Redruth, Cornwall
Brief Directions: Leave A30 at Scorrier exit, left past Cross Roads Hotel, at crossroads go straight across, ground just less than 1 mile on left
Hon Secretary: P.C Newcombe, 21 Martinvale Parc, Redruth, Cornwall TR15 1SD Tel: (H) 01209 212834
Tel: (W) 01872 266670
Fixtures Secretary: Michael Lawry, 4 Polwheal Road, Camborne, Cornwall Tel: (H) 01209 714878
Club Colours: White with cherry hoop.
League: Cornwall 1

ST. IVES RFC
Ground Address: The Clubhouse, Alexandra Road, St. Ives, Cornwall TR26 1EL
Tel: 01736 795346
Email Address: info@stives-rfc.co.uk
Brief Directions: M5/A30 to Hayle A3074 then B3311 coach route to St. Ives, Alexandra Road is second left after Fire Station
Hon Secretary: C. W. Trewhella, c/o CTG Windows, Hayle Ind. Park, Hayle, Cornwall
Tel: (W) 01736 754825
Fixtures Secretary: Mike Gee, 'Lowenna', 70 Halsetown, St. Ives, Cornwall TR26 3LZ
Tel: (H) 01736 797777 Tel: (W) 01736 797168
Email: swrfu@lineone.net
Club Colours: Navy and white Hoops
League: Western Counties West

ST. JUST RFC
Ground Address: St. Just RFC, Tregeseal, St. Just, Penzance, TR18 7PW Tel: 01736 788593
Email Address: strfc15@yahoo.co.uk
Web Address: www.stjustrfc.co.uk
Brief Directions: Follow the A30 down Cornwall to Penzance then take the A3071 to St.Just.The club can be found in Tregeseal Valley bellow the town of St.Just (6 miles from Lands End). See also the find us page at www.stjustrfc.co.uk
Hon Secretary: Nick Jelbert, 27 Penlee Street, Penzance, Cornwall TR18 2DE Tel: (H) 01736 366442
Tel: (M) 07833 151547 Tel: (W) 01736 756363
Email: gob39@dial.pipex.com
Fixtures Secretary: P. Whiteman, Ashmore Cottage, St. Just, Cornwall TR19 7MZ Tel: (H) 01736 788150
Club Colours: All black
League: Western Counties West

SOUTH WEST

ST. MARY'S OLD BOYS RFC
Ground Address: Trench Lane, Winterbourne
Tel: 01454 250489
Brief Directions: M5 J16 towards Bristol, turn left at 1st roundabout then left again onto Woodlands Lane, Bradley Stoke ground 1 mile on left
Hon Secretary: Gay Brewer, 19 Burchells Green Road, Bristol BS15 1DT Tel: (H) 0117 961 4104
Tel: (M) 07773 058256
Club Colours: Emerald green and black
League: South West 2 West

STITHIANS RFC
Ground Address: Playing Field, Stithians, Truro, Cornwall Tel: 01209 860148
Brief Directions: Opposite the church in the centre of the village. The village lies in the centre of the triangle formed by Redruth, Falmouth and Helston.
Hon Secretary: T.J. Knight, Carrine, Kea, Truro, Cornwall TR3 6EB Tel: (H) 01872 279608
Tel: (W) 01872 276116
Club Colours: Maroon
League: Cornwall 2

STOTHERT AND PITT RFC
Ground Address: Adamsfield, Corston, Bath, BA1 9AY
Tel: 01225 874802
Brief Directions: From junction 18 of the M4(Tormarton) take the third exit off roundabout, sign posted Bath(A46). When you come to the traffic lights at the junction of the A46 & the A4, head right, towards Bath City centre (A4 west). When you encounter the traffic lights at the Cleveland Bridge keep in the right-hand lane to go straight ahead, still on the A4. At the mini roundabout take the right fork, straight on until at the end of the Paragon get into the left-hand lane to go straight on past the face of the Royal York Hotel(Travel Lodge) do not turn left until you can not go any further, you will then enter Queens Square. Take the second exit off to continue on the A4 (past Charlotte Street car park & Registry Office) continue until you get to the Windsor Bridge, you have to be in the right-hand lane to go straight ahead. Keep on the A4 past the turning for the Royal United Hospital and past the Newbridge Park & Ride until you get to the junction of the A4 & A36. At the traffic lights turn right on to the dual carriageway. At the Globe Inn roundabout, take the third exit off(still on the A4 Bristol sign) over the rise and the Clubhouse is about 700 yards on the right.
Hon Secretary: Roger Vivian Garraway, 2 Westfield Park South, Bath, N.E.Somerset BA1 3HT
Tel: (H) 01225 316863
Tel: (W) 01225 328396
Fixtures Secretary: Carlos M Orzabal de la Quintana, 7a Clarence Street, Bath, N.E.Somerset BA1 5NS
Tel: (H) 01225 341845 Tel: (M) 07720 431875
Tel: (W) 0117 9674881
Email: clorzabal@yahoo.com
Club Colours: Blue,Black & Amber
League: Somerset 1

STOW-ON-THE-WOLD & DISTRICT RFC
Ground Address: Oddington Road, Stow-on-the-Wold, Glos GL54 1AH Tel: 01451 830 887
Brief Directions: From Stow take the A436 Chipping Norton Road for c. 1.5 miles. Stow RFC is sign posted up a tarmac drive to the right.
Hon Secretary: Nigel Drury, 2 Chesnut Corner, Whitehart Lane, Stow-on-the-Wold, GL54 1A2
Tel: (H) 01451 831686
Fixtures Secretary: Phil Lane, 24, Tinkers Close, Moreton in Marsh GL56 ONE Tel: (H) 01608 652609
Club Colours: Black and white hoops
League: South West 2 East

STROUD RFC
Ground Address: Fromehall Park, Dudbridge Hill, Stroud, Glos GL5 3HS Tel: 01453 863019
Brief Directions: 1 mile south of Stroud on A46 at Golden Cross cross roads - opposite 'Great Mills' store
Hon Secretary: Mike Jenkins, 31 Rowley, Cam, Gloucester, GL11 5NT Tel: (H) 01453 547085
Email: michaeljenkins@supanet.com
Club Colours: Blue and white hoops
League: South West 2 West

SUPERMARINE RFC
Ground Address: Supermarine Sports and Social Club, Highworth Road, South Marston, Nr Swindon, Wiltshire Tel: 01793 824828
Brief Directions: Take A419 M4 to Cirencester Rd, turn off at north or south 'Honda' junction, follow A361 signed Highworth, club entrance off roundabout for industrial estate
Hon Secretary: Geoff Bath, 2 Folly Drive, Swindon, Wiltshire, SN6 7JR Tel: (H) 01793 861619
Email: geebee5@ukonline.co.uk
Fixtures Secretary: Jamie Barrett, Honysuckle Cottage, 15 Hyde Road, Swindon, Wilts SN2 7RT
Tel: (H) 01793 825682
Club Colours: Sky Blue and dark blue quarters
League: Dorset & Wilts 2 North

SWANAGE & WAREHAM RFC
Ground Address: Bestwall, Wareham, Dorset.
Tel: 01929 552224
Email Address: swans@swanage-wareham-rfc.freeserve.co.uk Web Address: http://www.swanage-wareham-rfc.freeserve.co.uk
Brief Directions: Approach traffic lights at crossroads in Wareham town centre. Turn into Bestwall Road and the ground is at the bottom of the road on the left.
Hon Secretary: Keith Jeffrey, Purbeck Cottage, 20 Greenway Road, Weymouth, Dorset DT3 5BE
Tel: (H) 01305 815344
Fixtures Secretary: John Constable, Grand View, Puddletown Road, Wareham, Dorset BH20 6AD
Tel: (H) 01929 551468 Tel: (M) 07970 513088
Tel: (W) 01202 753670
Email: j.constable@swansrugby.freeserve.co.uk
Colours: Maroon shirts, white shorts, maroon socks.
League: South West 2 East

SWINDON COLLEGE OLD BOYS RFC
Ground Address: Nationwide Sports Social Club, Pipers Way, Swindon, Wilts. Tel No: 01793 513513
Web Address: http://www.scob38.freeserve.co.uk
Brief Directions: M4 J15.Take A419 and turn left at first roundabout into Marlborough Road. After one mile turn left into Pipers Way and ground is on left after 800 yards
Hon Secretary: Simon Reindl, 28 Dixon Street, Swindon, Wilts SN1 3PL Tel: (M) 07771 880909
Tel: (W) 01793 653839
Email: sreindl@swagrhino.freeserve.co.uk
Leagues Contact: Phillip Tyler, 13 Orchard Hill, Oxon SN7 7EH Tel: (M) 07885 874961
Tel: (W) 01367 241337
Fixtures Secretary: Phillip Tyler, as above
Club Colours: Black and Red
League: Dorset & Wilts 1

SWINDON RFC
Ground Address: Greenbridge Road, Swindon, Wilts. SN3 3LA Tel: 01793 521148
Email Address: glyn_barrett@hotmail.com
Web Address: http://www.swindonrfc.co.uk
Brief Directions: M4 Jct 15. Follow A419 towards Cirencester for 3 miles. Take Oxford Road follow signs to town centre for 1 mile. At Greenbridge R/about turn left, mini R/about turn right into Greenbridge Road.
Hon Secretary: Cliff Spanswick, 7 Avocet Close, St Pauls Drive, Swindon, Wiltshire, SN3 5HR
Tel: (H) 01793 538008 Tel: (W) 07976 700770
Email: cliff@ctedge.co.uk
Club Colours: Blue and amber hoops, white shorts
League: Southern Counties North

TADLEY RFC
Ground Address: Red Lane, Aldermaston, Reading, Berkshire, RG7 4PA Tel: 0118 970 0072
Web Address: www.tadleyrfc.co.uk
Brief Directions: M4 Junction 12 - follow A4 towards Newbury - left onto A340 - Aldermaston Village turn left follow road for approx I mile ground on left M3 Junction 6 - follow signs for A340 to Tadley - through Tadley Follow signs for Burghfield and Reading - Red Lane on left Approx 1 mile, ground 200 metres on right
Hon Secretary: R. W. Mears, 22 Winchfield Gardens, Tadley, Hampshire RG26 3TX Tel: (H) 0118 981 1648
Tel: (W) 01256 866703 Email: roy.mears@boeing.com
Fixtures Secretary: David Boshier
Tel: (H) 0118 9701 584
Club Colours: Black and amber
League: Southern Counties South

TAMAR SARACENS RFC
Ground Address: Parkway Sports Club, Ernesettle Lane, Plymouth Tel: 01752 363080
Email Address: john@hlmaintenance.fsnet.co.uk
Brief Directions: A38 to St Budeaux, turn off then towards Ernesettle
Hon Secretary: Ken Gianasi, 74 Kathleaven Street, Plymouth PL5 1PY Tel: (H) 01752 367466
Club Colours: Green & black. Change: Red &white
League: Devon 1

TAUNTON RFC LTD
Ground Address: Hyde Park, Hyde Lane, Taunton, Somerset TA2 8BU Tel: 01823 336363
Email Address: h@hydelane.fsnet.co.uk
Web Address: www.tauntonrfc.co.uk
Brief Directions: From Junction 25 of M5 head towards Taunton. At first set of traffic lights (Taunton RFC signposted before the lights) turn right onto A38 towards Bridgwater. 1/2 mile over railway bridge (again signposted) turn right at Bathpool Inn into Hyde Lane. Follow road around for further 1/2 mile - club entrance appears on right hand side.
Hon Secretary: Richard Walford, 16 Fullands Avenue, Taunton, Somerset TA1 3DE Tel: (H) 01823 335471
Tel: (W) 01823 356245
Email: rwalford@lineone.net
Leagues Contact: Andrew Fielding, 26 Wilton Street, Taunton, Somerset TA1 3JR Tel: (H) 01823 334470
Fixtures Secretary: Rodney Reed, 22 Barrow Drive, Taunton Tel: (H) 01823 276354
Club Colours: Crimson, black & white
League: South West 2 West

TAVISTOCK RFC
Ground Address: Sandy Park, Trelawney Road, Tavistock, Devon PL19 0JL Tel: 01822 618275
Brief Directions: From town centre take Brentor Road, under railway viaduct, 2nd right
Hon Secretary: Peter Garland, Rowes, Horndon, Tavistock, Devon PL19 9NQ Tel: (H) 01822 810619
Fixtures Secretary: M. Griffiths, 23 St. Maryhaye, Tavistock, PL19 8LR Tel: (H) 01822 613030
Club Colours: Black and red hoops
League: Devon 1

TEIGNMOUTH RFC
Ground Address: Bitton Sports Ground, 6 Fourth Avenue, Teignmouth, Devon TQ14 9DR
Tel: 01626 774714
Email Address: info@teignmouthrfc.co.uk
Web Address: www.teignmouthrfc.co.uk
Brief Directions: We are situated opposite County Garage.The main route from Cornwall is to get to Shaldon bridge and just carry on as if going to Teignmouth town. Alternative is to go down the Exeter Hill and turn right and follow road as if going to Newton Abbot.At bottom of Bitton Hill is Teignmouth RFC.
Hon Secretary: Robert Loveridge, 59 Second Avenue, Teignmouth, TQ14 9DN Tel: (H) 01626 775891
Tel: (W) 01626 774556 Email: r.loveridge@virgin.net
Club Colours: Red, white, black hoops
League: Cornwall/Devon

TETBURY RFC
Ground Address: The Recreation Ground, Hampton Street, Tetbury, Glos GL8 8JN Tel: 01666 505052
Brief Directions: On the B4014 (Hampton St.) out of Tetbury towards Avening, the ground is situated on the right behind the betting shop.

Hon Secretary: Tracey Wright, 67 Charlton Road, Tetbury, Gloucester, GL8 8DX Tel: (H) 01666 503098 Tel: (W) 01666 502901 Email: jeffwrightbuild@yahoo.co.uk
Fixtures Secretary: Ian Hancock, Summer Cottage, 39 Charlton Road, Tetbury GL8 8DX
Tel: (H) 01666 504505 Tel: (M) 07973 322950
Tel: (W) 01242 263747 Email: ian@softrain.co.uk
Club Colours: Black and gold
League: Gloucester 3 South

TEWKESBURY RFC
Ground Address: The Moats, Lankett Lane, Tewkesbury, Glos GL20 5PG Tel: 01684 294364
Email Address: tewkesbury-rfc@yahoo.co.uk
Brief Directions: From Cross in centre of town, take A38 to Gloucester. Take 1st left (after approx 200yds) into Gander Lane, past cricket club & car park enter lane alongside caravan clubsite. Follow lane to end.
Hon Secretary: John Williams, Kimberley, Lincoln Green Lane, Tewkesbury, Glos GL20 7DW
Tel: (H) 01684 298829 Tel: (M) 07976 294682
Tel: (W) 01452 529194
Email: tewkesbury_rfc@yahoo.co.uk
Fixtures Secretary: Heather Lampitt,, Tewkesbury, Glos Tel: (M) 07775 871454
Club Colours: Black and amber
League: Gloucester 1

THATCHAM RFC
Ground Address: Henwick Worthy Sports Fields, Henwick Lane, Thatcham, Berkshire
Brief Directions: Ground is situated midway between Thatcham and Newbury directly adjacent to the A4. Turn off the A4 (Bath Road) into Henwick Lane and after 100m turn left into the ground.
Hon Secretary: Andy Smith, 7 Charlock Close, Thatcham RG18 4DD Tel: (H) 01635 867142
Tel: (M) 07740 772134 Email: Asmith4975@aol.com
Club Colours: Navy blue & red quarters, blue shorts
League: Berks/Bucks & Oxon 1

THORNBURY RFC
Ground Address: Rockhampton Road, Thornbury, Bristol Tel: 01454 412 096
Brief Directions: From Thornbury: at Royal George pub take Gloucester rd out of town, after Anchor pub take 2nd left (ignore turn directly next to pub), club is down this lane approx 0.5 mile on the right
Hon Secretary: Howard Bowker, 2 Broncksea Road, Bristol, BS7 0ES Tel: (H) 0117 969 8744
Club Colours: Black and amber hoops
League: Western Counties North

TIVERTON RFC
Ground Address: Coronation Field, Bolham Road, Tiverton, EX16 6SG Tel: 01884 252 271
Brief Directions: M5 J27 north towards Tiverton, 7 miles r'about at end of d/carriageway left to Tiverton, ground 250mtrs on right just before footbridge over road
Hon Secretary: Margaret Sampson, 5 Shillands, Tiverton, EX16 5AA Tel: (H) 01884 255 287
Tel: (M) 07811 069 059
Club Colours: Light and dark blue
League: Western Counties West

TOPSHAM RFC
Ground Address: Bonfire Field, Topsham, Exeter, Devon EX3 0LY Tel: 01392 873651
Email Address: keethsmeeth@aol.com
Web Address: http://run.to/topshamrfc
Directions: Approaching Topsham from Exeter it is the last field on the left before the built up area.
Hon Secretary: Matt Shane, 33 Rayburn Close, Taunton, Somerset TA1 2RH Tel: (H) 01823 289420
Fixtures Secretary: Sam Pascoe, Flat 3, 7 Richmond Road, Exeter Tel: (H) 01392 491115
Tel: (W) 01392 849 275
Email: samlpascoe@aol.com
Club Colours: Light & dark blue hoops
League: Devon 1

TOR RFC
Ground Address: Lowerside Park, Lowerside Lane, Glastonbury, Somerset Tel: 01458 832236
Brief Directions: Adjacent to and signposted off A39 Glastonbury bypass
Club Secretary: Mrs Caro; Mountain, 16 Badgers Green Road, street, Somerset. BA16 0PT
Tel: 01458 446582
Email: hmountain@ tinyworld.co.uk
Fixtures Secretary: Mr Keith Elver,18 Hurmans Close, Ashcott, Bridgwater,somerset TA7 9PT
Tel: (H) 01458 211044 (W) 01749 673199
Club Colours: Maroon shirts with blue shorts
League: Somerset Premier

TORQUAY ATHLETIC RFC
Ground Address: Torquay Recreation Ground, Rathmore Drive, Seafront, Torquay, Devon TQ2
Tel: 01803 293842
Email Address: RicH@torquayrugby.co.uk
Web Address: www.torquayrugby.co.uk
Brief Directions: 1 Begin at Newton Abbot's Penn Inn on Torquay Road, A380 2 Follow signs and exit for Torquay, onto the Newton Road 3 Continue on Newton Road until you reach Torre (rail) Station/Halfords, here turn right at the lights down Avenue Road (the Rugby Club is signposted from the station) 4 Continue along this road, until you reach the lights on the Seafront 5 Turn Right at the lights, staying in the Right-hand lane, turning immediately right at the next lights (adjacent to the Grand Hotel) 6 The entrance to the Rugby Club is now in front of you, on the right-side of the Road
Hon Secretary: Richard Harris, 52 Chatsworth Road, Torquay, Devon TQ1 3BL Tel: (H) 01803 294115
Tel: (M) 07778 547119 Tel: (W) 01803 208471
Email: rich@torquayrugby.co.uk
Fixtures Secretary: Dave Thompson, 44 Bidwell Brook Drive, Paignton TQ4 7NF Tel: (H) 01803 845115
Email: daveliz44@dthompson49.freeserve.co.uk
Club Colours: Black & white hoops, black shorts & socks
League: South West 2 West
Leagues Contact: Dave Thompson - as above

TORRINGTON RUFC
Ground Address: Donnacroft, Torrington.
Tel: 01805 622055
Directions: Situated on B3227 South Molton Road.
Club Secretary: Daren Nudds, 4 South Street, Torrington, Devon Tel: 01805 624899
Fixtures Secretary: David Hickman
Tel: (H) 01769 560131
Club Colours: Green black and white hoops
League: Devon 1

TOTNES RFC
Ground Address: Borough Park, Totnes, Devon TQ9 5XW Tel: 01803 867796
Brief Directions: Pitch on public park adjacent to British Rail station
Hon Secretary: Aubrey Bourne, 18 Hunters Moon, Totnes, Devon TQ9 6JT Tel: (H&W) 01803 864462
Tel: (M) 07885 748871
Email: abourne@members.shines.net
Club Colours: Royal blue, white shorts
League: Devon 2

TREDWORTH RFC
Ground Address: The Lannet, King Edwards Avenue, Gloucester Tel: 01452 308939
Brief Directions: Along A38 towards Glos turn right into Tuffley Ave, then 5th into the OVAL which then leads to ground on right hand side
Hon Secretary: Ken Broady, 25 Stonechat Avenue, Abbeydale, Gloucester
Club Colours: Green shirts with black shorts
League: Gloucester 3 North

TROWBRIDGE RFC
Ground Address: Green Lane, Trowbridge, Wiltshire, BA14 7DJ Tel: 01225 351044
Email Address: brynparfitt@yahoo.co.uk
Web Address: http://www.trowbridgerugby.co.uk
Brief Directions: Directions - 1. From Devizes (A361) - at 2nd roundabout turn left and after 200 yards turn left into Green Lane. 2. From Frome/Bath - follow signs into Trowbridge then towards Devizes - on dual carriageway go under pedestrian bridge by Tescos. Turn right at roundabout. After 200 yards turn left into Green Lane. 3. From Westbury follow A350 to Yarnbrook - turn right at roundabout and left at next traffic lights - after 1 1/2 miles go straight over roundabout and turn right into Green Lane. Follow Green Lane until it changes to a track - club is on right.
Hon Secretary: Bryn Parfitt, 60 Paxcroft Way, Trowbridge, Wiltshire, BA14 7DJ
Tel: (H) 01225 351044
Email: brynparfitt@yahoo.co.uk
Hon Fixtures: Micky Milton, 6 Clarence Road, Trowbridge, Wiltshire Tel: (H) 01225 767204
Leagues Contact: Alistair Morrison, 22 Campion Drive, Trowbridge, Wilts BA14 0XZ Tel: (H) 01225 755135
Email: alistair.morrison24@virgin.net
Club Colours: Dark blue, light blue and gold hoops
League: Dorset & Wilts 1

VEOR RFC
Ground Address: Wheal Gerry, Cliff View Road, Canborne, Cornwall Tel: 01209 710974
Email Address: CazUren@aol.com
Brief Directions: Turn off A30 signed Canborne & Pool, right at traffic lights down hill, right again before pedestrian crossing, 0.5 mile right again after TA centre, ground 100 yds on right
Club Secretary: Colin Pascoe, 40 Barripper Road, Camborne, Cornwall TR14 7QW
Tel: (H) 01209 716172
Fixtures Secretary: Colin Pascoe, as above
Club Colours: Black and Gold
League: Cornwall 2

WADEBRIDGE CAMELS RFC
Ground Address: Molesworth Field, Egloshayle, Wadebridge, Cornwall Tel: 01208 815311
Web Address: www.wadebridgecamelsrfc.co.uk
Brief Directions: Opposite Egloshayle Church
Hon Secretary: Mark Richards, Trevanger Farm, Wadebridge, Cornwall PL27 6QR
Tel: (H) 01208 869092 Tel: (W) 01726 860308
Email: mark-richards@msn.com
Fixtures Secretary: M. Gee, Lowenna, 70 Halsetown, St. Ives TR26 3LZ Tel: (H) 01736 797777
Email: swrfu@aol.com
Club Colours: Chocolate and gold
League: Cornwall/Devon

WALCOT OLD BOYS
Ground Address: Albert Field, Lansdown, Bath BA1 9AF Tel: 01225 330199
Brief Directions: Follow signs from city centre to Lansdown, proceed along top to racecourse/golf club, halfway on right is ground opposite Bath car park & ride sign
Hon Secretary: S. J. Mills, 23 Heritage Close, Peasedown St. John, Bath, BA2 8TJ
Tel: (H) 01761 439102
Club Colours: Black and white hoops
League: Western Counties North

WALLINGFORD RFC
Ground Address: Hithercroft Sports Club, Wallingford, OX10 9ES Tel: 01491 835044
Email Address: rugby@wallingfordrfc.com
Web Address: www.wallingfordrfc.com
Brief Directions: Situated on Wallingford bypass on west side of town, bypass signposted on all approaches to Wallingford
Hon Secretary: Norma Henderson, 12 Lapwing Lane, Cholsey, Wallingford, OX10 0QR
Tel: (H) 01491 652075
Club Colours: Amber and black
League: Southern Counties North

WARMINSTER RFC
Ground Address: Folly Lane Sports Ground, Folly Lane, Warminster, Wilts. Tel: 01985 301788
Email Address: eve.jenkins@blueyonder.co.uk
Web Address: warminsterrfc.org.uk

Brief Directions: From A350 r'about on by-pass head into Warminster. Past 'Bell & Crown' on left, next left into Fore St.. At next r;'about 2nd left into Thornhill Rd, then left into Folly Lane. Ground 200 yds on right
Hon Secretary: Eve Jenkins, 15 Were Close, Warminster, Wilts BA12 8TB Tel: (H) 01985 212261
Email: eve.jenkins@blueyonder.co.uk
Fixtures Secretary: Steve Evans, Flat 3, The Maltings, Warminster, Wilts BA12 9AW Tel: (H) 01985 212750
Club Colours: Royal blue and gold hoops.
League: Dorset & Wilts 2 South

WELLINGTON RFC
Ground Address: The Athletic Ground, Corams Lane, Wellington, Somerset. TA21 8LL Tel: 01823 663758
Brief Directions: Leave M5 J25 or from A38 from Taunton, right at central traffic lights into North St, left at Sportsman Inn, enter via sports centre car park
Club Secretary: N. Robins, 37 Bircham Road, Taunton, Somerset. TA2 8EX.
Fixtures Secretary: G R Vickery, 7 Seymour Street, Wellington, Somerset TA21 8JT
Tel: (H) 01823 664695 (W) 01823 335166
Club Colours: Red and black hoops.
League: Cornwall/Devon

WELLS RFC
Ground Address: Charter Way, Wells, Somerset BA5 2FB Tel: 01749 672823
Email Address: contact@wellsrugbyclub.co.uk
Web Address: www.wellsrugbyclub.co.uk
Brief Directions: Off the Portway A371 or follow signs to the Leisure Centre (which is next door)
Hon Secretary: Dawn Hickman, Sunset, Mount Pleasant, Somerset BA4 4BL Tel: (H) 01749 890746
Tel: (M) 07946 742462
Email: contact@wellsrugbyclub.co.uk
Fixtures Secretary: Dawn Hickman, Sunset, Mount Pleasant, Somerset BA4 4BL Tel: (H) 01749 890746
Tel: (M) 07946 742462
Email: contact@wellsrugbyclub.co.uk
Club Colours: Black & white hoops
League: Somerset 1

WESSEX RFC
Ground Address: Flowerpot Field, Exwick Playing Fields, Exwick, Exeter
Tel: 01392 211959
Brief Directions: From J31 M5 to A30 follow signs to Exeter then Exwick, along Buddle Lane turn right into Oakhampton Road, turn left onto Western Road
Hon Secretary: Phil Langford, 7 Kinnerton Way, Exeter, EX4 2BL Tel: (H) 01392 211959
Tel: (W) 01392 414304
Email: mail@wessexrfc.co.uk
Fixtures Secretary: R. Richardson, 69 Parkway, Exeter, EX2 9BN Tel: (H) 01392 251629
Tel: (W) 01392 208205
Club Colours: Bottle green shirts with amber collars and white shorts
League: Cornwall/Devon

WESTBURY RFC
Ground Address: Leighton Sport Ground, Wellhead Lane, Westbury, Wiltshire Tel: 01373 826438
Email Address: jrugbymaster@aol.com
Web Address: www.westburyrfc.co.uk
Brief Directions: Warminster Road (A350), opposite Cedar Hotel turn into Wellhead Lane, ground 300 metres on left
Hon Secretary: Ron Jones, 36 Westbury Road, Trowbridge, Wiltshire, BA14 6AG
Tel: (H) 01225 766647 Tel: (M) 07713 619535
Tel: (W) 01373 828466
Email: jrugbymaster@aol.com
Club Colours: Irregular Green and black hoops
League: Southern Counties South

WESTBURY-ON-SEVERN RFC
Ground Address: Parish Grounds, Westbury-on-Severn, Glos. Tel: 01452 760359
Email Address: hollies@pbleathman.freeserve.co.uk
Brief Directions: A48 from Gloucester to Chepstow. Ground on left hand side before entering Westbury-on-Severn.
Hon Secretary: Phil Bleathman, The Hollies, Elton, Glos GL14 1JJ Tel: (H) 01452 760751
Email: hollies@pbleathman.freeserve.co.uk
Club Colours: Royal blue and white hoops
League: Gloucester 2

WEYMOUTH RFC
Ground Address: Monmouth Avenue, Weymouth, Dorset DT3 5HZ Tel: 01305 778889
Email Address: Bim.d@virgin.net
Web Address: www.weymouthrfc.supanet.com
Brief Directions: Travelling from Dorchester towards Weymouth take the third turning left after passing Safeways store on LHS after the Manor roundabout where the Club is signposted.
Hon Secretary: Bim Downes, 19 Coombe Valley Road, Weymouth, Dorset DT3 6NJ Tel: (H) 01305 834601
Email: Bim.d@virgin.net
Fixtures Secretary: John Lloyd, 43 Overcombe Drive, Weymouth, Dorset DT3 6QF Tel: (H) 01305 833574
Tel: (M) 07760 205435
Email: john.lloyd11@btinternet.com
Club Colours: Light blue with dark blue circlet and black shorts
League: Dorset & Wilts 1

WHEATLEY RUFC
Ground Address: Playing Fields, Holton, Wheatley, Oxford OX33 1QL Tel: (01865) 873476
Brief Directions: From Oxford, leave the A40 at the "Wheatley" signs. Turn left at the T-junction and the ground will be found on the left about 500 yards from the turn. From London, take the turning from the A40 or A418 to Wheatley and follow the signs to Oxford. Turn right at the mini-roundabout, pass over the A40 and the ground will be found about 800 yards to the left.
Hon Secretary: Andy Caldicott, 60 Church Road, Oxford, OX33 1LZ Tel: (H) 01865 427 974 Tel: (W) 01865 880 880 ext 310
Fixtures Secretary: Simon Wilde, Ivy Cottage, Crowell, Chinnor, Oxfordshire, OX39 4RR Tel: (H) 01844 353341 Tel: (M) 07768 993116
Colours: Purple, white & black hoops, black shorts
League: Berks/Bucks & Oxon 2

WHITEHALL RFC
Ground Address: Speedwell Recreation Ground, Foundry Lane, Speedwell, Bristol Tel: 0117 965 9636
Brief Directions: Off B4465 Whitehall Road at Crofts End, turn right into Deep Pit Rd, take 2nd left. From M32 J2 follow sign post up Muller Rd, left at roundabout
Hon Secretary: Richard Haycock, 393 Speedwell Road, Bristol, BS15 1EN Tel: (H) 0117 967 086 Tel: (W) 0117 317 1616
Fixtures Secretary: Wayne Millard, 263 Forest Road, Bristol, BS16 3QY Tel: (H) 0117 940 0778
Club Colours: Myrtle green and gold
League: Western Counties North

WIDDEN OLD BOYS RFC
Ground Address: Memorial Ground, Tuffley Avenue, Gloucester Tel: 01452 530 122
Web Address: www.wob.moonfruit.com
Brief Directions: M5 north J12, right at 1st roundabout at end of bypass, left at next roundabout into Stroud Rd, approx 150m left into Tuffley Avenue
Hon Secretary: Stuart McWalter, 52 The Causeway, Quedgeley, Gloucester, GL2 4LD Tel: (H) 01452 724 739 Tel: (M) 07747 7655 84 Tel: (W) 01452 332 604
Email: stuart.mcwalter@tesco.net
Fixtures Secretary: Andy Adler, 21 Chiltern Road, Gloucester Tel: (H) 01452 540 071 Tel: (M) 07957 979 569
Club Colours: Green shirts with red band & white hoops
League: Gloucester 2

WIMBORNE RFC
Ground Address: Leigh Park, Gordon Road, Wimborne, Dorset Tel: 01202 841478
Email Address: mmoysey@wimbornerugbyclub.co.uk
Web Address: www.wimbornerugbyclub.co.uk
Brief Directions: From A31 take B3073(approx 2 miles east of Wimborne)follow road towards town centre for about 1.5 miles and turn left in to Gordon Road. Wimborne RFC Leigh Park 250 yards ahead.
Hon Secretary: Michael Moysey, 42 Lacy Drive, Wimborne, Dorset BH21 1DG Tel: (H) 01202 841 478 Tel: (M) 07720 534818 Tel: (W) 01202 633 068
Email: michael@mmoysey.freeserve.co.uk
Fixtures Secretary: Bert Whitby Tel: (H) 01202 885836
Club Colours: All Black
League: South West 2 East

WINCANTON RUFC
Ground Address: Wincanton Sports Ground, Balsam Fields, Wincanton, Somerset
Brief Directions: Into Wincanton from A303, after Fire station turn right down Moor Lane 0.5 mile
Club Secretary: Mr. J. Bastable, Church Farm, Charlton Musgrove, Wincanton, Somerset. BA9 8ES.
Fixtures Secretary: Mr Glen Ware, c/o Dolphin Hotel, High Street, Wincanton, Somerset. BA9 9JF.
Colours: Black and amber Change C olours: Yellow
League: Dorset & Wilts 2 South

WINDSOR RFC
Ground Address: Home Park, Datchet Road, Windsor, Berkshire, SL4 6HX Tel: 01753 860 807
Web Address: www.windsorrugbyclub.com
Brief Directions: Off M4, signed Windsor, follow d/carriageway to 1st slip road off left, left at roundabout, left at next roundabout, keep left past railway station, next left into Home Park
Hon Secretary: Ian Potter, 3 Little Woodlands, WINDSOR, Berkshire, SL4 3RF Tel: (H) 01753 854572
Club Colours: Black, Maroon, Bottle & Gold quarters
League: South West 2 East

WINSCOMBE
Ground Address: Longfield Recreation Ground, The Lynch, Winscombe Tel: 01934 842 720
Brief Directions: Turn off A38 into Winscombe, turn left at right hand bend to ground.
Hon Secretary: Alun George, 3 Landseer Close, Worle, Weston-super-Mare, BS22 6UL Tel: (H) 01934 518 270
Email: alun@landseer.fsbusiness.co.uk
Club Colours: Black with white hoops
League: Somerset 2

WINSLOW RFC
Ground Address: Winslow Centre, Park Road, Winslow, Buckinghamshire, MK18 3DN Tel: 01908 566 233
Email Address: steve.hodges@pcg-intl.com
Brief Directions: A413 through Winslow, 0.5 mile towards Buckingham from town centre, turn left into Avenue Road, 1st right into Park Road
Hon Secretary: Steve Hodges, Giles Cottage, 54 Cross Tree Road, Wicken, MK19 6BT Tel: (H) 01908 566 233 Tel: (M) 07887 545 136
Email: steve.hodges@pcg-intl.com
Club Colours: Blue and gold hoops
League: Berks/Bucks & Oxon 2

WITHYCOMBE RFC
Ground Address: Raleigh Park, 36, Hulham Road, Exmouth, Devon EX8 3HS Tel: 01395 266 762
Brief Directions: M5 south J30, take A376 to Exmouth,

at Box Junction before traffic lights turn left into Hulham Rd, ground 200 yards on right
Hon Secretary: David Josey, 2 Larch Close, Marley Gardens, Exmouth, Devon EX8 5NQ Tel: (H) 01395 275 038
Email: davejosey@hotmail.com
Fixtures Secretary: David Field, 4 Mossop Close, Ottery St. Mary, Devon Tel: (H) 01404 811 102
Club Colours: Emerald green and black hoops
League: Western Counties West

WITNEY RFC
Ground Address: Witney Road, Hailey, Witney, Oxon, OX28 4AB Tel: 01993 771 043
Email Address: wrfc.co@virgin.net
Web Address: www.witneyrfc.co.uk
Brief Directions: Leave Witney centre by Bridge St, towards Oxford & Bicester, left at mini roundabout, keep along main road passing garage on right, ground on left after about 1 mile
Hon Secretary: Chris Tucker, 5 Highworth Place, Witney, Oxon, OX8 7AB Tel: (H) 01993 200376 Tel: (M) 0780 252 0252
Email: wrfc.co@virgin.net
Fixtures Secretary: Pete Holiday, 88 Blakin Avenue, Witney, Oxon, OX8 6SX Tel: (H) 01993 201 301
Email: wrfc.co@virgin.net
Club Colours: Black hoops on sky blue
League: Southern Counties North

WIVELISCOMBE RFC
Ground Address: Recreation Ground, West Road, Wiveliscombe Tel: 01984 623 897
Brief Directions: Take B3227 from Taunton to Barnstaple, ground is on left towards end of town
Hon Secretary: Guy Mabley, 3 Manor Park, Norton Firzwarren, Taunton, TA2 6SG Tel: (H) 01823 270 002
Club Colours: Navy blue with red sash
League: Somerset Premier

WOOTTON BASSETT RFC
Ground Address: Rylands Field, Stoneover Lane, Wootton Bassett, Wiltshire Tel: 01793 851425
Email Address: elias@tinyworld.co.uk
Web Address: WWW.bassettrfc.com
Brief Directions: M4 J16, follow signs for Wootton Bassett over R/about, up hill, Stoneover Lane on left, club 300 metres on left.
Hon Secretary: Chris Elias, Ty Canol, Wanshot Close, Swindon, Wilts SN4 0RF Tel: (H) 01793 845 396 Tel: (W) 01793 512 002
Email: elias@tinyworld.co.uk
Club Colours: Black shirts & shorts
League: Southern Counties South

WOTTON RFC
Ground Address: Ground Address: K L B School Ground, Kingswood Road, Wotton-under-Edge Tel: 01453 842138 (Falcon Hotel)
Email Address: helek_99@hotmail.com
Web Address: www.wottonrfc.com
Brief Directions: Take b4058 towards M5 out of Wotton, Ground on Left at foot of hill.
Hon Secretary: Helen King, 3 Gloucester Street, Gloucester, GL12 7DN Tel: (H) 01453 844 527
Email: helenk_99@hotmail.com
Club Colours: Black and amber hoops
League: Gloucester 3 South

YATTON
Ground Address: The Park, North End, Yatton Tel: 01934 832 085
Brief Directions: From centre of village, travel towards Clevedon, club is on right 300 yards after Railway bridge
Hon Secretary: Paul Edwards, c/o Yatton RFC, The Park, Yatton, Somerset Tel: (H) 01934 822 425
Club Colours: Amber and black
League: Western Counties North

ASSOCIATE MEMBERS

ANTI-ASSASSINS
Hon. Secretary Ms S B Gardiner, Blossoms Farm, Blossoms Lane, Woodford, Cheshire SK7 1RF
Hon. Fixture Sec. Mr P E Hughes, Height Top Smithy, Higham, Burnley, Lancashire BB12 9BU

BARBARIAN **1890**
Hon. Secretary Mr G Windsor-Lewis, Wilcote Place, Ramsden, Oxfordshire OX7 3BA

BRISTOL AND DISTRICT COMBINATION **1909**
Headquarters Bristol FC, Memorial Ground, Filton Avenue, Bristol BS7 0AG Tel: 0117 908 5500
Hon. Secretary Mr A J Weaver, 8 Lower Chapel Lane, Frampton Cotterell, Bristol BS36 2RL
Hon. Fixture Sec. Mr T Webb, 50 Monks Park Avenue, Filton, Bristol BS7 0UH

CHELTENHAM AND DISTRICT COMBINATION **1963**
Hon. Secretary Mr B F Didlick, 15 Stoneville Street, Cheltenham, Glos. GL51 8PH
Hon. Fixture Sec. Mr M Kedward, 35 Bishops Cleeve, Cheltenham, Glos. GL52 4NU

COMBINED BIRMINGHAM OLD BOYS **1951**
Hon. Secretary & Hon. Fixture Sec.
Mr C W Hayward, 6 Princethorpe Close, Shirley, Solihull, West Midlands B90 2LP

DERBYSHIRE COUNTY UNION **1922**
Hon. Secretary Mr P Fuller, Ednaston Lodge Farm, Ednaston, Ashbourne, Derbyshire DE6 3BA
Hon. Fixture Sec. Mr G Morgan, 55 Lower Market Street, Broadbottom, Hyde SK14 6AA

FOREST OF DEAN COMBINATION **1923**
Hon. Secretary Mr G Ward, Willow Brae, Gorsley, Ross-on-Wye, Herefordshire HR9 7SH
Hon. Fixture Sec. Mr C Edwards, Windbourne, High Beech Road, Bream, Nr Lydney, Glos. GL15 6JG

GREATER BIRMINGHAM **1936**
Hon. Secretary Mr C Humphreys, 75 Loxley Avenue, Shirley, Solihull, West Midlands B90 2QL
Hon. Fixture Sec. Mr K Jordan, 74 William Road, Warley, West Midlands B67 6LW

LEICESTER THURSDAY **1888**
Hon. Secretary Mr R Mitchell, 8 Begonia Close, Leicester Forest Close, Leicester LE3 3QY
Hon. Fixture Sec. Mr M Higgins, 36 Beechwood Avenue, Leicester Forest East, Leicester LE3 3PL

LINCOLNSHIRE COUNTY UNION **1947**
Hon. Secretary Mr M A Ross, Blacksmith's House, 26 Lincoln Road, Branston, Lincoln LN4 1PA
Hon. Fixture Sec. Mr C Moon, 5 Manor Close, Welton, Lincoln LN2 3TQ

LONDON **1911**
Hon. Secretary Mr D S Straw, London, 161 High Street, Hampton Hill, Middlesex TW12 1NL

NORTH GLOUCESTER COMBINATION **1912**
Hon. Secretary Mr M S Slatter, 135 Grange Road, Tuffley, Gloucester GL4 0PR
Hon. Fixture Sec. Mr D L Howell, 255c Stroud Road, Gloucester GL1 5JZ

NOTTINGHAMSHIRE COUNTY UNION **1920**
Hon. Secretary Mr D Sutton, 22 Vernon Avenue, Wilford Village, Nottingham HG11 7AE
Hon. Fixture Sec. Mr V P Williams, 1 Carisbrooke Drive, Mapperley Park, Nottingham NG3 5DS

PENGUIN INTERNATIONAL **1959**
Hon. Secretary Mr A G L Wright, 11 Little St James's Street, London SW1A 1DP
Hon. Fixture Sec. Mr I M Bullerwell, Duncombe Heights, Avenue Farm Lane, Wilden, Beds, MK44 2PY

PLYMOUTH & DISTRICT RUGBY COMBINATION **1901**
Hon. Secretary Mr S Reeves, 129 York Road, Weston Mill, Plymouth PL5 1AU

SHROPSHIRE **1959**
Hon. Secretary Mr I B Roberts, 2 Mount Cottages, Knighton, Adbaston, Stafford ST20 0QQ

STROUD AND DISTRICT COMBINATION **1974**
Hon. Secretary Mr R Edmonds, Woodlands Cottage, 205 Slad Road, Stroud, Glos. GL5 1RJ

THE WANDERERS (PSW) **1940**
Hon. Secretary Mrs J G Lowe, 46 Kingston Lane, Shoreham by Sea, West Sussex BN43 6YB
Hon. Fixture Sec. Brigadier R N R P James CBE, 3 Upper Court, Old Church Rd, Colwall, Malvern, Worcs WR13 6ET

WORCESTERSHIRE AND HEREFORDSHIRE **1923**
Hon. Secretary Mr J P Hartley, Nightingate House, Bishampton, Worcs WR10 2NH
Hon. Fixture Sec. Mr D S Price, Uplands Farm, Wellington Heath, Ledbury HR8 1NF

AFFILIATED CLUBS

AEI (RUGBY) 1917
Hillmorton Road
Rugby
Warwickshire
CV22 4AR
01788 576921

Mr R I Stephens
Hon. Secretary
AEI (Rugby)
10 Northampton Lane
Dunchurch, Rugby
Warwickshire
CV22 6QA

Mr A G Chronnell
Hon. Fixture Secretary
AEI (Rugby)
24 Kirkby Close
Brownsover, Rugby
Warwickshire
CV21 1TT

AESCULAPIANS 1986
The Rugby Club
49 Hallam Street
London
W1
020 7580 7917

Mr S D W Payne FRCS LLM
Hon. Secretary
Aesculapians
28 Emanuel Avenue
Acton
London
W3 6JJ

Mr J E T Payne
Hon. Fixture Secretary
Aesculapians
28 Emanuel Avenue
Acton
London
W3 6JJ

ALDBOURNE DABCHICKS 1992
Ewins Hill
Aldbourne
Wiltshire

Mr A Woodrow
Hon. Secretary
Aldbourne Dabchicks
61 Whitley Road
Aldbourne
Marlborough,
Wilts. SN8 2BU

Mr C Flett
Hon. Fixture Secretary
Aldbourne Dabchicks
71 Cottage Road
Aldbourne
Marlborough
SN8 2EB

ANDERSEN 1990

Mr D J Evans
Hon. Secretary
Andersen
c/o Arthur Andersen
1 Surrey Street
London
WC2R 2PS
020 7438 3000

Mr Richard Llewellyn
Hon. Fixture Secretary
Andersen
c/o Arthur Andersen
1 Surrey Street
London
WC2R 2PS

ANGLIA (CAMBRIDGE)
1990
c/o The Gymnasium
Anglia Polytechnic University
East Road, Cambridge
CB1 1PT

Hon. Secretary
Doug Cosnett
Anglia (Cambridge)
c/o The Gymnasium
Anglia Polytechnic University
East Road, Cambridge
CB1 1PT

Mr C Upham
Hon. Fixture Secretary
Anglia (Cambridge)
APU
Cambridge

ANSTEY 1980
Bennion Road
Beaumont Leys
Leicester
0116 235 5585

Mr Alan Chapman
Hon. Secretary
Anstey
1 Groby Road
Anstey
Leics
LE7 7FN

Mr Ian Pollock
Hon. Fixture Secretary
Anstey
14 Pinewood Close
Leicester
LE4 1ER

ASH 1995
Recreation Ground
Queens Road, Ash,
Canterbury, Kent,

Mr Julian Gugenheim
Hon. Secretary
Ash
Bourne Park Cottage
Bourne Park Bridge
Canterbury, Kent
CT4 5BJ

Mr Alan Warner
Hon. Fixture Secretary
Guilton Lodge
Guilton
Ash
Kent
CT3 2H2

AXMINSTER 1989
Gammons Hill
Kilmington
Axminster
EX13
01297 35989

Mrs Karen Hussey
Hon. Secretary
Axminster
Cranmere
Musbury Road
Axminster Devon
EX13 5JS

Mr M Carlisle
Hon. Fixture Secretary
Axminster
Apple Tree Corner
Colyford
Axminster, Devon
EX13 6QQ

AYLESTONE ATHLETIC 1919
Victoria Park
Victoria Park Road
Leicester

Mr R H Dann
Hon. Secretary
Aylestone Athletic
32 Monsell Drive
Aylestone
Leicester
LE2 8PN

Mr Mark Walters
Hon. Fixture Secretary
Aylestone Athletic
113 Holmfield Road
Leicester
LE2 1SF

AYLESBURY ATHLETIC

HM Prison
Bierton Road
Aylesbury HP20 1EH
01296 424435 x318

PEO D Beer
Hon. Secretary
Aylesbury Athletic
HMYOI Aylesbury
Bierton Road
Aylesbury HP20 1EH

PEO R Hemming
Hon. Fixture Secretary
Aylesbury Athletic
HM Young Offender Inst
Bierton Road
Aylesbury, Bucks
HP20 1EH

BAE WARTON 1992
Bank Lane Playing Fields
Bank Lane
Warton, Preston
PR4 1AX
01772 856354/852788

Mr M.D Hubble
Hon. Secretary
BAe Warton
2 Ribble View Close
Warton
Nr Prescot, Lancashire
PR4 1LD

Mr M Jagger
Hon. Fixture Secretary
BAe Warton
6 Hazel Coppice
Lea
Preston, Lancashire
PR2 1XG

BALLIOL COLLEGE 1906
c/o Balliol college
Oxford
OX1 3BJ
01865 277777

Mr E Rees
Hon. Secretary
Balliol College
c/o Balliol College
Oxford 0X1 3BJ

BARCLAYS BANK 1921
Barclays Bank Sports Club
Park View Road
Ealing, London
W5 2JF
020 8998 4904

Mr S C Payne
Hon. Secretary
Barclays Bank
Barclays Acquisition Finance
1st Floor, 54 Lombard Street
London EC3P 3AH

Mr D M Bevan-Jones
Hon. Fixture Secretary
Barclays Bank
23 Cypress Avenue
Whitton, Twickenham
Middlesex TW2 7JY

BARCLAYS BANK BIRMINGHAM DISTRICT
1955
Sunnybank Avenue
Perry Common
Birmingham B44 0HP

Mr K R Patterson
Hon. Secretary & **Fixture Secretary**
Barclays Bank Birmingham District
42 Pennymore Close
Trentham, Stoke on Trent
Staffordshire ST4 8YQ

BASILDON (BERKSHIRE) 1978
The Recreation Ground
Bethesda Street
Upper Basildon, Berkshire

Mr D Butcher
Hon. Secretary
8 Gratwicke Road
Tilehurst
Reading
Berkshire RG30 4TT

Mr J Hayes
Hon. Fixture Secretary
Basildon (Berkshire)
53 Willowtree Glade
Calcot
Reading

BEDFORD SCHOOL 1870
Burnaby Road
Bedford
01234 362200

Hon. Secretary
Bedford School
Burnaby Road, Bedford

BELGRAVIA
Imber Court
Ember Court Road
East Molesey, Surrey
020 8398 1267

Mr Shaun O'Neill
Hon. Secretary
Belgravia
6 Priory Close
Sunbury on Thames
Middlesex
TW16 5AB

Mr R Thorne
Hon. Fixture Secretary
Belgravia
Crime Prevention Office
Belgravia Police Station
Buckingham Palace Road
London

BENTON 1964
Civil Service Sports Ground
(Darsley Pk), Old Whitley Road
Newcastle-upon-Tyne
0191 2662726

Mr G Parker
Hon. Secretary
Benton
9 Wilson Terrace
Forest Hall
Newcastle upon Tyne
NE12 7JP

Mr R Jones
Hon. Fixture Secretary
Benton
9 Wilson Terrace
Forest Hall
Newcastle upon Tyne
NE12 7JP

BERWICK 1968
Scremerston
Berwick-upon-Tweed
TD15 2QY
01289 306416

Mr J H Greenwood
Hon. Secretary
Berwick
Ava Lodge
Castle Terrace
Berwick upon Tweed
TD15 1NP

Mr C Budzynski
Hon. Fixture Secretary
Berwick
17 Springfield Park
East Ord
Berwick Upon Tweed
TD15 2FD

BICTON COLLEGE OF AGRICULTURE 1947
Bicton College of Agriculture
East Budleigh
Budleigh Salterton
EX9 7BY
01395 562335

Mr I Wallace
Hon. Secretary
Agriculture
Bicton College of Agriculture
Agriculture
Bicton College of Agriculture
East Budleigh
Budleigh Salterton, Devon
EX9 7BY

Hon. Fixture Secretary
Bicton College of
Bicton College of
East Budleigh
Budleigh Salterton, Devon
EX9 7BY

BIRKENHEAD SCHOOL
11 Kingsmead Road South
Birkenhead
Merseyside
L43 6TA
0151 652 4014

Master I/C Rugby
Hon. Secretary
Birkenhead School
Birkenhead School
11 Kingsmead Road South
Birkenhead, Merseyside
L43 6TA

For Attention Of:
Hon. Fixture Secretary
Birkenhead School
11 Kingsmead Road South
Birkenhead
Merseyside
L43 6TA

BIRSTALL 1975
Longslade Community College
Wanlip Lane
Birstall, Leicestershire
LE4 4GH
0116 267 7107

Mr G Cree
Hon. Secretary
64 Branting Hill Avenue
Glenfield
Leicester
LE3 8GB

Mr S Cox
Hon. Fixture Secretary
Birstall
7 Roman Road
Birstall
Leicestershire
LE4 4BB

BISHOP'S STORTFORD COLLEGE 1920
Maze Green Road
Bishop's Stortford
Hertfordshire
CM23 2QZ
01279 657911

Master I/C Rugby
Hon. Secretary
Bishop's Stortford College
Bishops Stortford College
Bishops Stortford
Hertfordshire

For Attention Of:
Hon. Fixture Secretary
Bishop's Stortford College
Maze Green Road
Bishop's Stortford
Hertfordshire
CM23 2QZ

BLACK BAA BAAS 1994
23a Varna Road
London
SW6 7LB

Mr Julian Samuel
Hon. Secretary
Black Baa Baas
23A Varna Road
Fulham
London
SW6

Mr Julian Samuel
Hon. Fixture Secretary
Black Baa Baas
23A Varna Road
Fulham
London
SW6

BLACK HORSE 1977
Balls Park
Mangrove Road
Hertford, Hertfordshire
SG13 8AJ

Mr C R Daniels
Hon. Secretary
Black Horse
9 Currie Street
Hertford
Hertfordshire
SG13 7DA

Mr S Martin
Hon. Fixture Secretary
Black Horse
25 Gladstone Road
Ware
Hertfordshire
SG12 0AG

BLACKPOOL POLICE 1968
c/o Blackpool RUFC
Fleetwood Road
Blackpool, Lancashire
FY5 1RN
01253 853308

Mr D Crocombe
Hon. Secretary
Blackpool Police
53 Kendal Avenue
High Furlong, Blackpool
Lancashire
FY3 7LG

Mr C Farrow
Hon. Fixture Secretary
Blackpool Police
10 Newton Road
St Annes on Sea
Lancashire
FY8 3JW

BLUE BOAR 1977
c/o Oxford RFC
North Hinksey Village
Southern Bypass, Oxford
01865 243984

Mr B Kentish
Hon. Secretary
Blue Boar
Old Farmhouse
Longworth
Abingdon, Oxfordshire
OX13 5ET

Mr B Kentish
Hon. Fixture Secretary
Blue Boar
Old Farmhouse
Longworth
Abingdon, Oxfordshire
OX13 5ET

BLUNDELL'S SCHOOL 1868
Tiverton
Devon
EX16 4DN
01884 252543

Mr N Ridgway
Hon. Secretary
Blundell's School
Blundell's School
Tiverton
Devon
EX16 4DN

For Attention Of:
Hon. Fixture Secretary
Blundell's School
Tiverton
Devon
EX16 4DN

BORDER PARK 1961

Symons Park
Butteryhaugh
Kielder, Hexham
NE48 1HG

Mr C Earsman
Hon. Secretary
Border Park
Gladstone House,
Stannersburn
Falstone, Hexham
Northumberland
NE48 1DD

Mr W.J Turnbull
Hon. Fixture Secretary
Border Park
The Old Manse
Otterburn Rd,
Bellingham
Hexham, Northumberland
NE48 2DT

BOLSOVER RUFC
Oxcroft Miners Welfare
Clowne Road
Stranfree
Nr Chesterfield
Derbyshire

Hon. Secretary & **Fixture Secretary**
MR F Skinner
17 Oxcroft Lane
Bolsover
Chesterfield
Derbyshire
S44 6DJ

BP CHEMICALS 1972
BP Sports & Social Club
Salt End
Hedon Road, Hull
HU12 8DS
01482 896251

Mr S M Ladd
Hon. Secretary
BP Chemicals
56 Lindengate Avenue
Rockford Green
Hull, east Yorkshire
HU7 0ED

For Attention Of:
Hon. Fixture Secretary
BP Chemicals
BP Sports & Social Club
Salt End
Hedon Road, Hull
HU12 8DS

BRASENOSE COLLEGE
Abingdon Road
Oxford
01865 243478

Mr M Forbes	Mr M Forbes
Hon. Secretary	**Hon. Fixture Secretary**
Brasenose College RFC	Brasenose College RFC
Brasenose College	Brasenose College
Oxford	Oxford
OX1 4AJ	OX1 4AJ

BRAUNSTONE TOWN 1983
Mossdale Meadows
Kingsway
Braunstone
0116 263 0018

Mr R Bailey	Mr P Tyers
Hon. Secretary	**Hon. Fixture Secretary**
32 Ambleside Drive	9 Ivanhoe Street
Eyres Monsell	Newfoundpool
Leics. LE29 9LB	Leicester LE3 9GX

BRITISH STEEL 1953
The Bungalow
6th Form Centre, Needham Drive
Workington, Cumbria
01900 603570

Ms L Storey	For Attention of:
Hon. Secretary	**Hon. Fixture Secretary**
British Steel	British Steel
31 Pilgrim Street	The Bungalow
Workington	6th Form Centre,
Needham Drive	
Cumbria CA14 2RA	Workington, Cumbria

BRITISH UNIVERSITIES SPORTS ASSOCIATION 1919
8 Union Street
London SE1 1SZ
020 7357 8555

Mr G Gregory-Jones	C Dean
Hon. Secretary	**Hon. Fixture Secretary**
BUSA	BUSA
8 Union Street	8 Union Street
London SE1 1SZ	London SE1 1SZ

BROADMOOR STAFF - 2000
36 Pinewood Ave
Crowethorne
Berkshire RG45 6RP
01344 762038

Mr C G Pole	Mr Ian Hodsdon
Hon. Secretary	**Fixture Secretary**
19 South Meadow	36 Pinewood Avenuef
Crowthorne	Crowthorne
Berkshire RG45 7HJ	Berkshire RG45 6RP

BROMSGROVE SCHOOL
Bromsgrove
Worcestershire B16 7DU
01527 32863

Master I/C Rugby	For Attention Of:
Hon. Secretary	**Hon. Fixture Secretary**
Bromsgrove School	Bromsgrove School
Bromsgrove	Bromsgrove
Worcestershire B16 7DU	Worcestershire B16 7DU

BURBAGE 1983
Britannia Road Playing Fields
Britannia Road
Burbage
01455 636108

Mr C M Startin	Mr R Sansome
Hon. Secretary	**Hon. Fixture Secretary**
Burbage	Burbage
102 Strathmore Road	39 Duport Road
Hinckley	Burbage, Hinckley
Leicestershire LE10 0LR	Leicestershire LE10

BURTON JOYCE
The Poplars Burton Joyce Sport Ground
Station Road
Burton Joyce
Notts, NG14 5AN

Mr T Hallam	Mr C Maltby
Hon. Secretary	33 The Spinney
9 Copse Close	Bylcote
Burton Joyce	Nottingham
Nottingham NG14 5DD	NG14 5GX

BURTONWOOD 1964
Burtonwood Community Centre
Fir Tree Lane
Burtonwood, Warrington
01925 224480/225584

Mrs E Southern	Mr J Harper
Hon. Secretary	**Hon. Fixture Secretary**
25 Knight Road	8 Camborne Road
Burtonwood	Burtonwood
Warrington WA5 4QQ	Warrington WA5

CAMBRIDGE UNIVERSITY 1872
Univ. Football Ground
Grange Road
Cambridge
CB3 9BN
01223 354131 (355301 Fax)

Mr A W Jessop	Dr F J Clough
Hon. Secretary	**Hon. Fixture Secretary**
32 Highfield Avenue	33 Bridgewater Drive,
Cambridge	Great Glen,
CB2 2AD	Leicester LE8 9DX

CASTLETOWN 1991
Castletown RFU
Poulsom Park

Mr P D Martin	Mr J Quayle
Hon. Secretary	**Hon. Fixture Secretary**
16 Queen's Terrace	41 Campion Way RFC
Douglas	Abbeyfieldsk
Isle of Man	Doulglas, Isle of Man
IM1 4BZ	IM2 7DT

CENTAURS RFC
Gower Road
Syon Lane
Isleworth
Middlesex
TW7 5QB

Mr M W Root	Mr J Goldie
Hon. Secretary	**Hon. Fixture Secretary**
116 Uxbridge Road	23 Northumberland Avenue
Hatch End	Isleworth
Pinner	Middlesex
Middlesex HA5 4DS	TW5 5HZ

CENTURIONS STH KENT POLICE SC 1984
New Burlington Field
Bargrove, Newington
Folkestone, Kent CT18 8BH
01303 266887

Mr R Thomas
Hon. Secretary
Centurions S. Kent Police SC
196 Canterbury Road
Folkestone
Kent
CT19 5PF

Mr K Howland
Hon. Fixture Secretary
Centurions S. Kent Police SC
Morton Cottage
Mill Lane
Monks Morton
Ashford, Kent

CHELTENHAM COLLEGE 1944
Cheltenham
Gloucestershire GL53 7LD
01242 513540

Master I/C Rugby
Hon. Secretary
Cheltenham College
Cheltenham
Glos. GL53 7LD

For Attention Of:
Hon. Fixture Secretary
Cheltenham College
Cheltenham
Glos. GL53 7LD

CHISWICK POLICE 1989
c/o Grasshoppers RFC
McFarlane Lane
Syon Lane, Osterley

Sgt N Baillie
Hon. Secretary
Chiswick Police Station
209 High Rd, Chiswick
London
W4 2DU

Sgt N Baillie
Hon. Fixture Secretary
Chiswick Police Station
209 High Rd, Chiswick
London
W4 2DU

CHRIST'S COLLEGE
College Sports Ground
162a Huntingdon Road
Cambridge
01223 276218

Mr D Till
Hon. Secretary
Christ's College
College Rugby Club
Christ's College
Cambridge
CB2 3BU

Mr D Till
Hon. Fixture Secretary
Christ's College
College Rugby Club
Christ's College
Cambridge
CB2 3BU

CHRIST'S HOSPITAL SCHOOL 1553
Christ's Hospital School
Horsham
Sussex RH13 7LS
01403 255283

Hon. Secretary
Christ's Hospital School
Horsham
Sussex RH13 7LS
01403 255283

CHRIST CHURCH
Iffley Road
Oxford
01865 243992

Mr B Gripaioss
Hon. Secretary
Christ Church
The Steward's Office,
Christ Church College
Oxford 0X1 1DP

CHURCHILL COLLEGE 1961
Churchill College
Cambridge CB3 0DS
01223 336000

Mr G de Rose
Hon. Secretary
Churchill College
Storey's Way
Cambridge CB3 0DS

For Attention Of:
Hon. Fixture Secretary
Churchill College
Cambridge
CB3 0DS

CITIZENS 1929
Old Dunstonians Sports Ground
St Dunstans Lane
Langley Park, Beckenham, Kent BR3 3SS
020 8650 1779

Mr C R Southgate
Hon. Secretary
Citizens
Sunny Bank, Kingsland
Nr Leominster
Herefordshire HR6 9SE

Mr P Upton
Hon. Fixture Secretary
Citizens
68 Addington Road
West Wickham
Kent BR4 9BJ

CLACTON RFC
The Recreation Ground
Valley Road
Clacton on Sea
Essex
CO15 4NA

Mr D Jaffray
Hon. Secretary
30 Craigfield Avenue
Clacton on Sea
Essex CO15 4HS

Mr G Wiggins
Hon. Fixture Secretary
39 Victoria Road
Clacton-On-Sea
Essex

CLAPHAM 1982
Twinwoods Road
Clapham
Bedfordshire
01234 353633

Mr D R Tough
Hon. Secretary
Millbrook House
109 High Street
Riseley, Bedfordshire
MK44 1DF

Mr M Baker
Hon. Fixture Secretary
82 High Street
Oakley
Bedfordshire
MK43 7RH

CLARE COLLEGE 1908
Clare College Sports Ground
Bentley Rd
Cambridge

Mr H M Vann
Hon. Secretary
Clare College
Cambridge
CB2 1TL

For Attention Of:
Hon. Fixture Secretary
Clare College Sports Ground
Bentley Rd
Cambridge

CLEVELAND CONSTABULARY 1968
Police HQ,
Ladgate Lane
Middlesborough TS8 9EH
01642 301461

PC 848 Barfield
PC 848 Barfield
Hon. Secretary & Hon. Fixture Secretary
Cleveland Constabulary
c/o ARV Unit
Police HQ, PO Box 70
Ladgate Lane, Middlesborough TS8 9EH

COLWORTH HOUSE RFC
Sharbrook
Bedfordshire
MK44 1LQ

Mr A Reynolds
Hon. Secretary
21 Alburgh Close
Bedford
MK41 0HG

Mr J Ainley
Bourn Cottage
Wilstead Road
Elstow
Bedfordshire

CLIFTON COLLEGE
32 College Road
Clifton
Bristol BS8 3JH
0117 315 7000

Mr I Williams
Mr I Williams
Hon. Secretary & Hon. Fixture Secretary
Clifton College
School House, College Road
Clifton, Bristol BS8 3HY

CORPUS CHRISTI
Leckhampton
Cranmere Road
Cambridge
CB3 9BL
01223 353231

Hon. Secretary **Hon. Fixture Secretary**
Corpus Christi College Rugby Club
Cranmere Road
Cambridge
CB3 9BL

CORPUS CHRISTI & SOMERVILLE COLLEGES 1990
Corpus Christi College
Merton Street
Oxford
OX1 4JF
01865 276737

Mr J Barry
Hon. Secretary & **Hon. Fixture Secretary**
Corpus Christi & Somerville Colleges
Corpus Christi College
Merton Street, Oxford OX1 4JF

COSBY 1990
Victory Park
Park Road
Cosby, Leicester
0116 284 9244

Mr C W Elliott
Hon. Secretary & Hon. Fixture Secretary
Cosby
9 Wavertree Close
Cosby
Leicester LE9 1TNN

CRICKLADE 1992
VOWH Club
Cricklade High St.
Cricklade, Wilts
01793 750325

Mr P Gardiner
Hon. Secretary
Cricklade
4 Collett Place
Latton
Wiltshire SN6 6EH

Mr P Clements
Hon. Fixture Secretary
Cricklade
2 North Wall,
Cricklade
Wilts SN6 6DU

CUACO 1926
Cuaco Club
Copers Cope Road
Beckenham, Kent BR3 1RJ
020 8650 9902

Mr A P Wells
Hon. Secretary
CUACO
3rd Floor, CU House
69 Park Lane
Croydon, Surrey
CR9 1BG

For Attention Of:
Hon. Fixture Secretary
CUACO
Cuaco Club
Copers Cope Road
Beckenham, Kent
BR3 1RJ

CUMBRIA CONSTABULARY 1953
Winters Park
Penrith
Cumbria
CA11 8RG
01768 863151

Mr P D Hutton
Hon. Secretary
Cumbria Constabulary
24 Landsdown Close
Kendal
Cumbria LA9 7SB

Mr K Greenhow
Hon. Fixture Secretary
Cumbria Constabulary
County Police HQ
Carleton Hall
Penrith CA10 2AH

DARLINGTON RAILWAY ATHLETIC 1925
Brinkburn Road
Darlington
01325 468125

Mr T P Sanderson
Hon. Secretary
Darlington Railway Athletic
School House, Chapel Street
Street
Middleton-St-George
Darlington DL2 1DA

Mr T P Sanderson
Hon. Fixture Secretary
Darlington Railway Athletic
School House, Chapel
Middleton-St-George
Darlington DL2 1DA

DARWIN COLLEGE

The Hon Secretary
Hon. Secretary
Darwin College College Rugby Club
Darwin College
Cambridge CB3 9EU

DE LA SALLE (SHEFFIELD) 1956
De La Salle Association Club
(Behind Beauchief Hall)
Off Abbey Lane Sheffield
0114 236 7756

Mr J Halliday
Hon. Secretary
De La Salle (Sheffield)
Mayfield House
443 Greystones Rd
Sheffield S11 7BY

For Attention Of:
Hon. Fixture Secretary
De La Salle (Sheffield)
De La Salle Assoc. Club
(Behind Beauchief Hall)
Off Abbey Lane Sheffield

DERBYSHIRE CONSTABULARY 1926
Force Headquarters
Butterley Hall
Ripley, Derbyshire DE5 3RS
01773 570100

Mr I T Roe
Hon. Secretary
Derbyshire Constabulary
10 Otterburn Drive
Kedlaston Grange
Allestree, Derby DE22 2TJ

Mr I T Roe
Hon. Fixture Secretary
Derbyshire Constabulary
10 Otterburn Drive
Kedlaston Grange
Allestree, Derby DE22 2TJ

DEREHAM 1974
Moorgate Road
Dereham
Norfolk

Ms B Endresen
Hon. Secretary
Dereham
1 Bayfield Ave
Dereham
Norfolk NR19 1PH

DOVER COLLEGE 1870
Effingham Crescent
Dover
Kent CT17 9RX
01304 205969

Hon. Secretary
Dover College
Dover College
Effingham Crescent
Dover, Kent
CT17 9RX

For Attention Of:
Hon. Fixture Secretary
Dover College
Effingham Crescent
Dover
Kent
CT17 9RX

DOWNING COLLEGE
Long Road
Cambridge

Hon Secretary
Hon. Secretary
Downing College
College Rugby Club
Downing College
Cambridge CB3 9EU

For Attention Of:
Hon. Fixture Secretary
Downing College
Long Road
Cambridge

DOWTY 1961
Dowty Sports & Social Society
Staverton Division
Down Hatherley Lne, Gloucester GL2 9QD
01452 714567

Mrs G Blackwell
Hon. Secretary
Dowty
6 Kaybourne Crescent
Churchdown
Gloucestershire
GL3 2HL

Mr D Rose
Hon. Fixture Secretary
Dowty
7 Wren Terrace
Innsworth
Gloucester

DULWICH COLLEGE 1859
Dulwich Common
London SE21 7LD
020 8299 9237

Mr I Martin
Hon. Secretary
Dulwich College
Dulwich College
Dulwich
London

For Attention Of:
Hon. Fixture Secretary
Dulwich College
Dulwich Common
London
SE21 7LD

DURHAM SCHOOL 1850
Quarryheads Lane
Durham City DH1 4SZ
0191 386 4783

Mr P Gerrard
Hon. Secretary
Durham School
Quarryheads Lane
Durham City
DH1 4SZ

Mr P Gerrard
Hon. Fixture Secretary
Durham School
Quarryheads Lane
Durham City
DH1 4SZ

EASTBOURNE COLLEGE 1990
Old Wish Road
East Sussex
01323 21528

Master I/C Rugby
Hon. Secretary
Eastbourne College
Eastbourne College
Eastbourne
Sussex

For Attention Of:
Hon. Fixture Secretary
Eastbourne College
Old Wish Road
East Sussex

EAST PECKHAM & CAPEL (THE VILLAGERS) RFC 1977
Putlands Sport & Leisure Ctr
Mascalls Court Road
Paddock Wood, Kent TN12
01892 838290

Mr P Hale
Hon. Secretary & **Fixture Secretary**
East Peckham & Capel (The Villagers) RFC
52 Midsummer Road
Snodland, Kent ME6 5RP

ECCLES & ATTLEBOROUGH 1978
Gaymer's Ground
Attleborough
Norfolk NR17

Ms L Norman
Hon. Secretary
Eccles & Attleborough
Grove Lodge
Howard Street
Norwich, Norfolk
NR1 3RN

Mr N Young
Hon. Fixture Secretary
Eccles & Attleborough
48 Tedder Close,
Watton
Norfolk
IP25 6HX

EGOR 1978
Old Salians RFC
Clarendon Road
Sale, Manchester
0161 973 7250

Mr B Minor
Hon. Secretary
EGOR
45 Gorton Street
Peel Green
Eccles, Lancashire
M30 7LZ

Mr John Rogers
Hon. Fixture Secretary
EGOR
21 Dee Road
Astley
Manchester
M29 7HW

EMMANUEL COLLEGE
Wilberforce Road
Cambridge CB3 0EQ
01223 353961

Hon. Secretary
For Attention Of:
Hon. Secretary
Emmanuel College
Wilberforce Road
Cambridge CB3 0EQ

For Attention Of:
Hon. Fixture Secretary
Emmanuel College
Wilberforce Road
Cambridge
CB3 0EQ

EMANUEL SCHOOL 1910
Battersea Rise
London SW11 1HS
020 8874 4601

Hon. Secretary
Emanuel School
Emmanuel School
Wandsworth Common
London
SW11

For Attention Of:
Hon. Fixture Secretary
Emanuel School
Battersea Rise
London
SW11 1HS

ENGLAND FIRE SERVICE 1970

Mr Stuart Irwin
Hon. Secretary
England Fire Service
4 Linwood Grove
Leighton Buzzard
Bedfordshire LU7 8RP

ENTERTAINERS 1963
c/o Wimbledon RFC
Barham Road
London SW20 0ET
020 8946 3156

Mr C R Nicholas
Hon. Secretary & **Fixture Secretary**
Entertainers
68 Sutherland Grove
London
SW18 5QW

EPSOM COLLEGE 1870
Epsom
Surrey
KT17 4JQ
013727 24810

Mr A Wolstenholme
Hon. Secretary
Epsom College
Epsom
Surrey
KT17 4JQ

ESSEX POLICE
Coronation Park
Timson's Lane
Chelmsford, Essex
01245 452922

Hon. Secretary
Essex Police
c/o Sports Secretary,
Police HQ,
Springfield
Chelmsford
Essex CM2 1DA

Mr P Daly
Hon. Fixture Secretary
Essex Police
c/o Sports Secretary,
Police HQ, Springfield,
Chelmsford
Essex CM2 1DA

EXETER COLLEGE
Exeter College Sports Ground
Edgeway Road
New Marston, Oxford
01865 243710

Mr C Watts
Hon. Secretary
Exeter College,
Oxford
OX1 3DP

For Attention Of:
Hon. Fixture Secretary
Exeter College Sports Ground
Edgeway Road
New Marston, Oxford

FAIRBAIRN/CHIGWELL 1995
Salamander Sports Ground
Leigh Road
East Ham E6 2AS

Mr P Evans
Hon. Secretary & **Fixture Secretary**
Fairbairn/Chigwell
350 Ripple Road
Barking
Essex
IG11 7PQ

FAKENHAM 1982
Old Wells Road
Fakenham, Norfolk NR21 0BJ
01328 851007

Mr D J Swift
Hon. Secretary
Fakenham
19 North Park
Fakenham
Norfolk
NR21 9RG

Mr C Evans
Hon. Fixture Secretary
Fakenham
64 Boyd Avenue
Toftwood
East Dereham, Norfolk
NR19 1ND

FELIXSTOWE 1930
The Clubhouse,
Coronation Park
Felixstowe, Suffolk IP11 8LN
01394 270150

Mr D Cain
Hon. Secretary
Felixstowe
16 Berners Road
Felixstowe
Suffolk
IP11 7LF

Mr Ian Bignell
Hon. Fixture Secretary
Felixstowe
7 Cloncurry Gardens
Felixstowe
IP11 2QY

FERMAIN TAVERN 1981
Footes Lane
St Peter Port, Guernsey
01481 54590

Mr A Coulson
Hon. Secretary
Fermain Tavern
Jabulami
Les Petites Capelles
St Sampson, Guernsey
GY2 4GX

Mr M T P Cahill
Hon. Fixture Secretary
Fermain Tavern
Le Marecage
Le Marais
L'eree
G77 9LD

FITZWILLIAM COLLEGE 1966
93 Oxford Road
Cambridge CB4 3PH
01223 353382

Mr Richard Rowstron
Hon. Secretary
Fitzwilliam College
Fitzwilliam College
Cambridge CB3 ODG

For Attention Of:
Hon. Fixture Secretary
Fitzwilliam College
93 Oxford Road
Cambridge CB4 3PH

FIVE HORSESHOES 1982
Dry Leas
Marlow Road, Henley on Thames
Oxfordshire
01491 574499/641282

Mr G Cromack
Hon. Secretary
Five Horseshoes
4 Milton Close
Henley on Thames
Oxon RG9 1UJ

Mr P Cawthra
Hon. Fixture Secretary
Five Horseshoes
Beavers Lodge
Mill Road
Shiplake Oxon RG9 3LH

FORD LEAMINGTON RFC
Newbold Comyn
Leamington Spa

Mr J Cronin
Hon. Secretary
26 Alibone Close
Whitnash
Leamington
CV31 2SR

Mr E Newton
Hon. Fixture Secretary
86 Bury Road
Leamington Spa
Warwickshire
CV31 3HW

FOREST OLD BOYS 1990
Redingensians
Old Bath Road, Sonning
Reading, Berkshire
01189 695259

Mr T Walters
Hon. Secretary
Forest Old Boys
Azalea Cottage
Merryhill Green Lane
Winnersh, Wokingham, Berks
Berks

Mr T Walters
Hon. Fixture Secretary
Forest Old Boys
Azalea Cottage
Merryhill Green Lane
Winnersh, Wokingham,

GIRTON COLLEGE
Huntingdon Road
Cambridge CB3 0JG
01223 338999

Mr Andrew Holland
Hon. Secretary & **Fixture Secretary**
Girton College
Cambridge
CB3 0JG

GLOUCESTERSHIRE CONSTABULARY 1948
Dowty Rotol RFC
Down Hatherley Lane
Gloucester GL2 9QD
01452 714567

Mr A M Drummond
Hon. Secretary
Gloucestershire Constabulary
Constabulary
The Orchard
Green Lane
Churchdown, Gloucester
GL3 2LB

Mr P Haines
Hon. Fixture Secretary
Gloucestershire
Savannah
Church Road, Caincross
Stroud
GL5 4JE

GONVILLE & CAIUS COLLEGE
Gonville & Caius College
Cambridge
CB2 1TA
01223 332400

Hon Secretary
Hon. Secretary
Gonville & Caius College
College Rugby Club
Gonville & Caius College
Cambridge
CB2 1TA

For Attention Of:
Hon. Fixture Secretary
Gonville & Caius College
Gonville & Caius College
Cambridge
CB2 1TA

GREENWICH ACADEMICALS 1937
Kidbroke Lane
Eltham, London SE9
020 8850 1221

Mr H Davies
Hon. Secretary
Greenwich Academicals
29 Cumberland Avenue
Welling
Kent
DA16 2PT

Mr D Hoggan
Hon. Fixture Secretary
Greenwich Academicals
270 Bedonwell Road
Upper Belvedere
Kent
DA17 5NZ

GREATER MANCHESTER FIRE SERVICE 1965

Mr M E Higgins
Hon. Secretary & **Fixture Secretary**
Greater Manchester Fire Service
1 Langside Drive
Ladybridge, Bolton BL3 4US

GREATER MANCHESTER POLICE 1974
Police Club
Hough End Centre
Mauldeth Road West, Manchester M21 1SX
0161 856 1798

Sgt M Sutton
Hon. Secretary
Greater Manchester Police
GMP Rugby Section
Mottram Police Station
Atherton Grove, Mottram,
Hyde SK14 6JE

Hon. Fixture Secretary
Greater Manchester Police RFC
Police Club
Hough End Centre
Mauldesh Road West
Manchester
M21 1SX

HAILEYBURY 1863
Hertford Heath
Hertford SG13 7NU
01992 462352

Master I/C Rugby
Hon. Secretary
Haileybury
Haileybury College
Hertford

For Attention Of:
Hon. Fixture Secretary
Haileybury
Hertford Heath
Hertford SG13 7NU

HARTPURY COLLEGE 1970
Hartpury House
Nr Gloucester GL19 3BE
01452 700283(T) 700629 (F)

Mr S Holley
Hon. Secretary & **Fixture Secretary**
Hartpury College
Hartpury House
Hartpury College, Gloucester GL19 3BE

HARRODIANS 1912
Barn Elms, Queen Elizabeth Wlk
Barnes
London SW13 9SA
020 8876 7685

Mr P Kirby
Hon. Secretary & **Fixture Secretary**
Harrodians
53 Stanhope Gardens, London SW7 5RF

HERTFORDSHIRE FIRE & RESCUE SERVICE 1974
Hertford RFC
Hoe Lane
Ware, Hertfordshire SG12 9NZ

Mr J Horastead
Hon. Secretary
Herts Fire & Rescue Service
61 Acme Road
Watford
Herts WD2 5HQ

Mr C Strickland
Hon. Fixture Secretary
Herts Fire & Rescue Service
HFRS HQ
Old London Road
Hertford SG13 7LD

HERTFORDSHIRE POLICE 1949
Police HQ
Stanborough Road
Welwyn Garden City AL8 6XF
01992 533327

Mr R Larter
Hon. Secretary
Hertfordshire Police
Police Station
Baldock Road
Buntingford
Hertfordshire, SG9 9DB

Mr S Gibbs
Hon. Fixture Secretary
Hertfordshire Police
Youth Offending Team
c/o County Police Stn,
Ware Road, Hertford

HERTFORD COLLEGE
Catte Street
Oxford OX13BW
01865 279400

Mr P Clememts
Hon. Secretary
Hertford College
Catte street
Oxford OX1 3BW

Mr J Wilson
Hon. Fixture Secretary
Hertford College
Catte Street
Oxford OX1 3BW

HMP ACKLINGTON
HM Prison Acklington
Morpeth
Northumberland NE65 9XF
01670 760411 Ext 333

Mr P Sanderson
Hon. Secretary
HMP Acklington
10 Foxhill Close
Fallowfield Estate
Ashington, Northumberland

Mr B Taylor
Hon. Fixture Secretary
HMP Acklington
HMP Acklington
Morpeth
Northumberland

HMP GARTH 1989
H.M.Prison Garth
Ulnes Walton Lane
Leyland, Preston PR5 3NE
01772 622722

Mr T Probert
Hon. Secretary & **Fixture Secretary**
H M Prison Garth
Ulnes Walton Lane
Leyland, Preston PR5 3NE

HMP LINCOLN 1989
HMP Lincoln
Greetwell Road
Lincoln LN2 4BD
01522 533633 Ext 401

Mr C K Lewis
Hon. Secretary & **Fixture Secretary**
HMP Lincoln
PE Dept, HMP Lincoln
Greetwell Road
Lincoln LN2 4BD

HM PRISON SERVICE 1976
HM Prison Service College
Newbold Revel, Nr Rugby
Warwickshire
01788 832666

Mr S N Sporcic
Hon. Secretary
HM Prison Service
HMP Birmingham
Winson Green Rd
Birmingham B18 4AS

Mr R Sawbridge
Hon. Fixture Secretary
HM Prison Service
c/o H M Prison Leicester
Welford Rd,
Leicester

HODDESDON WHITE SWANARIANS 1991
King George v Playing Fields
Wormley
Hertfordshire EN11 8TN

Mr S Stagg
Hon. Secretary
Hoddesdon White Swanarians
Swanarians
10 Briscoe Rd
Hoddesdon
Herts EN11 9DQ

Mr P Reast
Hon. Fixture Secretary
Hoddesdon White

15 Stafford Drive
Broxbourne
Herts EN10 7JT

HOMERTON COLLEGE
Hills Road
Cambridge CB2 2PH
01223 507235/6

Mr A S Dinatar
Hon. Secretary & **Fixture Secretary**
Homerton College
College Rugby Club
Homerton College
Cambridge
CB2 2PH

HONDA 1990
Supermarine Sport/Social Club
Highworth Rd, South Marston
Swindon, Wiltshire SN3 4TZ
01793 824828

Mr T Lee
Hon. Secretary
Honda
c/o Honda Engineering Europe
Highworth Road, South Marston
Swindon, Wiltshire
SN3 4TZ

Mr N Harper
Hon. Fixture Secretary
Honda
385 Cricklade Road
Goarse Hill
Swindon
SN2 2AQ

HUGHES HALL

Hon Secretary
Hughes Hall
College Rugby Club
Hughes Hall
Cambridge CB1 2EW

HUMBERSIDE POLICE 1961
Inglemire Lane Police Club
Inglemire Lane
Hull, East Yorks
01482 856954

Mr J Harris
Hon. Secretary
Humberside Police
3 Stewart Garth
Cottingham
Police St
East Yorkshire HU16 5YQ

Mr P Snowden
Hon. Fixture Secretary
Humberside Police
c/o Humberside Police
F.I.B, Queens G'dens

Hull

IMBER COURT 1947
Imber Court Sports Club
Ember Lane
East Molesey, Surrey KT8 0BT
020 8398 1267/6609

Mr J Bailey
Hon. Secretary
Imber Court
39 Hurstdene Avenue
Staines
Middlesex TW18 1JG

Mr J Bowens
Hon. Fixture Secretary
Imber Court
10 Anette Way
Rickmansworth
WD3 2DA

JERSEY UNITED BANKS 1969
Grainville Playing Fields
St Saviour's Hill
St Saviour, Jersey JE2 7LG
01534 34350

Mr S Young
Hon. Secretary
Jersey United Banks
La rue de la Vallee
St Mary
Jersey JE3 3DL

Mr A Cotton
Hon. Fixture Secretary
Jersey United Banks
c/o Geest Limited
31 The Parade
St Helier, Jersey JE2 3QQ

JERSEY POLICE 1998
Granville
St Saviour
Jersey JE2 7LG
01534 34350

Mr D A Joshua
Hon. Secretary
Jersey Police
Rouge Bouillon Police Station
Station
St Helier, Jersey
Channel Islands
JE4 8ZZ

Mr S Cross
Hon. Fixture Secretary
Jersey Police
Rouge Bouillon Police
St Helier, Jersey
Channel Islands
JE4 8ZZ

JESUS COLLEGE
Jesus College
Cambridge CB5 8BL
01223 339339

Mr Chris Trimble
Hon. Secretary & **Fixture Secretary**
Jesus College
Cambridge CB5 8BL

JESUS COLLEGE 1890
Jesus College
Oxford OX1 3DW
01865 279700

Mr M Benjamin
Hon. Secretary
Jesus College,
Oxford 0X1 3DW

KEBLE COLLEGE
University Parks
Oxford OX1 3PG
01865 272727

Mr S Craig
Hon. Secretary
Keble College
Keble College
University Parks
Oxford

For Attention Of:
Hon. Fixture Secretary
Keble College
University Parks
Oxford
OX1 3PG

KEW OCCASIONALS 1988
Richmond Athletic Ground
Kew Foot Road
Richmond TW9 2SS
020 8940 0397

Mr R Clark
Hon. Secretary & **Fixture Secretary**
Kew Occasionals
5 Maze Road
Kew, Richmond
Surrey
TW9 3DA

KING EDWARD'S SCHOOL, BIRMINGHAM 1875
Edgbaston Park Road
Birmingham B15 2UA
0121 472 1672

Hon. Secretary
King Edward's School, Birmingham
King Edward's School
Edgbaston Park Road
Birmingham 15

For Attention Of:
Hon. Fixture Secretary
K E School, Birmingham
Edgbaston Park Road
Birmingham
B15 2UA

KING'S COLLEGE

Mr J Wasey
Hon. Secretary & **Fixture Secretary**
King's College
Cambridge
CB2 1ST

LADY MARGARET HALL & TRINITY COLLEGE
Marston Road
Oxford

Mr G Samual-Gibbon
Hon. Secretary
L M Hall & Trinity College
Lady Margaret Trinity
Marston Rd
Oxford

For Attention Of:
Hon. Fixture Secretary
L M Hl & Trinity College
Marston Road
Oxford

LEICESTERSHIRE CONSTABULARY 1951
c/o Syston RFC
Barkby Road
Queniborough, Leicester
LE7 3FE
0116 260 1223

Mr T Perridge
Hon. Secretary
Leicestershire Constabulary
Constabulary
Leics. Constabulary HQ.
St. John's
Narborough, Leics
LE3 5BX

Mr C Cary
Hon. Fixture Secretary
Leicestershire
Syston Police Station
Melton Road
Syston, Leics

LEYHILL 1988
HMP Leyhill
Wotton-under-Edge
Gloucester GL12 8BT
01454 260681 Ext 332

Mr P.E.O.T Probert
Hon. Secretary & **Fixture Secretary**
Leyhill
H.M.Prison Leyhill
Wooton-under-Edge
Glouscestershire

LEYS HIGH SCHOOL 1875
Woodrow Drive
Redditch
Worcestershire
01527 23088

Master I/C Rugby
Hon. Secretary
Leys High School
Leys School
Cambridge

For Attention Of:
Hon. Fixture Secretary
Leys High School
Woodrow Drive
Redditch
Worcestershire

LFB SOUTHERN COMMAND (MOOSEHEAD) 1986
Fire Station
Sunbury Street
London
SE18 5LU

Mr C Knight
Hon. Secretary
LFB Southern Command (Moosehead)
29 Cyclamen Road
Swanley
Kent BR8 8HH

Mr A Buss
Hon. Fixture Secretary
LFB Southern
Command (Moosehead)
52 Bransdale Crescent
Orpington
Kent

LINCOLNSHIRE POLICE 1958
Police HQ, Deep Dale Lane
Nettleham
Lincoln LN5 7PH
01522 532222

Mr C Moon
Hon. Secretary & **Fixture Secretary**
Lincolnshire Police
5 Manor Lane
Welton
Lincoln LN2 3JQ

LINCOLN COLLEGE
Bartlemas Close
Oxford OX4 2AA
01865 242357

Mr C Houston
Hon. Secretary
Lincoln College
Lincoln College
Bartlemas Close
Oxford OX4 2AA

Mr J Wynne
Hon. Fixture Secretary
Lincoln College
Lincoln College
Turl Street
Oxford OX1 3DR

LITTLEHEY 1988
HMP Littlehey
Perry
Huntingdon, Cambridgeshire PE18 0SR
01480 812202 Ext 248/249

Mr A P Curtis
Hon. Secretary & **Fixture Secretary**
Littlehey
6 Riverside Way
Islip, Kettering
Northamptonshire NN14 3LF

LLOYDS TSB 1913
Lloyds T.S.B.Sports Club
59 Lorne Gardens
Shirley, Croydon CR0 7RZ
020 8656 3901

Mr B Brazier
Hon. Secretary
Lloyds TSB
2 Crushes Close
Hutton
Brentwood, Essex
CM13 1PB

Mr P Wedderspoon
Hon. Fixture Secretary
Lloyds TSB
4 Lucerne Court
Abbey Park
Brackley Road
Beckenham BR3 1RB

LOGGERHEADS 1976
Sundorne Castle Ground
Shrewsbury
01743 53380

Mr R Macken
Hon. Secretary & **Fixture Secretary**
7 Raby Crescent,Longden
Road, Shrewsbury
Shropshire SY3 7JN

LONDON MANX 1987
Westminster Lodge
St Albans
Hertfordshire

Mr C J P Haslam
Hon. Secretary
Pennine Lodge
24 Gerard Avenue, Thorley
Bishops Stortford, Herts
CM23 4DU

Mr R White
Hon. Fixture Secretary
Trees
Wycke Lane, Tollesbury
Maldon, Essex

LONDON FIRE BRIGADE NW AREA 1989
Northolt RFC
Cayton Green Park, Cayton Road
Greenford, Middlesex UB6 8BJ
020 8813 1701

Mr K A Heymer
Hon. Secretary
London Fire Brigade NW Area
57 Manor Way
North Harrow
Middlesex HA2 6BZ

Mr Padraig McKeon
Hon. Fixture Secretary
London Fire Brigade
NW Area
16 Brinsley Road
Harrow Weald HA3 5HY

MAGDALENE COLLEGE
St John's Sports Field
Queens Road
Cambridge CB3 OAG
01223 508880

Hon. Secretary
Magdalene College
College Rugby Club
Magdalene College
Cambridge CB3 0AG

Hon. Fixture Secretary
Magdalene College
St John's Sports Field
Queens Road
Cambridge CB3 OAG

MAGDALEN COLLEGE
Marston Road
Oxford OX1 4AU
01865 247358

Mr M Blayford-Baker
Hon. Secretary
Magdalen College
Marston Road
Oxford OX1 4AU

Mr V Kashyap
Hon. Fixture Secretary
Magdalen College
Oxford
OX1 4AU

MALTON AND NORTON RUFC
The Club House
The Gannock
Old Malton Road
Malton
YO17 0EY

Mr W Laider
Hon. Secretary & **Fixture Secretary**
Ashdale
8 Second Avenue
Beacon Park Second Avenue
Pickering
North Yorkshire YO18 8AH

MANCHESTER YMCA 1903
The Hollies, Mersey Meadows,
Mersey Road, Didsbury
Manchester
M20 2GB

Mr Kennedy
Hon. Secretary & **Fixture Secretary**
Manchester YMCA
14 Beeston Close
Sharples
Bolton BL1 7RT

MARLBOROUGH COLLEGE 1861
Marlborough
Wiltshire SN8 1PA
01672 515511

Mr J E Patching
Hon. Secretary & **Fixture Secretary**
Marlborough College
Elmhurst Boarding House
Bath Road, Marlborough SN8 1PA

MENWITH HILL 1982
Menwith Hill Station
Harrogate
North Yorkshire HG3 2RF
01423 777788

Mr Steven Wilhelm
Hon. Secretary
Menwith Hill
RAF Menwith Hill
Box 494
North Yorkshire
HG3 2RF

Mr Jan Swenson
Hon. Fixture Secretary
Menwith Hill
Sports and Fittness Centre
RAF Menwith Hill
North Yorkshire
HG3 2RF

MERCHANT TAYLORS' SCHOOL (CROSBY) 1871
Crosby
Liverpool, Merseyside L23 0QP
0151 928 3618

For Attention Of: **Hon. Secretary**
Hon. Fixture Secretary

Merchant Taylors' School (Crosby)
Crosby
Liverpool, Merseyside L23 0QP

MERCHANT TAYLORS' SCHOOL (LONDON) 1859
Sandy Lodge Lane
Northwood
Middlesex HA6 2HT

For Attention Of: **Hon. Secretary**
Hon. Fixture Secretary

Merchant Taylors' School (Lon)
Sandy Lodge Lane
Northwood, Middlesex HA6 2HT

MERSEYSIDE FIRE BRIGADE
Newbrigton RUFC
Reeds Lane
New Brighton Wirral L46 3RH
0151 677 1873

Mr S Smith
Hon. Secretary
Merseyside Fire Brigade
4a The Parade, Wood Rd
Halewood
Liverpool
L26 1UZ

For Attention Of:
Hon. Fixture Secretary
Merseyside Fire Brigade
Newbrigton RUFC
Reeds Lane
New Brighton Wirral
L46 3RH

MERSEYSIDE POLICE 1960
Police Sports Ground
Riversdale Road
Aiburth, Liverpool
0151 427 2208

Sgt E Sheppard
Hon. Secretary
Merseyside Police
38 Lynmouth Road
Aigburth
Merseyside L17 6AW

Mr A Doyle
Hon. Fixture Secretary
Merseyside Police
c/o Walton Lane Police Stn
Liverpool
L5 6RB

MERTON AND MANSFIELD COLLEGES
Manor Road
Oxford
01865 276289

Mr R Amlot
Hon. Secretary
Mansfield College
Oxford OX1 3TF

Mr Damian King
Hon. Fixture Secretary
Mansfield College
Oxford OX1 3TF

METROPOLITAN POLICE (CHIGWELL) 1943
Met Police Sports Club
Chigwell Hall, High Road
Chigwell, Essex IG7 6BD
020 8500 2735

Mr D Fleming
Hon. Secretary
108 Swanshope
Loughton
Essex IG10 2NB

Mr J Harding
Hon. Fixture Secretary
19 Amanda Close
Chigwell
Essex IG7

MILL HILL SCHOOL
The Ridgeway
Mill Hill, London NW7 1QS
020 8959 1176

For Attention Of: **Hon. Secretary**
Hon. Fixture Secretary

Mill Hill School
The Ridgeway
Mill Hill, London NW7 1QS

MONTELL CARRINGTON RUFC
Carrington Works
Urmston
Manchester M31 4AJ

Mr A Kelly
Hon. Secretary & **Hon. Fixture Secretary**
The Farmers Arms
Longley Lane
Northerndon
Manchester M22 4JR

NESTLE ROWNTREE RFC
Mille Crux Sports Ground
Nestle UK
Haxby Road
York YO1 1XY

Hon. Secretary
Nestle Rowntree RFC
Mille Crux Sports Ground
Nestle UK
Haxby Road
York YO1 1XY

Mr G Lavender
Hon. Fixture Secretary
Nestle Rowntree RFC
52 Wilton Rise
Holgate
York

NEW COLLEGE & TEMPLETON
St Cross Road
Holywell
Oxford OX1 3BN

Mr C Houghton
Hon. Secretary
New College & Templeton
New College
St Cross Rd, Holywell
Oxford
OX1 3BN

For Attention Of:
Hon. Fixture Secretary
New College & Templeton
St Cross Road
Holywell
Oxford
OX1 3BN

NEWLAND PARK/BUCKS COLLEGE 1955
Gorelands Lane
Chalfont St Giles
Buckinghamshire HP8 4AD
01494 603084

Miss M Tremlin
Hon. Secretary
Newland Park/Bucks College
Newlands Park,Gorelands Lane
Chalfont St Giles
Bucks
HP8 4AD

Mr R Brooks
Hon. Fixture Secretary
New Parks
44 Bateman Road
New Parks Estate
Leicester
LE3 9HD

NEW PARKS 1968
New Parks Community College
St Oswalds Road
New Parks, Leicester
0116 287 2115

Mr T Smith
Hon. Secretary
New Parks
10 The Birds Nest Avenue
New Parks Estate
Leicester LE3 9NB

NORTH MIDLANDS FOOTBALL UNION

Mr C S Potts
Hon. Secretary
North Midlands F. U.
17 Ellesmere Court,
Newport
Shropshire
TF10 7SD

Mr D I Robins
Hon. Fixture Secretary
North Midlands F. U.
Flat 4 Halas House
Holywell Road
Malvern Worcs
WR14 4LE

NORTHAMPTONSHIRE POLICE 1966
NCC Sports & Social Club
Wootton Hall Park
Mereway, Northampton
01604 700934

Sgt A M Collins
Hon. Secretary
Northamptonshire Police
Traffics Ops, Mere Way
Northampton NN4 8BH

NORTHUMBRIA POLICE
North Road
Ponteland
Northumberland
01661 72555 Ext 4306

Sgt J Chappell
Hon. Secretary
Northumbria Police
Cedar House
61A Dunsgreen
Ponteland, Newcastle-Upon-Tyne
NE20 9EJ

PC A Park
Hon. Fixture Secretary
Northumbria Police
7 Axwell Park Road,
Blaydon
Tyne & Wear
NE21 5NR

NORTH YORKSHIRE POLICE 1974
c/o York Railway Inst RUFC
New Lane, Acomb
York
01904 798930

Mr S Smith
Hon. Secretary & **Fixture Secretary**
North Yorkshire Police
7 Whitehouse Dale
Pulleyn Drive
York YO2 2EB

OAKLANDS COLLEGE 1921
Oaklands Campus
Hatfield Road, St Albans
Hertfordshire AL4 0JA
01727 737000

Mr L Brown
Hon. Secretary & **Fixture Secretary**
Oaklands College
Oaklands Campus, Hatfield Rd
St Albans, Herts AL4 0JA

OLD AMPLEFORDIANS 1985
KCS Old Boys Rugby Club
Arthur Rd,Off West Barnes Lane
Motspur Park, London SW20
020 8336 2512

Mr Nick Dumbell
Hon. Secretary
Old Amplefordians
25 Greencroft Gardens
Hampstead
Lane
NW6 3LN

For Attention Of:
Hon. Fixture Secretary
Old Amplefordians
KCS Old Boys Rugby Club
Arthur Rd,Off West Barnes
Motspur Park, London
SW20

OLD DOWEGIANS 1956
Douai School
Upper Woolhampton
Reading, Berkshire RG7 5TH
01635 862735

Mr A Foster
Hon. Secretary
Old Dowegians
Chardith, Station Road
Gomshall, Guildford
Surrey
GU5 9LQ

J D Dukney
Hon. Fixture Secretary
Old Dowegians
6 Chisbury
Marlborough
Wiltshire
SN8 3JA

OLD EPSOMIAN 1963

Mr I R Edmond
Hon. Secretary
Old Epsomian
Little Orchards
Prince of Wales Road
Outwood, Surrey
RH1 5QU

Mr S T Schlaefli
Hon. Fixture Secretary
Old Epsomian
40 Broadhurst Gardens
Reigate
Surrey
RG2 8AW

OLDHAM COLLEGE (VETS) 1964
Tudor Lodge
Victoria Avenue East
Moston, Manchester M10 9SH
0161 682 9234

Mr J K McGuire
Hon. Secretary
Oldham College (Vets)
5 Gleneagles Avenue
Hopwood
Heywood, Lancashire
OL10 2BZ

Mr M Garner
Hon. Fixture Secretary
Oldham College (Vets)
21 Stansfield Street
Failsworth
Manchester
M35 9FA

OLD JOHNIANS 1960
Oaken Lane
Claygate
Surrey

Mr C D J Pearce
Hon. Secretary
C/o Pinecroft
The Barton
Cobham
Surrey KT11 2NJ

Mr D Devine
Hon. Fixture Secretary
Old Johnians
135e New Kings Road
Fulham
London SW6 4SL

OLD MALVERNIAN 1989
c/o Staines RUFC
Felthamhill Road
Feltham, Middlesex
020 8890 3051
For Attention Of:
Hon. Secretary
Hon. Fixture Secretary
Old Malvernian, c/o Staines RUFC
Felthamhill Road, Feltham, Middlesex

OLD NEWBURIANS 1991
St Bartholomews School
Andover Road
Newbury, Berkshire RG14 6JP
01635 521255

Mr C O Hobbs
Hon. Secretary & **Fixture Secretary**
Old Newburians
19 York Road
Newbury
Berkshire RG14 7NJ

OLD PALMERIANS RUFC
Palmers College
Chadwell Road
Grays, Essex

Mr A Platt
Hon. Secretary
17 McLoud Close
Grays
Essex
RM17 5RD

Mr A Cresswell
Hon. Fixture Secretary
16 Parkstone Road
Cricket Hill
Felixtowe
Suffolk IP11 8NF

OLD PERSEAN 1949
The Perse School for Boys
Hills Road
Cambridge CB2 2QF

Mr P Harvey
Hon. Secretary & **Fixture Secretary**
Old Persean
Rosemary Cottage
49 Woodditton Road
Newmarket, Suffolk CB8 9BQ

SALIANS RFC
Rockwood
Clarendon Crescent
Sale, Cheshire

Mr J Tracey
Hon. Secretary
12a Poolcroft
Sale
Cheshire
M33 2LF

Mr N Foster
Hon. Fixture Secretary
Flat 8, 21 Clyde Road
West Didsbury
Manchester
M20 2NJ

OLD STONEHAMIANS 1961
Berkshire Sports/Social Club
Sonning Lane
Reading, Berkshire
01189 691340

Mr R J Eccleston
Hon. Secretary & **Fixture Secretary**
Old Stonehamians
99 Blenheim Road
Caversham Heights
Reading, Berkshire
RG4 7RP

OLD STANDFORDIANS 1984
Luynes Riseane
Buntingford, Hertfordshire
01763 273062

Mr E T Moody
Hon. Secretary
Old Standfordians
522 Hatfield Road
St Albans
Hertfordshire AL4 0SX

Mr A Watson
Hon. Fixture Secretary
Old Standfordians
37 Downhall Ley
Buntingford
Herts SG99 9JT

OLD WELLINGBURIAN 1981
Sports Ground
The Embankment
Wellingborough, Northants NN8 1LD
01933 225922

Mr N J Fry
Hon. Secretary
Old Wellingburian
25 St. Mary's Road
Kettering
Northants
NN15 7BP

Mr M Thompson
Hon. Fixture Secretary
Old Wellingburian
25 Neath Avenue
Bedford
MK41 0RJ

ONLEY PARK 1972
HMY01
Onley
Rugby CV23 8AP
01788 522022 Ext 333/332

Mr N T Mapletoft
Hon. Secretary
Onley Park
10 Avon Street,
Clifton, Rugby
Warwickshire CV23 ODQ

Hon. Fixture Secretary
Onley Park
c/o HMY01 Onley
Rugby
CV23 8AP

ORIEL COLLEGE
Oriel Avenue
Gorleston, Gt Yarmouth
Norfolk NR31 7JJ
01865 726440

Mr J Schad
Hon. Secretary
Oriel College
Bartlemas Farm
Cowley Rd
Oxford

Mr C Nelson
Hon. Fixture Secretary
Oriel College
Oriel College
Oxford
OX1 4EW

ORWELL 1969

Mr S R J Bevan
Hon. Secretary
Orwell
34 Princethorpe Rd
Ipswich
Suffolk
IP3 8NX
01473 726134

Mr D Botwright
Hon. Fixture Secretary
Orwell
12 Vermont Road
Ipswich
Suffolk
IP4 2SR

OUNDLE SCHOOL
Oundle
Peterborough PE8 4EN
01832 73536

Master in Charge
Hon. Secretary
Oundle School
Oundle
Peterborough
PE8 4EN

Mr J Olver
Hon. Fixture Secretary
The Mill
Mill Land
Tallington
Lincolnshire

OXFORD UNIVERSITY 1869
Jackdaw Lane
Off Iffley Road
Oxford OX4 1EQ
01865 432000

Mr D J R Cole
Hon. Secretary & **Hon. Fixture Secretary**
Oxford University
Lavender Hill
6 Braybrook Close, Oxford OX7 4NT

OXTED 1983
Holland Rd
Hurst Green
Oxted
01883 717468

Mr N Madgett
Hon. Secretary & **Fixture Secretary**
Oxted
69 Hurst Green Road
Oxted, Surrey RH8 9AJ

PELHAMIANS
Taunton Avenue
Raynes Park
London SW20
020 894683855

Mr J Nichols
Hon. Secretary & **Fixture Secretary**
Pelhamians
28 Presburg Road
New Malden, Surrey KT3 5AH

PEMBROKE COLLEGE
Pembroke College
Cambridge CB2 1RF
01223 359543

Mr R Macfarlane
Hon. Secretary & **Fixture Secretary**
Pembroke College
College Rugby Club
Pembroke College, Cambridge CB2 1RF

PEMBROKE COLLEGE
Oxford OX1 1DW
01865 276444

Mr M J Clayton-Stead
Hon. Secretary & **Fixture Secretary**
Pembroke College, Oxford OX1 1DW

PETERHOUSE
Bentley Road
Cambridge CB2 1RD
01223 338200

Mr A Smith
Hon. Secretary
Peterhouse
Cambridge CB2 1RD

Mr A Smith
Hon. Fixture Secretary
Peterhouse
Cambridge CB2 1RD

PHOENIX GAS 1985
British Gas Eastern SSC
Whitewebbs Lane
Enfield, Middlesex
01992 760716

Mr W K Shorter
Hon. Secretary
8 Thatchers Drive
Elmstead Market
Colchester, Essex
CO7 7YE

Mr P Clarke
Hon. Fixture Secretary
British Gas
Hertford Reporting Centre
Marshgate Drive, Hertford

PHYLLOSANS 1969

Mr A E Walsham
Hon. Secretary
Phyllosans
The New House
Queens St
Hook Norton, Oxon OX15 5PJ

Mr S Samra
Hon. Fixture Secretary
Phyllosans
7 Granton Avenue
Upminster
Essex RM14 2RX

PILNING 1972
Beach Road
Severn Beach
Bristol
014545 633549

Mr J R Cox
Hon. Secretary
Pilning
Oregon, Ableton Lane,
Severn Beach
Nr Bristol BS35 4PP

Mr S Hinksman
Hon. Fixture Secretary
Pilning
16 Station Road,
Pilning
Nr Bristol BS35 4JP

PLYMSTOCK 1988
Staddiscombe Playing Fields
Staddiscombe Road
Plymstock, Plymouth

Ms L Stewart
Hon. Secretary
Laburnham House
Fields
4 Woodland Avenue
Elburton, Plymouth
PL9 8JE

For Attention Of:
Hon. Fixture Secretary
Staddiscombe Playing
Staddiscombe Road
Plymstock, Plymouth

POTTON 1978
2nd Meadow
Henry Smith Playing Fields
Brook End, Potton
01767 261433

Mr P Carroll
Hon. Secretary
1 Catherine Close
Potton
Nr Sandy, Beds SG19 2PR

Mr G Corrin
Hon. Fixture Secretary
22 Mill Lane
Potton
Beds, SG19 2PG

PREP SCHOOL WANDERERS 1987
Wellington College
Crowthorne
Berkshire RG45 7PU
01344 772262

Mr M Farrow
Hon. Secretary
Orchard Cottage
Station Road
Cookham, Berkshire
SL6 9BU

Mr G Ruck
Hon. Fixture Secretary
Dorton House School
Seal Drive
Seal, Nr Sevenoaks, Kent

PRESCOT-RAINHILL 1949
Haresfinch Social Club
Haresfinch Road
St Helens, Merseyside

Mr K O'Keefe
Hon. Secretary
Prescot-Rainhill
39 French St
Toll Bar, St Helens
Merseyside

For Attention Of:
Hon. Fixture Secretary
Prescot-Rainhill
Haresfinch Social Club
Haresfinch Road
St Helens, Merseyside

PRUDHOE & STOCKSFIELD RFC
Stocksfield Cricket & Football
Stocksfield
Northumberland NE43 7NN

Mr P Jones
Hon. Secretary
152 New Ridley Road
Stocksfield
Northumberland
NE43 7EH

Mr J Reed
Hon. Fixture Secretary
Warden Flat
1 Gill Street
Newcastle upon Tyne
NE4 8BH

PRUDENTIAL IBIS 1993
Prudential Ibis Club
Scours Lane
Reading, Berkshire RG3 6AY
01189 424130

Mr P J Bishop
Hon. Secretary
Prudential Ibis
16 The Fells
Tilehurst
Reading, Berkshire
RG31 5XY

Mr G McCoy
Hon. Fixture Secretary
Prudential Ibis
27 Shaftesbury Road
Reading
Berkshire

QUEENS' COLLEGE
Queens College Playing Grounds
Barton Road
Cambridge
01223 335511

Mr Freddie New
Hon. Secretary
Queens' College
Queens College
Grounds
Cambridge
CB3 9ET

For Attention Of:
Hon. Fixture Secretary
Queens' College
Queens College Playing
Barton Road
Cambridge

QUEEN'S COLLEGE
Abingdon Road
Oxford
01865 242129

Mr A Parsons
Hon. Secretary
Queen's College RFC
Queen's College
OX1 4AW

Mr E Slim
Hon. Fixture Secretary
Queens College RFC
Queen's College
OX1 4AW

RACAL DECCA RFC
Raccal Decca S & S Club
Kingston Road
Tolworth
Surrey KT5 9NT

Mr D Donald
Hon. Secretary
4 Donalds Wood Gardens
Tolworth
Surrey
KT5 9NP

Hon. Fixture Secretary
Raccal Decca RFC
Raccal Decca S & S Club
Kingston Road
Tolworth
Surrey KT5 9NT

RAMSEY IOM 1981
New Ground,
Mooragh Promenade
Ramsey, Isle of Man

Mr D M Christian
Hon. Secretary
Ramsey IOM
Beaconsfield Cottage
Bowring Road
Ramsey, Isle Of Man
IM8 3EV

Mr Tommy Callister
Hon. Fixture Secretary
Ramsey IOM
3 Chapel Close
Ballaugh
Isle of Man

READING SCHOOL
Reading
Berkshire
01189 61406

Hon. Secretary
Reading School
Reading School
Reading, Berkshire

For Attention Of:
Hon. Fixture Secretary
Reading School
Reading, Berkshire

READING WEST INDIANS 1975
Redingensians Sports Ground
Old Bath Road, Sonning
Nr Reading, Berkshire
RG4 0TQ
0118 969 5259

Mr K H Hinds
Hon. Secretary
Reading West Indians
243 Waverley Road
Reading
Berkshire RG30 2QH

Mr J R Bell
Hon. Fixture Secretary
Reading West Indians
36 Lismore Close
Woodley, Nr Reading
BerkshireRG5 3RT

ROBINSON COLLEGE
Cambridge CB3 9AN
01223 741270

For the attn. of
Hon. Secretary
Hon. Fixture Secretary

Robinson College
College Rugby Club
Robinson College
Cambridge CB3 9AN

RUGBY SCHOOL 1823
The Senior Common Room
20-22 Horton Crescent
Rugby, Warwickshire CV22 5DJ
01788 578006

Mr R D R Ray
Hon. Secretary & **Fixture**
Rugby School
Flat 2, 12 Hillmorton Road
Rugby, Warwickshire CV25 4DR

RUGBY WELSH 1936
Bakehouse Lane
Rugby
Warwickshire CV21 2DB
01788 565605

Mr K E Mills
Hon. Secretary
Rugby Welsh
18 Beatty Drive
Bilton, Rugby
Warwickshire CV22 7ET

Mr M James
Hon. Fixture Secretary
Rugby Welsh
17 Watson Road
Chapelfields
Coventry CV5 8EW

SEDGEFIELD 1985
Sedgefield Community College
Sedgefield, Stockton-on-Tees
Cleveland
01740 621097

Mr N Hetherington
Hon. Secretary
Sedgefield
8 West End
Sedgefield, Stockton-on-Tees
Cleveland TS21 2BS

Mr S Bintoff
Hon. Fixture Secretary
Sedgefield
3 Pineridge Avenue
Sedgefield
Cleveland TS21 3EF

SELWYN COLLEGE 1882
Fulbrooke Road
Cambridge CB3 14G
01223 741201

Mr C Dale
Hon. Secretary
Selwyn College
Selwyn College
Cambridge
CB39 DLE

For Attention Of:
Hon. Fixture Secretary
Selwyn College
Fulbrooke Road
Cambridge
CB3 14G

SHADWELL 1993
Aveley Sports And Social Club
Purfleet Road
Aveley, South Ockendon, Essex RM15 4DT
01708 863611

Mr S Fryatt
Hon. Secretary & Fixture Secretary
Shadwell
104 Hornchurch Road
Hornchurch, Essex RM11 1DL

SHEPSHED 1987
Hind Leys College
Forest Street, Shepshed
Loughborough, Leicestershire
01509 503592

Mr J Ryan
Hon. Secretary
Shepshed
23a Chapel Street
Shepshed
Leicestershire LE12 9AF

Mr R Short
Hon. Fixture Secretary
Shepshed
Hind Leys Cottage
Forest Street, Shepshed
Leicestershire

SHERBORNE SCHOOL 1846
Sherborne
Dorset
01935 81891

For Attention Of:
Hon. Secretary
Sherborne School,
Sherborne,
Dorset DT9 3AP

Hon. Fixture Secretary
Sherborne School,
Sherborne,
Dorset DT9 3AP

SHOTTERY 1985
Shottery Field
Shottery Road
Stratford Upon Avon

Mr D Evans
Hon. Secretary
Shottery
21 Oak Lane, Tiddington
Stratford upon Avon
Warwickshire CV37 7BU

Mr S Burford
Hon. Fixture Secretary
Shottery
20 Valetta Way
Wellesbourne
Warwicks

SIDNEY SUSSEX COLLEGE
Cambridge
CB2 3HU

Mr M Petevinos
Hon. Secretary
Sidney Sussex College
College Rugby Club
Sidney Sussex College
Cambridge CB2 3HU

For Attention Of:
Hon. Fixture Secretary
Sidney Sussex College
CB2 3HU

SNOWDOWN COLLIERY WELFARE 1937
Snowdown Colliery Welfare Recreation
Aylesham
Canterbury, Kent
01304 840278

Mr D Price
Hon. Secretary
Snowdown C.W.
157 Cornwallis Avenue
Aylesham
Canterbury
Kent CT3 3HJ

Mr I Prosser
Hon. Fixture Secretary
Snowdown C.W.
7 Dorman Avenue South,
Aylesham
Canterbury,
Kent CT3 3AB

SOUTHAMPTON POST OFFICE 1985
Test Park Playing Fields
Lower Brownhill Road
Southampton SO16 9HE
02380 737777

Mr P F Evans
Hon. Secretary & Fixture Secretary
Southampton Post Office
68 Northlands Road, Romsey, Hants SO51 5SE

SOUTHERN NOMADS 1982
King Williams College
Castletown, Isle of Man

Mr D Stewart
Hon. Secretary
Southern Nomads
Bay View House
Victoria St., Porterin,
Isle of Man IM9 6LD

Mr R Hirst
Hon. Fixture Secretary
Southern Nomads
Beulah
Fistard Road, Port St Mary
Isle of Man IM9 5HE

SOUTH LIVERPOOL 1963
Dunlop Sports and Social Club
Speke Hall Avenue
Speke, Liverpool L24
0151 486 1588

Mr L Sherrington
Hon. Secretary
South Liverpool
14 Brook Way
Great Sankey
Warrington, Cheshire
WA5 1RZ

Mr D Edge
Hon. Fixture Secretary
South Liverpool
93 Millwood Road
Speke
Liverpool
L24 2UR

SOUTH YORKSHIRE FIRE SERVICE 1975
Thornensians RUFC
Coulman Rd
Thorne, Doncaster DN8 5BU
01405 812746

Mr P R Shillito
Hon. Secretary
S. Yorkshire Fire Service
26 Westminster Close
Bramley, Rotherham
S. Yorks. S66 1WJ

Mr M Wordsworth
Hon. Fixture Secretary
S. Yorkshire Fire Service
2 Scott Walk
Maltby, Rotherham
S. Yorks. S66 8RA

SOUTH YORKSHIRE POLICE 1972
Niagra Sports Ground
Niagra Road, Sheffield S6 1LU
0114 2764946

PC S W Stokes
Hon. Secretary
South Yorkshire Police
c/o West Bar Police Station
West Bar
Sheffield S1 2DA

Mr John Turner
Hon. Fixture Secretary
South Yorkshire Police
c/o Crime Prevention Dept.
Woodseats Police Station
Sheffield S8 0SL

ST ANNE'S AND ST JOHN'S COLLEGES
St Johns College Sports Ground
Woodstock Road
Oxford X1 3JP
01865 515561

Mr Peter Singfield
Hon. Secretary
St Anne's & St John's Colleges
St John's College
Oxford
OX1 3JP

For Attention Of:
Hon. Fixture Secretary
St A. & St J. Colleges
St Johns Coll. Sports Gnd
Woodstock Road
Oxford

STANDARD TELEPHONES (GREENWICH) 1936

Mr R Williams
Hon. Secretary
Standard Telephones (Greenwich)
59 High St
Bexley
Kent
DA5 1AB

Mr G Dorton
Hon. Fixture Secretary
Standard Telephones (Greenwich)
698 Downham Way
Downham
Kent

ST BEES SCHOOL 1870
The Foundation
St Bees
Cumbria
CA27 0DS
01946 822286 / 822254

Mr H Lewis
Hon. Secretary & **Fixture Secretary**
St Bees School
School House
St Bees School
Cumbria
CA27 0DS

ST CATHARINE'S COLLEGE
Grantchester Meadows
South Green Road
Cambridge
01223 352474

Hon. Secretary
St Catharine's College
College Rugby Club
St Catharine's College
Cambridge
CB2 1RL

For Attention Of:
Hon. Fixture Secretary
St Catharine's College
Grantchester Meadows
South Green Road
Cambridge

ST CATHERINE'S COLLEGE 1963
The Parks
Oxford OX1 3UJ
01865 271700

Mr Mohamed Hassam
Hon. Secretary & **Fixture Secretary**
St Catherine's College
St Catherine's College
Manor Road
Oxford
OX1 3UJ

ST EDMUND HALL 1930
Oxford
OX1 4AR
01865 557106 (Groundsman)

Mr S Gough
Hon. Secretary
St Edmund Hall
St Edmund Hall
Oxford
OX1 4AR

For Attention Of:
Hon. Fixture Secretary
St Edmund Hall
St Edmund Hall
Oxford
OX1 4AR

ST EDMUND'S COLLEGE

Hon Secretary
Hon. Secretary
St Edmund's College
College Rugby Clube
St Edmund's College
Cambridge CB2 0BN

ST HELIER 1892
1 Anley Street
St Helier
Jersey, Channel Islands JE2 3QE
01534 888179

Mr A Blaby
Hon. Secretary
St Helier
8 Valley Court
Les Grands Vaux, St Helier
Jersey
JE2 4NA

Mr M Preston
Hon. Fixture Secretary
St Helier
4 Maitland Barn
Trinity Hill
St Helier, Jersey
JE2 4JP

ST HUGH'S COLLEGE 1987
St Hughes College
St Margrets Rd
Oxford OX2 6LE

Mr N Fox
Hon. Secretary & **Fixture Secretary**
St Hugh's College
Oxford OX2 6LE

ST JACQUES 1978
KGV Playing Fields
Rue Cohu, Castel
Guernsey, Channel Isles
GY5 7SZ
01481 56617

Miss C Moxon
Hon. Secretary
St Jacques
The Willows
Blanche Carrier Lane, Vale
Guernsey, Channel Isles
GY3 5DL

Mr A R Ingroville
Hon. Fixture Secretary
St Jacques
Bordeaux Cottage
Brock Road, St Sampsons
Guernsey
GY2 4PN

ST JOHN'S COLLEGE 1867
Cambridge CB2 1TP
01223 338600

Mr D P Langford
Hon. Secretary
St John's College
College Rugby Club
St John's College
Cambridge
CB2 1TP

Mr I A De Weymarn
Hon. Fixture Secretary
St John's College
College Rugby Club
St John's College
Cambridge
CB2 1TP

ST PAUL'S SCHOOL
Lonsdale Road
Barnes SW13 9JT
020 8748 9162

Hon. Secretary
St Paul's School
St Paul's School
Barnes
London
SW13 9JT

For Attention Of:
Hon. Fixture Secretary
St Paul's School
Lonsdale Road
Barnes
SW13 9JT

ST PETER'S COLLEGE
Southern Bypass
Oxford OX1 5AA
01865 727468

Mr A Salvoni
Hon. Secretary
St Peter's College
St Peter's College
Southern Bypass
Oxford OX1 5AA

For Attention Of:
Hon. Fixture Secretary
St Peter's College
Southern Bypass
Oxford
OX1 5AA

ST PETER'S SCHOOL, YORK 1874
Clifton
Yorkshire YO3 6AB
01904 623213

Hon. Secretary
St Peter's School, York
St Peter's School
York

For Attention Of:
Hon. Fixture Secretary
St Peter's School, York
Clifton
Yorkshire YO3 6AB

SURREY CONSTABULARY 1967
Police HQ
Mount Browne
Sandy Lane, Guildford GU3 1HG
01483 571212

Mr D Harriott
Hon. Secretary
Surrey Constabulary
Police Helicopter Unit
Fairoaks Airport
Chobham, Surrey
GU24 8HU

Mr J Bennett
Hon. Fixture Secretary
Surrey Constabulary
Guildford Police Station,
Margaret Road,
Guildford, Surrey
GU1 4QS

SUTTON VALENCE SCHOOL 1874
Maidstone
Kent

Hon. Secretary
Sutton Valence School
Sutton Valence School
Sutton, Surrey

For Attention Of:
Hon. Fixture Secretary
Sutton Valence School
Maidstone

SUTTON BONINGTON
School of Agriculture
Sutton Bonington
Nr Loughborough LE12 5RD
0115 951 5151 Ext 8648

Mr John Hughes
Hon. Secretary
Sutton Bonington
SBRFC, Ameneities Building
University of Nottingham
Sutton Bonington Campus
Campus
LE12 5RD

Mr S Jones
Hon. Fixture Secretary
Sutton Bonington
SBRFC Ameneties Building
University of Nottingham
Sutton Bonnington
LE12 5RD

TESCO 1977
Tesco Country Club
Theobalds Lane
Cheshunt, Hertfordshire EN8 8YA
01992 625278

Mr S W Wyatt
Hon. Secretary
Tesco
7 Hazeldell
Watton at Stone
Herts SG14 3SL

Mr I Bundock
Hon. Fixture Secretary
Tesco
41 Telfords Yarde
6-8 The Highway
Wapping, London E1 9BQ

THE MOUNT 1989
HMP The Mount
Molyneaux Avenue HP3 0QL
01442 834363 Ext 252

Mr I Harris
Hon. Secretary
The Mount
PE Instructor, HMP The Mount
Molyneaux Avenue
Bovingdon, Hertfordshire
HP3 0NZ

For Attention Of:
Hon. Fixture Secretary
The Mount
HMP The Mount
Molyneaux Avenue
HP3 0QL

TONBRIDGE SCHOOL 1870
The '50'
Tonbridge School
High Street, Tonbridge, Kent TN9 1JP
01732 365555

Mr G P Gales
Hon. Secretary & **Fixture Secretary**
Tonbridge School
Clare House
57 London Road
Tonbridge, Kent

TRINITY COLLEGE 1872
Trinity Old Field
Grange Rd
Cambridge CB2 1TQ
01223 359566

For Attention Of:
Hon. Secretary
Trinity College, Trinity Old Field,
Grange Rd, Cambridge CB2 1TQ

For Attention Of:
Hon. Fixture Secretary

TRINITY HALL
Cambridge CB2 1TJ
01223 332500

For Attention of:
Hon. Secretary
Trinity Hall, College Rugby Club
Cambridge CB2 1TJ

For Attention Of:
Hon. Fixture Secretary
Cambridge

UNITED HOSPITALS 1875
St Mary's Hospital Athletic
Ground, Udney Park Road
Teddington, Middlesex
020 89773100

Mr David Badenock FRCS
Hon. Secretary
United Hospitals
123 Harley Street
London
W1N 1HE

Dr Andy Platts
Hon. Fixture Secretary
United Hospitals
Dept. Radiology
The Royal Free Hospital
Pond St. Hampstead
NW3 2QG

UNIVERSITY COLLEGE
Abingdon Road
Oxford
01865 243490

Mr T Rutherford
Hon. Secretary
University College
Abington Road,
Oxford 0X1 4BH

For Attention Of:
Hon. Fixture Secretary
University College
Abingdon Road
Oxford 0X1 4BH

UNIVERSITY COLLEGE SCHOOL 1882
Frognal
London
NW3
020 7435 2215

Hon. Secretary
University College School
University College School
Frogal, Hampstead
London
NW3 6XH

For Attention Of:
Hon. Fixture Secretary
University College School
Frognal
London
NW3

UPPINGHAM SCHOOL 1889
Uppingham
Leicestershire LE15 9QE
01572 822533

Mr Master I/C Rugby	For Attention Of:
Hon. Secretary	**Hon. Fixture Secretary**
Uppingham School	Uppingham School
Common Room, Uppingham School	Uppingham
Uppingham	Leicestershire
Rutland	LE15 9QE

WADHAM COLLEGE
Marston Ferry Road
Oxford OX1 3PN
01865 53819

Mr B O'Grady
Hon. Secretary & **Fixture Secretary**
Wadham College
Parks Rd, Oxford OX1 3PN

WARWICK 1976
Hampton Fields
Hampton Road
Warwick
01926 410972

Mr P O'Rourke
Hon. Secretary & **Fixture Secretary**
Warwick
35 Moreall Meadows
Gibbett Hill
Coventry CV4 7HL

WARWICKSHIRE CONSTABULARY 1947
Police HQ-P O Box 4
Leek Wootton
Warwickshire CV35 7QB
01926 415000

Mr G T Moreton	Mr S Foster
Hon. Secretary	**Hon. Fixture Secretary**
Warwickshire Constabulary	Warwickshire Constabulary
118 Higham Lane	Police Station
Nuneaton	Vicarage St, Nuneaton
Warwickshire	Warwickshire
CV11 6AX	CV11 4DW

WASHINGTON 1976
Northern Area Playing Fields
Stephenson Industrial Estate
Washington, Tyne & Wear

Mr P Guy	Mr J Watlen
Hon. Secretary	**Hon. Fixture Secretary**
Washington	Washington
13 Beech Terrace	7 Bridekirk
South Moor, Stanley	Albany
County Durham	Washington
DH9 7EL	NE37 1ND

WATERLOOVILLE 1981
Rowlands Avenue
Waterlooville, Hampshire
01705 264080

Mr R Mowatt	Mr I Day
Hon. Secretary	**Hon. Fixture Secretary**
Waterlooville	Waterlooville
9 Holst Way	Bodywork Gym
Purbrook	270a London Road
Waterlooville, Hants	Waterlooville, Hants
PO7 5SJ	PO7 7HG

WATTON
Dereham Road Sports Centre
Watton
Norfolk
01953 881281

Mr R Watson	Mr S Blackwood
Hon. Secretary	**Hon. Fixture Secretary**
Watton	Watton
4 Guarnock Terrace	36 Queensway
King's Lynn	Watton
Norfolk PE30 5QT	Norfolk IP25 6BL

WELLINGTON COLLEGE 1859
Crowthorne
Berkshire
01344 772262

Hon. Secretary	For Attention Of:
Wellington College	**Hon. Fixture Secretary**
Wellington College	Wellington College
Crowthorne	Crowthorne
Berkshire	Berkshire

WEST CORNWALL POLICE 1947
Truro Rugby Grounds
Truro TR4 8NG
01209 714881

Mr M Boyling
Hon. Secretary & **Fixture Secretary**
West Cornwall Police
44 Messack Close
Falmouth
Cornwall TR11 4SH

WEST MIDLANDS POLICE 1935
W Mids Police Training Centre
Tally Ho!, Pershore Road
Edgbaston, Birmingham B5 7RN
0121 472 2944

Mr D Ashford	Mr J Grante
Hon. Secretary	**Hon. Fixture Secretary**
West Midlands Police	West Midlands Police
c/o Crime Manager	c/o CID Office

Sutton Coldfield Police Station, Lichfield Road,
Sutton Coldfield, W Midlands B74 2NR

WHEATSHEAF CABIN CREW 1992
Holders Rd
Amesbury
Wiltshire

Mrs L Gollop	For Attention Of:
Hon. Secretary	**Hon. Fixture Secretary**
Wheatsheaf Cabin Crew	Wheatsheaf Cabin Crew
39a Upperwoodford	Holders Rd
Salisbury	Amesbury
Wiltshire	Wiltshire

WHITGIFT SCHOOL 1871
Haling Park
Nottingham Road
South Croydon CR2 6YT
020 8688 9222

Hon. Secretary	For Attention Of:
Whitgift School	**Hon. Fixture Secretary**
Whitgift School	Whitgift School
Croydon	Haling Park
Surrey	Nottingham Road
CR2 6YT	South Croydon
	CR2 6YT

WHITWELL 1985
Markland Campus,
N Derbyshire Tertiary College
Sheffield Rd, Creswell, Notts F80 4HW
01909 724908

Mrs J Marshall
Hon. Secretary
Whitwell
3 Duke Street
Whitwell, Worksop
Nottingham S80 4TH

Mr M Passey
Hon. Fixture Secretary
Whitwell
40 Chesterfield Road
Barlborough
Derbyshire S43 4TT

WILTSHIRE POLICE
Police Headquarters
London Road
Devizes, Wiltshire SN10 2DN
01380 722341

Sgt. A Peach
Hon. Secretary
Wiltshire Police
Div. HQ. Wiltshire Police
Wood Lane, Chippenham SN15 3DH

WOLFSON COLLEGE
Cambridge CB3 9BB

Dr F Walclron - Lynch
Hon. Secretary
Wolfson College
Cambridge
CB3 9BB

Mr M Daniels
Hon. Fixture Secretary
Wolfson College
Cambridge
CB3 9BB

WOODRUSH RFC
Icknield Street
Forhill
Birmingham B38 0EL

Mr P Leahy
Hon. Secretary
8 Burns Close
Headless Cross
Redditch, Worcs
B97 5BS

Mr L Frogatt
Hon. Fixture Secretary
70 Meadow Road
Wythall
Birmingham
B47 6EQ

WORCESTER COLLEGE
Worcester Street
Oxford OX1 2HB
0836 251002

Dr J D Bradshaw
Hon. Secretary & **Fixture Secretary**
Worcester College
Oxford OX1 2HB

MAIN FIXTURES - 2002-03

UGUST 2002

at, 17th	Middlesex Charity Sevens	Twickenham
ri, 30th/Sat, 31st	Celtic League Pools A & B (1)	
at, 31st	English Premier League (1)	
	English Nationals Leagues 1,2,3N,3S (1)	
	English Senior Cup Qualifying Round	
	Scottish Premiership Leagues 1-3 (1)	
	Scottish National Leagues 1-5 (1)	
	Welsh National Leagues Divs 1,2,3W (1)	

EPTEMBER 2002

ri, 6th/Sat 7th	Celtic League Pools A & B (2)	
at, 7th	English Premier League (2)	
	English National Leagues 1,2,3N,3S (2)	
	English National Leagues 12s (1)	
	English Senior Cup Preliminary Round	
	Scottish Premiership Leagues 1-3 (2)	
	Scottish Cups First Round	
	Welsh National Leagues Divs 1,2,3W (2)	
	Welsh National League Division 3E (1)	
ri, 13th/Sat, 14th	Celtic League Pools A & B (3)	
at, 14th	English Premier League (3)	
	English National Leagues 1,2,3N,3S (3)	
	English National Leagues 12s (2)	
	English National Leagues 10s (1)	
	Scottish Premiership Leagues 1-3 (3)	
	Scottish National Leagues 1-5 (2)	
	Welsh National Leagues Divs 1,2,3W (3)	
	Welsh National League Division 3E (2)	
ri, 20th/Sat, 21st	Celtic League Polls A & B (4)	
Sat, 21st	English Premier League (4)	
	English National Leagues 1 & 2 (4)	
	English Senior Cup Round One	
	English Intermediate Cup Round One	
	English Junior Cup Round One	
	Scottish Premiership Leagues 1-3 (4)	
	Scottish National Leagues 1-5 (3)	
	Welsh National Leagues Divs 1 & 2 (4)	
Wed, 24th	Welsh National League Division 1 (5)	
Fri, 27th/Sat, 28th	Celtic League Pools A & B (5)	
Sat, 28th	English Premier League (5)	
	English National Leagues 1 & 2 (5)	
	English National Leagues 3N & 3S (4)	
	English National Leagues 12s (3)	
	English National Leagues 10s (2)	
	Scottish Premiership Leagues 1-3 (5)	
	Scottish National Leagues 1-5 (4)	
	Welsh National League Division 1 (6)	
	Welsh National League Division 2 (5)	
	Welsh National League Division 3W (4)	
	Welsh National League Division 3E (3)	

OCTOBER 2002

Fri, 4th/Sat, 5th	Celtic League Pools A & B (6)	
Sat, 5th	English Premier League (6)	
	English National League 1 (6)	
	English National Leagues 12s (4)	
	English National Leagues 10s (3)	
	English Senior Cup Round Two	
	Scottish Premiership Leagues 1-3 (6)	
	Scottish National Leagues 1-5 (5)	
	Welsh National League Division 1 (7)	
	Welsh National League Division 2 6)	
	Welsh National League Division 3W (5)	
	Welsh National League Division 3E (4)	
Fri,11th/Sun, 13th	Heineken Cup Round One	
	Parker Pen Challenge Cup Round One (first legs)	
Sat, 12th	English National League 1 (7)	
	English National League 2 (6)	
	English National League 3N & 3S (5)	
	English National Leagues 12s (5)	
	English National Leagues 10s (4)	
	Scottish Premiership Leagues 1-3 (7)	
	Scottish Cups Second Round	
	Welsh National League Division 1 (8)	
	Welsh National League Division 2 (7)	
	Welsh National League Division 3W (6)	
	Welsh National League Division 3E (5)	
Fri, 18th/Sun, 20th	Heineken Cup Round Two	
	Parker Pen Challenge Cup Round One (second legs)	
Sat, 19th	English National Leagues 3N & 3S (6)	
	English Senior Cup Round Three	
	English Intermediate Cup Round Two	
	English Junior Cup Round Two	
	Scottish Premiership Leagues 1-3 (8)	
	Scottish National Leagues 1-5 (6)	
	Welsh National League Division 1 (9)	
	Welsh National League Division 2 (8)	
	Welsh National League Division 3W 7)	
	Welsh Challenge Cup Round (provisional)	
Tue, 22nd	Welsh National League Division 1 (10)	
Fri, 25th/Sun, 26th	Celtic League Pools A & B (7)	
Sat, 26th	English Premier League (7)	
	English National League 1 (8)	
	English National Leagues 3N & 3S	
	English National Leagues 12s (6)	
	English National Leagues 10s (5)	
	Irish Leagues Divisions 1,2,3 (1)	
	Scottish Premiership Leagues 1-3 (9)	
	Scottish National Leagues 1-5 (7)	
	Welsh National League Division 1 (11)	
	Welsh National League Division 2 (9)	
	Welsh National League Division 3W 8)	
	Welsh National League Division 3E (6)	

NOVEMBER 2002

Sat, 2nd	English Premier League (8)	
	English National League 1 (9)	
	English National Leagues 2,3N,3S (8)	
	English National Leagues 12s (7)	
	English National Leagues 10s (6)	
	Irish Leagues Divisions 1,2,3 (2)	
	Scottish Cups Third Round	
	Welsh National League Division 1 (12)	
	Welsh National League Division 3W (9)	
	Welsh National League Division 3E (7)	
	Welsh Challenge Cup Round (provisional)	
Sat, 9th	ENGLAND v NEW ZEALAND	Twickenham
	IRELAND v AUSTRALIA	Dublin
	SCOTLAND v ROMANIA	Murrayfield
	WALES v FIJI	Cardiff
	English Premier League (9)	
	English National Leagues 3N & 3S (9)	
	English Senior Cup Round Four	
	English Intermediate Cup Round Three	
	English Junior Cup Round Three	
	Welsh National League Division 1 (13)	
	Welsh National League Divisions 2,3W (10)	
	Welsh National League Division 3E (8)	
Sun, 10th	Scottish Premiership Leagues 1-3 (10)	
	Scottish National Leagues 1-5 (8)	
Tue, 12th	Scotland 'A' v South Africa	TBA
	Combined Services v Barbarians	Plymouth
Sat, 16th	ENGLAND v AUSTRALIA	Twickenham
	SCOTLAND v SOUTH AFRICA	Murrayfield
	WALES v CANADA	Cardiff
	English Premier League (10)	
	English National Leagues 1,3N & 3s (10)	
	English National League 2 (9)	
	English National Leagues 12s (8)	
	English National Leagues 10s (7)	
	Irish Leagues Divisions 1,2,3 (3)	
	Welsh National League Division 1 (14)	
	Welsh National League Divisions 2,3W 11) Wales	
Sun, 17th	IRELAND v FIJI	Dublin
Wed. 20th	Scotland 'A' v Fiji	TBA
Sat, 23rd	ENGLAND v SOUTH AFRICA	Twickenham
	IRELAND v ARGENTINA	Dublin
	WALES v NEW ZEALAND	Cardiff
	English Premier League (11)	
	English National Leagues 1,3N & 3S (11)	
	English National League 2 (10)	
	English National Leagues 12s (9)	
	Scottish Premiership Leagues 1-3 (11) Scotland	
	Scottish Premiership Leagues 1-3 (12) Scotland	

	Scottish National Leagues 1-5 (9) Scotland	
	Welsh National League Division 1 (15)	
Sun, 24th	SCOTLAND v FIJI Murrayfield	
	Irish League Division 1 (4)	
Fri 29th-Sun, 1/12	Celtic League Quarter-finals	
Sat, 30th	NORTH v SOUTH (Challenge Match)	Cardiff
	English Premier League (12)	
	English National League 2 (11)	
	English National Leagues 3N & 3S (12)	
	English National Leagues 12s (10)	
	English National Leagues 10s (8)	
	English Senior Cup Round Five	
	English Intermediate Cup Round Four	
	England Junior Cup Round Four	
	Irish League Division 1 (4 continued)	
	Irish Leagues Divisions 2 & 3 (4)	
	Scottish Premiership Leagues 1-3 (13) Scotland	
	Scottish National Leagues 1-5 (10)	
	Welsh National League Division 1 (16)	
	Welsh National League Divisions 2,3W (12)	
	Welsh National League Division 3E (9)	
	Welsh Challenge Cup Round (provisional)	

DECEMBER 2002

Fri 6th/Sun 8th	Heineken Cup Round Three	
	Parker Pen Challenge Cup Round Two (first legs)	
	Parker Pen Shield Round One (first legs)	
Sat, 7th	English National Leagues 1 & 2 (12)	
	English National Leagues 3N & 3S (13)	
	English National Leagues 12s (11)	
	English National Leagues (9)	
	Irish Leagues Divisions 1,2,3 (5)	
	Scottish Premiership Leagues 1-3 (14)	
	Scottish National Leagues 1-5 (11)	
	Welsh National League Division 1 (17)	
	Welsh National League Divisions 2,3W (13)	
	Welsh National League 3E (10)	
Tue, 10th	Oxford v Cambridge (Bowring Bowl)	Twickenham
	Oxford v Cambridge u 21s (Bowring Plate)	Twickenham
Fri 13th/Sun 15th	Heineken Cup Round Four	
	Parker Pen Challenge Cup Round Two (second legs)	
	Parker Pen Shield Round One (second legs)	
Sat, 14th	English National Leagues 1 & 2 (13)	
	English National Leagues 3N & 3S (14)	
	English National Leagues 12s (12)	
	English National Leagues 10s (10)	
	Irish Leagues Divisions 2 & 3 (6)	
	Scottish Cups Fourth Round	
	Welsh National League Division 1 (18)	
	Welsh National League Divisions 2,3W (14) Wales	
	Welsh National League Division 3E (11) Wales	
Sat, 21st	English National League 2 (14)	
	English National Leagues 3N & 3S (15)	
	English National Leagues 12s (13)	
	English Senior Cup Round Six	
	English Intermediate Cup Round Five	
	English Junior Cup Round Five	
	Scottish National Leagues 1-3 (15) Scotland	
	Welsh National League Divisions 2,3W (15)	
	Welsh National League Division 3E (12)	
	Welsh Challenge Cup Round (provisional)	
Sat, 28th	English Premier League	
	Irish League Division 1 (6)	
	Welsh National League Division 1 (19) Wales	
	Welsh National League Divisions 2,3W 16) Wales	
	Welsh National League Division 3E (13) Wales	

JANUARY 2003

Sat, 4th (w/e)	Celtic League Semi-final	
Sat, 4th	English Premier League (14)	
	English National League 1 (14)	
	English National League 2 (15)	
	English National Leagues 3N & 3S (16)	
	English National Leagues 12s (14)	
	English National Leagues 10s (11)	
	Irish Leagues Divisions 2 & 3 (7)	
	Scottish Premiership Leagues 1-3 (16)	
	Scottish National Leagues 1-5 (12)	
	Welsh National League Division 1 (20)	
	Welsh National League Divisions 2,3W (17)	
	Welsh National League Division 3E (14)	
Fri 10th/Sun 12th	Heineken Cup Round Five	
	Parker Pen Challenge Cup Quarter-finals (first legs)	
	Parker Pen Shield Quarter-finals (first legs)	
Sat, 11th	English National League 1 (15)	
	English National League 2 (16)	
	English National Leagues 3N & 3S (17)	
	Rnglish National Leagues 12s (15)	
	Irish Leagues Divisions 2 & 3 (8)	
	Scottish Cups Fifth Round	
	Welsh National League Division 1 (21)	
	Welsh National League Divisions 2,3W (18)	
	Welsh National League Division 3E (15)	
Fri 17th/Sun 19th	Heineken Cup Round Six	
	Parker Pen Challenge Cup Quarter-finals (second legs)	
	Parker Pen Shield Quarter-finals (second legs)	
Sat, 18th	English National League 1 (16)	
	English National League 2 (17)	
	English National Leagues 3N & 3S (18)	
	English National Leagues 12s (16)	
	English National Leagues 10s (12)	
	English Intermediate Cup Round Six	
	English Junior Cuo Round Six	
	Irish League Division 1 (7)	
	Dublin Univ v Malone (Irish Div 3)	Dublin
	Scottish Premiership Leagues 1-3 (17)	
	Scottish National Leagues 1-5 (13)	
	Welsh National League Division 1 (22)	
	Welsh National League Divisions 2,3W (19)	
	Welsh National League Division 3E (16)	
Sat, 25th	English National League 1 (17)	
	English National League 2 (18)	
	English National Leagues 3N & 3S (19)	
	English Senior Cup Quarter-final	
	Irish League Division 1 (8)	
	Irish Leagues Divisions 2 & 3 (9)	
	Scottish Premiership Leagues 1-3 (18)	
	Scottish National Leagues 1-5 (14)	
	Welsh National League Divisions 2,3W (20)	
	Welsh National League Division 3E (17)	
	Welsh Challenge Cup Round (provisional)	

FEBRUARY 2003

Sat, 1st	English Premier League (15)	
	English National League 1 (18)	
	English National League 2 (19)	
	English National Leagues 3N & 3S (20)	
	English National Leagues 12s (17)	
	English National Leagues 10s (13)	
	Irish League Division 1 (9)	
	Irish Leagues Divisions 2 & 3 (10)	
	Scottish Cups Quarter-finals	
	Welsh National League Division 1 (23)	
	Welsh National League Divisions 2,3W (21)	
	Welsh National League Division 3E (18)	
Sat, 8th	English Premier League (16)	
	English National League 1 (19)	
	English National League 2 (20)	
	English National Leagues 3N & 3S (21)	
	English National Leagues 12s (18)	
	English National Leagues 10s (14)	
	Celtic League Final	
	Irish League Division 1 (10)	
	Irish Leagues Divisions 2 & 3 (11)	
	Scottish Premiership Lg stand-by date	
	Scottish National Leagues 1-5 (15)	
	Welsh National League Division 1 (24)	
	Welsh National League Divisions 2,3W (22)	
	Welsh National League Division 3E (19)	
Fri, 14th	England 'A' v France 'A'	England
	England Under 21 v France Under 21	England
	Italy 'A' v Wales 'A'	Italy
	Italy Under 21 v Wales Under 21	Italy
	Scotland 'A' v Ireland 'A'	Scotland
	Scotland Under 21 v Ireland Under 21	Scotland
Sat, 15th	ENGLAND v FRANCE (Six Nations)	Twickenham
	ITALY v WALES (Six Nations)	Rome

Date	Fixture	Venue
	SCOTLAND v IRELAND (Six Nations)	Murrayfield
	Scottish National Leagues 1-5 (16)	
ed, 19th	Welsh National League Division 1 (25)	
i, 21st	France 'A' v Scotland 'A'	France
	France Under 21 v Scotland Under 21	France
	Italy 'A' v Ireland 'A'	Italy
	Italy Under 21 v Ireland Under 21	Italy
	Wales 'A' v England 'A'	Wales
	Wales Under 21 v England Under 21	Wales
at, 22nd	FRANCE v SCOTLAND (Six Nations)	Paris
	ITALY v IRELAND (Six Nations)	Rome
	WALES v ENGLAND (Six Nations)	Cardiff
	English National League 1 (20)	
	English National League 2 (21)	
	English National Leagues 3N & 3S (22)	
	English Intermediate Cup - Quarter-finals	
	English Junior Cup - Quarter-finals	
ARCH 2003		
at, 1st	English Premier League (17)	
	English National League 1 (21)	
	English National League 2 (22)	
	English National Leagues 3N & 3S (23)	
	English National Leagues 12s (19)	
	English National Leagues 10s (15)	
	English Senior Cup Semi-finals	
	English Challenge Shield Semi-finals	
	Irish League Division 1 (11)	
	Irish Leagues Divisions 2 & 3 (12)	
	Scottish National Leagues 1-5 (17)	
	Welsh National League Division 1 (26)	
	Welsh National League Divisions 2,3W (23)	
	Welsh National League Division 3E (20)	
ed, 5th	Welsh National League Division 1 (27)	
i, 7th	England 'A' v Italy 'A'	England
	England Under 21 v Italy Under 21	England
	Ireland 'A' v France 'A'	Ireland
	Ireland Under 21 v France Under 21	Ireland
	Scotland 'A' v Wales 'A'	Scotland
	Scotland Under 21 v Wales Under 21	Scotland
at, 8th	ENGLAND v ITALY (Six Nations)	Twickenham
	IRELAND v FRANCE (Six Nations)	Dublin
	SCOTLAND v WALES (Six Nations)	Murrayfield
at, 15th	English Premier League (18)	
	Rnglish National League 1 (22)	
	English National League 2 (23)	
	English National Leagues 3N & 3S (24)	
	English National Leagues 12s (20)	
	English National Leagues 10s (16)	
	English Intermediate Cup	Semi-finals
	English Junior Cup	Semi-finals
	Irish League Division 1 (12)	
	Irish Leagues Divisions 2 & 3 (13)	
	Scottish National Leagues 1-5 (18)	
	Welsh National League Division 1 (28)	
	Welsh National League Divisions 2,3W (24)	
	Welsh National League Division 3E (21)	
i, 21st	England 'A' v Scotland 'A'	England
	England Under 21 v Scotland Under 21	England
	Italy 'A' v France 'A'	Italy
	Italy Under 21 v France Under 21	Italy
	Wales 'A' v Ireland 'A'	Wales
	Wales Under 21 v Ireland Under 21	Wales
at, 22nd	ENGLAND v SCOTLAND (Six Nations)	Twickenham
	ITALY v FRANCE (Six Nations)	Rome
	WALES v IRELAND (Six Nations)	Cardiff
i, 28th	France 'A' v Wales 'A'	France
	France Under 21 v Wales Under 21	France
	Ireland 'A' v England 'A'	Ireland
	Ireland Under 21 v England Under 21	Ireland
	Scotland 'A' v Italy 'A'	Scotland
	Scotland Under 21 v Italy Under 21	Scotland
at, 29th	FRANCE v WALES (Six Nations)	Paris
	IRELAND v ENGLAND (Six Nations)	Dublin
	SCOTLAND v ITALY	Murrayfield
	English National League 1 (23)	
	English National League 2 (24)	
	English National Leagues 3N & 3S (25)	

Date	Fixture	Venue
	English National Leagues 12s (21)	
	English National Leagues 10s (17)	
APRIL 2003		
Sat, 5th	English Senior Cup, Intermediate Cup	Twickenham
	Junior Cup, Challenge Shield Finals	
	Irish League Division 1 (13)	
	Irish Leagues Divisions 2 & 3 (14)	
	Scottish Cups Semi-finals	
	Welsh Challenge Cup Quarter-finals	
	(provisional)	
	Welsh National League Division 1 (29)	
	Welsh National League Divisions 2,3W (25)	
	Welsh National League Division 3E (22)	
Wed, 9th	Royal Air Force v Royal Navy	TBA
Fri,11th/Sun, 13th	Heineken Cup Quarter-finals	
	Parker Pen Challenge Cup Semi-finals (first legs)	
	Parker Pen Shield Semi-finals (first legs)	
Sat, 12th	English Premier League (19)	
	English National League 1 (24)	
	English National League 2 (25)	
	English National Leagues 3N & 3S (26)	
	English National Leagues 12s (22)	
	English National Leagues 10s (18)	
	English National U20 Quarter-finals	
	Irish League Division 1 (14)	
	Monkstown v City of Derry (Irish Div 3)	Dublin
	Welsh National League Division 1 (30)	
	Welsh National League Divisions 2,3W (26)	
	Welsh National League Division 3E (23)	
Sat, 19th	English Premier League (20)	
	English National League 1 (25)	
	Irish League Divisions 1,2,3 (15)	
	Welsh National League Division 1 (31)	
	Welsh National League Division 2,3W (27)	
	Welsh National League Division 3E (24)	
Sat,26th/Sun 27th	Heineken Cup Semi-finals	
	Parker Pen Challenege Cup Semi-finals (second legs)	
	Parker Pen Shield Semi-finals (second legs)	
Sat, 26th	English National League 1 & 2 (26)	
	English National Leagues 3N & 3s Play-offs	
	English National Leagues 12s Play-offs	
	English National Leagues 10s Play-offs	
	English County Shield (botton 11) Rd 1	
	Scottish Cups Finals Day	Murrayfield
	Welsh Challenge Cup Semi-finals (provisional)	Cardiff
	Welsh National League Division 1 (32)	
	Welsh National League Divisions 2,3W (28)	
	Welsh National League Dicvision 3E (25)	
Tue, 29th	Army v Royal Air Force	Aldershot
MAY 2003		
Sat, 3rd	English Premier League (21)	
	Royal Navy v Army	Twickenham
	County Championships Round One	
	County Shield Round Two	
	Welsh National League Division 1 (33)	
	Welsh National League Divisions 2,3W (29)	
	Welsh National League Division 3E (26)	
Sat, 10th	English Premier League (22)	
	County Championships Quarter-finals	
	County Shield Semi-finals	
	Welsh National League Division 1 (34)	
	Welsh National League Divisions 2,3W (30)	
Tue, 13th	East Midlands v Barbarians (prov)	Northampton
Sat, 17th	Premier League Play-offs	
	County Championship & Shield S-finals	
Fri, 23rd	Parker Pen Shield Final (provisional)	TBA
Sat, 24th	Heineken Cup Final	TBA
	County Championships Play-offs	
Sun, 25th	ENGLAND v BARBARIANS	Twickenham
	Parker Challenge Cup Final	TBA
Tue, 26th	WALES v BARBARIANS	Cardiff
Sat, 31st	SCOTLAND v BARBARIANS	Murrayfield
	Welsh Challenge Cup Final (provisional)	Cardiff
	English Premier Championship S-finals	
	County Championship & Shield Finals	Twickenham
JUNE 2002		
Sat, 7th	English Premier Championship Final	Twickenham

PARKER PEN SHIELD

POOL ONE

Saturday, 29th September 2001
Agen 20 Ebbw Vale 9
Sunday, 30th September 2001
Rovigo 21 Montauban 41
Saturday, 6th October 2001
Ebbw Vale 28 Rovigo 26
Montauban 28 Agen 26
Friday, 26th October 2001
Ebbw Vale 16 Montauban 5
Sunday, 28th October 2001
Rovigo 3 Agen 43
Saturday, 3rd November 2001
Agen 66 Rovigo 7
Montauban 19 Ebbw Vale 15
Friday, 4th January 2002
Agen 34 Montauban 13
Sunday, 6th January 2002
Rovigo 10 Ebbw Vale 26
Saturday, 12th January 2002
Ebbw Vale 59 Agen 10
Montauban 40 Rovigo 9

TABLE	P	W	D	L	F	A	T	Pts
Agen	6	4	0	2	199	119	25	8
Ebbw Vale	6	4	0	2	153	90	15	8
Montauban	6	4	0	2	146	123	10	8
Rovigo	6	0	0	6	78	244	8	0

POOL TWO

Saturday, 29th September 2001
Pau 35 Petrarca 0
Sunday, 30th September 2001
Madrid 16 Colomiers 36
Saturday, 6th October 2001
Colomiers 12 Pau 18
Petrarca 41 Madrid 12
Saturday, 27th October 2001
Pau 62 Madrid 10
Petrarca 12 Colomiers 74
Saturday, 3rd November 2001
Colomiers 45 Patrarca 6
Sunday, 4th November 2001
Madrid 10 Pau 30
Saturday, 5th January 2002
Madrid 29 Petrarca 36
Pau 40 Colomiers 12
Saturday, 12th January 2002
Colomiers 80 Madrid 13
Petrarca 19 Pau 28

TABLE	P	W	D	L	F	A	T	Pts
Pau	6	6	0	0	217	63	27	12
Colomier	6	4	0	2	259	105	32	8
Petrarca	6	2	0	4	114	223	14	4
Madrid	6	0	0	6	90	289	8	0

POOL THREE

Saturday, 29th September 2001
Beziers 23 Pontypridd 12
Overmach Parma 41 Leeds 10
Saturday, 6th October 2001
Pontypridd 31 Overmach Parma 10
Sunday, 7th October 2001
Leeds 48 Beziers 17
Saturday, 27th October 2001
Overmach Parma 41 Beziers 29
Sunday, 28th October 2001
Leeds 30 Pontypridd 27
Saturday, 3rd November 2001
Beziers 34 Overmach Parma 19
Pontypridd 28 Leeds 16
Saturday, 5th January 2002
Beziers 25 Leeds 26
Sunday, 6th January 2002
Overmach Parma v Pontypridd postponed - frozen pitch
(match switched to Gloucester, but Parma fail to appear
and tie awarded to Pontypridd)
Saturday, 12th January 2002
Pontypridd 41 Beziers 8
Sunday, 13th January 2002
Leeds 58 Overmach Parma 16

TABLE	P	W	D	L	F	A	T	Pts
Leeds	6	4	0	2	188	154	27	8
Pontypridd	6	4	0	2	139	87	12	8
Beziers	6	2	0	4	135	187	15	4
Overmach Parma	6	2	0	4	127	182	11	4

Pontypridd declared pool winners as a result of a better aggregate performance against Leeds (55-46).

POOL FOUR

Friday, 28th September 2001
Connacht 18 Narbonne 6
Saturday, 29th September 2001
Sale 93 Roma 0
Saturday, 6th October 2001
Narbonne 10 Sale 13
Roma 10 Connacht 20
Saturday, 27th October 2001
Connacht 30 Sale 33
Narbonne 40 Roma 0
Saturday, 3rd November 2001
Roma 17 Narbonne 22
Sale 44 Connacht 6
Saturday, 5th January 2002
Connacht 61 Roma 13
Wednesday, 9th January 2002
Sale 41 Narbonne 16
Saturday, 12th January 2002
Narbonne 34 Connacht 22
Roma 17 Sale 62

TABLE	P	W	D	L	F	AT	Pts	
Sale	6	6	0	0	286	79	40	12
Connacht	6	3	0	3	167	140	14	6
Narbonne	6	3	0	3	128	121	8	6
Roma	6	0	0	6	57	298	7	0

POOL FIVE

Saturday, 29th September 2001
Neath 41 Viadana 14
Sunday, 30th September 2001
Bourgoin 28 Bristol 34
Sunday, 7th October 2001
Bristol 10 Neath 6
Viadana 26 Bourgoin 10
Saturday, 27th October 2001
Neath 27 Bourgoin 20

Sunday, 28th October 2001
Viadana 16 Bristol 42
Sunday, 4th November 2001
Bourgoin 25 Neath 27
Bristol 31 Viadana 15
Saturday, 5th January 2002
Bourgoin 60 Viadana 16
Neath 33 Bristol 29
Saturday, 12th January 2002
Viadana 33 Neath 26
Sunday, 13th January 2002
Bristol 43 Bourgoin 17

TABLE	P	W	D	L	F	A	T	Pts
Bristol	6	5	0	1	175	88	17	10
Neath	6	4	0	2	160	131	15	8
Viadana	6	2	0	4	120	210	13	4
Bourgoin	6	1	0	5	160	173	19	2

POOL SIX

Saturday, 29th September 2001
L'Aquila 25 Valladollid 14
Dax 22 London Irish 29
Sunday, 7th October 2001
London Irish 48 L'Aquila 12
Valladollid 11 Dax 26
Saturday, 27th October 2001
L'Aquila 29 Dax 41
Sunday, 28th October 2001
Valladolid 5 London Irish 71
Sunday, 4th November 2001
Dax 94 L'Aquila 10
London Irish 76 Valladolid 10
Saturday, 5th January 2002
L'Aquila 8 London Irish 32
Sunday, 6th January 2002
Dax 99 Valladolid 3
Sunday, 13th January 2002
London Irish 28 Dax 28
Valladolid 10 L'Aquila 14

TABLE	P	W	D	L	F	A	T	Pts
London Irish	6	5	1	0	284	85	37	11
Dax	6	4	1	1	306	119	42	9
L'Aquila	6	2	0	4	107	239	10	4
Valladolid	6	0	0	6	53	307	7	0

POOL SEVEN

Saturday, 29th September 2001
Caerphilly 41 GRAN Parma 30
Gloucester 34 La Rochgelle 15
Saturday, 6th October 2001
GRAN Parma 5 Gloucester 48
La Rochelle 44 Caerphilly 39
Saturday, 27th October 2001
Gloucester 98 Caerphilly 14
La Rochelle 28 GRAN Parma 14
Saturday, 3rd November 2001
Caerphilly 16 Gloucester 47
GRAN Parma 25 La Rochelle 30
Saturday, 5th January 2002
Caerphilly 29 La Rochelle 32
Gloucester 99 GRAN Parma 0
Saturday, 12th January 2002
GRAN Parma 30 Caerphilly 31
La Rochelle 12 Gloucester 36

TABLE	P	W	D	L	F	A	T	Pts
Gloucester	6	6	0	0	362	62	44	12
La Rochelle	6	4	0	2	161	177	20	8
Caerphilly	6	2	0	4	170	281	18	4
GRAN Parma	6	0	0	6	104	277	11	0

POOL EIGHT

Saturday, 29th September 2001
Bologna 17 Dinamo Bucharest 49
Saracens 34 Bordeaux-Begles 14
Saturday, 6th October 2001
Bordeaux-Begles 89 Bologna 11
Dinamo Bucharest 12 Saracnes 75
Sunday, 28th October 2001
Bordeaux-Begles 82 Dinamo Bucharest 23
Saracens 113 Bologna 3
Saturday, 3rd November 2001
Dinamo Bucharest 5 Bordeaux-Begles 83
Bologna 10 Saracens 75
Saturday, 5th January 2002
Bologna 19 Bordeaux-Begles 62
Sunday, 6th January 2002
Saracens 113 Dinamo Bucharest 3
Saturday, 12th January 2002
Bologna 33 Dinamo Bucharest 10
Bordeaux-Begles 24 Saracens 25

TABLE	P	W	D	L	F	A	T	Pts
Saracens	6	6	0	0	435	66	63	12
Bordeaux-Begles	6	4	0	2	354	117	53	8
Dinamo Bucharest	6	1	0	6	102	403	15	2
Bologna	6	1	0	5	93	398	9	2

QUARTER-FINALS:

Friday, 25th January 2002
At Kingsholm, Gloucester. Att.: 6,816.

GLOUCESTER 46-11 EBBW VALE

Half-time: 9-11.

GLOUCESTER: D O'Leary; J Simpson-Daniel, T Fanolua, R Todd, D Albanese; L Mercier, A Gomarsall; P Collazzo, C Fortey, F Pucciariello, J Boer (captain), M Cornwell, A Eustace, A Hazell, J Paramore. Replacements: R Fidler for Eustace 10 mins., A Deacon for Pucciariello 22 mins., H Paul for O'Leary 68 mins., J Forrester for Hazell 68 mins., M Garvey for Albanese 68 mins., D Yachvili for Gomarsall 72 mins., M Irish for Collazzo 79 mins..
Scorers: Tries: O'Leary, Simpson-Daniel, Boer, Forrester. Pens: Mercier (6). Cons: Mercier (4).
EBBW VALE: M James; A Takarangi, R Shorney, P Matthews, A Wagstaff; G Cull, K Ellis; I Thomas, L Phillpis, M Jones, K Tuipolutu, C Billen (captain), N Edwards, P Williams, W Thomas. Replacements: G Booyse for Billen 57 mins., J Eavns for Phillips 69 mins., R Williams for Tuipolutu 72 mins., D Penisini for M Jones 78 mins..
Scorers: Try: Wagstaff. Pens: Cull (2).
Referee: G De Santi, Italy. Att.:

At Heywood Road, Sale. Att.: 3,607.

SALE 25-20 BRISTOL

Half-time: 15-13.

SALE: V Going; M Cueto, J Robinson, M Deane, S Hanley; C Hodgson, B Redpath (captain); K Yates, A Titterell, S Turner, A Perelini, I Fullarton, S Lines, S Pinkerton, A Sanderson. Replacements: C Marais for Titterell 60 mins., C Jones for Perelini 2nd half, A Black for Jones 76 mins..

Scorers: Tries: Going, Hanley, Redpath. Pens: Hodgson (2). Cons: Hodgson (2).
BRISTOL: M Carrington; L Nabaro, A Higgins, J Little (captain), P Christophers; F Contepomi, A Pichot; P Johnstone, N McCarthy, J White, A Sheridan, G Archer, A Brown, M Salter, C Short. Replacements: B Sturnham for Salter 40 mins., B Daniel for Nabaro 70 mins..
Scorers: Tries: Christophers, Contepomi. Pens: Contepomi (2). Cons; Contepomi (2).

Saturday, 26th January 2002
In Pau. Att.: 6,000.

PAU 9-38 LONDON IRISH

Half-time: 3-12.

PAU: D Traille; P Bomati, J-C Cistacq, P Carbonneau (captain), L Arbo; M Pearson, M Siro; M Larrouy, A Racine, D Laperne, I Harinodoquy, A Lahouarde, T Cleda, A Aqueb, E Goulomet. Replacements: G Pedaille for Racine 18 mins., C Warner for Pearson 40 mins., G Chasserieau for Lagouarde 40 mins., P Capdevielle for Laperne 40 mins., D Laperne for Larrouy 56 mins., G Combes for Goulomet 58 mins., B Bordenave for Harinodoquy 76 mins.. Yellow cards: Cleda 7-17 mins., Agueb 35-45 mins.. Sent off: Chasserieau 76 mins..
Scorers: Pens: Traille (2), Pearson.
LONDON IRISH: M Horak; J Bishop, G Appleford, B Venter, P Sackey; B Everitt, S Martens; M Worsley, R Kirke, S Halford, J Cockle, R Strudwick (captain), S Williams, D Danaher, C Sheasby. Replacements: S Brown for Everitt 39 mins., R Hardwick for Halford 46 mins., J Wright for Venter 71 mins., K Barrett for Martens 73 mins., G Delaney for S Williams 73 mins.. Temporary replacement: G Delanney for Sheasby 15-17 mins., Hardwick for Danaher 38-48 mins..
Scorers: Tries: Sackey, Worsley. DGs: Everitt, Brown. Pens: Everitt (3), Brown (3). Cons: Brown (2).
Referee: R Dickson, Scotland.

Sunday, 27th January 2002

At Vicarage Road, Watford. Att.: 6,182.

SARACENS 15-17 PONTYPRIDD

Half-time: 6-10.

SARACENS: T Horan; G Arasa, T Shanklin, K Sorrell, D O'Mahoney; J de Beer, K Bracken (captain); D Flatman, R Russell, P du Randt, K Chesney, S Hooper, S Murray, T Roques, R Hill. Replacements: A Winnan for Sorrell 47 mins., K Roche for Hooper 47 mins., N Walshe for Bracken 55 mins., M Cairns for Flatman 70 mins..
Scorer: Pens: De Beer (5).
PONTYPRIDD: B Davey; G Wyatt, S Parker, J Bryant, N Simpson; C Sweeney, P John (captain); G Jenkins, M Davies, D Bell, M Kelly, B Cockbain, R Sidoli, R Parks, M Owen. Replacements: D McIntosh for Kelly 46 mins., G Remnant for Cockbain 50 mins..
Scorer : Tries: Owen, Wyatt. Pen: Davey. Cons: Davey (2).
Referee: A Rolland, Ireland.

SEMI-FINALS:

Saturday, 27th April 2002.
In The Kassam Stadium, Oxford.

LONDON IRISH 27-33 PONTYPRIDD

Half-time: 21-24.
LONDON IRISH: M Horak; P Sackey, G Appleford, B Venter, J Bishop; B Everitt, S Martens; N Hatley, R Kirke, S Halford, E Halveg, R Strudwick (captain), S Williams, D Danaher, C Sheasby. Replacements: G Delaney for Williams 13 mins., D Edwards for Martens 38 mins., N Drotske for Kirke 45 mins., D Wheatley for Hatley 49 mins..
Scorers: Tries: Halvey, Kirke, Horak. Pens: Everitt (2). Cons: Everitt (3).
PONTYPRIDD: B Davey; G Wyatt, S Parker, J Bryant, G Baber; C Sweeney, P John (captain); G Jenkins, M Davies, D Bell, M Kelly, B Cockbain, R Sidoli, R Parks, M Owen. Replacement: D McIntosh for Kelly 72 mins..
Scorers: Tries: Wyatt, Jenkins, M Davies. Pens: Davey (4) Cons: Davey (3).
Referee: R Dickson, Scotland.
Att.: 7,882.

Sunday, 28th April 2002.
Franklin's Gardens, Northampton. Att.: 5,785.

GLOUCESTER 27 - 28 SALE

Half-time: 13-13
GLOUCESTER: C Catling; D O'Leary, T Fanolua, R Todd, J Simpson-Daniel; L Mercier, A Gomarsall; T Woodman, O Azam, P Vickery (captain), J Forrester, M Cornwell, E Pearce, K Sewabu, J Paramore. Replacements: D Albanese for O'Leary 40 mins., P Collazzo for Woodman 50 mins., R Fidler for Pearce 50 mins., J Boer for Sewabu 50 mins., H Paul for Catling 73 mins., C Fortey for Azam 73 mins..
Scorers: Tries: Fanloua (2), Forrester. DG: Mercier. Pen: Mercier. Cons: Mercier (3).
SALE: J Robinson; M Cueto, M Shaw, D Harris, S Hanley; C Hodgson, B Redpath (captain); K Yates, C Marais, S Turner, A Sanderson, I Fullarton, C Jones, S Pinkerton, P Anglesea.
Replacements: R Wilks for Sanderson 60 mins., A Black for Turner 68 mins., M Deane for Harris 76 mins..
Scorers: Tries: Cueto, Hanley, Marais, Harris. Pens: Hodgson (2). Con: Hodgson.
Referee: N Whitehouse, Wales.

FINAL

Sunday, 26th May 2002.
Kassam Stadium, Oxford. Att.: 12,000

SALE 25-22 PONTYPRIDD

Half-time: 0-15.

SALE: J Robinson; M Cueto, M Shaw, M Deanes, S Hanley; C Hodgson, B Redpath (captain); K Yates, C Marais, S Turner, A Sanderson, S Lines, C Jones, S Pinkerton, P Anglesea.
Replacements: D Harris for Deane 65 mins., A Titterell for Marais 65 mins.. Temp. replacements: J Baxendell for Hodgson 12-17 mins., A Black for Sanderson 31-40 mins..
Scorers; Tries: Shaw, Hanley, Harris.Pens: Hodgson (2). Cons: Hodgson (2).

PONTYPRIDD: B Davey; G Wyatt, S Parker, J Bryant, R Johnston; C Sweeney, P John (captain); G Jenkins, M Davies, D Bell, M Kelly, B Cockbain, R Sidoli, R Parks, M Owen. Replacements: G Remnant for Kelly 73 mins., M Rees for M Davies 80 mins..
Scorers: Try: M Davies. DG: Sweeney. Pens: Davey (4). Con: Davey.
Referee: A Lewis, Ireland.

HEINEKEN EUROPEAN CUP 2001-02

POOL ONE

Saturday, 29th September 2001
Leicester 12 Llanelli 9
Perpignan 56 Calvisano 3
Friday, 5th October 2001
Llanelli 20 Perpignan 6
Sunday, 7th October 2001
Calvisano 3 Leicester 37
Saturday, 27th October 2001
Perpignan 30 Leicester 31
Sunday, 28th Ocoober 2001
Calvisano 13 Llanelli 31
Saturday, 3rd November 2001
Llanelli 93 Amatori & Calvisano 14
Leicester 53 Perpignan 15
Friday, 4th January 2002
Perpignan 42 Llanelli 10
Saturday, 5th Jabuary 2002
Leicester 29 Calvisano 7
Saturday, 12th January 2002
Calvisano 18 Perpignan 33
Llanelli 24 Leicester 12

POOL 1	P	W	D	L	F	A	T	Pts
Leicester	6	5	0	1	175	88	17	10
Llanelli	6	4	0	2	187	99	22	8
Perpignan	6	3	0	3	182	136	19	6
Calvisano	6	0	0	6	58	379	6	0

Leicester and Llanelli qualify.

POOL TWO

Saturday, 29th September 2001
Treviso 28 Ulster 33
Sunday, 30th September 2001
Wasps 19 Stade Francais 25
Friday, 5th October 2001
Ulster 42 Wasps 19
Saturday, 6th October 2001
Stade Francais 42 Treviso 9
Saturday, 27th October 2001
Stade Francais 40 Ulster 11
Sunday, 28th October 2001
Wasps 29 Treviso 24
Friday, 2nd November 2001
Ulster 19 Stade Francais 16
Saturday, 3rd November 2001
Benetton Treviso 32 Wasps 17
Saturday, 5th January 2002
Treviso 6 Stade Francais 59
Sunday, 6th January 2002
Wasps 36 Ulster 32
Friday, 11th January 2002
Ulster 9 59 Treviso 3
Saturday, 12th January 2002
Stade Francais 31 Wasps 0

POOL 2	P	W	D	L	F	A	T	Pts
Stade Francais	6	5	0	1	213	64	23	10
Ulster	6	4	0	2	198	142	17	8
Wasps	6	2	0	4	120	186	9	4
Treviszo	6	1	0	5	102	230	2	2

Stade Francais qualify.

POOL THREE

Saturday, 29th September 2001
Biarritz 6 Bath 14
Swansea 21 Edinburgh 16
Friday, 5th October 2001
Edinburgh 6 Biarritz 6
Saturday, 6th October 2001
Bath 38 Swansea 9
Saturday, 27th October 2001
Edinburgh 6 Bath 37
Swansea 15 Biarritz 10
Saturday, 3rd November 2001
Bath 15 Edinburgh 10
Biarritz Olympique 24 Swansea 15
Saturday, 5th January 2002
Biarritz 45 Edinburgh 14
Swansea 12 Bath 24
Friday, 11th January 2002
Edinburgh 30 Swansea 20
Saturday, 12th January 2002
Bath 31 Biarritz 13

POOL 3	P	W	D	L	F	A	T	Pts
Bath	6	6	0	0	161	56	16	12
Biarritz	6	2	1	3	104	95	11	5
Swansea	6	2	0	4	92	142	2	4
Edinburgh	6	1	1	4	82	146	6	2

Bath qualify.

POOL FOUR

Saturday, 29th September 2001
Munster 28 Castres Olympique 23
Bridgend 24 Harlequins 30
Saturday, 6th October 2001
Castres Olympique 35 Bridgend 23
Harlequins 8 Munster 24
Friday, 26th October 2001
Bridgend 12 Munster 16
Sunday, 28th October 2001
Harlequins 17 Castres Olympique 39
Saturday, 3rd November 2001
Munster 40 Bridgend 6
Castres Olympique 24 Harlequins 18
Saturday, 5th January 2002
Munster 51 Harlequins 17
Bridgend 26 Castres Olympique 37
Saturday, 12th January 2002
Castres Olympique 21 Munster 13
Harlequins 29 Bridgend 25

POOL 4	P	W	D	L	F	A	T	Pts
Castres Olymp	6	5	0	1	179	125	19	10
Munster	6	5	0	1	172	87	17	10
Harlequins	6	2	0	4	119	187	14	4
Bridgend	6	0	0	6	116	187	11	0

Castres Olympique and Munster qualify.

POOL FIVE

Friday, 28th September 2001
Cardiff 25 Northampton 17
Glasgow 19 Montferrand 19
Saturday, 6th October 2001
Montferrand 37 Cardiff 10
Sunday, 7th October 2001
Northampton 30 Glasgow 9
Saturday, 27th October 2001
Cardiff 46 Glasgow 7
Northampton 15 Montferrand 21
Saturday, 3rd November 2001
Montferrand 50 Northampton 17
Sunday, 4td November 2001
Glasgow 47 Cardiff 32
Friday, 4th January 2002
Glasgow 31 Northampton 27
Saturday, 5th January 2002
Cardiff 26 Montferrand 20
Saturday, 12th January 2002
Northampton 26 Cardiff 15
Sunday, 13th January 2002
Montferrand 44 Glasgow 13

TABLE	P	W	D	L	F	A	T	Pts
Montferrand	6	4	1	1	191	100	23	9
Cardiff	6	3	0	3	154	154	16	6
Glasgow	6	2	1	3	126	198	10	5
Northampton	6	2	0	4	132	151	12	4

Montferrand qualify.

POOL SIX

Friday, 28th September 2001
Leinster 40 Tououse 10
Saturday, 29th September 2001
Newcastle 21 Newport 34
Friday, 5th October 2001
Leinster 28 Newcastle 9
Saturday, 6th October 2001
Newport 21 Toulouse 20
Friday, 26th October 2001
Leinster 21 Newport 6
Sunday, 28th October 2001
Tououse 33 Newcastle 13
Friday, 2nd November 2001
Newport 21 Leinster 26
Saturday, 3rd November 2001
Newcastle 42 Toulouse 9
Saturday, 5th January 2002
Toulouse 36 Newport 23
Newcastle v Leinster postponed
Tuesday, 8th January 2002
Newcastle 15 Leinster 17 (at Headingley, Leeds)
Friday, 11th January 2002
Newport 53 Newcastle 17
Sunday, 13th January 2002
Toulouse 43 Leinster 7

TABLE	P	W	D	L	F	A	T	Pts
Leinster	6	5	0	1	139	104	15	10
Toulouse	6	3	0	3	151	146	17	6
Newport	6	3	0	3	158	141	16	6
Newcastle	6	1	0	5	117	174	8	2

Leinster qualify.

QUARTER-FINALS:

Saturday, 26th January 2002 In Castres

CASTRES OLYMPIQUE 22-21 MONTFERRAND H.T.: 15-9

CASTRES OLYMPIQUE: R Teulet; F Plisson, E Artiguste, N Berryman, S Longstaff; G Townsend, A Albouy; M Reggiardo, R Vigneaux, B Moyle, R Froment, T Bourdet, N Spanghero, J Diaz, C Fernandez-Lobbe. Replacements: I Lassissi for Diaz 45 mins., S Chinamo for Bourdet 67 mins., O Sarramea for Teulet 80 mins.. Yellow card: Spanghero 15-25 mins.. **Scorers**: Try: Froment. DG: Townsend. Pens: Teulet (4). Con: Teulet.

MONTFERRAND: J Marlu; A Rougerie, J Ngaumo, T Marsh, D Bory; G Merceron, A Troncon; B Reidy, M Caputo, A Galasso, A Audebert, D Barrier (captain), S Boome, O Magne, E Vermeulen. Replacements: A Tolofua for Reidy 16 mins., I Gomez for Galasso 61 mins., C Dongieu for Audebert 75 mins.. Temp. replacement: O Machacek for Audebert 41-49 mins.. Yellow card: Bory 40-50 mins.. **Scorer**: Pens: Merceron (7). .

Referee: C White, England. Attendance: 9,500.

At Stade de France, Paris.

STADE FRANCAIS 14-16 MUNSTER H.T.: 3-16

STADE FRANCAIS: S Jonnet; N Williams, F Comba, N Raffault, R Poulain; D Dominguez, F Galthie (captain); S Marconnet, M Blin, P de Villiers, R Martin, D Auradou, M James, P Rabadan, C Juillet. Replacements: P Lemoine for Marconnet 66 mins., C Moni for Martin 78 mins.. Yellow card: Rabadan 67-77 mins..

Scorers: Try: Juillet. Pens: Dominguez (3). Con: Dominguez.

MUNSTER: D Crotty; J Kelly, R Henderson, J Holland, R Horgan; R O'Gara, P Stringer; P Clohessy, F Sheahan, J Hayes, J Williams, M Galwey (captain), P O'Connell, D Wallace, A Foley. Replacement: M Horan for Clohessy 79 mins.. Temp. replacement: Horan for Hayes 6-9 mins.. **Scorers**: Try: Horgan. DG: O'Gara. Pens: O'Gara (2). Con: O'Gara..

Referee: N Whitehouse, Wales. Attendance: 12,000.

Sunday, 27th January 2002 At Recreation Ground, Bath.

BATH 10-24 LLANELLI H.T.: 3-15

BATH: M Perry; I Balshaw, O Barkley, M Tindall, K Maggs; M Catt, A Williams; G Barnes, A Long, S Emms, G Thomas, S Borthwick, D Grewcock, M Gabey, N Thomas. Replacements: D Lyle for Gabey 41 mins., M Regan for Long 41 mins., G Cooper for Williams 56 mins., R Thirlby for Tindall 53 mins., D Dorsey for Emms 74 mins..

Scorer: Try: G Thomas. Pen: Barkley. Con: Barkley.

LLANELLI: G Evans; W Proctor, N Boobyer, L Davies, S Finau; S Jones, G Easterby; M Madden, R McBryde, J Davies, D Jodges, V Cooper, C Wyatt, S Easterby, S Quinnell. Replacements: B Davies for G Evans 42 mins., P Jones for Madden 78 mins., D Jones for S Easterby 78 mins.. **Scorers**: DG: S Jones. Pens: S Jones (8). .
Referee: A Lewis, Ireland. Attendance: 8,200.

At Welford Road, Leicester.
LEICESTER 29-18 LEINSTER H.T.: 24-13

LEICESTER: G Murphy; O Smith, L Lloyd, R Kafer, F Tuilagi; A Healey, J Hamilton; G Rowntree, R Cockerill, D Garforth, L Moody, M Johnson (captain0, B Kay, N Back, M Corry. Replacements: H Ellis for Hamilton 59 mins., J Kronfeld for Back 68 mins., A Balding for Corry 70 mins.. Yellow card: Moody 72-82 mins.. **Scorers**: Tries: Back (2), Lloyd (1), Healey (1), Murphy (1). Cons: Murphy (2).
LEINSTER: G Dempsey; D Hickie, B O'Driscoll, S Horgan, G D'Arcy; N Spooner, B Willis; R Corrigan (captain), S Byrne, P Wallace, E Miller, L Cullen, B Casey, K Gleeson, V Costello. Replacements: A Magro for Horgan 49 mins., A McCullen for Cullen 50 mins., S Keogh for D'Arcy 69 mins., P Coyle for Wallace 70 mins., G Hickie for Byrne 79 mins., T Brennan for Miller 79 mins. **Scorers**: Tries: Hickie (1), Willis (1). Pens: Spooner (2). Con: Spooner. .
Referee: J Jutge, France. Attendance: 16,249.

SEMI-FINALS:

Saturday, 27th April 2002
In Stade de la Mediterranee, Beziers.
CASTRES 17-25 MUNSTER Half-time: 9-6

CASTRES: R Teulet; U Mola, E Artiguste, N Berryman, S Longstaff; G Townsend (captain), A Albouy; M Reggiardo, R Ibanez, B Moyle, R Froment, I Fernandez-Lobbe, N Spanghero, I Lassissi, A Costes. Replacements: R Vigneaux for Ibanrz 40 mins., G Delmotte for Artiguste 51 mins., D Dima for Reggiardo 69 mins., S Chinarro for Spanghero 69 mins., F Plisson for Mola 79 mins., O Sarramea for Teulet 76 mins.. Temp. replacements: Dima for Froment 17-30 mins., Chinano for Costes 65-67 mins.. Yellow card: Moyle 19-29 mins..
Scorers: Try: Lomgstaff. Pens: Teulet (4).
MUNSTER: D Crotty; J Kelly, R Henderson, J Holland, R Horgan; R O'Gara, P Stringer; P Clohessy, F Sheahan, J Hayes, A Quinlan, M Galwey (captain), P O'Connell, D Wallace, A Foley. Replacements: D O'Callaghan for Foley 15 mins., M Horan for Clohessy 69 mins., J Staunton for Crotty 84 mins., M Mullins for Genderson 84 mins.. Temp. replacements: Horan for O'Connell 16-30 mins., Mullins for O'Gara 45-50 mins.. Yellow card: Clohessy 19-29 mins.. Scorers: Try: Kelly. Pens: O'Gara (6). Con: O'Gara.
Referee: C White, England. Attendance: 20,400

Sunday, 28th April 2002.
In City Ground, Nottingham.
LEICESTER 13-12 LLANELLI Half-time: 3-9.

LEICESTER: T Stimpson; G Murphy, O Smith, R Kafer, F Tuilagi; A Healey, H Ellis; G Rowntree, D West, D Garforth, L Moody, M Johnson (captain), B Kay, N Back, M Corry. Replacements: J Hamilton for Ellis 63 mins., L Lloyd for Tuilagi 71 mins..
Temp. replacement: A Balding for Corry 24-29 mins.. Scorers: Try: Ellis. Pens: Stimpson (2). Con: Stimpson.
LLANELLI: G Evans; M Jones, N Boobyer, L Davies, F Finau; S Jones, G Easterby; M Madden, R McBryde, J Davies, D Hodges, V Cooper, C Wyatt, S Easterby, S Quinnell (captain). Replacements: L Gross for Wyatt 70 mins., W Proctor for G Evans 71 mins., I Boobyer for Hodges 74 mins.. Scorer: Pens: S Jones (4).
Referee: D McHugh, Ireland. Attendance: 29,849

FINAL

Saturday, 25th May 2002
At Millennium Stadium, Cardiff Attendance: 74,000

LEICESTER 15-9 MUNSTER Half-time: 5-6

LEICESTER: T Stimpson; G Murphy, O Smith, R Kafer, F Tuilagi; A Healey, J Hamilton; G Rowntree, D West, D Garforth, L Moody, M Johnson (captain), B Kay, N Back, M Corry. Replacements: H Ellis for Hamilton 49 mins., P Freshwater for Rowntree 72 mins., G Gelderbloom for Smith 76 mins..
Scorers: Tries: Murphy (1), Healey (1). Pen: Stimpson. Con: Stimpson.
MUNSTER: D Crotty; J O'Neill, R Henderson, J Holland, J Kelly; R O'Gara, P Stringer; P Clohessy, F Sheahan, J Hayes, A Quinlan, M Galwey (captain), P O'Connell, D Wallace, A Foley.
Replacements: J Williams for Foley 51 mins., M Horan for Clohessy 60 mins., M O'Driscoll for O'Connell 60 mins., M Mullins for Henderson 65 mins., J Staunton for Crotty 65 mins.. Temp. replacement: J Blaney for Sheahan 16-28 mins..
Scorer: Pens: O'Gara (3).
Referee: J Jutge, France.

PowerGen Cup 2001-02

First Round

(Saturday 15th September)

Barking 26 Old Patesians 16
Barnstaple 7 Launceston 35
Blackheath 26 Haywards Heath 11
Bromsgrove 6 Darlington MP 48
Doncaster 79 Sandal 8
Dudley K 59 West Hartlepool 3
Hull Ionians 13 Westoe 12
Kettering 16 Lydney 29
Marlow 24 Clifton 14
Morley 23 Liverpool St Helens 28
Morpeth 17 Bedford Ath 32
New Brighton 35 Whitchurch 21
Norwich 22 Redruth 13
Nuneaton 17 Tynedale 9
Penzance & Newlyn 80 Cinderford 12
Scunthorpe 20 Winnington Park 18
Staines 15 North Walsham 28
Stroud 32 Camberley 12
Swanage & Wareham 10 Old Colfeians 34
Tabard 23 London Nigerians 38
Walsall 17 Blaydon 21
Westcombe Park 16 Reading 18

Reading releagted to South West One last season beat Westcombe Park away from home to progress to the second round. as sides from National Three South suffered at the hands of sides from lower down the league structure.
Other sides from lower division beating opposition from higher leagues were all to involve teams from National Three with four more falling by the wayside.
London Nigerians traveled to Tabard and came away convincing winners.
Stroud played host to Camberley and ran out 32-8 comfortable winners Marlow beat Clifton 24-14 to progress to the second round whilst the other side to suffer was Redruth who went down to London One side Norwich.
Penzance & Newlyn were the big scorers in the round with 80 points at home to Cinderford. They ran in 11 tries which were all converted by Nat Saumi who also added a penalty in a 25 point haul.

Second Round

(Saturday 29th September)

Barking 27 Old Colfians 18
Bedford Ath 16 Preston 44
Blackheath 18 Newbury 37
Blaydon 22 Fylde 28
Dudley K 36 Nottingham 3
Kendal 30 Doncaster 17
Launceston 19 Esher 10
Liverpool St H 37 Hull Ionians 15
London Nigerians 18 Marlow 15
Lydney 21 Reading 10
New Brighton 13 Harroagte 5
North Walsham 20 Penzance & Newlyn 10
Norwich 21 Stround 16
Nuneaton 31 Wharfedale 29
Orrell 83 Scunthorpe 8
Rosslyn Park 15 Plymouth 6
Sedgley Park 33 Stourbridge 13
Waterloo 20 Darlington MP 32

Two sides from outside the National league qualified for the nxt round after playing other sides from outside the National leagues. London Nigerians were winners at home to Marlow whilst Norwich also had the better with home advantage to beat Stround.
The biggest scorers of the round were Orrell who ran in 83 points at home to Scunthrpe. Leading the way for Orrell was Phil Jones with 33 points from two tries, 10 conversions and a penalty whilst Scottish centre Andy Craig scored a hat trick of tries.
High flying Plymouth Albion suffered a shock when they were beaten by Rosslyn Park who had nearly beaten them in the league a few weeks earlier.
Esher had the tough trip to Launceston from the division below them and were tunred over by the powerful Cornish side. The only other side to beat a team from below them in the league structure was Darlington MP who won at Waterloo.

Third round

(Saturday 13th October)

Bedford 19 Wakefield 22
Darlington MP 31 Dudley K 25
Henley Hawks 54 Liverpool St H 14
Kendal 6 Manchester 16
Launceston 26 Exeter 40
London Nigerians 8 London Welsh 43
Lydney 0 Worcester 45
Moseley 25 North Walsham 17
Newbury 36 Barking 23
Norwich 20 Fylde 32
Nuneaton 31 New Brighton 7
Otley 23 Bracknell 19
Preston 15 Birmingham & Sol 49
Rosslyn Park 32 Orrell 40
Rotherham 48 Rugby Lions 3
Sedgley Park 22 Coventry 40

There were no real shocks with no team from a lower division able to beat a side from above them in the league ladder. National One side Wakefield went to Bedford, wh started well in the league, and came away with a surprise narrow win.
Nuneaton were comfortable winners against New Brighton who over the last few years have done well in the Cup but started the season in less than convincing style.
Orrell were involved in a tough high scoring match at Rosslyn Park before coming away with a 40-32 win.
National Three South side North Walsham went to Moseley and gave them a run for their money before going down after putting up a spirited display

Fourth Round

(Saturday 3rd November)

Birmingham & Sol 35 Wakefield 6
Darlington MP 27 Manchester 39
Exeter 30 London Welsh 3
Henley Hawks 48 Otley 30
Moseley 3 Worcester 50
Newbury 29 Nuneaton 8
Orrell 37 Fylde 9
Rotherham 51 Coventry 27

Another round in which there were no shock results. Darlington Mowden Park, two leagues below, gave Manchester a good match before going down to the National One Side.
Only Orrell and Newbury from outside National One qualified for the next round of the competition.

Fifth Round

(Saturday 24th November)

Birmingham & Sol 35 Henley Hawks 22
Manchester 20 Exeter 30
Newbury 25 Orrell 30
Worcester 19 Rotherham 26

Three of the Fifth round matches went to the away side but in each one you would have expected that with maybe the exception of Worcester having home advantage against Rotherham. Orrell were the only non National One sides to make the next round after their win at fellow National Two side Newbury.

Sixth Round

(Saturday 15th December)
Bath 12 London Irish 20
Leicester 27 Exeter 0
Orrell 22 Leeds Tykes 31
Northampton 32 Birmingham & Solihull 19
Sale 25 Harlequins 32 aet
(Sunday 16th December)
Bristol 23 Gloucester 37
Newcastle 24 London Wasps 22
Saracens 43 Rotherham 17

The Zurich Premiership sides joined the PowerGen Cup in the sixth round along with the four remaining sides from the previous round, three from National One and one from National Two. By the end of the weekend fixtures we were left with eight Premiership sides.
In the Orrell v Leeds Tykes matcg we had two Rugby League stars confronting each other - Gary Connolly playing for Orrrell against Graham Mackay of Leeds Tykes.

Quarter Finals

Saturday 19th Janaury

Harlequins 22 Leicester Tigers 20

Saracens 28 Northampton 30

Sunday 20th Janauryr

Leeds Tykes 24 Newcastle Falcons 41

London Irish 25 Gloucester 10

Despite their poor league form Harlequins continue to do well in the Cup with a narrow win against Leicester for the second successive season.
If proved the difference.
Newcastle ran out winners at Leeds but not before they were given a run for their money.
London Irish use home advantage to beat Gloucester and reach just their fourth ever semi final.

Semi- Finals

Saturday 9th March

Harlequins 27 London Irish 32

Attendance: 8,274
Referee: S Leyshon (Bristol)

HARLEQUINS: D Sleman (rep B Gollings 63): R Jewell, W Greenwood, N Burrows, D Luger, P Burke, N Duncombe; J Leonard, A Tiatia, A Olver, A Codling, S White-Cooper (rep G Morgan 27), R Winters, P Sanderson (rep L Sherriff 73), A Diprose.
LONDON IRISH: M Horak: J Bishop, G Appleford, B Venter, P Sackey, B Everitt, H Martens (rep D Edwards 46); R Hardwick (rep D Wheatley 52), R Kirke (rep A Drotske 46), S Halford, R Strudwick, S Williams (rep G Delaney 67, E Halvey, D Danaher, C Sheasby.
Scoring sequence: (Harlequins first) 00-3, 0-6, 0-13, 0-19, 0-26, 7-26, 10-26 (half time), 13-26, 20-26, 27-26, 27-29, 27-32.
Scorers: Harlequins: Tries: Codling (34), Tiatia (56), Diprose (69). Conversions: Burke 3. Pens: Burke 2 (40, 42)
London Irish: Tries: Venter (15), Horak (29). Conversions: Everitt 2. Penalty goals Everitt 6 (6, 9, 19, 24, 76, 80+4)

The Irish reach just their second National Cup final in 28 attempts.
For Quins it was a 8th semi final defeat in thirteen appearances as they attempted to reach successive Twickenham finals.

Saturday 9th March

Northampton 38 Newcastle Falcons 7

Attendance: 11,652
Referee: T Spreadbury (RFU)

NORTHAMPTON: N Beal: C Moir, P Jorgensen, J Leslie (rep M Tucker 69), B Cohen, P Grayson (J Brooks 58), M Dawson (rep I Vass 74): R Morris (rep T Smith 41), D Richmond (rep S Thompson 50), M Stewart (rep R Morris 71), J Ackermann, O Brouzet, A Blowers (rep R Hunter 71), B Pountney (sin bin 49-59), G Seely (rep M Soden 67).
NEWCASTLE : L Botham: M Stephenson, J Noon, T May, I Tuigamala, J Wilkinson, G Armstrong: G Graham, M Thompson(rep N Makin 65), M Hurter, H Vyvyna (sin bin 19-29), S Grimes, E Taione, A Mower, P Lam.
Scoring sequence: (Northampton first): 7-0, 10-0, 13-0, 18-0, 23-0, 26-0, 33-0 (half time), 38-0, 38-7.
SCORERS: Northampton: Tries: Seely 2 (3, 33), Jorgensen 2 (29, 76), Moir (37). Cons: Grayson 2 Pens: Grayson 3 (7, 19, 36).
Newcastle: Try: Stephenson (80+3). Con: Wilkinson.

Northampton reach their third National Cup final and will be hoping to make it third time lucky having lost on both their previous Twickenham finals.

FINAL

Saturday 20th April

London Irish 38 Northampton Saints 7

Attendance: 75,000
Referee: Steve Lander (RFU)

LONDON IRISH: M Horak: P Sackey, G Appleford, B Venter (rep R Hoadley 76), J Bishop, B Everitt (rep J Brown 80), H Martens (rep D Edwards 57): M Worsley (sin bin 59-69), N Drotske (rep R Kirke 46), R Hardwick (rep S Halford 46), R Strudwick (capt), S Williams (rep G Delaney 73), E Halvey (rep J Cockle 76), D Danaher (rep Hardwick 64-69), C Sheasby.
NORTHAMPTON SAINTS: N Beal: C Moir (rep J Brooks 41), P Jorgensen, J Leslie (rep M Tucker 76), B Cohen, P Grayson, M Dawson: T Smith, S Thompson (rep D Richmond 51), M Stewart (rep R Morris 51; sin bin 59-69), J Ackermann (rep J Phillips 57 rep Stewart 64-69), O Brouzet, A Blowers, B Pountney, G Seely.

SCORERS:
London Irish:
Tries:
Appleford 2 (14, 25),
Bishop 2 (35, 78),
Horak (20).
Cons: Everitt 5
Pen: Everitt (32).

Northampton:
Try: Cohen (60).
Con: Grayson.

Scoring sequence:
(London Irish first):
7-0,
14-0,
17-0,
24-0
(half time),
24-7,
31-7,
38-7.

London Irish won their first ever National Cup in their second appearance in a final.
For the Saints it was a third defeat in a National Cup final and they still search for that elusive win.
Chris Sheasby, after having picked up two losers medals for Harlequins, make it third time lucky.

RFU SENIOR CUP
INDIVIDUAL MEDALLISTS

(asterisk signifys an appearance as a substitute)*

Name	Club	Result
ACKERMAN, RA	Lon. Welsh	L - 85
ACKERMANN, J	Northampton	L - 02
ACKFORD, PJ	Harlequins	W - 88, 91 L - 92
ADCASTER, SD	Moseley	W - 82
ADEBAYO, AA	Bath	W - 90, 94, 95, 96
ADEY, GJ	Leicester	W - 79, 80, 81 L - 78
AKENHEAD, R	Moseley	L - 79
ALEXANDER, JR	Harlequins	L - 93
ALLEN, M	Northampton	L - 00
ALSTON, P	Northampton	L - 91
ANDERSON, TR	Gosforth	L - 81
ANDERSON, PG	Rosslyn Park	L - 75
ANDREW, CR	Wasps	L - 87, 95
APPLEFORD, G	London Irish	W - 02
ARCHER, G	Newcastle	L - 99
ARCHER, JS	Gosforth	W - 77 L - 81
ARMSTRONG, G	Newcastle	W - 01.L - 99
ARNOLD, R	Newcastle	W - 01.L - 99
ASHURST, N	Sale	L - 97
ASTLEY, KJ	Moseley	L - 79
AYRE, B	Moseley	L - 79
BACK, NA	Leicester	W - 93, 97 L - 94, 96
BAILEY, MD	Wasps	L - 86, 87
BAILWARD, CJ	Bedford	W - 75
BAINBRIDGE, S	Gosforth	L - 81
BAKER, SJW	Gloucester	W - 82
BALCOMBE, P	Wasps	L - *86
BALDWIN, D	Sale	L - 97
BALDWIN, G	Northampton	L - 91
BALL, I	Waterloo	L - 77
BARKER, RG	Leicester	L - 78
BARKER, N	Bedford	W - 75
BARLOW, RL	Rosslyn Park	L - 75
BARNES, S	Bath	W - 86, 87, 89, 90, 92, 94
	BristoL	W - 83 L - 84
BARNWELL, RC	Coventry	W - 74
	Leicester	W - 79, 80, 81 L - 83
BARTON, J	Coventry	W - 73
BATEMAN, A	Northampton	L - 00
BATES, SM	Wasps	L - 86, 87, 95
BATES, I	Leicester	W - 93 L - *83, 89
BAXENDALE, J	Sale	L - 97
BAYLISS, JA	Gloucester	W - 72
BAZALGETTE, MB	Rosslyn Park	L - 75
BEAL, N	Northampton	L - 00, 02
BEALE, JD	Moseley	L - 79
BEATTIE, R	Newcastle	L - 99
BEIM, T	Sale	L - 97
BELL, JAH	Gosforth	L - 81
BELL, TP	Harlequins	W - 88
BELL, DE	Lon. Scot	L - 74
BENNETT, WN	Bedford	W - 75
BERINGER, GG	Lon. Irish	L - 80
BESS, G	Bath	W - 85, *87
BIGGAR, AG	Lon. Scot	L - 74
BIGGAR, MA	Lon. Scot	L - 74
BILLINGHAM, MF	Waterloo	L - 77
BISHOP, J	London Irish	W - 02
BLACK, A	Wasps	L - *98
BLACKHURST, F	Waterloo	L - 77
BLACKMORE, AG	Bristol	L - 88
BLAKEWAY, PJ	Gloucester	W - 82
BLOWERS, A	Northampton	L - 02
BOGIRA, MK	Bristol	W - 83
BONNER, J	Wasps	L - 86, 87
BOOTH, MH	Gloucester	W - 72
BOWRING, K	Lon. Welsh	L - 85
BOYLE, LS	Leicester	L - 94
BOYLE, SB	Gloucester	W - 78 82
BRACKEN, K	Saracens	W - 98
BRADLEY, B	Lon. Welsh	L - 85
BRAIN, J	Gloucester	L - 90
BRAY, KA	Harlequins	L - 93
BREAKEY, RW	Gosforth	W - 76, 77 L - 81
BREEZE, J	Gloucester	L - 90
BRINN, A	Gloucester	W - 72
BRITTEN, JK	Gosforth	W - 76, 77
BRODERICK, JM	Coventry	W - 73, 74
BROOKS, J	Northampton	L - *02
BROWN, J	London Irish	W - *02
BROUZET, O	Northampton	L - 02
BULPITT, MA	Rosslyn Park	L - 76
BURKE, P	Harlequins	L - 01
BURROWS, N	Harlequins	L - 01
BURTON, MA	Gloucester	W - 72, 78
BURWELL, T	Leicester	W - 79, 80
BUTLAND, R	Bath	W - 95
BUTLER, JL	Gosforth	L - 81
BUTLER, PE	Gloucester	W - 78
BYRNE, L	Rosslyn Park	L - *76
CALLARD, JEB	Bath	W - 90, 94, 95, 96
CARDUS, RM	Wasps	L - 86
CARDWELL, R	Coventry	W - 74
CARFOOT, DJ	Waterloo	L - 77
CARLING, WDC	Harlequins	W - 88, 91 L - 92, 93
CARR, JF	Bristol	W - 83 L - 84, 88
CARTMELL, J	Newcastle	L - *99
CASKIE, D	Gloucester	L - 90
CATT, MJ	Bath	W - 94, 96
CHADWICK, R	Bedford	W - 75
CHALLINOR, AP	Harlequins	L - 92, 93
CHIDGEY, DL	Bristol	L - 84
CHILCOTT, GJ	Bath	W - 84, 85, 86, 87, 89, 90, 92
CHILDS, G	Wasps	L - 95
CHRISTOPHERSON, SF	Waterloo	L - 77
CHUTER, G	Saracens	W - 98
CLARKE, BB	Bath	W - 92, 94, 95
CLEWS, RJ	Gloucester	W - 72, 78
COCKERILL, R	Leicester	W - 93, 97 L - 94, 96
COCKLE, J	London Irish	W - *02
CODD, RA	Rosslyn Park	L - 75
CODLING,A	Harlequins	L - *01
COHEN, B	Northampton	L - 00, 02
COKER, T	Harlequins	W - 91
COLLINGS, P	Bristol	L - 88
COLLINS, J	Lon. Welsh	L - 85
CONDON, HC	Lon. Irish	L - 80
CONSTABLE, R	Saracens	W - 98
CONNOR, L	Waterloo	L - 77
COOPER, MJ	Moseley	W - 82 L - 79
CORLESS, TF	Moseley	W - 82
CORLESS BJ	Coventry	W - 74
	Moseley	L - 79
CORSTORPHINE, AE	Lon. Scot	L - 74

COWLING, RJ	Leicester	W - 79, 80, 81
	Gloucester	W - 72
COWMAN, AR	Coventry	W - 73, 74
COX, GNJ	Moseley	W - 82 L - 79
CREED, RN	Coventry	W - 73
CRERAR, RD	Lon. Scot	L - 74
CRONIN, DF	Bath	W - 89, 90
CUE, PC	Bristol	L - 84
CUNNINGHAM, R	Gosforth	L - 81
	Bath	W - 84
CURTIS, PS	Harlequins	W - 88
CUSWORTH, L	Leicester	W - 79, 80, 81 L - 83, 89
CUTTER, AJ	Gosforth	W - 76, 77
DALLAGLIO, LBN	Wasps	W-99, 00 L - 95, 98
DANAHER, D	London Irish	W - 02
DANDY, MJW	Bristol	L - 73
DANIEL, B	Saracens	W - 98
	Harlequins	L - 01
DARNELL, IR	Coventry	W - 73, 74
DAVIDSON, JS	Moseley	W - 82
DAVIES, GH	Wasps	L - 87
DAVIS, EG	Harlequins	W - 88, 91 L - 92
DAWE, RGR	Bath	W - 86, 87, 89, 90, 92, 94, 95, 96
DAWSON, J	Harlequins	L - 01
DAWSON, M	Northampton	L - 00, 02
DELANEY, G	London Irish	W - *02
DEMMING, R	Bedford	W - 75
DENNEY, M	Wasps	W - 99, 00 L - 98
DESBOROUGH, JE	Moseley	W - 82
DEVONSHIRE, R	Newcastle	W - 01
DIAMOND, S	Sale	L - 97
DIPROSE, A	Saracens	W - 98
DIX, J	Gloucester	W - 72
DIXON, PJ	Gosforth	W - 76, 77
DOBLE, SA	Moseley	L - 72
DOBSON, I	Leicester	L - 83
DODGE, PW	Leicester	W - 79, 80, 81 L - 78, 83, 89
DOUBLEDAY, RJ	Bristol	W - 83 L - 84, 88
DOUGLAS, MHJL	Lon. Welsh	L - 85
DROTSKE, A	London Irish	W - 02
DUCKHAM, DJ	Coventry	W - 73, 74
DUGGAN, MJ	Leicester	L - 78
DUGGAN, IH	Bristol	W - 83 L - 88
DUN, AF	Bristol	L - 88
DUNN, KA	Wasps	L - 95
	Gloucester	L - 90
DUNSTON, I	Wasps	L - 95
EBSWORTH, M	Lon. Welsh	L - 85
EDWARDS, NGB	Harlequins	W - 88 L - 92
EDWARDS, EF	Bedford	W - 75
EDWARDS, D	London Irish	W - * 02
EGERTON, DW	Bath	W - 87, 89, 90
ELKINGTON, D	Northampton	L - 91
ERSKINE, D	Sale	L - 97
ETHERIDGE, J	Northampton	L - 91
EVANS, BJ	Leicester	L - 83, 89
EVANS, GW	Coventry	W - 73
EVERITT, B	London Irish	W - 02
FAIRBROTHER, KE	Coventry	W - 73, 74
FALLON, JA	Bath	W - 92
FIDLER, JH	Gloucester	W - 78
FIELD, R	Moseley	L - 79
FINLAN, JF	Moseley	L - 72

FISHER, RG	Rosslyn Park	L - 75
FISHER, CD	Waterloo	L - 77
FLETT, MA	Waterloo	L - 77
FLUSKEY, S	Rosslyn Park	L - 76
FORD, P	Gloucester	W - 82
FORFAR, DJ	Leicester	L - 78
FOUHY, D	Lon. Welsh	L - 85
FOULKES-ARNOLD, M	Leicester	L - 83, 89
FOULKS, D	Coventry	W - 74
FOWLIE, DG	Lon. Scot	L - 74
FRASER, G	Lon. Scot	L - 74
FRIDAY, M	Wasps	W-"99 L - 98
FRIELL, AAS	Lon. Scot	L - 74
FRY, MJ	Bristol	L - 73
GADD, J	Gloucester	W - 82 L - 90
GALLAGHER, J	Coventry	W - 74
GARFORTH, DJ	Leicester	W - 93, 97 L - 94, 96
GAYMOND, N	Bath	W - 84, 85
GIFFORD, CJ	Moseley	L - 79
GILLINGHAM, NK	Leicester	W - 80 L - 83
GITTINGS, WJ	Coventry	W - 73, 74
DE GLANVILLE, PR	Bath	W - 92, 94, 95, 96
GLENISTER, RJ	Harlequins	W - 91 L - 93
GOLLINGS, B	Harlequins	L - *01
GOMERSALL, A	Wasps	W-99 L - *98
GOODWIN, JM	Moseley	W - 82
GRAHAM, G	Newcastle	L - 99
GRAU, R	Saracens	W - 98
GRAY, JD	Coventry	W - 73
GRAYSON, P	Northampton	L - 00, 02
GREAVES, WH	Moseley	L - 79
GREEN, W	Wasps	W-99, 00 L - 98
GREENSTOCK, N	Wasps	L - 95
	Harlequins	L - 01
GREENWOOD, M	Wasps	L - 95
GREENWOOD, W	Leicester	W - 97
	Harlequins	L - 01
GREWCOCK, D	Saracens	W - 98
GRIFFIN, SM	Gosforth	W - 76
GRIFFITHS, J	Moseley	L - 72
GRIMES, S	Newcastle	W - 01
GUSCOTT, JC	Bath	W - *85, 87, 89, 90, 92, 95
GUSTARD, JS	Gosforth	W - 76, 77
HAAG, M	Bath	W - 92, 95, 96
HACKNEY, S	Leicester	L - 96
HADLEY, A	Sale	L - 97
HADLEY, N	Wasps	L - 95
HALFORD, S	London Irish	W - *02
HALL, C	Northampton	L - 91
HALL, BP	Leicester	L - 78
HALL, JP	Bath	W - 84, 85, 86, 87, 89, 94
HALLIDAY, SJ	Harlequins	W - 91 L - 92
	Bath	W - 85, 86, 87, 89, 90
HALVEY, E	London Irish	W - 02
HAMLIN, M	Gloucester	L - 90
HANCOCK, K	Waterloo	L - 77
HANNAFORD, M	Gloucester	L - 90
HANNAFORD, RC	Bristol	L - 73
HARDING, RM	Bristol	W - 83 L - 84, 88
HARDWICK, R	London Irish	W - 02
HARE, WH	Leicester	W - 79, 80, 81 L - 78, 89
HARRIMAN, AT	Harlequins	W - 88, 91
HARRIS, JC	Leicester	W - 93 L - 94

Name	Club	Result
HATTER, K	Moseley	L - 72
HAZLERIGG, AG	Leicester	W - 79 L - 78
HEALEY, A	Leicester	W - 97
HEDLEY, J	Gosforth	W - 77
HENDERSON, R	Wasps	W - *99, 00 L - 98
HESFORD, R	Bristol	W - 83
HILL, RJ	Bath	W - 84, 85, 86, 87, 89, 90, 92, 94
HILTON, DIW	Bath	W - 94, 96
HINTON, NP	Rosslyn Park	L - 75, 76
HOADLEY, R	London Irish	W - 02
HOBLEY, MJ	Harlequins	L - 92
HOGG, ST	Bristol	W - 83 L - 84, 88
HOLLINS, AJ	Bedford	W - 75
HOLMES, G	Wasps	L - 86
HOLT, BC	Coventry	W - 73
HONE, W	Bristol	L - 88
HOOKER, C	Bedford	W - 75
HOPLEY, P	Wasps	L - 95
HOPLEY, DP	Wasps	L - 95
HORAK, M	London Irish	W - 02
HORTON, JP	Bath	W - 84, 85
HORTON, NE	Moseley	L - 72
HOWARD, JM	Bedford	W - 75
HOWELL, PR	Gloucester	W - 78
HUGHES, J	Lon. Welsh	L - 85
HUNTER, I	Northampton	L - 91
HURTER, M	Newcastle	L - 99. W 01
JACKSON, N	Leicester	W - 81
JACKSON, GT	Waterloo	L - 77
JARDINE, R	Gloucester	W - 78
JARRETT, JS	Gloucester	W - 72
JEAVONS, NC	Moseley	W - 82 L - 79
JENKINS, R	Harlequins	L - 01*
JENNER, J	Newcastle	W - 01
JOHNS, P	Saracens	W - 98
JOHNSON, D	Gosforth	L - 81
JOHNSON, G	Saracens	W - 98
JOHNSON, SR	Leicester	W - 79, 80, 81 L - 78, 83
JOHNSON, MO	Leicester	W - 93, 97 L - 94, 96
JOINER, C	Leicester	W - 97
JONES, W	Lon. Irish	L - 80
JONES, TW	Lon. Welsh	L - 85
JONES, B	Leicester	L - 78
JONES, L	Gloucester	W - 82
JORDEN, AM	Bedford	W - 75
JORGENSEN, P	Northampton	L - 02
JOYCE, NJ	Leicester	W - 79, 80, 81 L - 78
KARDOONI, A	Leicester	W - 93,* 97 L - 89, 94, 96
KEDDIE, RR	Lon. Scot	L - 74
KEEN, B	Bedford	W - 75
d'A KEITH-ROACH,	Rosslyn Park	L - 75, 76
KENNEY, S	Leicester	W - 79, 80, 81 L - 78
KENT, CP	Rosslyn Park	L - 76
KERR, R	Moseley	L - 72
KILFORD, WA	Leicester	L - 94
KILLICK, N	Harlequins	L - 93
KING, A	Wasps	W - 99, 00 L - 98
KING, S	Moseley	L - *79
KIRKE, R	London Irish	W - *02
KNIBBS, RA	Bristol	W - 83 L - 84, 88
KNIGHT, S	Bath	W - "90
KNIGHT, PM	Bristol	L - 73
LAIRD, R	Moseley	L - 79
LAM, P	Northampton	L - 00
LANE, DE	Moseley	L - 72
LANGHORN, RS	Harlequins	W - 88, 91 L - 93
LAWSON, RD	Moseley	W - 82
LE CHEVALIER	Wasps	W - *00
LEE, MR	Bath	W - 84, 85, 86, 89
LEGG, S	Newcastle	L - 99
LEONARD, J	Harlequins	W - 91 L - 93, 01
LEOPOLD, DA	Lon. Irish	L - 80
LEOTA, T	Wasps	W - 99, 00 L-"98
LEWIS, E	Lon. Welsh	L - 85
LEWIS, A	Bedford	W - 75
LESLIE, J	Northampton	L - 02
LEWSEY, J	Wasps	W - 99, 00
LIGHT, B	Lon. Welsh	L - 85
LILEY, J	Leicester	W - 93 L - 96
LINK, G	Rosslyn Park	L - 75
LLOYD, L	Leicester	W - 97
LLOYD-ROBERTS, G	Rosslyn Park	L - 76
LOGAN, K	Wasps	W - *99, 00
LONGSTAFF, M	Gloucester	W - 82
LOVETT, MS	Lon. Scot	L - 74
LOZOWSKI, RAP	Wasps	L - 87
LUMSDEN, A	Bath	W - 96
LUNT, K	Waterloo	L - 77
LUXTON, TC	Harlequins	L - 92
LYNAGH, M	Sarecens	W - 98
MacKINNON	Northampton	L - *00
MacMILLAN, AJ	Gosforth	L - 81
MADDERSON, CS	Harlequins	L - 93
MADSEN, DF	Gosforth	W - 76, 77
MALLETT, J	Bath	W - *95, 96
MALLINDER, J	Sale	L - 97
MALONE, NG	Leicester	W - 97 L - 96
MANNIX, S	Sale	L - 97
MANTELL, ND	Rosslyn Park	L - 75, 76
MARTENS, H	London Irish	W - 02
MARTIN, CR	Bath	W - 84, 85, 86, 87
MAY, T	Newcastle	W - 01.L - 99
McDOWELL, NH	Gosforth	L - 81
McFADYAN, CW	Moseley	L - 72
McHARG, AF	Lon. Scot	L - 74
McKAY, DJ	Rosslyn Park	L - 75
McKENZIE, RA	Lon. Scot	L - 74
McKIBBIN, R	Lon. Irish	L - 80
McKIBBIN, AR	Lon. Irish	L - 80
MEANWELL, CA	Lon. Irish	L - 80
MENDEZ, F	Northampton	L - 00
METCALFE, R	Northampton	L - 00
MILLER, E	Leicester	W - 97
MILLS, SGF	Gloucester	W - 78, 82
MITCHELL, J	Sale	L - 97
MITCHELL, S	Wasps	L - 98
MOGG, RR	Gloucester	W - 78, 82 L - 90
MOIR, C	Northampton	L - 00, 02
MOLLOY, D	Wasps	W - 99, 00 L - 95, 98
MOON, RHQB	Harlequins	W - 88
MOORE, BC	Harlequins	W - 91 L - 92
MORDELL, R	Rosslyn Park	L - 76
MORGAN, D	Gloucester	L - 90
MORGAN, G	Harlequins	L - 01
MORLEY, AJ	Bristol	W - 83 L - 73, 84
MORRELL, CC	Moseley	L - 72
MORRIS, D	Sale	L - 97
MORRIS, R	Gloucester	W - 72
MORRIS, R	Moseley	L - 72

Name	Club	Result
MORRIS, R	Northampton	L - *02
MORRISON, JSC	Bath	W - 86, 87, 89
MOSS, P	Northampton	L - 91
MOWER, A	Newcastle	W - 01
MOYLES, JL	Rosslyn Park	L - 76
MULLINS, AR	Harlequins	W - 88, 91 L - 92, 93
MUNDEN, AC	Bristol	L - 73
MURPHY, BW	Lon. Irish	L - 80
NANCEKIVELL, R	Northampton	L - 91
NAYLOR, J	Newcastle	L - 99
NEEDHAM, RJ	Leicester	L - 78
NESDALE, R	Newcastle	W - 01.L - 99
NEWBERRY, JA	Lon. Irish	L - 80
NEWMAN, A	Northampton	L - 00
NEWTON, M	Leicester	W - 79
NICHOLLS, MJ	Gloucester	W - 72
NICHOLLS, AH	Bristol	L - 73
NICOL, AD	Bath	W - 96
NINNES, BF	Coventry	W - 73, 74
NOON, J	Newcastle	W - 01
NUTT, DR	Moseley	W - 82 L - 79
O'DONNELL, P	Lon. Irish	L - 80
O'DRISCOLL, JB	Lon. Irish	L - 80
O'GRADY, D	Sale	L - 97
O'NEILL, R	Harlequins	L - 01
OJOMOH, SO	Bath	W - 92, *94, 95, 96
OLSEN, M	Saracens	W - *98
OLVER, A	Saracens	W - *98
OLVER, JC	Northampton	L - 91
	Harlequins	W - 88
ORLEDGE, RJ	Bristol	L - 73
ORWIN, J	Gloucester	W - 82
PACKMAN, F	Northampton	L - 91
PAGEL, G	Northampton	L - 00
PALMER, JA	Bath	W - 84, 85, 86, 87, 89
PALMER, T	Gloucester	W - 72
PALMER, DJ	Bristol	W - *83 L - 84, 88
PARSLOE, SG	Gloucester	W - 82
PASCALL, R	Gloucester	L - 90
PASK, P	Northampton	L - 91
PATRICK, B	Gosforth	W - 76, 77 L - 81
PATRICK, HE	Gosforth	W - 76, 77
PEARCE, GS	Northampton	L - 91
PEARN, AFA	Bristol	L - 73
PEARS, D	Harlequins	W - 91 L - 92
PEEL, I	Newcastle	W - *01.L - *99
PEGLAR, DJ	Wasps	L - 86, 87
PELLOW, R	Wasps	L - 86
PERRY, MH	Moseley	W - 82
PETERS, EW	Bath	W - 96
PHILLIPS, CA	Bristol	L - 88
PHILLIPS, J	Northampton	L - *02
PICKERING, DA	Lon. Scot	L - 74
PIENNAAR, F	Saracens	W - 98
PINNEGAR, MCF	Wasps	L - 86, 87
POLLEDRI, P	Bristol	W - 83 L - 84
POMPHREY, NJC	Bristol	W - 83 L - 84, 88
POOLE, MD	Leicester	W - 93, 97 L - 94, 96
POTTER, S	Leicester	W - 93, 97 L - 94, 96
POTTER, MJ	Gloucester	W - 72
POUNTNEY, A	Northampton	L - 00, 02
POWELL, M	Harlequins	L - 01
PREECE, PS	Coventry	W - 73
PREEDY, M	Gloucester	W - 82 L - 90
PRESTON, AJ	Gosforth	W - 76
PRICE, C	Lon. Welsh	L - 85
PRINGLE, IN	Moseley	L - 72
PRITCHARD, P	Gloucester	W - 82
PROBYN, JA	Wasps	L - 86, 87
PULLIN, JV	Bristol	L - 73
RAFTER, M	Bristol	W - 83 L - 84
RALSTON, CS	Rosslyn Park	L - 76
RAVENSCROFT, S	Saracens	W - 98
RECARDO, A	Moseley	W - 82
REDFERN, SP	Leicester	W - 79, 80, 81 L - 78, 83, 89
REDFERN, SB	Leicester	L - 83
REDMAN, NC	Bath	W - 84, 85, 86, 87, 90, 92, 94, 95, 96
REED, AI	Bath	W - 94
	Wasps	W - 00 L - *98
REED, D	Waterloo	L - 77
REES, CWF	Lon. Welsh	L - 85
REES, D	Sale	L - 97
REES, GL	Wasps	W-99 L - 86, 98
REES, A	Bath	W - 84
RENDALL, PAG	Wasps	L - 87
RICHARDS, D	Leicester	W - 93, *97 L - 83, 89, 94, 96
RICHARDSON, WP	Leicester	L - 89
RICHMOND, D	Northampton	L - *02
RIGBY, MA	Wasps	L - 86, 87
RIPLEY, AG	Rosslyn Park	L - 75, 76
ROBERTS, TC	Gosforth	W - 76, 77 L - 81
ROBINSON, D	Gosforth	W - 76, 77
ROBINSON, RP	Leicester	L - 96
ROBINSON, RA	Bath	W - 87, 89, 90, 92, 94, 95, 96
RODBER, T	Northampton	L - 91, 00
RODGERS, AJ	Bristol	L - 73
RODGERS, AK	Rosslyn Park	L - 75, 76
ROGERS, DP	Bedford	W - 75
ROISER, S	Wasps	W - 00 L - 98
ROLINSON, LJ	Coventry	W - 74
ROLLITT, DM	Bristol	L - 73
ROSE, MA	Wasps	L - 86, 87
ROSSBOROUGH, PA	Coventry	W - 73, 74
ROWNTREE, GC	Leicester	W - 93, 97 L - 94, 96
RUSSELL, S	Lon. Welsh	L - 85
RUSSELL, MP	Harlequins	L - 92, 93
RYAN, D	Wasps	L - 95
SACKEY, P	London Irish	W - 02
SAGOE, FK	Bath	W - 89
SALMON, JLB	Harlequins	W - 88
SAMPSON	Wasps	W-99 L - *98
SANDERS, I	Bath	W - 95
SANDERSON, P	Harlequins	L - 01
SARGENT, GAF	Gloucester	W - 78, *82
SAVILLE, CD	Rosslyn Park	L - 75
SCELZO, M	Northampton	L - *00
SCRASE, L	Wasps	L - 98
SCRIVENER, P	Wasps	W-99
SCRIVENS, N	Gloucester	L - 90
SEELY, G	Northampton	L - 02
SELLA, P	Saracens	W - 98
SHAW, M	Newcastle	L - 99
SHAW, S	Wasps	W - 99, 00 L - 98
SHEASBY, CMA	Harlequins	W - 02.L - 92, 93

SHEEHAN, JM	Lon. Irish	L - 80
SHEPARD, A	Bristol	W - 83 L - 84
SHORROCK,, DW	Moseley	W - 82
SHORT, JJO	Gosforth	W - 76
SHORT, KS	Lon. Irish	L - 80
SHORT, KF	Waterloo	L - 77
SIMMONS, A	Wasps	L - 86, 87
SIMMS, KG	Wasps	L - 87
SIMONETT, JF	Gloucester	W - 78
SIMPSON, PD	Bath	W - 84, 85, 86, *89
SINGER, M	Saracens	W - *98
SKINNER, MG	Harlequins	W - 88, 91
SLEIGHTHOLME, J	Bath	W - 96
SMITH, A	Sale	L - 97
SMITH, SM	Gosforth	L - 81
SMITH, ST	Wasps	L - 86, 87
SMITH, IR	Leicester	W - 79, 80, 81
		L - 83, 89
SMITH, T	Leicester	L - 89
SMITH, R	Glouceste	W - 72
SMITH, T	Gloucester	L - 90
SMITH, I	Gloucester	L - 90
SMITH, TJ	Moseley	L - 72
SMITH, T	Northampton	L - 02
SMYTHE, MJ	Lon. Irish	L - 80
SNOW, ACW	Harlequins	L - 93
SOLE, DMB	Bath	W - 87
SPAVEN, JN	Waterloo	L - 77
SPURRELL, RA	Bath	W - 84, 85, 86
STARLING, D	Rosslyn Park	L - 76
STARR, B	Harlequins	L - *01
STEELE, J	Northampton	L - 91
STEPHENS,EJF	Gloucester	W - 72
STEPHENSON, M	Newcastle	W - 01
STEVENSON, GB	Lon. Scot	L - 74
STEWART, M	Northampton	L - 00, 02
STIFF, PJ	Bristol	L - 84
STRANSKY, J	Leicester	W - 97
STRINGER, NC	Wasps	L - 86
STRUDWICK, R	London Irish	W - 02
STURNHAM, B	Saracens	W - 98
SUTHERLAND, IS	Moseley	W - 82
SWAIN, MK	Moseley	L - 72, 79
SWATFIELD, RJ	Bristol	L - 73
SWIFT, AH	Bath	W - 86, 87, 89, 90, 92, 94, 95
TAYLOR, PA	Gloucester	W - 82
TEAGUE, MC	Gloucester	W - 82 L - 90
THACKER, T	Leicester	L - 89
THAME, J	Northampton	L - 91
THOMAS, DG	Bristol	L - 88
THOMAS, A	Moseley	L - 79
THOMPSON, AL	Harlequins	W - 88
THOMPSON, GJ	Harlequins	L - 93
THOMPSON, S	Northampton	L - *00, 02
THORBURN, CW	Lon. Scot	L - 74
THORNEYCROFT, H	Northampton	L - 91
THRESHER, SE	Harlequins	W - 88, 91
TICKLE, SG	Waterloo	L - 77
TRESEDER, PA	Rosslyn Park	L - 75, 76
TREVASKIS, B	Bath	W - 84, 85, 87
TRICK, DM	Bath	W - 84, 85, 86
TROUGHTON, AH	Bristol	W - 83
TUCKER, M	Northampton	L - *02

TUIGAMALA, V	Newcastle	W - 01.L - 99
UBOGU, VE	Bath	W - 90, 92, 94, 95
UFTON, J	Wasps	L - 95
UNDERWOOD, R	Leicester	W - 93 L - 89, 94, 96
UNDERWOOD, T	Leicester	W - 93 L - 94
	Newcastle	L - 99
UTTLEY, RM	Gosforth	W - 77
VENTER, B	London Irish	W - 02
VINE, BJ	Gloucester	W - 78
VOLLEY, P	Wasps	W - 00 L - 98
VYVYAN, H	Newcastle	W - *01
WALDER, D	Newcastle	W - 01
WALKER, R	Coventry	W - 74
WALLACE, P	Saracens	W - 98
WALLACE, R	Saracens	W - *98
WALTER, S	Northampton	L - *00
WALTON, P	Newcastle	L - 99
WARD, B	Northampton	L - *91
WARD, M	Newcastle	W - 01
WARDLOW, CS	Coventry	W - 73
WARREN, DG	Moseley	W - 82
WATERS, F	Wasps	W-99
WATKINS, M	Lon. Welsh	L - 85
WATKINS, JA	Gloucester	W - 72, 78
WATSON-JONES, A	Moseley	L - *79
WATT, DEJ	Bristol	L - 73
WEBB, JM	Bath	W - 92
	Bristol	L - 88
WEBSTER, JG	Moseley	L - 72
WEDDERBURN, MA	Harlequins	L - 92
WEEDON, M	Wasps	W - 99, 00 L - 98
WEIR, D	Newcastle	W - 01.L - 99
WELLS, JM	Leicester	W - 93, 97
		L - 89, 94, 96
WESTON, LE	Rosslyn Park	L - 75, 76
WHEELER, PJ	Leicester	W - 79, 80, 81
		L - 78, 83
WHITE, C	Gosforth	W - 76, 77 L - 81
WHITE, L	Lon. Irish	L - 80
WHITE, M	Wasps	L - 95, *98
WHITE, JC	Moseley	L - 72
WHITE-COOPER, S	Harlequins	L - 01
WILKINSON, J	Newcastle	W - 01.L - 99
WILKINSON, RM	Bedford	W - 75
WILLIAMS, K	Leicester	W - 81
WILLIAMS, CG	Gloucester	W - 78
WILLIAMS, CJ	Bristol	L - 73
WILLIAMS, S	London Irish	W - 02
WILSON, D	Harlequins	L - 01
WINSTANLEY, P	Sale	L - 97
WINTERBOTTOM, PJ	Harlequins	W - 91 L - 92, 93
WINTERS, R	Harlequins	L - 01
WITHEY, K	Bath	W - 90
WOOD, K	Harlequins	L - 01
WOOD, M	London Wasps	W - 00
WOOD, P	Gloucester	W - *82
WOODWARD, C	Leicester	W - 80, 81 L - 83
WOOLEY, VJ	Gloucester	W - 78
WORSLEY, J	Wasps	W - 99, 00 L - 98
WORLSEY, M	London Irish	W - 02
WYATT, D	Bedford	W - 75
YATES, K	Bath	W - 95
YOUNG, M	Gosforth	W - 76, 77 L - 81
YOUNGS, NC	Leicester	L - 83

Year	Winners	Captain	Points Scored	Tries	Cons	Pens	DG
1972	**Gloucester**	*M Nicholls*	**17**	2		1	2
1973	**Coventry**	*D Duckham*	**27**	4	1	4	1
1974	**Coventry**	*D Duckham*	**26**	4	2	2	
1975	**Bedford**	*D Rogers*	**28**	5	4		
1976	**Gosforth**	*M Young*	**23**	4	2	2	
1977	**Gosforth**	*R Uttley*	**27**	5	2	1	
1978	**Gloucester**	*J Watkins*	**6**	1	1		
1979	**Leicester**	*P Wheeler*	**15**	1	1	2	1
1980	**Leicester**	*P Wheeler*	**21**			4	3
1981	**Leicester**	*P Wheeler*	**22**	3	2	3	
1982	**Gloucester**	*S Mills*	**12**			4	
1983	**Bristol**	*M Rafter*	**28**	4	3	1	
1984	**Bath**	*R Spurrell*	**10**	1		1	1
1985	**Bath**	*R Spurrell*	**24**	2	2	4	
1986	**Bath**	*J Palmer*	**25**	4	3	1	
1987	**Bath**	*R Hill*	**19**	3	2	1	
1988	**Harlequins**	*J Olver*	**28**	3	2	4	
1989	**Bath**	*S Barnes*	**10**	1		2	
1990	**Bath**	*S Barnes*	**48**	8	5	2	
1991	**Harlequins**	*P Winterbottom*	**25**	4	2	1	
1992	**Bath**	*A Robinson*	**15**	1	1	2	1
1993	**Leicester**	*J Wells*	**23**	2	2	2	1
1994	**Bath**	*J Hall*	**21**	2	1	3	
1995	**Bath**	*P de Glanville*	**36**	5	4	1	
1996	**Bath**	*P de Glanville*	**16**	1	1	2	1
1997	**Leicester**	*M Johnson*	**9**			3	
1998	**Saracens**	*A Diprose*	**48**	7	5		1
1999	**Wasps**	*M Weedon*	**29**	2	2	4	1
2000	**Wasps**	*L Dallaglio*	**31**	4	1	3	
2001	**Newcastle**	*G Weir*	**30**	4	2	2	
2002	**London Irish**	*R Strudwick*	**38**	5	5	1	

Year	Runners-up	Captain	Points Scored	Tries	Cons	Pens	DG	Losing Semi-Finalists
1972	**Moseley**	*J Webster*	**6**	1	1			Coventry, Wilmslow
1973	**Bristol**	*A Nicholls*	**15**			5		Sale, London Welsh
1974	**London Scottish**	*M Biggar*	**6**				2	Rosslyn Park, Orrell
1975	**Rosslyn Park**	*P Keith-Roach*	**12**	3				Coventry, Morpeth
1976	**Rosslyn Park**	*P Keith Roach*	**14**	2		1	1	Sale, Wakefield
1977	**Waterloo**	*C Fisher*	**11**	2		1		London Welsh, Saracens
1978	**Leicester**	*B Hall*	**3**			1		Harlequins, Coventry
1979	**Moseley**	*M Cooper*	**12**	1	1	1	1	Wasps, Gosforth
1980	**London Irish**	*J O'Driscoll*	**9**	1	1	1		Rosslyn Park, Harlequins
1981	**Gosforth**	*C White*	**15**	1	1	3		London Scottish, Moseley
1982	**Moseley**	*D Nutt*	**12**			3	1	Coventry, Leicester
1983	**Leicester**	*S Johnson*	**22**	2	1	4		Coventry, London Scottish
1984	**Bristol**	*M Rafter*	**9**	1	1	1		Nottingham, Harlequins
1985	**London Welsh**	*C Rees*	**15**			5		Gloucester, Coventry
1986	**Wasps**	*R Cardus*	**17**	3	1	1		Leicester, London Scottish
1987	**Wasps**	*D Pegler*	**12**	1	1	1	1	Orrell, Leicester
1988	**Bristol**	*N Pomphrey*	**22**	2	1	3	1	Wasps, Moseley
1989	**Leicester**	*P Dodge*	**6**			2		Gloucester, Harlequins
1990	**Gloucester**	*M Hamlin*	**6**	1	1			Moseley, Northampton
1991	**Northampton**	*G Pearce*	**13**	1		3		Nottingham, Orrell
1992	**Harlequins**	*P Winterbottom*	**12**	1	1	3		Gloucester, Leicester
1993	**Harlequins**	*P Winterbottom*	**16**	1	1	3		Northampton, Wasps
1994	**Leicester**	*D Richards*	**9**			3		Harlequins, Orrell
1995	**Wasps**	*D Ryan*	**16**	2		2		Harlequins, Leicester
1996	**Leicester**	*D Richards*	**15**	2	1	1		Gloucester, London Irish
1997	**Sale**	*J Mallinder*	**3**			1		Gloucester, Harlequins
1998	**Wasps**	*L Dallaglio*	**18**	2	1	2		Northampton, Sale
1999	**Newcastle**	*G Armstrong*	**19**	1	1	4		Gloucester, Richmond
2000	**Northampton**	*M Dawson*	**23**	1		6		Bristol, London Irish
2001	**Harlequins**	*D Wilson*	**27**	2	1	5		Sale, Leicester
2002	**Northampton**	*B Pountney*	**7**	1	1			Harlequins, Newcastle

RFU SENIOR CUP FINAL TRIVIA

MOST WINNERS MEDALS

9	Nigel Redman (Bath).
8	Richard Hill (Bath)
	Graham Dawe (Bath).
7	Stuart Barnes (Bristol 1, Bath 6)
	Andy Robinson (Bath)
	Tony Swift (Bath)
	Gareth Chilcott (Bath)
6	Jeremy Guscott (Bath-2 as Rep)
	John Hall (Bath)
	Simon Halliday (Bath 5, Harlequins 1)

MOST LOSERS MEDALS

4	Dean Richards (Leicester)
3	Steve Bates (Wasps)
	Paul Dodge (Leicester)
	Adel Kardooni (Leicester)
	Steve Redfern (Leicester)
	Rory Underwood (Leicester)
	John Wells (Leicester)

WINNERS MEDALS FOR TWO CLUBS

Stuart Barnes (Bristol, Bath)
Roger Barnwell (Coventry, Leicester)
Roger Cowling (Gloucester, Leicester)
Andy Reed (Bath, Wasps)

LOSERS MEDALS FOR TWO CLUBS

Kevin Dunn (Gloucester, Wasps)
Tony Underwood (Leicester, Newcastle)
Nick Greenstock (Wasps, Harlequins)

PLAYERS APPEARING FOR TWO CLUBS

Stuart Barnes (Bristol, Bath); Roger Barnwell (Coventry, Leicester); Barrie Corless (Coventry, Moseley); Roger Cowling (Gloucester, Leicester); Rob Cunningham (Gosforth, Bath); Kevin Dunn (Gloucester, Wasps); Simon Halliday (Bath, Harlequins); John Olver (Harlequins, Northampton); Jonathan Webb (Bristol, Bath); Andy Reed (Bath, Wasps); Tony Underwood (Leicester, Newcastle); Nick Greenstock (Wasps, Harlequins); Will Greenwood (Leicester, Harlequins); Brendon Daniel (Saracens, Harlequins), Chris Sheasby (Harlequins, London Irish

PLAYERS SENT OFF

Player	Match	Year	Referee
Nigel Horton	Moseley v Gloucester	1972	Ron Lewis
Bob Mordell	Rosslyn Park v Gosforth	1976	Norman Sanson
John Gadd	Gloucester v Bath	1990	Fred Howard

RFU SENIOR CUP

OVERALL PLAYING RECORD
OF TEAMS WHO HAVE REACHED THE LAST 8

	Winners	R-up	SF	QF	Years in competition	Played	Won	Drawn	Lost
Bath	10	0	10	13	30	80	60	-	20
Leicester	5	5	16	21	30	102	77	-	25
Gloucester	*3	1	10	18	30	89	61	1	27
Wasps	2	4	9	14	27	73	48	-	25
Harlequins	2	3	13	21	29	91	64	-	27
Newcastle	3	2	7	13	31	83	55	-	28
Coventry	2	0	8	10	31	80	51	-	29
Bristol	1	3	5	12	30	76	47	-	29
Moseley	*1	2	6	12	31	79	48	1	30
London Irish	1	1	4	8	28	63	36	-	27
Saracens	1	0	2	7	28	62	35	-	27
Bedford	1	0	1	3	30	54	25	-	29
Northampton	-	3	6	12	30	74	44	-	30
Rosslyn Park	-	2	4	7	30	71	41	-	30
London Welsh	-	1	3	9	29	75	46	-	29
London Scottish	-	1	4	6	27	59	32	-	27
Sale	-	1	5	12	29	72	43	-	29
Waterloo	-	1	1	6	25	51	26	-	25
Orrell	-	-	4	6	26	55	29	-	26
Nottingham	-	-	2	7	29	60	31	-	29
Wakefield	-	-	1	4	23	53	30	-	23
Wilmslow	-	-	1	2	5	11	6	-	5
Morpeth	-	-	1	1	3	6	3	-	3
Richmond	-	-	-	5	26	59	33	-	26
West Hartlepool	-	-	-	4	22	45	23	-	22
Penryn	-	-	-	2	4	9	5	-	4
Metropolitan Police	-	-	-	2	17	36	19	-	17
Exeter	-	-	-	2	24	60	36	-	24
Liverpool St Helens	-	-	-	2	26	47	21	-	26
Halifax	-	-	-	1	3	6	3	-	3
Roundhay	-	-	-	1	7	10	3	-	7
Manchester	-	-	-	1	8	22	14	-	8
Leeds Tykes	-	-	-	1	10	21	11	-	10
Fylde	-	-	-	1	21	46	25	-	21
Plymouth Albion	-	-	-	1	23	34	11	-	23
Total	32	30	124	248					

CLUB NAME	LEAGUE	Page Ref.	Level
Abbey	South West 2 East	SW - 679-707	6
Abingdon	Berks/Bucks & Oxon 2	SW - 679-707	9
Acklam	Durham/N'thm'land 1	N - 521-550	7
Adwick le Street	Yorkshire 5	N - 521-550	11
Aireborough	Yorkshire 5	N - 521-550	11
Alcester	Warwickshire 1	M - 569-596	9
Aldermaston	Berks/Bucks & Oxon 1	SW - 679-707	8
Aldridge	North Midlands 2	M - 569-596	10
Aldwinians	North 2 West	N - 521-550	6
Alnwick	North 2 East	N - 521-550	6
Alresford	Hampshire 2	L - 619-660	10
Alton	London 3 South West	L - 619-660	7
Altrincham Kersal	North 2 West	N - 521-550	6
Amber Valley	NLD/Leics 1 West	M - 569-596	9
Ambleside	Cumbria	n - 521-550	8
Amersham & Chiltern	South West 2 East	SW - 679-707	6
Ampthill	Midlands 2 East	M - 569-596	6
Andover	London 2 South	L - 619-660	6
Anselmians	South Lancs/Cheshire 2	N - 521-550	8
Anstey	NLD/Leics 1 West	M - 569-596	9
Appleby Frodingham	NLD/Leics 2 East	M - 569-596	10
Aretians	Gloucester Premier	SW - 679-707	8
Arun	Sussex 3	L - 619-660	11
Ashbourne	Midlands 4 East (North)	M - 569-596	8
Ashby	NLD/Leics 1 West	M - 569-596	9
Ashfield	Midlands 4 East (North)	M - 569-596	8
Ashford	Kent 1	L - 619-660	9
Ashington	Durham/N'thm'land 1	N - 521-550	7
Ashley Down Old Boys	Gloucester 1	SW - 679-707	9
Ashton on Mersey	South Lancs/Cheshire 2	N - 521-550	8
Ashton-under-Lyne	North Lancs 1	N - 521-550	8
Askeans	Kent 1	L - 619-660	9
Aspatria	North 1	N - 521-550	5
Aspull	North 2 West	N - 521-550	6
Aston Old Edwardians	Midlands 3 West (North)	M - 569-596	7
Atherstone	Warwickshire 2	M - 569-596	10
Avon	Somerset Premier	SW - 679-707	8
Avonmouth OB	Gloucester Premier	SW - 679-707	8
Avonvale	Somerset 1	SW - 679-707	9
Aylesbury	Southern Counties North	SW - 679-707	7
Aylesford	Kent 1	L - 619-660	9
Aylestone Athletic	NLD/Leics 2 West	M - 569-596	10
Aylestone St James	NLD/Leics 2 West	M - 569-596	10
Aylestonians	NLD/Leics 1 West	M - 569-596	9
Baildon	Yorkshire 4	N - 521-550	10
Bakewell Mannerians	NLD/Leics 1 West	M - 569-596	9
Banbury	Midlands 2 East	M - 569-596	6
Bancroft	East Counties 2 South	L - 619-660	10
Bank Of England	London 2 North	L - 619-660	6
Barkers Butts	Midlands 1	M - 555-558	5
Barking	National Division Three South	433	4
Barnard Castle	Durham/N'thm'land 2	N - 521-550	8
Barnes	London 3 South West	L - 619-660	7
Barnet Saracens Elizabethans	London 3 North West	L - 619-660	7
Barns Green	Sussex 2	L - 619-660	10
Barnsley	Yorkshire 4	N - 521-550	10
Barnstaple	South West 1	SW - 665-668	5
Barton & District	NLD/Leics 1 East	M - 569-596	9
Barton Hill	Gloucester Premier	SW - 679-707	8
Basildon	London 3 North East	L - 619-660	7
Basingstoke	National Division Three South	437	4

Charlton Park	London 3 South East	L - 619-660	7
Cheddar Valley	Somerset 2	SW - 679-707	10
Chelmsford	London 4 North East	L - 619-660	8
Cheltenham	South West 1	SW - 665-668	5
Cheltenham Civil Service	Gloucester 3 North	SW - 679-707	11
Cheltenham North	Western Counties North	SW - 679-707	7
Cheltenham Saracens	Gloucester 2	SW - 679-707	10
Chesham	Berks/Bucks & Oxon 2	SW - 679-707	9
Cheshunt	South West 1	L - 601-604	5
Chess Valley	Herts/Middlesex 2	L - 619-660	10
Chester	North 1	N - 521-550	5
Chester le Street	Durham/N'thm'land 3	N - 521-550	9
Chesterfield	NLD/Leics 2 West	M - 569-596	10
Chew Valley	Somerset Premier	SW - 679-707	8
Chichester	London 4 South East	L - 619-660	8
Chichester IHE	Sussex 1	L - 619-660	9
Chineham	Hampshire 3	L - 619-660	11
Chingford	London 3 North East	L - 619-660	7
Chinnor	South West 1	SW - 665-668	5
Chippenham	South West 2 East	SW - 679-707	6
Chipping Norton	Berks/Bucks & Oxon 1	SW - 679-707	8
Chipping Sodbury	Gloucester 1	SW - 679-707	9
Chipstead	Surrey 3	L - 619-660	11
Chiswick	Herts/Middlesex 1	L - 619-660	9
Chobham	London 3 South West	L - 619-660	7
Chorley	North Lancs 2	N - 521-550	9
Chosen Hill F. P.	Gloucester Premier	SW - 679-707	8
Christleton	South Lancs/Cheshire 5	N - 521-550	11
Cinderford	South West 1	SW - 665-668	5
Cirencester	Gloucester Premier	SW - 679-707	8
Civil Service	London 4 North West	L - 619-660	8
Claverdon	Warwickshire 1	M - 569-596	9
Cleckheaton	North 1	N - 521-550	5
Clee	North Midlands 2	M - 569-596	10
Cleethorpes	NLD/Leics 2 East	M - 569-596	10
Cleobury Mortimer	North Midlands 1	M - 569-596	9
Cleve	South West 2 West	SW - 679-707	6
Clevedon	South West 2 West	SW - 679-707	6
Clifton	South West 1	SW - 665-668	5
Clitheroe	North Lancs 2	N - 521-550	9
Coalville	Midlands 4 East (South)	M - 569-596	8
Cobham	London 2 South	L - 619-660	6
Cockermouth	Cumbria	n - 521-550	8
Colchester	East Counties 1	L - 619-660	9
Colerne	Dorset & Wilts 2 North	SW - 679-707	9
Colne & Nelson	North Lancs 2	N - 521-550	9
Combe Down	Somerset 1	SW - 679-707	9
Coney Hill	Western Counties North	SW - 679-707	7
Congleton	South Lancs/Cheshire 4	N - 521-550	10
Consett	Durham/N'thm'land 2	N - 521-550	8
Cooper Avon Tyres	Dorset & Wilts 1	SW - 679-707	8
Corby	East Midlands 2	M - 569-596	10
Corsham	Dorset & Wilts 1	SW - 679-707	8
Cotham Park	Gloucester 3 South	SW - 679-707	11
Coventrians	Warwickshire 2	M - 569-596	10
Coventry	National Division One	127	2
Coventry Saracens	Warwickshire 2	M - 569-596	10
Coventry Technical	Warwickshire 2	M - 569-596	10
Coventry Welsh	Midlands 4 West (South)	M - 569-596	8
Cranbrook	Kent 1	L - 619-660	9
Cranleigh	London 4 South West	L - 619-660	8
Crawley	London 4 South East	L - 619-660	8
Crediton	South West 2 West	SW - 679-707	6
Creighton	Cumbria	n - 521-550	8
Crewe and Nantwich	South Lancs/Cheshire 2	N - 521-550	8
Crewkerne	Somerset 1	SW - 679-707	9

CLUB INDEX

CLUB INDEX

London Tribes	Herts/Middlesex 3 South	L - 619-660	11
London Wasps	Zurich Premiership	63	1
London Welsh	National Division One	139	2
Long Buckby	Midlands 3 East (South)	M - 569-596	7
Long Eaton	Midlands 4 East (North)	M - 569-596	8
Longlevens	Gloucester Premier	SW - 679-707	8
Longton	Midlands 1	M - 555-558	5
Lonsdale Wanderers	North Lancs 2	N - 521-550	9
Lordswood	Kent 1	L - 619-660	9
Loughborough	Midlands 3 East (North)	M - 569-596	7
Loughborough Students	Midlands 3 East (North)	M - 569-596	7
Loughton	East Counties 3 South	L - 619-660	11
Lowestoft & Yarmouth	London 4 North East	L - 619-660	8
Luctonians	Midlands 1	M - 555-558	5
Ludlow	Midlands 4 West (North)	M - 569-596	8
Luton	Midlands 2 East	M - 569-596	6
Lutterworth	Midlands 3 East (South)	M - 569-596	7
Lydney	National Division Three South	453	4
Lymm	North 2 West	N - 521-550	6
Lytchett Minster	Hampshire 2	L - 619-660	10
Lytham	North Lancs 1	N - 521-550	8
Macclesfield	North 1	N - 521-550	5
Maidenhead	South West 2 East	SW - 679-707	6
Maidstone	London 2 South	L - 619-660	6
Maldon	East Counties 1	L - 619-660	9
Malton and Norton	Yorkshire 2	N - 521-550	8
Malvern	Midlands 1	M - 555-558	5
Manchester	National Division One	145	2
Manchester Wanderers	South Lancs/Cheshire 4	N - 521-550	10
Manor Park	Warwickshire 1	M - 569-596	9
Mansfield	Midlands 2 East	M - 569-596	6
March BRAZA	East Counties 3 North	L - 619-660	11
Marconi Coventry	Midlands 4 West (South)	M - 569-596	8
Marist	Yorkshire 6	N - 521-550	12
Marjons	Devon 2	SW - 679-707	10
Market Bosworth	Midlands 2 East	M - 569-596	6
Market Rasen	Midlands 4 East (North)	M - 569-596	8
Marlborough	Dorset & Wilts 2 North	SW - 679-707	9
Marlow	South West 1	SW - 665-668	5
Marple	South Lancs/Cheshire 3	N - 521-550	9
Martock	Dorset & Wilts 2 South	SW - 679-707	9
Matlock	Midlands 3 East (North)	M - 569-596	7
Matson	South West 2 West	SW - 679-707	6
May & Baker	East Counties 3 South	L - 619-660	11
Meden Vale	NLD/Leics 2 East	M - 569-596	10
Medicals	Durham/N'thm'land 3	N - 521-550	9
Medway	Kent 2	L - 619-660	10
Melbourne	NLD/Leics 1 West	M - 569-596	9
Mellish	Midlands 4 East (North)	M - 569-596	8
Melton Mowbray	Midlands 3 East (North)	M - 569-596	7
Mersea Island	London 4 North East	L - 619-660	8
Merton	Surrey 1	L - 619-660	9
Met. Police, Hayes	Kent 3	L - 619-660	11
Metropolitan Police	London 3 North West	L - 619-660	7
Middlesbrough	North 2 East	N - 521-550	6
Midhurst	Sussex 2	L - 619-660	10
Midsomer Norton	Somerset Premier	SW - 679-707	8
Mill Hill	Herts/Middlesex 2	L - 619-660	10
Millbrook	Hampshire 1	L - 619-660	9
Millfield O.B.	Herts/Middlesex 4 South	L - 619-660	12
Millom	Cumbria	n - 521-550	8
Millwall Albion	East Counties 3 South	L - 619-660	11
Milton Keynes	Berks/Bucks & Oxon 1	SW - 679-707	8
Minchinhampton	Gloucester 2	SW - 679-707	10
Minehead Barbarians	Somerset Premier	SW - 679-707	8
Minety	Dorset & Wilts 2 North	SW - 679-707	9

Old Abingdonians	Surrey 2	L - 619-660	10
Old Actonians	Herts/Middlesex 2	L - 619-660	10
Old Albanians	London 2 North	L - 619-660	6
Old Alleynian	Surrey 2	L - 619-660	10
Old Amplefordians	Surrey 2	L - 619-660	10
Old Ashmoleans	Herts/Middlesex 4 North	L - 619-660	12
Old Ashtonians	Somerset 1	SW - 679-707	9
Old Bealonians	East Counties 3 South	L - 619-660	11
Old Bedians	North Lancs 1	N - 521-550	8
Old Bevonians	Surrey 3	L - 619-660	11
Old Blues	London 3 South West	L - 619-660	7
Old Brentwoods	East Counties 2 South	L - 619-660	10
Old Brightonians	Sussex 3	L - 619-660	11
Old Bristolians	Gloucester 1	SW - 679-707	9
Old Brodleians	Yorkshire 1	N - 521-550	7
Old Caterhamians	Surrey 1	L - 619-660	9
Old Centralians	Western Counties North	SW - 679-707	7
Old Colfeians	National Division Three South	461	4
Old Colstonians	Gloucester 3 South	SW - 679-707	11
Old Cooperians	East Counties 3 South	L - 619-660	11
Old Coventrians	Midlands 3 West (South)	M - 569-596	7
Old Cranleighans	Surrey 1	L - 619-660	9
Old Crossleyans	Yorkshire 1	N - 521-550	7
Old Cryptians	Gloucester 2	SW - 679-707	10
Old Culverhaysians	Somerset Premier	SW - 679-707	8
Old Dunstonians	London 4 South East	L - 619-660	8
Old Edwardians	East Counties 2 South	L - 619-660	10
Old Elizabethans	Gloucester 2	SW - 679-707	10
Old Elthamians	Kent 2	L - 619-660	10
Old Emanuel	London 4 South West	L - 619-660	8
Old Freemens	Surrey 1	L - 619-660	9
Old Grammarians	Herts/Middlesex 3 North	L - 619-660	11
Old Gravesendians	Kent 2	L - 619-660	10
Old Griffinians	North Midlands 2	M - 569-596	10
Old Haberdashers	Herts/Middlesex 3 North	L - 619-660	11
Old Haileyburians	Surrey 2	L - 619-660	10
Old Halesonians	Midlands 4 West (South)	M - 569-596	8
Old Hamptonians	London 4 North West	L - 619-660	8
Old Isleworthians	Herts/Middlesex 2	L - 619-660	10
Old Laurentians	Midlands 2 West	M - 569-596	6
Old Leamingtonians	Midlands 3 West (South)	M - 569-596	7
Old Merchant Taylors	London 4 North West	L - 619-660	8
Old Mid-Whitgiftian	London 2 South	L - 619-660	6
Old Millhillians	Herts/Middlesex 2	L - 619-660	10
Old Modernians	Yorkshire 4	N - 521-550	10
Old Newtonians	Midlands 4 East (South)	M - 569-596	8
Old Northamptonians	Midlands 3 East (South)	M - 569-596	7
Old Olavians	Kent 2	L - 619-660	10
Old Otliensians	Yorkshire 3	N - 521-550	9
Old Patesians	National Division Three South	465	4
Old Paulines	Surrey 1	L - 619-660	9
Old Plymothian & Mann.	Devon 1	SW - 679-707	9
Old Public Oaks	Devon 2	SW - 679-707	10
Old Redcliffians	Western Counties North	SW - 679-707	7
Old Reedonians	Surrey 1	L - 619-660	9
Old Reigatian	Surrey 1	L - 619-660	9
Old Richians	Western Counties North	SW - 679-707	7
Old Rishworthians	Yorkshire 5	N - 521-550	11
Old Rutlishians	Surrey 1	L - 619-660	9
Old Saltleians	Midlands 4 West (North)	M - 569-596	8
Old Streetonians	Herts/Middlesex 3 North	L - 619-660	11
Old Sulians	Somerset 1	SW - 679-707	9
Old Suttonians	Surrey 3	L - 619-660	11
Old Technicians	Devon 2	SW - 679-707	10
Old Tiffinians	Surrey 1	L - 619-660	9
Old Tottonians	Herts/Middlesex 3 North	L - 619-660	11

CLUB INDEX

West Park Bramhope	Yorkshire 2	N - 521-550	8
West Park St Helens	North 1	N - 521-550	5
West Park Warriors	North Lancs 2	N - 521-550	9
Westbury	Southern Counties South	SW - 679-707	7
Westbury on Severn	Gloucester 2	SW - 679-707	10
Westcliff	East Counties 2 South	L - 619-660	10
Westcombe Park	National Division Three South	481	4
Westoe	North 2 East	N - 521-550	6
Weston-Super-Mare	National Division Three South	485	4
Westwood	East Midlands 1	M - 569-596	9
Wetherby	Yorkshire 4	N - 521-550	10
Weymouth	Dorset & Wilts 1	SW - 679-707	8
Wharfedale	National Division Two	333	3
Wharfedale Rams	Yorkshire 5	N - 521-550	11
Wheatley	Berks/Bucks & Oxon 2	SW - 679-707	9
Wheatley Hills	Yorkshire 1	N - 521-550	7
Whitby	Durham/N'thm'land 2	N - 521-550	8
Whitchurch	Midlands 1	M - 555-558	5
Whitehall	Western Counties North	SW - 679-707	7
Whitehaven	Cumbria	N - 521-550	8
Whitley Bay Rockcliff	Durham/N'thm'land 3	N - 521-550	9
Whitstable	Kent 1	L - 619-660	9
Wibsey	Yorkshire 5	N - 521-550	11
Wickersley Exel	Yorkshire 6	N - 521-550	12
Widden Old Boys	Gloucester 2	SW - 679-707	10
Widnes	South Lancs/Cheshire 1	N - 521-550	7
Wigan	South Lancs/Cheshire 1	N - 521-550	7
Wigton	North 2 West	N - 521-550	6
Willenhall	Midlands 3 West (North)	M - 569-596	7
Wilmslow	North 2 West	N - 521-550	6
Wimbledon	London 2 South	L - 619-660	6
Wimborne	South West 2 East	SW - 679-707	6
Wincanton	Dorset & Wilts 2 South	SW - 679-707	9
Winchester	South West 1	L - 601-604	5
Windermere	Cumbria	n - 521-550	8
Windsor	South West 2 East	SW - 679-707	6
Winlaton Vulcans	Durham/N'thm'land 2	N - 521-550	8
Winnington Park	North 2 West	N - 521-550	6
Winscombe	Somerset 2	SW - 679-707	10
Winslow	Berks/Bucks & Oxon 2	SW - 679-707	9
Wirral	South Lancs/Cheshire 1	N - 521-550	7
Wisbech	East Counties 2 North	L - 619-660	10
Witham	East Counties 3 North	L - 619-660	11
Withernsea	Yorkshire 6	N - 521-550	12
Withycombe	Western Counties West	SW - 679-707	7
Witney	Southern Counties North	SW - 679-707	7
Wiveliscombe	Somerset Premier	SW - 679-707	8
Woking	Surrey 2	L - 619-660	10
Wolverhampton	Midlands 2 West	M - 569-596	6
Woodbridge	London 4 North East	L - 619-660	8
Woodford	London 2 North	L - 619-660	6
Woodrush	North Midlands 1	M - 569-596	9
Wootton Bassett	Southern Counties South	SW - 679-707	7
Worcester	National Division One	193	2
Worcester Wanderers	North Midlands 1	M - 569-596	9
Workington	North Lancs/Cumbria	N - 521-550	7
Worksop	NLD/Leics 1 West	M - 569-596	9
Worth Old Boys	Surrey 3	L - 619-660	11
Worthing	London 2 South	L - 619-660	6
Wotton	Gloucester 3 South	SW - 679-707	11
Wymondham	London 3 North East	L - 619-660	7
Yardley & District	Midlands 4 West (North)	M - 569-596	8
Yarm	Durham/N'thm'land 3	N - 521-550	9
Yarnbury	Yorkshire 1	N - 521-550	7
Yatton	Western Counties North	SW - 679-707	7
York	Yorkshire 1	N - 521-550	7
York Railway Institute	Yorkshire 3	N - 521-550	9